How To Use The Edge Index

Bend the pages of the book nearly double and hold them that way with your left hand.

Locate the letter you want in the Edge Index.

Match up the 1- or 2-line symbol next to the letter you have selected with the corresponding 1- or 2-line symbol on the page edge, and open there.

В
Г
Д
Е
Ж
З
И
К
Л
М
Н
О
П
Р
С
Т
У
Ф
Х
Ц
Ч
Ш
Щ
Э
Ю
Я

Russian-English Physics Dictionary

Russian-English

Physics Dictionary

---

by IRVING EMIN and the

CONSULTANTS BUREAU STAFF

OF PHYSICIST-TRANSLATORS

JOHN WILEY & SONS, INC., NEW YORK AND LONDON

Library of Congress Catalog Card Number: 63-8056

Printed in the United States of America

Preface

The achievements of Russian physical scientists during the last decade have stimulated universal interest in the physical literature of the Soviet Union. As one of the initial translators for the Consultants Bureau physics program, I became acutely aware of the need for an adequate general Russian-English physics dictionary. The available technical dictionaries were (and still are) obsolete, highly specialized, or lacking very much of the terminology employed in physical research. English-Russian dictionaries for some fields of physics, notably nuclear science, published in the Soviet Union were based generally on incomplete compilations of either English or Russian terminology, and failed to include a large number of the terms actually employed by Russian physicists. Determination of the valid English equivalent for a given Russian phrase frequently required hours of linguistic-scientific detective work in various sources; even then, the final choice was sometimes supported largely by intuition.

My experience paralleled that of other translators of Soviet physics material. Thus it was that in 1956, with the encouragement and pledges of cooperation of a number of other bilingual physicist-translators and the backing of Consultants Bureau, I undertook the compilation of this dictionary. Perhaps fortunately, we did not realize the magnitude of the task. What we had expected to complete in three years has taken seven, during the course of which I have learned that no lexicographer can ever truly consider a work completed, and most certainly not in a field of science expanding and developing as rapidly as is physics in this second half of the twentieth century.

I derived the core of this new *Russian-English Physics Dictionary* from the careful reading of well over 10,000 pages of Soviet physics journals published from 1955 to 1962. Nearly two-thirds of this material I translated completely, for publication in current American translation journals of Russian physics. The great majority of these translated articles were from the most widely known and important Soviet journals of the physical sciences—*The Journal of Experimental and Theoretical Physics*, the *Proceedings* (*Doklady*) *of the U.S.S.R. Academy of Sciences*, the geophysical and physical series of the *Bulletin* (*Izvestiya*) *of the U.S.S.R. Academy of Sciences*, the *Journal of Technical Physics*, *Progress* (*Uspekhi*) *in the Physical Sciences*, *The Astronomical Journal*, and the *Soviet Journal of Atomic Energy*. A determined effort was made to supply authentic English equivalents for all scientific expressions encountered in these pages, including the basic chemical, engineering, instrumentation, and materials vocabulary. Almost all of the accompanying general nontechnical vocabulary has also been included—both because in very many instances common words assume unusual meanings in physics, and also so that the user will be relatively rarely inconvenienced by the need to refer to a general Russian-English dictionary.

Among the valuable features of this dictionary are:

1. The actual vocabulary, including synonyms for many concepts, employed by Soviet physicists in reporting current research.

2. Additional Russian vocabulary compiled from Russian-language physics encyclopedias, dictionaries, glossaries, monographs, textbooks, and official terminology lists published by the U.S.S.R. Academy of Sciences.

3. A critical selection of vocabulary from numerous bilingual dictionaries published in the Soviet Union.

4. Russian abbreviations for scientific units, journal titles, institutions, and other expressions frequently encountered in the Russian periodical literature.

5. Russian transliterations, which are often ambiguous or not immediately recognizable, of the names of many prominent non-Russian scientists, past and present.

6. The basic vocabulary of chemistry and electronics, and general technical terminology, including the names of instruments, machine parts, and materials (especially alloys), that have been found in the physics literature.

7. Astrophysical and astronomical vocabulary, including the Russian names of constellations, stars, planets, satellites, meteors, lunar features.

8. The inclusion of the terminology of all important branches of physics—theoretical, experimental, mathematical, and applied. Among the applied branches nuclear-reactor terminology is especially important.

9. Geophysical vocabulary, especially in the fields of meteorology and geophysical prospecting; also much of the related geological vocabulary and the vocabulary of minerals.

10. A reference section containing grammatical and other material in an especially useful form.

11. Blank pages provided at the end of the dictionary—a do-it-yourself supplement to enable the user to record additional Russian words and/or English equivalents as they are located in the course of his work, or as they are added to the rapidly expanding vocabulary of physics in both languages.

12. Reproduction of the transliteration scheme and of the abbreviations used in this dictionary on the back end papers, for the most convenient possible ready reference.

This dictionary furnishes meanings of many compound words and phrases which have not previously appeared in any dictionary. The significance of many of the phrases and compound words would not be obvious from the translations of the separate words; however, numerous word combinations that can be translated literally have been included as illustrations.

In the course of the preparation of the dictionary during the past seven years, dozens of bilingual physicists associated with Consultants Bureau as translators or advisors contributed specialized Russian terms and their English equivalents, or assisted in determining the identification of certain obscure terms. Special thanks are due to J. E. S. Bradley, S. Chomet, R. Des Verney, W. H. Furry, D. Harker, M. G. Jacobson, H. Lashinsky, C. V. Mulholland, P. Robeson, Jr., R. B. Rodman, A. F. Setteducati, F. L. Sinclair, N. Solntseff, S. H. Taylor, R. N. Thurston, and E. B. Uvarov.

Mr. M. G. Zimmerman, a prominent Soviet dictionary compiler, and his associates at the Soviet Institute of Scientific Information rendered invaluable assistance by supplying some otherwise-unobtainable information, and by devoting much time to a search for the meanings of several difficult and obscure expressions. I am also indebted to Professor N. V. Belov of the Institute of Crystallography of the U.S.S.R. for supplying a list of the most common Soviet transliterations of the names of minerals.

Invaluable assistance in editing and preparing material for the printer was rendered by Mrs. Helen Posner-Kagen and by her assistants at the Consultants Bureau Interlanguage Dictionaries division, who also bore the main burden of reading the galley and page proofs.

The alphabetical listing of technical and grammatical endings and of Russian phonetic transliteration forms, the inclusion of blank pages for recording new vocabulary, and the reproduction of the most frequently consulted reference material on the back end papers follow the suggestions of Mrs. Frances Coleman, editor of Consultants Bureau.

IRVING EMIN

North Miami Beach, Florida
February, 1963

Sources

The core of the vocabulary in the dictionary was derived from over 10,000 pages of Soviet physics journals. The following groups of sources were also read carefully, analyzed, or consulted for additional vocabulary:

Russian-language dictionaries and encyclopedias published in the U.S.S.R.
Terminology lists published in the U.S.S.R.
Russian physics books.
Russian-English dictionaries.
English-Russian dictionaries published in the U.S.S.R.

RUSSIAN-LANGUAGE DICTIONARIES AND ENCYCLOPEDIAS PUBLISHED IN THE U.S.S.R.

Fizicheskiĭ slovar' (*Physics Dictionary*), P. N. Belikov, Ed., 5 v., 1936–1939.

Kratkaya éntsiklopediya-atomnaya energiya (*Brief Encyclopedia of Atomic Energy*), V. S. Emel'yanov, Ed., 1958.

Slovnik fizicheskogo slovarya (*Glossary of the Encyclopedic Physics Dictionary*).

Fizicheskiĭ éntsiklopedicheskiĭ slovar' (*Encyclopedic Physics Dictionary*), Vols. I (1960) and II (1962).

Kratkiĭ politekhnicheskiĭ slovar' (*Brief Technical Dictionary*), Yu. A. Stepanov, Ed., 1955.

Kratkiĭ technicheskiĭ spravochnik I (*Brief Technical Reference Manual*), V. A. Zinov'eva, 1952.

Bol'shaya sovetskaya éntsiklopediya (*Large Soviet Encyclopedia*).

Kratkiĭ fotograficheskiĭ slovar' (*Brief Dictionary of Photography*), A. A. Lapauri and V. I. Sheberstova, Eds., 1956.

Biograficheskiĭ slovar' deyateleĭ estestvoznaniya i tekhniki (*Biographical Dictionary of Scientists*), A. A. Zvorykin, Ed., 2 v., 1959.

Orfograficheskiĭ slovar' russkogo yazyka (*Orthographical Dictionary of the Russian Language*), 1958.

Slovar' inostrannykh slov (*Dictionary of Foreign Words*), I. V. Lekhin and F. N. Petrov, 1954.

TERMINOLOGY LISTS PUBLISHED IN THE U.S.S.R.

International Electrochemical Vocabulary

Group 07, *Electronics*, 1959 (Russian-English).

Group 05, *Fundamental Definitions*, 1957 (Russian-English).

U.S.S.R. Academy of Sciences, Technical Terminology Committee.

Terminology of Hydromechanics, 1947 (Russian-English).

Terminology of Theoretical Electrical Engineering, 1958 (Russian-English).

Dielectrics, 1960 (Russian-English).

Terminology of General Mechanics, 1955.

Terminology of the Theory of Elasticity, Testing and Mechanical Properties of Materials, and Structural Mechanics, 1952.

Fundamental Astronomical Symbols, 1959.

Terminology of Illumination, 1956.

RUSSIAN PHYSICS BOOKS

G. S. Landsberg, *Optics*, 1952.
A. F. Ioffe, *Semiconductors in Modern Physics*, 1954.
A. A. Chechulin, *Wave Processes, Optics and Elementary Nuclear Physics*, 1954.
Ya. I. Frenkel, *Principles of Atomic Theory*, 1955.
N. A. Kaptsov, *Electric Phenomena in Gases and in a Vacuum*, 1950.
B. A. Vorontsov-Vel'yaminov, *Astronomy*, 1959.
M. V. Vol'kenshtein, *Structure and Physical Properties of Molecules*, 1955.
A. Kh. Khrgian, *Physics of the Atmosphere*, 1958.
G. M. Popov and I. I. Shafranovskiĭ, *Crystallography*, 1948.
V. A. Kireev, *A Course in Physical Chemistry*, 1951.
M. A. Blokhin, *Physics of X-Rays*, 1953.
L. G. Loitsyanskiĭ, *Mechanics of Liquids and Gases*, 1957.
A. G. Samoĭlovich, *Thermodynamics and Statistical Physics*, 1953.
V. I. Levantovskiĭ, *By Rocket to the Moon*, 1960.
L. D. Landau and E. M. Lifshitz, *Electrodynamics of Continuous Media*, 1959.
S. L. Sobolev, *Equations of Mathematical Physics*, 1950.
V. A. Ambartsumyan, *Theoretical Astrophysics*, 1952.
A. I. Akhiezer and V. B. Berestetskiĭ, *Quantum Electrodynamics*, 1953.
I. E. Tutov, *Metal Structure*, 1954.
L. I. Landau and E. M. Lifshitz, *Mechanics*, 1958.
E. S. Venttsel', *Theory of Probability*, 1958.
B. B. Gnedenko, *A Course in the Theory of Probability*, 1954.
M. N. Marchevskiĭ, *Theory of Numbers*, 1958.

RUSSIAN-ENGLISH DICTIONARIES

Russian-English Dictionary, A. I. Smirnitskiĭ, 1958.

Russian-English Technical and Chemical Dictionary, first edition, L. I. Callaham, Wiley, 1947.

Russian-English Polytechnical Dictionary, L. N. Kondratov, 1948.

Russian-English Glossary of Guided Missile, Rocket and Satellite Terms, A. Rosenberg, Library of Congress, 1958.

Russian-English Glossary of Metallurgical and Metal-Working Terms, A. Akhonin, 1955.

Glossary of Soviet Military Technology, English-Russian and Russian-English, U.S. Army Technical Manual TM30–544, 1955.

Electronics Dictionary, English-Russian and Russian-English, U.S. Army Technical Manual TM30–545, 1956.

Mathematical Dictionary, Russian-German-English, Berlin, 1959.

Russian Abbreviations, A. Rosenberg, Library of Congress, 1957.

Russian-English Glossary of Aeronautical and Miscellaneous Technical Terms, U.S. Dept. of Commerce, OTS, 1956.

Atomic Energy—Glossary of Technical Terms, United Nations, 1958.

Russian-English Nuclear Dictionary, D. I. Voskoboĭnik and M. G. Zimmerman, 1960.

Russian-English Dictionary of Mathematical Sciences, A. J. Lohwater, Am. Math. Soc., 1961.

ENGLISH-RUSSIAN DICTIONARIES PUBLISHED IN THE U.S.S.R.

English-Russian Nuclear Dictionary, D. I. Voskoboĭnik and M. G. Zimmerman, 1960.

English-Russian Dictionary of Nuclear Physics and Engineering, E. V. Shpol'skiĭ, 1955.

English-Russian Dictionary of Radio and Electronics, N. I. Dozorov, 1959.

English-Russian Dictionary on Pure and Applied Chemistry, K. M. Herzfeld, 1953.

English-Russian Electrotechnical Dictionary, L. B. Heiler and N. I. Dozorov, 1951.

English-Russian Meteorological Dictionary, M. Aĭnbinder, 1959.

English-Russian Meteorological Dictionary, L. I. Mamontova and S. P. Khromov, 1959.

English-Russian Geological Dictionary, T. A. Sofiano, 1957.

English-Russian Dictionary on Civil Engineering, P. G. Amburger, 1951.

English-Russian Dictionary on Machine Elements, L. D. Belkind, 1959.

English-Russian Dictionary on Automation and Instruments, L. K. Ptashnyĭ, 1957.

English-Russian Rocket Dictionary, A. M. Murashkevich, 1958.

English-Russian Dictionary of Oceanographical Terms, N. N. Gorskiĭ and V. I. Gorskaya, 1957.

THE ENGLISH-LANGUAGE SOURCES WHICH WERE FREQUENTLY CONSULTED INCLUDED:

Glossary of Geology and Related Sciences, Am. Geol. Inst., 1957.

Glossary of Meteorology, Am. Meteorol. Soc., 1959.

Mathematics Dictionary, G. James and R. C. James, Van Nostrand, 1959.

A Dictionary of Named Effects and Laws in Chemistry, Physics and Mathematics, D. W. G. Ballenteyne and L. E. Q. Walker, Chapman and Hall, 1958.

American Institute of Physics Handbook, 1957.

Encyclopedic Dictionary of Electronics and Nuclear Engineering, R. I. Sarabacher, Prentice-Hall, 1959.

International Dictionary of Physics and Electronics, Van Nostrand, 1956.

Systematic Mineralogy of Uranium and Thorium, Geological Survey Bulletin 1064, 1958.

A Dictionary of Statistical Terms, M. G. Kendall and W. R. Buckland, Hafner, 1957.

A Glossary of Terms in Nuclear Science and Technology, ASME, 1955.

Dictionary of Guided Missiles and Space Flight, Van Nostrand, 1959.

International Dictionary of Applied Mathematics, Van Nostrand, 1960.

In addition to the listed sources, terminology was selected critically from numerous Soviet translations of English-language textbooks and monographs in specialized fields of physics.

Introduction

The scope and arrangement of the dictionary are described in this introduction, with an account given of the procedures adhered to in order to attain maximum consistency. Regular users will benefit by keeping these explanations in mind.

Alphabetical Order. All words, phrases, names, and abbreviations are entered in strictly alphabetical order. Words sharing an identical stem are generally included in a single paragraph. Hyphenated compounds and phrases consisting of two or more words are most frequently listed under the constituent having the least literal or obvious meaning. Frequently, however, many phrases are included in a single paragraph under a key word such as **антенна.**

Paragraphs of more than 25 lines are frequently broken into two or more parts. In such cases the main entry word is repeated, followed by the abbreviation *cont.* (continued).

English Synonyms. The English-language equivalents are generally those most useful for scientific comprehension and translation. In many instances several English synonyms will frequently become apparent from an examination of nearby related or associated words. Nonsynonymous English equivalents are separated by semicolons, synonyms and near-synonyms by commas.

Parenthetical Explanations. Parenthetical abbreviations or complete words designating branches of science are used, as a rule, only to eliminate ambiguities. Parentheses also enclose words which can be used optionally to form phrases, which can be used as synonyms, or which clarify the meanings of adjacent words.

Abbreviations. We have incorporated abbreviations (in their most frequently encountered form) of: scientific and engineering terms and measurement units; journals frequently cited in Soviet physics literature; institutes, laboratories, learned and technical societies; major Soviet universities, libraries, publishing and other agencies; grammatical, bibliographic, and lexicographic terms; and many other expressions frequently abbreviated in the Soviet literature of the physical sciences. The explanations of abbreviations of physical terms are followed (in parentheses) by the equivalent abbreviations most usual in the physics literature of the United States.

Some Russian abbreviations, particularly those of Soviet agencies, republics, etc., appear in the Soviet literature in more than one form (capitalized or lower-cased, with or without periods, as one or more words, etc.). In this dictionary, only the most frequently encountered form is given as a rule.

Some of the abbreviations for Soviet agencies may have meanings in addition to those identified herein.

Russian Spelling. The Russian literature, like that of other languages, reveals inconsistent spellings of many words and names. In this dictionary predominant usage is followed in all instances for which sufficient evidence has been recorded. For other words the *Orthographical Dictionary of the Russian Language* has been used as an authority. In the case of proper names the *Russian Biographical Dictionary*, the *Large Soviet Encyclopedia*, and the *Encyclopedic Physics Dictionary* have been used as authorities. Bibliographic information on these sources is given on page ix.

Proper Names of Non-Russian Scientists have been listed most frequently as they appear in the literature, that is, combined with a Russian word designating a law, theory, equation, process, etc. The Russian name in such instances usually appears in the genitive case, but the English equivalent is not generally given in the possessive form. Uncapitalized Russian adjectives formed from proper names are often substituted for the genitive case of the name. In some instances both the proper name and the corresponding adjective are given. Cross references are given to alternative Russian spellings of some of the most frequently occurring names.

Russian Proper Names. The explanation already given regarding the listed forms of non-Russian names also applies to the names of Russian scientists. The English equivalents generally follow the British-American Standard Transliteration Scheme. Alternative spellings found frequently in the English-language literature are included in parentheses.

General Vocabulary. The general vocabulary is that of contemporary Soviet physics. However, some obsolete, nearly obsolete, or historical terms and proper names are included to facilitate the reading of the older Russian physics literature.

Phrases that are obvious literal combinations of the constituent words have been listed relatively infrequently. The included instances serve to eliminate doubt regarding the validity of a literal translation, or as examples for less-experienced users.

Minerals. The names of many common minerals, especially those mentioned very frequently in the geophysical or crystallographic literature or in connection with uranium prospecting and processing, have been included. The selection of this vocabulary emphasizes words that are not obvious transliterations of the English equivalents, or which illustrate the Russian spellings of the proper names incorporated in the names of the minerals.

Chemical and Electronic Terminology. The fundamental chemical and electronic terminology used in physical science is included. Some examples of chemical compounds are given. Innumerable additional words and phrases can be translated on the basis of the constituent words, prefixes, and suffixes given in this vocabulary.

GRAMMAR

It is assumed that most users of the dictionary have at least an elementary knowledge of Russian grammar.

Nouns. All nouns are listed in the nominative case, accompanied frequently by instances of other cases used idiomatically to form useful expressions.

Adjectives. All adjectives are listed in the masculine singular nominative form. Illustrative combinations are given in the traditional order: masculine, feminine, neuter, and plural. Cases other than the nominative are sometimes incorporated in phrases, which appear at the end of the entry.

Alternative forms of adjectives (with different endings but identical meanings) are sometimes listed (*Ex.* **полиморфный** and **полиморфический**), although usually only one form is given. Alternative adjective endings are also found in the English language, but less frequently than in Russian (*Ex.* symmetr*ic* and symmetr*ical*, isotherm*ic* and isotherm*al*, amorph*ic* and amorph*ous*). The dictionary may in specific instances include both forms or only one, in Russian and in English.

A few very common comparative forms of adjectives are included.

Verbs are listed in the infinitive form. The imperfective and perfective infinitives are frequently given together as one entry, but either infinitive may be listed alone. Many frequently used verb forms, including participles and gerunds, are included without specific identification as verbs. Reflexive infinitives (having the suffix —**ся** or —**сь**) are not generally listed unless their meanings differ considerably from a literal reflexive translation.

Adverbs are usually formed by changing the adjective endings —**ый** and —**ой** to —**о**; —**ский** to —**ски**; and sometimes —**ий** to —**е**. Adverbs are not consistently listed along with the adjectives from which they are derived. Occasionally the adverb alone is listed; in such instances the corresponding adjective would be recognizable immediately.

Pronouns. Inflected forms of the personal pronouns are listed.

Reference Section

The dictionary is not accompanied by a summary of Russian grammar. However, the following pages contain reference material which will be valuable to users irrespective of their knowledge of the Russian language. The various lists will facilitate the translation of words not contained in the dictionary. The alphabetized lists of technical word endings, and of the grammatical endings of verbs, nouns, and adjectives, will be especially helpful in deducing the meanings of Russian words from a knowledge of what their roots signify. A brief discussion of Russian participles and gerunds is included because these forms are often confused and translated incorrectly.

Russian Alphabet

STANDARD		ITALICS	TRANSLITERATION
А	а	*а*	a
Б	б	*б*	b
В	в	*в*	v
Г	г	*г*	g
Д	д	*д*	d
Е	е	*е*	e
Ж	ж	*ж*	zh
З	з	*з*	z
И	и	*и*	i
Й	й	*й*	ĭ
К	к	*к*	k
Л	л	*л*	l
М	м	*м*	m
Н	н	*н*	n
О	о	*о*	o
П	п	*п*	p
Р	р	*р*	r
С	с	*с*	s
Т	т	*т*	t
У	у	*у*	u
Ф	ф	*ф*	f
Х	х	*х*	kh
Ц	ц	*ц*	ts
Ч	ч	*ч*	ch
Ш	ш	*ш*	sh
Щ	щ	*щ*	shch
Ъ	ъ	*ъ*	,,
Ы	ы	*ы*	y
Ь	ь	*ь*	'
Э	э	*э*	é
Ю	ю	*ю*	yu
Я	я	*я*	ya

COMMENTS ON RUSSIAN ALPHABET

1. The letter ё is usually written as е although the pronunciation "yo" is retained. The letter э has been retained in the Soviet orthography but has been replaced by е in some words.

2. The following letters of the pre-Revolutionary orthography were eliminated by the Soviet government:

DISCARDED LETTERS	REPLACEMENTS
І і	И и
Ѣ ѣ	Е е
Ѵ ѵ	И и
Ѳ ѳ	Ф ф

3. Russian italic letters are generally used for the same purposes as English italics, and especially for abbreviations of scientific terms and measurement units (not followed by periods), and in stating theorems. The Russian standard letters which differ considerably in appearance from the corresponding italic letters are: а (*а*); в (*в*); г (*г*); д *д*; и (*и*); п (*п*); and т (*т*).

TRANSLITERATION

1. The transliteration scheme given here is the British-American Standard system, which has been adopted by the American Institute of Physics, by Consultants Bureau, and by many other institutions and publishers. Additional rules of this system are:

a. The combination тс is transliterated as "t-s" to distinguish it from the consonant ц (ts).

b. The combination ыа is transliterated as "ȳa" to distinguish it from the letter я (ya).

c. The combination ыу is transliterated as "ȳu" to distinguish it from the letter ю (yu).

2. Differences between this system and the Library of Congress transliteration system are given in the following table:

RUSSIAN LETTERS	LIBRARY OF CONGRESS	BRITISH-AMERICAN STANDARD
е	ye	e
й	y	ĭ
тс	ts	t-s
ы (before у or а)	y	ȳ
э	e	é
ю	iu	yu
я	ia	ya

3. In the interest of eliminating unnecessary diacritical marks, many publishers use "i" instead of "ĭ" in transliterating the endings of Russian proper names, since this causes no ambiguity.

COMMON RUSSIAN TECHNICAL WORD ENDINGS

The most common Russian endings of technical words which are not exact transliterations of the equivalent English words are included in the following alphabetical list, together with illustrations of the corresponding English endings. (*Some of the examples are not grammatical suffixes.*)

RUSSIAN ENDINGS	ENGLISH ENDINGS	RUSSIAN EXAMPLES	ENGLISH EQUIVALENTS
—аза *f.*	—ase	лактаза	lactase
—айший *a.*	—est	нижайший	lowest
—амма *f.*	—am	диаграмма	diagram
—ан *m.*	—an	меркаптан	mercaptan
	—ane	октан	octane
—ат *m.*	—ate	борат	borate
—атный *a.*	—ate	сульфатный	sulfate
—аф *m.*	—aph	спектрограф	spectrograph
	—apher	фотограф	photographer
—в, ва, во *a.*	—ian	Броуново движение	Brownian motion
—ватый *a.*	—ish	зеленоватый	greenish
—вый *a.*	—ic	ацетиленовый	acetylenic
—е *a. comp.*	—er	больше	larger
		легче	easier
—ее *a. comp.*	—er	слабее	weaker
adv. comp.	more		more weakly
—ез *m.*	—esis	синтез	synthesis
—еза *f.*	—esis	гипотеза	hypothesis
—ейший *a.*	—est	новейший	newest
—ема *f.*	—em	проблема	problem
—ен *m.*	—ene	антрацен	anthracene
	—en	глутен	gluten
—ентность *f.*	—ence	турбулентность	turbulence
—ентный *a.*	—ent	турбулентный	turbulent
—енция *f.*	—ency	тенденция	tendency
—есть *f.*	—ity	летучесть	volatility
—зионный *a.*	—sion	телевизионный	television
—зия *f.*	—sion	телевизия	television
—ивность *f.*	—ivity	селективность	selectivity
—ивный *a.*	—ive	селективный	selective
—ид *m.*	—ide	сульфид	sulfide
—идный *a.*	—ide	сульфидный	sulfide
—иевый *a.*	—ium, —ic	талиевый	thallium, thallic

RUSSIAN ENDINGS	ENGLISH ENDINGS	RUSSIAN EXAMPLES	ENGLISH EQUIVALENTS
—из *m.*	—ysis	гидролиз	hydrolysis
—изация *f.*	—ization	ионизация	ionization
—изированный *a.*	—yzed	анализированный	analyzed
—изировать *v.*	—yze	анализировать	analyze
—ий *m.*	—ium	бериллий	beryllium
—ик *m.*	—ist	физик	physicist
	diminutive	столик	small table
—ика *f.*	—ics	физика	physics
—ил *m.*	—yl	бензил	benzyl
	—ile	нитрил	nitrile
—иловый *a.*	—yl	бензиловый	benzyl
—ин *m.*	—in	парафин	paraffin
	—ol	глицерин	glycerol
	—ine	бензин	benzine
	—ene	керосин	kerosene
—иновый *a.*	—ine	анилиновый	aniline
—ирование *n.*	—ation	галоидирование	halogenation
—ированный *a.*	—ated	метилированный	methylated
	—ed	окклюдированный	occluded
—иссионный *a.*	—ission	трансмиссионный	transmission
—иссия *f.*	—ission	трансмиссия	transmission
—истый *a.*	—ous, —iferous	железистый	ferrous, ferriferous
	—y	серебристый	silvery
—ит *m.*	—ite	гранит	granite
	—yte	электролит	electrolyte
	—itis	неврит	neuritis
—итный *a.*	—ite, —itic	гранитный	granite, granitic
	—ytic	электролитный	electrolytic
—ификация *f.*	—ification	ректификация	rectification
—ифицированный *a.*	—ified	ректифицированный	rectified
—ифицировать *v.*	—ify	ректифицировать	rectify
—ический *a.*	—ic	металлический	metallic
	—ical	физический	physical
—ичный *a.*	—ical	типичный	typical
	—ous	аналогичный	analogous
—ия *f.*	—y	энергия	energy
	—ion	прогрессия	progression
	—ism	изомерия	isomerism
	—ia	анемия	anemia

RUSSIAN ENDINGS	ENGLISH ENDINGS	RUSSIAN EXAMPLES	ENGLISH EQUIVALENTS
—ка *f.*	—let	капелька	droplet
	diminutive	цепочка	small chain
—мость *f.*	—bility	растворимость	solubility
—мый *a.*	—ble	растворимый	soluble
—ние *n.*	—tion	основание	foundation
	—ing	кипение	boiling
—ник *m.*	—or	проводник	conductor
—нный *a.*	—ed	поглощенный	absorbed
—ный *a.*	—ic	магнитный	magnetic
	—ous	аномальный	anomalous
—о *adv.*	—ly	легко	easily
—ог *m.*	—ogist	биолог	biologist
—од *m.*	—ode	электрод	electrode
—оз *m.*	—osis	симбиоз	symbiosis
—оза *f.*	—ose	целлюлоза	cellulose
—ол *m.*	—ol	этанол	ethanol
	—ene	бензол	benzene
—оль *m.*	—ol	алкоголь	alcohol
—ольный *a.*	—olic	алкогольный	alcoholic
—ом *m.*	—ome	аэродром	aerodrome
—он *m.*	—on	фотон	photon
	—one	ацетон	acetone
—онный *a.*	—onic	электронный	electronic
—ость *f.*	—ness	твердость	hardness
	—ity	емкость	capacity
—ота *f.*	—ity	чистота	purity
	—cy	частота	frequency
	abstract noun	теплота	heat
—рный *a.*	—ar	молекулярный	molecular
—ски *adv.*	—ally	физически	physically
—ский *a.*	—ic	палеозойский	Paleozoic
	—ian	кембрийский	Cambrian
—ство *n.*	—ity	количество	quantity
	abstract noun	вещество	matter
—тель *m.*	—er	окислитель	oxidizer
	—or	ускоритель	accelerator
—тельный *a.*	—ent	поглотительный	absorbent
	—ive	уничтожительный	destructive
—тор *m.*	—er	трансформатор	transformer
	—or	генератор	generator

RUSSIAN ENDINGS	ENGLISH ENDINGS	RUSSIAN EXAMPLES	ENGLISH EQUIVALENTS
	—yst	катализатор	catalyst
—тый *a.*	—ed	тянутый	pulled
—ура *f.*	—ure	номенклатура	nomenclature
—ца *f.*	diminutive	частица	particle
—ционный *a.*	—tion, —tional	фрикционный	friction, frictional
—ция *f.*	—tion	порция	portion
—чик *m.*	—er	летчик	flyer
—шко *n.*	diminutive	пятнышко	small spot
—ще *adv.*	—ingly	исчезающе	vanishingly
—щий *a.*	—ing, —ent	поглощающий	absorbing, absorbent
—щийся *a.*	—ble	окисляющийся	oxidizable

ENDINGS OF NOUNS AND ADJECTIVES

The case endings are those of singular nouns except where adjectives (*a.*) or plural (*pl.*) nouns are specified. The symbol * indicates that the ending is also a verb ending.

—а*	*m., n. (gen.); f. (nom.); n. pl. (nom., acc.)*
—ай	*m. (nom., acc.)*
—ам	*pl. (dat.)*
—ами	*pl. (instr.)*
—ах	*pl. (prep.)*
—ая	*a. f. (nom.)*
—е	*m., f., n. (prep.); f. (dat.); n. (nom., acc.); adv.*
—ев	*m. pl. (gen.)*
—его	*a. m., n. (gen.)*
—ее	*a. n. (nom., acc.)* or *adv. comp.*
—ей	*f. (instr.); m., f., n. pl. (gen.); a. f. (gen., dat., instr., prep.)*
—ем*	*m., n. (instr.); a. m., n. (prep.)*
—ему	*a. m., n. (dat.)*
—ею	*f. (instr.); a. f. (instr.)*
—и	*f. (gen., dat., prep.); m., f. pl. (nom., acc.)*
—ие	*a. pl. (nom., acc.)*
—ии	*m., n. (prep.); f. (gen., dat., prep.)*
—ий	*m. (nom., acc.); f., n. pl. (gen.); a. m. (nom.)*
—им*	*a. m., n. (instr.); pl. (dat.)*
—ими	*a. pl. (instr.)*
—их	*a. pl. (gen., prep.)*
—о	*n. (nom., acc.); adv.*
—ов	*m. pl. (gen.)*
—ого	*a. m., n. (gen.)*
—ое	*a. n. (nom., acc.)*
—ой	*m. (nom., acc.); f. (instr.); a. m. (nom., acc.), f. (gen., dat., instr., prep.)*
—ом	*m., n. (instr.); a. m., n. (prep.)*
—ому	*a. m., n. (dat.)*
—ою	*f. (instr.); a. f. (instr.)*
—у*	*m., n. (dat.); f. (acc.)*
—ую*	*a. f. (acc.)*
—ы	*f. (gen.); m., f. pl. (nom., acc.)*
—ые	*a. pl. (nom., acc.)*
—ый	*a. m. (nom., acc.)*
—ым	*a. m., n. (instr.); a. pl. (dat.)*
—ыми	*a. pl. (instr.)*

—ых	*a. pl. (gen., prep.)*
—ь	*m., f. (nom., acc.); f. pl. (gen.)*
—ью	*f. (instr.)*
—ю *	*m., n. (dat.); f. (acc.)*
—юю *	*a. f. (acc.)*
—я *	*m., n. (gen.); f. (nom); n. pl. (nom., acc.)*
—ям	*pl. (dat.)*
—ями	*pl. (instr.)*
—ях	*pl. (prep.)*
—яя	*a. f. (nom.)*

VERB ENDINGS

The 1st, 2nd, and 3rd persons, singular and plural, and the past tense, infinitive, participle, and gerund endings are indicated.

—а	present gerund
—ат	3 *pl.*
—в	past gerund
—вши	past gerund
—вший	past active participle
—ем	1 *pl.*
—ет	3 *sing.*
—ете	2 *pl.*
—ешь	2 *sing.*
—им	1 *pl.*
—ит	3 *sing.*
—ите	2 *pl.*
—ишь	2 *sing.*
—л	past tense (*m.*)
—ла	past tense (*f.*)
—ли	past tense (*pl.*)
—ло	past tense (*n.*)
—мый	present passive participle
—нный	past passive participle
—сь	reflexive verb
—ся	reflexive verb
—ти	infinitive
—тый	past passive participle
—ть	infinitive
—у	1 *sing.*
—ую	1 *sing.*
—ший	past active participle
—щий	present active participle
—ю	1 *sing.*
—ют	3 *pl.*
—юю	1 *sing.*
—я	present gerund
—ят	3 *pl.*

VERB FORMATION

Verbs can be formed from the positive or comparative forms of adjectives or from nouns. Important points to remember are: (1) most of these verbs are formed with the prefix у— (less frequently по—, о—, за—, or other prefixes), but the prefix usually has no specific meaning; (2) consonants are sometimes interchanged.

RUSSIAN VERB	ENGLISH EQUIVALENT	RUSSIAN ROOT	ENGLISH EQUIVALENT
улучшать	improve	лучше	better
уменьшать	diminish	меньше	less
ускорять	accelerate	скорый	rapid

RUSSIAN VERB	ENGLISH EQUIVALENT	RUSSIAN ROOT	ENGLISH EQUIVALENT
повторять	repeat	второй	second
объяснять	clarify, explain	ясный	clear
обугливать	carbonize	уголь	carbon
освещать	illuminate	свет	light
затруднять	impede	трудный	difficult
испарять	evaporate	пар	vapor
превышать	exceed	выше	higher
ухудшать*	impair	хуже	worse

* Note substitution of дш for ж in forming the verb.

PARTICIPLES AND GERUNDS

Present Active Participles are formed only from imperfective verbs, by substituting the ending —щий for the final —т in the 3rd person plural of the present tense:

работать (работают)	работающий	working
составлять (составляют)	составляющий	constituting

The meaning is the present performing of an action.

Present Passive Participles are formed only from transitive imperfective verbs, by adding —ый to the 1st person plural of the present tense:

освещать (освещаем)	освещаемый	(being) illuminated
проницать (проницаем)	проницаемый	(being) permeated; permeable
видеть (видим)	видимый	(being) seen; visible

The meaning is either submission to an action (being done) or susceptibility to an action.

Past Active Participles are usually formed by substituting —вший for the final —л of the masculine past tense form, or by adding —ший if the past tense does not end in —л:

взять (взял)	взявший	having taken [perfective]
тереть (тер)	терший	(which was) rubbing [imperfective]
идти (шёл)	шедший	having gone [perfective]
нагреться (нагрелся)	нагревшийся	having been heated [perfective]

The meaning is the past performance of an action.

Past Passive Participles are formed only from transitive, mainly perfective, verbs, most frequently by substituting either —нный or —тый for the ending —ть of the infinitive; consonant or vowel changes also occur in the stems of some verbs:

сделать	сделанный	done
сфотографировать	сфотографированный	photographed
покрыть	покрытый	covered

понять	понятый	understood
достигнуть	достигнутый	attained
окислить	окисленный	oxidized
сжечь	сожженный	burnt
унести	унесенный	carried away
найти	найденный	found
осветить	освещенный	illuminated

The meaning is that of an adjective representing past submission to an action.

Present Gerunds are formed only from imperfective verbs, by adding —а or —я (or rarely —учи) to the stem of the 3rd person plural of the present tense:

исследовать (исследуют)	исследуя	(when, or while) investigating
слышать (слышат)	слыша	hearing
быть (будут)	будучи	being
развиваться (развиваются)	развиваясь	being developed (developing itself)

Past Gerunds are usually formed, mainly from perfective verbs, by substituting either —в or —вши for the ending —ть of the infinitive; many verbs can have either ending:

сделать	сделав, сделавши	having done
взять	взяв, взявши	having taken
быть	быв, бывши	having been
разделить	разделив, разделивши	having divided
открыть	открыв, открывши	having discovered
идти	шедши	having gone
нести	несши	having carried

RUSSIAN SPELLING OF BORROWED WORDS AND NAMES

Transliteration into the Russian is based on phonetics rather than a letter-by-letter scheme. Since the Russian alphabet cannot represent all the sounds of foreign languages from which words and names have been borrowed, transliteration back to the original Latin-alphabet name is frequently very difficult. The Russian versions can be classified, but numerous inconsistencies are encountered in Russian publications. The following list contains examples of many of the rules that are usually followed in rendering English, German, and French words and names into Russian. The sounds represented are of the English language unless followed by (F)—signifying French, or (G)—signifying German. It should also be borne in mind that French names and words are sometimes transliterated into Russian as they would be pronounced in German.

RUSSIAN	SOUND	RUSSIAN EXAMPLE	ORIGINAL NAME OR WORD
ав	au	автор	author
ай	i	таймер	timer
	ei (G)	Майсснер	Meissner
ан	en (F)	жанр	genre
ау	ow	Браун	Brown
в	w	Вильсон	Wilson
г	h	гелий	helium
дж	g	Джермер	Germer
	j	Джонс	Jones
е	a	Чедвик	Chadwick
	u	Рессел	Russell
	ä (G)	Трегер	Träger
	er (F)	Оже	Auger
ев	eu	псевдо	pseudo
ей	a	Бейтс	Bates
	eu	нейтральный	neutral
	eu (G)	Гейслер	Heusler
ж	g	Женева	Geneva
	j (F)	журнал	journal
з	s	квази	quasi
	s (G)	Бунзен	Bunsen
	s (F)	зонд	sonde
	th	Резерфорд	Rutherford
и	y	Йорк	York
	e	Истмэн	Eastman
	ie (G)	Вин	Wien
	j (G)	Иод	Jod
к	c	Кембридж	Cambridge
кв	qu	эквивалент	equivalent
кз	x	экзотермный	exothermic
кс	x	гексан	hexane
о	a	Уокер	Walker
	au	боксит	bauxite
	au (F)	Оже	Auger
	eau (F)	Шевено	Chéveneau
с	th	Раус	Routh
т	th	теория	theory
у	oo	Вуд	Wood
	w	Уокер	Walker

RUSSIAN	SOUND	RUSSIAN EXAMPLE	ORIGINAL NAME OR WORD
	ou (F)	ампула	ampoule
уа	ois (F)	Дю Буа	Du Bois
ф	ph	фот	phot
	th	логарифм	logarithm
х	h	Холл	Hall
	ch (G)	характер	Charakter
ц	z	цинк	zinc
	z (G)	принцип	Prinzip
	tz	кварц	quartz
це	ce	цемент	cement
ци	cy	циклотрон	cyclotron
ш	ch (F)	шифр	chiffre
шт	st (G)	Штрих	Strich
ье	ier (F)	Фурье	Fourier
э	a	Чэдвик	Chadwick
	ai	Эри	Airy
	u	Фэрри	Furry
	et (F)	Сорэ	Soret
эв	eu	эвтектика	eutectic
эй	ai	Эйри	Airy
ю	hughe	Юз	Hughes
	ju	Юпитер	Jupiter
	u (F)	Дю Буа	Du Bois
	ü (G)	Мюллер	Müller
я	ja	Якобсон	Jacobson

CONSONANT INTERCHANGES

The relationships between many words become apparent when certain frequently occurring interchanges of sounds are observed. Among the common alternations of consonants are:

г ↔ ж	к ↔ ч	т ↔ ч
д ↔ ж	с ↔ ш	т ↔ щ
д ↔ жд	ск ↔ щ	ц ↔ ч
з ↔ ж	ст ↔ щ	х ↔ ш

Ex.

много ↔ множество	свет ↔ освещать
низкий ↔ ниже	частица ↔ частичный
наука ↔ научный	воздух ↔ воздушный

ALTERNATIVE SPELLINGS

Many borrowed words and names appear with more than one Russian spelling. Some of the most frequent alternative spellings have been indicated in the dictionary by cross references. Among the alternative letters and letter combinations are:

б ↔ п	л ↔ лл	с ↔ сс
г ↔ гг	л ↔ ль	т ↔ тт
г ↔ х	м ↔ мм	у ↔ ю
е ↔ э	н ↔ нн	ф ↔ фф
	п ↔ пп	

Ex. Доплер ↔ Допплер (Doppler)
коэфициент ↔ коэффициент (coefficient)

Abbreviations

a.	adjective
abbr.	abbreviation
acc.	accusative
acous.	acoustics
adv.	adverb
aero.	aerodynamics, aeronautics
astr.	astronomy, astrophysics
bio.	biology, biophysics
chem.	chemistry
comp.	comparative
conj.	conjunction
cont.	continued
cosm.	cosmic rays
cryst.	crystallography
dat.	dative
elast.	elasticity
elec.	electricity, electronics
esp.	especially
Ex.	example
f.	feminine
fluor.	fluorescence
gen.	genitive
geo.	geology, geophysics
geod.	geodesy
geom.	geometry
hyd.	hydrodynamics
imp.	imperative
instr.	instrumental
m.	masculine
mach.	machinery
mag.	magnetism
math.	mathematics
mech.	mechanics
med.	medicine
mes.	meson physics
met.	metals, metallurgy
meteor.	meteorology
micros.	microscopy
mil.	military
min.	mining
mol.	molecular physics
mus.	music
n.	neuter
naut.	nautical
nucl.	nuclear physics, nuclear power
obs.	obsolete
opt.	optics
petr.	petrology
phot.	photography
photom.	photometry
pl.	plural
plast.	plasticity
prep.	preposition, prepositional
pron.	pronoun
quant.	quantum mechanics, quantum electrodynamics
rad.	radio, radar
rel.	relativity
seis.	seismology
semicond.	semiconductors
sing.	singular
sol.	solid state physics
spec.	specifically
spect.	spectroscopy
stat.	statistics
surv.	surveying
tech.	technology
telev.	television
therm.	thermodynamics, heat
v.	verb

А

а *conj.* but; and; **а не** rather than; **а так как** and since; **а (не) то** otherwise.

а *abbr.* (**ампер**) ampere (amp); (**ар**) are.

А *abbr.* (**нормальная атмосфера**) standard atmosphere.

Å *abbr.* (**ангстрем**) ångström, angstrom (Å, A), Ångström unit.

ААН *abbr.* (**Архив Академии наук СССР**) Archives of the Academy of Sciences, USSR.

ААО *abbr.* (**Абастуманская горная астрофизическая обсерватория**) Abastumani Astrophysical Mountain Observatory.

абака *f.* abacus.

абампер *m.* abampere.

Аббе конденсатор (micros.) Abbe condenser; **А. условие синусов** Abbe sine condition.

абвольт *m.* abvolt.

абгенри *m.* abhenry.

АБГИЗ *abbr.* (**Абхазское государственное издательство**) Abkhasian State Press.

Абегга правило Abegg rule.

абелева группа Abelian group.

Абеля прибор Abel tester; **признак сходимости А.** A. test for convergence.

аберрация *f.* aberration.

абзац *m.* paragraph, item; indentation.

абихит *m.* abichite.

абляция *f.* ablation.

абрадировать *v.* abrade, wear off.

абраз/ив *m.* **—ивный** *a.* **—ивный материал, —ионный материал** abrasive, abradant; **—ионный** *a.* abrasion, abrasive; **—ия** *f.* abrasion.

абревиатура *f.* abbreviation.

абриаканит *m.* abriachanite.

абрис *m.* contour, outline, sketch.

абс. *abbr.* (**абсолютный**) absolute.

абс. ед. *abbr.* (**абсолютная единица**) absolute unit.

абсолютиров/ание *n.* dehydration (of alcohol); **—ать** *v.* dehydrate.

абсолютн/о *adv.* absolutely; **а. черное тело** ideal black body; **—ый** *a.* absolute; **—ый нуль** absolute zero; **—ый поглотитель** perfect absorber; **—ый радиатор** perfect radiator; **—ый эфир** absolute ether; **—ая пустота** total vacuum; **—ая система единиц** absolute system of units.

абсорб/ат *m.* absorbate; **—ент** *m.* absorbent; **—ер** *m.* absorber; absorbent; **—ированный** *a.* absorbed; **—ировать** *v.* absorb; **—ируемый** *a.* absorbable.

абсорбирующ/ий *a.* absorbing, absorbent, absorptive; **—ая сила** absorbing power; **—ее вещество** absorber, absorbing medium; **—ее средство** *see* **абсорбент.**

абсорбциометр *m.* absorptiometer; **—ический** *a.* absorptiometric; **—ия** *f.* absorptiometry.

абсорбц/ионный *a.* absorption, absorptive; **—ионная колонна** absorption column; **—ионная способность** absorptive power; **—ионное выделение** absorption extraction; **—ия** *f.* absorption.

абстатампер *m.* abstatampere.

абстра/гировать *v.* abstract; **—ктный** *a.* abstract; **—кция** *f.* abstraction.

абсурд *m.* absurdity; **—ный** *a.* absurd, incongruous, foolish; inept.

абсцисса *f.* abscissa.

абс. эл. ст. ед. *abbr.* (**абсолютная электростатическая единица**) absolute electrostatic unit.

Абульфеда Abulfeda (lunar crater).

абфарада *f.* abfarad.

Абхазская АССР, АбхАССР Abkhazian ASSR.

абцуг *m.* **—овый шлак** (met.) dross, scum.

абшайдер *m.* separator; refiner.

абштрих *m.* (met.) scum, skim, dross.

ав *abbr.* (**ампервиток**) ampere turn; **ав.** (**авиационный, авиация**) aviation.

Авангард Vanguard (satellite).

аванкамера *f.* forechamber; (hyd.) forebay, prechamber.

авантюрин *m.* aventurine.

аванцистерна *f.* preceding tank, preliminary tank; feed tank.

авар/ийный *a.* accident, emergency; **а. стержень** emergency rod, shut-down rod; safety rod, scram rod; **а. тормоз** emergency brake; —**ийная бригада** emergency crew; —**ийная остановка** emergency shut-down, scram; —**ийное положение** emergency; —**ия** *f.* accident, breakdown, failure, trouble, emergency; damage; casualty.

аваруит *m.* awaruite.

авг. *abbr.* (**август**) August.

авгит *m.* augite.

август *m.* August.

авиа— *prefix* aviation, airplane, air, aerial, aero—.

Авиавнито *abbr.* (**Всесоюзное авиационное научно-инженерно-техническое общество**) All-Union Aeronautical Scientific, Engineering and Technical Society.

авиа/горизонт *m.* gyrohorizon; —**двигатель** *m.* aircraft engine; —**звено** *n.* flight.

авиаинженер *abbr.* (**авиационный инженер**) aviation engineer.

авиаинститут *abbr.* (**авиационный институт**) aviation institute.

авиа/крыло *n.* airplane wing; —**левый** *a.* avialite; —**линия** *f.* airline.

авиалит *m.* Avialite (copper-aluminum-iron alloy).

авиа/магистраль *f.* main air route; —**матка** *f.*, —**носец** *m.* aircraft carrier.

авиамет *abbr.* (**авиационная метеорологическая станция**) aerometeorological station.

авиаметеорологическая станция aerometeorological station.

Авиаметеослужба *abbr.* (**авиационная метеорологическая служба**) air meteorological service.

авиа/отряд *m.* squadron; —**перехват** *m.* air interception; —**прицел** *m.* bomb-sight; —**разведка** *f.* air reconnaissance; —**съемка** *f.* aerial survey; —**техник** *m.* aircraft mechanic.

авиац. *abbr.* (**авиация**) aviation; (**авиационный**) aeronautical.

авиац/ионный *a.* aviation, aircraft, air, aeronautical; —**ионная метеорологическая станция** aerometeorological station; —**ионная метеорология** aeronautical meteorology; —**ия** *f.* aviation.

аво, а-во *abbr.* (**агентство**) agency.

Авогадро Avogadro; **А. закон** A. law; **А. число** A. number.

авось *adv.* perhaps, maybe; **на а.** at random, haphazardly.

австр. *abbr.* (**австрийский**) Austrian.

австрал. *abbr.* (**австралийский**) Australian.

Австралия Australia.

австрийский *a.* Austrian.

Австрия Austria.

авт. *abbr.* (**автоматический**) automatic, mechanical, unmanned; (**автономный**) autonomous; (**автор**) author, writer.

авто— *prefix* auto—, automatic; automobile.

автобаротроп/ия *f.* autobarotropy —**ный** *a.* autobarotropic.

авт. обл. *abbr.* (**автономная область**) autonomous region, oblast.

авто/блокировка *f.* automatic blocking; self-locking; —**воз** *m.* carrier, truck.

автогамма-радиометр carborne gamma-ray counter.

автоген. *abbr.* (**автогенный**) autogenous.

автогенератор *m.* self-excited oscillator

автогенн/ый *a.* autogenous; —**ая сварка** autogenous welding.

автогетеродин *m.* autoheterodyne, autodyne.

автодин *m.*, —**ный** *a.* autodyne.

авто/ионизация *f.* auto-ionization; —**жир** *m.* autogyro; —**камера** *f.* inner tube (of tire); —**катализ** *m.* autocatalysis; —**каталитический** *a.* autocatalytic; —**кисление** *n.* autooxidation.

автоклав *m.*, **—ировать** *v.* autoclave; **—ирование** *n.* autoclaving; **—ированный** *a.* autoclaved.

автокластический *a.* autoclastic.

автоколеб/ания *pl.* auto-oscillations, self-oscillations, natural oscillations; **—ательный** *a.* self-oscillating, auto-oscillating.

автоколлимац/ионный *a.* autocollimating; **—ия** *f.* autocollimation.

автоконвек/тивный *a.* autoconvective; **—ция** *f.* autoconvection.

автокоррел/ятивный *a.*, **—яция** *f.* autocorrelation; **—ятивная функция** autocorrelation function.

автолиз *m.* autolysis.

Автолик Autolycus (lunar crater).

автомат *m.* robot; automatic machine; **—изация** *f.* automatization, automation; **—изм** *m.* automatism, automatic performance; **—ика** *f.* automation; automatic equipment; **—ически записывающий** self-recording, self-registering.

автоматическ/ий *a.* automatic, mechanical, unmanned; **а. потенциометр** self-balancing potentiometer; **а. спутник** robot satellite; **—ая пишущая машина** automatic pen recorder; **—ая подстройка частоты** automatic frequency control; **—ая регулировка, —ое регулирование** self-regulation, automatic adjustment, automatic control; **—ая регулировка громкости** automatic volume control; **—ая регулировка избирательности** automatic selectivity control; **—ая регулировка усиления** automatic gain control; **—ое управление** automatic control.

автомашина *f.* motor vehicle, truck.

автомобиль *m.* automobile, car; **—ный** *a.* automobile, car, carborne; **грузовой а.** truck.

автомодельн/ость *f.* (hyd.) self-similarity; **—ый** *a.* self-similar.

автомор/физм *m.* automorphism; **—фический** *a.* automorphic.

автон., автоном. *abbr.* (**автономный**) autonomous.

автономный *a.* autonomous, independent; isolated; self-contained.

авто/пилот *m.* automatic pilot; **—подстройка частоты** automatic frequency control; **—полярный** *a.* self-polar; **—проводимость** *f.* autoconduction.

автор *m.* author, writer.

авторадиограмма *f.* autoradiogram, radioautogram.

авторадиограф *m.* autoradiograph, radioautograph; **—ирование** *n.*, **—ия** *f.* autoradiography, radioautography.

авторадиолиз *m.* autoradiolysis.

авторегресс/ивный *a.* autoregressive; **а. ряд** autoregressive series; **—ия** *f.* autoregression.

авторегулир/овка *f.* automatic control (system); **а. усиления** automatic gain control, automatic volume control; **—уемый** *a.* automatically controlled.

автореферат *m.* author's abstract.

авторизованный *a.* authorized.

авторитет *m.* authority; **—ный** *a.* authoritative; **—ный специалист** authority.

авторотация *f.* (aero.) autorotation, windmilling.

авторс/кий *a.* author's; **а. гонорар** author's honorarium; royalty, royalties; **—кое право** copyright; **—кое свидетельство** author's (inventor's) certificate; **—тво** *n.* authorship.

автосин *m.* autosyn.

автосцепка *f.* automatic coupler.

автотрансформатор *m.* autotransformer.

автофазировка *f.* phase stability (in accelerators).

автохром *m.* autochrome.

автохтонный *a.* autochthonous; **а. массив** terrane.

автоэлектронн/ый *a.* autoelectronic; **а. микроскоп** field emission microscope; **—ая эмиссия** field emission.

автоэмиссионая картина field emission pattern.

авт. рег. *abbr.* (**регулирование автоматическое**) automatic control.

авт. реф. *abbr.* (**авторский реферат**) author's abstract.

авт. свид. *abbr.* (**авторское свидетельство**) author's (inventor's) certificate.

А/Г *abbr.* (**отношение альбуминов к глобулинам**) albumin-globulin ratio (A/G).

агатовый подшипник jewel bearing.

агвиларит *m.* aguilarite.

агг— *see also* **аг—**.

агглютин/ация *f.* agglutination; **—ированный** *a.* agglutinated; **—ировать** *v.* agglutinate.

агент *m.* agent, factor; **а. удерживания** hold-back agent; **—ский** *a.* agent, acting; **—ство** *n.* agency.

агеострофический *a.* ageostrophic.

агирный *a.* triclinic.

агит/атор *m.* agitator, stirrer; **—ационный** *a.* agitation; **—ация** *f.* agitation, stirring; **—ировать** *v.* agitate, stir.

агломер/ат *m.* agglomerate, sinter, sinter cake; **—ационный** *a.* agglomeration; **—ационный обжиг** sintering; **—ация** *f.*, **—ирование** *n.* agglomeration, sintering; **—ировать** *v.* agglomerate; **—ирующее средство** agglomerant.

аглюкон *m.* aglucone.

Агнези ведьма witch of Agnesi.

АГНИИ *abbr.* [**Астрономо-геодезический научно-исследовательский институт (при Московском университете)**] Astronomy and Geodesy Scientific Research Institute (at Moscow University).

агометр *m.* agometer.

агон/а *f.*, **—альная линия, —ическая линия** agonic line.

агония *f.* agony.

аграрный *a.* agrarian, agricultural.

агрег/ат *m.* aggregate; apparatus, set, assembly, outfit, unit; plant, plant unit; **а. высокого давления** high-pressure unit; **—атный** *a.* aggregation; **—атное состояние** state of aggregation; **—ация** *f.* aggregation, clustering.

агресс/ивный *a.* aggressive; corrosive; **—ия** *f.* aggression.

агриколит *m.* agricolite.

агрикультура *f.* agriculture.

агрилит *m.* Agrilite (copper-tin-lead, etc., alloy).

Агриппа Agrippa (lunar crater).

агро— *prefix* agro—, agricultural.

агро/гидрология *f.* agrohydrology; **—климатология** *f.* agroclimatology; **—метеорология** *f.* agrometeorology.

агроном *m.* agriculturist; **—ический** *a.* agricultural; **—ия** *f.* agronomy, agriculture.

Агроприбор *abbr.* (**Завод агротехнических приборов и лабораторного стекла**) Factory for Agronomic Apparatus and Laboratory Glass.

агротех. *abbr.* (**агротехника**) agricultural technology; (**агротехнический**) agrotechnological.

агро/техника *f.* agricultural technology; **—технологический** *a.* agrotechnological; **—физика** *f.* agricultural physics; **—химия** *f.* agricultural chemistry.

АГУ *abbr.* [**Азербайджанский государственный университет) (им. С. М. Кирова)**] S. M. Kirov Azerbaidzhan State University.

а. д. *abbr.* (**авиационный двигатель**) aircraft engine.

адамантовый *a.* adamantine; firm, steadfast.

адамон *m.* adamon.

адапт/ация *f.* adaptation; **—ер** *m.* adapter; (sound) pickup; **—ированный** *a.* adapted; **—ометр** *m.* (optics) adaptometer.

адатом *m.* adatom, adsorbed atom

адванс *m.* Advance (copper-nickel alloy).

адвективный *a.* advective, advection; **а. заморозок** advection frost; **а. слой** advection layer; **а. туман** advection fog.

адвекция *f.* advection; **а. вихря скорости** vorticity advection; **а. холода** cold advection.

адгез/иограмма *f.* adhesiogram; **—иометр** *m.* adhesiometer; **—ионный** *a.* adhesive, adhesion; **—ионная способность** adhesiveness; **—ия** *f.* adhesion, adherence.

адденд *m.* addend.

аддитивн/ость *f.* additivity; **—ый** *a.* additive; **—ый член** additive term; **—ая интерференция** constructive interference.

адекватн/о *adv.* adequately, sufficiently; **—ость** *f.* adequacy; **—ый** *a.* adequate, sufficient.

Аджарская АССР, АджАССР Adzhar ASSR.

адиабата *f.* adiabatic curve; **а. влажная** moist adiabat; **а. сухая** dry adiabat.

адиабатическ/ий *a.* adiabatic; **а. градиент** adiabatic gradient, adiabatic lapse rate; **а. перепад температур** (meteor.) adiabatic lapse rate; **—ое падение для сухой атмосферы** dry adiabatic lapse rate; **—ое понижение температуры влажного воздуха с высотой** saturated adiabatic lapse rate, moist adiabatic lapse rate; **—ое понижение температуры сухого воздуха с высотой** dry adiabatic lapse rate.

адиабат/ичный, —ный *see* **адиабатический; —ная бумага** adiabatic diagram (chart).

адиактинический *a.* adiactinic.

адиатермический *a.* adiathermal, athermanous.

адион *m.* adion.

Адкока антенна Adcock antenna.

адм. *abbr.* (**административный**) administrative, administration; [**адмирал (при фамилии)**] admiral (when modifying a name).

администра/тивный *a.* administrative, administration; **—ция** *f.* administration.

адмирал *m.* admiral; **—тейский металл** admiralty metal.

адмитанс *m.* admittance.

Адмот *abbr.* (**административный отдел**) administrative division.

адм. центр. *abbr.* (**административный центр**) administrative center.

адник *m.* Adnic (copper-nickel-tin alloy).

адрес *m.* address; **по —у** concerning (someone); **—ная книга** directory; **—овать** *v.* address, direct; refer.

адский камень lunar caustic, silver nitrate.

адсорб/ат *m.* adsorbate; **—ент** *m.* adsorbent; **—ер** *m.* adsorber; adsorbent; **—ирование** *see* **адсорбция; —ированный** *a.* adsorbed; **—ировать** *v.* adsorb; **—ируемое вещество** adsorbate; **—ирующий** *a.* adsorbent.

адсорбц/ионный *a.* adsorption; **—ионная колонка** adsorption column; **—ионная способность** adsorptivity, adsorptive capacity; **—ионное осаждение** adsorption precipitation; **—ия** *f.* adsorption; **—ия на ионообменной смоле** ion-exchange resin adsorption.

адуляр *m.* adularia.

адурол *m.* (phot.) adurol.

адус/ация, —сация *f.* (met.) malleablizing.

адъюнгированный *a.* adjoint.

адъюнкт *m.* adjunct; **—а** *f.* cofactor, signed minor.

а.е.в. *abbr.* (**атомная единица веса**) atomic weight unit (awu).

а.е.м. *abbr.* (**атомная единица массы**) atomic mass unit (amu).

АЖ *abbr.* (**Астрономический журнал**) Astronomical Journal (Soviet Astronomy—AJ).

ажурный *a.* open, skeleton; fret (saw).

аз. *abbr.* (**азиатский**) Asiatic.

азартная игра game of chance.

азбест *see* **асбест.**

азбука *f.* alphabet.

АзГИЗ *abbr.* (**Азербайджанское государственное издательство**) Azerbaidzhan State Press.

АзГНИ *abbr.* (**Азербайджанский государственный научный институт**) Azerbaidzhan State Scientific Institute.

АзГНИИ *abbr.* (**Азербайджанский государственный научно-исследовательский институт**) Azerbaidzhan State Scientific Research Institute.

Азгостехиздат *abbr.* (**Азербайджанское государственное техническое издательство**) Azerbaidzhan State Technical Press.

азеотроп *m.* azeotrope; **—ический** *a.* azeotropic.

Азербайджанская ССР, Азерб. ССР Azerbaidzhan SSR.

ази— *prefix* azi—.

азиатский *a.* Asiatic.

азид *m.* azide.

азид—, азидо— *prefix* azid—, azido—.

азимидо—, азимино— *prefix* azimido—, azimino—.

азимут *m.* azimuth; bearing; **—альный** *a.* azimuthal.

азин *m.*, **—овый** *a.* azine; **—окраски** *pl.* azino dyes.

Азия Asia.

АзНИИ *abbr.* (**Азербайджанский научно-исследовательский институт**) Azerbaidzhan Scientific Research Institute.

азо— *prefix* azo—.

Азовсталь *abbr.* (**Азовский металлургический завод**) Azov Metallurgical Plant.

азойский *a.* (geo.) azoic.

азокислотный *a.* azo acid.

азокси— *prefix* azoxy—.

азоксисоединение *n.* azoxy compound.

Азорский максимум Azores high.

азосоединение *n.* azo compound.

азот *m.* nitrogen (N); **двуокись —а** nitrogen peroxide; **закись —а** nitrous oxide; **окись —а** nitric oxide.

азотиров/ание *n.* nitration; (met.) nitriding; **—анный** *a.* nitrated; nitrided; **—анная сталь** nitrided steel, nitralloy steel; **—ать** *v.* nitrate; nitride.

азотист/ый *a.* nitrous, nitrogenous, nitride (of); **—ая кислота** nitrous acid; **соль —ой кислоты** nitrite.

азотноват/истая кислота hyponitrous acid; **соль —истой кислоты** hyponitrite; **—истокислый** *a.* hyponitrous acid, hyponitrite (of); **—истокислая соль** hyponitrite; **—ый ангидрид** nitrogen peroxide.

азотно/глицериновый эфир nitroglycerin; **—железистая соль** ferrous nitrate; **—железная соль** ferric nitrate; **—кислый** *a.* nitric acid, nitrate (of); **—кислая соль** nitrate; **—медная соль** cupric nitrate; **—метиловый эфир** methyl nitrate; **—этиловый эфир** ethyl nitrate.

азотн/ый *a.* nitric, nitrogen, nitrogenous; **а. ангидрид** nitric anhydride; **а. мостик** nitrogen bridge; **—ая дуга** nitrogen arc; **—ая кислота** nitric acid; **соль —ой кислоты** nitrate.

азот/ометр *m.* azotometer; **—содержащий** *a.* nitrogenous.

Азофи Azophi (lunar crater).

АИ *abbr.* (**Астрономический институт**) Institute of Astronomy.

АИЗ *abbr.* (**Ассоциация изобретателей**) Inventors' Association.

АИМ *abbr.* (**Амплитудно-импульсная модуляция**) pulse-amplitude modulation (PAM).

Айвс Ives.

айдырлит *m.* aidyrlite.

айкинит *m.* aikinite.

Айри *see* **Эри.**

айсберг *m.* iceberg.

Айх *see* **Эйч.**

акад. *abbr.* (**академик**) academician; (**академия**) academy.

академ/ик *m.* academician, member of an academy; **—ический** *a.* academic; **—ия** *f.* academy.

Академкнига *abbr.* (**Издательство Академии наук СССР**) USSR Academy of Sciences Press.

акадиалит *m.* acadialite.

акалидавин *m.* akalidavynite.

акантит *m.* acanthite.

акарбодавин *m.* acarbodavynite.

аква/даг *m.* Aquadag; **—жел** *m.* aquagel.

аквамарин *m.* aquamarine.

Аквариды Aquarids (meteors).

акватория *f.* water area.

акведук, —т *m.* aqueduct, conduit.

Аквилон Aquilon (French reactor).

акклиматиз/ация *f.* acclimatization **—ованный** *a.* acclimatized.

аккомод/ация *f.* accommodation, adaptation; **—ированный** *a.* accommodated.

аккомпанировать *v.* accompany.

аккорд *m.* (mus.) chord; **—ная работа** piece work.

аккреция *f.* accretion.

аккумулиров/ание *n.* accumulation, storage; **—анный** *a.* accumulated, stored; **—ать** *v.* accumulate, store; retain (heat).

аккумулятор *m.* storage cell, storage battery; **—ная** *f.* battery room; **—ный** *a.* battery, storage cell; **—ный сосуд** battery jar; **—ный элемент** battery cell, storage cell; **—ная батарея** storage battery; **—ная кислота** battery acid.

аккумуляц/ионный *a.* accumulation; **—ия** *see* **аккумулирование.**

аккуратн/о *adv.* accurately, exactly; neatly; **—ость** *f.* accuracy, exactness; punctuality; precision, regularity; neatness; **—ый** *a.* accurate, exact, precise; punctual; neat; conscientious.

аклин/а *f.* acline, magnetic equator; **—ический** *a.* aclinic.

акмит *m.* acmite.

аком *abbr.* (**акустический ом**) acoustic ohm.

АКП *abbr.* (**анилинокрасочная промышленность**) aniline dye industry.

акр *m.* acre.

акрил *m.* acryl; **—ил** *m.* acrylyl; **—овый** *a.* acryl, acrylic.

акровакс *m.* acrowax.

акрофут *m.* acre-foot.

акселер/атор *m.* accelerator; **—ограмма** *f.* accelerogram; **—ограф** *m.* accelerograph; **—ометр** *m.* accelerometer.

аксессуары *pl.* accessories.

аксиальн/о: **а.-векторное взаимодействие** axial-vector interaction; **а.-симметричный** axially symmetric, axisymmetric; **—ый** axial; *see also* **осевой**; **—ое давление** end thrust.

аксинит *m.* axinite.

аксиома *f.* axiom; **а. мощности** axiom of power; **а. отделимости** axiom of separability; **а. произвольного выбора** axiom of choice; **а. счетности** denumerability axiom; **—тика** *f.* axiomatics; **—тический** *a.* axiomatic.

аксиотрон *m.* axiotron.

аксонометр/ический *a.* axonometric, clinographic; **—ия** *f.* axonometry.

акт *m.* act, event; document; statement, report; **а. ионизации** ionizing event.

актив *m.* assets; active members.

актив/атор *m.* activator, catalyst, promoter; **—аторный центр** activator center; **—ационный** *a.* activation, activating; **—ация** *f.* activation; sensitization; **—изировать** *see* **активировать.**

активирован/ие *n.* activation; **—ный** *a.* activated; **—ный излучением** radioactivated; **—ный уголь** activated carbon.

актив/ировать *v.* activate, promote, stimulate, accelerate; **—ирующее вещество** activating agent; **—ность** *f.* activity.

активн/ый *a.* active; (nucl.) radioactive; effective; operating; industrious; **а. объем** sensitive volume, active volume; **—ая зона** active zone; core (of nuclear reactor); **—ая зона с высокой плотностью потока** high-flux (reactor) core; **—ая зона с малой плотностью потока** low-flux (reactor) core; **—ая масса** filling paste, grid plug (of storage battery); **—ая проводимость** conductance; **—ая составляющая** (elec.) resistive component, active component; **—ое напряжение** active voltage; **—ое сопротивление** resistance; **—ое сопротивление антенны** antenna (effective) resistance; **—ое сопротивление катушки** coil resistance.

актинид *m.* actinide.

актиниевый ряд actinium series.

актин/изм *m.* actinism; **—ий** *m.* actinium (Ac); **—ический, —ичный** *a.* actinic; **—ичность** *f.* actinism.

актино/грамма *f.* actinogram; **—граф** *m.* actinograph; **—ид** *see* **актинид**; **—климатология** *f.* actinoclimatology; **—логия** *f.* actinology.

актинометр *m.* actinometer; **а.-самописец** actinograph; **—ический** *a.* actinometric; **—ия** *f.* actinometry.

актинон *m.* actinon (An).

актиноскоп *m.* actinoscope, solar radiation meter; **—ия** *f.* actinoscopy.

актиноуран *m.* actinouranium (AcU); **—овый ряд, —овое семейство** uranium-actinium series.

актино/фотометр *m.* actinic photometer; **—химия** *f.* actinochemistry; **—электрический** *a.* actinoelectric; **—электричество** *n.* actinoelectricity.

актор *m.* (chem.) actor, donor.

актуальн/ость *f.* actuality; urgency, timeliness; **—ый** *a.* actual; present, modern, timely, current; pressing, urgent, essential.

актуатор *m.* actuator.

акуметр *m.* acoumeter.

акуст. *abbr.* (**акустика**) acoustics; (**акустический**) acoustic.

Акуст. ж. *abbr.* (**Акустический журнал**) Acoustics Journal (Soviet Physics—Acoustics).

акусти/ка *f.* acoustics; **—метр** *m.* acoustimeter.

акустическ/ий *a.* acoustic, sonic; *see also* **звуковой**; **а. ветер** acoustic streaming, quartz wind; **а. дальномер** sound ranger; **а. детектор смещения** acoustic displacement detector; **а. звукосниматель** acoustic pickup; **—ая емкость** acoustic capacitance; **—ая жесткость** acoustic stiffness; **—ая инертность** acoustic inertance; **—ая податливость** acoustic compliance; **—ая проводимость** acoustic admittance; **—ая проницаемость** acoustic transmittivity; **—ая реагированность** acoustic responsiveness; **—ая реактивность** acoustic reactance; **—ое активное сопротивление** acoustic resistance; **—ое измерение расстояний** sound ranging; **—ое поле** sound field; **—ое согласование** acoustic matching; **—ое течение** sound streaming.

акцент *m.* accent, accentuation; **—ирование** *n.* accentuation; **—ировать, —овать** *v.* accent, accentuate, emphasize.

акцепт/ировать *v.* accept; **—ор** *m.* acceptor; **—орный** *a.* (sol.) acceptor.

акцессорный *a.* accessory.

акцидентный *a.* accidental.

ал— *see also* **аль—**.

алабамий *m.* alabamium, alabamine (Ab).

алабастриновый процесс (phot.) alabastrine process.

Аламогордо Alamogordo.

аламозит *m.* alamosite.

алб. *abbr.* (**албанский**) Albanian.

Албания Albania; *see also* **Народная Республика Албания.**

алгебра *f.* algebra; **—ический** *a.* algebraic; **—ический знак** algebraic sign; **—ическое дополнение** algebraic complement, cofactor (of matrix element).

алгоритм (**алгорифм**) *m.* algorithm; **—ический** *a.* algorithmic.

алдебараний *m.* aldebaranium (Ad).

алебастр *m.* alabaster.

алевр/итовая частица silt particle; **—олит** *m.* siltstone.

Александерсона машина Alexanderson alternator.

александрит *m.* alexandrite.

алембик *m.* alembic, retort.

алеть *v.* redden, glow.

алеф-нуль *m.* aleph-null, aleph-zero.

алжирский металл Algerian metal (tin alloy).

алидада *f.* (surv.) alidade.

ализонит *m.* alisonite.

аликвантный *a.* (math.) aliquant.

аликвотн/ый *a.*, **—ая проба** aliquot; **—ая часть** aliquot part.

али/фатический *a.* aliphatic; **—циклический** *a.* alicyclic.

алкали *n.* alkali; *see also* **щелочь**; **—зировать** *v.* alkalize; **—метр** *m.* alkalimeter; **—метрический** *a.* alkalimetric; **—метрия** *f.* alkalimetry; **—ческий** *a.* alkaline.

алкил *m.* alkyl; alkyle; **—ирование** *n.* alkylation; **—ированный** *a.* alkylated; **—ировать** *v.* alkylate; **—овый, —ьный** *a.* alkyl.

алклэд *see* **алькла**д.

алкогель *m.* alcogel.

алкогол/из *m.* alcoholysis; **—изация** *f.* alcoholization; **—ический** *a.* alcoholic; **—ь** *m.* alcohol; **—ьный** *a.* alcohol, alcoholic.

алкумит *m.* Alcumite (copper-aluminum-iron-nickel alloy).

аллактит *m.* allactite.

алланит *m.* allanite.

аллеганит *m.* alleghanyite.

аллелотроп/ический *a.* allelotropic; **—ия** *f.* allelotropism.

алленовый *a.* allenic.

аллигаторный зажим alligator clip.

аллобар *m.* allobar.

аллогипсография *f.* allohypsography.

аллодельфит *m.* allodelphite.

аллоклазит *m.* alloclasite.

алломер/ия *f.* (cryst.) allomerism; **—ный** *a.* allomerous.

алломорф/изм *m.* allomorphism; **—ный** *a.* allomorphic.

аллонж *m.* adapter; extension.

аллотриоморфный *a.* allotriomorphic.

аллотроп/изм *m.*, **—ия** *f.* allotropy, allotropism; **—ический** *a.* allotropic.

аллофан *m.* allophane.
аллохроит *m.* allochroïte.
аллохроматический *a.* allochromatic.
аллувиальный *see* **аллювиальный.**
аллюв/иальный *a.* alluvial; **—ий** *m.* alluvium.
алм— *see also* **альм—.**
алмаз *m.* diamond.
алмазилиум *see* **альмасилиум.**
алмазный *a.* diamond; **а. порошок** diamond dust; **а. шпат** adamantine spar, corundum.
аловольт *m.* alowalt (abrasive).
алодайн *m.* Alodyne (coating on aluminum).
алоизит *m.* aloisite.
алперм *m.* Alperm (aluminum-iron alloy).
алудель *m.* aludel.
алудур *m.* Aludur (aluminum-magnesium alloy).
алунд *m.*, **—овый** *a.*, **—ум** *m.* alundum.
алфавит *m.* alphabet; **—ный** *a.* alphabetical; **—ный указатель** index.
алфер *m.* Alfer (iron-aluminum alloy).
алый *a.* reddish, blood red, ruby-colored.
Альбатегний Albategnius (lunar crater).
альбедо *n.* albedo; **—метр** *m.* albedometer.
альбион-металл *m.* Albion metal (lead-tin laminate).
альбумин *m.* albumin; albumen; **—ат** *m.* albuminate; **—иметр** *m.* albuminimeter; **—ин** *m.* albuminin; **—ный, —овый** *a.* albumin, albuminoid, albuminous; albumen; **—ная бумага** (phot.) albumin paper; **—озный** *a.* albuminous; **—оид** *m.* albuminoid.
Альголь Algol (Beta Persei).
Альдебаран Aldebaran.
альдегид *m.* aldehyde; **а. муравьиной кислоты** formaldehyde.
альдо— *prefix* aldo—.
аль/дрей *m.* Aldrey (aluminum-magnesium alloy); **—дюраль** *m.* Aldural (aluminum-coated Duralumin sheet); **—зен** *m.* Alzene (aluminum-zinc alloy).
Альиацен Aliacensis (lunar crater).
алькл/ад, —эд *m.* Alclad (aluminum-coated Duralumin).
алькомакс *see* **альнико.**
алькусин *m.* Alcusin (aluminum-copper-silicon casting alloy).
альмаг *abbr.* (**алюминиево-магниевый сплав**) aluminum-magnesium alloy.
Альмагест Almagest.
Альманун Almanon (lunar crater).
аль/масилиум *m.* Almasilium (aluminum alloy); **—мелек** *m.* Almalec (aluminum alloy); **—неон** *m.* Alneon (aluminum-zinc alloy).
альмукантар *m.* almucantar.
альни *m.* Alni (aluminum-nickel-copper alloy).
альнико *m.* Alnico (aluminum-nickel-cobalt alloy).
альпакс *m.* Alpax (aluminum-silicon alloy).
Альпетрагий Alpetragius (lunar crater).
альпийский свет Alpine glow.
альсифер *m.* Alsifer, Sendust (aluminum-silicon-iron alloy).
альтазимут *m.* altazimuth.
Альтаир *m.* Altair.
альтакс *m.* Altax (dibenzothiazole disulfide rubber accelerator).
альтернатив/а *f.* alternative, choice; **—ный** *a.* alternative.
альтерн/атор *m.*, **—аторный** *a.* alternator; **—ирующий** *a.* alternating.
альтиграф *m.* altigraph.
альтиметр *m.* altimeter; **а.-анероид** aneroid altimeter; **—ия** *f.* altimetry.
альтма *f.* Altma (aluminum alloy).
альто/кумулюс *m.* altocumulus; **—стратус** *m.* altostratus.
альфа *f.* alpha (Greek letter); **а.-излучатель** alpha-ray emitter, alpha-emitter; **а.-излучение, а.-лучи** alpha-rays; **а.-спектрометр** alpha-ray spectrometer; **а.-уран** alpha-uranium; **а.-частица** alpha-particle; **—лучевой** *a.* alpha-ray; **—толщиномер** *m.* alpha-ray thickness gauge; **—трон** *m.* alphatron.
Альфвена волна Alfvén wave.
альфенид *m.* Alfenid (nickel-plated silver alloy).
альфоль *m.* Alfol (aluminum foil).
Альфонс Alphons (lunar crater).
Альциона Alcyone.
алюмель *m.* Alumel (nickel alloy).
алюминиево/кислый *a.* aluminic acid;

aluminate (of); **а. натрий, —натриевая соль** sodium aluminate; **—кислая соль** aluminate.

алюминиев/ый *a.* aluminum, aluminiferous; **—ая кислота** aluminic acid; **соль —ой кислоты** aluminate; **—ые квасцы** potash alum.

алюмин/ий *m.* aluminum (Al); **азотнокислый а.** aluminum nitrate; **гидрат окиси —ия** aluminum hydroxide; **окись —ия** aluminum oxide; alumina; **—ированный** *a.* aluminized.

алюминотерм/ический *a.* aluminothermic; **—ия** *f.* aluminothermy.

алюмо— *prefix* alumo—; *see also* **алюмино—**.

алюмогель *m.* alumogel.

алюмосиликат *m.* aluminosilicate.

аляскаит *m.* alaskaite.

ам. *abbr. see* **амер.**

АМ *abbr.* (**амплитудная модуляция**) amplitude modulation.

Амага-Ледюка правило Amagat-Leduc rule.

амальгам/а *f.* amalgam; **—ационный** *a.*, **—ация** *f.*, **—ирование** *n.* amalgamation; **—ированный** *a.* amalgamated; **—ировать** *v.* amalgamate; **—ирующий** *a.* amalgamating.

амбар *m.* warehouse, storehouse.

амберлит *m.* Amberlite (ion-exchange resin).

амбиполярный *a.* ambipolar.

амблигонит *m.* amblygonite.

амблистегит *m.* amblystegite.

амбулатория *f.* dispensary.

амбушюр *m.* opening; mouthpiece (of telephone).

амезит *m.* amesite.

амелиорация *f.* melioration, improvement.

амер. (*abbr.*) (**американский**) American.

Америка *f.* America.

американский *a.* American.

америций *m.* americium (Am).

Амершем Amersham.

аметист *m.* amethyst.

аметропи/ческий *a.* ametropic; **—я** *f.* ametropy.

амиант *m.* amianthus.

амигдо— *prefix* amygdo—.

амид *m.* amide; **—ирование** *n.* amidation; **—ировать** *v.* amidate.

амидо— *prefix* amido—; amino—.

амидоген *m.* amidogen.

амикрон *m.* amicron.

амил *m.* amyl.

амило— *prefix* amylo—.

амило/кластический *a.* amyloclastic, amylolytic; **—лиз** *m.* amylolysis; **—метр** *m.* amylometer.

амин *m.* amine; **—ирование** *n.* amination; **—ировать** *v.* aminate.

амино— *prefix* amino—.

аминокислота *f.* amino acid.

Амичи призма Amici prism.

аммиа/к *m.* ammonia; **едкий а.** aqua ammonia, ammonium hydroxide; **—кат** *m.*, **—т** *m.* ammoniate.

аммиачн/ожелезные квасцы ammonium iron alum; **—охромовые квасцы** ammonium chrome alum; **—ый** *a.* ammonium, ammonia, ammoniacal; **—ая вода** ammonia water, ammonium hydroxide; **—ые часы** ammonia clock.

аммоний *m.* ammonium.

АМН *abbr.* (**Академия медицинских наук СССР**) Academy of Medical Sciences of the USSR.

АМО *abbr.* (**Московский автомобильный завод**) Moscow automobile plant.

амозит *m.* amosite.

амортиз/атор *m.* shock absorber, bumper; dashpot; damper; buffer; **—ационный** *a.* shock-absorbing; **—ационная пружина** shock absorber; **—ация** *f.*, **—ирование** *n.* amortization, depreciation; shock-absorbing; damping; buffer action; **—ированный** *a.* shockproof; damped; **—ировать** *v.* absorb shock; damp; **—ирующий** *a.* absorptive (shock).

аморф/изм *m.*, **—ность** *f.* amorphism; **—ный** *a.* amorphous; **—ная масса** amorphous mass.

АМП *abbr.* (**аэрометрический пост**) aerometrical station.

ампангабеит *m.* ampangabéite.

ампер *m.* ampere; **а.-весы** ampere balance; **а.-вольт-омметр** multimeter; **а.-секунда** ampere-second; **а.-час** ampere-hour.

Ампера весы *see* **ампер-весы; закон А.** Ampere law; **А. контурный закон** Ampere circuital law.

ампер/аж *m.* amperage; **—виток** *m.* ampere turn; **—вольтметр** *m.* ampere voltmeter; **—метр** *m.* ammeter; **—метр тепловой** hot-wire ammeter, thermal ammeter; **—ный** *a.* ampere; **—ова дуга** ampere arc; **—часовая емкость** ampere-hour capacity.

амплидин *m.*, **—ный** *a.* amplidyne.

амплитуд/а *f.* amplitude, range; **а. двойная** double amplitude, peak-to-peak amplitude; **а. импульса** pulse amplitude, pulse height; **а. прилива** tidal range; **коэффициент —ы** amplitude factor, crest factor; **—но-модулированный** *a.* amplitude-modulated.

амплитудн/ый *a.* amplitude; **а. анализатор** pulse-height analyzer; **а. вольтметр** peak voltmeter; **а. дискриминатор импульсов** pulse-height discriminator; **а. селектор импульсов** pulse-height selector; **—ое значение** peak value.

амплификация *f.* amplification.

ампула *f.* ampoule, vial; **а. с отбиваемым кончиком** breakseal ampule.

амп-ч *abbr.* (**ампер-час**) ampere-hour.

амфибол *m.* amphibole.

амфиген *m.* amphigene.

амфидная соль amphoteric salt.

амфидромия *f.* amphidrome.

амфихро/ический *a.* amphichroic; **—матический** *a.* amphichromatic.

амфоделит *m.* amphodelite.

амфолит *m.* ampholyte, amphoteric electrolyte.

амфотер *m.* amphoteric substance; **—ность** *f.* amphoteric character; **—ный** *a.* amphoteric.

АН *abbr.* (**Академия наук СССР**) Academy of Sciences of the USSR; (**авианосец**) aircraft carrier.

ан. *abbr.* (**английский**) English; (**аэростат наблюдения**) observation balloon.

анабатический *a.* anabatic.

анализ *m.* analysis; **качественный а.** qualitative analysis; **количественный а.** quantitative analysis; **а. размерностей** dimensional analysis; **не поддающийся —у** unanalyzable; **—атор** *m.* analyzer, analyst; (met.) assayer; **—атор импульсов** pulse analyzer; **—атор совпадений** coincidence analyzer; **—ирование** *n.* analyzing; **—ировать** *v.* analyze.

аналист *m.* analyzer, analyst; (met.) assayer.

аналитик *see* **анализатор; —а** *f.* analysis; analytics, analytic geometry.

аналитическ/и *adv.* analytically; **—ий** *a.* analytical, analytic; **—ая геометрия в пространстве** solid analytic geometry; **—ая геометрия на плоскости** plane analytic geometry; **—ое расширение** analytic continuation.

аналитичность *f.* analyticity, analytic functionality.

аналлобара *f.* anallobar.

аналог *m.* analog; **—ический, —ичный** *a.* analogous, analogic, similar; **—ия** *f.* analogy, similarity; **—о-цифровое моделирование** analog-digital simulation.

анальцим *see* **цеолиты.**

анаморф/изм *m.* anamorphism; **—ный** *a.* anamorphous, anamorphic; **—оза** *f.* anamorphosis, anamorphism.

анастигмат *m.* anastigmat; **—ический** *a.* anastigmatic.

анат. *abbr.* (**анатомия**) anatomy; (**анатомический**) anatomical.

анатексис *m.* anatexis.

анатом/ический *a.* anatomical; **—ия** *f.* anatomy.

анафорез *m.* anaphoresis.

анафронт *m.* anafront.

ангар *m.* hangar.

ангармон/изм *m.*, **—ичность** *f.* anharmonicity; **—ическое отношение** anharmonic (or cross) ratio.

Ангера функция Anger function.

ангидр/ид *m.* anhydride; **—изация** *f.* dehydration.

ангидро— *prefix* anhydro—.

ангиетизм *m.* anhyetism.

англ. *abbr. see* **английский.**

англезит *m.* anglesite.

английск/ий *a.* English; British; **а. цемент** marble cement, Keene's cement; **—ая соль** *see* **ипсомская соль; —ие белила** white lead.

ангстрем *m.* ångström, angstrom (Å,A), Ångström unit.

андалузит *m.* andalusite.

андезин *m.* andesine.

андро— *prefix* andro—.

Андромеда Andromeda (And) (constellation).

Андромедиды Andromedids (meteors).

андрьюсит *m.* andrewsite.

анезин *m.* anesin, chloretone.

анем/ичный *a.* anemic; **—ия** *f.* (med.) anemia.

анемо/грамма *f.* anemogram; **—граф** *m.* anemograph; **—клинограф** *m.* anemoclinograph; **—клинометр** *m.* anemoclinometer; **—логия** *f.* anemology.

анемометр *m.* anemometer, wind gauge; **а. с крестом из чашек** cup anemometer; **а. с крыльями** windwheel anemometer; **—ический** *a.* anemometric; **—ический столб** anemometer mast; **—ическая вышка** wind tower; **—ия** *f.* anemometry.

анемо/румбометр *m.* anemorhumbometer; **—скоп** *m.* anemoscope; **—тахометр** *m.* anemotachometer, airspeed indicator; **—фикация** *f.* utilization of wind power.

анемузит *m.* anemousite.

анероид *m.* aneroid (barometer); **а. циклонометр** barocyclonometer; **—ный** *a.* aneroid; **—ная коробка** aneroid capsule (box); **—ограмма** *f.* aneroidogram; **—ограф** *m.* aneroidograph.

АНИ *abbr.* (**Издательство Академии наук СССР**) USSR Academy of Sciences Press.

анизаллобара *f.* anisallobar.

анизо/барический, —барный *a.* anisobaric; **—метр** *m.* torque magnetometer; **—метрический** *a.* anisometric.

анизотроп/ический, —ный *a.* anisotropic; **—ия, —ность** *f.* anisotropy; **—ия формы** form anisotropy (of a macromolecule).

АНИИ *abbr.* (**Арктический научно-исследовательский институт**) Arctic Scientific Research Institute; (**Артиллерийский научно-исследовательский институт**) Artillery Scientific Research Institute; (**Ассоциация научно-исследовательских институтов**) Association of Scientific Research Institutes.

анил *m.* anil, indigo; **—иновый** *a.* aniline.

анимикейская система (geo.) Animikean series, Upper Huronian.

анион *m.* anion; **—ит** *m.*, **—обменная смола** anion-exchange resin; anion exchanger; **—ный дефект** anion defect; **—ная смола** anion resin.

анкер *m.* anchor; stay, tie rod; **—ный** *a.* anchor; **—ный болт** anchor bolt; **—ный спуск** anchor escapement; **—ная балка** tie beam; **—ная плита** anchor plate; **—ные часы** lever watch.

анкета *f.* questionnaire, inquiry.

анкилит *m.* ancylite.

анналы *pl.* annals, records.

аннекс/ировать *v.* annex; **—ия** *f.* annexation.

аннигиляц/ионный *a.* annihilation; **—ия** *f.* annihilation; **—ия на лету** annihilation in flight.

аннот/ационный журнал abstract journal; **—ация** *f.* annotation; **—ировать** *v.* annotate.

аннулиров/ание *f.* annulment, cancellation; **—анный** *a.* annulled, canceled; **—ать** *v.* annul, cancel.

анод *m.* anode, plate; **—изация** *f.*, **—ирование** *n.* anodizing; **—ировать** *v.* anodize.

анодн/ый *a.* anode, anodic, plate; **—ая нагрузка** plate load; **—ая цепь** anode loop; **—ое выпрямление** anode (or plate) rectification; **—ое падение** anode fall, anode drop; **—ое покрытие** anodizing, anodic oxidation; **—ое растворение** anodic dissolution; **—ое свечение** anode glow; **—ые лучи** positive rays, canal rays; **—ые рейки** anode strips.

анодо-сеточная характеристика grid-plate characteristic.

аноксит *m.* anauxite.

анолит *m.* anolyte.

аномал/ия *f.* anomaly, abnormality; **а. силы тяжести** gravity anomaly; **—оскоп** *m.* anomaloscope; **—ьно дисперсный** *a.* anomalous-dispersion, selective; **—ьный** *a.* anomalous, abnormal, unusual, nonstandard, ir regular; —**ьная рефракция** anomalous refraction; (meteor.) superstandard refraction, super-refraction.

анонимный *a.* anonymous.

анонс *m.* advertisement.

анормальный *a.* abnormal, anomalous.

анортит *m.* anorthite.

анотрон *m.* anotron.

ансамбль *m.* ensemble, assembly.

антагон/изм *m.* antagonism; —**истический** *a.* antagonistic.

антантрен *m.* anthanthrene.

антарктический *a.* antarctic.

антелий *m.* anthelion.

антенна *f.* antenna; **а. антифединговая** antifading antenna, diversity antenna; **а. арфообразная** harp antenna; **а. биконическая, а. двухконусная** biconical antenna; **а. веерная** fan antenna, spiderweb antenna; **а. витковая** loop antenna; **а. возбуждаемая в центре** center-driven antenna; **а. волноводно-щелевая** leaky-pipe antenna; **а. воронкообразная** horn(-type) antenna; **а. горизонтальная синфазная** broadside array, binomial array; **а. диапазонная** multiple-tuned antenna; **а. ёмкостная** capacity antenna; **а. из наклонных проводов** lattice-wire broadside array; **а. квадратная рамочная** square-loop antenna; **а. коаксиально-дипольная** sleeve dipole antenna; **а. колбасообразная** cage antenna; **а. колинеарная** collinear (Franklin) antenna; collinear array.

антенна лестничная fishbone antenna; **а.-мачта** tower-type antenna, mast antenna; **а. нагруженная в основании** base-loaded antenna; **а. направленная** directional antenna; **а. ненастроенная** aperiodic antenna, untuned antenna; **а. определения знака направления** sense antenna; **а. пассивная** parasitic antenna, passive antenna; **а. переключаемая разрядником** spark-gap switched antenna; **а. питаемая у основания** base-driven antenna; **а. поисковая** scanning antenna; **а. профильно-лучевая** shaped-beam antenna, phase-shaped antenna; **а. радиоотметчика** marker antenna; **а. рамочная** loop antenna, frame antenna; **а. ромбическая** diamond antenna.

антенна с веерным лучом fanned-beam antenna; **а. с горизонтальной поляризацией** ground-plane antenna; **а. со змеем** kite-hoisted antenna; **а. с качающимся лучом** eagle antenna; **а. с неподвижной рамкой** fixed-coil antenna; **а. с нижним питанием** base-driven antenna; **а. с параболоидным отражателем** parabolic (reflector) antenna; **а. с переключением диаграммы** lobe-switching antenna; **а. спиральная** helical antenna; **а. с прижатым излучением** low-angle dish, low-altitude dish antenna; **а. с серединным питанием** center-fed antenna; **а. с управляемой диаграммой** steerable antenna; **а. сыровидная** cheese(box) antenna; **а. с экранированным снижением** screened antenna; **а. Татаринова** collinear array; **а. типа уголкового отражателя** angle-reflector antenna, corner-reflector antenna; **а. цилиндрически-параболическая** pillbox antenna.

антенн/ый *a.* antenna; **а. колпак** radome; **а. переключатель** antenna change-over switch; **а. разделительный фильтр** antenna diplexer; —**ая решетка** antenna array; —**ая решетка излучающая вдоль оси** endfire array, end-on directing array; —**ая решетка линейная** linear array.

антецедент *m.* antecedent.

анти— *prefix* anti—; non—.

антиапекс *m.* antapex.

антибарическое течение (meteor.) antibaric flow.

антивещество *n.* antibody.

антивибратор *m.* vibration mount.

антигелий *m.* anthelion.

анти/гигиеничный *a.* unsanitary; —**гнилостное средство** preservative.

антигризутное взрывчатое вещество (min.) safety explosive.

антидетона/тор *m.* antiknock (compound); —**ционный** *a.* antiknock.

антидинатронная сетка suppressor grid.

анти/катализатор *m.* anticatalyst; **—катод** *m.* anticathode, target cathode; **—каузальный** *a.* noncausal; **—каустик** *m.* anticaustic, antialkali; **—кластический** *a.* anticlastic.

антиклиналь *f.* (geo.) anticline; **—ный** *a.* anticlinal.

антикоагулянт *m.* anticoagulant.

антикоммут/ативность, —ация *f.* anticommutation; **—атор** *m.* anticommutator (bracket); **—ировать** *v.* anticommute.

анти/коррозийный, —коррозионный *a.* anticorrosive, corrosion-resisting, antirust, rust-inhibiting; **—крепускулярный луч** anticrepuscular ray; **—логарифм** *m.* antilogarithm; **—локационное устройство** antiradar device.

антимагнитные часы nonmagnetic watch.

антимодальное распределение (stat.) antimodal distribution.

антимуссон *m.* antimonsoon.

антинаучный *a.* unscientific.

антинейтр/ино *n.* antineutrino; **—он** *m.* antineutron.

анти/нуклон *m.* antinucleon; **—обледенитель** *m.* deicer; **—окислитель, —оксидант** *m.* antioxidant.

антипаразитное сопротивление (elec.) grid suppressor.

анти/параллельный *a.* antiparallel; **—пассат** *m.* antitrade wind, counter trade wind.

антипатия *f.* antipathy, aversion.

анти/плейон *m.* antipleion; **—производная** *a.* antiderivative; **—протон** *m.* antiproton; **—резонанс** *m.* antiresonance.

антипод *m.* antipode; **а. эпицентра** anticenter.

анти/самосопряженный *a.* skew Hermitian; **—санитарный** *a.* unsanitary; **—связывающая орбита** antibonding orbital.

антисегнетоэлектр/ик *m.* antiferroelectric (material); **—ический** *a.* antiferroelectric; **—ичество** *n.* antiferroelectricity.

анти/сейсмический *a.* earthquakeproof, quake-resistant; **—сиккатив** *m.* antisiccative, humidifier.

антисимметр/изация *f.* antisymmetrization; **—изованный** *a.* antisymmetrized; **—ический, —ичный** *a* antisymmetric, skew-symmetric. **—ия** *f.* antisymmetry.

антискорч *m.* antiscorch; **—инг** *m.* antiscorching.

антисовпаден/ие *n.* anticoincidence, **—ий схема** anticoincidence circuit.

антисолнечная точка (astr.) antisolar point.

антистоксова линия anti-Stokes line.

антитеза *f.* antithesis, contrast.

анти/тело *see* **антивещество**; **—триптический** *a.* antitryptic; **—узел** *m.* antinode; **—фазный** *a.* antiphased, oppositely phased.

антиферро/магнетизм *m.* antiferromagnetism; **—магнетик** *m.* antiferromagnet, antiferromagnetic (material); **—магнитный** *a.* antiferromagnetic; **—электрический** *a.* antiferroelectric.

антифрикционный *a.* antifriction; **а. металл, а. сплав** antifriction metal, antifriction alloy.

анти/центр *m.* anticenter; **—циклогенез** *m.* anticyclogenesis; **—циклолиз** *m.* anticyclolysis.

антициклон *m.* anticyclone, high-pressure area; **—иальный, —ический** *a.* anticyclonic; **—ический вихрь** anticyclonic eddy; **—ическое понижение** anticyclone subsidence.

античастица *f.* antiparticle.

античный *a.* antique; ancient; **а. мир** Ancient World.

антиэкранирован/ие *n.* antishielding; **коэффициент —ия** antishielding factor (in magnetic resonance).

антиэлектрон *m.* antielectron.

антиэрмитов, —ый *a.* skew-Hermitian, anti-Hermitian.

АНТО *abbr.* (**Авиационное научно-техническое общество**) Aeronautical Scientific and Technical Society.

Антонова правило Antonov (Antonow, Antonoff) rule.

антофиллит *m.* anthophyllite.

антрацен *m.*, **—овый** *a.* anthracene.

антрац/ил *m.* anthracyl; **—ин** *m.* anthracine, anthrazine; **—ит** *m.*

anthracite; —**итовый** *a.* anthracite, anthraciferous.

антропогеновый период Quaternary period.

АНУ *abbr.* (**Академия наук Украины**) Academy of Sciences of the Ukraine.

АНУзССР *abbr.* (**Академия наук Узбекской ССР**) Academy of Sciences of the Uzbek SSR.

аншлиф *m.* (micros.) polished section.

Аньези локон witch of Agnesi.

анэлектрический *a.* anelectric.

АОЛГУ *abbr.* (**Астрономическая обсерватория при Ленинградском государственном университете**) Astronomical Observatory at Leningrad State University.

АОЭ *abbr.* [**Астрономическая обсерватория им. В. П. Энгельгардта (при Казанском государственном университете)**] V. P. Engel'gardt Astronomical Observatory (at the Kazan' State University).

апастр/ий, —он *m.* apastron.

апатит *m.* apatite.

апджонит *m.* apjohnite.

апекс *m.* apex; **а. солнца** solar apex.

апериодич/еский *a.* aperiodic; **а. прибор** dead-beat instrument; —**ность** *f.* aperiodicity.

апертур/а *f.* aperture, opening, orifice; —**ный** *a.* aperture; —**ный угол** (opt.) angular aperture; —**ная диафрагма** aperture stop; objective aperture (of microscope).

Апиан Apianus (lunar crater).

апикальный *a.* apical.

апланат *m.* aplanat; —**изм** *m.* aplanatism; —**ический, —ичный** *a.* aplanatic; —**ическая линза** aplanatic lens.

Аплегейта диаграмма Applegate diagram.

АПН *abbr.* (**Академия педагогических наук РСФСР**) Academy of Pedagogical Sciences of the RSFSR.

апо— *prefix* apo—.

апогей *m.* apogee; climax, culmination; peak, summit; acme; —**ный** *a.* apogean; —**ное расстояние** apogean distance.

Аполлон Apollo.

Аполлоний Apollonius (lunar crater).

Аполлония теорема Apollonius theorem.

аполярный *a.* apolar.

апостериорный *a.* a posteriori.

апостильб *m.* apostilb.

апофема *f.* apothem.

апофиз *m.*, —**а** *f.* apophysis.

апохромат *m.* apochromat.

апп. *abbr. see* **аппарат.**

аппарат *m.* apparatus, instrument, device; (phot.) camera; —**ная** *f.* control room; —**ный** *a.* apparatus, instrument; —**ура** *f.* apparatus, equipment; —**урный спектр** spectrogram; —**урное уширение** instrumental broadening.

аппендикс *m.* appendix (neck of aerostat).

аппликата *f.* y—coordinate (in two dimensions); z—coordinate (in three dimensions).

аппликатор *m.* applicator.

апр. *abbr.* (**апрель**) April.

априорн/о *adv.*, —**ый** *a.* a priori.

апроб/ация *f.* approbation, approval, confirmation; —**ированный** *a.* approved, tested; —**ировать** *v.* approbate, approve, test.

апроксим/ационный *a.* approximate, approximation; —**ированный** *a.* approximate, approximated; —**ировать** *v.* approximate; —**ируемость** *f.* approximability.

апсида *f.* apse; —**льный** *a.* apsidal; **линия апсид** line of apsides.

АПЧ *abbr.* (**автоматическая подстройка частоты**) automatic frequency control (AFC).

апьезон *m.* apiezon.

ар *m.* are.

ар. *abbr.* (**арабский**) Arabic; (**армянский**) Armenian.

арабский *a.* Arabic.

Араго Arago (lunar crater).

аракаваит *m.* arakawaite.

арамайоит *m.* aramayoite.

арандизит *m.* arandisite.

аранжировать *v.* arrange, set, put in order.

АРГ *abbr.* (**автоматическая регулировка громкости**) automatic volume control (AVC).

Арганда газовая горелка, аргандова горелка Argand burner; **А. диаграмма** A. diagram.
аргент. *abbr.* (**аргентинский**) Argentine.
аргентан *m.* argentan, German silver (copper-nickel-zinc alloy).
Аргентина Argentina.
аргентинский *a.* Argentine.
аргиродит *m.* argyrodite.
аргирометр/ический *a.* argyrometric; **—ия** *f.* argyrometry.
аргиропирит *m.* argyropyrite.
аргон *m.* argon (A, Ar).
Аргонавт Argonaut (reactor).
аргоннский *a.* Argonne.
аргумент *m.* argument, reasoning; **—ация** *f.* argument, line of reasoning; **—ированный** *a.* argued, proved, deduced; **—ировать** *v.* argue, prove, deduce.
Аргуса-Шмидта труба Argus-Schmidt tube (pulse-jet engine).
ардометр *m.* ardometer (radiation pyrometer).
ареа/синус *m.* inverse hyperbolic sine; **—тангенс** *m.* inverse hyperbolic tangent; **—функция** *f.* inverse hyperbolic function.
арена *f.* arena, area.
Арентса сифон (met.) Arents tap (for lead).
ареоксен *m.* araeoxen.
арео/метр *m.* areometer, hydrometer; **—метрический** *a.* areometric; **—метрия** *f.* areometry, hydrometry; **—пикнометр** *m.* areopycnometer.
Арзахель Arzachel (lunar crater).
аридн/ость *f.* aridity; **—ый** *a.* arid.
Ариель Ariel (satellite of Uranus).
Ариетиды Arietids (meteors).
арил *m.* aryl; **—ирование** *n.* arylation; **—овать** *v.* arylate.
Аристарх Aristarchus (lunar crater).
Аристилл Aristillus (lunar crater).
Аристотель Aristoteles (lunar crater).
аристотипная бумага (phot.) a silver chloride printing paper.
аритмичный *a.* arrhythmic.
арифмет/ика *f.* arithmetic; **—ический** *a.* arithmetical; **—ическая прогрессия, —ический ряд** arithmetical progression; **среднее —ическое** arithmetical mean.
арифмо/граф *m.* arithmograph; **—метр** *m.* arithmometer, adding machine, calculating machine.
арка, —да *f.* arc, arch.
арканзит *m.* arkansite.
арканит *m.* arcanite.
аркверит *m.* arquerite.
арккосинус *m.* arc cosine.
Арко Arco.
аркоген *m.* arcogen.
аркообразный *a.* arched.
арксинус *m.* arc sine.
арктангенс *m.* arc tangent; **—оидальная кривая** inverse tangent curve.
Арктика Arctic regions.
арктический *a.* arctic; **а. пояс** frigid zone.
Арктур Arcturus.
арм. *abbr.* (**армянский**) Armenian.
армалак *m.* Armalac.
арматур/а *f.* fittings, fixtures, accessories, outfit, equipment; mounting, framework; reinforcement; (elec.) armature; **—ный** *a.* fitting, fixture; armature.
Армгосиздат *abbr.* (**Армянское государственное издательство**) Armenian State Press.
армейский *a.* army.
армиллярная сфера armillary sphere.
армиров/ание *n.* armoring, reinforcement; **—анный** *a.* armored, reinforced; **—анное стекло** wire glass; **—ать** *v.* armor, reinforce, sheathe; **—ка** *f.* armoring.
армия *f.* army.
армко-железо *n.* Armco iron.
АРМС (**автоматическая радиометеорологическая станция**) automatic radio meteorological station.
Арм ССР *abbr. see* **Армянская ССР.**
Армстронга кислота Armstrong acid; **А. приемник** A. (superheterodyne) receiver; **А. схема** A. circuit.
Армфан *abbr.* (**Армянский филиал Академии наук**) Armenian Branch of the Academy of Sciences.
Армянская ССР Armenian SSR.
Арндт Arndt; **синтез по —у-Эйстерту** A.-Eistert synthesis.
арочн/о-гравитационная плотина arch-gravity dam; **—ый** *a.* arch, arched, arching; **—ая плотина** arch dam.

АРП *abbr.* (**автоматический радиопеленгатор**) automatic radio direction finder.

Аррениуса теория Arrhenius theory; **А. уравнение** A. equation.

арретир *m.*, **—овка** *f.* arrester, stop, checking device, detainer; locking device, catch; **—овать** *v.* arrest, stop, check; secure; **—овочный** *a.* arresting, stopping, stop; **—ующий палец** pickup finger.

арроядит *m.* arrojadite.

арсенал *m.* arsenal.

арсен/ат *m.* arsenate; **—ид** *m.* arsenide; **—ик** *m.* arsenic; *see also* **мышьяк.**

арсеноклазит *m.* arsenoclasite.

арсеномарказит *m.* arsenomarcasite.

арсин *m.* arsine, arsenic hydride.

артезианский *a.* artesian.

артель *f.* artel, workmen's association, company; crew (of workers).

артикуляция *f.* articulation.

АРУ *abbr.* (**автоматическое регулирование усиления**) automatic volume control (AVC).

арх. *abbr.* (**архив**) archives; [**архитектор (при фамилии)**] architect (when modifying a name).

Архбюро *abbr.* (**архивное бюро**) archives, Hall of Records.

археозойская эра Archeozoic era.

архив *m.*, **—ный** *a.* archives; **—ный метр** standard meter bar.

Архимед Archimedes (lunar crater).

Архимеда аксиома Archimedes axiom; **закон А., принцип А.** A. principle; **спираль А.** A. spiral.

архимедов винт Archimedean screw; **—а спираль** *see* **спираль Архимеда**; **—ски расположенный** with Archimedean ordering.

архитект/ор *m.* architect; **—ура** *f.* architecture; **—урный** *a.* architectural.

Арцела теорема Arzelà theorem.

АРЧ *abbr.* (**автоматическое регулирование чувствительности**) automatic sensitivity control (ASC).

а-с *abbr.* (**ампер-секунда**) ampere-second.

асб *abbr.* (**апостильб**) apostilb.

асбест *m.* asbestos; **а.-сырец** crude asbestos; **—овидный** *a.* asbestiform, fibrous; **—овый** *a.* asbestos.

асбо/картон *m.* asbestos board; **—цемент** *m.* asbestos cement.

Асгейрссона теорема Asgeirsson theorem.

асек *abbr.* (**ампер-секунда**) ampere-second.

асидерит *m.* asiderite.

асиметрия *see* **асимметрия.**

асимметр/ический, —ичный *a.* asymmetric, asymmetrical, unsymmetric, nonsymmetric, dissymmetric; **—ия** *f.* asymmetry, skewness; **—ии коэффициент** (nucl.) asymmetry parameter; (stat.) coefficient of skewness; **—ии множитель** asymmetry factor.

асимптот/а *f.* asymptote; **—ика** *f.* asymptotic form (or behavior); **—ический** *a.* asymptotic.

асинхрон/ичный, —ный *a.* asynchronous, nonsynchronous.

аспазиолит *m.* aspasiolite.

аспект *m.* aspect, appearance.

аспидн/ый *a.* slate, schistous; scaly, flaky, foliated; **а. сланец, —ая доска** slate; blackboard.

аспирант *m.*, **—ка** *f.* aspirant, graduate student; **—ура** *f.* postgraduate training (or scholarship).

аспира/тор *m.* aspirator, suction apparatus; **—ционный** *a.* aspiration, suction; **—ционный психрометр** aspiration psychrometer.

асс. *abbr.* (**ассистент**) assistant.

ассигнов/ание *n.* assignment; appropriation; **—ать** *v.* assign, grant, appropriate; **—ка** *f.* assignment, grant.

ассимил/ированный *a.* assimilated; **—ировать** *v.* assimilate; **—ируемость** *f.* assimilability; **—ируемый** *a.* assimilable; **—яторный** *a.* assimilatory; **—яция** *f.* assimilation.

ассист. *abbr. see* **ассистент.**

ассист/ент *m.* assistant, lecturer, instructor; **—ировать** *v.* assist.

ассортимент *m.* assortment, selection; set.

ассоци/ативность *f.* associative property; **—ативности закон** associative law; **—ативный** *a.* associative; **—ация** *f.* association; combination; **—ированный** *a.* associated; **—ировать, —ироваться** *v.* associate, join, unite (with).

АССР *abbr.* (**Автономная Советская Социалистическая Республика**) Autonomous Soviet Socialist Republic.

астазир/ование *n.* astatization; **—овать** *v.* astaticize; **—ующая сила** labilizing force.

астатин *m.* astatine (At).

астатич/еский *a.* astatic; **—еское регулирование** floating control; **—ность** *f.* astaticism.

астер/изм *m.* (cryst.) asterism; **—ин** *m.* asterin; **—оид** *m.* asteroid.

Астеропа Asterope.

астигмат/изатор *m.* astigmatizer; **—изм** *m.* astigmatism; **—ический** *a.* astigmatic.

Астона закон Aston rule (of isotopes); **А. темное пространство, астоновское темное пространство** A. dark space.

астр. *abbr.* (**астрономический**) astronomical; (**астрономия**) astronomy.

астральный *a.* astral.

астр. ед. *abbr.* (**астрономическая единица**) astronomical unit (a.u.).

астрионика *f.* astrionics, astronomical electronics.

астрогородок *abbr.* (**астрономический городок**) astronomical observatory and settlement.

астрограф *m.* astrograph; **—ика** *f.* astrography; **—ический** *a.* astrographic.

астроида *f.* (math.) astroid.

астро/компас *m.* astrocompass, celestial compass; **—купол** *m.* astrodome.

астролябич/еский *a.*, **—ия** *f.* astrolabe.

астрометрия *f.* astrometry.

астрон. *abbr.* (**астрономический**) astronomical.

астронав/игация *f.* astronavigation; **—тика** *f.* astronautics; **—тический** *a.* astronautical.

Астрон. ж. *see* **АЖ.**

астроном *m.* astronomer; **—ический** *a.* astronomical; **—ический пункт** astronomic position; **—ическая ориентировка** *see* **астроориентировка**; **—ия** *f.* astronomy; **—о-геодезический** astrogeodetic.

астро/ориентировка *f.* celestial orientation (or fix); celestial navigation; **—система** *f.* star system, planetary system; **—спектроскопия** *f.* stellar spectroscopy; **—физика** *f.* astrophysics.

астрофиллит *m.* astrophyllite.

астрофотометрия *f.* astrophotometry.

астр. п. *abbr.* (**астрономический пункт**) astronomical position.

асфальт *m.* asphalt; **—ирование** *n.* asphalting; **—ированный** *a.* asphalted; **—ировать** *v.* asphalt; **—ит** *m.* asphaltite.

асфальто/бетон *m.* asphalt concrete; **—вый** *a.* asphalt, asphaltic; **—тип** *m.* asphaltotype.

асцен/дент *m.* ascendent; **—зия** *f.* ascension.

ат *abbr.* (**атмосфера техническая**) technical atmosphere (735.5 mm Hg); **ат.** (**атом**) atom; (**атомный**) atomic.

АТ *abbr.* (**абсолютная топография**) absolute topography.

ат. % *abbr.* (**атомный процент**) atomic percent.

ата *abbr.* (**атмосфера абсолютная**) absolute atmosphere.

Атабаска (озеро) Athabaska Lake.

атак/а *f.* attack; **угол —и** angle of attack, angle of incidence.

атакамит *m.* atacamite.

атаковать *v.* attack.

ат. в. *abbr.* (**атомный вес**) atomic weight (at. wt.).

Атвуда машина Atwood machine; **формула А.** A. formula.

ат. ед. *abbr.* (**атомная единица**) atomic unit.

ат. ед. массы *see* **а.е.м.**

атермический *a.* athermanous, athermous, adiathermal.

ати *abbr.* (**атмосфера избыточная**) gauge atmosphere.

атлантический *a.* Atlantic.

Атлас Atlas (lunar crater).

атлас *m.* satin; atlas; **а. льдов** ice atlas; **—истый** *a.* satin, satiny; **—истый шпат**, **—ный шпат** satin spar.

атм. *abbr.* (**атмосфера**) atmosphere (atm); (**атмосферный**) atmospheric.

атмидо/метр *m.* atmidometer, atmometer; **—метрия** *f.* atmidometry, atmometry; **—скоп** *m.* atmidoscope.

атмо/генный *a.* (petr.) atmogenic;

—**кластический** *a.* (petr.) atmoclastic; —**лиз** *m.* atmolysis; —**логия** *f.* atmology; —**метр** *m.* atmometer; —**метрия** *f.* atmometry; —**стойкий** *a.* weatherproof.

атмосфера *f.* atmosphere; air; **а. абсолютная** absolute atmosphere; **а. избыточная** gauge atmosphere; **а. нормальная** standard atmosphere; **а. техническая** technical atmosphere (735.5 mm Hg).

атмосфер/ика *f.* atmospherics, static; —**ический,** —**ный** *a.* atmospheric, weather; —**ный воздух** free air; —**ный ливень** (cosm.) air shower; —**ный слой** air stratum, atmospheric layer; —**ное давление** atmospheric pressure; —**ные осадки** atmospheric precipitation; atmospheric condensation; —**остойкий** *see* **атмостойкий.**

ат. н. *abbr.* (**атомный номер**) atomic number.

атолл *m.* atoll.

атом *m.* atom; **а. внедрения** interstitial atom; **а.-донор** donor atom; **а. лишенный внешних электронов** stripped atom; **а. отдачи** recoil atom; **разделившийся а.** fissioned atom; **знак —а** atomic symbol; **порядковое число —ов** atomic number.

атом/арный *a.* atomic, elemental; —**изатор** *m.* atomizer; —**изм** *m.*, —**истика** *f.* atomic theory, atomics; —**ический** *see* **атомный.**

атомн/ик *m.* atomic scientist; —**оводородная сварка** atomic-hydrogen welding; —**ость** *f.* atomicity, valency.

атомн/ый *a.* atomic; **а. вес,** —**ая масса** atomic weight; **а. двигатель** nuclear engine; —**а. котел** nuclear reactor; **а. номер,** —**ое число,** —**ое порядковое число** atomic number; —**ый объем** atomic volume; **а. фактор рассеяния** atomic scattering factor; —**ая единица** atomic unit; —**ая теплоемкость** atomic heat; —**ая техника** nuclear engineering; —**ая энергетика** atomic power (engineering).

атомоход *m.* atomic ship.

атрибут *m.* attribute; —**ивный** *a.* attributive.

атро— *prefix* atro—.

АТС *abbr.* (**автоматическая телефонная станция**) dial telephone exchange.

аттаколит *m.* attacolite.

аттенюатор *m.* attenuator.

аттест/ат *m.* testimonial, certificate; —**ация** *f.* attestation, testimony; —**овать** *v.* testify, certify.

аудиенция *f.* audience.

аудио/грамма *f.* audiogram; —**граф** *m.* audiograph.

аудиоллой *m.* Audiolloy (nickel-iron-alloy).

аудио/метр *m.* audiometer; —**метрия** *f.* audiometry; —**н** *m.* audion.

аудитория *f.* auditorium, lecture hall; audience.

Ауригиды Aurigids (meteors).

аури/пигмент *m.* orpiment; —**хальцит** *m.* aurichalcite.

ауробисмутинит *m.* aurobismuthinite.

аустенит *m.* austenite; —**ный,** —**овый** *a.* austenite, austenitic; —**ная сталь** austenitic steel.

Аустина-Когена формула Austin-Cohen law.

ауто— *prefix* auto—; *see also* **авто**—.

аутооксидация *f.* self-oxidation.

АФ *abbr.* (**арктический фронт**) arctic front.

афанезит *m.* aphanesite.

афвиллит *m.* afwillite.

афелий *m.* aphelion.

афиний *m.* athenium (einsteinium).

афиш/а *f.* poster, placard; —**ная краска** lithographic color.

афокальный *a.* afocal.

афр. *abbr.* (**африканский**) African.

Африка *f.* Africa.

африканский *a.* African.

африт *m.* aphrite.

африцит *m.* aphrizite.

афросидерит *m.* aphrosiderite.

афтершок *m.* aftershock.

афтиталит *m.* aphthitalite.

аффин/аж *m.*, —**ирование** *n.* refining (of gold).

аффинн/ость *f.* affinity; —**ый** *a.* (math.) affine.

аффинор *m.* affinor; dyadic; **а. отражения** reflectance dyadic; —**ный** *a.* dyadic.

ахматит *m.* achmatite.

ахроит *m.* achroite.
ахромат *m.* achromat; **—изация** *f.* achromatization, achromatizing; **—изированный** *a.* achromatized; **—изм** *m.* achromatism; **—изованный** *a.* achromatized; **—ический** *a.* achromatic.
ахтарагдит *m.* achtaragdite.
АХТТ *abbr.* (**Ассоциация химии твердого топлива**) Solid Fuel Chemistry Association.
аце— *prefix* ace—.
ацет— *prefix* acet—.
ацетил/ен *m.*, **—еновый** *a.* acetylene; **—ированный** *a.* acetylized; **—ировать** *v.* acetylate, acetylize; **—ируемый** *a.* acetylizable.
ацетиметр *m.* acetimeter; **—ия** *f.* acetimetry.
ацето— *prefix* aceto—.
ацетон *m.* acetone.
аци— *prefix* aci—.
ацид/иметр *m.* acidimeter; **—иметрия** *f.* acidimetry; **—ометр** *m.* acidometer.
ациклический *a.* acyclic.
ацил *m.* acyl; **—ирование** *n.* acylation; **—ировать** *v.* acylate.
а-ч *abbr.* (**ампер-час**) ampere-hour (amp-hr).
Ачесона электропечь Acheson furnace.
ашарит *m.* ascharite.
Ашберри сплав Ashberry metal.
ашкрофтин *m.* ashcroftine.
АЭ *abbr.* [**Атомная энергия** (**журнал**)] Atomic Energy (The Soviet Journal of Atomic Energy).
АЭО *abbr.* (**экспериментально-аэродинамический отдел**) division of experimental aerodynamics.
аэр/атор *m.* aerator; **—ация** *f.*, **—ирование** *n.* aeration; **—ировать** *v.* aerate.
аэро— *prefix* aero—, air; *see also* **авиа—**.
Аэроби Aerobee (rocket).
аэро/гамма поиски aerial gamma-ray prospecting; **—грамма** *f.* aerogram.
аэрограф *m.* aerograph; air brush; **—ист** *m.* aerographer; **—ический** *a.* aerographic; **—ия** *f.* aerography.
аэродвигатель *m.* airplane engine.
аэродинамик *m.* aerodynamicist; **—а** *f.* aerodynamics.
аэродинамическ/ий *a.* aerodynamic; **—ая продувка** wind-tunnel test; **—ая труба** wind tunnel; **—ая труба открытого типа** free-jet wind tunnel, open-jet tunnel; **—ая труба с закрытой рабочей частью** closed-jet wind tunnel; **—ая труба со свободной струей** open-jet wind tunnel; **—ая характеристика** aerodynamic performance, aerodynamic characteristic; **—ое качество** aerodynamic quality, lift-drag ratio; **—ие весы** aerodynamic balance, wind-tunnel balance.
аэродром *m.* airfield.
аэро/дромный маяк airfleld beacon; **—земный ток** air-earth current; **—золь** *m.* aerosol; **—карта** *f.* aeronautical chart; **—климатология** *f.* aeroclimatology; **—кулер** *m.* air cooler.
аэро/лак *m.* dope (for airplanes); **—лит** *m.* aerolite; **—лифт** *m.* air lift.
аэролог *m.* aerologist; **—ический** *a.* aerological; **—ический теодолит** balloon theodolite; **—ия** *f.* aerology.
аэро/магнитомер *m.* aeromagnetometer; **—метеорограф** *m.* aerometeorograph.
аэрометр *m.* aerometer; **—ический** *a.* aerometric; **—ия** *f.* aerometry.
аэромеханика *f.* aeromechanics.
аэрон *m.* Aeron (aluminum alloy).
аэронав/игатор *m.* air navigator; **—игационная карта** aeronautical chart; **—игация** *f.* aerial navigation; **—тика** *f.* aeronautics; **—тический** *a.* aeronautical.
аэро/план *m.* airplane; **—психограф** *m.* aeropsychograph; **—пыль, —смесь** *f.* dust-laden air, dust cloud; **—радиометрия** *f.* aerial radiometry; **—разведка** *f.* aeroprospecting; **—сидерит** *m.* aerosiderite.
аэростат *m.* aerostat, balloon; **змейковый а.** kite balloon; **управляемый а.** dirigible, airship; **—ика** *f.* aero statics; **—ный** *a.* aerostatic, airborne.
аэро/сфера *f.* aerosphere; **—съемка** *f.* aerial survey, aerial photography, aerial mapping; **—термометр** *m.* air-temperature indicator, aerothermometer; **—танк** *m.* air tank.

аэроупруг/ий *a.* aeroelastic; **—ость** *f.* aeroelasticity.

аэроф. *abbr.* (**аэрофотометрия**) aerial photometry.

аэро/фильный *a.* aerophilic, capable of absorbing air; **—фильтр** *m.* air filter; **—флот** *m.* aerofloat.

Аэрофлот *abbr.* (**Главное управление гражданского воздушного флота**) Main Administration of the Civil Air Fleet.

аэро/фобный *a.* aerophobic; **—фон** *m.* aerophone.

аэрофото/аппарат *m.* aerial camera; **—грамметрист** *m.* aerophotogrammetrist; **—грамметрия** *f.* aerophotogrammetry; **—граф** *m.* aerial photographer; **—графия** *f.* aerial photography; **—метрия** *f.* aerial photometry; **—разведка** *f.* aerial reconnaissance mapping; **—снимок** *m.* aerial photograph.

аэрофотосъем/ка *f.* aerial photography; **—очный аппарат** air survey camera; **—щик** *m.* aerial photographer.

аэроэлектроразведка *f.* airborne electromagnetic prospecting.

АЭС *abbr.* (**атомная электростанция**) atomic electric power plant.

Аюи *see* **Гаюи.**

Б

б *see* **бы.**

б *abbr.* (**бар**) bar (unit of pressure); **б.** (**бывший**) former.

Б [*in steel mark* (**ниобий**)] niobium (Nb).

Б *abbr.* [**Бомэ** (**Боме**)] Baumé, Bé.

Ба *abbr.* (**число Барстоу**) Barstow number.

баба *f.* ram; head of hammer; drop weight.

Баба Bhabha.

баббит *m.* babbitt (tin-antimony-copper alloy).

Бабине (**Бабинэ**) **компенсатор** Babinet compensator; **Б. принцип** B. principle; **Б.-Солейля компенсатор** B.-Soleil compensator; **Б. точка** B. point; **Б. формула** B. formula.

бабка *f.* (mach.) monkey; headstock; block; chuck; mandrel.

Бабо закон Babo law.

бабочк/а *f.* butterfly; **клапан —ой** butterfly valve.

бабье лето Indian summer.

бавенский двойник Baveno twin.

баган *m.* heap, pile.

багер *m.* dredging shovel, dredge.

багет *m.* baguet, molding, fillet.

багио *n.* (meteor.) baguio.

багор *m.* boat hook, harpoon.

багров/еть *v.* redden, become reddish purple; **—ый** *a.* reddish purple, crimson.

баддеккит *m.* baddeckite.

бадделеит *m.* baddeleyite.

бад/ейка *f.* bucket; small basin; **—ья** *f.* tub.

база *f.* base, basis, base line; **б. интерференции, б. интерферометра** (rad. astr.) interferometer spacing.

базальт *m.* basalt; **—овый** *a.* basalt, basaltic; **—ообразный** *a.* basaltiform.

базанит *m.* basanite, lydite.

баз/ировать, —ироваться *v.* base (on); **—ис** *m.* basis, base.

базисн/ый *a.* basis, base, base line; basic, basal; **б. вектор** basis vector; **б. пункт** reference point; **—ая клетка** (cryst.) elementary cell; **—ая линия** base line; **—ая плоскость** (cryst.) basal plane.

базит *m.* (petr.) basic rock.

базобисмутит *m.* basobismutite.

базовый *a.* base, basic, basal.

базоцентрир. *abbr.* *see* **базоцентрированный.**

базоцентрированный *a.* base-centered.

Байера теория напряжений Baeyer strain theory.

Байес *see* **Бейес.**

байкалит *m.* baikalite.

байльдонит *m.* bayldonite.

байонетный *a.* bayonet.

байпас, *m.*, **—ный** *a.* by-pass.

бак *m.* tank, reservoir; **б.-дегазатор** degassing tank; **б. для конденсата** condensate catch tank; **б.-хранилище** storage tank.

бакалавр *m.* bachelor; baccalaureate.

бакел/изированный, —изованный *a.* bakelized; **—изованная бумага** bakelized paper; **—ит** *m.* bakelite.

бакен *m.* beacon, buoy.

бакштаг *m.* backstay.

баланс *m.* balance; **б. нейтронов** neutron balance; **б. тепловой** heat balance, thermal balance; **б. энергии** energy balance; **—ер** *m.* balancer.

балансир *m.*, **—ный** *a.* bob; balance wheel; balance beam, equalizer; balance, balanced.

балансиров/ание *n.* balancing; **—анный** *a.* balanced; **—ать** *v.* balance, compensate; **—ка** *f.*, **—овочный** *a.* balancing.

балансн/ый *a.* balance, balanced, balancing; **—ая модуляция** balanced modulation; **—ая схема** balanced circuit.

балда *f.* sledge hammer.

балка *f.* beam, girder; gorge, gully, ravine.

балкон *m.* balcony.

балл *m.* mark; number, point (on a scale).

балласт *m.* ballast; **—ирование** *n.*, **—ировка** *f.* ballasting; **—ированный** *a.* ballasted; **—ировать** *v.*, **—ный** *a.* ballast; **—ный резервуар** ballast tank.

Баллинга ареометр Balling hydrometer.

баллистика *f.* ballistics; **б. внутренняя** interior ballistics.

баллистический *a.* ballistics; **б. аппарат** ballistic vehicle; **б. гальванометр** ballistic galvanometer.

баллон *m.*, **—ный** *a.* balloon; (gas) cylinder, bottle, vessel, container, tank; bulb; **б.-зонд** air sonde, test balloon, weather balloon, sounding balloon; **—ет** *m.* (aero.) ballonet.

баллоэлектрический эффект balloelectric effect.

балоптикон *m.* balopticon.

балочный *a.* beam, girder.

балт. *abbr. see* **балтийский.**

балтийский *a.* Baltic.

бальзам пихтовый Canada balsam.

Бальмера серия Balmer series.

бальмеровский декремент Balmer decrement; **б. скачок** B. discontinuity.

бальмэна *pl.* fluorescent colors.

БАН *abbr.* (**Белорусская Академия наук**) Academy of Sciences of Belorussia; (**Библиотека Академии наук СССР**) Library of the Academy of Sciences of the USSR.

банахово вектор-пространство Banach vector space.

бандаж *m.* bandage; tire, band, hoop, binding; **—ный** *a.* bandage; tire, band; belt; **—ная проволока** binding wire.

Бандровского основание Bandrowski base.

Банерджи равенство Banerjee equation.

банка *f.* tin can; jar; sand bank; shoal; bank.

банник *m.* (tube) brush, cleaner; reamer.

баночный *a.* jar, pot.

баня *f.* bath.

бар *m.* bar (unit of pressure), barye; bar, ledge.

барабан *m.* drum; cylinder, barrel, roll, reel; **—ный** *a.* drum, barrel-type, revolver-type, turret-type; **—ная перепонка** ear drum; drum membrane.

баран *m.* ram.

баран/ка *f.* steering wheel; **—ок** *m.* (tech.) plane.

бараш/ек *m.* wing nut; thumbscrew; kink (in wire); **—ки** *pl.* whitecaps; fleecy clouds; **—ковая гайка** wing nut, flanged nut.

барбот/аж *m.* bubbling; **—ер** *m.* bubbler; **—ировать** *v.* bubble; **—ирующий воздух** flushing air.

барбьерит *m.* barbierite.

Бардин Bardeen; **—а модель** B. model (of nucleus).

баржа *f.* barge.

бар/иевый *a.* barium, bariated; **—ий** *m.* barium (Ba); **окись —ия** barium oxide, baryta.

барикальцит *m.* baricalcite.

барико-циркуляционный режим barometric circulation regime.

барилит *m.* barylite.

бариоанортит *m.* barium anorthite.
бариомусковит *m.* bariomuscovite.
барион *m.*, **—ный** *a.* baryon.
барированный *a.* bariated.
барисилит *m.* barysilite.
барисфера *f.* (geo.) barysphere, centrosphere.
барит *m.* baryta, barium oxide; (min.) barytes.
барито— *prefix* baryto—.
баритов/ый *a.* barytic, baryta, baryto—; barytes.
барицентр *m.* barycenter; **—ический** *a.* barycentric.
барическ/ий *a.* baric, barometric, pressure; **б. закон** Buys Ballot law; **—ая система** pressure system; **—ая топография** baric topography.
барка *f.* barge, boat, bark; **красильная б.** dye vat; **—с** *m.* barge, launch.
Баркгаузена-Курца генератор Barkhausen oscillator; **Б.-Курца колебания** B.-Kurtz oscillations; **Б. эффект (явление)** B. effect.
Барло/ва колесо, —у колесо (elec.) Barlow wheel.
барн *m.* barn (unit of cross-sectional area, 10^{-24} cm^2).
Барнетта эффект Barnett effect.
баро/грамма *f.* barogram; **—граф** *m.* barograph; **—камера** *f.* pressure chamber.
бароклин/а *f.* barocline; **—ия, —ность** *f.* baroclinicity; **—ный** *a.* baroclinic.
бароключатель *see* **баропереключатель.**
барометр *m.* barometer; **б.-анероид, металлический б.** aneroid barometer; **инспекторский (или контрольный) б.** inspector's barometer (for calibration); **б. чашечный** cup (cistern) barometer.
барометрическ/ий *a.* barometric, barometer; **—ая ступень** barometric step; **—ая тенденция** pressure tendency, barometric tendency; **—ая формула** barometric height formula.
барометрия *f.* barometry.
баро/переключатель *m.* baroswitch; **—скоп** *m.* baroscope; **—стат** *m.* barostat; **—термограф** *m.* barothermograph, meteorograph.
баротроп/ический *a.* barotropic; **—ия, —ность** *f.* barotropy; **—ный** *a.* barotropic.
Бароций Barocius (lunar crater).
бароциклонометр *m.* barocyclonometer.
барочный *a.* barge.
барретер *m.* current regulator, ballast tube, barretter.
барруазит *m.* barroisite.
Барстоу число Barstow number.
бартит *m.* barthite.
Бартки тождество Bartky identity.
Бартлета сила Bartlett force.
Бартолин Bartholinus.
бархат *m.* velvet.
барценит *m.* barcenite.
барьер *m.* barrier; **б. (для) деления** fission barrier; **—ный** *a.* barrier; **—ный слой** barrier layer.
бас *m.* bass.
басс. *abbr. see* **бассейн.**
бассейн *m.* tank, (swimming) pool, basin; coal field; **—ный реактор** swimming-pool reactor.
Бастиана счетчик Bastian meter.
бастнезит *m.* bastnäsite.
батал *m.*, **—овый** *a.* batalum (barium-tantalum alloy).
Бата металл Bath metal (brass alloy).
батар/ейка *f.* small battery; **—ейный** *a.* battery; **—ейный зажим** battery terminal; **—ея** *f.* battery; bank; **—ея накала** (elec.) A battery; **—ея сеточного смещения** (elec.) C battery; **—ея сухих элементов** dry battery.
батилимнион *m.* bathylimnion.
бати/метрический *a.* bathymetric; **—сейсмический** *a.* bathyseismic; **—скаф** *m.* bathyscape; **—сфера** *f.* bathysphere; **—термограф** *m.* bathythermograph.
бато/лит *m.* (petr.) batholite, batholith; **—литовый** *a.* batholitic; **—метр** *m.* bathometer, water sampler.
батохром *m.* bathochrome; **—ный** *a.* bathochromic; **—ное смещение** bathochromic shift.
батрахит *m.* batrachite.
Бау способ обозначения усилий Bow's notation.
баумгауерит *m.* baumhauerite.
Бауш-Лома микроскоп Bausch and Lomb microscope.

Баушингера эффект Bauschinger effect.

бафтинг *m.* buffeting.

бахром/а *f.*, **—очный** *a.* fringe; **—чатость** *f.* fringing; **—чатый** *a.* fringed.

баццит *m.* bazzite.

Бачинского формула Bachinskii formula.

бачок *m.* can, small tank.

башен/ка *f.* turret, tower; **—кообразный** *a.* (meteor.) castellatus, towering; **—кообразные облака** castellatus.

башенн/ый *a.* tower; **б. водозабор** (hyd.) intake tower; **б. кран** tower crane; **б. процесс** tower process; **б. солнечный телескоп** solar tower; **б. холодильник** cooling tower; **—ая антенна** tower antenna; **—ое облако** towering cloud.

Башкирская АССР Bashkir ASSR.

башм/ак *m.* shoe; (mag.) pole piece; **—ачный** *a.* shoe.

башня *f.* tower, turret; **б.-конденсатор** condensation tower; **б. облачная** *see* **башенное облако**; **б. пусковая** launching tower.

б.г. *abbr.* (**без года**) year not given (in bibliography).

БГМП *abbr.* (**Бюро гидрометеорологических прогнозов**) hydrometeorological forecasts bureau.

БГУ *abbr.* (**Белорусский государственный университет**) Belorussian State University.

бдительн/ость *f.* vigilance, alertness; **—ый** *a.* vigilant, alert.

беватрон *m.* bevatron.

Бевереджа антенна Beverage antenna, wave antenna.

бег *m.* run, running, course; **—ание** *n.* running, wandering; **—ать** *v.* run; **—ать от** avoid.

бегающ/ий *a.* running; **б. луч** scanning beam; **—ее катодное пятно** free cathode spot.

бегство *n.* flight, escape.

бегун *m.* runner; traveler; roll; **—ковая тележка** trailer; **—ок** *m.* runner; traveler; roller.

бегучести коэффициент traveling-wave ratio.

бег/учий, —ущий *a.* running; **—ущие слои, —ущие страты** moving striations.

беда *f.* misfortune, trouble.

бедантит *m.* beudantite.

Беджера формула Badger rule.

бедн/еть *v.* grow poor; **—ость** *f.* poverty; **—ый** *a.* poor, lean, low-grade, meager; **—ая руда** lean ore (low-grade); **—ая смесь** weak mixture, lean mixture.

бедрок *m.* (geo.) bedrock.

бедств/енный *a.* distress; disastrous; **—ие** *n.* calamity, disaster, distress; **сигнал —ия** distress signal, SOS call.

Беера *see* **Бера.**

бежать *v.* run, flow.

без, безо *prep. gen.* without; minus, less, free (of); **б. даты** undated.

без— *prefix* dis—, il—, in—, ir—, un—, —less, —free, de—, non—; *see also* **бес—.**

без/аберрационный *a.* nonaberrational; **—аварийный** *a.* accident-free; **—активаторный** *a.* nonactivated, inactive.

безалаберн/ость *f.* disorder, inconsistency; **—ый** *a.* disorderly, unsystematic.

без/батарейный *a.* self-powered; **—брежный** *a.* boundless; **—бурный** *a.* calm; **—вариантный** *a.* invariant.

безваттн/ый *a.* wattless, reactive; **—ая составляющая** reactive component.

безвестный *a.* obscure, unknown.

безветр/енный *a.* windless, calm; **—ие** *n.* calm.

без/вихревой *a.* irrotational, nonvortical, vortex-free, eddy-free; **—вкусный** *a.* tasteless, flat, insipid; **—влажный** *a.* dry, arid.

безвод/ность *f.*, **—ье** *n.* dryness, aridity, anhydrous state; **—ный** *a.* anhydrous, nonaqueous, water-free; dry, arid; **—ная соль** anhydrous salt; **—ородный** *a.* hydrogen-free.

без/возвратный *a.* irrevocable, irreversible; **—воздушный** *a.* air-free, vacuum; **—возмездный** *a.* without cost.

безвредн/о *adv.* harmlessly; **—ость** *f.* harmlessness; **—ый** *a.* harmless, noninjurious; —**ые дозы радиации** radiation tolerance standards.

безвременн/ость *f.* untimeliness, prematureness; —**ый** *a.* inopportune, ill-timed, premature.

безвыгодн/ость *f.* disadvantage; —**ый** *a.* disadvantageous.

без/вязкостный *a.* nonviscous, inviscid; —**гистерезисный** *a.* anhysteretic.

безграмотн/ость *f.* illiteracy; —**ый** *a.* illiterate, ignorant, ungrammatical.

безграничн/о *adv.* infinitely, without limit; **б.-делимый** infinitely divisible; —**ость** *f.* infinity, limitlessness; —**ый** *a.* unbounded, infinite.

безгранный *a.* anhedral.

бездейств/енность *f.* inactivity; ineffectiveness, inefficiency; —**енный,** —**ующий** *a.* inoperative, idle; —**енный воздух** dead air; —**ие** *n.* idling, inaction, inoperation; outage; **быть в** —**ии** be out of service, not run; —**овать** *v.* remain inactive.

бездел/ица *f.* trifle; —**ье** *n.* idleness.

бездеятельн/о *adv.* passively; —**ость** *f.* passivity, inaction, inactivity; —**ый** *a.* passive, inactive, inoperative.

бездипольный *a.* nondipolar.

бездна *f.* chasm, abyss; a great number of, a great deal of.

бездождие *n.* drought, dry weather.

без/доказательный *a.* unproved, unsubstantiated; —**донный** *a.* bottomless, very deep; —**дорожный** *a.* pathless, impassable, roadless.

бездоходн/ость *f.* unprofitableness; —**ый** *a.* unprofitable.

бездымный *a.* smokeless.

безжелезн/ый *a.* iron-free, air-cored; **б. спектрометр** iron-free spectrometer; —**ая катушка** air-core coil.

без/жизненный *a.* inanimate, dead; insipid, dull; —**заботный** *a.* careless; —**законный** *a.* illegal, lawless; —**защитный** *a.* defenseless, unprotected; —**звездный** *a.* starless; —**звучный** *a.* soundless, noiseless, silent.

безламповый *a.* tubeless.

безличный *a.* impersonal.

без/лучевой *a.* unpronged, zero-pronged; —**магнитный** *a.* nonmagnetic; —**мезонный** *a.* nonmesonic.

безмерн/о *adv.* immeasurably, excessively; —**ость** *f.* immeasurableness, immensity, excess; —**ый** *a.* immeasurable, immense, excessive.

безмолв/ный *a.* silent, speechless, unspoken; —**ствовать** *v.* be silent.

безмоментный *a.* zero-moment, zero-spin, zero-torque.

безнадежн/ость *f.* hopelessness; —**ый** *a.* hopeless, desperate.

безнакальный тиратрон cold-cathode thyratron.

безнулевая шкала supressed-zero scale.

безоблачный *a.* cloudless, clear.

безобраз/ить *v.* disfigure, deform; —**ный** *a.* disfigured, deformed.

безоговорочн/о *adv.* unconditionally; —**ый** *a.* unconditional, unrestricted.

безопасн/о *adv.* safely, without danger; —**ость** *f.* safety, security; **техника** —**ости** accident prevention; —**ый** *a.* safe, safety; permissible (load); —**ая пленка** safety film; —**ая работа** safe operation, safe work.

безоружный *a.* unarmed.

безосновательн/о *adv.* groundlessly, without basis; —**ый** *a.* groundless, unfounded, unsubstantiated.

безостановочн/о *adv.* continuously, ceaselessly; —**ый** *a.* continuous, uninterrupted; nonstop.

безотбойный *a.* uninterrupted.

безответственн/ость *f.* irresponsibility; —**ый** *a.* irresponsible.

безотказн/ость *f.* dependability, reliability; —**ый** *a.* reliable, failure-proof, trouble-free.

безоткатный *a.* nonrecoil.

безотлагательн/о *adv.* without delay, urgently, promptly; —**ость** *f.* urgency; —**ый, безотложный** *a.* urgent, pressing.

без/отлучный *a.* uninterrupted; —**отменный** *a.* irrevocable.

безотносительн/о *adv.* without reference to, regardless of; —**ый** *a.* irrespective of, irrelative; absolute.

безотраженный *a.* reflectionless.

безотчетный *a.* involuntary; unaccountable.

безошибочн/о *adv.* correctly, —**ость** *f.* faultlessness, infallibility, certainty; —**ый** *a.* infallible, correct.

безрадиоактивный *a.* nonradioactive, "cold."
безразлич/ие *n.* indifference; **—ный** *a.* indifferent, neutral; **—ное равновесие** neutral (or indifferent) equilibrium.
безразмерн/ый *a.* dimensionless; **—ая величина** dimensionless value.
безразрядный *a.* nondischarge.
безрезультатн/о *adv.* without result, to no effect; **—ость** *f.* futility, ineffectiveness; failure; **—ый** *a.* futile, ineffective; unsuccessful.
безрельсовый *a.* railless; **б. транспорт** highway transportation.
без/рессорный *a.* without springs; **—роторный** *a.* irrotational; **—рупорный** *a.* hornless.
безуаттный *see* **безваттный.**
безубыточный *a.* without loss.
безугольный *a.* nonangular; without coal; carbon-free.
безударный *a.* unstressed, unaccented, unemphasized.
безузловой *a.* nodeless.
безуклон/ный, —чивый *a.* undeviating, straight.
безукоризненный *a.* irreproachable, faultless, spotless.
безумол/кный, —чный *a.* ceaseless, incessant (noise).
безупречн/ость *f.* faultlessness; **—ый** *a.* faultless.
безусадочный *a.* nonshrink, nonshrinking.
безусловн/о *adv.* certainly, undoubtedly, unconditionally, absolutely; **—ость** *f.* certainty; **—ый** *a.* absolute, unconditional, categorical, positive.
безуспешн/о *adv.* unsuccessfully; **—ость** *f.* failure; **—ый** *a.* unsuccessful.
безустанный *a.* incessant, indefatigable.
безъемкостный *a.* noncapacitive.
безызвестн/ость *f.* obscurity, uncertainty; **—ый** *a.* obscure, unknown.
безызлучательный *a.* nonradiative, nonradiating, radiationless; **б. переход** nonradiative transition.
безым/енный, —янный *a.* nameless, anonymous.
безындукционный *a.* noninductive.
безынерционн/ость *f.* noninertia, rapid response; **—ый** *a.* inertialess.
безыскр/истый, —овой *a.* sparkless.
безысходный *a.* endless.
безэлектродный *a.* electrodeless.
безэховый *a.* anechoic.
бейделлит *m.* beidellite.
Бейеса формула Bayes formula, Bayes theorem.
бейлеит *m.* bayleyite.
Бейли Baily (lunar crater).
Бейли волны Bailey waves; **Б. металл** B. metal; **Б. печь** Baily furnace; **Б. четки** Baily beads.
Бейльби слой Beilby layer.
бейрихит *m.* beyrichite.
Бейс-Балло закон (правило) Buys Ballot law.
бейц/евание *n.*, **—овка** *f.* staining (of woods); (met.) scouring, pickling.
Бека ареометр Beck hydrometer; **Б. лампа** B. arc lamp; **Б. призма** B. prism.
бекар *m.* (mus.) natural (note).
Бекке полоска Becke line.
беккелит *m.* beckelite.
беккерелит *m.* becquerelite.
Беккереля лучи, беккерелевы лучи Becquerel rays; **Б. эффект** B. effect.
беккерит *m.* beckerite.
Бекмана перегруппировка Beckmann rearrangement; **Б. спектрофотометр** Beckmann spectrophotometer; **Б. термометр** Beckmann thermometer.
бекмановск/ая перегруппировка *see* **Бекмана перегруппировка**; **—ое превращение** Beckmann molecular transformation.
бекстремит *m.* bäckströmite.
бел *m.* (acous.) bel.
белен/ие, —ье *n.* bleaching; blanching; **—ый** *a.* bleached.
бел/еть *v.* grow white, whiten, bleach; **—изна** *f.* whiteness, white; **—ила** *pl.* white mineral pigment, whiting; **—ильный** *a.* bleaching; **—ить** *v.* whiten, bleach.
беличь/е колесо, —я клетка (mach.) squirrel cage.
белки *pl. of* **белок.**
белков/ина *f.*, **—ое вещество** albumin; **—ый** *a.* albumin, albuminous, protein.
Беллятрикс Bellatrix.

белов/атый *a.* whitish; **—ой экземпляр** clean copy.
белок *m.* albumen; albumin; protein; white (of eye).
белокалильн/ость *f.* incandescence, white heat; **—ый** *a.* incandescent, white hot, glowing; **—ый жар** incandescence, white heat.
белокровие *n.* leukemia.
белонезит *m.* belonesite.
белорусс. *abbr.* (**белорусский**) Belorussian.
Белорусская ССР Belorussian SSR.
белоснежный *a.* snow-white.
белочный *see* **белковый.**
бел/ый *a.* white; **б. камень** granulite, whitestone (metamorphic rock); **б. кружок** open circle, unfilled circle; **б. металл, б. сплав** white metal; **б. накал** white heat; **б. свет** white light; **б. шум** white noise; **—ая крыса** white rat; **—ая мышь** white mouse.
бельг. *abbr.* **бельгийский** *a.* Belgian.
Бельгия Belgium.
белье *n.*, **—вой** *a.* linen.
бельмо *n.* (med.) cataract.
бельтинг *m.* belting.
Бельтрами, *m.*, **бельтрамиевый** *a.* Beltrami.
беляк *m.* foam (of waves).
бемит *m.* boehmite.
бемоль *m.* (mus.) flat.
Бемпорада формула Bemporad formula.
бемск/ий *a.* Bohemian; **—ое стекло** Bohemian glass.
Бенара ячейка Bénard (convection) cell.
бенжаминит *m.* benjaminite.
бенз— *prefix* benz—, benzo—.
бензин *m.*, **—овый** *a.* gasoline, benzine; **—овый двигатель, —овый мотор, —омотор** *m.* gasoline engine, gasoline motor.
бензоил *m.* benzoyl.
бензо/ин, —й *m.* benzoin; **—йный** *a.* benzoic.
бензол *m.* benzene.
Бенндорфа электрометр Benndorf electrometer.
бентонит *m.* bentonite.
Бенуа шкала Benoit scale (of x-ray hardness).
БЕПО, Бепо Bepo (British Experimental Pile O).
Бера закон Beer law.
Бербера правило Barber rule (magnetic focusing).
Бергмана серия Bergmann series.
Берд Baird; **—а денситометр** B. densitometer.
берег *m.* shore, coast, seashore, seacoast; **отвесный б.** bluff.
берегов/ой *a.* coastal, littoral, shore; **б. ветер** shore wind; **б. интерферометр** cliff-top interferometer; **—ая черта** shore line.
бережн/о *adv.* carefully, cautiously; **—ость** *f.* caution; **—ый** *a.* cautious, careful.
берем *present pl. of* **брать,** we take, let us take.
беременная *a.* pregnant.
берется *v.* is taken.
беречь *v.* take care of; preserve; spare; **—ся** *v.* guard against.
берженит *m.* börszönyite.
Бержерона-Финдайзена гипотеза Bergeron-Findeisen hypothesis.
берил, —л *m.* (min.) beryl; **благородный б.** emerald (gem).
берилл/ат *m.* beryllate; **—иевый** *a.* beryllium, *see also* **берилловый; —иевый реактор** beryllium reactor.
берилл/ий *m.* beryllium (Be); **окись —ия** beryllium oxide, beryllia.
берилло/вый *a.* beryllium; **—вая земля** beryllia, beryllium oxide; **—ид** *m.* berylloid.
бериллонит *m.* beryllonite.
берк *m.* dynamic meter.
беркелий *m.* berkelium (Bk).
берма *f.* berm.
бермудский антициклон Bermuda high.
Бернсайд Burnside.
Бернулли дифференциальное уравнение Bernoulli differential equation; **Б. полиномы (многочлены)** Bernoullian polynomials; **Б. уравнение** Bernoulli equation; **Б. числа, бернуллиевы числа** B. numbers.
Бертена поверхность Bertin surface.
Бертло (Бертело) бомба Berthelot bomb, B. calorimeter; **Б.-Томсена принцип** B.-Thomsen principle; **Б. уравнение** B. equation.

бертолетова соль Berthollet's salt.
Бертолле Berthollet.
бертоллид *m.*, **—ный** *a.* berthollide.
бертонит *m.* berthonite.
Бертрана линза Bertrand lens; **Б. признак** B. criterion, B. test.
бертьерин *m.* berthierine.
бертьерит *m.* berthierite.
берцелианит *m.* berzelianite.
берцелиит *m.* berzeliite.
Берцелиуса лампа Berzelius lamp.
бес— *see also* **без—**.
бесед/а *f.* talk, discussion, debate; **—овать** *v.* talk.
бескатушечный *a.* coilless.
бескислородный *a.* oxygen-free.
бесконечно *adv.* indefinitely, infinitely, ad infinitum; **б. большой** infinite; **б. малый, б. малая величина** infinitesimal; **б. удаленная точка** (math.) point at infinity, ideal point; **—мерный** *a.* infinite dimensional.
бесконечност/ь *f.* infinity; singularity; **обращаться в б.** become infinite; **в —и** at infinity; **до —и** to infinity; ad infinitum.
бесконечн/ый *a.* infinite, unbounded; nonterminating, perpetual; **б. винт** endless screw, worm; **—ая цепь** endless chain; **—ое полотно** conveyer belt.
бесконтактный *a.* noncontact, noncontacting.
бесконтрольн/о *adv.*, **—ый** *a.* uncontrolled.
бескорыстный *a.* disinterested.
бескров/ие *n.*, **—ность** *f.* anemia; **—ный** *a.* anemic.
бескрылый *a.* wingless.
бесперебойн/ость *f.* steadiness, continuity; **—ый** *a.* steady, uninterrupted, smooth, constant.
беспереводный *a.* nontransferable.
бесперемен/о *adv.* without change; **—ый** *a.* changeless, invariable.
беспечный *a.* unconcerned, careless.
беспилотный *a.* pilotless.
беспламенный *a.* flameless.
беспланов/ость *f.* planlessness; **—ый** *a.* haphazard, planless.
бесплатн/о *adv.*, **—ый** *a.* free, free of charge.
бесплод/ие *n.*, **—ность** *f.* sterility, infertility; fruitlessness, futility; **—ный** *a.* sterile, fruitless, futile.
бесповоротн/ость *f.* irreversibility, irrevocability; **—ый** *a.* irreversible, irrevocable; nonrotary.
бесподобн/ость *f.* incomparableness; **—ый** *a.* incomparable, excellent.
беспокоить *v.* disturb; **—ся** *v.* worry.
беспокой/ный *a.* agitated, disturbed, turbulent; **—ство** *n.* unrest, agitation, disturbance; worry; turbulence.
бесполезн/о *adv.* uselessly, in vain; **—ость** *f.* uselessness; ineffectiveness; **—ый** *a.* useless, ineffective; **—ый захват** nonproductive capture.
бесполый *a.* sexless, asexual, neuter.
бесполюсный *a.* poleless.
беспомощн/ость *f.* helplessness; **—ый** *a.* helpless, feeble.
беспористый *a.* nonporous, dense.
беспороговый *a.* nonthreshold.
беспорочный *a.* immaculate, faultless, pure, spotless.
беспорядок *m.* disorder, confusion; scattering; irregularity.
беспорядочн/о *adv.* randomly, confusedly; **б. распределенный** randomly distributed; **—ость** *f.* disorder; **—ый** *a.* random; irregular, disordered, confused; **—ое движение** random motion; **—ое рассеяние** random scattering; **—ые отражения** clutter (radar).
беспосадочный *a.* nonstop.
беспотерный *a.* lossless.
беспочвенн/о *adv.* without basis, without foundation; **—ость** *f.* groundlessness; **—ый** *a.* groundless, unfounded, unsubstantiated.
беспредельн/о *adv.* infinitely, ad infinitum, boundlessly; **—ость** *f.* infinity, boundlessness; **—ый** *a.* infinite, boundless, limitless, unbounded.
беспредметный *a.* aimless, pointless.
беспрекословный *a.* incontestable, absolute.
беспрепятственн/о *adv.* without hindrance; **—ый** *a.* unimpeded, unobstructed, unhindered.
беспрерывн/о *adv.* continuously; **—ость** *f.* continuity; **—ый** *a.* continuous, uninterrupted, incessant; **—ый процесс** continuous process.

беспрестанный *see* **беспрерывный.**

бесприбыльный *a.* unprofitable; unremunerative.

беспримерный *a.* unprecedented, unparalleled.

беспримесный *a.* pure, uncontaminated; unalloyed.

беспристраст/ие *n.*, **—ность** *f.* impartiality, disinterestedness; **—но** *adv.* impartially, without bias; **—ный** *a.* impartial, unbiased, objective.

бесприцельный *a.* aimless, random, haphazard.

беспричинн/о *adv.* without reason; **—ый** *a.* causeless; gratuitous; motiveless.

беспроводный *a.* wireless.

беспроигрышный *a.* without loss, sure, safe.

беспыльный *a.* dustless.

бессвязн/ость *f.* inconsistency, incoherence; **—ый** *a.* inconsistent, incoherent, disconnected.

бесселева функция *see* **Бесселя функция.**

Бессель Bessel (lunar crater).

Бесселя/-Клиффорда дифференциальное уравнение Bessel-Clifford differential equation; **Б. неравенство** B. inequality; **Б. функция** B. function; **Б. функция с нулевым значком** zero-order B. function.

Бессемера процесс Bessemer process.

бессемеров/ание *n.* (met.) bessemerizing, Bessemer process; **—ать** *v.* bessemerize; **—о железо, —ское железо** Bessemer iron; **—ский** *a.* Bessemer; **—ская сталь** Bessemer steel.

бессердечниковый *a.* coreless.

бессерный *a.* sulfur-free.

бессеточный *a.* gridless.

бессил/ие *n.* impotence, weakness; **—ьный** *a.* impotent, weak.

бессистемный *a.* unsystematic, haphazard, unmethodical.

бесследный *a.* traceless.

бессменн/о *adv.* without change, continuously; **—ость** *f.* changelessness, permanency; **—ый** *a.* changeless, permanent, fixed, set, continuous.

бессмертный *a.* immortal.

бессмысленный *a.* senseless, absurd, meaningless.

бесснежье *n.* lack of snow.

бес/совестный *a.* dishonest, unscrupulous; **—содержательный** *a.* empty; **—сознательный** *a.* unconscious, involuntary.

бесспиновый *a.* spinless, spin-zero.

бес/спорный *a.* indisputable; **—срочный** *a.* indefinite, permanent; **—столкновительный** *a.* collisionless; **—структурный** *a.* structureless; **—ступенчатый** *a.* continuously variable; **—счетный** *a.* innumerable, countless; **—теневой** *a.* shadowless.

бестоковая полоса (sol.) nonconduction band.

бестол/ковщина, —ковица, —очь *f.* disorder, muddle, confusion, chaos.

бестрансформаторный *a.* transformerless.

бесфланцевый *a.* flangeless.

бесфоновый *a.* hum-free, background-free.

бесформенный *a.* shapeless, formless, amorphous.

бесфосфорный *a.* phosphorus-free; dephosphorized.

бесхлопотный *a.* trouble-free.

бесцветн/ость *f.* colorlessness, achromatism; **—ый** *a.* colorless, achromatic.

бесцельн/о *adv.* aimlessly, at random; **—ость** *f.* aimlessness, purposelessness; **—ый** *a.* aimless, futile.

бесценный *a.* priceless, invaluable.

бесцентровый *a.* centerless.

бесциркуляционный *a.* (hyd.) irrotational.

бесцокольн/ый *a.* baseless; **—ая лампа** baseless tube.

бесчестный *a.* dishonest, dishonorable.

бесчисленн/ый *a.* innumerable, countless.

бесчувств/енность *f.*, **—ие** *n.* insensibility; **—енный** *a.* insensible, unfeeling.

бесшовный *a.* seamless, jointless.

бесшумный *a.* noiseless, silent, quiet.

бесщелевой *a.* slitless.

БЕТ *abbr.* [**Брунауер, Эмметт и Теллер** (**БЕТ уравнение, метод**)] Brunauer, Emmett and Teller (BET equation, method).

бета *f.* beta (Greek letter); **б.-активное вещество** beta-active substance, beta emitter; **б.-измеритель** beta gauge; **б.-латунь** (met.) beta-brass (copper-zinc alloy); **б.-лучи** beta rays; **б.-радиоактивный** beta-radioactive; **б.-распад** beta decay; **б.-спектрометр** beta spectrometer, beta-ray spectrometer; **б.-уранотил** beta-uranotile; **б.-устойчивый** beta-stable; **б.-фаза** beta phase; **б.-фон** beta background; **б.-функция** beta function; **б.-частица** beta particle.

бетаизлуч/атель *m.* beta emitter, beta-radioactive substance; **—ающий** *a.* beta-emitting; **—ение** *n.* beta radiation.

бета/лучевой спектрометр beta-ray spectrometer; **—толщиномер** *m.* beta-ray thickness gauge; **—топический** *a.* betatopic.

бетатрон *m.*, **—ный** *a.* betatron.

Бете Bethe; **Б.-Салпетера уравнение** B.-Salpeter equation.

Бетельгейзе Betelgeuse.

бетон *m.* concrete; **—ирование** *n.* concreting; **—ированный** *a.* concrete, treated with concrete; **—ировать, —ить** *v.* concrete, treat with concrete, lay concrete (on); **—ит** *m.* concrete (building) block; **—ный** *a.* concrete; **—ный камень** concrete block.

Бетса процесс Betts process.

Бетти теорема Betti theorem.

Беттин Bettinus (lunar crater).

Бетца-Кноллера эффект Betz-Knoller effect.

беумлерит *m.* baeumlerite.

бехилит *m.* bechilite.

Бехштейна фотометр Bechstein (flicker) photometer.

беч *m.* batch.

Бечвара поток Bečvař's stream (Ursid meteors).

бечев/а *f.* towline; **—ка** *f.* twine.

би— *prefix* bi—, di—.

Бианкини (Бианчини) Bianchini (lunar crater).

бианкит *m.* bianchite.

биберит *m.* bieberite.

библ. *abbr.* (**библиография**) bibliography.

библиограф *m.* bibliographer; **—ический** *a.* bibliographic; **—ия** *f.* bibliography.

библиоте/ка *f.* library; **б.-справочник** reference library; **—карь** *m.* librarian; **—чный** *a.* library.

бивариантный *a.* bivariant, bivariate; two-variable.

биверит *m.* beaverite.

Биверлодж Beaverlodge.

бигармоническая функция biharmonic function.

бигидрат *see* **дигидрат.**

бидистиллат *m.* doubly distilled water.

бидон *m.* can, container, vessel.

Биелиды Bielids (meteors).

биен/ие *n.* beat, pulsation; wobble; **—ия** *pl.* wobbling; **принцип —ий** beat-frequency principle.

Бийе билинза Billet split lens.

бикарбонат *m.* bicarbonate, *specif.* sodium bicarbonate.

биквадрат *m.* biquadrate; **—ный** *a.* biquadratic.

бикварц *m.* bi-quartz.

би/компактный *a.* bicompact; **—конический** *a.* biconical.

бикристалл *m.* bicrystal.

бикрон *m.* bicron (one billionth of a meter).

биксбиит *m.* bixbyite.

Бикфорда, бикфордов шнур Bickford (safety) fuse.

билатеральный *a.* bilateral.

билет *m.* ticket, pass, permit; **кредитный б.** bank note.

б. или м. *abbr.* (**более или менее**) more or less.

билинейный *a.* bilinear.

билинза *f.* bilens, split lens.

Билли Billy (lunar crater).

биллиардный шар billiard ball.

биллион *m.*, **—ный** *a.* billion; **—ная часть** one billionth.

биллон *m.* (met.) billon (coinage alloy).

било *m.* beater.

билогарифмический *a.* log-log (plot).

бильд *m.* photograph, picture, facsimile; **б.-аппарат** phototelegraph; **—телеграмма** *f.* facsimile telegram, wire photo; **—телеграфия** *f.* phototelegraphy.

биметалл *m.* bimetal; **—ический** *a.* bimetallic.

имолекулярный *a.* bimolecular, dimolecular.
иморфный элемент bimorph cell.
имс *m.*, **—овый** *a.* beam.
инантный электрометр binant electrometer.
инарн/ый *a.* binary; **—ая пересчетная схема** binary scaler, scale-of-two circuit; **—ая смесь** binary mixture.
инауральный *a.* binaural.
ингама формула Bingham equation.
индгеимит *m.* bindheimite.
ине (Бинэ) теорема Binet theorem.
инейтрон *m.* dineutron.
инок/ль *m.* binoculars; **полевой б.** field glasses; **—улярный** *a.* binocular; **—улярное зрение** binocular vision.
ином *m.* (math.) binomial; **—альный ряд** binomial series; **—иальный, —инальный** *a.* binomial.
инормаль *f.* binormal.
инт *m.* bandage; **—овать** *v.* bandage, swathe.
ио— *prefix* bio—.
ио закон Biot law; **Б.-Савара закон** B.-Savart relation; **Б. число** B. number.
иограф *m.* biographer; **—ический** *a.* biographic; **—ия** *f.* biography.
иоклимат/ический *a.* bioclimatic; **—ология** *f.* bioclimatology, bioclimatics.
иоколлоид *m.*, **—ный** *a.* biocolloid.
иол. *abbr.* **(биология)** biology; **(биологический)** biological, biologic.
иолит *m.* (min.) biolith.
иолог *m.* biologist; **—ически** *adv.* biologically; **—ический** *a.* biological, biologic; **—ический эквивалент рентгена** man roentgen equivalent (rem); **—ический экран** biological shield; **—ия** *f.* biology.
иолюминесценция *f.* bioluminescence.
иомагнет/изм *m.* biomagnetism; **—ический** *a.* biomagnetic.
ио/математика *f.* biomathematics; **—метрия** *f.* biometry; **—механика** *f.* biomechanics.
иоплазма *f.* bioplasm.
иортогональный *a.* biorthogonal.
иоскоп *m.* bioscope.
иосфера *f.* biosphere.
иотрон *m.* biotron.
иофизика *f.* biophysics.

биохим/ический *a.* biochemical; **—ия** *f.* biochemistry.
био/электрический *a.* bioelectric; **—энергетика** *f.* bioenergetics.
бипирамида *f.* bipyramid; **—льный** *a.* bipyramidal.
биплан *m.* biplane.
биполярн/ость *f.* bipolarity; **—ый** *a.* bipolar; **—ый коэффициент диффузии** ambipolar diffusion coefficient.
бипотенциальн/ый *a.* bipotential; **—ая линза** bipotential lens.
бипризма *f.* biprism.
бипятеричный *a.* biquinary.
бирадикал *m.* diradical.
бирка *f.* tally; tag, ticket; name plate.
Биркхоф Birkhoff.
бирюз/а *f.*, **—овый** *a.* turquoise.
бис— *prefix* bis—.
бисазо— *prefix* bisazo—.
бисбиит *m.* bisbeeite.
бисдиазо— *prefix* bisdiazo—, tetrazo—.
бисекция *f.* bisection.
бисер *m.* beads; **—ный** *a.* bead, beaded; **—ообразная молния** beaded lightning.
бисиликат *m.* disilicate.
биск *m.* bisque.
бисквит *m.*, **—ный** *a.* biscuit; **—ный обжиг** biscuit firing.
бисмутинит *m.* bismuthinite.
бисмуто— *prefix* bismutho—, bismuto—.
биспинор *m.* bispinor.
биспираль *f.* double helix.
биссектриса *f.* bisector, bisectrix, bisecting line.
биссолит *m.* byssolite.
бисульф/ат *m.* bisulfate; **—ид** *m.* bisulfide; **—ит** *m.* bisulfite.
бисфеноид *m.* bisphenoid; **—альный** *a.* bisphenoidal.
бисферический *a.* bispherical.
битиит *m.* bityite.
битовнит *m.* bytownite.
биток *m.* beetle, mallet.
Битти-Бриджмена уравнение Beattie-Bridgman equation (of state).
битум *m.* bitumen, asphalt; **—инизировать** *v.* bituminize; **—инозный, —ный** *a.* bituminous; asphalt, asphaltic.
бит/ый *a.* struck, cracked, broken; **—ь** *v.* break; shoot; strike, flap, whip;

wobble; —**ь на** aim at; —**ь струей** spout, squirt; —**ье** *n.* beating; breaking; —**ься** *v.* beat, throb, pulsate.

бифилярн/ый *a.* bifilar, double-wound; **б. маятник** bifilar pendulum; **б. подогреватель** double-helical heater; —**ая обмотка** bifilar winding.

бифуркация *f.* bifurcation.

бихарактеристика *f.* bicharacteristic.

бихлорид *m.* bichloride.

бихромат *m.* bichromate.

бицикл *m.* dicycle, bicycle; —**ический** *a.* dicyclic, bicyclic.

бицикло— *prefix* bicyclo—.

бициркулярный *a.* bicircular.

Бишопа кольцо Bishop ring.

бишофит *m.* bischofite.

Благдена закон Blagden law.

благодар/ить *v.* thank; —**ность** *f.* thanks, gratitude, appreciation; **в —ность** in acknowledgment; —**ный** *a.* thankful, grateful, appreciative; —**я** owing to, due to, because of, by virtue of.

благополучный *a.* safe; satisfactory.

благоприят/но *adv.* favorably; —**ность** *f.* favorableness; —**ный** *a.* favorable, opportune; —**ный фактор** contributory factor; —**ствующий** *a.* favorable.

благоразумный *a.* reasonable, sensible.

благородный *a.* noble; precious (stone); **б. газ** noble gas, inert gas; **б. змеевик** precious serpentine; **б. металл** noble metal; precious metal; **б. опал** precious opal.

благотворный *a.* beneficial.

благоустроенный *a.* well-organized, well-arranged, well-managed.

Блазиуса (Блязиуса) формула Blasius equation.

бланк *m.* blank; form.

Бланкан Blancanus (lunar crater).

бланк/ирование *n.*, —**ирующий** *a.* blanking.

блатгаллер Blatthaller loudspeaker.

блаугаз *m.* Blau gas.

бледит *m.* blödite.

бледн/еть *v.* lose color; —**оватый** *a.* rather pale; —**оокрашенный** *a.* pale-colored, dull; —**ость** *f.* paleness; —**ый** *a.* pale; faint, weak (color).

блекл/ость *f.* fading; —**ый** *a.* faded, pale; —**ая руда** fahlerz, gray copper ore.

бленд/а *f.* (astr.) blend, blending; (phot.) blind; (min.) blende, zinc blende; —**ирование** *n.* blend, blending.

блес/к *m.* brightness, luminosity, brilliance; light, flash, glitter, glare; (min.) glance; **угол —ка** blaze angle; —**кость** *f.* glare; —**нуть** *v.* flash.

блест/еть *v.* shine, glitter, sparkle; —**як, —ян** *m.* galena; mica; —**ящий** *a.* brilliant, bright, shiny, sparkling.

ближ/айший *a.* nearest, next; immediate; —**е** *comp. of* **близко,** nearer.

ближн/ий *a.* near, next, neighboring; **б. порядок** short-range order; —**яя инфракрасная область** near-infrared region; —**яя точка** near point (of the eye); —**яя упорядоченность** short-range order, local order; —**ее ультрафиолетовое излучение** near ultraviolet radiation.

близ *prep. gen.* near, in the vicinity of; —**иться** *v.* approach, approximate.

близк/ий *a.* near, close; similar; **б. к резонансу** near resonance; **б. уровень** adjacent level; —**ое столкновение** near collision, close encounter; —**о** *adv.* near, close; near by, close by; —**одействующий** *a.* short-range.

близлежащий *a.* adjacent, contiguous, neighboring, near-by.

близмеридиональная высота ex-meridian altitude.

близнец *m.* twin; —**ы** *pl.* twins; (math.) twin primes.

Близнецы Gemini (Gem) (constellation).

близорук/ий *a.* short-sighted, myopic; —**ость** *f.* myopia.

близост/ный эффект proximity effect; —**ь** *f.* nearness, proximity, vicinity, neighborhood.

блик *m.* highlight; bright spot; (met.) fulguration, flashing.

Бликера диаграмма влажности Bleeker humidity diagram.

блинд/аж *m.* dugout, shelter; —**ированный** *a.* iron-clad, armor-clad.

блинкмикроскоп *m.* blink microscope.

блинчатый лед pancake ice.

блист/ание *n.* shining, glittering; **—ательность** *f.* brilliance.
блитит *m.* blythite.
блок *m.* block; unit, assembly; chassis; (nucl.) slug, lump; pulley; **б. питания** power (supply) unit, power pack; **сложный б.** hoisting tackle; **б.-схема** block diagram; **б. управления** control unit; **б.-эффект** blocking effect; self-blocking, disadvantage factor.
блокинг *m.* blocking; **б.-генератор** blocking generator.
блокиров/ание *n.*, **—ка** *f.* blocking, holding; lock, locking, interlock; **—анный** *a.* blocked; **—ать** *v.* block, lock, interlock; **—очный** *a.* blocking, locking, interlocking; **—очный конденсатор** bypass capacitor; **—очное приспособление** interlock.
блок/ирующий *see* **блокировочный**; **б. антициклон** (meteor.) blocking high; **—овый** *a.* block, pulley.
бломстранд, —ит *m.* blomstrandite; **—ин** *m.* blomstrandine, blomstrandinite.
блонделя люменометр Blondel nitometer (surface-brightness meter).
блоха закон $T^{3/2}$ для намагниченности Bloch $T^{3/2}$ law for magnetization; **Б. стенка, блоховская стенка, блоховская граница** B. wall; **Б. теорема для сверхпроводимости** B. theorem of superconductivity; **Б. функции** B. functions.
блочн/ый *a.* block, lump; unit type, plug-in type; modular; **б. полимер** block polymer; **—ая матрица** partitioned matrix; **—ая схема** block diagram; **—ое расположение урана** lumping of uranium.
блочок *m.* slug.
блуждание *n.* wandering, straying; **беспорядочное б., случайное б.** (math.) random flight (or walk); **б. ионов** migration of ions.
блужд/ать *v.* wander, stray, move at random; **—ающий** *a.* stray, wandering, migratory; devious; **—ающий блик** (telev.) ghost (image); **—ающий ток** stray current.
блэкман Blackman.

блюд/о *n.* dish, plate; **—цеобразный** *a.* saucer-shaped.
блюм *m.* (met.) bloom; **—инг** *m.* blooming, blooming mill, bloomery.
бляха *f.* plate.
б. м. *abbr.* (**без места**) place not given (in bibliography).
б. м. и г. *abbr.* (**без места и года**) place and year not given (in bibliography).
БМЭ *abbr.* (**Большая Медицинская Энциклопедия**) Large Medical Encyclopedia.
бн *abbr.* (**барн**) barn (unit of cross-sectional area, 10^{-24} cm^2).
бобина *f.* bobbin, spool, reel.
бобовидный *a.* bean-like, bean-shaped.
бобообразный *see* **бобовидный.**
бобылевская задача Bobylev problem.
бобыш/ек *m.* cam; **—ка** *f.* boss, lug; nipple, spool.
бобьеррит *m.* bobierrite.
бовенит *m.* bowenite.
богат/еть *v.* grow rich, prosper; **—ство** *n.* wealth; **—ства** *pl.* resources **естественные —ства** natural resources; **—ый** *a.* rich, high-grade; abundant.
богхед *m.* boghead coal.
бод *m.* baud (unit of telegraph signal speed).
Боде (Бодэ) диаграмма Bode diagram; **Б. правило** B. law.
боев/ой *a.* combat; war, military; **б. заряд** warhead; **б. молот** sledge hammer; **б. отсек** warhead; **—ое радиоактивное вещество** radiological warfare agent.
боек *m.* block; head (of hammer); firing pin; striker.
боеприпасы *pl.* ammunition, munitions.
Бозе-частица Bose particle, boson; **Б.-Эйнштейна статистика** B.-Einstein statistics; **бозевский** *a.* Bose.
бозон *m.* boson.
бой *m.* battle; struggle; face (of hammer); beating.
бойк/ий *a.* clever, brisk, alert; **—ость** *f.* briskness, alertness.
бойлер *m.* boiler.
Бойля закон Boyle's law; **Б.-Мариотта закон** B. law, Mariotte's law; **Б. точка (температура)** B. temperature (point).

бойница *f.* vent.

Бойса камера Boys rotating lens-type camera.

бойсограмма *f.* Boys-camera photograph.

бок *m.* side, flank; wall; **б.-о-б.** side by side, alongside; **в б.** to the side, sideways; **к —у** laterally; **на б.** on the side, sideways; **по —ам** on each side; **по —у** set aside; **с —у** at the side of, at hand; **с —у на б.** from side to side.

бокал *m.* beaker.

боккран *m.* trestle crane.

боковик *m.* measuring jaw.

боков/ой *a.* side, lateral, edgewise; neighboring, marginal; supplementary; extraneous; (meteor.) horizontal; (geo.) wall; **б. ветер** side wind; **б. зазор** side play; **б. канал** bypass; **б. ливень** inclined shower, lateral shower; **б. мираж** lateral mirage; **—ая волна** (seis.) refraction (or head) wave; **—ая грань, —ая поверхность** lateral face, flat side, facet; **—ая группа** side group (of polymer); **—ая диффузия** lateral diffusion; **—ая жидкость** auxiliary liquid; **—ая реакция** side reaction; **—ая сила** lateral force, side force, yawing force; **—ая цепь** side chain; **—ое давление** lateral pressure, lateral thrust; (meteor.) horizontal pressure; **—ое излучение** fringe radiation, lateral radiation; **—ое колебание** transverse oscillation; **—ое перемешивание** lateral mixture; **—ое прогибание** bowing; **—ое рассеяние** side scattering; **—ое спускное течение** side stream; **—ое усилие** side thrust.

боком *adv.* sideways, sidewise, edgewise.

боксит *m.* bauxite; **—овый** *a.* bauxite, bauxitic.

болванка *f.* pig, ingot, bar, slug.

болг. *abbr.* (**болгарский**) Bulgarian.

Болгария Bulgaria; *see also* **Народная Республика Болгария.**

болгарский *a.* Bulgarian.

боле, —е *adv.* more; *see also* **больше; все —е** increasingly, progressively; **—е или менее** more or less; **тем —е** all the more; **тем —е, что** especially as; **—е того** and what is mor **—е чем** more than.

болезн/етворный *a.* disease-producin pathogenic; **—ь** *f.* disease; **морска —ь** seasickness, nausea.

боле/ть *v.* be ill, ache; **—утоляющий** *a* **—утоляющее средство** sedativ anodyne.

Болиай Bolyai.

болид *m.* bolide, fire-ball.

Болина камера Seeman-Bohlen camer

боло/грамма *f.* bologram; **—граф** *n* bolograph.

болометр *m.* bolometer; **—ический** bolometric.

болонский камень, б. шпат bologn stone.

болот/истый, —ный *a.* bog, bogg swampy, marshy; **—ный газ** mars gas, methane; **—ная вода** pe water; **—ная руда** bog ore; **—о** bog, swamp, marsh, morass.

болото Гнилое Palus Putredinis (lunar **б. Сонное** Palus Somnii (lunar); **Туманное** Palus Nebularum (lunar

болт *m.* bolt; pin; **б.-барашек** butterf bolt, wing bolt.

болт/ание *n.* shaking, stirring; **—анка** (aero.) bump; bumpy air; **—ать** shake, stir, mix; **—аться** *v.* dangl swing.

болтов/ой *a.* bolt; pin; **б. шарнир** p hinge; **—ое крепление** bolting.

болус *see* **болюс.**

Больцано Bolzano.

Больцмана закон излучения (**зако Стефана-Больцмана**) Boltzmann la of radiation (Stefan-Boltzmann law **Б. постоянная** B. constant; **Б. ра пределение** B. distribution; **Б. урав нение** B. equation.

большак *m.* highway.

Большая Медведица Ursa Major (UM (constellation).

больше *comp. of* **большой, много,** mor larger, bigger; **как можно б.** as muc as possible; **много б.** much mor **б. не** no longer; **чем б., тем** the mo the . . . .

больш/ий *a.* greater, larger; major; **—е частью** for the most part; **самое —** at the most; **—инство** *n.* majorit most of.

Большое Магеллановое Облако Large Magellanic Cloud.

Большое Медвежье озеро Great Bear Lake.

больш/ой *a.* big, large, bulky, great, high; strong (current); coarse (grain); heavy (machine); **б. круг** great circle; **б. резонанс** giant resonance; **—ая энергия** high energy.

болюс *m.* bole, bolus.

бомб/а *f.* bomb; vessel, cylinder; **калориметрическая б.** oxygen-bomb calorimeter; **сбрасывать —ы** bomb.

бомбардир/ование *n.*, **—овка** *f.* bombardment; bombing; **—овать** *v.* bombard; bomb; **—овщик** *m.* bomber; **—уемый** *a.* bombarded, struck; **—ующий** *a.* incident, bombarding; **—ующая частица** projectile.

бомбиччит *m.* bombiccite.

бомонтит *m.* beaumontite.

Бомэ (**Боме**) Baumé, Bé; **ареометр Б.** Baumé hydrometer; **шкала Б.** Baumé scale.

бонанца *f.* bonanza.

бондеризация *f.* bonderizing.

Бонплан Bonpland (lunar crater).

боотит *m.* boothite.

бор *m.* boron (B); **б. трехфтористый** boron trifluoride.

бора *m.* bora (wind).

Бора атом Bohr atom; **Б. принцип соответствия** B. correspondence principle.

боразон *m.* borazon.

боракс *m.* borax.

Боракс Borax (reactor).

бор/аль *m.* boral (mixture of B_4C and aluminum); **—ан** *m.* borane, boron hydride; **—ат** *m.* borate.

бораско *m.* borasca.

боратное стекло borax glass.

борацит *m.* boracite.

боргстремит *m.* borgströmite.

Борда Borda (lunar crater).

Борда насадка Borda mouthpiece.

бордюр *m.* border; curb; **—ный** *a.* border.

борей *m.* north wind.

борелевское тело множеств (math.) class of all Borel sets; **Бореля разложение** Borel expansion.

боржицкит *m.* bořickite.

боридный катод boride cathode.

бор/ил *m.* boryl; **—ин** *m.* borine.

борирован/ие *n.* borating; **—ный** *a.* borated.

борист/ый *a.* boron, boride (of); **б. счетчик** boron counter tube; **—ая камера** boron chamber; **—ая сталь** boron steel.

Борна/-Габера цикл, Б. круговой процесс Born-Haber cycle; **Б.-Инфельда теория** B.-Infeld theory; **Б. приближение** B. approximation; **Б. формула** B. equation.

борнил *m.* bornyl.

борно— *prefix* boro—.

борновское приближение *see* **Борна приближение.**

борн/ый *a.* boric, boracic; **б. счетчик** boron counter, boron-filled counter; **—ая ионизационная машина** boron-filled ionization chamber.

боров, *m.*, **—ковый** *a.* flue; **—ковый порог** baffle.

бороводород *m.* boron hydride.

боровок *m.* baffle.

боровольфрамовая кислота borotungstic acid.

боровская орбита Bohr orbit.

боровый *a.* flue.

бородчатый *a.* barbed.

борозд/а, —ка *f.* furrow; **—чатый** *a.* grooved, channeled, fluted; striated.

бороскоп *m.* boroscope.

борт *m.* edge, rim, border, side, flange, bead; (min.) bort; board; **загибать б.** *v.* bead; **—овый** *a.* edge, rim, border, flange; **—овая сварка** double-flanged butt weld.

борьба *f.* struggle, fight; prevention, control.

Боскович Boscovich (lunar crater).

босон *m.* boson.

босфорит *m.* bosphorite.

ботан. *abbr.* (**ботаника**) botany; (**ботанический**) botanical.

ботан/ик *m.* botanist; **—ика** *f.* botany; **—ический** *a.* botanical.

ботриоген *m.* botryogen.

ботриолит *m.* botryolite.

боулингит *m.* bowlingite.

Боуэна нефрит Bowen nephrite.

Бофорта балл Beaufort number; **Б. код (для состояния погоды)** B. notation; **Б. шкала** B. (wind) scale.

бочар *m.* cooper.

бочка *f.* barrel, cask, tub, vat; (aero.) roll.

бочкообразн/ый *a.* barrel-shaped; **—ая дисторсия** barrel-shaped distortion; **—ое поле** barrel field.

бояться *v.* fear.

БП *abbr.* (**бюро погоды**) weather bureau.

бра-вектор (Dirac) bra vector.

Браве решетка Bravais lattice.

браз. *abbr.* (**бразильский**) Brazilian.

Бразилия Brazil.

бразильский *a.* Brazilian.

брак *m.* defect; discard, reject.

бракебушит *m.* brackebuschite.

бракет *m.* bracket.

браков/анный *a.* rejected; defective; **—ать** *v.* reject, discard; **—ка** *f.* quality inspection, discarding, rejecting, rejection; **—щик** *m.* quality checker, inspector, examiner.

брандизит *m.* brandisite.

брандмауер *m.* fire wall, fireproof wall.

Бранли Branly tube; **Б. когерер** B. coherer; **Б.-Ленарда эффект** B.-Lenard effect.

браннерит *m.* brannerite.

бранхит *m.* branchite.

брат *m.* brother.

брать *v.* take; **не б.** fail; **—ся** *v.* undertake.

Брауна трубка Braun (cathode-ray) tube.

брауновское *see* **броуново.**

брахи— *prefix* brachy—.

брахи/ось *f.* (cryst.) brachyaxis; **—пирамида** *f.* brachypyramid; **—стохрона** *f.* brachistochrone. **—типный** *a.* brachytype.

брашпиль *m.* windlass.

брев/енчатый *a.* log, beam, timber; **—но** *n.* beam, log, block.

бревий *m.* brevium.

бревицит *m.* brevicite.

Бревстера *see* **Брюстера.**

бреггерит *m.* bröggerite.

бредень *m.* dragnet.

Бредта теорема Bredt theorem.

брезент *m.*, **—овый** *a.* tarpaulin, canvas.

бреинерит *m.* breunerite.

Брейт, брейтовский *a.* Breit; **Б.-Вигнера максимум** B.-Wigner peak; **Б.-Вигнера формула** B.-Wigner formula.

брейтгауптит *m.* breithauptite.

брекватер *m.* breakwater.

брекч/иа, —ия *f.* breccia; **—ирование** *n.* brecciation; **—ированный** *a.* brecciated.

бремсберг *m.* slope.

бремя *n.* burden, load.

бренный *a.* perishable; transitory.

Брента уравнение Brunt equation.

брести *see* **бродить.**

бретонский *a.* Bretonian.

брешь *f.* breach, gap, flaw.

Брианшона теорема Brianchon theorem.

бригада *f.* brigade, squad, crew, team.

Бриггс Briggs (lunar crater).

бригговы логарифмы Briggsian logarithms.

бридер *m.* breeder; **—ный** *a.* breeder, converter, conversion; **—ное отношение** breeding ratio.

бриз *m.* breeze.

БРИЗ *abbr.* (**Бюро содействия рационализации и изобретательству**) Office for the Promotion of Industrial Efficiency and Inventions.

бризантн/ость *f.* **—ые взрывчатые вещества** high explosives.

бризовая циркуляция breeze circulation.

брикерит *m.* brickerite.

брикет *m.* briquet, cake, preform; **—ирование** *n.* briquetting, caking, preforming; **—ированный** *a.* briquetted; **—ировать** *v.* briquet, preform; **—ировочный, —ный** *a.* briquetting, briquet, preforming.

брикфилдер *m.* brickfielder, southerly buster (wind).

бриллиант *m.* diamond; **—овый** *a.* diamond; brilliant.

Бриллюэна зона Brillouin zone; **Б. функция** B. function.

Брина метод Brin process.

Бринел/я метод для определения твердости Brinell hardness test; **—я проба** B. test; **твердость по —ю** B. hardness.

брит. *abbr.* *see* **британский.**

британ/ский *a.* British; **б. металл** Britannia metal (tin-antimony-copper alloy); **—ская тепловая единица** British thermal unit (Btu).
бритва *f.* razor.
бритолит *m.* britholite.
брод/ить *v.* ferment; wander; **—ящий** *a.* fermenting; wandering, straying.
Бродхуна сектор Brodhun sector disk.
брожение *n.* fermentation.
брокат *m.* bronze powder.
брокенский призрак Brocken bow, Brocken specter.
бром *m.* bromine (Br).
бром— *prefix* brom—.
бромаргирит *m.* bromargyrite.
бромат *m.* bromate.
Бромвича интеграл Bromwich integral; **Б. (интегральная) формула** B. (integral) formula; **теорема разложения Б.** B. expansion theorem.
бромирит *m.* bromyrite.
бром/ирование *n.* bromination; **—истый** *a.* bromine.
бромноватистокисл/ый *a.* hypobromous acid, hypobromite (of); **—ая соль** hypobromite.
бромный *a.* bromine, (higher, —ic) bromide.
бромо— *prefix* bromo—.
бромозамещенный *a.* brominated.
бромосеребряный фотоэлемент silver bromide photocell.
бромциан *m.* bromocyanogen.
бронев/ой *a.* armor, armoring, sheathing; **б. трансформатор** shell-type transformer; **—ая обмотка** (elec.) drum winding.
броненосный *a.* armor-clad, armored, iron-clad, steel-clad.
бронза *f.* bronze.
бронзиров/альный *see* **бронзовый**; **—ание** *n.*, **—ка** *f.* bronzing; **—анный** *a.* bronzed.
бронзит *m.* bronzite.
бронзовый *a.* bronze.
брониров/ание *n.* armoring, armor-plating; **—анный** *a.* armored, armor-clad; jacketed; **—анный кабель** armored cable; **—ать** *v.* armor, armor-plate.
Бронсона сопротивление Bronson resistance.
бронто/граф *m.* brontograph; **—метр** *m.* brontometer.
броньярдит *m.* brongniardite.
броньяртит *m.* brongniartite.
броня *f.* armor, casing, jacket; armoring.
брос/ание *n.* throwing, tossing; abandonment; projection; **угол —ания** angle of departure, angle of deviation; **—ать, —ить** *v.* throw, abandon; project; cast; **ать, —ить жребий** cast the die; **—аться, —иться** *v.* throw oneself, plunge; **—ающийся в глаза** conspicuous, outstanding; **—ок** *m.* throw, kick; rush, surge; (aero.) bump; **—ок тока** surge.
Броунинга (солнечная) призма Browning (solar) prism.
броунов/о движение, —ское движение Brownian movement.
брошантит *m.* brochantite.
брошенн/ое тело projectile, **—ый** *a.* thrown; abandoned; dropped.
брошь *f.* broach.
брошюра *f.* brochure, paper-back book.
БРСД *abbr.* (**баллистическая ракета средней дальности**) intermediate range ballistic missile (IRBM).
брукит *m.* brookite.
Брукхейвен Brookhaven.
брульон *m.* draft, sketch, outline.
Брунса эйконал eikonal of Bruns.
бруньятеллит *m.* brugnatellite.
брус *m.* beam, squared beam, timber; bar, block; **—ковый** *a.* bar; **—ковая щетка** block brush; **—ковое железо** bar iron; **—овка** *f.* file; **—овой** *a.* girder, joist, beam; **—ок** *m.* (met.) ingot, bar, pig, slug; **—чатка** *f.* block; **—чатый** *a.* block, square beam.
брусит *m.* brucite.
брутто *adv.* gross weight, gross; **вес б.** gross weight; **б.-формула** molecular formula; **—вый** *a.* gross.
брызг *m.* splash, spatter, spray; **—алка** *f.*, **—ало** *n.* sprinkler, sprayer; **—альный** *a.* spray; **—ание, —анье** *n.* sprinkling; spatter; jet; **—ать** *v.* sprinkle; spatter; spray, squirt; **—аться** *v.* splash, spatter; **—и** *pl.* spray; **давать —и** spurt; **—озащищенный, —остойкий** *a.* splash-proof.

брызнуть *see* **брызгать.**

Брэгга закон Bragg law; **Б. уравнение** B. equation; **брэгговский угол** B. angle.

Брэкетта серия Brackett series; **брэкеттовский континуум** B. continuum.

БРЭС *abbr.* (**Белорусская электрическая станция**) Belorussian Electric Power Plant.

Брэттен Brattain.

Брюкнера теория Brueckner theory; **брюкнеров период** B. cycle.

брюкнереллит *m.* brücknerellite.

брюниров/ание *n.* browning; bronzing; burnishing; **—анный** *a.* browned; burnished; **—ать** *v.* brown; burnish.

Брюстера закон Brewster law.

брюстерит *m.* brewsterite.

БС *abbr.* (**белый свет**) white light.

БСАМ *abbr.* (**Большой Советский Атлас Мира**) Large Soviet World Atlas; Institute for the Large Soviet World Atlas.

БССР *abbr. see* **Белорусская ССР.**

БСт. *abbr.* (**бессемеровская сталь**) Bessemer steel.

БСЭ *abbr.* (**Большая Советская Энциклопедия**) Large Soviet Encyclopedia.

БТ *abbr.* (**барическая топография**) baric topography, pressure pattern.

б.т.е. *abbr.* (**британская тепловая единица**) British thermal unit (Btu).

БТИ *abbr.* (**Бюро технической информации**) Bureau of Technical Information.

б-то *abbr.* (**брутто**) gross weight, gross.

Бубнова метод Bubnov (Ritz, Galerkin) method.

Бувар Bouvard (lunar crater).

Буво Блана реакция Bouveault-Blanc reaction; **восстановление по Б. и Блану** B.-B. reduction.

Буге гало Bouguer halo.

бугель *m.* band, loop, hoop, yoke.

Бугера закон Bouguer law.

буг/ор *m.* heap, mound; protuberance; **—орок** *m.* prominence; **—ристый** *a.* uneven, hilly; **—ристый лед** knobby ice.

будем *future pl. of* **быть,** let us.

будень *m.* workday, weekday.

будет *future of* **быть.**

будить *v.* wake, rouse.

будка *f.* booth; box, cabin; **английская б.** (meteor.) Stevenson shelter (screen); **б. метеорологическая, б. психрометрическая** Stevenson screen.

будничн/ость *f.* triviality; **—ый** *a.* unimportant; weekday; **—ый день** weekday, workday.

будочка *see* **будка.**

будто, б. бы *conj.* as if, as though.

будучи *participle of* **быть:** being.

будущ/ее *n.* the future; **—ий** *a.* future, coming, next, ensuing; prospective; **в —ем году** next year; **на —ее время** for the future; **—ность** *f.* future.

будь *imp. of* **быть.**

буек *m.* buoy.

буер *m.* iceboat.

буер/ак *m.*, **—ачный** *a.* ravine, gorge, deep gully; **—ачистый** *a.* full of ravines.

бузинный шарик pith ball.

буй *m.* buoy.

буй/ный *a.* violent, turbulent; **—ство** *n* tumult, violence, turbulence.

букарамангит *m.* bucaramangite.

букв/а *f.* letter, character; **гласная б** vowel; **прописная б.** capital letter **согласная б.** consonant; **строчная б.** small letter; lower-case letter.

буквальн/о *adv.* literally, verbatim **—ость** *f.* literalness; **—ый** *a.* literal.

букв/арный *a.* alphabetic; **—енный** *a* literal; **—опечатающий** *a.* printing.

Буки лучи grenz rays.

Букингема П-теорема Buckingham I theorem.

букландит *m.* bucklandite.

буксир *m.* tow, towline; tug, tugboat **—ный, —овочный** *a.* tow, tug **—ование** *n.* towing, tugging; **—оват** *v.* tow, tug; **—овка** *f.* towing.

буксов/ание *n.* slipping, skidding; **—ат** *v.* slip, skid.

булав/ка *f.*, **—очный** *a.* pin; **—очна коррозия** pitting.

буланжерит *m.* boulangerite.

булань *see* **булинь.**

булат *m.* damask steel.

булев/а алгебра, —ская алгебра Boolean algebra.
булинь *m.* bowline.
Буллиальд Bullialdus (lunar crater).
бульб, *m.* **—овый** *a.* bulb.
бульк/ание *n.* gurgle, gurgling; **—ать** *v.* gurgle.
бультфонтейнит *m.* bultfonteinite.
бум. *abbr.* **(бумажный)** paper; cotton.
бума/га *f.* paper; **—жка** *f.* slip of paper.
бумаго—, бумажно— *prefix* paper; cotton.
бумажный *a.* paper; cotton.
Бум. пром. *abbr.* (**Бумажная промышленность**) Paper Industry (journal).
буна *f.* Buna (rubber).
Бунзена, бунзеновская горелка Bunsen burner; **Б.-Роско закон** B.-Roscoe law; **Б. фотометр** B. photometer.
бунзенит *m.* bunsenite.
бункер *m.*, **—ный** *a.* bin, bunker, hopper; **—ный затвор** bin gate; **—ный фидер** hopper, feed bin.
бунт *m.* bale, pack.
Бунте бюретка Bunte gas buret.
бунтовать *v.* bale.
Буняковского неравенство Bunjakowski (Bunyakowskii) inequality, Schwarz inequality.
бур *m.* auger, drill; bit; **головка —а, долото —а** bit, drill bit.
бур/а *f.* borax; **сплавленный шарик —ы** borax bead; **стекло —ы** fused borax.
бурав *m.* auger, drill; **—ить** *v.* bore, drill; **—ление** *n.* boring, drilling; **—чатый** *a.* auger-shaped; **—чик** *m.* gimlet; **—чика правило** right-hand screw rule, thumb rule.
буран *m.* buran, blizzard.
Бург Buerg (lunar crater).
Бургерса вектор Burgers vector; **Б. дислокация** B. (screw) dislocation.
Бурдона, бурдоновский манометр Bourdon pressure gauge; **Б. трубка** B. tube.
бурение *n.* boring, drilling.
буреть *v.* grow brown, turn brown.
буриль/ный *a.* boring; **б. молоток** hammer drill, rock drill; **—щик** *m.* borer, driller.
бур/имость *f.* drillability; **—ить** *v.* bore, drill; **—ка** *f.* drill hole, blast hole.
бурл/ение *n.* swirling, turbulence; **—ивость** *f.* turbulence; **—ивый** *a.* tempestuous, stormy, turbulent; **—ить** *v.* swirl, seethe.
бурно *adv.* vigorously, violently.
бурнонит *m.* bournonite.
бурн/ость *f.* violence, storminess, intensity; **—ый** *a.* vigorous, rapid; turbulent, stormy, rough; **—ый поток** turbulent flow; **—ая реакция** violent reaction; **—ое газообразование** gassing, boiling; **—ое море** rough sea; **—ые сороковые** (meteor.) roaring forties.
буроватый *see* **бурый.**
буровить *v.* bubble, ferment.
буров/ой *a.* drilling, boring; **б. зонд** drill-hole probe; **б. раствор** drilling fluid (or mud); **б. резец, —ое долото** boring bit, drill bit; **б. станок** drill; **—ая вышка** derrick; **—ая запись** drill-hole logging; **—ая мука** bore meal, borings, drillings; **—ая муть, —ая грязь** drill mud, sludge; **—ая скважина** bore, bore hole, drill hole.
буровый *a.* borax, boracic.
буроугольный *a.* lignite.
бурт, —ик *m.* bead, crimp, shoulder, collar.
бурун *m.* surf, breaker.
бур/ый *a.* brownish (or reddish) black; grayish brown; **б. железняк** limonite, brown hematite, brown iron ore; **—ая руда** vivianite; limonite; sphalerite.
буря *f.* storm, gale.
Бурятская АССР Buryat ASSR.
бусин/а, —ка *f.*, **—ковый** *a.* bead; **—ковый спектромер** bead spectrometer.
Буссинеска уравнение Boussinesq equation.
буссинготит *m.* boussingaultite.
буссоль *f.* compass; **б. магнитного наклонения** dip compass (needle, circle), inclinometer; **б. склонения** declinometer; **б.-угломер** aiming circle.
бустер *m.*, **—ный** *a.* booster.
бусы *pl.* beads.
бутадиен *m.*, **—овый каучук** butadiene rubber.
бутан *m.* butane.
бутен *m.* butene, butylene.
бутербродный тип sandwich type.

бутил *m.*, **—овый** *a.* butyl.
бутиро— *prefix* butyro—.
бутит *m.* boothite.
бутов/очный, —ый *a.* rubble; **б. материал** filling, filler; **—ый камень** rubble stone.
буттгенбахит *m.* buttgenbachite.
бутыл/ка *f.* bottle; **—кообразный** *a.* bottle-shaped; **—очный** *a.* bottle; **—ь** *f.*, **—ьный** *a.* large bottle, vessel; (gas) cylinder.
буфер *m.* buffer, shock absorber, cushion; **воздушный б., масляный б.** dashpot; **б.-компенсатор** compensating buffer; **паровой б.** steam cushion; **—ный** *a.* buffer; **—ный раствор** buffer solution; **—ная ступень** buffer stage; **—ное действие** buffer action.
буферовка *f.* buffing, polishing.
бухнуть *v.* swell, dilate.
бухольцит *m.* bucholzite.
бухта *f.* bay; coil.
буч/ение *n.* washing in lye; **—ить** *v.* steep (in lye), scour.
бушинг *m.* bushing.
бушит *m.* buszite.
бушменит *m.* bushmanite.
б.ц. *abbr.* **(без цены)** price not given.
бы *sign of conditional and subjunctive moods:* should, would; **где б.** wherever; **если б.** if.
быв/ало *past of* **бывать,** used to; **—алость** *f.* experience; **—алый** *a.* experienced, skilled; past; **—ать** *v.* happen, occur; be; be held, take place; *see also* **быть; —ший** *a.* former, late; ex—.
бык *m.* pier; buttress.
было *past of* **быть;** nearly, on the point of; **—й** *a.* past, bygone.
быль *f.* fact; past occurrence.
быстрина *f.* rapid, swift course.
быстро *adv.* quickly, rapidly, swiftly; **—вяжущий** *a.* quick-setting; **—горящий** *a.* quick-burning, conflagrant, deflagrant; **—движущийся** *a.* fast-moving.
быстродейств/ие *n.* quick operation, speed of response; **—ующий** *a.* fast, quick, quick-acting, high-speed; **—ующий выключатель** quick-break switch.
быстро/летящий *a.* fast-moving, fast; **—накальный катод** quick-heating cathode; **—отпускающий** *a.* quick-release; **—охлажденный** *a.* rapidly cooled, "rapid cool"; **—размыкающийся** *a.* quick-break; **—режущий** *a.* fast-cutting, high-speed; **—режущая сталь** high-speed steel; **—сгорающий** *a.* free-burning; **—сканирующий** *a.* rapid-scanning; **—сменный** *a.* quick-change; **—сохнущий** *a.* quick-drying; **—схватывающийся** *a.* quick-setting (cement).
быстрота *f.* speed, velocity, celerity, rapidity; rate; **б. реагирования** responsiveness (of an instrument); **б. сходимости** rapidity of convergence.
быстро/течный *a.* transient; **—ток** *m.* chute; **—уплотняющийся** *a.* quick-sealing; **—устанавливающийся** *a.* quick-adjusting, readily adjustable; **—ходный** *a.* high-speed, fast, rapid.
быстрый *a.* quick, fast, high-speed; prompt; **б. нейтрон** fast neutron; **б. нейтрон деления** prompt fission neutron; **б. ход** high speed.
быт *m.* way of life; **—ие** *n.* being, existence, reality; **—ность** *f.* stay, sojourn, presence.
бытовой *a.* actual, everyday.
быть *v.* be, exist; **б. вправе** have a right to, be justified.
бьелькит *m.* bjelkite.
бьерк *see* **берк.**
Бьеркнеса теорема Bjerknes (circulation) theorem.
Бьеррума теория молекулярных спектров Bjerrum theory of molecular spectra.
бьеф *m.* water race, millrace; reach, level; **верхний б.** headwater, headrace, upstream water; **нижний б.** tailwater, tailrace, downstream water.
бьющийся *a.* beating, pulsating.
Бэв *abbr.* **(биллион электроновольт)** billion electron volts (Bev).
Бэйли *see* **Бейли.**
Бэкон Bacon (lunar crater).
б.э.р. *abbr.* **(биологический эквивалент рентгена)** roentgen equivalent, man (rem).
Бэра *see* **Бера.**

бэровское пространство Baire space.
БЭСМ *abbr.* (**быстродействующая электронная счетная машина**) high-speed electronic computer.
Бэчер Bacher.
бюджет *m.*, **—ный** *a.* budget; **предусматривать в —е** budget for estimate.
бюкс *m.* weighing bottle.
бюл. *see* **бюллетень.**
бюллетень *m.* bulletin; report.
бюретка *f.* buret.
бюро *n.* bureau, office, department; desk; **справочное б.** information bureau.
бюрократ/изм *m.* bureaucracy, red tape; **—ический** *a.* bureaucratic; **—ия** *f.* bureaucracy.
бюстовое облако mammato cloud; **б. кучевое облако** mammato-cumulus.
Бюффона задача Buffon (needle) problem.
Бюхнера воронка Büchner filter.

В

в *prep.* in, into; on; to; for (directional); at, per; **в год** per annum, yearly; **в час** per hour; **в этом году** this year.
в *abbr.* (**вольт**) volt (v); **в.** *abbr.* (**век**) century, epoch, age; (**верхний**) upper, top, overhead; (**верховный**) supreme; (**восточный**) east, eastern, easterly; (**вращение**) rotation.
В [*in steel mark* (**вольфрам**)] tungsten (W).
В. *abbr.* (**вестник**) bulletin; (**восток**) east; (**всесоюзный**) All-Union.
ва *abbr.* (**вольтампер**) volt-ampere (va).
ВА *abbr.* (**воздушная армия**) Air Force.
вавеллит *m.* wavellite.
Вавилова-Черенкова излучение Cerenkov radiation.
вага *f.* crowbar, bar, lever.
вагнерит *m.* wagnerite.
ВАГО *abbr.* (**Всесоюзное астрономо-геодезическое общество**) All-Union Astronomical and Geodetic Society.
вагон *m.* (railroad) car, coach; **—етка** *f.* trolley, truck, carriage, car; **—ный** *a.* car; **—ный парк** rolling stock.
вагран/ка *f.*, **—очный** *a.* (met.) cupola, cupola furnace.
вад *m.* wad.
важн/о *adv.* significantly; it is important; **—ость** *f.* importance; **—ый** *a.* important, significant.
вазелин *m.*, **—овый** *a.* petroleum jelly, Vaseline; **—овое масло** Vaseline oil.
ВАИ *abbr.* (**Всесоюзный арктический институт**) All-Union Arctic Institute; (**Всесоюзная ассоциация инженеров**) All-Union Association of Engineers.
вайсенбергограмма *f.* Weissenberg rotating-crystal photograph.
Вайцзеккер Weizsäcker.
вакан/сия *f.* vacancy; **—тный** *a.* vacant, unoccupied.
вакуметр *see* **вакуумметр.**
вакуум *m.* vacuum; **в.-насос** vacuum pump; **в.-спектрограф** vacuum spectrograph; **испарение в —е** vacuum evaporation; **перегонка под —ом** vacuum distillation; **—метр** *m.* vacuum gauge; **—метрическое давление** vacuum gauge pressure; **—но плотный** vacuumtight.
вакуумн/ый *a.* vacuum; **в. затвор, в. люк, в. шлюз** vacuum lock; **в. насос** vacuum pump; **в. триод** vacuum tube triode; **—ая арматура** vacuum fittings; **—ая камера бетатрона** betatron "doughnut" **—ая лампа** vacuum tube; **—ая пайка, —ое уплотнение** vacuum seal; **—ая петля** vacuum loop; **—ая плавка** vacuum fusion; **—ая течь** vacuum leak; **—ая установка** vacuum system.
Вакье магнитные весы Vaquier magnetic balance.
вал *m.* roller, roll; shaft, spindle; drum; bank, embankment; (meteor.) billow; **лунный в.** lunar ridge.
валенсианит *m.* valencianite.
валентийский век (geo.) Valentian stage.
валентн/о-силовая модель valence-force model; **—ость** *f.*, **—ый** *a.* valence, valency, valence bond; **—ый угол**

valence angle; **—ый штрих** valence bond; **—ый электрон** valence electron; **—ая зона** (sol.) valence band; **—ая сила** valence force; **—ая связь** valence bond, valence link; **—ые колебания** (mol.) stretching vibrations.

валец *m.* roller, cylinder.

валик *m.* roller, cylinder, drum; shaft.

валить *v.* throw down, overturn, upset; **—ся** *v.* fall, collapse.

валковый *a.* roller.

Валле-Пуссен de la Vallée-Poussin.

валов/ой *a.* gross, total; **в. вес** gross weight; **в. выход** gross yield; **—ая формула** molecular formula.

валок *m.* roller, roll, cylinder.

валун *m.* boulder; rubble; **—ы** *pl.* (geo.) detritus.

валховит *m.* walchowite.

Вальдена правило Walden rule; **вальденовское обращение** W. inversion.

валькерит *m.* walkerite.

вальпургин *m.* walpurgite.

Вальтер Walter (lunar crater).

вальц *m.* roll, roller; **—евание** *see* **вальцовка**; **—евать** *see* **вальцовать.**

вальцов/анный *a.* rolled; **—ать** *v.* roll; **—ка** *f.* rolling; **—ый** *a.* roller, rolling; **—ый затвор** roller gate; **—ая мельница** rolling mill.

валяльная глина, в. глинка fuller's earth.

ВАМИ *abbr.* (**Всесоюзный алюминиево-магниевый институт**) All-Union Aluminum and Magnesium Institute.

вамоскоп *m.* wamoscope.

ВАН *abbr.* (**Вестник Академии наук**) Herald (Bulletin) of the Academy of Sciences (journal).

ванадат *m.* vanadate.

ванад/иевый, —овый *a.* vanadium, vanadic; **—ий** *m.* vanadium (V); **—ил** *m.* vanadyl; **—истый** *a.* vanadium, vandous.

Ван-де-Граафа генератор Van de Graaf generator; **В.-де-Г. ускоритель** V. de G. accelerator.

ванденбрандит *m.* vandenbrandeite.

вандендрисшейт *m.* vandendriesscheite.

ван-дер-Ваальса уравнение van der Waals equation.

ван-дер-ваальсов/а адсорбция van der Waals adsorption; **—ы силы** v. der W. forces.

Вандермонда теорема Vandermondes theorem.

Ван-дер-Поля уравнение Van der Pol equation.

Ван-Левен (**Лейвен**) Van Leeuwen.

ванна *f.* bath; tub, tank, vat.

Ваннера пирометр Wanner pyrometer.

ванночка *f.* (phot.) tray; dish.

ваноксит *m.* vanoxite.

Вант-Гоффа закон Van't Hoff law; **В.-Г.-Ле Беля теория** V. H.-Le Bel theory; **В.-Г. принцип** V. H. principle; **В.-Г. принцип суперпозиции** V. H. principle of superposition; **В.-Г. уравнение** (**для осмотического давления**) V. H. equation (for osmotic pressure); **В.-Г. формула** V. H. equation.

вантгоффит *m.* vanthoffite.

вантуз *m.* air vent.

Ван-Флек Van Vleck; **ван-флековский парамагнетизм** V. V. paramagnetism.

ВАО *abbr.* (**Всесоюзное объединение авиационной промышленности**) All-Union Association of the Aircraft Industry.

вапориметр *m.* vaporimeter.

ваплерит *m.* wapplerite.

вар *m.* pitch; (elec.) var.

Варбурга формула Warburg law.

варвикит *m.* warwickite.

Варгентин Wargentin (lunar crater).

вардит *m.* wardite.

вариак *m.* variac, transtat.

вариант *m.* variant, version, variation; alternative; **в. взаимодействия** interaction type; **—ность** *f.* variance; **—ный** *a.* variant, alternate, alternative.

вариатор *m.* variator; buncher.

вариац. *abbr. see* **вариационный.**

вариац/ионный *a.* variation, variational; **в. принцип** variational principle; **—ионное исчисление** calculus of variations; **—ия** *f.* variation, modulation, fluctuation; **—ия постоянных** variation of parameters.

варииров/ание *see* **варьирование**; **—ать** *see* **варьировать.**

варимю *m.* varimu, variable-mu tube.

варингтонит *m.* waringtonite.

Вариньона теорема Varignon theorem.

варио/граф *m.* variograph; **—куплер** *m.* varicoupler; **—метр** *m.* variometer.

варистор *m.* varistor.

варисцит *m.* variscite.

вар/ить *v.* boil, cook; found (glass); **—иться** *v.* boil, cook, be boiled; **—ка** *f.* melt; cooking; boiling.

Варнитсо *abbr.* (**Всесоюзная ассоциация работников науки и техники активных участников социалистического строительства в СССР**) All-Union Association of Scientists and Technicians Participating in the Building of Socialism in the USSR.

варренит *m.* warrenite.

вартаит *m.* warthaite.

варьиров/ание *n.* variation, modulation; **—ать** *v.* vary, range.

Васко да Гама Vasco da Gama (lunar crater).

ассерглас *m.* water glass.

ата *f.* wadding.

атержакет *m.*, **—ный** *a.* water jacket.

атер/линия *f.* water line; **—пас** *m.* (water) level; balance level.

атерпруф *m.* waterproof.

атный *a.* cotton wadded, quilted.

атт *m.* watt (w); **в.-секунда** (**джоуль**) watt-second (joule); **в.-час** watt-hour.

атт/метр *m.*, **—метровый** *a.* wattmeter; **—ность** *f.* wattage; **—ный** *a.* watt.

ашегиит *m.* vashegyite.

ашингтонит *m.* washingtonite.

б *abbr.* (**вебер**) weber; **вб.** [**вероятное боковое** (**отклонение**)] probable error (deflection).

бе/гать, —жать *v.* run in; flow into.

бив/ание *n.*, **—ка** *f.* driving in; **—ать** *v.* drive in, hammer; wedge.

бир/ание *n.* absorption; **—ать** *v.* absorb.

близи *adv.* near, in the vicinity, nearby, close, around.

бок *adv.* sideways.

брасывать, вбросить *v.* throw in.

брошенный *a.* thrown in.

брызгива/ние *n.* injection; **—ть** *v.* inject.

вв *abbr.* (**взрывчатые вещества**) explosives; **в.в.** (**века**) centuries.

ВВ *abbr.* (**выдержка времени**) time lag.

введение *n.* introduction, insertion; leading in; preface; **в. в эксплоатацию** putting in operation; **в. дырок** (semicond.) hole injection.

вверг/ать, —нуть *v.* fling, plunge.

ввернуть *see* **ввертывать.**

вверт/ка *f.*, **—ывание** *n.* screwing in; **—ный** *a.* screw-in; **—ная пробка, —ыш** *m.* screw stopper; **—ывать** *v.* screw in, twist in.

вверх *adv.* up, upward; **в. дном** upside down; **движение в., перемещение в., ход в.** upward motion, upstroke (of piston); **тяга в.** upward pull, lift; updraft; **—у** *adv.* above, overhead, at the top of.

вверчивать *see* **ввертывать.**

ввести *see* **вводить; в. в действие** put into operation.

ввиду *prep.* in view of.

ввин/тить, —чивать *v.* screw in; **—ченный** *a.* screwed in; **—чивание** *n.* screwing in.

в-во *abbr.* (**вещество**) substance, material, matter.

ввод *m.* leading in, induction, admission, introduction; inlet; (elec.) lead, lead-in; **—имый** *a.* input; introducible; **—ить** *v.* lead in, introduce, feed into, inject; insert, drive in; (math.) interpolate; **—ить в заблуждение** mislead, deceive.

вводн/ый *a.* introductory, entrance, input, inlet, intake, lead-in; parenthetical; quoted, cited; **в. провод** lead-in; **—ое отверстие** inlet.

ВВС *abbr.* (**военно-воздушные силы**) Air Force.

ввяз/анный *a.* tied in, involved; **—ать, —ывать** *v.* tie in, involve; **—ывание** *n.* tying in.

ВГБИЛ *abbr.* (**Всесоюзная государственная библиотека иностранной литературы**) All-Union State Library of Foreign Literature.

вгиб *m.* an inward bend; **—ание** *n.* bending inward; **—ать** *v.* bend in, curve inward, deform.

ВГИТИС *abbr.* (**Высший государственный институт телемеханики и связи**) Higher State Institute of Telemechanics and Communications.
вгладь *adv.* flush, even.
вглубь *adv.* deep into, deeply; deep down.
вгляд/еться, —ываться *v.* observe closely, examine.
вгнездиться *v.* take root in.
вгон *m.*, **—ка** *f.* driving in; **—ять** *v.* drive in, force in.
вгорячую *adv.* hot; **тянутый в.** (met.) hot-drawn.
ВГРО *abbr.* (**Всесоюзное геолого-разведочное объединение**) All-Union Geological-Prospecting Association.
вгру/жать, —зить *v.* load.
ВГУ *abbr.* (**Воронежский государственный университет**) Voronezh State University.
в.д. *abbr.* (**восточная долгота**) east longitude.
вдаваться *v.* protrude into; **в. в подробности** go into details; **в. в тонкости** elaborate.
вдавить *see* **вдавливать.**
вдавл/енный *a.* depressed; **—ивание** *n.* impression, indentation, depression; **—ивать** *v.* press in, force in; imbed; impress.
вдал/еке, —и *adv.* in the distance, far off; **—ь** *adv.* into the distance.
вдаться *see* **вдаваться.**
вдви/гание *n.* moving into, advance; **—гать, —нуть** *v.* move into; **—гаться, —нуться** *v.* enter; **—жной** *a.* movable; **—нутый** *a.* moved in; **—нутые один в другой** interpenetrating.
вдво/е *adv.* double, twice; di—; **в. больше** twice as much; **складывать в.** fold in two, double; **—ем** *adv.* (two) together; **—йне** *adv.* twofold, doubly; especially.
вдевать *v.* put in.
вдевятеро *adv.* ninefold.
вдел/анный *a.* set-in, built-in; **—ать, —ывать** *v.* fit in, set in; **—ка** *f.*, **—ывание** *n.* fitting in, setting in.
вдер/гать, —гивать, —нуть *v.* pull in.
вдесятерр *adv.* tenfold.
вдет/ый *a.* put in, drawn in; **—ь** *see* **вдевать.**
вдобавок *adv.* in addition, furthermore.
вдоволь *adv.* enough, sufficiently.
вдоль *adv.* lengthwise, longitudinally *prep.* along; **в. по** along.
вдребезги *adv.* in pieces.
вдруг *adv.* suddenly.
вдув/аемый *a.* blown in; **в. воздух** air blast; **—ание** *n.* blowing in, blast; **—ать** *v.* blow in.
вдум/аться, —ываться *v.* consider carefully.
вдут/ый *a.* blown in, injected; **—ь** *see* **вдувать.**
вдыхать *v.* inhale, breathe in.
вебер *m.* weber.
Вебера закон Weber law; **В. фотометр** W. photometer.
вебнерит *m.* webnerite.
Вебстера фонометр Webster phonometer.
вебстерит *m.* websterite.
вевеллит *see* **уэвеллит.**
Вега Vega.
вегазит *m.* vegasite.
Вегарда закон Vegard law; **В.-Каплан полоса** V.-Kaplan band.
Вегенера теория Wegener theory.
вед/ать *v.* know; manage, drive; supervise; **—ение** *n.* conducting, presiding management; authority; knowledge drive; **в —ении** under the authority (or supervision).
ведер/ко *n.* pail; **—ный** *a.* pail, bucket
ведомость *f.* list, record, catalog.
ведомств/енный *a.* departmental; **—** *n.* department.
ведом/ый *a.* controlled, guided; driven **в. вал** driven shaft; **—ая волна** guided wave.
ведро *n.* pail, bucket.
ведущ/ий *a.* leading, prominent, guiding; driving; pilot, master; **в. вал** drive shaft; **в. подшипник** guide bearing; **в. поток** (meteor.) steering current; **в. ролик, в. шкив** guide pulley, guide roller, guide; drive pulley, drive; **в. ток** (elec.) current carrying, live; **в. центр** guiding center; **в. член** leading term; **—ая ось** driving axle; **—ая частота**

control frequency; —**ее колесо** driving wheel; guide pulley.

ведь *conj.* (frequently not requiring translation) in fact.

веер *m.*, —**ный** *a.* fan; **в. нормалей** bundle (or cone) of normals; —**о-образный** *a.* fan-shaped.

везде *adv.* everywhere; **в. где угодно** anywhere; —**присутствующий, —сущий** *a.* omnipresent, ubiquitous; —**сущность** *f.* omnipresence.

везен/ие *n.* conveying, transportation; —**ный** *a.* conveyed, transported.

везти *see* **возить.**

везувиан *m.* vesuvian, vesuvianite, idocrase.

везущий *a.* carrying, conveying.

веибиеит *m.* weibyeite.

вейбуллит *m.* weibullite.

Вейгерта эффект Weigert effect.

Вейерштрасса неравенство Weierstrass inequality; **В. сфера** W. sphere; **В. функция** W. function.

Вейль Weyl.

Веймара сплав Weimar alloy (copper-manganese-aluminum alloy).

вейнбергерит *m.* weinbergerite.

вейншенкит *m.* weinschenkite.

вейсбахит *m.* weisbachite.

Вейса гипотеза Weiss hypothesis; **В. поле** W. field, molecular (or exchange) field; **В.-Форрера метод** W.-Forrer method.

вейссит *m.* weissite.

век *m.* century, age; (geo.) epoch, stage.

веков/ой *a.* secular; **в. ход, —ое колебание** secular variation; —**ое направление** secular trend; —**ое сжатие** (astr.) secular contraction; —**ое уравнение** secular equation.

вектолит *m.* Vectolite (mixture of iron and cobalt oxides).

вектор *m.* vector; **в. вихря** vorticity vector; **в. Герца** Hertzian vector; **в. гирации** gyration vector; **в. 4-импульса** 4-momentum vector; **в. намагниченности** direction of magnetization; **в. поляризации** polarization vector; **в.-потенциал** vector-potential; **в. состояния** state vector; **в. состояния вакуума** vacuum state vector; **в. трансляции** translation vector.

вектор/иальность *f.* vector (directional) character; —**иальный, —ный** *a.* vector, vectorial; —**ная функция** vector function; —**ное исчисление** vector analysis, vector calculus; —**ное произведение** vector product, cross product.

велер *m.* selector.

велерит *m.* wöhlerite.

Великобритания Great Britain.

величайший *a.* greatest, extreme.

величин/а *f.* quantity, entity; size, magnitude, value, amount; **в. мощности** power value; **в. нагревания** thermal value; **в. натуральная** actual value, full size; **в. нулевого порядка** zeroth-order quantity; **в. обратная** (math.) reciprocal; **в. отклонения от критического состояния** off-critical amount; **в. охлаждения** cooling power; **в. прилива** tidal range; **в. пульсации** percent ripple; **в. фона** background, noise level; **в натуральную —у** full size; **на значительную —у** to a considerable extent; **определять —у** measure.

велькерит *m.* voelckerite.

вельхит *m.* wölchite.

вена *f.* vein.

венг. *abbr.* (**венгерский**) Hungarian.

Венг/ерская Народная Республика Hungarian People's Republic; —**рия** Hungary.

Венделин Vendelinus (lunar crater).

Венельта прерыватель Wehnelt interruptor; **В. шкала** W. (x-ray) scale.

Венера Venus.

венерины волосы rutile needles in quartz.

венец *m.* (meteor.) corona, halo, aureole; heiligenschein, Cellini halo; **в. вокруг луны** lunar corona.

Венинг-Мейнес Vening-Meinesz.

венис/а *f.*, —**овый** *a.* garnet.

вентилир/ованный, —уемый *a.* ventilated; —**ованный психрометр** ventilated psychrometer; —**овать** *v.* ventilate.

вентиль *m.*, —**ный** *a.* valve; (elec.) tube, rectifier; gate; **в. с жидким катодом** (elec.) pool rectifier; —**ный выпрямитель** valve rectifier; —**ный слой** barrier layer, rectifying barrier;

—**ный фотоэлемент** barrier-layer cell; —**ный фотоэлемент с тыловым фотоэффектом** barrier-layer rear-wall photocell; —**ный фотоэлемент с фронтальным фотоэффектом** barrier-layer front-wall photocell; —**ный фотоэффект** barrier-layer photoeffect; —**ный эхо-заградитель** valve-type echo-suppressor.

вентиля/тор *m.*, —**торный** *a.* ventilator, fan, blower; **вытяжной в.** exhaust fan; —**ционный** *a.* ventilation, ventilating; —**ционный психрометр** ventilated psychrometer; —**ция** *f.* ventilation, aeration.

Вентури трубка Venturi tube.

Вентцеля-Крамерса-Бриллюэна (ВКБ) метод Wentzel-Kramers-Brillouin-Jeffreys method (W.K.B.J. method).

венцелит *m.* wenzelite.

Верде постоянная Verdet constant.

верев/ка *f.*, —**очный** *a.* cord, rope, string; —**ки** *pl.* cordage; —**очный многоугольник** funicular polygon, string polygon.

вереница *f.* row, line, train.

веретено *n.* spindle; —**образный** *a.* spindle-shaped.

верить *v.* believe, trust.

верлит *m.* wehrlite.

вермикулит *see* **слюда.**

вернее *comp. of* **верно, верный** rather, more likely.

Вернеля (Вернейля) печь Verneuil furnace.

Вернер Werner (lunar crater).

вернерит *m.* wernerite.

верно *adv.* correctly, accurately; probably.

верность *f.* correctness, accuracy, fidelity, truth; **в. звуковоспроизведения** acoustic fidelity.

вернуть *v.* return; recover; —**ся** *v.* return.

верный *a.* correct, accurate, right, true.

верньер *m.*, —**ный** *a.* vernier.

вероятно *adv.* probably; it is probable.

вероятностн/о-логарифмическая сетка logarithmic probability paper; —**ый** *a.* random, stochastic, chance; probability, probabilistic.

вероятност/ь *f.* probability, likelihood. **в. вылета** escape probability; **в. деления** fission probability; **в. избежания резонансного захвата** resonance escape probability; **в. перехода** transition probability; **в. прохождения** penetration probability **в. радиоактивного распада** disintegration probability; **схождение п**о —**и** convergence in probability, convergence in measure, stochastic convergence; **формула полной —и** **теорема сложения —ей** theorem of total probability; **теорема умножения —ей** theorem of compound probability; —**ей теория** theory of probability.

вероятный *a.* probable, likely.

версия *f.* version.

верстка *f.* (printing) imposition; form.

вертекс *m.* vertex.

вертеть *v.* turn; —**ся** *v.* turn around rotate.

вертикал *m.* (astr.) vertical circle.

вертикал/ь *f.* vertical; **по —и,** —**ьн**о *adv.* vertically; —**ьность** *f.* verticality.

вертикальн/ый *a.* vertical, erect, plumb **в. профиль** elevation profile; **в. разрез** elevation, front view; **в. электрический ток в атмосфере** air-earth current; —**ая камера** vertically operated camera; —**ая радиолокация** vertical-incidence radar; —**ая фокусировка** vertical focusing; —**ые магнитные весы** (mag.) vertical field balance.

вертиметр *m.* vertimeter.

вертит *m.* wörthite.

вертлюг *m.* pivot.

верт/олет *m.* helicopter; —**ушка** *f.* vane, current meter; —**ячий** *a.* rotary; —**ящий** *a.* rotatory; —**ящийся** *a.* revolving, rotating.

верх *m.* top, upper part, summit; —**и** *pl.* treble.

верхне/меловой *a.* (geo.) upper cretaceous; —**пропускающий фильтр** high-pass filter.

верхн/ий *a.* upper, top, overhead; **в. атмосферный слой** upper atmosphere, upper air; **в. бьеф** upstream water; **в. ветер** upper wind; **в. воздух** upper air; **в. значок** superscript; **в. мираж** superior mirage;

в. предел по углу места upper elevation limit; **в. привод** overhead drive; **—яя атмосфера** upper atmosphere; **—яя граница** upper limit; **—яя грань** upper boundary; **—ее состояние** upper state; **—ие звуковые частоты** treble; **—ие пассаты** upper trade winds; **—ие слои атмосферы** upper atmosphere.

верховн/ость *f.* superiority; **—ый** *a.* supreme.

верхов/ой *a.* top, upper; **в. ветер** mountain breeze; **—ая вода** upstream water; **—ая грань** upstream face (of dam); **—ье** *n.* headwater, river-head.

верхом *adv.* heaped; upwards, above.

верхуш/ка *f.*, **—ечный** *a.* top, summit, acme, apex, tip.

верчение *n.* pivoting, spinning, rotating.

вершина *f.* top, summit, peak; (geom.) vertex, apex; point, tip; **в. петли гистерезиса** tip of hysteresis loop.

вершинн/ый *a.* peak, apical, vertex; **в. угол** vertical angle; **—ая станция** mountain station; **—ая точка** vertex, apex; **—ая часть** vertex part.

вес *m.* weight; importance; **в. брутто** gross weight; **в. нетто** net weight; **удельный в.** specific weight, specific gravity; **на в., —ом** by weight, weighing.

вес % *abbr.* (**весовые проценты**) percent by weight.

весенн/ий *a.* spring, vernal; **—яя инверсия** spring inversion.

вес/ить *v.* weigh; **—кий** *a.* weighty; **—кий аргумент** strong argument; **—кость** *f.* weight, weightiness.

веслинит *m.* weslienite.

весна *f.* spring.

весов/ой *a.* weight, gravimetric; **в. анализ** gravimetric analysis; **в. барометр** balance barometer; **в. гигрометр** balance hygrometer; **в. коэффициент** weight, weight factor, weighting factor; **в. множитель** weight (ing) factor; **в. поток** weight flow, mass flow; **в. расход** mass flow weight rate (consumption); **в. снегомер** weighing-type snow gauge; **—ая скорость** mass flow rate; **—ая геплоемкость** specific heat per unit weight; **—ая функция** weighting function; **—ая часть** part by weight; **—ая чашка** balance pan; **—ое число** weight, weight factor, weighting number.

весом/ость *f.* ponderability; **—ый** *a.* ponderable.

весселиит *m.* veszelyite.

вест *m.*, **—овый** *a.* west (wind).

вести *v.* conduct, run, lead, drive.

вестн. *abbr.* (**вестник**) bulletin, herald.

Вестн. машин. *abbr.* (**Вестник машиностроения**) Mechanical Engineering Bulletin.

Вестн. МГУ *abbr.* (**Вестник Московского государственного университета**) Bulletin of the Moscow State University.

вестник *m.* bulletin, herald.

Вестона элемент Weston cell.

Вестфаля весы Westphal balance.

весть *f.* news, report.

вес. ч. *abbr.* (**весовая часть**) part by weight.

Весы Libra (constellation).

весы *pl.* scales, balance; **газовые в.** gas balance; **десятичные в.** decimal balance; **крутильные в.** torsion balance; **пружинные в.** spring balance; **точные в.** precision balance; **химикоаналитические в.** analytical balance.

весь *a. and pron.* all, entire, total, complete; **всего** altogether, in all, total; but, only; **во всем** in all respects; **во всю** fully; **при всем том** nevertheless.

весьма *adv.* extremely, very, highly, greatly, fairly, quite.

ветвеобразный кристалл dendritic crystal.

ветв/истый *a.* branched, ramified; **—ление** *n.* branching; **—ь** *f.* branch, arm; side; **—ь кривой** branch of a curve; **—ь термопары** arm (element) of thermocouple; **—ящийся** *a.* branching, dendritic; ramified.

ветер *m.* wind; **в. встречный** head wind, contrary wind; **в. в 1 балл** force-one wind; **в. низовой** valley breeze; **в. попутный** favorable wind; **в. порывистый** gusty wind; **в. противный** head wind, dead wind; **в. склона** slope wind; **в. слабый** gentle breeze (Beaufort number 3); **в. электрический** aura, electric wind; **—ок** *m.* breeze.

ветка *see* **ветвь.**

ветреный *a.* windy.

ветров/ой *a.* wind; **—ая волна** wind wave; **—ое зондирование** upper-wind sounding; **—ое перемешивание** wind-induced turbulence.

ветро/гон *m.* anemoscope, weathercock; **—двигатель** *m.* wind motor; **—мер** *m.* wind gauge, anemometer; **—указатель** *m.* (aero.) wind indicator; **—чет** *m.* (aero.) wind-speed indicator, course computer.

ветря/к *m.*, **—нка** *f.* air vane; wind turbine, vane wheel.

ветрян/ый *a.* wind, *see also* **ветро—**; **в. двигатель, —ая мельница** windmill; **в. конус** wind sleeve, cone.

ветхий *a.* old, dilapidated.

ветшание *n.* dilapidation, decay.

веха *f.* boundary mark; surveying rod; stake; **мерная в.** surveying rod.

вечер *m.*, **—ний** *a.* evening; **—ом** *adv.* in the evening, at nightfall.

вечно *adv.* perpetually, always; **—мерзлый** *a.* ever-frozen.

вечн/ый *a.* perpetual, endless; **в. двигатель (первого рода)** perpetual motion machine (of the first kind); **—ая мерзлота** permafrost; **—ое движение** perpetual motion.

веш/алка *f.* rack, stand; peg; **—ать** *v.* hang, suspend; weigh.

вещание *n.* broadcasting.

вещественн/ость *f.* substantiality, materiality; (math.) realness; **—ый** *a.* real; substantial, material; **—ое число** real number.

вещество *n.* substance, material, matter; **в. отравляющее катализатор** anticatalyst; **простое в.** element.

вещь *f.* thing, object, article.

Вея-Вигнера формула Way-Wigner formula.

вжигание *n.* brazing.

вжимать *v.* squeeze in, force in.

взад *adv.* back, backwards; **в. и вперед** back and forth, reciprocating.

взаимно *adv.* mutually, reciprocally, inter—; *see also* **взаимо—**; **в. заменимый, в. замкнутый** *a.* interlocked, intermeshed; **в. непрерывный** (math.) bicontinuous; **в. однозначно** one-to-one; **в. пересекающиеся силы** concurrent forces; **в. полярный** polar reciprocal; **в. расстроенные контуры** staggered circuits; **в. соединяться** interlock; **в. сопряженные точки** conjugate points; **в. уничтожающиеся погрешности** compensating errors.

взаимно/исключающий *a.* mutually exclusive, incompatible; **—обратно** *adv.* mutually opposing; **—обратные точки** inverse points; **—проникающий** *a.* interpenetrating; **—сопряженные точки** conjugate points.

взаимност/ь *f.* correlation, reciprocity, duality; **—и закон** (opt.) principle of reversibility; (rel.) reciprocity principle; **—и принцип** (math.) principle of duality; **соотношение —и** reciprocal relation; **—и теорема** reciprocity theorem.

взаимн/ый *a.* mutual, reciprocal, relative; *see also* **взаимо—**; **в. контроль** cross check; **в. потенциал** interaction potential; **—ая диффузия** interdiffusion; **—ая емкость** mutual capacitance; **—ая индикация** mutual indication; **—ая калибровка** intercalibration; **—ая корреляция** cross-correlation; **—ая модуляция** intermodulation; **—ая связь** coupling; interconnection; interrelation; **—ая смешиваемость** intermiscibility; **—ая энергия** mutual energy; **—ое отталкивание** mutual repulsion; **—ое положение** relative position; **—ое притяжение** mutual attraction; **—ое проникновение** interpenetration; **—ое усиление** mutual reinforcement; **—ые векторы** reciprocal vectors; **—ые глубины** conjugate depths; **—ые помехи от радиостанций** interstation interference; **—ые системы векторов** reciprocal systems of vectors; **—ые функции** reciprocal functions.

взаимо— *prefix* inter—; *see also* **взаимно.**

взаимовлияние *n.* interference.

взаимодейств/ие *n.* interaction, reciprocal action, reciprocity; (chem.)

reaction; cooperation; **в. различных видов колебаний** coupling of modes; **в. спина с орбитальным моментом** spin-orbit interaction; **в. спинов** spin-spin interaction; **константа —ия** coupling constant; **продукты —ия** reaction products; **—овать** *v.* interact; **—ующий** *a.* cooperative, interacting; reacting; **—ующая смесь** reaction mixture.

взаимозависим/ость *f.* interdependence; **—ый** *a.*, **—ые** *pl.* interdependent.

взаимозамен/а *f.* interchange; **—имый** *a.* interchangeable; **—яемость** *f.* interchangeability; **—яемый** *a.* interchangeable; **—яемая часть** duplicate, spare part.

взаимо/заместимость *f.* reciprocity; **—индуктивность** *f.* mutual inductance; **—индукции коэффициент** coefficient of mutual inductance; **—модуляционное искажение** intermodulation distortion; **—обмен** *m.* interchange; **—обменный** *a.* interchangeable; **—однозначное соответствие** one-to-one correspondence; **—отношение** *n.* interrelation, relationship, correlation; **—положение** *n.* relative position; **—помощь** *f.* mutual assistance.

взаимопревращаем/ость *f.* interconvertibility; **—ый** *a.* interconvertible, interchangeable.

взаимо/проникающий *a.* interpenetrating; **—растворение** *n.* mutual solution.

взаимосвяз/анный *a.* interconnected, interlocked, coupled; correlated; interrelated, related; **—анные величины** interrelated quantities; **—ь** *f.* interrelationship, relation; interlocking, interconnection; **—ь массы и энергии** mass-energy relation.

взамен *prep.* instead of, in exchange for.

ВЗАПИ *abbr.* (**Всесоюзный заочный политехнический институт**) All-Union Polytechnical Correspondence Institute.

взбаламу/ченный *a.* stirred, agitated; **—чивать, —тить** *v.* stir, agitate.

взбалтыв/ание *n.* shaking, agitation; **—ать** *v.* shake, agitate.

взбе/гание *n.* running up; **—гать, —жать** *v.* run up.

взбивать *v.* beat up, whip.

взбираться *v.* climb up.

взбить *see* **взбивать.**

взболтать *see* **взбалтывать.**

взбрасывать *v.* throw up.

взброс *m.* ramp; (geo.) upthrust; **в. прибоя** oversplash; **—ить** *see* **взбрасывать.**

взброшенный *a.* thrown up, upthrust.

взбрыз/гивание *n.* spraying; **—гивать, —нуть** *v.* spray.

взбудораж/ивать, —ить *v.* disturb.

взвед/ение *n.* leading up to; **—енный** *a.* led up to; erected, raised.

взвесить *see* **взвешивать.**

взвести *see* **взводить.**

взвесь *f.* suspended matter, suspension.

взвешенн/ость *f.* suspension, suspended state; **—ый** *a.* suspended; weighted; weighed; **—ое вещество** suspended matter, suspension.

взвешив/ание *n.* suspension; weighing; **двукратное в.** double weighing; **способ двойного —ания** method of double weighing; **—ать** *v.* suspend; weigh; weight; **—ающий коэффициент** weighting factor.

взвиваться *v.* rise, be raised.

взвизгивание *n.* squeal.

взвин/тить, —чивать *v.* wind up.

взвиться *see* **взвиваться.**

взвихривание *see* **взметание.**

взводить *v.* lead up; raise.

взгля/д *m.* glance; view, opinion; appearance; **—дывать, —нуть** *v.* look at, glance.

взгонять *v.* sublime.

вздваивать *v.* double up.

вздор *m.* nonsense; **—ность** *f.* absurdity; **—ный** *a.* absurd.

вздрагивать *v.* shudder.

вздув/ание *n.* swelling, bulging, inflation; (geo.) heave; **—ать** *v.* inflate; **—аться** *v.* swell, bulge, inflate.

вздут/ие *n.*, **—ость** *f.* swelling, bulge, inflation; **—ый** *a.* swelled, inflated; **—ь** *see* **вздувать.**

вздым/аться *v.* rise, heave; **—ающийся** *a.* rising.

взир/ать *v.* consider, look (at); **не —ая на** in spite of.

взламыв/ание *n.* breaking open; **—ать** *v.* break open, force open.

взлет *m.* upward flight, take-off (of plane); **—ать, —еть** *v.* fly up, take off.

взлом/анный, —ленный *a.* broken; **—ать, —ить** *see* **взламывать.**

взмах *m.* stroke, sweeping motion, swing; **—ивать, —нуть** *v.* flap, swing.

взмет/ание *n.* whirling, flying up, rising (dust, etc.); **—ать, —нуть, —ывать** *v.* throw up.

взму/тить, —щать *v.* make turbid, muddy; **—ченный** *a.* turbid; **во —ченном состоянии** in suspension; turbid.

взмыл/енный *a.* foamy, frothy; **—иваться, —иться** *v.* foam, froth.

взнос *m.* contribution.

взобраться *see* **взбираться.**

взогн/анный *a.* sublimated; **—ать** *see* **возгонять.**

взойти *see* **всходить.**

взорв/анный *a.* exploded, blown up; **—ать** *see* **взрывать.**

взраст/ать, —и *v.* grow; increase.

взрыв *m.* explosion, detonation; blast; burst, rupture, eruption; outbreak, outburst; **—ание** *n.* explosion, bursting; blasting, blowing up; **—атель** *m.* detonator, fuse; **—ать** *v.* explode, detonate, blow up; **—аться** *v.* explode, burst; **—ающий** *a.* exploding, explosive; **—ающийся** *a.* explosive.

взрывн/ой *a.* explosive, *see also* **взрывчатый; в. реактор** explosive reactor; **—ая волна** detonation wave, blast wave.

взрыво/безопасный, —непроницаемый *a.* explosion-proof; **—опасный** *a.* dangerously explosive; **—упорный** *a.* explosion-proof; **—чный** *see* **взрывной.**

взрывчат/ость *f.* explosiveness; **—ка** *f.*, **—ый** *a.* explosive; **—ый воздух** fire damp; **—ые вещества** explosives.

взрыть *v.* dig up.

взывать *v.* appeal, invoke.

взыскательный *a.* exacting, strict, severe.

взят/ие *n.* taking; **в. проб** sampling; **—ый** *a.* taken; in question; **—ь** *v.* take; **—ься** *v.* take hold of, undertake.

виадук *m.* viaduct.

вибратор *m.*, **—ный** *a.* vibrator, shaker; (rad.) oscillator; dipole; **в. в параболоиде** dipole-fed paraboloid; **в. коаксиальный** (rad.) sleeve stub; **—ная антенна** dipole antenna.

вибрационн/ый *a.* vibration, vibrational, vibrating, vibratory; **в. частотомер** vibrating-reed frequency meter; **—ая энергия** vibrational energy.

вибрация *f.* vibration, oscillation, (elec.) chatter; **в. кручения** torsional vibrations.

вибрир/ование *n.* vibration, oscillation; **—ать** *v.* vibrate, oscillate; quiver; **—ующий** *a.* vibrating, vibratory, vibration, oscillating; **—ующее зеркало** (meteor astr.) rocking mirror.

вибро/выпрямитель *m.* vibrating-reed rectifier; **—граф** *m.* vibrograph; **—датчик** *m.* vibro-pickup; **—движущая сила** vibromotive force; **—метр** *m.* vibrometer; **—преобразователь** *m.* vibrating-reed converter.

вибропрочн/ость *f.* vibration stability; **—ый** *a.* vibration-proof, shockproof.

вибро/скоп *m.* vibroscope; **—стойкий** *a.* vibration-proof, shockproof; **—трон** *m.* vibrotron; **—устойчивый** *a.* vibration-proof.

ВИГМ *abbr.* (**Всесоюзный институт гидромашиностроения**) All-Union Institute of Hydromachinery Construction.

Вигнера сила Wigner force.

вид *m.* view; species; appearance; form; type, kind; outlook; mode (of oscillations, etc.); **в. акустических колебаний** acoustic mode; **в. колебаний в волноводе** waveguide mode; **в. на погоду** weather prospect; **в. облаков** cloud species; **в. распада** mode of decay; **в. распространения** mode of propagation; **в. сбоку** side view; **в. сверху** top view; **в. сзади** rear view; **в. симметрии** crystal symmetry class, point group; **в. спереди** front view; **в. ядра** nuclide; **в —е** in the form of, as; **в —у** in view of; **в —у того, что** considering that; **иметь в —у** have in mind, intend, contemplate; imply.

вид/анный *a.* seen; **—ать** *v.* see often.

Видемана-Франца закон Wiedemann-Franz (and Lorentz) law; **В. эффект** W. effect.

вид/ение *n.* vision, sight; **в. в темноте** noctovision.

видео— *prefix* video—.

видео/блок *m.* video unit; **—детектор** *m.* video detector; **—импульс** *m.* video pulse; **—усилитель** *m.* video amplifier, video frequency amplifier (vfa); **—частота** *f.* video frequency.

видеть *v.* see, view; **в. с ребра** see edge-on.

Види коробка (**коробочка**) aneroid (or pressure) capsule, Vidi vacuum cell (or box).

видиа режущий металл, в.-сплав widia (cemented tungsten carbide).

видикон *m.* vidicon.

видимо *adv.* evidently, visibly, obviously, clearly; **—сть** *f.* visibility, visual range; appearance; **—сть исключительная** excellent visibility; **—сть слабая** poor visibility; **—сть средняя** moderate visibility.

видим/ый *a.* apparent, visible; **в. горизонт** apparent horizon, skyline; **в. полдень** (astr.) apparent noon; **в. спектр** visible spectrum; **в. шум** (telev.) visible noise; **делать —ым** visualize; **—ая величина** (astr.) apparent magnitude; **—ая температура** apparent temperature; **—ая траектория** apparent path; **—ое излучение** visible radiation.

видманштеттова структура Widmanstätten structure.

видн/еться *v.* be seen, show; **—о** *adv.*, **как видно** obviously, evidently; **—ость** *f.* luminosity, visibility; **—ый** *a.* visible, prominent, observable; *suffix* like, resembling, —shaped.

видоизмен/ение *n.* change, alteration, modification, version; **—енный** *a.* modified, altered; **—ять** *v.* change, alter, modify.

видоискатель *m.* viewfinder.

Виета Vieta (lunar crater).

визг *m.* squeal, whine.

визерин *m.* wiserine.

визж/ание *n.* spluttering (of arc); **—ать** *v.* squeal, whine.

визиочастота *f.* video frequency, visual frequency.

визир *m.* sight; sighting device; (phot.) viewfinder; **—ка** *f.* (surv.) ranging rod; **—ный** *a.* sighting; **—ный крест** cross line, reticle; **—ный пункт** (geo.) station; **—ная линейка** aiming rule; **—ная линия** sighting line, transit line; **—ная нить** cross-hair; **—ная трубка** telescopic sight; **—ное отверстие** peep hole.

визиров/ание *n.* sighting, sight; **обратное в.** (surv.) backsight; **в. через несколько точек** aligning, alignment sighting; **—ать** *v.* sight; level; align, collimate.

ВИЗМАЭ *abbr.* (**Всесоюзный институт земного магнетизма и атмосферного электричества**) All-Union Institute of Terrestrial Magnetism and Atmospheric Electricity.

визуал/изация *f.* visualization, visual representation; **—изировать** *v.* visualize, represent visually; **—ьный** *a.* visual.

виикит *m.* wiikite.

Вийяра явление Villard effect.

Вика теорема Wick theorem.

викаллой *m.* Vicalloy (cobalt-vanadium alloy).

Викерс: твердость по —у Vickers hardness.

викторит *m.* victorite.

вилк/а *f.* fork, two-pin plug; branching; **соединение —ой** forked connection, Y-connection; **—овый** *see* **вилочный.**

вилкообразн/ый *a.* fork-shaped, forked, Y-shaped; **—ая трубка** Y-tube.

Виллари явление Villari effect.

виллемит *m.* willemite.

виллиамит *m.* willyamite.

Виллио диаграмма (**перемещений**) Williot diagram.

виллиомит *m.* villiaumite.

вилльямсит *m.* williamsite.

вило/образный *a.* forked, bifurcate; **—чка** *f.* Y-connector; **—чный** *a.* fork; **—чный контакт** (elec.) plug.

вилтширеит *m.* wiltshireite.

Вильгельм Wilhelm (lunar crater).

Вильда доска Wild pressure-plate anemometer.
вилькеит *m.* wilkeïte.
Вильсон Wilson (lunar crater).
Вильсона камера Wilson cloud chamber; **В. теорема** W. theorem; **В. электрометр** W. electroscope.
вильсонит *m.* wilsonite.
вильчат/ость *f.* bifurcation; **—ый** *a.* forked, Y-shaped; **—ый рычаг** yoke lever.
виля/ние *n.*, **—ть** *v.* wobble (of wheel).
ВИМС *abbr.* (**Всесоюзный научно-исследовательский институт метрологии и стандартизации**) All-Union Scientific Research Institute of Metrology and Standardization.
Вимшерста электростатическая машина Wimshurst machine.
вина *f.* fault, blame.
Вина закон смещения Wien displacement law; **В. эффект** W. effect.
Винера-Хопфа уравнение Wiener-Hopf equation.
винил *m.* vinyl; **—ит** *m.* vinylite; **—овый, —ильный** *a.* vinyl.
ВИНИТИ *abbr.* (**Всесоюзный институт научной и технической информации**) All-Union Institute of Scientific and Technical Information.
винкель *m. see* **угольник.**
винклерит *m.* winklerite.
винн/окаменная кислота tartaric acid; **—ый** *a.* tartaric.
винт *m.* screw; propeller; **в. бесконечный** endless screw, worm; **б. воздушный** propeller, airscrew; **в. геликоптерный** lifting propeller; **в. двухлопастный** two-bladed propeller; **отдавать в., отпустить в.** unscrew; **в. правого вращения** right-hand propeller.
винт/ик *m.* small screw; **—ить** *v.*, **—овальный** *a.* screw; **—овальная доска, —овальня** *f.* screw plate, die plate.
винтов/ой *a.* screw, spiral, helical; **—ая дислокация** screw (or Burgers) dislocation; **—ая зубчатая передача, —ая передача** helical gear; worm gear; **—ая линия** helical line, spiral; **—ая нарезка** thread (of screw); **—ая настройка** screw tuning; **—ая ось** screw axis; **—ая пружина** helical spring; **—ое перемещение** twist; **—ое развертывание** helical scanning; **—ые свойства пространства** chirality.
винто/образный *a.* screw-shaped, helical; **—образная линия** helical line, helix; **—резный** *a.* screw-cutting.
винчит *m.* winchite.
виньет/ирование *n.* vignetting; **—ка** *f.* vignette.
Виолля эталон Violle standard.
вираж *m.* (aero.) veering, banking, turning; (phot.) toning; **—ировать** *v.* veer, turn; (phot.) tone, shade.
ВИРГ *abbr.* (**Всесоюзный научно-исследовательский институт разведочной геофизики**) All-Union Scientific Research Institute of Geophysical Prospecting.
вириал *m.* virial; **—ьный коэффициент** virial coefficient.
вирировать *v.* (phot.) tone, shade.
виртуальн/ый *a.* virtual; **в. источник** image source; **в. катод** virtual cathode; **в. уровень** virtual level; **—ая частица** virtual particle; **—ое состояние** virtual state.
вирус *m.*, **—ный** *a.* virus; **—ология** *f.* virology.
висеть *v.* hang.
вискоз/а *f.* (text.) viscose, (viscose) rayon; **—иметр** *m.* viscosimeter; **емкостный —иметр** capacitance-change viscosimeter; **—иметрия** *f.* viscosimetry; **—итет** *m.* viscosity.
висмут *m.* bismuth (Bi); **—ид** *m.* bismuthide; **—овокислый** *a.* bismuthic acid, bismuthate (of); **—овый** *a* bismuth, bismuthic.
виснуть *v.* hang.
високосный год leap year.
вися/чий, —щий *a.* hanging, suspended; **в. клапан** drop valve; **в. мост** suspension bridge; **—чая антенна** trailing antenna.
вита-глас *m.* Vitaglass (permeable to ultraviolet rays).
витамит *m.* withamite.
витафон *m.* vitaphone.
Витворта резьба Whitworth thread.

ВИТР *abbr.* (**Всесоюзный научно-исследовательский институт методики и техники разведки**) All-Union Scientific Research Institute of Prospecting Methods and Techniques.
Вителло Vitello (lunar crater).
витерит *m.* witherite.
витнеит *m.* whitneyite.
вит/ой *a.* twisted, cabled; **—ок** *m.* coil, loop; turn; **мертвый —ок** idle turn; **—ок связи** coupling loop, pickup loop.
Витрувий Vitruvius (lunar crater).
Витстона мостик Wheatstone bridge.
виттит *m.* wittite.
виттихенит *m.* wittichenite.
вить *v.* twist, whirl, wind; **—е** *n.* twisting, torsion; **—ся** *v.* twist, spin.
Вихардта аналогия Wieghardt analogy.
вихляться *v.* dangle.
вихрев/ой *a.* vortical, vortex, rotational; turbulent, eddy; rotary; **в. ветер** whirlwind; **в. градиент** vortex gradient; **в. поток** vortex flow; **в. провал** vortex sink, vortex depression; **в. свисток** vortex whistle; **в. слой** vortex sheet; **в. шнур** vortex filament; **в. элемент** vortex element.
вихрев/ой *cont.*, **—ая воронка** vortex; **—ая вязкость** eddy viscosity; **—ая депрессия** vortex sink; **—ая дорожка** vortex street, vortex trail; **—ая линия** vortex line; **—ая нить** vortex filament; **—ая пелена** vortex sheet; **—ая поверхность** vortex surface; **—ая струя** vortex stream; **—ая трубка** vortex tube; **—ая форсунка** swirl injector, swirl jet; **—ая энергия** eddy energy; **—ое движение** turbulence, eddy, vortex motion, eddying; **—ое кольцо** vortex ring; **—ое облако** eddy cloud; **—ое поле** vorticity field; **—ые токи** eddy currents.
вихре/источник *m.* (hyd.) vortex-source combination; **—образование** *n.* eddy formation, vortex formation; **—проводность** *f.* eddy conductivity; **—сток** *m.* (hyd.) vortex-sink combination.
вихр/ь *m.* vortex, vorticity; eddy; whirlpool; (math.) curl; **в. вектора** curl (of a vector); **в. осевой** axial eddy; **связанный в.** bound vortex; **в. скорости** vorticity; **—я вектор** vorticity vector.
вице— *prefix* vice—.
вициналь *f.* (cryst.) vicinal form; **—ный** *a.* vicinal; **—ное правило** vicinal rule.
вишневит *m.* wischnewite.
вишневокалильный жар cherry-red heat.
вкат/ить, —ывать, —иться, —ываться *v.* roll in.
ВКБ метод Wentzel-Kramers-Brillouin method.
вкл. *abbr.* (**включенный**) switched on; (**включительно**) inclusively.
вклад *m.* contribution, portion; **—ка** *f.* putting in; insertion, insert; **—ывание** *n.* insertion; **—ывать** *v.* put in, enclose; embed; sheathe.
вкладыш *m.* bearing, bushing; brass; insert; **в. подшипника** bushing; brass.
вклеивать, вклеить *v.* glue in, cement in, paste in.
вклейка *f.* pasting in; inset.
вклепанный *a.* riveted.
вклин/ение, —ивание *n.* wedging in; **—ивать, —ить** *v.* wedge in; **—иваться, —иться** *v.* wedge in, be wedged in.
включ/атель *m.* switch, circuit closer, cut-in; **—ать** *v.* include, enclose, insert; occlude (gas); switch on, close (switch); put in gear, engage; **—ать скорость** put in gear; **—аться** *v.* engage, interlock; **—ающий** *a.* enclosing, including; engaging; **—ающий кулачок** actuating cam; **—ающий механизм** gear; **—ающее реле** cut-in relay; **—ая** *a.* including, comprising.
включен/ие *n.* inclusion, insertion; occlusion (of gas); switching on; connection; engaging; **в. ступенями** cascade connection; **схема —ия** (elec.) wiring diagram; **—ия** *pl.* inclusions; impurities; **газовые —ия** occluded gas, entrapped gas.
включ/енный *a.* included, enclosed, inner; occluded (gas); incorporated; embedded; switched on; in gear,

engaged; **в. навстречу** connected in opposition; **—ительно** *adv.* inclusively; **—ить** *see* **включать.**

вкол/ачивание *n.* driving in, packing; **—ачивать, —отить** *v.* drive in, ram, pack in.

вконец *adv.* entirely.

вкорен/ение *n.* inculcation; **—ить, —ять** *v.* inculcate.

вкось *adv.* obliquely.

вкра/дываться, —сться *v.* slip in (error).

вкрапл/ение *n.* **—енность** *f.* dissemination, impregnation; **—енный** *a.* disseminated, impregnated; **—ивать, —ять** *v.* disseminate, impregnate (ore).

вкратце *adv.* briefly, in short.

вкрест *adv.* transversely, transverse to.

вкру/тить, —чивать *v.* screw in, twist in.

ВКС *abbr.* (**Всесоюзный комитет по стандартизации**) All-Union Standardization Committee.

вкус *m.* taste.

влаг/а *f.* moisture, humidity; **количество —и** moisture content, humidity; **—и поток** moisture transport.

влагать *see* **вкладывать.**

влаго— *prefix* moisture, hygro—.

влаго/емкость *f.* moisture capacity; **—мер** *m.* hygrometer; **—непроницаемый** *a.* moistureproof; **—оборот** *m.* hydrologic cycle; **—отделитель** *m.* moisture separator; **—перенос** *m.* moisture transfer; **—содержание** *n.* moisture content; **—стойкий, —устойчивый** *a.* moistureproof, moisture-resistant; **—температурный индекс** moisture-temperature index; **—удалитель** *m.* moisture extractor.

владеть *v.* own, possess.

влажно *adv.* moistly, wet; **—адиабатический** *a.* moist-adiabatic; **—неустойчивый** *a.* moist-labile, wet-unstable.

влажност/ь *f.* moisture, humidity; moisture content; **—и дефицит** (meteor.) humidity deficit, saturation deficit; **содержание —и** moisture content, humidity.

влажн/ый *a.* moist, humid; **в. шарик** wet bulb; **—ая адиабата** moist adiabat; **—ая неустойчивость** wet instability; **—ая температура** wet-bulb temperature.

Влакк Vlacq (lunar crater).

власт/вование *n.* domination; **—вовать** *v.* dominate, rule; **—ь** *f.* power, authority, rule.

влево *adv.* to the left, counterclockwise; **вращающийся в.** levorotatory.

влет *m.* flight in; entrance; **—ать, —еть** *v.* fly in; enter.

влеч/ение *n.* inclination, tendency; **—ь** *v.* attract; **—ь за собой** involve, necessitate, entail, imply.

влив/ание *n.* pouring in, infusion; **—ать** *v.* pour (in), infuse.

влит/ый *a.* poured in; **—ь** *see* **вливать.**

влия/ние *n.* influence, action, effect; **в. близости** proximity effect; **в. масштаба** scale effect; **в. рассеяния** diffusion effect; **линия —ния** influence line; **—тельный** *a.* influential; **—ть** *v.* influence, affect.

влож/ение *n.* insertion, imbedding, enclosure; **—ить** *see* **вкладывать.**

влучение *n.* incident radiation.

вмаз/ать, —ывать *v.* cement in, putty in, paste in; **—ка** *f.*, **—ывание** *n.* cementing in, pasting in.

вмерз/ать *v.* freeze in; **—ший** *a.* frozen-in.

вместе *adv.* together; **в. с тем** at the same time, moreover.

вмести/лище *n.* receptacle, container, tank; **—мость, —тельность** *f.* capacity; space, volume; contents; **—мый** *a.* (math.) imbeddable; **—тельный** *a.* spacious, large; **—ть** *see* **вмещать; —ться** *v.* fit in.

вместо *prep. gen.* instead (of); **в. того, чтобы** instead of.

вмеш/ательство *n.* interference; **—ать, —ивать** *v.* mix in, add; **—аться, —иваться** *v.* interfere.

вмещ/ать *v.* hold, contain; insert; **в. угол** subtend an angle; **—аться** *v.* fit in; **—ающий** *a.* holding, containing, enclosing; **—ающая порода** enclosing (or country) rock; **—ение** *n.* putting in, insertion; (math.) imbedding; **—енный** *a.* put in, inserted, contained.

вмиг *adv.* in a flash.

ВМО *abbr.* (**Всемирная метеорологическая организация**) World Meteorological Organization.

вмонтиров/анный *a.* built-in, fixed; **—ать** *v.* build in.

вмороженность *f.* freezing in.

ВМС *abbr.* (**военно-морские силы**) navy.

вмятина *f.* dent, depression.

ВН *abbr.* (**вакуум насос**) vacuum pump; (**высокое напряжение**) high voltage.

ВНАИЗ *abbr.* (**Всесоюзный научно-исследовательский институт звукозаписи**) All-Union Scientific Institute of Sound Recording.

внакладку *see* **внахлестку.**

внаклон *adv.* slant-wise.

внакрой, внапуск *see* **внахлестку.**

внасыпную *adv.* in bulk.

внахлестку *adv.* overlapping; **соединение в., шов в.** lap joint, overlapping joint.

вначале *adv.* first of all, at first.

вне *prep.* out of, outside, beyond; irrespective of; **в. сомнения** without doubt.

вне— *prefix* extra—, out—, outside—.

вневписанн/ый *a.* circumscribed, escribed; **—ая окружность** escribed circle, excircle.

внегалактический *a.* extragalactic.

внедр/ение *n.* inculcation, implanting, penetration, incorporation; introduction, injection; (geo.) intrusion; **в. электронов** injection of electrons; **—енный** *a.* implanted, interstitial; imbedded; intruded; **—ить, —ять** *v.* inculcate; introduce, inject; imbed, intrude, thrust; **—иться, —яться** *v.* enter, be incorporated (in).

внезапн/о *adv.* suddenly; **—ое начало** (astr.) sudden commencement; **—ое похолодание** cold snap; **—ость** *f.* suddenness; **—ый** *a.* sudden.

вне/земной *a.* extraterrestrial; **—осевой** *a.* off-axis; extra-axial; **—осевая точка** extra-axial point.

внеинтегральный *a.* outside the integral.

внеочередной *a.* extra; out of order.

внес/ение *n.* introduction, insertion, entry; **в. дырок** hole injection; **—ти** *see* **вносить.**

внетропический *a.* extratropical.

внефокальный *a.* extrafocal.

внешкальный *a.* off-scale; **в. нуль** inferred zero.

внешне *adv.* outwardly, externally.

внешн/ий *a.* outer, exterior, external, outside, outward; extraneous; surface, superficial; extrinsic; foreign; **в. вид** outside diameter; **в. газ** foreign gas; **в. диаметр** outside diameter; **в. размер** overall dimension, overall size; **в. угол** exterior angle; **в. фотоэффект** (surface) photoelectric effect, photoemissive effect; **в. электрон** outer electron, orbital electron; **—яя атмосфера** outer atmosphere; **—яя баллистика** external ballistics; **—яя линия** outline; **—яя нарезка** male thread; **—яя нормаль** outward normal; **—яя оболочка** outer(most) orbit; **—яя резьба** male thread, external screw thread; **—яя совместность** external consistency; **—яя среда** environment, ambient; **—яя электронная оболочка** outermost electronic shell; **—ее поле** external field, applied field; **—ее пространство** outer space; **—ее тормозное излучение** outer bremsstrahlung; **—ее трение** external friction; **—ие свойства** (semicond.) extrinsic properties.

внешность *f.* exterior, form, appearance; superficiality.

Внешторг *abbr.* (**Министерство внешней торговли**) Ministry of Foreign Trade.

внеэкваториальная зона extra-equatorial zone.

внеядерный *a.* extranuclear.

ВНИГМИ *abbr.* (**Всесоюзный научно-исследовательский гидромашиностроительный институт**) All-Union Scientific Research Institute of Hydromachinery Construction.

вниз *adv.* down, downwards, underneath; **направленный в., сверху в.** downward; **в. по течению** downstream; **ход в.** descent, down stroke.

внизу *adv.* below, underneath; *prep. gen.* at the foot of, at the bottom of.

ВНИИ *abbr.* (**Всесоюзный научно-исследовательский инструментальный институт**) All-Union Instrument Research Institute.

ВНИИГ *abbr.* (**Всесоюзный научно-исследовательский институт галургии**) All-Union Scientific Research Institute for the Study of Halurgy; (**Всесоюзный научно-исследовательский институт гидротехники**) All-Union Scientific Research Institute of Hydroengineering.

ВНИИГАЗ *abbr.* (**Всесоюзный научно-исследовательский нститут газовой промышленности**) All-Union Scientific Research Institute of the Gas Industry.

ВНИИГС *abbr.* (**Всесоюзный научно-исследовательский институт гидротехнических и санитарно-технических работ**) All-Union Scientific Research Institute of Hydro- and Sanitary Engineering.

ВНИИК *abbr.* (**Всесоюзный научно-исследовательский институт керамики**) All-Union Scientific Research Institute of Ceramics.

ВНИИКИМАШ *abbr.* (**Всесоюзный научно-исследовательский институт кислородного машиностроения**) All-Union Scientific Research Institute of Oxygen Machinery Construction.

ВНИИМ *abbr.* (**Всесоюзный научно-исследовательский институт метеорологии**) All-Union Scientific Research Institute of Meteorology; [**Всесоюзный научно-исследовательский институт метрологии (им. Д. И. Менделеева)**] The D. I. Mendeleev All-Union Scientific Research Metrological Institute.

ВНИИС *abbr.* (**Всесоюзный научно-исследовательский институт стекла**) All-Union Scientific Research Institute of Glass.

ВНИИСВ *abbr.* (**Всесоюзный научно-исследовательский институт стеклянного волокна**) All-Union Scientific Research Institute of Glass Fibers.

ВНИИЭЭ *abbr.* (**Всесоюзный научно-исследовательский институт энергетики и электрификации**) All-Union Scientific Research Institute of Power Engineering and Electrification.

вник/ание *n.* investigation; **—ать, —нуть** *v.* investigate, scrutinize.

ВНИЛ *abbr.* (**Всесоюзная научно-исследовательская лаборатория**) All-Union Scientific Research Laboratory.

вниман/ие *n.* attention, notice; **обращать в.** pay attention, notice; **принимая во в.** in view of; **не принимая во в.** disregarding; **достойный —ия** noteworthy; noticeable.

внимательн/о *adv.* attentively; **—ость** *f.* attentiveness; **—ый** *a.* attentive.

ВНИСИ *abbr.* (**Всесоюзный научно-исследовательский светотехнический институт**) All-Union Scientific Research Institute of Lighting Engineering.

ВНИТО *abbr.* (**Всесоюзное научное инженерно-техническое общество**) All-Union Scientific Engineering and Technical Society.

ВНИТОМАШ *abbr.* (**Всесоюзное научное инженерно-техническое общество машиностроителей**) All-Union Scientific Engineering and Technical Society of Mechanical Engineers.

Внитоприбор *abbr.* (**Всесоюзное научное инженерно-техническое общество приборостроения**) All-Union Scientific Engineering and Technical Society of Instrument Making.

ВНИТОСС *abbr.* (**Всесоюзное научное инженерно-техническое общество судостроителей**) All-Union Scientific Engineering and Technical Society of Shipbuilders.

ВНИТОЭ *abbr.* (**Всесоюзное научное инженерно-техническое общество энергетиков**) All-Union Scientific Engineering and Technical Society of Power Engineers.

вновь *adv.* again; newly; re—.

внос, —ка *see* **внесение; —имый** *a.* inserted; **—имая реактивность** insertion reactance; **—имое сопротивление** reflected (or coupled) impedance, added resistance; **—ить** *v.* bring in, contribute; introduce, insert, enter, list; **—ить поправку** rectify, correct.

ВНР *abbr.* *see* **Венгерская Народная Республика.**

ВНТО *abbr.* (**Всесоюзное научно-техническое общество**) All-Union Scientific-Technical Society.

внутр. *abbr.* (**внутренний**) inner, inside, interior, internal.

внутренне *adv.* internally, intrinsically.

внутренне— *prefix* inside, internal.

внутренний *a.* inner, inside, interior, internal, inward; inland; inherent, intrinsic; female (screw thread); domestic; **в. габарит** inside dimensions, internal section; **в. диаметр** inside diameter; **в. комптон-эффект** internal Compton effect; **в. момент количества движения** intrinsic angular momentum, spin; **в. пучок** internal beam; **в. фотоэффект** photoconductive effect; **в. циклотронный пучок** internal cyclotron beam; **в. электрон** inner-shell electron; core electron.

внутренн/ий *cont.*, **—яя баллистика** interior ballistics; **—яя волна** internal wave; **—яя конверсия** internal conversion; **—яя нормаль** inner normal; **—яя оболочка** inner shell; **—яя орбита** inner orbit; **—яя проводка** interior wiring; **—яя проницаемость** intrinsic permeability; **—яя пучка** internal beam; **—яя согласованность** internal consistency, **—яя фильтрация** inherent filtration; **—яя энергия** internal energy; intrinsic energy; **—ей конверсии коэффициент** internal conversion coefficient.

внутренн/ий *cont.*, **—ее горение** internal combustion; **—ее изображение** latent image; **—ее квантовое число** inner quantum number; **—ее напряжение** internal strain; **—ее отражение** internal reflection; **—ее падение отражения** tube voltage drop; **—ее поле** internal (or local) field; **—ее сгорание** internal combustion; **—ее сопротивление** internal resistance; **—ее сопротивление лампы** plate resistance; **—ее тормозное излучение** inner bremsstrahlung; **——ее трение** internal friction, viscosity; **—ее фотографическое изображение** latent (photographic) image; **—ее экранирование** internal screening; **—ие размеры** inside dimensions; **—ие свойства** intrinsic properties.

внутренность *f.* interior.

внутри *adv. and prep. gen.* inside, within.

внутри— *prefix* intra—, inside.

внутриатомн/ый *a.* intratomic, subatomic; **—ая энергия** atomic energy, nuclear energy; **—ое изменение** subatomic change.

внутри/земной *a.* intratelluric; **—клеточный** *a.* intracellular; **—комплексная группа** chelate group; **—кристаллический** *a.* intracrystalline.

внутримассов/ый туман air-mass fog; **—ые облака** internal clouds.

внутри/молекулярный *a.* intramolecular; **—нуклонный** *a.* subnucleonic; **—поровый** *a.* pore, interstitial; **—реакторный** *a.* in-pile, in-reactor; **—тропический** *a.* intertropical; **—ядерный** *a.* intranuclear; **—ячейковый** *a.* intracellular.

внутрь *adv.* in, inside, inward; *prep. gen.* in, into, inside.

внуш/ать, —ить *v.* suggest, impress; **—ение** *n.* suggestion; **поддающийся —ению** open to suggestion; **—енный** *a.* suggested; **—ительный** *a.* imposing, impressive.

внятн/о *adv.* audibly; **—ость** *f.* intelligibility, audibility; **—ый** *a.* intelligible, audible.

во *see* **в.**

вобрать *see* **вбирать.**

вобулированный *a.* (elec.) wobbulated.

вовле/кать, —чь *v.* draw in, involve; **—каться в движение** be set in motion; **—чение** *n.* drawing in, implication, involving; **—ченный** *a.* drawn in, involved.

вовремя *adv.* in time.

вовсе *adv.* completely, entirely; **в. нет** not at all.

во-вторых *adv.* secondly.

вогнать *see* **вгонять.**

вогнуто— *prefix* concavo—.

вогнутовыпукл/ый *a.* concavo-convex; **—ая чечевица** concavo-convex lens; meniscus.

вогнут/ость *f.* concavity; **—ый** *a.* concave, bent in; **—ый вверх** concave upward; **—ый вниз** concave downward; —**ое место** dent; —**ь** *see* **вгибать.**

вода *f.* water; **движущая в., рабочая в.** power water; **в. для питания котла** feed water; **легкая в.** light water; **проточная в.** running water; **тяжелая в.** heavy water; **охлаждение —ой** water cooling; **присоединение —ы** hydration; **сила —ы** water power; **удалять —у** dehydrate.

воданит *m.* wodanite.

водвор/ение *n.* installation; —**ить, —ять** *v.* install, establish.

вод/итель *m.* driver; —**ить** *see* **вести;** —**иться** be found.

водка крепкая aqua fortis; **в. царская** aqua regia.

водно— *prefix* water, aqueous; *see also* **водо—.**

водно/спиртовый *a.* water-alcohol; —**сть** *f.* water content.

водн/ый *a.* water, aqueous, hydrous; *see also* **водяной; в. гомогенный реактор** aqueous homogeneous reactor; **в. кадастр** hydrographic survey; **в. остаток** water residue, hydroxyl; **в. путь** waterway; **в. раствор** aqueous solution; **в. эквивалент** water equivalent; **в. экран** water shield; —**ая соль** hydrated salt; —**ая фаза** aqueous phase; —**ая энергия** water power; —**ое зеркало** water table; —**ые ресурсы** water resources.

водо— *prefix* water, hydraulic; aqua—.

водо/бой *m.* (hyd.) apron; —**вместилище** *n.* reservoir; —**вод** *m.* water pipe, conduit; —**ворот** *m.*, —**воротный** *a.* whirlpool, swirl, eddy, vortex.

водовыпускн/ой *a.* water-discharge; **в. кран** water cock, water faucet; —**ая труба** water discharge pipe, drain.

водоем *m.* reservoir, basin; —**истый,** —**кий** *a.* containing or absorbing considerable water; —**кость** *f.* water-retaining capacity; reservoir capacity; —**ный** *a.* reservoir, tank.

водо/забор *m.* (hyd.) intake; —**заборное сооружение** intake structure; —**зор** *m.* hydroscope; —**измещение** *n.* (water) displacement; —**качальный** *a.* water-pumping; —**качка** *f.* pumping station.

водолаз *m.* diver; —**а** *f.*, —**ный шлем** diving helmet; —**ный** *a.* diving, diver's.

Водолей Aquarius (Aqu) (constellation).

водомер *m.*, —**ный** *a.* water meter, water gauge; —**ная рейка** depth gauge; —**ное стекло** gauge glass.

водонапорн/ый *a.* water pressure; **в. насос** hydraulic pump; —**ая башня** water tower; —**ая колонка** water column.

водонепро/мокаемость, —**ницаемость** *f.* watertightness; —**никаемый,** —**ницаемый** *a.* waterproof, watertight.

водоносн/ый *a.* water-bearing, aquiferous; **в. грунт,** —**ая порода** water-bearing soil.

водоот/ведение *n.* water diversion; —**вод** *m.* drain, drainage; —**водная труба** drain(pipe).

водо/отделитель *m.* dehydrator, water trap; —**отливный** *a.* discharge; —**отнимающий** *a.* dehydrating; —**отнимающее средство** dehydrating agent, dehydrant; —**охладительный** *a.* water-cooling; —**охлаждаемый** *a.* water-cooled.

водоочиститель *m.* water purifier; —**ный** *a.* water-purifying.

водо/очищение *n.* water purification, water treatment; —**пад** *m.*, —**падный** *a.* waterfall, cascade, cataract; —**падь** *f.* decrease of water; —**поглощающий** *a.* water-absorbing, hygroscopic; —**подготовка** *f.* water treatment.

водоподъемный *a.* water-raising; **в. таран** hydraulic ram.

водо/потребление *n.* water consumption; —**приемник** *m.* water intake; —**приемный** *a.* water-receiving.

водопровод *m.* water pipe, water conduit, aqueduct; water supply; —**ец** *m.* hydraulic engineer; —**ный** *a.* water-conducting; —**ная вода** tap water; —**ная задвижка** sluice gate; —**ная магистраль** water main; —**ная раковина** sink, basin; —**ная система** water supply system; —**ная станция,** —**ные сооружения** water works; —**ная труба** water pipe; —**ящий** *a.* water-conducting.

водопроницаем/ость *f.* water permeability; **—ый** *a.* permeable (to water).

водо/пропускная способность (geo.) transmission constant; **—разборный кран** hydrant; **—раздел** *m.* watershed, water divide; **—раздельный хребет** divide; **—распыление** *n.* water spraying; **—распылительный** *a.* water-spray.

водород *m.* hydrogen (H); **легкий в.** light hydrogen; **в. сверхтяжелый** tritium; **сернистый в.** hydrogen sulfide; **тяжелый в.** heavy hydrogen, deuterium; **хлористый в.** hydrogen chloride; **перекись —а** hydrogen peroxide.

водородистый *a.* hydrogen, hydride (of); **в. калий** potassium hydride.

водородн/ый *a.* hydrogen, hydrogenous; **в. замедлитель** hydrogenous moderator; **в. показатель** pH value; **—ая бомба** hydrogen bomb, H-bomb; **—ая связь** hydrogen bond.

водородо/-воздушная смесь hydrogen-air mixture; **—кислородный** *a.* oxyhydrogen; **—подобный** *a.* hydrogen-like; **—содержащий** *a.* hydrogenous.

водосбор *m.* water collection; **—ник** *m.* water-collecting header; **—ный** *a.* water-collecting; **—ный резервуар** catch basin; **—ная площадь** catchment basin.

водосброс *m.*, **—ное сооружение** spillway.

водослив *m.* **—ный** *a.* spillway, weir; **в. со свободной струей** ventilated overfall; **—ная плотина** overflow (or spillway) dam; **—ная труба** water-discharge tube; **—ное течение** (water) discharge current.

водо/снабжающее устройство water supply (system); **—снабжение** *n.* water supply, water works; **—содержащий** *a.* water-containing, hydrated.

водоспуск *m.* **—ной** *a.* floodgate; drain outlet; **—ное сооружение** outlet works.

водостойк/ий *a.* water-resistant; **—ость** *f.* water resistance, stability in water.

водосто/к *m.*, **—чный** *a.* drain; gully; **—чный жолоб** gutter.

водо/струйный *a.* water-jet; **—тек** *m.*, **—течь** *f.* current of water; leak; **—ток** *m.* water course; **—трубный котел** tubular boiler; **—удерживательный** *a.* water-retaining.

водоуказатель *m.*, **—ный прибор, —ное стекло** water gauge.

водо/упорность *f.* water resistance; **—упорный, —устойчивый** *a.* waterproof, watertight.

водо/хозяйственный кадастр water resources survey; **—хранилище** *n.* reservoir, tank; **—чистилище** *n.* filtering basin, filtering tank.

водру/жать, —зить *v.* erect; **—жение** *n.* erection.

вод. ст. *abbr.* (**водяной столб**) water column.

водянист/ость *f.* wateriness; **—ый** *a.* watery, aqueous, hydrous.

водян/ой *a.* water, aqueous; aquatic; hydraulic; *see also* **водный, водо—**; **в. гомогенный реактор** aqueous homogeneous reactor; **в. затвор** water seal, hydraulic seal; **в. защитный слой** water shield; **в. котел** water boiler; **в. отблеск** (meteor.) water sky; **в. пар** steam, water vapor; **в. смерч** water spout; **в. экран** water shield; **—ая взвесь** water suspension, water slurry; **—ая закалка** water quenching (or hardening); **—ая защита** water shielding; **—ая подогревная секция** water preheater section; **—ая турбина** hydraulic turbine; **—ое облако** water cloud; **—ое охлаждение** water cooling; **—ое число** water equivalent (of calorimeter).

водящий *a.* leading, guiding.

воедино *adv.* together, jointly.

воен. *abbr.* (**военный**) military.

военинженер *abbr.* (**военный инженер**) military engineer.

воен.-мор. *abbr. see* **военно-морской.**

военн/о-морской naval; **—ый** *a.* military; **—ые запасы** munitions.

вождение *n.* driving, navigation, piloting.

возб. *abbr.* (**возбужденный**) excited, induced, activated.

возбран/ительный *a.* prohibitory; **—ить, —ять** *v.* prohibit.

возбуд/имость *f.* excitability; —**итель** *m.* stimulant, energizer; (elec.) exciter, driver; —**итель модулятора** modulator driver; —**ительный** *a.* stimulating, exciting; —**ительный анод** excitation anode; —**ить** *see* **возбуждать.**

возбужд/аемый *a.* excitable; —**ать** *v.* excite, stimulate; create, give rise to; actuate, establish; induce; —**аться** *v.* be excited.

возбуждающ/ий *a.* exciting, stimulating; —**ая обмотка** exciting (or energizing) coil; —**ая сила** exciting force; —**ая частота** driver frequency; exciting frequency; —**ее напряжение** driving voltage; exciting voltage.

возбужден/ие *n.* (elec.) excitation, energizing; activation; energization; **в. большое** strong excitation; **в. недокомпаундированное** undercompound excitation; **в. перекомпаундированное** overcompound excitation; **напряжение —ия** exciting voltage; **цепь —ия** energizing circuit; —**ный** *a.* excited, induced, activated; —**ное состояние** excited state.

возведение *n.* erection; **в. в квадрат** squaring; **в. в степень** raising to a power; involution.

возвести *see* **возведение, возводить.**

возве/стить, —**щать** *v.* announce, —**щение** *n.* announcement.

возводить *v.* raise; erect; deduce; —**ся** *v.* be raised, be elevated.

возврат *m.* return, recovery; regression; (rocket) re-entry; **точка —а (первого рода)** cuspidal point (of first kind); —**имый** *a.* revertible; recoverable; —**ить** *see* **возвращать.**

возвратно-поступательн/ый *a.* reciprocating; —**ое движение** reciprocating motion.

возвратн/ый *a.* returning, return; recurrent; retrogressive; —**ая волна** reflected wave; —**ая пружина** return spring; —**ое действие** retroaction; —**ое уравнение** reciprocal equation.

возвращать *v.* return; restore; —**ся** *v.* return; regress; recur; revert; —**ся назад** *v.* regress.

возвращающ/ий *a.* returning; —**ийся** *a.* returning, resurgent; —**ая конвекция** return convection; —**ая сила** restoring force.

возвращен/ие *n.* return; recovery; restoration, replacement; reversion; regression; back stroke (of piston); **в. в исходное положение** reset, return to normal; —**ный** *a.* returned; restored.

возвыш/ать, возвысить *v.* raise, elevate; —**ать в квадрат** (math.) square; —**аться** *v.* be raised; rise above; —**аться на** stand out against (a background).

возвышен/ие *n.* raising, elevation; rise, increase; —**ность** *f.* height, elevation, altitude; protuberance; prominence, mountain; upland; —**ный** *a.* elevated; raised, increased.

возгла/сить, —**шать** *v.* proclaim.

возгон *m.* sublimate; —**ка** *f.* sublimation; volatilization; —**очный** *a.* sublimation; —**яемость** *f.* sublimability; —**яемый,** —**яющийся** *a.* sublimable; volatilizable; —**ять,** —**яться** *v.* sublimate, sublime.

возгор/аемость *see* **воспламеняемость;** —**ание** *n.* inflammation, deflagration, flare up, ignition; —**ание люминесценции** rise of luminescence emission; **точка —ания** flash point; —**аться,** —**еться** *v.* ignite, deflagrate; —**ающийся** *a.* inflammable, ignitable, combustible.

воздвиг/ание *n.* erection, raising; —**ать,** —**нуть** *v.* erect, set up.

воздейств/ие *n.* influence, action, effect; attack; **(активное) в. на облака** cloud modification; **в. на погоду** weather control (or modification); —**овать** *v.* influence, act, affect; react, attack; —**ующий механизм** actuator; —**ующий сигнал** actuating signal.

воздерживаться *v.* refrain; decline.

воздух *m.* air; **в. жидкий** liquid air; **в. наружный, в. окружающий** ambient air; **в. отработанный** return air; **в. приземный** surface air; **в. при нормальных условиях** standard air; **в. пыльный** dust-laden air.

воздухо— *prefix* air.

воздуховыпускной кран air cock.

воздуходув/ка *f.* blower; **—ный** *a.* air-blowing, blast; **—ный мех** bellows; **—ный прибор** blast apparatus; **—ный счетчик** bellows meter; **—ная коробка** blast box; **—ная машина** blower, blowing machine, pressure blower; **—ная труба** (met.) blast pipe, tuyere pipe; **—ная установка** blower plant; blast apparatus.

воздухо/заборник *m.* air intake; **—измещение** *n.* air displacement; **—летательные аппараты** aircraft; **—мер** *m.* aerometer; **—мерия** *f.* aerometry, **—нагреватель** *m.* blast heater; **—непроницаемый** *a.* air-tight; **—отвод** *m.* drawoff; **—отсасывающий** *a.* exhaust; **—охладительный** *a.* air-cooling; **—охлаждаемый** *a.* air-cooled; **—очиститель** *m.* air purifier.

воздухоплав/ание *n.* aeronautics, aerostatics; **—атель** *m.* balloonist; **—ательный** *a.* aeronautical; aerostatic; **—ательное дело** aeronautics.

воздухо/подводящий *a.* air-supply, air-feed; **—провод** *m.* air-duct; flue; (met.) blast pipe; **—проводящий** *a.* air-conducting; **—разделительный аппарат** air-fractionating apparatus; **—сборник** *m.* air collector; **—уловитель** *m.* air trap.

воздухоэквивалентн/ый *a.* air-equivalent; **—ая камера** air-equivalent chamber.

воздушносухой *a.* air-dry.

воздушн/ый *a.* air, aerial, overhead; *see also* **воздухо—**; **в. ваттметр** air-flow wattmeter; **в. винт** air screw, propeller; **в. зазор** air gap; **в. конденсатор** air-speed capacitor; **в. ливень** air shower; **в. свет** air glow; **в. сердечник** air core; **в. трансформатор** air-core transformer; **в. шар** balloon; **—ая ионизационная камера** free-air ionization chamber; air-filled ionization chamber; **—ая масса фронтальной зоны** frontal air mass; **—ая разведка** aerial reconnaissance, airborne prospecting; **—ая съемка** aerial mapping, aerial surveying; **—ая яма** air pocket; **—ое лобовое сопротивление** air drag; **—ое сопло** air blast nozzle; **—ое тело** air mass; **—ое успокоение** air cushioning.

возить *v.* convey, transport.

возл/агать, —ожить *v.* lay, place.

возле *prep. gen.* beside, by, near, alongside.

возмещ/ать, возместить *v.* compensate; **—ение** *n.* compensation.

возможн/о *adv.* possibly, it is possible; it is likely; **—ость** *f.* potentiality; possibility, feasibility, opportunity; performance; **—ости** *pl.* resources, potentialities; **—ость выбора** option; **давать —ость** enable; **по —ости** as far as possible; **—ый** *a.* possible, feasible; available; virtual; **—ое перемещение** (mech.) virtual displacement; **принцип —ых перемещений** virtual work principle; **сделать все —ое** do one's utmost.

возмущ/ать, возмутить *v.* disturb, perturb; agitate; **—ающий** *a.* disturbing, perturbing; **—ающая сила** disturbing force; **—ающая функция** perturbation function.

возмущен/ие *n.* disturbance, perturbation; **магнитное в.** magnetic disturbance; **—ий теория** perturbation theory; **—ный** *a.* disturbed, perturbed; **—ное солнце** disturbed sun.

вознагражд/ать, вознаградить *v.* reward, compensate; **—ение** *n.* reward, remuneration, compensation.

возник/ание *see* **возникновение**; **—ать,** *see* **возникнуть**; **—ающий** *a.* originating, generated, rising (from); incipient; incremental.

возникн/овение *n.* formation, emergence; origin, origination, initiation, genesis; incipient formation, onset; **в. течения** (plast.) incipient yielding; **—уть** *v.* arise, appear, emerge, develop, originate, be initiated.

Возничий Auriga (Aur) (constellation).

возобнов/ить, —лять *v.* renew, resume, recommence; **—ление** *n.* renewal, restoration; resumption; **—ленный** *a.* renewed, restored; **—ляемый** *a.* renewable; **—ляющийся** *a.* regenerative.

возогнанный *a.* sublimated.

возраж/ать *v.* object, disapprove; **—ающий** *a.* objecting; **—ение** *n.* objection.

возраст *m.* age; **в. волны** wave age; **в. нейтрона** neutron age; **в. нейтронов по Ферми** Fermi age; **в. по радиоуглероду** radiocarbon age; **в. прилива** age of tide.

возраст/ание *n.* increase, rise, growth; **порядок —ания** ascending order; **—ать, —и** *v.* grow, increase; **—ающий** *a.* increasing, rising; **—ающий степенной ряд** ascending power series.

возрастн/ой, —ый *a.* age; **—ая теория** age theory; **—ое распределение** age distribution; **—ое уравнение** age-diffusion equation.

возрожд/ать, возродить *v.* regenerate; reactivate; **—аться** *v.* regenerate, revive; **—ающий** *a.* regenerative; **—ение** *n.* regeneration; reactivation; **—енный** *a.* regenerated; reactivated.

ВОИЗ *abbr.* (**Всесоюзное общество изобретателей**) All-Union Inventors' Society.

вой *m.* howl.

войлок *m.* felt.

вой/на *f.* war; **в. с применением ядерного (атомного) оружия** nuclear warfare, atomic warfare; **—ска** *pl.* troops.

войти *see* **входить.**

вокал *m.* vowel; **—ьный** *a.* vocal.

вокеленит *m.* vauquelinite.

вокодер *m.* vocoder.

вокруг *adv. and prep. gen.* round, around.

воксит *m.* vauxite.

волевой *a.* volitional.

Волк Lupus (Lup) (constellation).

волканит *m.* volcanite.

Волластона призма Wollaston prism.

волластонит *m.* wollastonite.

волн. *abbr.* (**волновой**) wave.

волна *f.* wave; **в. бегущая** traveling wave; **в. взрывная** detonation wave; **в. давления** pressure wave, compression wave; **в. модулированная импульсами** pulse-modulated wave; **в. несущая** carrier wave; **в. нормальная** (geo.) compressional wave; **в. перемагничивания** wave of magnetization; **в. перемещения** surge; **в. переходная** intermediate wave; **в. поверхностная** ground wave; **в. по оси X** X-wave; **в. приливная** tidal wave; **в. пространственная** sky wave.

волн/а разгрузки unloading wave, rarefaction wave; **в. разрежения** rarefaction wave, expansion wave; **в. расширения** wave of dilatation, dilatational wave; expansion wave, rarefaction wave; **в. световая** light wave; **в. сгущения** compressional wave; **в. сдвига** shear wave; **в. сжатия** compression wave; **в. сжатия-расширения** compressional-dilatational wave; **в. тяготения** gravity wave; **длина —ы** wavelength.

волнение *n.* agitation, disturbance; roughness; swell (of sea); **в. большое** high sea; **в. жестокое** precipitous sea; **в. легкое** slight sea (Douglas number 2); **в. сильное** very high sea.

волнин *m.* wolnyn.

волнист/ость *f.* undulation, ripple; corrugation; **—ый** *a.* undulating, wavy; sinuous; corrugated; crimped; (meteor.) undulatus; **—ые облака** undulatus, billow clouds.

волничность *f.* (elec.) ripple factor.

волновать *v.* agitate, disturb; **—ся** *v.* be agitated; wave, billow, surge.

волновод *m.* wave guide; **—ная ячейка** wave guide cell.

волнов/ой *a.* wave; **в. вектор** wave vector; propagation vector; **в. вибратор, в. диполь** wave dipole; **в. пакет** wave packet; **в. преобразователь** wave converter; **—ая аберрация** wave aberration; **—ая антенна** wave antenna; **—ая механика** wave mechanics; **—ая оптика** physical optics; **—ая проводимость** characteristic admittance, surge admittance; **—ая функция** wave function; **—ое сопротивление** (hyd.) wave resistance (or drag); (aero.) wave drag; (elec.) characteristic (or wave) impedance; **—ое уравнение** wave equation; **—ое число** wave number.

волново-корпускулярный дуализм wave-particle duality.

волно/лом *m.* breakwater; **—мер** *m.*

ondometer, wavemeter; —**мерный прибор** wave recorder.

волнообраз/ный *a.* wavy, undulating; —**ная обмотка** (elec.) wave winding; —**ователь** *m.* (rad.) oscillator.

волно/отвод *m.* breakwater; —**повышающий** *a.* (rad.) booster; —**прибойный** *a.* wave-cut; —**прибойные знаки** ripple marks; —**рез** *m.* breakwater; —**стойкий** *a.* surgeproof; —**формующая схема** wave-shaping circuit.

волны материи matter waves; **в. метровые** ultrashort waves, meter waves.

волокнисто— *prefix* fiber, fibro—.

волокнисто/образный *a.* fibroid; —**пористый** *a.* fibroporous; —**сть** *f.* fibrousness, fibrous structure; —**эластичный** fibroelastic.

волокн/истый *a.* fibrous, filamentary; **в. агрегат** (geo.) columnar aggregate; —**о** *n.* fiber, filament, thread; **нейтральное —о** (elast.) neutral fiber (or line).

воломит *m.* wolomite (tungsten alloy).

Волопас Bootes (Boo) (constellation).

волос *m.*, —**ы** *pl.* hair.

волосн/ой *a.* hair; capillary; **в. гигрометр** hair hygrometer; **в. гидрометр** hair hydrometer; —**ая пружина** hair spring; —**ая трубка** capillary tube; —**ость** *f.* capillarity; **действие —ости** capillary action.

волосо/видный *a.* hairlike; capillary; —**вина** *f.* fine crack, hairline; —**к** *m.* hair; filament, fiber; hairline; catwhisker.

Волосы Вероники Coma Berenices (Com) (constellation).

волосяной *a.* hair; capillary; **в. гигрометр** (meteor.) hair hygrometer; **в. канал** capillary duct.

волоч/ение *n.* dragging, drag; traction; drawing (of wire); **ось —ения** drag axis; —**енный** *a.* dragged; drawn.

волочильн/ый *a.* drawing; **в. глазок**, —**ое очко** draw hole; **в. станок** draw bench, wire-drawing machine; —**ая доска** draw plate; —**ая матрица** drawing die; —**я** *f.* draw plate.

волоч/ить, —**ь** *v.* draw (wire); prolong.

волчок *m.* (spinning) top; gyroscope.

вольн/о *adv.* freely; —**ость** *f.* freedom; —**ый** *a.* free.

вольт *m.* volt (v).

вольта/ж *m.* voltage; —**ический** *a.* voltaic; —**метр** *m.* voltameter; —**метрический** *a.* voltametric; —**скоп** *m.* voltascope.

вольтампер *m.* volt-ampere (va); —**метр** *m.* voltammeter; —**ная характеристика** volt-ampere characteristic, current-voltage characteristic.

Вольта эффект (явление) Volta effect.

Вольтерра Volterra; **В. уравнение** (math.) V. integral equation.

вольтметр *m.* voltmeter; **в. амплитудный** peak voltmeter, crest voltmeter; **в. ламповый** vacuum-tube voltmeter; **в. тепловой** hot-wire voltmeter.

вольтов столб voltaic pile; —**а дуга** voltaic arc, electric arc; —**ый** *a.* volt, voltage.

вольто/добавочная машина booster; —**мметр** *m.* voltohmyst; —**понижающая электрическая машина** negative booster; —**трансформатор** *m.* (voltage) transformer.

вольтцит *m.* voltzite.

Вольфа/-Райе звезда Wolf-Rayet star; **В. число** W. (sunspot) number.

вольфахит *m.* wolfachite.

вольфрам *m.* tungsten, wolfram (W).

вольфрамат *m.* tungstate.

вольфрамит *m.* wolframite.

вольфрамо— *prefix* tungsten.

вольфрамов/ый *a.* tungsten, tungstic; —**ая лампа** tungsten lamp; —**ая нить накала** tungsten filament; —**ая сталь** tungsten steel.

вольфсбергит *m.* wolfsbergite.

вольфтонит *m.* wolftonite.

волюм/енометр *m.* volumenometer; —**етр,** —**инометр,** —**метр,** —**ометр** *m.* volumeter; —**етрический** *a.* volumetric.

воля *f.* will; freedom, liberty

вонз/ать, —**ить** *v.* thrust.

вон/ь *f.* stench; —**ючий** *a.* malodorous; —**ять** *v.* have a bad odor.

вообра/жаемый *a.* imaginary, fictitious; **в. источник** image source; **в. поток** fictitious flow; —**жать,** —**зить** *v.* imagine, visualize, conceive, figure;

—жение *n.* imagination, idea; **—женный** *a.* imaginary, virtual, image, assumed; **—зимый** *a.* imaginable.
вообще *adv.* in general, generally, on the whole; broadly; at all; **в. не** not at all.
воодушев/ить, —лять *v.* inspire; **—ление** *n.* enthusiasm, inspiration.
ВООМП *abbr.* (**Всесоюзное объединение оптико-механической промышленности**) All-Union Optical Equipment Industry Association.
вооруж/ать, —ить *v.* arm; outfit; **—ение** *n.* armament; fitting out; **—енный** *a.* armed; fitted out.
во-первых *adv.* first, firstly, in the first place.
вопло/тить, —щать *v.* embody.
вопр. *abbr.* (**вопросы**) problems (e.g. **Вопросы физики** — Problems of Physics).
вопреки *prep. dat.* in spite of, despite, regardless of; contrary to.
вопрос *m.* question; problem; **под —ом** undecided; **—ительный** *a.* interrogative; **—ительный знак** question mark; **—ник** *m.* questionnaire.
ворваться *see* **врываться.**
воробьевит *m.* worobieffeite, vorobyevite.
Ворон Corvus (Crv) (constellation).
ворон/еный *a.* burnished, polished; browned; blued; **—еная сталь** blue steel; **—ить** *v.* (met.) burnish; brown; bronze; blue.
воронк/а *f.* funnel; hopper; crater; eddy; **в. депрессии** cone of influence (of well); **капельная в.** drop funnel; **—ообразный** *a.* funnel-shaped; cone-shaped; **—ообразное облако** funnel cloud.
ворот *m.* windlass, winch.
ворота *pl.* gate(s); **в. шлюза** lock gate.
ворот/ило *n.* mill handle; **—ить** *v.* recall; **—иться** *v.* return.
воротник *m.* collar, flange, lip.
воротный *a.* gate; windlass, winch.
ворох *m.* heap, pile.
ворочать *v.* turn, roll; **—ся** *v.* turn, rotate.
ворошить *v.* stir, disturb.
вортекс *m.* vortex.
восемнадцат/ый *a.* eighteenth; **—ь** eighteen.
восемь eight; **—десят** eighty; **—сот** eight hundred.
воск *m.* wax; **—овка** *f.* tracing paper; **—овой** *a.* wax, waxy; **—овая бумага** tracing paper; wax paper; **—ообразный, —оподобный** *a.* waxlike, waxy.
воскресенье *n.* Sunday.
воспаленный *a.* inflamed.
воспит/ание *n.* education, training; **—ательный** *a.* educational; **—ать, —ывать** *v.* bring up, educate.
воспламенен/ие *n.* ignition, combustion; setting fire to; **проба на в.** flash test; **камера —ия** combustion chamber; **температура —ия, точка —ия** flash point; ignition point, kindling point.
воспламен/итель *m.* igniter, ignition device; **—ить, —ять** *v.* ignite, **—иться, —яться** ignite; **—яемость** *f.* combustibility, inflammation; **—яемый, —яющийся** *a.* combustible, inflammable.
восполн/ить, —ять *v.* fill in, make up, complete.
воспользоваться *v.* take advantage of, use, employ.
воспомин/ание *n.* recollection; **—ания** *pl.* memoirs; **—ать** *v.* remember, recollect.
воспрепятствовать *v.* hinder, prevent.
воспре/тительный *a.* prohibitive; **—тить, —щать** *v.* prohibit, **—щение** *n.* prohibition.
восприимчив/ость *f.* susceptibility, sensitivity; **магнитная в.** magnetic susceptibility; **—ый** *a.* susceptible, receptive, sensitive.
восприн/имаемость *f.* perceptibility; **—имаемый** *a.* perceptible, discernible; **—имать, —ять** *v.* take, receive; absorb; perceive; **—имающий элемент** sensing element (or unit), sensor.
восприят/ие *n.* perception; receiving; **коэффициент —ия** coefficient of perception.
воспроизв/едение *see* **воспроизводство**; **—еденный** *a.* reproduced; **—ести** *see* **воспроизводить.**
воспроиз-во *abbr.* (**воспроизводство**) reproduction, breeding.
воспроизвод/имость *f.* reproducibility,

restoration; —**имый** *a.* reproducible; —**ительный** *a.* reproductive, reproducing; —**ить** *v.* reproduce.

воспроизводств/о *n.* reproduction; (nucl.) breeding, conversion, regeneration; **в. расщепляющегося материала** breeding of fissionable material; **в. ядерного топлива** nuclear fuel reproduction, nuclear fuel breeding; —**а коэффициент** (nucl.) conversion ratio; breeding ratio; reproduction factor.

воспроизводящий материал breeder material; **в. реактор** breeding reactor, breeder.

воспротив/иться, —**ляться** *v.* oppose, resist; —**ление** *n.* resistance.

воссоедин/ение *n.* recombination; —**ения коэффициент** recombination coefficient; —**ять,** —**яться** *v.* recombine.

воссозда/вать *v.* reconstruct; —**ние** *n.* reconstruction.

восставить перпендикуляр erect a perpendicular.

восстанавлив/аемость *see* **восстановляемость**; —**аемый** *a.* reducible; —**ать** *v.* reduce; reestablish, restore; regenerate, recover; erect (a perpendicular); set up; —**ающий** *a.* restoring; —**ающийся** *a.* reducible; recovering, recovery; —**ающая сила** restoring force.

восстание *n.* rise; uprising.

восстанов/имость *f.* reducibility; —**имый** *see* **восстановляемый**; —**итель** *m.* reducing agent, reductant; regenerator, restorer.

восстановительн/ый *a.* reducing, reduction; regenerating, reactivating, restoration; —**ая атмосфера** reducing atmosphere; —**ая способность** reducing power; —**ое время** recovery time; —**ые работы** recovery.

восстановить *see* **восстанавливать.**

восстановлен/ие *n.* reduction; recovery, regeneration, recuperation, restoration, re-establishment, reconstruction; restitution; **в. водородом** hydrogen reduction; **в. импульсов** pulse regeneration; **в. совместное** coreduction; **коэффициент** —**ия** (mech.) coefficient of restitution; —**ный** *a.* reduced; restored; recovered; —**ное состояние** reduced state.

восстановл/яемость *f.* reducibility; —**яемый,** —**яющийся** *a.* reducible; —**ять** *see* **восстанавливать**; —**яющий** *see* **восстановительный.**

вост. *abbr.* (**восточный**) east, eastern, easterly.

восток *m.* east.

востор/г *m.* enthusiasm; —**женный** *a.* enthusiastic, zealous.

восточн/о-западный эффект east-west effect; —**ый** *a.* east, eastern, easterly; —**ая долгота** east longitude; —**ое поясное время** Eastern Standard Time.

востребовани/е *n.* claiming; **до** —**я** general delivery.

восхо/д *m.* rise, ascent; —**дить** *v.* rise, ascend; go back to (time); —**дящий** *a.* rising, ascending, anabatic; upward; uptake (flue); —**дящий поток** ascending current, updraft, upcurrent, upgust; —**дящий узел** (astr.) ascending node; —**ждение** *n.* ascent; (cryst.) climb.

восьмер/ичный *a.* octuple, octal; —**ка,** —**о** eight; figure eight.

восьми— *prefix* oct—, octa—, octo—, eight.

восьми/валентный *a.* octavalent; —**гранник** *m.* octahedron; —**гранный** *a.* octahedral; —**десятый** *a.* eightieth; —**кратный** *a.* octuple; —**летний** *a.* octennial; —**угольник** *m.* octagon; —**угольный** *a.* octagonal; —**штырьковый цоколь** octal base.

восьмой *a.* eighth.

вот *adv.* there, here; there is, here is.

воткнуть *see* **втыкать.**

вохейнит *m.* wocheinite.

вощ/анка *f.* wax paper; wax cloth; —**аной,** —**аный** *a.* wax, waxed; —**ение** *n.* waxing; —**еный** *a.* waxed; —**еная бумага** wax paper; —**ить** *v.* wax.

воющий тон howling tone.

впад/ать *v.* fall in; flow, discharge; —**ающий** *a.* falling into; flowing into, inflowing; —**ение** *n.* inflow; mouth (of river); —**ение в синхронизм** lock-in; —**ина** *f.* hollow, cavity, depression, dent, indentation; trough, recess, notch; lowland;

—ина волны wave trough; **—истый** *a.* full of cavities.

впаив/ание *n.*, **впай** *m.*, **впайка** *f.* soldering in, sealing in; **—ать** *v.* solder in, seal in.

впал/ость *f.* hollowness; **—ый** *a.* hollow, sunken.

впасть *see* **впадать.**

впаять *see* **впаивать.**

впервые *adv.* first, for the first time.

вперед *adv.* on, forward, ahead, henceforth; first; **взад и в.** back and forth; **движение в.** advance, progress; **идущий в.** advancing, progressive; **ход в.** forward running; forward stroke.

впереди *adv.* in front, in advance, ahead; *prep. gen.* in front of, before.

вперекрой, вперекрышку, *see* **внахлестку.**

вперемежку *see* **попеременно.**

впечатл/ение *n.* impression; **—ительность** *f.* impressibility; **—ительный** *a.* sensitive, susceptible.

впивать *v.* absorb.

впис/анный угол inscribed angle; **—ывать** *v.* record, inscribe.

впит/анный *a.* absorbed; **—ать, —ывать** *v.* absorb; **—аться** *v.* be absorbed, soak in; **—ывание** *n.* absorption; **—ывающий** *a.* absorbent, absorbing; **—ывающий в себя** absorptive; **—ь** *see* **впивать.**

впих/ать, —ивать, —нуть *v.* push in, cram in.

вплав/ить, —лять *v.* fuse in; **—ленный контакт** (semicond.) alloyed junction, diffused junction.

впластов/анный *a.* imbedded; interbedded; interstratified; **—ываться** *v.* be imbedded; interbed; interstratify.

вплет/ание, —ение *n.* interweaving, intertwining; implication; **—ать, вплести** *v.* interweave, intertwine, interlace; splice in; implicate, involve; **—енный** *a.* interwoven, interlaced; implicated, involved.

вплотную *adv.* close, closely; **в. к** up against, close to.

вплоть *adv.* up to, till; close; **в. до** (right) up to, down to.

вполне *adv.* fully, entirely, totally, quite; **в. возможно** it may well be; **в. законно** fully valid; **в. упорядоченный** (math.) well-ordered; **не в.** incompletely, under, sub—.

вполовину *adv.* half.

вполу/накрой, —нахлест, —нахлестку *adv.* half-lap.

впопад *adv.* timely, apropos.

впопыхах *adv.* hurriedly.

впоследствии *adv.* subsequently, later.

впотай *adv.* flush, even; **головка в.** countersunk head; **клепка в.** flush riveting; **углубление в.** countersinking.

вправ/ить, —лять *v.* adjust, insert.

вправо *adv.* to the right, clockwise; **вращающийся в.** dextrorotatory; **вращение в.** clockwise rotation.

впредь *adv.* henceforth, in future.

впрессованный *a.* pressed in, imbedded.

впритык *adv.* flush, end to end; **накладка в.** butt; **сваривать в.** butt weld; **сварка в.** butt welding; **соединение в., сращивание в.** butt joint.

впрочем *adv.* however; otherwise; besides.

впрыг/ивать, —нуть *v.* jump in.

впрыск *m.*, **—ивание** *n.*, **—ивательный** *a.* injection.

впрыскив/ать, впрыскать *v.* inject, spray in; **—ающий** *a.* injecting, spray; **—ающий холодильник** jet condenser; **—ающее сопло** spray nozzle.

впрыснут/ый *a.* injected; **—ь** *see* **впрыскивать.**

впуск *m.* intake, inlet, inflow; admission; **в. воздуха** air intake; **ход —а** admission stroke, instroke; **—ать** *v.* admit.

впускн/ой *a.* admission, entrance, intake, inlet; **в. канал** inlet (or admission port); **в. клапан** inlet valve, intake valve; **в. конец** feed end; **—ая труба** feed pipe, intake pipe; **—ое окно** entrance window; **—ое отверстие** inlet, intake.

впустить *see* **впускать.**

впустую *adv.* to no purpose.

впут/анный *a.* implicated, involved; **—ать, —ывать** *v.* implicate, involve; **—аться, —ываться** *v.* be mixed up with, be entangled; interfere.

впущенный *a.* admitted, let in, injected.
впятеро *adv.* five times (as many).
вразбежку *adv.* alternately; **размещение в.** staggering; **расположенный в.** staggered, alternated.
вразбро/д *adv.* separately, disunitedly; **—с** *adv.* scattered, haphazard.
вразвилку *adv.* forked, pronged; **ось в.** forked axle.
вразрез *adv.* contrarily, in opposition.
вразум/ительность *f.* comprehensibility; **—ительный** *a.* comprehensible, intelligible; **—ить, —лять** *v.* teach, convince.
врасплох *adv.* unexpectedly.
врассыпную *adv.* in all directions; helter-skelter.
враст/ание *n.* growing in; intergrowth, interlocking; **—ать, —и** *v.* grow in; intergrow, interlock; **—ающий** *a.* ingrowing; interlocking.
врастяжку *adv.* at full length.
врасщеп *adv.* split, forked; **сварка в.** split welding, fork welding, V-welding.
врач *m.* doctor, surgeon, physician; **—ебный** *a.* medical.
вращаемый *a.* rotatable.
вращатель *m.* rotator; **—но-колебательная полоса** vibration-rotation band.
вращательн/ый *a.* rotational; rotary, rotatory; **в. магнитный гистерезис** rotary magnetic hysteresis; **в. приливный поток** rotary tidal current; **—ая дисперсия** dispersion of the rotation; **—ая линия** rotational line; **—ая релаксация** rotational relaxation; **—ое движение** rotary motion, orbital motion; gyration; **—ое квантовое число** rotational quantum number; **—ые спектры** band spectra.
вращать *v.* revolve, rotate, turn; circulate; **—ся** *v.* revolve, rotate, turn, gyrate.
вращающ/ий *a.* rotating, spinning; **в. анемометр** rotary anemometer; **в. момент** torque; **—ая пара** force couple; **—ая сила** rotary force, angular force; **—ая способность** rotatory power; **—ая среда** rotatory medium; **—ее зеркало** rotating mirror; **—ийся** *a.*, **вращаясь** rotary, rotatory, rotating, revolving; spinning; turning, gyrating; swivel; pivoted; **—ийся влево** levorotatory, rotating counterclockwise; **—ийся вправо** dextrorotatory; rotating clockwise; **—ийся поршень** impeller (of pump); **—ийся стол** turntable; **—ийся электрон** spinning electron; **—аяся волна** rotary wave; **—аяся сила** rotatory power.
вращен/ие *n.* rotation, rotary motion, revolution, revolving, turning, roll, gyration, spin; pivoting; circulation (of liquid); **в. в левую сторону, левое вращение** levorotation, counterclockwise rotation; backing (of wind); **в. в правую сторону, правое вращение** dextrorotation, clockwise rotation; veering (of wind); **круговое в.** revolution; **в. перигелия** rotation of the perihelion; **момент —ия** torque; **точка —ия** pivot, fulcrum.
вред *m.* damage, injury; **—ить** *v.* damage, injure, impair; **—но** *adv.* harmfully; it is harmful; **—ность** *f.* damage, injury; harmfulness.
вредн/ый *a.* harmful, injurious, poisonous; noxious (gas); **в. захват** capture by "poisons"; **—ая емкость** stray capacitance; **—ая примесь в люминофоре** phosphor poison; **—ая связь** spurious coupling; **—ое биологическое воздействие** biological damage; **—ое излучение** harmful radiation; **—ое поглощение нейтронов** neutron poisoning; **—ое пространство** idle space, dead space; clearance.
вредоносн/ый *see* **вредный**; **—ые испарения** noxious vapors.
врез/ание *n.* incision, gash, notch; **—анный** *a.* incised, notched; serrated; **—ать, —ывать** *v.* cut in; **—ка** *f.* cutting in, engraving; setting in; **—ной** *a.* cut in; fit in, set in.
временн/ик *m.* annals; **—о** *adv.* temporarily; **—ой** *a.* time, temporal; **—ой анализатор** time-delay analyzer; **—ой режим** time behavior; **—ой ход** time dependence; **—оподобный** *a.* timelike; **—ость** *f.* temporariness.
временн/ый *a.* temporary, tentative; intermittent, transient; **в. контакт** intermittent contact; **в. подъем**

transient rise; **—ая вариация** time variation; **—ое затишье** lull; **—ое сопротивление** ultimate strength (or resistance); **—ое уравнение** time-dependent equation.

врем/я *n.* time; interval, period; **в. восстановления** recovery time; **в. выдерживания** storage (or holdup) time; (nucl.) decay (or cooling) time; **в. выдержки, в. задержки** time lag; delay time; **в. высвечивания** decay time, de-excitation time; lifetime (of radiation); **в. года** season; **в. жизни** lifetime; **в. замедления** slowing-down time; **в. запаздывания** time lag, lag time; **в. запуска** starting time; **в. затухания** decay time, damping time; **в. импульсная модуляция** pulse-time modulation; **в. круговорота** life cycle; **в. нагрева** warm-up time; **в. нарастания** rise time; **в. нечувствительности** dead time; **в. ограничения** clipping time; **в. отклика** response time; **в. отключения** clearing time.

врем/я *cont.*, **в. перемещения** transit time; **в. поколения** generation time; **в. полной фазы** (astr.) totality; **в. прихода** arrival time; **в. пробега** time of travel, traveling time; transit time; **в. пролета** transit time; time of flight; **в. пропускания, в. прохождения** transit time; **в. разрешения** resolving time; **в. релаксации** relaxation time; **в. сбора** collecting time; **в. свободного пробега** mean free time; **в. собирания** collection time; **в. спада, в. спадания** decay time; **в. срабатывания** actuation time, operating time, response time, opening time; **в. съемки** time of exposure; **в. торможения** stopping time; **в. успокоения** relaxation time; transient time; **в. установления** transient period, time constant; settling time, stabilization time; **—ени подобный** *see* **временноподобный; —ени постоянная** time constant.

врем/я *cont.*, **в настоящее в.** at present, now; **во в.** in time, at the right time; during, while; **в. от времени** from time to time; **в свое в.** at one time; in due time; **все в.** consistently; **в то в. как** whereas; **в это же в.** at the same time; **за в.** during; **за последнее в.** lately, recently; **на в.** for a while; **на некоторое в.** for some time, for a while; **неопределенное в.** indefinitely; **до недавнего —ени** until recently; **к тому —ени** by then, by that time; **по —енам** at times; **со —енем** in time, in due time; **тем —енем** meanwhile.

времяисчисление *n.* chronology, calendar.

вровень *adv.* level (with), flush.

вроде *prep. gen.* like, such as.

врожденн/ость *f.* innateness; **—ый** *a.* innate, inherent, native, natural.

врозь *adv.* apart, separately.

вронскиан *m.*, **определитель или детерминант Вронского** Wronskian.

вруб *m.* cut, notch, channel; **—ать, —ить** *v.* cut in; groove, notch; **—ка** *f.* cut, notch; grooving; **соединять —кой** *v.* mortise; **—ленный** *a.* cut in, notched, grooved.

врубовой *a.* chopping, cutting; **в. молот** pickax, pick.

вруч/ать, —ить *v.* give, deliver, entrust; **—ение** *n.* committing, entrusting.

вручную *adv.* manually; **откованный в.** hand-forged; **подача в.** hand feed, manual feed; **приводимый в.** hand-operated, manual; **сделанный в.** handmade.

вры/вать, —ть *v.* dig in; **—ваться** *v.* burst in.

вряд ли *adv.* scarcely, hardly.

всадить *see* **всаживать.**

всаж/енный *a.* set in, imbedded; planted; **—ивать** *v.* set in, imbed, thrust, plunge, drive in; plant.

всасыв/аемость *f.* absorbability; **—аемый** *a.* absorbable; suction; **—ание** *n.* suction; intake; **—ать** *v.* draw in; absorb.

всасывающ/ий *a.* suction, pull; absorbing, absorptive; intake; **в. вентилятор** suction fan, exhaust fan; **в. клапан** suction valve, inlet valve; **в. насос** suction pump; **в. ход** admission stroke; **—ая сила** suction force; **—ая система** exhaust system; **—ая**

склянка suction bottle; **—ая способность** absorptivity; **—ая труба** suction pipe; **—ее действие** suction; **—ее окно, —ее устройство** intake.

все *n. of* **весь**; *pl.* all, everybody, everyone.

все *adv.* always, all the time; (ever) increasingly; **в. (еще)** still; **в. же** nevertheless; **в. лишь** at most; **в.-таки** nevertheless.

все— *prefix* omni—, pan—, all.

всевозможный *a.* every kind of, all kinds of.

всеволнов/ой, —ый *a.* wide-range, all-wave; **—ый счетчик** long (flat, flat-response) counter.

всегда *adv.* always.

ВСЕГИНГЕО *abbr.* (**Всесоюзный научно-исследовательский институт гидрогеологии и инженерной геологии**) All-Union Scientific Research Institute of Hydrology and Engineering Geology.

всего *gen. of* **весь;** *adv.* in all; only.

вседневный *a.* daily, everyday, common.

вселен/ная *f.* universe, world; **—ский** *a.* universal.

всем *see* **весь.**

всемерн/о *adv.* in every possible way; **—ый** *a.* of every kind.

всемеро *adv.* seven times; **—м** *adv.* seven (together).

всемирн/ый *a.* universal; worldwide; **—ое время** universal time (U.T.), Greenwich time; **—ое тяготение** universal gravitation.

все/направленный *a.* omnidirectional; **—народный** *a.* national, nation-wide; **—общий** *a.* common, general, universal; **—объемлющий** *a.* universal; **—охватывающий** *a.* comprehensive; **—проникающий** *a.* highly penetrating, pervasive.

всероссийский *a.* All-Russian.

всес. *abbr. see* **всесоюзный.**

всесоюзный *a.* All-Union.

Всестандартком *abbr.* (**Всесоюзный комитет по стандартизации**) All-Union Committee for Standardization.

всесторонн/ий *a.* thorough, comprehensive; manifold; uniform, isotropic; omnidirectional; **—ее комплексное изучение** comprehensive study; **—ее сжатие** hydrostatic stress (pressure).

всецел/о *adv.* completely; **—ый** *a.* complete, entire.

всечасн/о *adv.*, **—ый** *a.* every hour.

вскакивать *v.* spring up.

вскальзыв/ание *n.* slipping in; **—ать** *v.* slip in, slide in.

вскип/ание *n.* boiling up; effervescence; **—ать, —еть** *v.* boil up; effervesce; **—ающий** *a.* boiling up; effervescing; **—ятить** *v.* bring to a boil; **—ятиться** *v.* come to a boil.

всколых/ать, —нуть, всколебать *v.* stir up.

всколькз/нуть *see* **вскальзывать;** **—ь** *adv.* casually.

вскопанный *a.* dug up.

вскоре *adv.* soon, shortly after.

вскочить *see* **вскакивать.**

вскры/вать, —ть *v.* open; find out, reveal; dissect; **—тие** *n.* opening; discovery; dissection; **—тый** *a.* opened; revealed, discovered.

вслед *prep.* after; **в. за** following; **—ствие** *prep. gen.* in consequence of, owing to, by virtue of.

вслепую *adv.* blindly.

вслуш/аться, —иваться *v.* listen.

всматриваться, всмотреться *v.* scrutinize.

ВСНИТО *abbr.* (**Всесоюзный совет научно-инженерно-технических обществ**) All-Union Council of Scientific Engineering and Technical Societies.

всовывать *v.* slip in, thrust in.

всос/анный *a.* sucked in; absorbed; **—ать** *see* **всасывать.**

вспенив/ание *n.* foaming, frothing; **—ать, вспенить** *v.* froth, foam; **—аться** *v.* froth; **—ающий** *a.* frothing; **—ающее средство** frothing agent.

всплес/к *m.* splash; (rad. astr.) burst; **в. излучения** burst (flash of light); **в. на импульсах** pulse spike; **большой в.** (rad. astr.) outburst; **—кивание** *n.* splashing; **—кивать, —нуть** *v.* splash.

всплош/ную, —ь *adv.* without interruption, in quick succession.

всплыв/ание *n.* floating up, emersion, buoyancy; **—ать** *v.* float up, come to the surface, come to light, emerge; **—ающий** *a.* supernatant; **—ной** *a.* floating; **—ной процесс** flotation process; **—ная сила** buoyant force.

всплыт/ие *see* **всплывание**; **—ый** *a.* floated; **—ь** *see* **всплывать.**

всполз/ание *n.* creeping; **—ать** *v.* creep.

вспом/инать, —нить *v.* recall, remember.

вспомогательн/ый *a.* auxiliary, accessory, subsidiary, branch; booster; relief, emergency, spare; **в. агрегат, —ое устройство** booster; **в. анод** relieving anode; **в. двигатель** auxiliary motor; **в. материал** accessory material; **в. насос** booster pump; **в. передатчик** satellite transmitter; **—ая несущая** subcarrier; **—ая схема** accessory circuit; **—ая установка** branch (establishment); **—ая функция** auxiliary function; **—ая часть** accessory; **—ое оборудование** auxiliary equipment; **—ое предложение** lemma; **—ое приспособление** attachment; **—ые принадлежности** appurtenances.

вспрыг/ивать, —нуть *v.* jump up.

вспрыс/кивание *n.* sprinkling, injection; **—кивать, —нуть** *v.* sprinkle, inject.

вспух/ать, —нуть *v.* swell; **—лый** *a.* swollen.

вспуч/енный *a.* swollen, distended; **—ивание** *n.* distention, bulging, swelling, expanding; (geo.) heaving; **—ивать, —ить** *v.* swell, distend; **—ивающий** *a.* swelling; heaving.

вспых/ивание *see* **вспышка**; **—ивать, —нуть** *v.* flash, flare up, deflagrate; **—ивающий** *a.* flashing, flaring; deflagrating.

вспышк/а *f.* flash, scintillation; flare-up; (astr.) (solar) flare; outburst (of nova); burst (of cosmic rays); **в. ионизации** burst of ionization; **тепловая в.** thermal spike; **момент —и** ignition point; **проба на —у** flash test; **сгорание со —ой** deflagration; **температура —и, точка —и** flash point.

встав/ить *see* **вставлять**; **—ка** *f.* insertion; mounting; fuse; **—ление** *n.* insertion, introduction, installation; **—ленный** *a.* inserted; mounted; **—лять** *v.* insert, set in, introduce into, fit in; **—ной** *a.* inserted, insertion; **—ная катушка** plug-in coil.

встретить *see* **встречать.**

встреч/а *f.* encounter, meeting; **в. дискретная** discrete encounter; **—ать** *v.* meet, encounter, find; **—аться** *v.* meet, coincide; be found, occur; **линия —и** line of impact; **точка —и** contact point.

встречно-включенные катушки opposing coils; **в.-параллельный** antiparallel.

встречн/ый *a.* contrary, counter, opposed, encountered; **в. ветер** head wind; **в. годограф** (seis.) counter travel-time curve; **в. поток** counter-current, counterflow; **в. ток** counter-current, reverse current; **—ая диффузия** interdiffusion; **—ое излучение** counterradiation; **—ое приливное течение** countertide; **—ое смешанное возбуждение** differential compound excitation; **—ое течение** countertide, counterflow.

встроенный *a.* built in, imbedded.

встряхив/ание *n.*, **встряска** *f.* shaking (up); **—атель** *m.* scrambler, shaker; **—ать, встряхнуть** *v.* shake; **—ающий** *a.* shaking.

вступ/ать, —ить *v.* enter; **—ающий** *a.* entering, incoming; **—ительный** *a.* introductory, ingoing; **—ление** *n.* entry, entrance; introduction; preface.

встык *adv.* butt; **приделанный в.** butted; **сваренный в.** butt-welded; **сваривать в.** butt-weld; **сварка в.** butt welding; **соединение в.** butt joint.

всунут/ый *a.* put in, inserted; **—ь** *see* **всовывать.**

всухую *adv.* dry; **шлифовать в.** dry grind.

всход *m.* ascent, rise; **—ить** *v.* mount, ascend.

всып/ание *n.*, **—ка** *f.* filling, pouring in (dry material); **—анный** *a.* poured in; **—ать** *v.* fill with, pour in; **—ной** *a.* pouring.

всюду *adv.* everywhere; **в. плотный** *a.* (math.) everywhere dense.

вся *f. of* **весь**; **—кий** *a. and pron.* any, every; anyone, everyone; **на —кий случай** to make sure, just in case; **—чески** *adv.* in every possible way; **—ческий** *a.* of every kind.

вт *abbr.* (**ватт**) watt (w); (**вторник**) Tuesday.

втайне *adv.* secretly, confidentially.

вталкив/ание *n.* pushing in, forcing in; **—ать, —аться** *v.* push in, force in.

втек/ание *n.* inflow, influx; **—ать** *v.* flow in; **—ающий** *a.* inflowing.

втереть *see* **втирать.**

втеч/ение *see* **втекание**; **—ь** *see* **втекать.**

ВТИ *abbr.* [**Всесоюзный теплотехнический институт (им Ф. Дзержинского)**] F. Dzerzhinskii All-Union Heat Engineering Institute.

втирать *v.* rub in.

втис/кать, —кивать, —нуть *v.* squeeze in, force in.

втолкнуть *see* **вталкивать.**

вторг/ание *n.* invasion; **—аться, —нуться** *v.* encroach upon, impinge; invade; **—ающийся** *a.* (geo.) intrusive, incoming.

вторжение *n.* intrusion; invasion; (geo.) irruption; surge.

вторично *adv.* a second time, again; re—; secondary; **в.-квантованный** *a.* second-quantized; **в.-электронный катод, в.-эмитирующий электрод** dynode; **в. электронный ток** secondary-electron current, dynode current.

вторичн/ый *a.* secondary, second-order; re—; **в. продукт** secondary material, afterproduct; **в. реактор** secondary reactor, power pile; **в. спектр** secondary spectrum; **в. электрон** secondary electron; **в. элемент** secondary cell; **—ая ионизация** secondary ionization; **—ая нарезка** rethreading; **—ая обмотка** secondary winding; **—ая реакция** secondary reaction, second-order reaction; **—ая частица** secondary particle; **—ой эмиссии коэффициент** secondary emission coefficient; **—ое зажигание** reignition; **—ое замерзание** regelation; **—ое излучение** secondary radiation; **—ое квантование** second quantization; **—ое квантовое число** secondary quantum number; **—ое столкновение** secondary collision; **—ое ядро** product nucleus; **—ые нейтроны деления** fission neutrons.

вторник *m.* Tuesday.

втор/ой *a.* second; **в. звук** second sound; **—ого порядка** of second order; **—ая радуга** secondary rainbow; **—ая стадия ползучести** secondary creep; **—ое квантование** second quantization; **—ые соседи** second nearest neighbors; **во —ых** secondly.

второклассный *a.* second-class, secondary.

второ/разрядный, —сортный *a.* inferior, second-rate; **—сортная руда** (min.) seconds; **—степенный** *a.* secondary, minor, subsidiary.

втро/е *adv.* triply, threefold; **—ем** *adv.* three (together); **—йне** *adv.* threefold.

вт-с, вт-сек, втсек *abbr.* [**ватт-секунда (джоуль)**] watt-second (joule).

ВТТИ *abbr.* (**Всесоюзный трест точной индустрии**) All-Union Precision Instrument Industry Trust.

ВТУ *abbr.* (**высшее техническое училище**) Higher Technical School.

втуз *abbr.* (**высшее техническое учебное заведение**) engineering college, institute of technology.

втул/ка *f.*, **—очный** *a.* bushing, sleeve, collar; plug, insert; hub (of wheel); **—очный ключ** socket wrench; **—очный подшипник** bush bearing; **—очная муфта** sleeve coupling.

вт-ч *abbr.* (**ватт-час**) watt-hour.

в т. ч. *abbr.* (**в том числе**) among them.

втыкать *v.* thrust into, drive into.

втя/гивание *n.* drawing in, pulling in, suction; **—гивать, —нуть** *v.* draw in, pull in, suck in; absorb; implicate, involve; **—гиваться, —нуться** *v.* become accustomed to.

втяжной сердечник plunger (of electromagnet); **в. электромагнит** plunger electromagnet.

втянутый *a.* drawn in, pulled in, sucked in.

ВУ *abbr.* (**вертикальный угол**) vertical angle; (**видеоусилитель**) video amplifier, video frequency amplifier (vfa).

вуаль *f.* (phot.) fog; film, veil.

ВУАН *abbr.* (**Всеукраинская Академия наук**) Ukrainian Academy of Sciences.

Вуда металл, В. сплав (met.) Wood's alloy (bismuth-lead-tin-cadmium alloy); **вудовский фильтр** W. filter.

вуз *abbr.* (**высшее учебное заведение**) university.

вузовец *abbr.* (**учащийся высшего учебного заведения**) university student.

вулка/бестон *m.* Vulcabeston (insulator); —**лоза** *f.* Vulcalose (insulator).

вулкан *m.* volcano.

вулканиз/ат *m.* vulcanized rubber; —**атор** *m.* vulcanizer; —**ационный** *a.*, —**ация** *f.* vulcanization; **ускоритель —ации** rubber accelerator; —**ированный,** —**ованный** *a.* vulcanized; —**ировать,** —**овать** *v.* vulcanize; —**м** *m.* (geo.) volcanism; —**ование** *n.* vulcanization.

вулкан/ит *m.* vulcanite (a hard rubber); —**ический** *a.* volcanic.

вулканолог/ический *a.* volcanological; —**ия** *f.* volcanology.

вультекс *m.* vultex (a rubber latex).

Вульфа/-Брэгга формула Bragg law; **В. стереографическая сетка** Wulff stereographic net; **В. (однонитный) электрометр** W. (string) electrometer.

вульфенит *m.* wulfenite.

Вумера Woomera (Australia).

Вурцельбауер Wurzelbauer (lunar crater).

вурцит *m.* wurtzite (a zinc sulfide).

вход *m.* entrance, admission; intake, inlet; input section, front; —**а угол** angle of incidence.

входить *v.* enter, penetrate; **в. в расчет** be taken into account; **в. в состав** be a member of; comprise; participate in; **в. в сцепление** engage.

входн/ой *a.* inlet, intake; input; entrance, incoming; **в. зрачок** entrance pupil; **в. канал** access duct; **в. контакт** emitter (of transistor); **в. люк** entrance port; **в. ток** input current; **в. участок** intake (channel); —**ая емкость** input capacitance; —**ая мощность** power input; —**ая щель** entrance slit; —**ое отверстие** inlet; intake orifice; —**ое сопротивление** input impedance; —**ые ворота** entrance gate; —**ые данные** input information.

входящ/ий *a.* incoming, intake, entrance, ingoing; **в. в** entering into, appearing in; **в. угол** re-entrant angle (or corner); —**ие в состав** components, constituents.

вхождение *n.* entry.

вхолодную *adv.* cold; **ковать в.** forge cold.

вхолостую *adv.* idle, empty, no-load.

ВХТУ (**Высшее химико-технологическое училище**) Higher School of Chemical Engineering.

вцеп/иться, —**ляться** *v.* catch hold of.

ВЧ *abbr.* (**высокая частота, высокочастотный**) radio frequency (rf), high frequency (hf).

вчерне *adv.* in the rough.

вчетверо *adv.*, **в. больше** fourfold; **сложить в.** *v.* fold in four; —**м** *adv.* four (together).

вчистую *adv.* finally; **обрабатывать в.** *v.* finish, dress.

вшестеро *adv.* sixfold; —**м** *adv.* six (together).

въед/аться *v.* corrode; —**чивость** *f.* corrosiveness; —**чивый** *a.* corrosive.

въесться *see* **въедаться.**

вы *pron. pl.* you.

выбег *m.* running out, coasting; overtravel, overshoot, overswing; —**а метод** (mach.) retardation method.

выбив/ание *n.* knocking out, expulsion, beating out, stamping; **протон —ания** knock-on (or knocked-on) proton; —**ать** *v.* hammer out, knock out, dislodge; stamp, punch; —**ной** *a.* knock-out; stamping.

выбират/ель *m.* selector; switch; —**ь** *v.* select.

выбит/ый *a.* knocked out, ejected; stamped, punched; **в. электрон** knock-on (or knocked-on) electron; —**ь** *see* **выбивать.**

выбо/ина *f.*, —**й** *m.* hollow, dent.

выбор *m.* choice, selection; sampling; sampling option; **—ка** *f.* sample; selection; **—ный** *a.* selective, selected.

выборочн/ый *a.* selective; sample, sampling; **в. контроль, в. метод** sampling; **—ая проверка, —ое испытание** random test; spot check; **—ое распределение** sampling distribution; **—ым путем** by sampling.

выбранный *a.* selected.

выбрасыв/ание *n.* ejection, expulsion; discarding; discomposition; projection; **—атель** *m.* ejector, extractor; **—ать** *v.* throw out, discard, drop, reject; eject; project.

выбрать *see* **выбирать.**

выбро/с *m.* ejection, emission; (astr.) surge; (rad. astr.) outburst; (rad.) blip, pip, overshoot, overswing, peaked trace, "horn"; spike; **в. мощности** power excursion; **отрицательный в.** undershoot, underswing; **—сить** *see* **выбрасывать**; **—ски, —сы** *pl.* refuse; **—шенный** *a.* thrown out, rejected, ejected.

выбы/вать, —ть *v.* leave, be out.

вывал/ивать, —ить *v.* throw out; **—иваться** *v.* fall out.

вывар/енный *a.* boiled, extracted; **—ивание** *n.* boiling, extraction; **—ивать, —ить** *v.* extract; boil down; **—ка** *f.* boiling; extraction, residue; **—очная соль** sodium chloride.

вывед/ать, —ывать *v.* find out; **—енный** *a.* brought out, derived; developed; **—енный пучок** extracted beam; **—енная средняя точка** center tap.

вывер/енный *a.* adjusted, aligned; calibrated; checked; **—ить** *see* **выверять**; **—ка** *f.* adjustment, alignment.

вывернут/ый *a.* inverted, reversed; **—ь** *see* **вывертывать, выворачивать.**

выверочн/ый *a.* straightening, aligning, adjustment; **в. винт** adjusting screw; **—ая доска** straightedge.

вывертывать *v.* unscrew; *see also* **выворачивать**; **—ся** *v.* get out.

вывер/щик *m.* adjuster; **—ять** *v.* adjust, align, straighten; verify, check; calibrate; regulate; **—яющийся** *a.* adjustable.

вывести *see* **выводить.**

выветр/енный *a.* weathered, eroded; **—ивание** *n.* airing; weathering; **—ивать, —ить** *v.* air ventilate, **—иваться, —иться** *v.* be aired; weather, erode; **—ившийся** *a.* weathered.

вывин/тить, —чивать *v.* unscrew; **—ченный** *a.* unscrewed.

вывод *m.* conclusion, deduction, inference; result; (math.) derivation; (elec.) lead out, tap; outlet, bringing out, outward flow; **в. из работы** disabling; **в. пучка** beam extraction; **сделать —ы** draw conclusions, conclude; **—ить** *v.* lead out, withdraw, help out of; conclude, deduce, infer; develop, evolve; (math.) derive.

выводн/ой *a.* leading out; **—ая труба** vent pipe.

вывоз *m.* export, removal; **—ить** *v.* export; remove.

вывор/ачивание *n.* turning inside out, reversing; **—ачивать, —отить** *v.* turn inside out, reverse; **—от** *m.* reverse; **—отный, —оченный** *a.* turned out, reversed, inverted.

выгад/ать, —ывать *v.* economize, spare; gain (time); **—ывание** *n.* economy; gain.

выгар *m.*, **—ки** *pl.* slag.

выгиб *m.* bend, curve; **—ание** *n.* curving; **—ать** *v.* curve, bend.

выгла/дить, —живать *v.* smooth.

выглядеть *v.* look, appear.

выгнать *see* **выгонять.**

выгнут/ость *f.* convexity, bulging; **—ый** *a.* convex, cambered; **—ь** *see* **выгибать.**

выгов/аривать, —орить *v.* pronounce; stipulate.

выгод/а *f.* advantage, benefit, gain; **—нейшая величина** optimum value; **—но** *adv.* profitably; **—ность** *f.* economy, advantageousness; utility, efficiency; **—ный** *a.* advantageous, favorable, favored, suitable; profitable.

выгон/ка *f.* distillation; **—ять** *v.* drive out; distil.

выгор/ание *n.* burn-up, depletion (fuel); (elec.) burnout; burning out; **ионное в.** ion burning; **—ать, —еть** *v.* burn out, burn up; **—елый** *a.* burned out.

выгруз/ить, выгружать *v.* unload, discharge; —**ка** *f.* unloading, discharge; —**очный** *a.* unloading.

выдавать *v.* distribute, issue; **в. себя** pass for; —**ся** *v.* protrude, project; swell out.

выдав/ить, —ливать *v.* squeeze out, extrude; spin (on lathe); —**ка** *f.*, —**ливание** *n.* extrusion; stamping, pressing; spinning; —**ленный** *a.* squeezed out, extruded; stamped, pressed out.

выдалбливать *v.* excavate, hollow out.

выдать *see* **выдавать.**

выдача *f.* distribution, delivery; output.

выдающийся *a.* prominent, eminent; protruding.

выдвиг/ать *v.* put forward, introduce, promote, advance; move (out), withdraw; **в. вперед** push forward, promote; —**ающийся** *a.* prominent, outstanding.

выдвижение *n.* promotion, advance, advancement; withdrawal.

выдвижной *a.* extensible, sliding, telescopic; **в. калибр** slide gauge; **в. ящик** drawer.

выдвинуть *see* **выдвигать.**

выдел/анный *a.* produced, manufactured; —**ать** *see* **выделывать.**

выделен/ие *n.* selection; discrimination; isolation, segregation, elimination, separation, separating out; deposition, precipitation; extraction, desorption, liberation, emanation; **в. на катоде** cathode deposition; **в. серебра** desilverization; **в. частоты** frequency discrimination (extraction, isolation); **в. энергии** energy release; **момент —ия, состояние —ия** nascent state.

выдел/енный *a.* isolated, separate; defined, separated out; precipitated; evolved, liberated; selected, distinguished, assigned; —**енное положение** distinct status; —**ившийся** *a.* separated; precipitated; evolved (gas); —**итель** *m.* separator, discriminator; eliminant; —**ить** *see* **выделять.**

выдел/ка *f.*, —**ывание** *n.* manufacture, production; —**ывать** *v.* manufacture, produce, prepare.

выдел/яемость *f.* separability; precipitability; —**яемый** *a.* separable; precipitable; —**ять** *v.* separate (out), isolate, exclude, segregate; resolve; distinguish, assign, select; precipitate; release, evolve, liberate, give off, discharge; extract; discriminate; assign; factor out; —**яться** *v.* separate out; precipitate out; escape, emanate; segregate; be distinguished; —**яющий** *a.* giving off, yielding; selecting; —**яющийся** *a.* evolved, released; separated, precipitated; prominent; selective.

выдергивать *v.* pull out, draw out.

выдерж/анный *a.* exposed; sustained, persistent, maintained; postponed; —**ать, —ивать** *v.* age; stand, endure, withstand; pass (a test); store, maintain; **не —ивать** fail; —**ивание** *n.* seasoning; keeping, storage; enduring; holding, hold-up; exposing; —**ка** *f.* extract, passage; endurance; (phot.) exposure; aging; holding time; —**ка времени** delay, time lag.

выдернуть *see* **выдергивать.**

выдолб/ить *see* **выдалбливать**; —**ленный** *a.* hollowed out; slotted.

выдув/альщик *m.* (glass) blower; —**ание** *n.*, —**ка** *f.* blowing (out); —**ать** *v.* blow (out); —**ной** *a.* blow, blow-out.

выдум/ать, —ывать *v.* invent, devise, contrive; —**ка** *f.* invention, fiction, —**щик** *m.* inventor.

выдуть *see* **выдувать.**

выдых/ание *n.* exhalation; —**ать** *v.* exhale.

выед/ание *n.* corrosion, eating away; —**ать** *v.* corrode, pit.

выез/д *m.* departure; —**жать** *v.* leave, depart.

выем/ка *f.*, —**очный** *a.* hollow, recess, slot, indentation; notch; groove, channel; excavation; removal, extraction (of ore); ditch.

выесть *see* **выедать.**

выжать *see* **выжимать.**

выжечь *see* **выжигать.**

выжив/аемость *f.*, —**ание** *n.* survival; —**ать** *v.* survive, outlive.

выжиг/ание *n.* burning out; bake-out; —**ать** *v.* burn, burn out; roast.

ыжим/ание *n.* squeezing out; **—ать** *v.* squeeze out, press out.

ыжить *see* **выживать.**

ызванный *a.* induced, initiated, caused; **в. облучением** radiation-induced.

ызвать *see* **вызывать.**

ыздоровление *n.* recovery.

ызревание *n.* ripening; aging.

ызыв/аемый *a.* producible; effected, caused; **—ать** *v.* give rise to; initiate, cause, effect; induce, produce; excite, generate (current); exert (pressure); call.

ыигр/ать, —ывать *v.* win, gain; **—ыш** *m.* gain; advantage; **—ышный** *a.* won, gained.

ыиск *m.*, **—ивание** *n.* search; **—ать, —ивать** *v.* search for; discover.

ыйти *see* **выходить.**

ыказ/ать, —ывать *v.* display, manifest; **—ной** *a.* exhibited.

ык/алывать, —олоть *v.* prick out.

ыкапыв/ание *n.* excavation; **—ать** *v.* excavate.

ыкат *m.*, **—ывание** *n.* rolling out; **—ать, —ывать** *v.* roll out.

ыкач/анный *a.* pumped out; **—ать, —ивать** *v.* pump out, evacuate, exhaust; **—ивание** *n.*, **—ка** *f.* pumping out, evacuation, exhaustion.

ыки/дать, —дывать, —нуть *v.* throw out, reject; eliminate, discard.

ыкип/ать, —еть *v.* boil away.

ыклад/ка *f.*, **—ывание** *n.* lining, facing; **—ки** *pl.* (math.) calculation, computation, operations; **делать —ки** compute; **—ывать** *v.* line, face.

ыклинивание *n.* tapering.

ыключаемый *a.* switching off.

ыключатель *m.* switch, trip, (contact) breaker, cut-out; releasing device; **дистанционный в.** teleswitch; **концевой в.** limit switch; **в. перекидного типа** toggle switch.

ыключать *v.* disconnect, disengage, uncouple, release; cut out, shut off; switch off, break (contact); put out of service; exclude; **в. скорость** throw out of gear.

ыключающ/ий *a.* disconnecting, disengaging, releasing; cut-off; tripping; **—ая катушка** trip coil; **—ее напряжение** release voltage; **—ее устройство** shut-down switch.

выключен/ие *n.* disconnecting, disengaging, release; shutting off; switching off, breaking contact; **муфта —ия** release clutch; **положение —ия** off position; **—ный** *a.* disconnected; turned off, cut off, off; (elec.) switched off.

выключить *see* **выключать.**

выков/ать, —ывать *v.* (met.) forge, hammer out.

выколачивать *v.* knock out.

выколка *f.* cutting out, chipping off.

выколотить *see* **выколачивать.**

выкопать *see* **выкапывать.**

выкристаллизов/ание *n.* crystallization; **—анный** *a.* crystallized out; **—ать, —ывать** *v.* crystallize out.

выкройка *f.* pattern.

выкру/гливать, —глить *v.* round off; **—жать, —живать, —жить** *v.* round; **—жка** *f.* rounding off.

выкру/тить, —чивать *v.* unscrew; **—чивание** *n.* unscrewing.

выламывать *v.* break (open).

вылеживание *n.* aging.

вылет *m.* escape, emission; emergence; exit; flight, take-off; overhang; boom (of crane); **в. нейтронов** neutron escape; **длина —а** range; **линия —а** line of departure; **—ать, —еть** *v.* be emitted, fly out; (aero.) take off; **—ающий** *a.* outgoing, emitted; **—ающая частица** outgoing particle.

вылив/ание *n.* pouring out; **—ать** *v.* pour out; **—аться** *v.* flow out, be discharged; **—аться через край** overflow.

вылит/ый *a.* poured out; **—ь** *see* **выливать.**

вылож/енный *a.* lined; **в. свинцом** lead-lined; **—ить** *see* **выкладывать.**

вылудить *v.* tin, tinplate.

вымасл/ивать, —ить *v.* oil, grease.

выматывать *v.* unwind; deplete.

вымачив/ание *n.* steeping, soaking; **—ать** *v.* steep, soak.

вымеобразн/ый *a.* (meteor.) mammatus; **—ые облака** mamma, mammatus.

вымер/ивание *n.* measuring; **—ивать, —ить, —ять** *v.* measure.

вым/етать, —ести *v.* sweep out.

вымот/анный *a.* depleted; **—ать** *see* **выматывать.**

вымоч/енный *a.* wetted, steeped, soaked; **—ить** *see* **вымачивать.**

вымощенный *a.* paved.

вымпел *m.* pennant, pendant; (aero.) message bag.

вымыв/ание *n.* washing, elution; **—ать** *v.* wash out.

вымысел *m.* invention.

вымыт/ый *a.* washed, washed out; **—ь** *v.* wash out, elute.

вымышлять *v.* invent, contrive, devise.

вынашивать *see* **выносить.**

вынес/енный *a.* outlying, extension; external, remote; **—ти** *see* **выносить.**

выним/ание *n.* removal, withdrawal; **—ать** *v.* take out, remove.

вынос *m.* carrying out, bearing out; (aero.) stagger; **—ить** *v.* take out, carry out; endure; **—ка** *f.* annotation, footnote.

вынослив/ость *f.* endurance, durability, resistance, strength; **в. вибрационная** fatigue limit; **в. на усталость** fatigue resistance; **—ости коэффициент** endurance ratio; **—ый** *a.* rugged, durable.

выносной *see* **вынесенный.**

выну/дить, —ждать *v.* force, induce.

вынужденн/ый *a.* forced, constrained; induced; **—ая волна** induced wave; **—ая конвекция** forced convection; **—ое движение** forced motion; **—ое деление** induced fission; **—ое испускание** stimulated emission; **—ые колебания** forced oscillations.

вынут/ый *a.* removed, withdrawn; **—ь** *see* **вынимать.**

вынyр/ивать, —нуть *v.* emerge.

выпавшая фаза precipitated phase, precipitate.

выпад *m.*, **—ка** *f.* falling out, precipitation; **—ать** *v.* fall out, drop out, separate out, precipitate; occur; **—ающая фаза** precipitate; **—ение** *n.* falling out, fallout, dropout, precipitation, deposit; occurrence; **—ение дождя** rainfall; **—ение радиоактивных веществ** radioactive fallout.

выпар/енный *a.* evaporated; **—ивание** *n.* evaporation, steaming; **—иватель, —итель** *m.* evaporator; vaporizer; **—ивать, —ить** *v.* evaporate steam; **—иваться** *v.* evaporate, vaporize; **—ительный** *a.* evaporating **—ной, —ный** *a.* evaporating.

выпасть *see* **выпадать.**

выпер/еть *see* **выпирать;** **—тый** *a* pushed out, bulging.

выпил/ивание *n.* sawing, sawing out **—ивать, —ить** *v.* saw, saw out; file out.

выпирать *v.* protrude, bulge out.

выпис/ать, —ывать *v.* write out, copy **—ка, —ь** *f.* extract, copy.

выпих/ивать, —нуть *v.* push out.

выплав/ить, —лять *v.* melt out, extract; smelt; **—ка** *f.*, **—ление** *n* melting, extraction; smelting; **—ленный, —ной** *a.* melted out, extracted smelted.

выплес/кать, —кивать, —нуть *v.* splash out, spatter, spill.

выплы/вать, —ть *v.* emerge, float up.

выполаживание *n.* flattening out.

выполн/ение *n.* execution, fulfilment realization, achievement, completion performance; **—енный** *a.* performed accomplished, completed, realized **—имость** *f.* feasibility, practicability; **—имый** *a.* workable; feasible practicable; **—ить, —ять** *v.* accomplish, achieve, fulfil, perform.

выпор *m.* air hole.

выправ/ить, —лять *v.* correct, straighten, smooth, flatten; direct; **—ка** *f* correction, straightening, smoothing **—ление** *n.* correcting, straightening **—ление рек** river improvement.

выпрям/итель *m.* (elec.) rectifier; **в. запирающим слоем** barrier-layer rectifier; **—ителя действие** rectification **—ительный** *a.* rectifying; **—ить —лять** *v.* straighten; (elec.) rectify **—ление** *n.* straightening; rectification; **—ления коэффициент** rectification factor; **—ления кривая** rectification characteristic; **—ления кристалла коэффициент** crystal ratio; **—ленный** *a.* straightened; rectified; **—ляющий** *a.* straightening rectifying; **—ляющая плоскость** rectifying plane.

выпукловогнутый *a.* convexo-concave.

выпукл/ость *f.* convexity, curvature, camber; prominence, bulge, protuberance; **—ости коэффициент** (mag.) fullness factor; **—ый** *a.* convex, arched; buckled, bulging; protuberant.

выпуск *m.* outlet, escape, exhaust; pouring, discharge, emptying, omission, withdrawal; outfall; expulsion; output; issue (of journal); **в. пара** steam exhaust, steam escape; **—ание** *n.* discharge; emission; **—ать** *v.* let out; exhaust, discharge; eject, release, issue, publish; omit; manufacture.

выпускн/ик *m.* graduating student, senior; **—ой** *a.* exhaust, outlet, discharge; **—ой канал** exhaust port; **—ой клапан** escape valve, release valve; **—ая антенна** trailing antenna; **—ая сторона** exit side, exit end; **—ая труба** outlet pipe, exhaust pipe; **—ое отверстие** vent.

выпустить *see* **выпускать.**

выпут/ать, —ывать *v.* disentangle.

выпуч/енный *a.* bulging, protruding, buckled; **—ивание** *n.* bulge, swelling; **—ивать, —ить** *v.* bulge, swell, protrude.

выпущен/ие *see* **выпускание**; **—ный** *a.* let out, discharged; *see* **выпускать.**

выпя/тить, —чивать *v.* protrude; **—чиваться** *v.* project, overhang.

выраб/атывать, —отать *v.* manufacture, produce; perfect; develop, improve; generate; work; exhaust, deplete; **—отанный** *a.* manufactured; improved, developed; generated; worked; exhausted, spent; **—отка** *f.* manufacture, production; development; generation; working, mining; yield, output; wear; depletion.

выравнив/ание *n.* equalizing, balancing, compensation; matching; smoothing, flattening; aligning, leveling, trimming; padding; **зонное в.** (cryst.) zone leveling; **в. импульсов** pulse matching; **в. характеристик линии** balancing of a circuit; **—атель** *m.* equalizer; **—ать** *v.* balance, equalize, align, straighten, smooth, level, flatten; adjust; **—ающий** *a.* compensating, balancing, equalizing; leveling, smoothing, straightening; padding.

выраж/ать *v.* express; **—ение** *n.* expression, formula; **—енный** *a.* expressed; **—енный через** expressed in terms of.

выраз/ительный *a.* expressive, significant; **—ить** *see* **выражать.**

выраст/ание *n.* growing; **—ать, —и** *v.* grow; **—ить, выращивать** *v.* grow, cultivate.

выращ/енный переход grown junction; **—ивание кристаллов** crystal growth (growing).

вырвать *v.* tear out, pull out.

вырез *m.* cut, notch, groove; **—аемый пучок** defined beam; **—ание** *n.* cutting out; excision; **—ать, —ывать** *v.* cut out; engrave; eliminate; **—ка** *f.* cut, cutout; indentation, notch.

вырисов/ать, —ывать *v.* draw carefully; **—аться, —ываться** *v.* appear, stand out.

выровн/енный *a.* straightened, leveled; trimmed; **—ять** *see* **выравнивать.**

выро/диться, —ждаться *v.* degenerate.

вырожден/ие *n.* degeneracy, degeneration; **в. колебаний** degeneration of oscillations; **—ия температура** degeneracy temperature; **—ный** *a.* degenerated; (math.) degenerate, confluent; **—ное гипергеометрическое уравнение** confluent hypergeometric equation; **—ное состояние** degenerated state.

вырон/ить, —ять *v.* let fall, drop.

вырост *m.* protuberance.

выруб *m.* cut, notch; **—ать, —ить** *v.* chop out; cut off, cut out; **—ка** *f.* cutting out; notching, indentation; **—ленный** *a.* cut out, cut off; **—ной** *a.* cutting, punching.

выруч/ать, —ить *v.* help; gain, profit; **—ка** *f.* assistance; gain.

вырыв/ание *n.* ejection, removal; extraction; pickup; **в. электронов полем** field-induced electron emission; **—ать** *v.* dig out; pull out; extract; **—аться** *v.* break loose.

вырыт/ый *a.* excavated; **—ь** *see* **вырывать.**

высажив/ать *v.* precipitate; **—аться** *v.*

settle out, precipitate; **—ающийся** *a.* settling out, precipitating.

высалив/ание *n.* salting out; **—ать** *v.* salt out.

высасыв/ание *n.* sucking out, exhaustion; **—ать** *v.* suck out; draw out, exhaust, evacuate.

высачив/ание *n.* leaking; **—аться** *v.* leak.

высверл/енный *a.* drilled, bored; **—ивание** *n.* drilling, boring; **—ивать, —ить** *v.* drill, bore.

высвечив/ание *n.* luminescence, de-excitation; **—ать** *v.* luminesce, de-excite; **—ающее действие** luminescence stimulation.

высвобо/дить, —ждать *v.* set free; disengage; **—ждение** *n.* release, freeing.

высе/вки *pl.* sifting, screenings; **—ивание** *n.* sifting out, screening; **—ивать** *v.* sift out, screen.

высекать *v.* cut out; stamp, punch.

высеч/ка *f.* cutting out, punching, cut; **—ь** *see* **высекать.**

высеять *see* **высеивать.**

выситься *v.* tower, rise above.

выскаблив/ание *n.* scraping out; **—ать** *v.* scrape out; erase.

высказ/анный *a.* expressed, explicit; **—ать, —ывать** *v.* express.

выскакив/ание *n.* springing out; **—ать** *v.* spring out, slip out.

выскальзыв/ание *n.* slipping out; **—ать** *v.* slip out.

выскобл/енный *a.* scraped out; **—ить** *see* **выскабливать.**

выскользнуть *see* **выскальзывать.**

выскочить *see* **выскакивать.**

выскре/бать, —бывать, —сти *v.* scrape off, scratch out; **—бывание** *n.* scraping (off).

высле/дить, —живать *v.* trace, track.

выслу/га *f.* service; **—живать, —жить** *v.* deserve, merit.

выслуш/ать, —ивать *v.* listen, hear; **—ивание** *n.* listening.

высматривать *v.* look out for, be on the alert for.

выс.-мол. *abbr.* (**высокомолекулярный**) high-molecular weight, high-molecular.

высмотреть *see* **высматривать.**

высовывать *v.* thrust out; **—ся** *v.* protrude, project.

высок/ий *a.* high, tall; eminent; (meteor.) high-level; **в. вакуум** high vacuum; **—ая верность воспроизведения** high fidelity; **—ая частота** radio frequency, high frequency; **—ое напряжение** high voltage.

высоко— *prefix* high, highly.

высоко/вакуумный *a.* high-vacuum; **—вольтный** *a.* high-voltage; **—вязкий** *a.* high-viscosity; **—горный** *a.* high-mountain, high-altitude; **—градусный** *a.* high-grade; **—дисперсный** *a.* highly dispersed; **—добротный** *a.* high-Q; **—зольный** *a.* high-ash.

высококачественн/ый *a.* high-grade; high-quality; high-Q, rich (ore); **—ая запись** high-fidelity recording; **—ое телевидение** high-definition television.

высоко/кипящий *a.* high-boiling; **—коэрцитивный** *a.* high-coercivity; **—кремнистый** *a.* high-silicon; **—кучевое облако** altocumulus.

высоко/легированный *a.* high (alloy); **—марганцовистый** *a.* high-manganese; **—молекулярный** *a.* high-molecular-weight, high-molecular; **—мощный** *a.* high-power; (mach.) heavy-duty; **—огнеупорный** *a.* highly refractory; **—омный** *a.* high-resistance, high-impedance.

высоко/плавкий *a.* high-melting; **—полимер** *m.* high polymer; **—пористый** *a.* highly porous; **—пробный** *a.* high-test; high-grade; **—продуктивный** *a.* highly efficient; high-yield; **—производительный** *a.* very productive, high-yield, high-performance; **—проницаемый** *a.* high-permeability; **—проходный фильтр** (elec.) high-pass filter; **—процентный** *a.* high-percentage, high-grade; **—процентная урановая руда** high-uranium ore.

высоко/радиоактивный *a.* highly radioactive; **—скоростной** *a.* high-speed, **—слоистое облако** high sheet cloud altostratus; **—сортный** *see* **высококачественный**; **—точный** *a.* high precision, precision; **—углеродистый** *a.* high-carbon.

высокочастотный *a.* high (or radio) frequency; **в. масс-спектрометр** radio frequency mass spectrometer.

высоко/чистый *a.* high-purity; **—чувствительный** *a.* highly sensitive; **—энергичная частица** high-energy particle; **—эффективный** *a.* highly efficient, high-performance.

высортиров/ать *v.* sort out; **—ка** *f.* sorting.

высосать *see* **высасывать.**

высот/а *f.* height, altitude; elevation; depth; pitch; **в. барьера** barrier height; **в. большая** high altitude; **в. в свету** inside height, clearance; **в.-дальность** height-range; **в. звука** pitch of sound; **в. малая** low altitude; **в. над уровнем моря** height above sea level; **в. напора** pressure head; **в. напора помпы** lift of pump; **в. положения** elevation; **в. прилива** rise of tide; **в. резонанса** resonance amplitude; **набирать —у** (aero.) climb; **по —е** vertically.

высотн/ость *f.* height, altitude; **—ый** *a.* upper-air, high-level, upper; altitude, high-altitude; **—ый репер** (surv.) bench mark; **—ый ход** altitude effect, height dependence; **—ый эффект** altitude effect; **—ая атмосфера** upper atmosphere; **—ая камера** altitude (test) chamber, pressure chamber; **—ая карта** upper-air map; **—ая климатология** upper-air climatology; **—ая кривая** altitude curve; **—ая радиолокация** height-finding radar; **—ая характеристика** altitude response; **—ое исследование** high-altitude research.

высото/граф *m.* altigraph; **—мер** *m.* altimeter; **—писец** *m.* altigraph.

высох/нуть *see* **высыхать; —ший** *a.* dry.

выстав/ить, —лять *v.* advance, expose; exhibit; **—ка** *f.* exhibition, display; **—ление** *n.* putting out, exposure; **—ленный** *a.* exposed.

выстаивать *v.* stand; withstand; **—ся** *v.* mature.

выст/илать, —лать *v.* pave, cover, line; **—илка** *f.* pavement, lining.

выстоять *see* **выстаивать.**

выстраив/ание *n.* alignment; **в. ядер** nuclear alignment; **—ать** *v.* build, erect, set up, align.

выстрел *m.* shot; **—ить** *v.* shoot.

выстро/енное ядро aligned nucleus; **—ить** *see* **выстраивать; —йка** *f.* building, construction.

высту/дить, —жать, —живать *v.* cool.

выстукив/ание *n.* percussion; **—ать** *v.* subject to percussion; tap.

выступ *m.* projection, protuberance, bulge, protrusion; cusp; lug; jog, flange; ledge; **—ать, —ить** *v.* address; protrude; come out; **—ающий** *a.* protruding; salient; coming out; **—ающий наружу** emerging; **—ление** *n.* (public) address, statement.

выстывать *v.* cool.

высунут/ый *a.* protruding; **—ь** *see* **высовывать.**

высуш/енный *a.* dried, desiccated; **—ивание** *n.* drying, desiccation; **—ивать, —ить** *v.* dry, desiccate; **—ивающий** *a.* drying, desiccating.

высчитывать *v.* calculate.

выс/ший *a.* higher, highest; **в. спин** higher spin; **—шая гармоника** higher harmonic; **—шая граница** upper limit; **—шая математика** higher mathematics; **—шая точка** peak; top, summit; **—шее учебное заведение** university.

высып/анный *a.* poured out; **—ать** *v.* pour out; **—аться** *v.* be poured out; **—ка** *f.* pouring out.

высых/ание *n.* drying, desiccation; **—ать** *v.* dry, dry up; **—ающий** *a.* drying.

высь *f.* height; top, summit, crest.

выталкив/ание *n.* ejection, extrusion; **в. потока** flux exclusion; **—атель** *m.* ejector; withdrawing device; extruder; **—ать** *v.* eject, expel, extrude.

вытаплив/ание *n.* melting down; smelting out; **—ать** *see* **вытопить.**

вытаскив/ание *n.* extraction, drawing out; **—ать** *v.* pull out, extract.

вытачивать *v.* machine, turn (on lathe).

вытащить *see* **вытаскивать.**

вытек/ание *n.* outflow, effluence; discharge; **скорость —ания** rate of discharge; **температура —ания** exit temperature; —**ать** *v.* flow out, discharge; result, follow, ensue; —**ающий** *a.* flowing out, effluent; resultant; —**ающая жидкость** effluent.

вытереть *see* **вытирать.**

вытерпеть *v.* endure, bear.

вытесн/ение *n.* displacement; —**енный** *a.* displaced, expelled; —**ить,** —**ять** *v.* displace, force out, expel; —**ять из обихода** render obsolete.

вытечь *see* **вытекать.**

вытирать *v.* wipe, dry.

вытолк/ать, —**нуть** *see* **выталкивать.**

вытопить *v.* heat; melt out.

выточ/енный *a.* cut, turned (on lathe); —**ить** *see* **вытачивать**; —**ка** *f.* turning (on lathe); recess, groove.

вытрав/ить, —**ливать,** —**лять** *v.* etch; —**ка** *f.*, —**ление,** —**ливание** *n.* corrosion, etching; **фигура** —**ления** etched figure; —**ленный** *a.* corroded, etched; —**ляющий** *a.* corroding, corrosive; —**ляющее средство** caustic.

вытягив/ание *n.* extraction, drawing off; extension, pulling out, elongation, stretching, spread; **в. кристаллов** crystal pulling; —**ать** *v.* extract, draw out; exhaust (air); extend, pull out, elongate, prolong; stretch (out), spread; —**аться** *v.* be extracted; stretch, extend; expand; —**ающее напряжение** extraction voltage.

вытяжка *f.* drawing; (drawn) shell; *see also* **вытягивание.**

вытяжн/ой *a.* drawing; exhaust, draft; **в. вентилятор** exhaust fan; **в. клапан** vent valve; **в. насос** vacuum pump; **в. пресс** drawing press; **в. трос** (parachute) rip cord; **в. шкаф** fume hood (cupboard, cabinet); **в. штамп** drawing die; —**ая труба** exhaust pipe; stack.

вытянут/ость *f.* elongation; —**ый** *a.* stretched, prolonged; (math.) prolate; extracted; —**ая дислокация** extended dislocation; —**ь** *see* **вытягивать.**

выуч/ивать, —**ить** *v.* teach; learn; —**иться** *v.* learn.

выхлоп *m.* exhaust, discharge; —**ной** *a.* exhaust, escape, waste; —**ной газ** exhaust gas, burned gas, combustion gas, propulsive gas, reaction gas; —**ной клапан** exhaust valve, outlet valve.

выход *m.* yield, efficiency, output; emergence, escape, outflow, discharge; outlet; outcrop; exit; publication; outcome, result; **в. из-под контроля** going out of control; **в. из строя** collapse, breakdown; **в. люминесценции** luminescence yield, luminescence efficiency; **в. на** arrival at; **в. нейтронов на деление** fission neutron yield; **в. по току** current efficiency, power yield; **в. сцинтилляций** scintillation response; **в. химического процесса** chemical efficiency; **в. энергии** energy production, energy generation; —**а внешняя работа** outer work function; —**а внутренняя работа** inner work function; —**а угол** (seis.) angle of emergence.

выходить *v.* go out, emerge, issue; escape; be published, be issued; front, face; **в. за пределы, рамки** fall outside the limits; **в. из строя** fail; **в. на** reach; go out to.

выходн/ой *a.* output; outgoing; outlet, exit; **в. зрачок** exit pupil; **в. импульс** output pulse; **в. каскад** output stage; **в. конец** outlet end; **в. контакт** collector (of transistor); **в. люк** exit port; **в. прибор** output meter; **в. слой** (geo.) outcrop; **в. трансформатор** output transformer; —**ая емкость** output capacitance; —**ая мощная лампа** power output tube; —**ая нагрузка** output load, termination; —**ая скорость** exit velocity, rate of discharge; —**ая щель** exit slit; —**ое отверстие** outlet, vent; —**ое отверстие коллиматора** collimator portal; —**ое сопротивление** output impedance.

выхо/дящий *a.* outgoing, outbound, emergent; (geo.) outcropping; **в. угол** salient angle (or corner); —**ждение** *n.* coming out, going out.

выхол/аживание *n.* cooling; —**аживать,** —**одить** *v.* chill.

выцвест/и, —**ь** *see* **выцветать.**

выцвет *m.* fading, bleaching; efflorescence; —**ание** *n.* fading, bleaching, discoloration; —**ать** *v.* fade, bleach, lose color; **—ший** *a.* faded, discolored.

выч. *abbr.* (**вычисленный**) calculated, computed.

вычерк/ивание *n.* deleting; canceling; **—ивать, —нуть** *v.* delete; cancel; **—нутый** *a.* crossed out, deleted; canceled.

вычерп/ать, —нуть, —ывать *v.* exhaust; scoop.

вычер/тить *v.* trace, draw, map out; **—чивание** *n.* tracing, plotting, drawing.

выч/есть *v.* deduct, subtract; **—ет** *m.* deduction; (math.) residue; **приведенная система —етов** reduced system of residues.

вычисл/ение *n.* calculation, computation; **—енный** *a.* calculated, computed; **—итель** *m.* calculator, calculating machine; **—ительный** *a.* calculating, computational; **—ительная машина непрерывного действия** analog computer; **—ить, —ять** *v.* calculate, compute; **—яемый** *a.* enumerable.

вычистить *see* **вычищать.**

вычит/аемое *n.* (math.) subtrahend; **—аемый** *a.* deductible; **—ание** *n.* deduction; subtraction; **—ательный** *a.* subtractive, subtractional; **—ать** *v.* deduct; subtract; read (through); **—ывать** *v.* read (through).

вычищать *v.* clean.

выше— *prefix* above—, super—.

выше *comp. of* **высокий, высоко;** *prep. gen.* higher, above; **—изложенный** *a.* foregoing, above-stated; **—исчисленный** *a.* above-numbered, above-calculated; **—лежащий** *a.* superincumbent; **—лежащий пласт** (geo.) superstratum, overburden, overlying stratum; **—объявленный, —означенный, —приведенный, —сказанный, —указанный, —упомянутый** *a.* above, foregoing, aforesaid, above-mentioned.

вышедший из строя disabled.

вышел *past tense of* **выходить.**

вышиб/ать, —ить *v.* knock out, dislodge.

выш/ина *f.* height; **—ка** *f.* tower; derrick; **—ний** *a.* high, superior.

выщел/ачивание *n.* leaching (out), depletion; **—оченность** *f.* leaching; **—оченный** *a.* leached (out).

выяв/ить, —лять *v.* show, exhibit, expose; develop; recognize; **—иться, —ляться** *v.* be revealed, manifest itself; **—ление** *n.* exposure; development, appearance.

выясн/ение *n.* clarification, explanation, determination; **—енный** *a.* cleared up, explained; **—ить, —ять** *v.* clarify, elucidate, illustrate; investigate; ascertain; develop; learn.

вью/га *f.*, **—жный** *a.* snowstorm.

вьюстит *m.* wüstite.

вьючить *v.* load, pack.

вьюшка *f.* damper.

ВЭИ *abbr.* (**Всесоюзный электротехнический институт**) All-Union Electrotechnical Institute.

ВЭК *abbr.* (**Всесоюзный энергетический комитет**) All-Union Power Engineering Committee.

ВЭО *abbr.* (**Всесоюзное электротехническое объединение**) All-Union Electrical Engineering Association.

ВЭТ *abbr.* (**Весоюзный электротехнический трест**) All-Union Electrotechnical Trust.

ВЭШ *abbr.* (**Военная электротехническая школа**) Military Electrical Engineering School.

вюртц/илит *m.* wurtzilite; **—ит** *m.* wurtzite.

Вюрца колба Wurtz flask; **В.-Фиттига реакция** W.-Fittig reaction.

вяжущ/ий *a.* binding, cementing; stringent; **в. материал, —ее вещество, —ее средство** binder, bonding material, cement; matrix; **—ая способность** binding power.

вяз/альный *a.* binding; **—ание** *n.* binding, tying; **—анка** *f.* bundle; **—ательный** *a.* binding; **—ать** *v.* bind, tie; **—аться** *v.* be compatible with, be consistent with; **—ка** *f.* binding, tying, tie.

вязк/ий *a.* viscous, viscid; tough; malleable, ductile; **в. металл** tough metal; **в. сдвиг** (hydr.) viscous shear; **—ая жидкость** viscous fluid; **—ое разрушение** ductile fracture.

вязко/сть *f.* viscosity; toughness; ductility; **в. в запиле** notch impact strength; **объемная в.** second (or dilatational) viscosity; **ударная в.** impact ductility, toughness; **—сти коэффициент** coefficient of viscosity; (mag.) lag coefficient; **—эластический** *a.* viscoelastic.

вязнуть *v.* stick, sink (in.)

вязочная проволока tie wire.

вянуть *v.* fade.

Г

г *abbr.* (**грамм**) gram (g); **г.** (**год**) year; (**гора**) mountain; (**город**) town, city; (**государственный**) state; government, federal.

Г [*in steel mark* (**марганец**)] manganese (Mn).

Г *abbr.* [**грамм (сила)**] gram (force).

га *abbr.* (**гектар**) hectare.

г-атом *abbr.* (**грамм-атом**) gram atom; **г-ион** (**грамм-ион**) gram ion; **г-моль** (**грамм-молекула**) mole, gram-molecule; **г-р** (**грамм-рентген**) gram roentgen; **г-экв** (**грамм-эквивалент**) gram equivalent.

габарит *m.*, **—ный** *a.* (overall) size; (external) dimensions; clearance; **г. внутренний** inside dimensions; **—ный контур** outline; **—ный размер** overall dimensions; **—ная высота** clearance height; **—ная стойкость** dimensional stability.

Габера процесс Haber process.

габитус *m.*, **—ный** *a.* (cryst.) habit; **—ная форма** habit, form.

Гавайские острова Hawaian Islands.

Гавелока формула Havelock law.

гагат *m.*, **—овый** *a.* jet (mineral).

ГАГО *abbr.* (**Государственное астрономо-геодезическое общество**) State Astronomy and Geodesy Society.

гад/ание *n.* guessing; **—ательно** *adv.* hypothetically, by conjecture; **—ательный** *a.* problematic, doubtful, conjectural; **—ать** *v.* guess.

гадолиний *m.* gadolinium (Gd).

гаечн/ый *a.* nut; **г. барашек** thumb nut, wing nut, butterfly nut; **г. ключ** wrench; **—ая резьба** female thread, inside thread.

газ. *abbr.* (**газета**) newspaper; (**газовый**) gas, gaseous.

газ *m.* gas; gauze; **г. инертный** inert gas; **превращать в г., образовывать г.** gasify; **сбавить г.** (mach.) throttle.

газ/гольдер *m.* gas holder, gas container, gas tank; **—ер** *see* **газовик.**

Газе Hase (lunar crater).

газет/а *f.*, **—ный** *a.* newspaper.

газиров/ание *n.* gassing, aeration; **—анный** *a.* gassed, aerated; **—ать** *v.* gas, aerate, aerify.

газифик/атор *m.* gasifier; **—ация** *f.* gasification; carburetion.

газо— *prefix* gas; gauze.

газо/баллон *m.* gas cylinder; **—видный** *see* **газообразный; —вик** *m.* gas generator; **—воздушная смесь** gas-air mixture; **—всасыватель** *m.* gas exhauster; **—выделение** *n.* gas generation, gassing; emanation.

газов/ый *a.* gas, gaseous; *see also* **газо—; г. карман** gas pocket; **г. пузырь** blowhole, gas cavity; **г. разряд** gas discharge; **г. счетчик** gas counter, gaseous counter; **—ая диффузия** gaseous diffusion; **—ая магистраль** gas main, gas pipeline; **—ая постоянная** gas constant; **—ая противоточная колонка** countercurrent gaseous exchange column; **—ая сажа** gas black, carbon black; **—ая ткань** wire gauze; **—ая электроника** gaseous electronics; **—ое включение** (occluded) gas pocket; **—ое месторождение** gas field; **—ое охлаждение** gas cooling; **—ое усиление** gas amplification; **—ые часы** gas meter.

газоген *m.* gasogen.

газогенератор *m.* gas generator; **—ный** *a.* gas-producing.

газодинам/ика *f.* gas dynamics; **—ический** *a.* gas-dynamical; **—о** *n.* gas-driven dynamo.

газо/ем *m.* gas holder, gasometer; **—затворный** *a.* gas-sealed.

газокалильн/ый *a.* incandescent; **г. колпачок, —ая сетка** gas mantle.

газокинетический *a.* gas kinetic.

газолин *m.*, **—овый** *a.* gasoline.

газомагнитный *a.* magnetohydrodynamic, hydromagnetic.

газомер, —итель *m.* gas meter; gasometer.

газометр *see* **газомер; —ический** *a.* gasometric; **—ический анализ** eudiometry; **—ия** *f.* gasometry.

газо/мотор *m.* gas engine; **—наполненный** *a.* gas-filled; **—наполненная лампа** gas-filled lamp; **—непроницаемый** *a.* gastight; **—носный** *a.* gas-bearing, gaseous.

газообразн/ость *f.* gaseousness; **—ый** *a.* gaseous **—ая жидкость** gaseous fluid, gas; **—ое тело** gas; **—ое топливо** gaseous fuel; fuel gas.

газообразов/ание *n.* gasification, gas formation; **—атель** *m.* gas producer.

газообразующий *a.* gas-forming; **г. аппарат** *see* **газообразователь.**

газоотвод *m.* gas vent, gas conduit; **—ная труба, —ящая труба** gas outlet; exhaust pipe.

газо/отделитель *m.* gas separator; **—отравленный** *a.* gas-poisoned; **—отсасывающий** *a.* gas-suction, exhaust; **—охладитель** *m.* gas condenser.

газоочист/итель *m.* gas purifier, scrubber; **—ительный** *a.* gas-purifying; **—ка** *f.* gas purification, scrubbing.

газо/поглотитель *m.* gas absorber, getter; **—подводящий** *a.* gas-intake, gas-feed; **—полный** *a.* gas-filled; **—полная лампа** gas-filled lamp; **—привод** *m.* gas inlet; **—приемник** *m.* gas collector; **—приемный** *a.* gas-collecting, gas-receiving; **—провод** *m.* gas pipe, gas main, gas supply; **—производитель** *m.* gas generator; **—промыватель** *m.* gas purifier, scrubber.

газопроницаем/ость *f.* gas permeability; **—ый** *a.* gas-permeable.

газоразрядн/ый *a.* gas-discharge; **г. электровакуумный прибор** gas-filled tube; **—ая лампа** gas-discharge tube, glow tube.

газораспределитель *m.* gas distributor, gas header; **—ный** *a.* gas-distributing.

газо/сборник *m.* gas collector; **—светная лампа** fluorescent lamp; **выпрямитель с —светной лампой** slow-discharge rectifier; **—сфокусированный** *a.* gas-focused; **—трон** *m.* gas divide, gas-filled tube rectifier; phanatron; **—турбина** *f.* gas turbine.

газо/уловитель *m.* gas trap, gas catcher, gas collector; **—упорный** *a.* gastight; **—фикация** *see* **газификация; —хранилище** *n.* gas holder; **—хромирование** *n.* diffusion chroming; **—чиститель** *see* **газоочиститель.**

газящий *a.* gassy.

ГАИ *abbr.* (**Главный астрономический институт**) Main Astronomical Institute.

гаиденит *m.* haydenite.

гаидингерит *m.* haidingerite.

ГАИЗ *abbr.* (**Государственное астрономическое издательство**) State Astronomical Press.

гаиит *m.* gajite

ГАИШ *abbr.* (**Государственный астрономический институт им. П. К. Штернберга**) P. K. Shternberg State Astronomical Institute.

Гайда сектор Hyde sector disk.

Гайдингера полосы Haidinger fringes.

гайка *f.* nut; **г. барашек, барашковая г.** wing nut.

Гайнцель Hainzel (lunar crater).

гайперник *m.* Hypernic (iron-nickel alloy).

гайперсил *m.* Hipersil, Hypersil (iron-silicon alloy).

Гайтлера *see* **Гейтлера; гайтлеровская** *see* **гейтлеровская.**

гайфлюкс *m.* Hyflux (permanent-magnet material).

гакманит *m.* hackmanite.

гал *m.* gal (unit cgs acceleration).

галаксит *m.* galaxite.

галактика *f.* galaxy; **плоская составляющая Галактики** population I of the Galaxy; **сферическая составляющая Галактики** population II of the Galaxy.

галактит *m.* galactite.

галактическ/ий *a.* galactic; **г. шум** galactic (radio) noise; **—ое ядро** galactic center.

гален, —ит *m.* galena; **—овый** *a.* galena.

Галеркина метод Galerkin method.

галет/а *f.* pancake coil; biscuit; **—ная батарея** (geo.) battery of flat dry cells.

галечник *m.*, **—овый** *a.* pebble.

галилеев/а зрительная трубка Galilean telescope; **—ы координаты** G. coordinates; **Галилея преобразование** G. transformation.

галит *m.* halite.

галлерея *f.* gallery.

галлерит *m.* hallerite.

галлефлинта *f.* (pet.) haelleflinta.

галлий *m.* gallium (Ga).

галлит *m.* hallite.

галловый *a.* gallic.

галлуазит *m.* halloysite.

галмей *m.* calamine.

гало *n.* halo.

галоген *m.* halogen; **—ация** *f.*, **—ирование** *n.* halogenation; **—ид** *m.* halide; **—ированный** *a.* halogenated; **—ный** *a.* halide, halogen, halogenous; **—ный счетчик** halogen counter.

галоид *m.*, **—ный** *a.* halogen, halide, haloid; **—ный самогасящий счетчик** halogen-quenched counter; **—ный течеискатель** halide leak detector; **—ное серебро** silver halide; **—оводород** *m.* hydrogen halide.

галоклина *f.* halocline.

галометр *m.* halometer; **—ический** *a.* halometric; **—ия** *f.* halometry.

галос *see* **гало.**

галотрихит *m.* halotrichite.

Галуа теория Galois theory.

гальваниз/атор *m.* galvanizer; **—ация** *f.*, **—ирование** *n.* galvanization; **—ированный** *a.* galvanized; **—ировать** *v.* galvanize.

гальванический *a.* galvanic; **г. элемент** galvanic cell.

гальвано/граф *m.* galvanograph; **—люминесценция** *f.* galvanoluminescence.

гальваномагнит/изм *m.* galvanomagnetism; **—ный** *a.* galvanomagnetic; **—ный эффект** magnetoresistive effect, magnetoresistance, galvanomagnetic effect.

гальванометр *m.* galvanometer; **—ический** *a.* galvanometric; **—ия** *f.* galvanometry.

гальванопластика *f.* galvanoplastics.

гальваноскоп *m.* galvanoscope; **—ический** *a.* galvanoscopic.

гальваностег/ировать *v.* electroplate; **—ия** *f.* electroplating.

гальвано/типия *f.* electrotype; **—упругий эффект** elastoresistance; **—хромия** *f.* (met.) galvanic coloring.

галька *f.* pebble.

гальмей *see* **галмей.**

Гальтона закон Galton law; **кривая Г.** Galtonian curve; **свисток Г.** Galton whistle.

гамартит *m.* hamartite.

Гамбар Gambart (lunar crater).

гамбергит *m.* hambergite.

Гамильтона оператор Hamiltonian (operator); **принцип Г.** Hamilton principle; **уравнение Г.-Якоби** Hamilton-Jacobi equation; **функция Г.** *see* **гамильтониан.**

гамильтон/иан *m.* Hamiltonian; **г. взаимодействия** interaction H.; **—овский** *a.* Hamiltonian.

гамлинит *m.* hamlinite.

гамма *f.* gamma; gamma ray (geo.; math.) gamma; (mus.) scale; **г.-железо** (met.) gamma iron; **г. излучатель** gamma emitter; **г.-излучение** gamma radiation, gamma-ray emission; **г.-квант** gamma(-ray) quantum, photon; **г.-лучи** gamma rays; **г.-лучи радиационного захвата** capture gamma radiation; **г.-переход** gamma(-ray) transition; **г.-пространство** (mech.) gamma space, phase space; **г.-снимок** gammagraph; **г. спектр** gamma-ray spectrum; **г.-уран** gamma-uranium; **г.-установка** gamma unit; gamma-ray source; **г.-фотон** gamma (-ray) photon; **г.-функция** gamma function.

гамма/грамма *f.* gammagram; **—графирование** *n.* gammagraph; **—графия** *f.* gammagraphy, gamma(-ray) radiography.

Гамметa уравнение Hammett equation.

Гамов Gamow.

гампденит *m.* hampdenite.

Гангийе-Коттера формула Ganguillet and Kutter formula.

Ганимед Ganymede (satellite of Jupiter).

ганит *m.* gahnite.

Ганкела преобразование Hankel transform; **Г. функция** H. function; **Г. функция первого ряда** H. function of the first kind.
ганкокит *m.* hancockite.
ганксит *m.* hanksite.
ганнеит *m.* hannayite.
ганофиллит *m.* ganophyllite.
Ганса правило Gans law.
Ганстин Hansteen (lunar crater).
гантелеобразный *a.* dumbbell-shaped.
Ганча синтез Hantzsch synthesis.
ГАО *abbr.* [**Главная астрономическая** (**Пулковская**) **обсерватория**] Main Astronomical Observatory (in Pulkovo).
гарантиров/ание *n.* guaranteeing; **—анный** *a.* guaranteed, assured; **—ать** *v.* guarantee.
гарантия *f.* guarantee, assurance.
гарбортит *m.* harbortite.
гарвезированная сталь Harvey steel.
Гарвея процесс Harvey process.
Гаргривс-Берда элемент Hargreaves-Bird (electrolytic) cell.
гардистонит *m.* hardystonite.
Гаркинса теория Harkins theory.
гармони/зация *f.* harmonization; **—ка** *f.* harmonic, harmonic component; **газовая —ка** gas harmonica, pyrophone.
гармоническ/ий *a.* harmonic; **г. анализ** harmonic analysis; Fourier analysis; **г. анализатор** harmonic analyzer; **г. ряд** harmonic series; **—ая величина** harmonic quantity; **—ая составляющая** harmonic component; **—ое среднее** harmonic mean; **—ие колебания** harmonic oscillations.
гармония *f.* harmony.
гармотом *m.* harmotome.
Гарнака теорема Harnack theorem.
гарнитура *f.* fittings.
гаррингтонит *m.* harringtonite.
гарстигит *m.* harstigite.
гарт *m.* type metal; **—блей** *m.* hard lead.
гартин *m.* hartine.
Гартмана генератор Hartmann generator; **Г. микрофотометр** H. microphotometer; **Г. уравнение** H. dispersion formula.
Гартри приближение Hartree approximation.
гарттит *m.* harttite.
гарь *f.* burning, fumes.
гасил/о *n.*, **—щик** *m.* extinguisher, quencher, damper; **—ьный** *a.* extinguishing, quenching.
гасит/ель *see* **гасило**; **г. энергии** energy dissipator; **—ельный** *see* **гасильный**; **—ельный контур** quenching circuit; **—ь** *v.* extinguish, quench; damp; cancel.
гаснуть *v.* go out; be slaked.
Гассенди Gassendi (lunar crater).
гастингсит *m.* hastingsite.
гасящ/ий *a.* extinguishing, quenching; **—ая примесь** quenching admixture, quenching impurity, quenching agent; **—ая схема** quench circuit; **—ее сопротивление** quenching resistance, voltage-dropping resistor; **—еся пробное устройство** quenching probe unit.
гатчеттит *m.* hatchettite.
гатчеттолит *m.* hatchettolite (tantaloniobate of uranium).
Гау ферма Howe girder.
гауерит *m.* hauerite.
гаузистор *m.* gaussistor.
Гаукинса элемент Hawkins cell.
Гаурик Gauricus (lunar crater).
гаусманит *m.* hausmannite.
гаусс *m.* gauss (unit).
Гаусс Gauss (lunar crater).
Гаусса кривая ошибок Gaussian error curve; **Г.-Остроградского теорема** (math.) Gauss theorem; **Г. принцип наименьшего принуждения** Gauss principle of least constraint; **Г. распределение** Gaussian distribution; **система единиц Г.** Gaussian units; **теорема взаимности Г.** Gauss reciprocal theorem; **Г. числовое поле** Gaussian plane, complex plane.
гауссиан *m.* Gaussian.
гауссметр *m.* gaussmeter.
гауссов потенциал Gaussian potential; **—а кривая** *see* **Гаусса распределение**; **кривая нормального (—а) распределения** Gauss error curve; **—а полимерная сетка** Gaussian polymer network; **—а система единиц** *see* **система единиц Гаусса**; **—а ширина** Gaussian width; **—ский** *a.* Gaussian.

гаухекорнит *m.* hauchecornite.
ГАФИ *abbr.* (**Государственный астрофизический институт**) State Astrophysical Institute.
гафний *m.* hafnium (Hf).
гашен/ие *n.* quenching, extinguishing, cancelation; **г. пучка** beam suppression; **г. разряда** quenching of discharge; **г. реактора** reactor shutdown; **—ка** *f.* slaked lime; **—ый** *a.* extinguished, quenched, slaked.
Гаюи закон Haüy law.
гаюин, —ит *m.* haüynite, haüne.
гб *abbr.* (**гильберт**) gilbert (unit).
гвадалкацарит *m.* guadalcazarite.
гваякилит *m.* guyaquilite.
гверсолт *m.* hversalt.
гвозд/ить *v.* nail; **—еобразный** *a.* nail-shaped; **—ь** *m.* nail; peg, spike; pin; **шляпка —я** nail head.
гвт *abbr.* (**гектоватт**) hectowatt; **гвт-ч** (**гектоватт-час**) hectowatt-hour.
гг *abbr.* (**гектограмм**) hectogram; **гг.** (**годы**) years; (**города**) cities; **г.г.** (**господа**) gentlemen.
ГГГТ *abbr.* (**Геолого-гидро-геодезический трест**) Geological-Hydrological-Geodetic Trust.
ГГИ *abbr.* (**Государственный гидрологический институт**) State Hydrological Institute.
ГГК *abbr.* (**Главный геодезический комитет**) Main Geodetic Committee.
ГГО *abbr.* (**Главная геофизическая обсерватория**) Main Geophysical Observatory.
ГГУ *abbr.* (**Главное геологическое управление**) Main Geological Administration; (**Горьковский государственный университет**) Gor'ki State University.
где *adv.* where; **г. бы ни** wherever; **г.-либо, г.-нибудь, г.-то** somewhere, anywhere.
ГДР *abbr.* (**Германская Демократическая Республика**) German Democratic Republic.
геантиклиналь *f.* geanticline.
Гебер Geber (lunar crater).
Геберлейна агломерационный процесс Heberlein (sintering) process.
гебронит *m.* hebronite.
Гевелий Hevelius (lunar crater).
Гевелиуса гало Hevelian halo, halo of Hevelius.
геветтит *m.* hewettite.
Гегенбауера (Гегенбауэра) полином Gegenbauer polynomial; **Г. функция** G. function.
Геде насос Gaede pump; **Г. ртутный насос** G. mercury pump.
Гедель Gödel.
геденбергит *m.* hedenbergite.
гедифан *m.* hedyphane.
гезенк *m.* (min.) blind shaft.
Гезиод Hesiodus (lunar crater).
геиерит *m.* geyerite.
геикилит *m.* geikielite.
гейбахит *m.* heubachite.
Гейгера/-Мюллера счетчик Geiger-Mueller counter; **Г.-Наттола (Неттола, Нэттола, Нуттола) закон** G.-Nuttall law; **Г. счетчик** G. (-Mueller) counter; **гейгеровская область** G. plateau.
Гейзенберга принцип неопределенности, гейзенберговский принцип Heisenberg uncertainty principle; **Г. соотношение неопределенностей** H. uncertainty relation.
гейзер *m.* geyser.
гейландит *m.* heulandite.
Гейли метод Gayley process.
Гей-Люссак Gay-Lussac (lunar crater).
Гей-Люссака башня Gay-Lussac tower; **Г.-Л. закон объемных отношений** G.-L. law of combining volumes; **Г.Л.-Шарля закон** G.-L. law; Charles law.
гейлюссит *m.* gay-lussite.
Гейнзий Heinsius (lunar crater).
гейнтцит *m.* heintzite.
Гейслера насос Geissler (mercury) pump; **Г. сплав** Heusler alloy (manganese-copper-aluminum ferromagnetic alloy); **Г. трубка, гейслерова трубка** Geissler tube.
Гейтеля эффект Geitel effect.
Гейтлера-Лондона модель Heitler-London model; **Г.-Л. теория ковалентной связи** H.-L. covalence theory; **гейтлеровская единица длины** H. unit (or length).
гекза—, гекса— *prefix* hexa—.
гексаг. *abbr.* (**гексагональный**) hexagonal.

гексагидрит *m.* hexahydrite.
гексагир/а *f.* sixfold axis of symmetry; —**ный** *a.* (cryst.) hexagonal.
гексагонально— *prefix* hexagonal.
гекса/гональный *a.* hexagonal; —**декан** *m.* hexadecane; —**замещенный** *a.* hexasubstituted; —**кисоктаэдр** *m.* (cryst.) hexakisoöctahedron, hexoctahedron; —**мер** *m.* hexamer.
гексан *m.* hexane.
гексасимметричная поверхность (cryst.) hexasymmetrical plane.
гексатетраэдр *m.* hexatetrahedron; —**ический** *a.* hexatetrahedral.
гекса/циклический *a.* hexacyclic; —**эдр** *m.* hexahedron; —**эдрический** *a.* hexahedral.
гексод *m.* hexode; **г. с переменной крутизной** variable-mu hexode.
гексоктаэдр *m.* hexoctahedron.
гектар *m.* hectare (10^4 m^2, 2.47 acres).
гекто— *prefix* hecto—.
гектоватт *m.* hectowatt; **г.-час** hectowatt-hour.
гекто/грамм *m.* hectogram; —**граф** *m.* hectograph; —**графический** *a.* hectographic; —**д** *see* **гексод**; —**литр** *m.* hectoliter; —**метр** *m.* hectometer; —**пьеза** *f.* hectopieza (hpz) (pressure unit equal to 1 bar, 10^6 dynes/cm^2).
геленит *m.* gehlenite.
гелеобраз/ный *a.* gel-like, gelatinous; —**ование** *n.* gelation.
гелиев/о-водяной теплообменник helium-water exchanger; —**ый** *a.* helium; —**ая температура** liquid-helium temperature; —**ое охлаждение** helium cooling.
гелий *m.* helium (He).
геликоид *m.* helicoid; —**альный** *a.* helicoid, helical, spiral.
Геликон Helicon (lunar crater).
геликоптер *m.* helicopter.
гелио— *prefix* helio—.
гелио/геофизика *f.* heliogeophysics; —**гравюра** *f.* heliogravure; —**грамма** *f.* heliogram.
гелиограф *m.* heliograph; —**ический** *a.* heliographic; —**ия** *f.* heliography.
гелиодор *m.* heliodor.
гелио/лампа *f.* heliolamp; —**метр** *m.* heliometer.
гелио/подобный *a.* heliumlike; —**скоп** *m.* helioscope; —**стат** *m.* heliostat; —**сфера** *f.* heliosphere; —**техника** *f.* applied solar energy.
гелиотроп *m.* (surv.) heliotrope, heliograph; —**ический ветер** heliotropic wind; —**овый** *a.* heliotrope, heliotropic.
гелио/физика *f.* solar physics; —**физический** *a.* heliophysical; —**центрический** *a.* heliocentric.
гелит *m.* hoelite.
Гелл Hell (lunar crater).
гелландит *m.* hellandite.
Геллезена элемент Hellesen cell.
Геллера процесс Heller process.
гель *m.* gel; **г. кремнекислоты** silica gel.
гельвин *m.* helvine.
Гельдера условие Hölder boundary condition.
гельдерберг/иан *m.*, —**ская формация** (geo.) Helderbergian formation.
Гельмгольца двойной слой Helmholtz double layer; **Г. кольца** H. coils; **Г. теорема** H. theorem; **Г. формула** H. equation.
Гельмерта формула Helmert formula.
гема— *prefix* hema—.
гематин *m.* hematin; —**овый** *a.* hematinic.
гематит *m.* hematite; —**овый** *a.* hematite, hematitic; —**овая руда** hematite; —**оподобный** *a.* hematitic.
гемато *prefix* hemato—, blood.
гемералопия *f.* hemeralopia.
геми— *prefix* hemi—, semi—.
гемикристаллический *a.* hemicrystalline, hypocrystalline, semicrystalline.
гемиморф/изм *m.* (cryst.) hemimorphism; —**ит** *m.* hemimorphite; —**ный** *a.* hemimorphic.
Гемин Geminus (lunar crater).
Геминиды Geminids (meteors).
геми/пирамида *f.* hemipyramid; —**призма** *f.* hemiprism.
гемисфер/а *f.* hemisphere; —**ический** *a.* hemispheric, hemispherical.
гемит *m.* (elec.) Hemit (insulation).
гемитроп/ический, —ный *a.* (cryst.) twinned, hemitropic, hemitrope.
гемиэдр *m.* hemihedron; —**ический** *a.* hemihedral; —**ия** *f.* hemihedrism.
гемма *f.* gem.

гемо— *prefix* hemo—.
гемоглобин *m.* hemoglobin.
Гемпеля бюретка Hempel gas buret.
Гемфри насос Humphrey pump.
ген *abbr.* (**генеральный**) general (used as a prefix).
ген *m.* gene.
генвудит *m.* henwoodite.
Гендерсона явление для pH Henderson equation for pH.
генеалогический *a.* genealogical, parentage; **г. коэффициент** (nucl.) fractional parentage coefficient.
генезис *m.* genesis, origin.
генеральн/ый *a.* general; **—ая совокупность** (stat.) population.
генератор *m.* generator, oscillator; **г. асинхронный** induction generator; **г. гармоник** harmonic oscillator; **г. для электрической молекулярной модуляции** Stark modulator; **г. задающий** master oscillator; **г. колебаний** oscillator; **г. модулированный импульсами** pulse-modulated oscillator; **г. нейтронов** neutron generator; **г. опорного напряжения** reference generator; **г. реактивный** reluctance generator; **г. сигнала** signal generator; **г. ультракоротких волн** ultra-high-frequency oscillator; **г. электромашинный** dynamo generator.
генераторн/ый *a.* generator, generating; **г. агрегат** generator, generating set; **г. триод** transmitting triode; **—ая станция** power station.
генератриса *f.* generatrix, generator.
генерац/ионная модель generation model; **—ия** *f.* generation, production; **—ия нейтронов** neutron production.
генерир/ование *see* **генерация**; **—ованный** *a.* generated; **—овать** *v.* generate; **—ующий кристалл** oscillating crystal.
генет/ика *f.* genetics; **—ический** *a.* genetic.
ген/иальный *a.* ingenious, brilliant; **—ий** *m.* genius.
Генки/-Прандтля сетка Hencky-Prandtl net; **Г. теорема** H. theorem.
Геннинга пирометр Henning pyrometer.
генри *n.* henry (unit) (h); **Генри закон** Henry law; **—метр** *m.* henrymeter.
гентит *m.* genthite.
гео— *prefix* geo—.
геогидрология *f.* geohydrology.
геогр. *abbr.* (**география**) geography; (**географический**) geographic.
геограмма *f.* geogram.
географ *m.* geographer; **—ический** *a.* geographic; **—ическая координата** geographic coordinate, bearing; **—ия** *f.* geography.
геод. *abbr.* (**геодезия**) geodesy; (**геодезический**) geodesic, geodetic.
геодез/ист *m.* geodesist; **—ический** *a.* geodesic, geodetic; **—ический базис** geodesic base line; **—ическая съемка** geodetic survey; **—ия** *f.* geodesy.
геодепрессия *f.* geodepression.
геоид *m.* geoid.
геоизотерма *f.* geoisotherm.
геокороний *m.* geocoronium.
геокриология *f.* cryopedology.
геол. *abbr.* (**геология**) geology; (**геологический**) geological.
геолог *m.* geologist; **—ический** *a.* geological; **—ическое летоисчисление** geochronology; **—ия** *f.* geology.
геомагнетизм *m.* geomagnetism.
геомагнит/ный *a.* geomagnetic; **г. полюс, —ная широта** geomagnetic latitude; **—ное возмущение** geomagnetic storm (disturbance); **—олог** *m.* geomagnetician.
геометрически *adv.* geometrically; **г. складывать** add vectionally.
геометрическ/ий, геометральный *a.* geometric; **г. параметр** geometric parameter; size-shape factor; **г. параметр кривизны** geometric buckling; **г. ряд** geometric progression; **г. фактор** geometry factor; **—ая оптика** geometrical optics; **—ая сумма** vector sum; **—ое место** locus; **—ое сечение** geometrical cross section; **—ие размеры** "the geometry" (of an experiment).
геометрия *f.* geometry; **г. положения** analysis situs, topology; **г. счета** counting geometry.
геоморф/ный *a.* geomorphic; **—ология** *f.* geomorphology.
геономия *f.* geonomy.

геопотенциал *m*., **—ьный** *a*. geopotential; **—ьный метр** geopotential meter.

геосинклиналь *m*. geosyncline; **—ный** *a*. geosynclinal.

геострофическ/ий перенос geostrophic transport; **—ая слагающая** geostrophic component; **—ое отклонение** geostrophic departure (deviation); **—ое течение** geostrophic current.

гео/строфия *f*. geostrophism; **—сфера** *f*. geosphere.

геотектонический *a*. geotectonic.

геотермика *f*. thermal studies (or history), geothermy, geothermometry.

геотерм/ический *a*. geothermic, geothermal; **г. градиент** geothermal gradient; **—ическая ступень** geothermic step; **—ия** *see* **геотермика**; **—ометр** *m*. geothermometer.

Геофиан *abbr*. (**Геофизический институт Академии наук СССР**) Geophysical Institute of the Academy of Sciences, USSR.

геофиз. *abbr*. (**геофизика**) geophysics; (**геофизический**) geophysical.

геофиз/ик *m*. geophysicist; **г.-разведчик** exploration geophysicist; **—ика** *f*. geophysics; **—ический** *a*. geophysical; **—ическая разведка** geophysical prospecting.

геофон *m*. geophone.

ГЕОХИ *abbr*. (**Институт геохимии и аналитической химии**) Institute of Geochemistry and Analytical Chemistry.

геохим/ический *a*. geochemical; **—ия** *f*. geochemistry.

геохронология *f*. geochronology.

гео/центрический *a*. geocentric; **—электрический** *a*. geoelectric.

гепта— *prefix* hepta—.

гептагональный *a*. heptagonal.

гептадекан *m*. heptadecane.

гептан *m*. heptane.

гептаэдр *m*. heptahedron; **—ический** *a*. heptahedral.

гептод *m*. heptode, pentagrid; **г.-смеситель** heptode mixer, pentagrid mixer.

Гепфнера процесс Höpfner process.

Геральд Herald (reactor).

герапатит *m*. herapathite.

герб *m*. head (of coin).

гергардтит *m*. gerhardtite.

гердерит *m*. herderite.

Гересгофа печь Herreshoff furnace.

Герике Guerike (lunar crater).

Герке осциллограф Gehrke oscillograph.

Геркулес Hercules (Her) (constellation); Hercules (lunar crater).

геркулой *m*. Herculoy (copper alloy).

Герлаха и Штерна опыт Stern-Gerlach experiment.

герм. *abbr*. (**германский**) German.

Германа-Могена символ Hermann-Maugin symbol.

герман/иевый фотоэлемент germanium photocell; **—ий** *m*. germanium (Ge).

Германия Germany; *see also* **ГДР, ФРГ.**

Германская Демократическая Республика German Democratic Republic.

Гермес Hermes.

герметизация *f*. hermetic sealing, canning, pressurization.

герметизирован/ие *n*. pressurizing; **—ный** *see* **герметический**; **—ный мотор** canned motor.

герметическ/и *adv*. hermetically; **г. закрытый, г. закупоренный, г. запаянный** hermetically sealed, leakproof, canned; vacuum-packed; **—ий** *a*. airtight, vacuumtight, hermetic, leakproof, canned; pressurized; **—ий затвор** hermetic seal; **—ий ртутный барометр** sealed mercury barometer; **—ая система** airtight system, leaktight system.

герметичн/ость *f*. vacuum seal, airtightness; **—ый** *see* **герметический.**

гернезит *m*. hoernesite.

Геродот Herodot (lunar crater).

геронов шар Heron sphere.

герполодия *f*. herpolhode.

герренгрундит *m*. herrengrundite.

Герстнера волны (hyd.) Gerstner waves.

Герти генератор Heurty generator.

Гертнер Goertner (lunar crater).

Геру дуговая печь Heroult furnace.

Герхардта правило Gerhardt law.

Герхольма спектрометр Gerholm spectrometer.

герц *m*. hertz, cycle per second (cps).

Герца волны Hertz waves; **Г. диполь** H. antenna, half-wave dipole; **Г. теория** H. theory.

герцин/ит *m.* hercynite; **—ская складчатость** (geo.) Hercynian folding.

Герцшпрунга разрыв Hertzsprung gap.

гершелит *m.* herschelite.

Гершель Herschel (lunar crater).

Гершеля эффект (**явлеине**) Herschel effect.

Гесса закон Hess law.

гессиан *m.* Hessian.

гессит *m.* hessite.

Гесслера сплав *see* **Гейслера сплав.**

гессонит *m.* hessonite.

гетеро— *prefix* hetero—.

гетероатом *m.* heteroatom; **—ный** *a.* heteroatomic.

гетерогальванометр *m.* heterogalvanometer.

гетероген/ит *m.* heterogenite; **—ность** *f.* heterogeneity.

гетерогенн/ый *a.* heterogeneous; **г. катализ** heterogeneous catalysis; **г. пучок** heterogeneous beam; **г. реактор** heterogeneous reactor; **—ая решетка** heterogeneous lattice.

гетеродин *m.*, **—ный** *a.* heterodyne, local oscillator, beat-frequency oscillator; **местный г.** local oscillator; **—ный прием** heterodyne reception.

гетеродирование *n.* heterodyning.

гетеролиз *m.* heterolysis.

гетеролит *m.* hetaerolite.

гетероморф/изм *m.* heteromorphism; **—ит** *m.* heteromorphite; **—ный** *a.* heteromorphous, heteromorphic.

гетеропический *a.* heteropic.

гетерополярн/ость *f.* heteropolarity; **—ый** *a.* heteropolar; **—ая связь** heteropolar bond, ionic bond; **—ое соединение** heteropolar compound.

гетеростатическ/ий способ heterostatic method; **—ое включение** heterostatic (electrometer) connection.

гетеро/сфера *f.* heterosphere; **—томный** *a.* heterotomous; **—трофный** *a.* heterotrophic; **—фазный** *a.* heterophase; **—хромный** *a.* heterochrome, heterochromatic.

гетероциклическ/ий *a.* (chem.) heterocyclic, heteronuclear; **—ое ядро** heteronucleus; **—ие соединения** heterocyclic compounds.

гетинакс *m.* laminated Bakelite insulation, micarta.

гетит *m.* goethite.

геттангский ярус (geo.) Hettangian stage.

геттер *m.* getter; **—ный порошок** getter powder; **—ная таблетка** getter pellet.

геферит *m.* hoeferite.

Гефнера свеча, гефнерова свеча Hefner lamp (or candle).

ГЗИП *abbr.* (**Государственный завод измерительных приборов**) State Measuring Instruments Plant.

ГИ *abbr.* (**Государственное издательство**) State Press.

Гиады (astr.) Hyades.

гиалиновый *a.* glassy.

гиалит *m.* hyalite.

гиало— *prefix* hyalo—, hyal—.

гиалограф/ический *a.* hyalographic; **—ия** *f.* hyalography.

гиалоидный *see* **гиалиновый.**

гиало/кристаллический *a.* hyalocrystalline; **—пилитовая структура** hyalopilitic texture; **—сидерит** *m.* hyalosiderite; **—текит** *m.* hyalotekite.

гиалофан *m.* hyalophane.

гиацинт *m.* hyacinth (variety of zircon).

гиб *m.* bend, bending; **испытание на г. с перегибом** backward-and-forward bending test.

Гиббса адсорбционное уравнение Gibbs adsorption equation; **Г. большое каноническое распределение** G. grand canonical ensemble; **Г. парадокс** G. paradox; **Г. правило** G. rule; **Г. правило фаз** G. phase rule; **уравнение Г.-Гельмгольца** G.-Helmholtz equation; **явление Г.** G. phenomenon.

гибель *f.* ruin, destruction, decomposition, loss; death; **—ный** *a.* destructive, disastrous.

гибк/а *f.* bending; **—ий** *a.* flexible, elastic, pliant; **—ий вал** flexible shaft; **—ая нить** torsion fiber; **—ое сочленение** flexible coupling (joint).

гибкость *f.* flexibility, pliability, ductility; **акустическая г.** acoustic compliance.

гибочный *a.* bending.

гибрид *m.* hybrid; **—изация** *f.* hybridization; **—изированная орбита** hybridized orbital; **—изованный** *a.* hybridized; **—ный** *a.* hybrid.

гибшит *m.* hibschite.

ГИВД *abbr.* (**Государственный научно-исследовательский институт высоких давлений**) State High Pressure Research Institute.

гига— *prefix* giga— (10^9).

гигагерц *m.* gigacycle.

гигант *m.* giant; **—ский** *a.* gigantic, huge; **—ский резонанс** giant resonance.

гигаэлектрон-вольт gigaelectronvolt, Gev.

гиггинсит *m.* higginsite.

гигиена *f.* hygiene, sanitation.

Гигин Hyginus (lunar crater).

гигро— *prefix* hygro—.

гигро/грамма *f.* hygrogram; **—граф** *m.* hygrograph; **—логия** *f.* hygrology.

гигрометр *m.* hygrometer; **г. весовой** balance hygrometer; **г. волосяной** hair hygrometer; **—ический** *a.* hygrometric; **—ия** *f.* hygrometry.

гигроскоп *m.* hygroscope; **—ический, —ичный** *a.* hygroscopic; **—ичность** *f.* hygroscopicity.

гигро/стат *m.* hygrostat; **—термограф** *m.* hygrothermograph; **—электрометр** *m.* hygroelectrometer.

гид *m.* guide.

гидато/генезис *m.* (geo.) hydatogenesis; **—генный** *a.* hydatogenic.

гидденит *m.* hiddenite.

гидирование *n.* guiding.

гидр— *prefix* hydr—.

Гидра Hydra (Hya) (constellation).

гидравлик *m.* hydraulician; **—а** *f.* hydraulics.

гидравлическ/ий *a.* hydraulic; **г. затвор** hydraulic seal; **г. прыжок** hydraulic jump; **г. уклон** hydraulic gradient; **—ая сила** water power; **—ое колесо** water wheel.

гидравличность *f.* hydraulicity.

гидразин *m.* hydrazine.

гидрат *m.* hydrate; **г. закиси** hydroxide (—ous hydroxide); **г. окиси** hydroxide (—ic hydroxide).

гидрат/ация, —изация *f.* hydration; **—изированный, —ированный** *a.* hydrated; **—изировать** *v.* hydrate; **—ный** *a.* hydrate, hydrated; **—ная вода** water of hydration.

гидрация *see* **гидратация.**

гидрид *m.* hydride; **г. лития** lithium hydride.

гидрир/ование *n.* hydrogenation; **—ованный** *a.* hydrogenated; **—овать** *v.* hydrogenate, hydrogenize; **—ующий** *a.* hydrogenant.

гидро— *prefix* hydro—, hydr—, hydraulic.

гидроген/изация *f.* hydrogenation; **—изированный, —изирующий** *a.* hydrogenant; **—изованный** *a.* hydrogenized, hydrogenated; **—изовать** *v.* hydrogenate; **—ный** *a.* hydrogen, hydrogenous.

гидро/геология *f.* hydrogeology; **—геохимический** *a.* hydrogeochemical.

гидрограф *m.* hydrograph; hydrographer; **г. наводнения** flood hydrograph; **—ический** *a.* hydrographic; **—ия** *f.* hydrography.

гидродинам/ика *f.* hydrodynamics; **—ический** *a.* hydrodynamic; **—ометр** *m.* hydrodynamometer.

гидрозатвор *m.* hydroseal, water seal.

гидрокластический *a.* hydroclastic.

гидрокрыло *n.* hydrofoil.

гидрокси— *prefix* hydroxy—.

гидроксил *m.*, **—ьный** *a.* hydroxyl.

гидроксоний *m.* hydroxonium, hydronium.

гидрол *m.* hydrol; water molecule.

гидролиз *m.* hydrolysis; **—ация** *f.* hydrolyzing, hydrolysis; **—ировать, —овать** *v.* hydrolyze; **—ующий** *a.* hydrolyzing; **—ующийся металл** hydrolyzable metal.

гидролит *m.* hydrolyte; **—ический** *a.* hydrolytic; **—ическое расщепление** hydrolytic dissociation.

гидролог. *abbr.* (**гидрологический**) hydrologic.

гидролог *m.* hydrologist; **—ический** *a.* hydrologic; **—ия** *f.* hydrology.

гидрометеор *m.* hydrometeor.

гидрометеоролог *m.* hydrometeorologist; **—ическая станция** hydrometeorological station; —**ия** *f.* hydrometeorology.

гидрометр *m.* hydrometer; flowmeter; —**ический** *a.* hydrometric; —**ическая вертушка** current meter; —**ия** *f.* hydrometry; —**ограф** *m.* hydrometrograph.

гидромехан/ика *f.* hydromechanics, fluid mechanics.

гидромодуль *m.* hydromodulus.

гидроналиум *m.* Hydronalium (aluminum alloy).

гидронастуран *m.* hydrouraninite.

гидро/окись *f.* hydroxide, hydrate; —**перекись** *f.* hydrogen peroxide.

гидро/почта *f.* hydraulic rabbit; —**прогноз** *m.* hydrologic forecasting; —**проект** *m.* hydroelectric power project; —**режим** *m.* hydrologic regime; —**самолет** *m.* hydroplane, seaplane; —**силовая установка** hydroelectric power plant; —**скоп** *m.* hydroscope; —**станция** *f.* hydroelectric power plant.

гидростат *m.* hydrostat; —**ика** *f.* hydrostatics.

гидростатическ/ий *a.* hydrostatic; —**ое давление, г. сжатие** hydrostatic pressure; —**ое напряжение** hydrostatic stress.

Гидростройпроект *abbr.* (**Государственный институт по строительному и рабочему проектированию гидроэнергоузлов**) State Institute for the Design and Layout of Hydroelectric Developments.

гидро/сфера *f.* hydrosphere; —**термальный,** —**термический** *a.* hydrothermal.

гидротехн/ик *m.* hydraulic engineer; —**ика** *f.*, —**ический** *a.* hydraulic engineering; —**ическое сооружение** hydraulic structure; —**ические изыскания** hydraulic engineering research.

гидроторит *m.* hydrothorite.

гидро/тропность *f.* hydrotropism; —**турбина** *f.* hydroturbine; —**физика** *f.* hydrophysics.

гидрофильн/ость *f.* hydrophilic nature; —**ый** *a.* hydrophilic.

гидро/фон *m.* hydrophone; —**фор** *m.* hydrophore; —**хинон** *m.* hydroquinone; —**хлорид** *m.* hydrochloride; —**целлюлоза** *f.* hydrocellulose; —**централь** *m.* hydroelectric plant; —**экстрактор** *m.* hydroextractor.

гидроэлектрическ/ий *a.* hydroelectric; —**ая станция** hydroelectric power plant.

гидроэнерг/етический *a.*, —**ия** *f.* water power.

Гидроэнергопроект *abbr.* (**Всесоюзный трест по проектированию гидроэлектростанций и гидроэлектроузлов**) All-Union Trust for the Design and Planning of Hydroelectric Power Plants and Hydroelectric Developments.

гиельмит *m.* hjelmite.

гиератит *m.* hieratite.

гиетный *a.* hyetal.

ГИЗ *abbr.* (**Государственное издательство**) State Press.

гизекит *m.* gieseckite.

гизингерит *m.* hisingerite.

Гийо Guillaud.

ГИКИ *abbr.* (**Государственный исследовательский керамический институт**) State Ceramics Research Institute.

гикомакс *m.* Hycomax (iron-cobalt-nickel-aluminum-copper alloy).

Гил-Шоу опыт Hele-Shaw experiment.

гиллебрандит *m.* hillebrandite.

Гиллери линейка (met.) Guillery ruler.

гильберт *m.* gilbert (unit).

Гильберта преобразование Hilbert transform; **Г.-Шмидта теорема** H.-Schmidt theorem; **гильбертово пространство** H. space.

гильдит *m.* guildite.

гильз/а *f.*, —**овый** *a.* case; sleeve, bushing.

Гильо способ Guillot method.

гильотин/а *f.*, —**ный** *a.*, —**ные ножницы** guillotine; —**ный множитель** (astr.) guillotine factor.

гильош *m.* guilloche.

гильпинит *m.* gilpinite.

ГИМ *abbr.* (**Государственный институт метеорологии**) State Institute of Meteorology.

гиместанция *abbr.* (**гидрометеорологическая станция**) hydrometeorological station.

гимназ/ист *m.*, **—истка** *f.* secondary school student; **—ия** *f.* secondary school, high school.

гимнит *m.* gymnite.

гиму *m.* Hymu (molybdenum-nickel-iron alloy)

Гин-Пластмасс *abbr.* (**Государственный научно-исследовательский институт пластических масс**) State Plastics Scientific Research Institute.

гинсдалит *m.* hinsdalite.

гинтцеит *m.* hintzeite.

Гинцветмет *abbr.* (**Государственный институт по цветным металлам**) State Institute of Nonferrous Metals.

гиортдалит *m.* hiortdahlite.

гипабиссальный *a.* hypabyssal.

гипаутоморфный *a.* hypautomorphic, hypidiomorphic.

гипер— *prefix* hyper—.

гипербол/а *f.* hyperbola; **—ический** *a.* hyperbolic.

гиперболоид *m.* hyperboloid.

гипер/борейский *a.* hyperborean; **—геометрическая функция** hypergeometric function; **—заряд** *m.* hypercharge; **—звук** *m.* hypersound, hypersonics; **—звуковой** *a.* hypersonic; **—квантование** *n.* hyperquantization.

гиперко *m.* Hiperco (iron-chromium-cobalt alloy).

гиперкоммутация *f.* (elec.) overcommutation.

гиперкомпаундирован/ие *n.* overcompounding.

гипер/комплексный *a.* hypercomplex; **—конъюгация** *f.* hyperconjugation.

гиперник *m.* Hipernik, Hypernick (iron-nickel alloy).

гиперон *m.* hyperon.

гипер/осколок *m.* hyperfragment; **—параллелепипед** *m.* hyperparallelepiped; **—плоскость** *f.* hyperplane; **—поверхность** *f.* hypersurface.

гиперсенсибилиз/ация *f.*, **—ирование** *n.* hypersensitizing, hypersensitization.

гиперсил *see* **гайперсил.**

гипер/синхронный *a.* hypersynchronous; **—тонический** *a.* hypertonic; **—форическое изменение** hyperphoric alteration; **—фрагмент** *see* **гиперядро.**

гипер/хроматическая линза hyperchromatic lens; **—хромный** *a.* hyperchromic; **—центрический** *a.* hypercentric; **—эллиптический интеграл** hyperelliptic integral; **—ядро** *n.* hyperfragment, hypernucleus.

гипидиоморфный *a.* hypidiomorphic.

гипнотический *a.* hypnotic.

гипо— *prefix* hypo—.

гипо/кристаллический *a.* hypocrystalline; **—синхронный** *a.* hyposynchronous.

гипосульфит *m.* hyposulfite.

гипотеза *f.* hypothesis; **г. небулярная** nebular hypothesis.

гипотенуза *f.* hypotenuse.

гипотермальный *a.* hypothermal.

гипотетич/ность *f.* hypothetical character; **—ный, —еский** *a.* hypothetical.

гипо/хромный эффект hypochromic effect; **—центр** *m.* (seis.) hypocenter, center of origin; **—циклоида** *f.* (math.) hypocycloid.

Гиппал Hippalus (lunar crater).

гипс *m.* gypsum; plaster of Paris; **—овый** *a.* gypsum, gypseous; plaster.

гипсограф *m.* hypsograph; **—ия** *f.* hypsography.

гипсометр *m.* hypsometer.

гипсотермометр *m.* hypsothermometer.

гипсохром *m.* hypsochrome.

гира/тор *m.* gyrator; **—ционный эллипсоид** ellipsoid of gyration.

гиргол *m.* hyrgol.

Гиредмет *abbr.* (**Государственный научно-исследовательский институт редких металлов**) State Rare Metals Research Institute.

гирлянда *f.* garland, chain; **г. изоляторов** insulator chain.

гирный *a.* weight (of balance).

гиро/вертикаль *f.* gyro-vertical, vertical gyroscope; **—горизонт** *m.* gyro-horizontal.

гироида *f.* rotoinversion axis; **—идальный** *a.* (cryst.) gyroidal.

гирокомпас *m.* gyrocompass.

гиролит *m.* gyrolite.

гиромагнитн/ый *a.* gyromagnetic; **—ая частота** Larmor (gyromagnetic) frequency; **—ое отношение** gyromagnetic ratio.

гирорезонанс *m.* gyro-resonance.

гироскопическ/ий *a.* gyroscopic; **г. компас** gyrocompass; **—ая частота** gyroscopic frequency.

гиростабилизованный *a.* gyrostabilized.

гиростат *m.* gyrostat; **—ика** *f.* gyrostatics; **—ический** *a.* gyrostatic.

гиро/тропный *a.* gyrotropic; **г. волновод** gyrotropic-medium waveguide; **—частота** *f.* gyrofrequency; **—эдрический** *see* **гироидальный.**

гиря *f.* weight.

гистерези/граф *m.* hysteresigraph; **—метр** *m.* hysteresimeter.

гистерезис *m.* hysteresis, lag; **г. вращения** rotating hysteresis; **вязкий г., ползучий г.** hysteresis lag, magnetic creeping; **коэффициент —а** hysteresis constant.

гистерезис/ный *see* **гистерезис**; **—ная петля** hysteresis loop; **—ограф** *m.* hysteresisograph.

гистеро/генный *a.* hysterogenetic; **—кристаллизация** *f.* hysterocrystallization; **—морфный** *a.* hysteromorphic.

гистограмма *f.* histogram, bar graph.

гистриксит *m.* histrixite.

гитерманит *m.* guitermanite.

ГИТТЛ *abbr.* (**Государственное издательство технической и теоретической литературы**) State Technical and Theoretical Press.

Гитторфа темное пространство Hittorf dark space, cathode dark space; **Г. трубка** H. tube.

гитчекокит *m.* hitchcockite.

Гифар Hifar (high-flux Australian reactor).

ГИФТИ *abbr.* (**Горьковский исследовательский физико-технический институт**) Gor'ki Research Institute of Physics and Technology.

ГИЭКИ *abbr.* (**Государственный исследовательский электрокерамический институт**) State Electroceramics Research Institute.

ГКП *abbr.* (**Главное управление кислородной промышленности**) Main Administration of the Oxygen Industry.

гл *abbr.* (**гектолитр**) hectoliter; **гл.** (**глава**) chapter (in bibliography); (**главный**) chief, principal, main; (**глубина**) depth.

глав. *abbr.* (**главный**) chief, principal, main.

глав— *prefix see* **главный.**

глав/а *f.* chapter; head; **—енство** *n.* supremacy, domination; **—енствовать** *v.* predominate.

главко— *prefix* glauco—.

Главмервес *abbr.* (**Главное управление мер и весов**) Bureau of Weights and Measures.

Главнаука *abbr.* (**Главное управление научными учреждениями**) Central Scientific Board.

главнейший *a.* chief, predominant.

главн/ый *a.* chief, principal, main, major, dominant, leading; (mech.) master; **г. канал** main channel; **г. луч** chief ray; **г. максимум** (opt.) principal maximum; **г. момент инерции** principal moment of inertia; **г. удар** (seis.) principal shock; **г. фокус** principal focus; **г. член** dominant term; **—ая балка** main beam; **—ая диагональ** principal diagonal; **—ая нормаль** (math.) principal normal; **—ая ось** major axis, principal axis; **—ая плоскость** (opt.) principal plane; **—ая последовательность** (astr.) main sequence; **—ая секция кристалла** principal crystal section; **—ая серия** principal series; **—ая точка** (opt.) principal point; **—ая хорда** principal chord.

главн/ый *cont.*, **—ое значение** (math.) principal value; **—ое квантовое число** principal quantum number; **—ое направление** principal direction; **—ое напряжение** principal stress; **—ое удлинение** principal extension; **—ое управление** central administration (or board); **—ые ветры** cardinal winds; **—ые румбы компаса** cardinal points; **—ым образом** mainly, for the most part, primarily, principally, chiefly.

Главприбор *abbr.* (**Главное управление приборостроения**) Main Instrument Industry Administration.

Главсевморпуть *abbr.* (**Главное управление Северного Морского Пути**) Main Administration of the Northern Sea Route.

глагол *m.* verb.

гладильный *a.* polishing, smoothing.

глад/ить *v.* polish, smooth; **—кий** *a.* smooth, plain, even; (math.) continuous, differentiable: **—ко** *adv.* smoothly; **—кое сшивание** smooth joining; **—кость** *f.* smoothness, evenness; **—ь** *f.* (water) smooth surface, even surface.

глаже *comp. of* **гладкий, гладко,** smoother, more even.

глаз *m.* eye; **г. бури** eye of storm; **вооруженный г.** aided eye; **на г.** estimated (by eye); **невооруженный г.** unaided (or naked) eye; **бросающийся в —а** conspicuous.

Глазебрука призма Glazebrook prism.

глазиров/ание *n.*, **—ка** *f.* glaze, glazing; **—анный** *a.* glazed; **—ать** *v.* glaze.

глаз/ной *a.* eye, ocular, optic, ophthalmic; **—ная впадина** eye socket, orbit; **—ное яблоко** eyeball; **—ок** *m.* eye, eyelet; inspection hole, peephole; aperture, hole (of die); (screen) mesh.

глазомер *m.*, **—ная оценка** visual estimate; **—ный** *a.* visual, by eye.

глазообразный *a.* eye-shaped, oculiform.

глазур/енный, —ованный *a.* glazed; enameled, lacquered; **—ь** *f.* glaze; enamel, lacquer.

Глана призма, Г.-Томсона призма Glan prism, G.-Thompson prism.

гласить *v.* state, read (have wording).

гласн/ость *f.* publicity, public knowledge; **—ый** *a.* public, open; vowel; **—ый звук** vowel sound.

глаубер/ит *m.* glauberite; **—ова соль** Glauber salt.

глауко— *see* **главко—**.

глациальный *a.* glacial.

глетчер *m.* glacier; **—ный айсберг** glacier iceberg.

глико— *prefix* glyco—; gluco—.

гликол *m.* glycol.

глина *f.* clay; loam; **белая г., фарфоровая г.** kaolin; **жирная г.** loam; **формовая г.** putty.

глинец *m.* clay sand; **квасцовый г.** alum shale.

глиний *see* **глинозем.**

глинисто— *prefix* argillo—.

глинист/ый *a.* clay, argillaceous; **г. песчаник** argillaceous sandstone; **г. сланец** slate, argillite, shale; **—ая порода** clay rock.

глиножелезистый *a.* argilloferruginous.

глинозем *m.* alumina, aluminum oxide; **белый г.** kaolin; **водный г., гидрат —а** aluminum hydroxide.

глиноносный *a.* clayey, argillaceous.

глиняный *a.* clay, clayey, argillaceous; loam.

глицерин *m.* glycerin.

глицерин— *prefix* glycero—.

глицерол glycerol.

глицин *m.* glycine.

глобальный *a.* total, combined; global.

глобар *m.* globar (lamp).

глобозит *m.* globosite.

глобоидальный *a.* globoid, globate, globular.

гл. обр. *abbr.* (**главным образом**) mainly, principally, chiefly.

глобул/а, —ь *f.* globule; **—ит** *m.* globulite; **—ярный** *a.* globular.

глобус *m.*, **—ный** *a.* globe.

глокерит *m.* glockerite.

глория *f.* glory.

глосса *f.* gloss.

глоссарий *m.* glossary.

глуб. *abbr.* (**глубина**) depth.

глубже *comp. of* **глубокий, глубоко,** deeper.

глубин/а *f.* depth; intensity; interior; **г. вдавливания** depth of penetration; **г. выгорания** burnup (fraction); **г. депрессии** depth of depression; **г. модуляции** percentage modulation, modulation index; **г. проникновения** skin thickness; depth of penetration; **г. резкости** depth of focus **г. трения** depth of frictional resistance; **г. фокуса** depth of focus; **на —е** deep.

глубинн/ость *f.* (depth of) penetration; **—ый** *a.* depth, deep; abyssal; bathymetric; **—ый ход интенсивности**

depth—intensity curve; **—ая доза** depth dose.

глубино/измерительный прибор, —мер *see* **глубомер.**

глубок/ий *a.* deep, deep-seated, thorough, extreme, profound; **—ая вытяжка** deep drawing; **—ая доза** depth dose; **—ое выгорание** high burnup; **—ое охлаждение** deep-freezing.

глубоко *adv.* deeply; **г. находящийся** deep-seated; **г. расположенный участок** deep-lying portion.

глубоко/водный взрыв deep-water explosion; **—мыслие** *n.*, **—мысленность** *f.* thoughtfulness, profundity; **—отпущенный** *a.* (met.) deep-drawn, cold-work drawn; **—полимеризованный** *a.* highly polymerized; **—сть** *f.* depth, profundity.

глуб/омер *m.* depth gauge, hydrobarometer; **—ь** *see* **глубина.**

глуп/ость *f.* nonsense, foolish mistake; **—ый** *a.* foolish, stupid.

глух/о *adv.* dully; **—ой** *a.* deaf; dull (sound); blind (passage), dead-end; blank; opaque (glass); **—ой диффузор** dummy diffusor; **—ой канал** (reactor) thimble; **—ой фланец** blank flange, blind flange; **—ая камера** dead-end chamber; (acous.) anecoic chamber; **—ая муфта** end sleeve; **—ое помещение** (acous.) dead room; **—ое соединение** dead joint; **—ота** *f.* deafness.

глуш/ение *n.* damping, silencing, extinguishing; (rad.) jamming; **—итель** *m.* silencer, damper, muffler; (rad.) jammer; **—ить** *v.* silence, muffle, damp; (rad.) jam.

глыб/а *f.* lump, block; **—истый, —оватый** *a.* lumpy; **—овая гора** block mountain.

глюкоза *f.* glucose, dextrose.

гляд/ение *n.* looking; **—еть** *v.* look, watch.

глянец *m.* polish, luster, gloss; **наводить г.** polish, gloss, glaze.

глянц/евание *n.* polishing, glossing, glazing; **—еватый** *a.* shiny; **—евать, —овать** *v.* polish, gloss; **—евый, —овый** *a.* glossy; **—евая бумага** glossy paper; **—ованный** *a.* polished, glossed.

гляцио/климатология *f.* glacioclimatology; **—логия** *f.* glaciology.

ГМ *abbr.* (**географическое место светила**) location of a heavenly body.

ГМК *abbr.* (**гиромагнитный компас**) gyromagnetic compass.

гн *abbr.* (**генри**) henry (unit) (h).

гнать *v.* drive, chase; race (engine).

ГНБ *abbr.* (**Государственная научно-техническая библиотека**) State Scientific and Technical Library.

гнезд/о *n.* **—ный, —овой** *a.* recess; socket; jack; nest, pocket; (dictionary) paragraph; **г. и шип** mortise and tenon; **г. клапана** valve seat; **осадок —ами** (geo.) nodular deposit; **—овой отбор** cluster sampling; **—овая панель** jack panel.

гнейс *m.* gneiss.

Гнейсена постоянная Gneisen constant.

гне/сти *v.* press, squeeze; **—т** *m.* press, pressure; **—тение** *n.* pressing, squeezing.

ГНИ *abbr.* (**Государственный научный институт**) State Scientific Institute.

ГНИГИ *abbr.* (**Государственный научно-исследовательский геофизический институт**) State Geophysical Scientific Research Institute.

гномо/н *m.* gnomon; **—ника** *f.* gnomonics; **—нический** *a.* gnomonic; **—ническая проекция** gnomonic projection; **—стереографическая проекция** gnomonic projection.

ГНТИ *abbr.* (**Государственное научно-техническое издательство**) State Science and Technology Press.

ГНТК *abbr.* [**Государственный научно-технический комитет** (**при Совете Министров СССР**)] State Scientific and Technical Committee (in the Council of Ministers, USSR).

гну/тый *a.* bent, curved; **—ть** *v.* bend, curve, flex, buckle; **—щийся** *a.* flexible, elastic, pliable.

Г-образный *a.* L-shaped; **Г-о. уравновешенный четырехполюсник** balanced L-network; **Г-образная антенна** gamma-type antenna, inverted L-type antenna.

гован *m.* (geo.) gowan.

говлит *m.* howlite.

говор/итель *m.* (rad.) speaker; **—ить** *v.* talk, say, speak, tell; mean; **—ить о** indicate, denote; discuss; **не —я** to say nothing (of); **собственно —я, строго —я** strictly speaking; **—ят** it is said, it is claimed; **—ной раструб, —ная воронка** mouthpiece.

гогманнит *m.* hohmannite.

год *m.* year; **г. звездный** sidereal year; **г. прошлый** last year; **г. световой** light year; **—ы** *pl.* years, age.

годжкинсонит *m.* hodgkinsonite.

Годин Godin (lunar crater).

годиться *v.* suit, fit, apply.

годичн/ость *f.* a year's time; **—ый** *a.* annual, yearly; **—ая вариация** seasonal distribution.

годн/ость *f.* suitability, fitness, validity; **—ый** *a.* suitable, fit, valid; **—ый к эксплоатации** fit for service.

годов/ой *a.* annual; **г. ход** annual variation; **—щина** *f.* anniversary.

годо/граф *m.* hodograph, (seis.) travel-time curve; **—скоп** *m.* hodoscope; **—скопический** *a.* hodoscopic.

ГОИ *abbr.* (**Государственный оптический институт**) State Optical Institute.

ГОИ, ГОИН *abbr.* (**Государственный океанографический институт**) State Oceanographic Institute.

гойяцит *m.* goyazite.

Гоклен Goclenius (lunar crater).

Голея элемент Golay cell.

голл. *abbr.* (**голландский**) Dutch.

голландит *m.* hollandite.

Голландия the Netherlands.

голландск/ий *a.* Dutch; **г. металл** Dutch metal (copper-zinc alloy); **—ая зрительная труба** Galilean telescope.

голоаксиальный *a.* holoaxial.

голов/а *f.* head; **—ка** *f.* head; cap; knob; attachment, end, tip; **—ка ключа** key button; **поворотная —ка** swivel head; **—ка регулятора** control knob; **—ка счетчика** counting head; **—ка сцинтилляционного счетчика** scintillation head.

головн/ой *a.* head, leading; **г. скачок уплотнения** bow shock, forward shock, front shock, bow wave; **г. телефон** earphone; **—ая волна** head wave; **—ая насадка** cap; **—ая установка** pilot plant.

головчат/ый *a.* bulbous; **—ое железо** bulb iron.

гололед *m.*, **—ица** *f.* glaze, glazed frost, ice-covered ground.

голометр *m.* holometer.

голоморфный *a.* holomorphic.

голономн/ость *f.* holonomy; **—ый** *a.* holonomic.

голос *m.* voice; **г. моря** oceanic noise.

голословн/о *adv.* without proof; **—ость** *f.* absence of proof, lack of substantiation; **—ый** *a.* unsubstantiated; unfounded.

голосов/ание *n.* vote, voting, ballot, poll; **—ать** *v.* vote; **—ой** *a.* vocal, voice; **—ая щель** glottis; **—ые связки** vocal chords.

голоцен *m.* (geo.) Holocene.

голоэдр *m.* holohedron; **—ический** *a.* holohedral.

голуб/еть *v.* become azure, become blue; **—оватый** *a.* bluish; **—ой** *a.* blue, sky-blue, azure.

Голубь Columba (Col) (constellation).

гол/ый *a.* bare, uncovered; **г. котел** (nucl.) bare pile; **г. мезон** bare meson; **г. нуклон** bare nucleon; **г. провод** bare conductor; **—ый реактор** bare reactor; **—ое ядро** bare nucleus.

голыш *m.* pebble, shingle, flint stone; **—евый** *a.* pebbly.

гольдфильдит *m.* goldfieldite.

Гольдшмидта закон Goldschmidt law.

гольмий *m.* holmium (H).

гольтский ярус (geo.) Gault stage.

Гольтхузена камера Holthusen (ionization) chamber.

Гольтца машина (elec.) Holtz machine.

Гольф/стром, —штрем, —штрим *m.* Gulf Stream.

гомео— *prefix* homeo—.

гомеографическое преобразование homographic transformation, collineatory transformation.

гомеоморф/изм *m.* homeomorphism; **—ный** *a.* homeomorphous.

гомеополяр/ный *a.* homopolar, covalent; **—ная связь** covalent bond; **—ное соединение** homopolar compound.

ГОМЗ *abbr.* (**Государственный оптико-механический завод**) State Optical Equipment Plant.
гомилит *m.* homilite.
гомихлин *m.* homichline.
Гоммель Hommel (lunar crater).
гомо— *prefix* homo—.
гомоатомный *a.* homoatomic.
гомогениз/атор *m.* homogenizer; **—ация** *f.* homogenizing, homogenization; **—ирование** *n.* homogenization; **—ованный** *a.* homogenized; **—овать** *v.* homogenize.
гомогенн/ость *f.* homogeneity, uniformity; **—ый** *a.* homogeneous, uniform; **—ый реактор** homogeneous reactor; **—ый реактор типа водяной котел** boiling homogeneous reactor; **—ая радиация** homogeneous radiation; **—ое распределение** homogeneous distribution.
гомо/графия *f.* homography; **—динамичный** *a.* homodynamic; **—дисперсный** *a.* monodisperse; **—клиналь** *f.* (geo.) homocline.
гомолог *m.* homolog; **—ический, —ичный** *a.* homologous; **—ический ряд** homologous series; **—ическое преобразование** homology transformation; **—ия** *f.* homology.
гомометрический *a.* homometric.
гомоморф/изм *m.* homomorphism; **—ный** *a.* homomorphic.
гомо/пауза *f.* homopause; **—сфера** *f.* homosphere.
гомотаксиальный *a.* (geo.) homotaxial.
гомотет/ичный *a.* homothetic; **—ия** *f.* similitude, homothety; **центр —ии** center of similitude.
гомотопн/ость *f.* homotopy; **—ый** *a.* homotopy.
гомохалинность *f.* homosalinity.
гомоцентрич/еский пучок homocentric (monocentric, concentric) rays; **—ность** *f.* homocentricity; **—ность следов** copunctuality of tracks.
гомоцикл *m.* homoatomic ring.
гондол/а *f.*, **—ьный** *a.* gondola, nacelle; balloon basket; (geo.) towed "bird".
гониометр *m.* goniometer; **отражательный г.** reflecting goniometer; **прикладной г.** protractor; **—ический** *a.* goniometric; **—ия** *f.* goniometry, direction finding.
гонорар, —ий *m.* fee, honorarium, compensation; **авторский г.** royalty.
ГОНТИ *abbr.* (**Государственное объединенное научно-техническое издательство**) State United Scientific and Technical Press.
гончарный *a.* ceramic, earthenware; clay.
Гончие Собаки, Гончие Псы Canes Venatici (CVn) (constellation).
гопеит *m.* hopeite.
Гопкинсона коэффициент Hopkinson coefficient; **Г. формула** (mag.) H. formula (divided-bar method); **Г. эффект** H. effect.
гор. *abbr.* (**горный**) mountain; mining; (**город**) city; (**городской**) city, municipal, urban.
гора *f.* mountain, hill.
гораздо *adv.* much, considerably; **г. больше** much more.
горб *m.* hump, protuberance, bulge; camber; **г. кривой** hump of a curve; **—атый** *a.* arched.
горбач *m.* compass plane.
горб/ина *f.* hump, bump; **—ить** *v.* bend, crook; **—ообразный** *a.* hump(-shaped); **—ыль** *m.* slab.
горд/иться *v.* be proud of; **—ость** *f.* pride; **—ый** *a.* proud.
Гордона формула Gordon formula.
горе *n.* misfortune.
горел/ка *f.* burner; (welding) torch; **—ый** *a.* burnt, scorched.
горельеф *m.* high relief.
гор/ение *n.* combustion, burning; **г. дуги** arcing; **теплота —ения** heat of combustion; **—еть** *v.* burn; shine; **быстро —еть** conflagrate, deflagrate.
горжа *f.* gorge, ravine.
горизонт *m.* horizon; level; **г. видимый** apparent horizon, visible horizon, skyline; **г. воды** water table; **г. истинный** true horizon; **вне —а** out of sight; **—аль** *f.* horizontal, level contour line; **установка по —али** horizontal adjustment.
горизонтальн/о *adv.* horizontally, on a level; **—ость** *f.* horizontal position; **—ый** *a.* horizontal, level, flat, lateral

—**ый канал** (nucl.) tangential channel; —**ый опытный канал** tangential beam hole (of reactor); —**ая линия,** —**ая плоскость** level; —**ая съемка** plane survey.

горизонтировать, —**ся** *v.* level off.

горист/ость *f.* mountainous character, mountainous state; —**ый** *a.* mountainous.

горка *f.* hill, knoll.

горл/о *n.* throat; neck (of vessel); —**овина** *f.* orifice, mouth, entrance, vent; throat; neck (of vessel); —**овина канала** canal (or duct) entrance; —**овой** *a.* throat; —**овая линия** striction line; —**овая трубка** throttle pipe; —**ышко** *n.* neck, mouth.

горн *see* **горнило.**

Горнера метод (схема) Horner method.

горн/ило *n.* hearth, forge; —**ильный,** —**овой,** —**овый** *a.* hearth, forge; —**овая сварка** forge welding.

горнодоб. *abbr. see* **горнодобывающий.**

горно/добывающий *a.* mining; —**долинный ветер** mountain valley breeze; —**заводский** *a.* metallurgical; —**промышленность** *f.* mining industry.

горн/ый *a.* mountain, mountainous; mining; **г. инженер** mining engineer; **г. компас** dip compass; **г. кряж** mountain ridge; **г. хрусталь** rock crystal; **открытая** —**ая выработка** open-pit mining, open-cut mining; —**ая порода** rock; —**ая станция** high-altitude station, mountain station; —**ая техника** mining engineering; —**ое дело** mining; —**ое масло** mineral oil; —**ое сало** hatchettite; —**ые квасцы** rock alum.

горн/як *m.,* —**яцкий** *a.* miner, mining engineer.

город *m.* city, town; **главный г.** capital.

городить *v.* enclose.

городской *a.* city, municipal, urban.

горо/дьба *f.* enclosure, fence; —**жение** *n.* enclosing, fencing.

горообраз/ование *n.* orogenesis; —**ующий** *a.* orogenic.

гороптер *m.* horopter.

горсейксит *m.* gorceixite.

горст *m.* (geo.) horst, upthrust, uplift.

горсть *f.* handful.

горсфордит *m.* horsfordite.

Гортера-Меллинка трение Gorter-Mellink friction.

гортикультура *f.* horticulture.

гортонолит *m.* hortonolite.

горчичный газ mustard gas.

горш/ечный, —**ковый** *a.* pot; —**ковый изолятор** pot insulator; —**ок** *m.* pot.

горький *a.* bitter; rancid.

горьковский эффект (rad.) Luxemburg effect, Tellegen effect.

горькозем *m.,* —**истый** *a.* magnesia; —**истая слюда** magnesium mica.

горюч/ее *n.* fuel; **газовое г.** gaseous fuel; fuel gas; **жидкое г.** liquid fuel; oil; **твердое г.** solid fuel; —**есть** *f.* combustibility, inflammability.

горюч/ий *a.* combustible, inflammable; **г. газ** fuel gas; **г. материал** fuel, combustible material; —**ая жидкость** flammable liquid; —**ая смесь** fuel mixture; —**ее масло** fuel oil.

горяче/катаный *a.* hot-rolled; —**ломкий** *a.* (met.) hot-short; —**тянутый** *a.* (met.) hot-drawn.

горяч/ий *a.* hot; —**ая камера** (nucl.) hot cave, hot cell; —**ая лаборатория** (nucl.) hot laboratory; —**ить** *v.* heat.

горящий *a.* burning.

гос. *abbr.* (**государственный**) state; government, federal.

гос-во *abbr.* (**государство**) state; government.

Гослегпром *abbr.* (**Государственное издательство легкой промышленности**) State Light Industry Press.

Госплан *abbr.* (**Государственная плановая комиссия**) State Planning Commission.

господств/о, —**ование** *n.* prevalence, predominance, domination; —**овать** *v.* predominate, govern, prevail; —**ующий** *a.* dominant, predominant, prevalent; —**ующий характер** dominant character.

ГОСТ *abbr.* (**Государственный общесоюзный стандарт**) All-Union State Standard.

Гостехиздат *abbr. see* **ГИТТЛ.**

Гостоптехиздат *abbr.* (**Государственное научно-техническое издательство нефтяной и горно-топливной промышленности**) State Scientific and Technical Press of the Petroleum and Mineral-Fuel Industry.

государств/енный *a.* state; government, federal; **—о** *n.* state; government.

Госхимиздат *abbr.* (**Государственное научно-техническое издательство химической литературы**) State Press for Chemical Literature.

Госхимтехиздат *abbr.* (**Государственное химико-техническое издательство**) State Chemical-Technical Press.

Госэнергоиздат *abbr.* (**Государственное энергетическое издательство**) State Power Engineering Press.

готовальня *f.* set of drawing instruments.

готов/ить *v.* prepare; **—ность** *f.* preparedness, readiness, willingness; **—ый** *a.* ready, prepared, fabricated, finished; willing.

гоугит *m.* houghite.

Гоуджа закрылок Gouge wing flap.

Гофман Hofmann, Hoffman, Hoffmann; **—а электрометр** Hoffman electrometer.

гофманнит *m.* hofmannite.

гофр *m.* corrugation, crimp.

гофриров/альный *a.* crimping; **—ание** *n.*, **—ка** *f.* crimping, corrugation; **—анный** *a.* corrugated; undulating; crimped; **—ать** *v.* corrugate, crimp.

Гофти *abbr.* (**Государственный физико-технический институт**) State Physics and Technology Institute.

гошкорнит *m.* hauchecornite.

Гоэлро *abbr.* (**Государственная комиссия по электрификации России**) State Commission for the Electrification of Russia.

гпз *abbr.* (**гектопьеза**) hectopieza (hpz) (pressure unit equal to 1 bar, 10^6 dynes/cm^2).

гп м *abbr.* (**геопотенциальный метр**) geopotential meter.

гр. *abbr.* (**градус**) degree; (**группа**) group.

грабен *m.* (geo.) graben.

грабшти/к, —х, —хель *m.* engraving tool.

гравер *m.* engraver, etcher.

гравий *m.*, **—ный** *a.* gravel; **горный г., карьерный г.** pit gravel.

гравиметр *m.* gravimeter, gravity meter, hydrometer; **—ический** *a.* gravimetric; **—ия** *f.* gravimetry.

гравиразведка *f.* gravitational prospecting.

гравировальн/ый *a.* engraving, carving; **—ая доска** engraver's plate; **—ая игла** etching needle, style.

гравиров/альщик *see* **гравер**; **—ание** *n.*, **—ка** *f.* engraving, etching, carving; **—анный** *a.* engraved, etched; **—ать** *v.* engrave, etch, carve; **—ать параллельными линиями** hatch; **—ать перекрещивающимися линиями** cross hatch; **—ать решетку** rule a grating.

гравитац *abbr. see* **гравитационный.**

гравитационн/ый *a.* gravitation, gravitational, gravity; **г. ветер** gravity wind; **—ая аномалия** gravity anomaly; **—ая волна** gravitational wave; (hyd.) gravity wave; **—ая горизонталь** gravity contour; **—ая плотина** gravity dam; **—ая постоянная** gravitational constant; **—ая энергия** gravitational energy; **—ое поле** gravitational field; **—ое потемнение** (astr.) gravity darkening; **—ое разделение** gravity separation.

гравит/ация *f.* gravitation; gravity; **—ирующий** *a.* gravitational, gravitating.

гравитон *m.* graviton.

гравюра *f.* engraving, print, cut.

грагамит *m.* grahamite.

град. *abbr.* (**градус**) degree.

град *m.* hail.

градация *f.* gradation; **г. изображения** gradation of image.

градиент *m.* gradient; (meteor.) lapse rate; **г. адиабатический** adiabatic lapse rate, adiabatic gradient; **г. концентрации** concentration gradient; **—ный ветер** gradient wind; **—ный тип взаимодействия** derivative coupling; **—ная инвариантность** gauge invariance; **—ная связь** derivative coupling; **—ное преобразование** gauge transformation; **—метр** *see* **градиометр.**

градина *f.* hailstone.

градиометр *m.* (geo.) gradiometer.

градирн/ый *a.* graduation, evaporation; **г. аппарат** graduator; **—я** *f.* water-cooling tower.

градиров/ание *n.*, **—ка** *f.* graduation, calibration; **—ать** *v.* graduate, calibrate.

град. мер. *abbr.* (**градус меридиана**) degree of meridian.

градовой дождь hail shower.

градуатор *m.* graduator.

градуиров/ание *n.*, **—ка** *f.* graduation, calibration; **—анный** *a.* graduated, calibrated, divided; **—анный диск** dial; **—ать** *v.* graduate, calibrate; **—очная кривая** calibration curve; **—очная таблица** calibration chart.

градус *m.*, **—ный** *a.* degree; **—ник** *m.* thermometer; **медицинский —ник** clinical thermometer; **180- —ное смещение** reversal; **—о-день** (meteor.) degree day.

град. экв. *abbr.* (**градус экватора**) degree of equator.

граждан/ин *m.* citizen; **—ский** *a.* civil; **—ский инженер** civil engineer; **—ское время** civil time; **—ское строительство** civil engineering.

Грама определитель (math.) Gram determinant, Gramian.

грамм *m.* gram (g); **г.-атом** gram atom; **г.-ион** gram ion; **г.-калория** gram calorie, small calorie; **г.-молекула** mole, gram molecule; **г.-молекулярный** gram-molecular, molar (M); **г.-рад** gram-rad; **г.-рентген** gram-roentgen; **г.-сантиметр** gram-centimeter; **г.-эквивалент** gram equivalent.

Грамма кольцевой якорь Gramme ring armature; **Г. кольцо** G. ring.

грамматика *f.* grammar; **—ический** *a.* grammatical.

граммовый *a.* gram; **г. эквивалент** *see* **грамм-эквивалент.**

граммолекула *see* **грамм-молекула.**

граммофон *m.* phonograph.

грамот/а *f.* reading and writing; certificate; **верительные —ы** credentials; **—ность** *f.* literacy; **—ный** *a.* literate.

грампластинка *abbr.* (**граммофонная пластинка**) phonograph record.

гран *m.* grain (weight).

гранат *m.* garnet.

граната *f.* grenade, shell.

гранатоподобный *a.* garnet-like.

грандидьерит *m.* grandidierite.

грандиозн/ость *f.* grandeur, vastness; **—ый** *a.* magnificent; immense, vast.

гранен/ие *n.* cutting (of gems); **—ый** *a.* cut, faceted; **—ое стекло** diamond-cut glass.

гранецентрированный *a.* face-centered; **г. кубический** face-centered cubic (fcc); **—ая решетка** face-centered lattice.

гранил/о *n.* cutter; **—ьный** *a.* cutting; **—ьная мастерская, —ьня** *f.* diamond-cutting shop.

гранистый *a.* faceted.

гранит *m.* granite; **—ный, —овый** *a.* granite, granitic.

гранито/гнейс *m.* gneissoid granite; gneissic granite; **—идный** *a.* granitoid.

гранить *v.* cut, facet.

границ/а *f.* boundary, limit, cutoff, border, (line of) demarcation; (math.) bound; **г. атмосферы** limit of atmosphere; **г. вечного снега** snow line; **г. дат** international date line; **г. диффузии** diffusion barrier; **г. допуска** tolerance limit; **г. звездообразности** (math.) star boundary; **г. зерна** grain boundary; **г. конденсации на ионах** ion limit (cloud chamber); **г. контакта** interface; **г. К-полосы поглощения** K-absorption edge; **г. поглощения в кадмии** cadmium cutoff; **г. пропускания** (transmission) cutoff; **г. раздела** interface, boundary, demarcation; **г. раздела фаз** phase boundary; **г. фотопроводности** photoconduction limit; **в —ах** within, in the range (of); **за —ей** abroad; **имеющий общую —у** coterminous (with).

гранич/ащий *a.* adjacent, adjoining; **—ение** *n.* demarcation; **—ить** *v.* border (on), be contiguous (to), abut.

граничн/ый *a.* boundary, border, bounding, limiting, cutoff; **г. континуум** series limit continuum; **г. оператор** boundary operator; **г. слой** boundary layer; **г. эффект** wall effect; **—ая аудиограмма** threshold audiogram;

—**ая задача** boundary value problem; —**ая поверхность** bounding surface; —**ая скорость** cutoff velocity, (seis.) boundary velocity; —**ая точка** end point, boundary point; threshold; —**ая частота** threshold frequency, cutoff frequency, frequency limit; —**ая частота фотоэффекта** photoelectric threshold frequency; —**ая энергия** wall energy, end-point energy, energy limit, cutoff; —**ое значение** boundary value; —**ое трение** boundary friction; —**ое условие** boundary condition.

гранка *f.* galley proof; slip.

—**гранн/ик** *suffix* —hedron; —**ый** *suffix* —hedral; —faced.

грановитый *a.* faceted.

гранул/а *f.* granule; —**езный** *a.* granulose, granulous.

гранулиров/ание *n.* granulation; —**анный** *a.* grained, granular, granulated; —**ать** *v.* granulate.

гранул/ометрия *f.* granulometry; —**ятор** *m.* granulator; —**яционный** *a.* granulation, granulating; —**яция** *f.* granulation.

грань *f.* (cryst.) face, facet; surface, side; edge; (math.) bound; **г. скола** cleavage surface.

ГРАО *abbr.* (**Главная российская астрономическая обсерватория**) Main Russian Astronomical Observatory.

Грасхофа число Grashof number.

граувакка *f.* graywacke.

граф *m.* graph.

графа *f.* column (of a table).

графекон *m.* graphecon.

график *m.* graph, diagram, plot; chart; **г. ветра и деривации** wind and drift chart; —**а** *f.* graphic representation, graph.

графил/ка *f.* marking tool; —**ьный** *a.* marking, ruling.

графит *m.* graphite; —**изация** *f.*, —**ирование** *n.*, —**ование** *n.* graphitization; —**ированный** *a.* graphitized; —**ировать** *v.* graphitize; —**истый** *a.* graphitic; —**ный** *a.* graphite, graphitic; —**ный уголь** graphitic carbon; —**о-водяной реактор** water-cooled graphite reactor.

графитовый *see* **графитный**; **г. з**[...] **медлитель** graphite moderator; [...] **реактор** graphite reactor, graphit[e-] moderated reactor.

графито/ид *m.* graphitoid; —**натри**[е]**вый реактор** graphite-moderate[d] sodium-cooled reactor; —**образны**[й] *a.* graphitic; —**урановый реакт**[ор] graphite-moderated uranium reacto[r].

графить *v.* rule (draw lines).

графическ/и *adv.* graphically; —**ий** [*a.*] graphic, graphical, diagrammati[c,] schematic; —**ая характеристи**[ка] characteristic curve; —**ое изображ**[е]**ние** graphic representation; plot, di[a]gram; —**ое интегрирование** graph[i]cal integration.

графный *a.* divided into columns.

графо/метр *m.* graphometer; —**стат**[и]**стика** *f.* graphostatics.

гребенка *f.* comb; chasing tool; rack.

гребенчатый *a.* comb, comb-shaped; [...] **колчедан** cockscomb pyrite; **г. по**[д]**шипник** collar thrust bearing.

гребень *m.* comb; ridge; crest; colla[r;] flange (of wheel); ledge; **г. вод**[о]**слива** crest of spillway; **г. волн**[ы] wave crest; **г. высокого давлени**[я] high-pressure ridge; **г. плотин**[ы] crest of dam.

гребешок *m.* comb; crest; lug; riser.

гребневидный *see* **гребенчатый.**

гребн/ой *a.* paddle; **г. вал** propell[er] shaft; **г. винт** (screw) propeller, wat[er] propeller; —**ое колесо** paddle whee[l;] —**ое облако** crest cloud.

Грегема *see* **Греэма.**

Грегори рефлектор Gregorian reflectin[g] telescope.

грейзен *m.* greisen.

грейнерит *m.* greinerite.

греметь *v.* fulminate, detonate; thunde[r].

гремучий *a.* fulminating, detonatin[g,] thundering; **г. газ** detonating gas.

гренвильская свита (geo.) Grenvil[le] series.

Грене элемент Grenet cell.

Греффе метод Gräffe method.

Греца критерий Grätz number.

Греция Greece.

грецовский выпрямитель Grätz bridg[e] circuit rectifier.

греч. *abbr.* (**греческий**) Greek.

грешить *v.* violate.

Греэма (Грэма) закон Graham law.

ГРИ *abbr.* (**Государственный радиевый институт**) State Radium Institute.

гриб *m.* mushroom; fungus; **—овидный, —ообразный** *a.* mushroom-shaped; **—овидное облако** mushroom cloud (in atomic blast).

гридлик *m.* grid leak.

Гримальди Grimaldi (lunar crater).

Гримальди опыт Grimaldi experiment.

Грина теорема, формула (math.) Green's theorem; **Г. функция** G. function.

гриналит *m.* greenalite.

Гринвич Greenwich; **гринвичское среднее время** G. mean time (GMT).

гриниан *m.* Green's function.

гриновит *m.* greenovite.

гриновская функция Green's function.

гринокит *m.* greenockite.

Гриньяра реактив Grignard reagent.

грифель *m.* slate pencil; **—ный сланец** (geo.) grapholite; **—ная доска** slate.

грифит *m.* griphite.

гриффитит *m.* griffithite.

Грове элемент Grove cell.

гроза *f.* thunderstorm, electrical storm; **г. с градом** hailstorm; **г. с ливнем** thundershower.

грозить *v.* threaten.

грозов/ой *a.* storm, thunderstorm; **г. разрядник** lightning arrester; **г. шквал** thundersquall; **—ая туча, —ое облако** thundercloud; **—ое возмущение** thunderstorm perturbation; **—ое электричество** thunderstorm electricity.

грозо/отметчик *m.* storm indicator; **—писец** *m.* brontograph, lightning recorder, sferics receiver.

грозящий *a.* threatening, imminent.

гром *m.* thunder; **г. гремит** it thunders.

громад/а *f.* mass, bulk; **—ность** *f.* immensity; **—ный** *a.* huge, immense.

громить *v.* destroy, ruin.

громкий *a.* loud.

громкоговоритель *m.* (rad.) loudspeaker; **г. для верхних частот** tweeter; **г. на нижние частоты** woofer; **г. с подвижным проводником** moving-conductor loudspeaker; **г. электродинамический** moving-coil loudspeaker, electrodynamic (dynamic) loudspeaker.

гром/кость *f.* loudness, volume (of sound); **—овой** *a.* thunder, thunderous.

громозд/ить *v.* pile up; **—кий** *a.* cumbersome, unwieldy, awkward; tedious, onerous.

громоотвод *m.*, **—ный** *a.* lightning rod, lightning arrester; **—ный стержень, громопрут** *m.* lightning rod.

громо/удар *m.* lightning stroke; **—шторм** *m.* lightning storm, thunderstorm.

громыхать *v.* rumble.

гроссуляр *m.* grossularite.

гротин *m.* grothine.

гротит *m.* grothite.

Гроттуса/(-Гершеля)-Дрейпера закон Grotthus and Draper law; **Г. цепная теория** G. chain theory.

грохот *m.* rumble, crash, rattle, roar; screen, sifter, sieve; **—ать** *v.* crash; **—ить** *v.* screen, sift.

грохочен/ие *n.* screening, sifting; **—ый** *a.* screened, sifted.

ГРУ (**Главное разведывательное управление**) Central Intelligence Administration.

груб/еть *v.* coarsen; **—о** *adv.* roughly, coarsely; **—оватый** *a.* rather coarse; **—оволокнистый** *a.* coarse-fibered, coarse-grained; **—озернистый** *a.* coarse-grained; **—ость** *f.* roughness, coarseness; crudeness; **—ый** *a.* rough, coarse; crude; **—ый индикатор дальности** coarse-range scope; **—ый регулирующий стержень** (nucl.) shim rod; **—ая линия скольжения** coarse slip line; **—ая настройка** coarse adjustment, coarse tuning; **—ая регулировка** coarse control, rough adjustment; **—ое приближение** rough approximation.

груда *f.* heap, pile.

груз. *abbr.* (**грузинский**) Georgian.

груз *m.* load, burden; charge; (pendulum) bob; **общий г.** gross weight; **—ик** *m.* (small) weight; **—ик центро-**

бежный flyweight; **—ило** *n.* plumb, plumb bob, sounding lead, sinker.
Грузинская ССР Georgian SSR.
Груз НИТО *abbr.* (**Грузинское научно-исследовательское техническое общество**) Georgian Scientific Research Engineering Society.
грузный *a.* heavy, massive, bulky.
грузо/вик *m.* truck; **—вместимость** *f.* carrying capacity.
грузов/ой *a.* load; freight; **—ая ватерлиния** flotation line, load water line; **—ая линия** load line; **—ая ракета** freight (cargo, transport) rocket.
грузоподъемн/ость *f.* lifting capacity, lifting power; load capacity; **—ый** *a.* hoisting; **—ое приспособление** lifting tackle.
Груз ССР *abbr. see* **Грузинская ССР.**
Грумбергер Gruemberger (lunar crater).
грунт *m.* ground, bottom, soil, earth, land; priming; **—ование** *n.* grounding, priming.
грунтов/ой, —очный *a.* ground, soil; prime; **г. лед** ground ice; **г. мороз** ground frost; **—ая вода** ground water, subterranean water.
групп/а *f.* group, cluster, bunch; series; set, bank, gang; **г. доменов** cluster of domains; **г. ионов** ionic cluster; **г. обслуживания** team; **г. редких земель** rare-earth series; **г. счетчиков** bank of counters; **групп теория** group theory.
группиров/ание *n.*, **—ка** *f.* clustering, clumping, grouping; classification; **г. электронов** electron bunching; **—анный** *a.* grouped, classified; **—атель** *m.* buncher; **—ать** *v.* group, classify; **—аться** *v.* group.
группов/ой *a.* group, grouped; **—ая дифузия** group diffusion; **—ая скорость** group velocity; **—ость** *f.* group property.
груш/а *f.* (elec.) bulb; **—евидный** *a.* pear-shaped.
гр. ц. куб. *abbr.* (**гранецентрированный кубический**) face-centered cubic (fcc).
грэбеит *m.* graebeit.
Грюнайзена (**Грюнейзена**) **постоянная** (**константа**) Grüneisen constant; **Г. формула** G. relation.
грюнерит *m.* grünerite.
грюнлингит *m.* grünlingite.
грюнштейн *m.* greenstone.
гряда *f.* ridge; range; bank; **г. облаков** cloud bank; **г. тумана** fog bank.
грязе/вит *m.* sludge pan, sump; **—отстойник** *m.* sump; sediment tank.
гряз/нить *v.* soil; pollute, contaminate; **—ный** *a.* soiled; contaminated, impure; **—ь** *f.* dirt; sludge; impurity.
гс *abbr.* (**гаусс**) gauss (unit).
ГСВ *abbr.* (**гринвичское среднее время**) Greenwich mean time (GMT).
гсм *abbr.* (**грамм-сантиметр**) gram-centimeter.
ГТД *abbr.* (**газотурбинный двигатель**) gas turbine engine.
ГУ *abbr.* (**государственное учреждение**) state institution, state office.
гуанахуатит *m.* guanajuatite.
гуантахайит *m.* huantajayite.
гуаяканит *m.* guayacanite.
губа *f.* (mech.) jaw; inlet, bay.
губить *v.* destroy, ruin.
губк/а *f.* (mach.) jaw, bit; sponge; **—оватый** *see* **губчатый.**
губчат/ость *f.* porosity; sponginess; **—ый** *a.* porous; spongy; **—ое железо** sponge iron.
гувернерит *m.* gouvernerite.
ГУГГН *abbr.* (**Главное управление государственного горного надзора**) Central Board, State Supervision and Control of Mineral Resources.
ГУГК *abbr.* (**Главное управление геодезии и картографии**) Main Administration of Geodesy and Cartography.
ГУГМС *abbr.* (**Главное управление гидрометеорологической службы**) Central Board of the Hydrometeorological Service.
Гудвина газовая сажа Goodwin gas black.
гудение *n.* hum, buzzing.
гудерманиан *m.* Gudermannian.
гудеть *v.* hum, buzz.
гудзонит *m.* hudsonite.
гудок *m.* horn, whistle; hooting.
гудрон *m.* tar.
гузнек *m.* gooseneck.
Гуи метод Gouy method.

Гука закон Hooke law; **Г. шарнир** universal joint.
Гукера элемент Hooker cell.
гул *m.* rumble, din; (rad.) hum.
Гулда пояс (astr.) Gould belt.
гулк/ий *a.* booming; resonant, resounding, reverberating; **—ость** *f.* boominess; reverberation.
гуллит *m.* hullite.
гулсит *m.* hulsite.
Гульдберга и Вааге закон Guldberg and Waage law, law of mass action.
Гумбольдт (В.) Wilhelm Humboldt (lunar crater).
Гумбольдта течение Humboldt current.
гумбольдтилит *m.* humboldtilite.
гумбольтин *m.* humboltine.
гуминовая кислота humic acid.
гумит *m.* humite.
гумми *n.* gum; **—лак** *m.* shellac.
гуммит *m.* gummite.
гумучионит *m.* gumucionite.
Гунда правило Hund rule.
гунтерит *m.* hunterite.
гунтилит *m.* huntilite.
гуперовский провод (elec.) Hooper wire.
Гупта формализм Gupta formalism.
гур *m.* guhr, kieselguhr.
Гурвица (Гурвича) критерий Hurwitz criterion.
гурон/ит *m.* huronite; **—ский** *a.* (geo.) Huronian.
ГУС *abbr.* (**Государственный ученый совет**) State Scientific Council.
гусен/ица *f.* caterpillar track; **—ичный** *a.* caterpillar; **—ичный волновод** flexible wave guide.
гуссакит *m.* hussakite.
густ/еть *v.* thicken; **—ой** *a.* thick, dense; heavy (oil); deep (color); fine (screen); **—ой туман** dense fog, thick fog; **—ота** *f.* thickness, density.
гуськом *adv.* single file; tandem.
Гуттенберг Guttenberg (lunar crater).
гутчинсонит *m.* hutchinsonite.
Гуча тигель Gooch crucible.
гуща *f.* sediment.
гуэхарит *m.* guejarite.
гц *abbr.* (**герц**) hertz, cycle per second (cps).
гцк *abbr. see* **гр. ц. куб.**
Гэде *see* **Геде.**
гэз *m.* gaize.
ГЭИ *abbr.* (**Государственное энергетическое издательство**) State Power Engineering Press.
ГЭМЗ *abbr.* (**гармоническое электромагнитное зондирование**) harmonic electromagnetic sounding.
ГЭС *abbr.* (**гидроэлектрическая станция**) hydroelectric power plant; (**Государственная электрическая станция**) State Electric Power Plant.
гюбнерит *m.* hubnerite.
гюгелит *m.* hügelite.
Гюгонио Hugoniot.
Гюйгенса окуляр Huygens eyepiece.
Гюккель Hueckel.
гюнцский век (geo.) Gunzian stage.
гюролит *m.* hureaulite.

Д

д *abbr.* (**деци**) deci—; **д.** (**долгота**) longitude.
Д [*in steel mark* (**медь**)] copper (Cu).
да *adv.* yes; *conj.* but, and.
даваемый *a.* given.
давать *v.* give; provide; yield; **д. возможность** enable; **д. осадок** settle, deposit; **д. усадку** contract, shrink.
давизит *m.* daviesite.
давило *n.* weight; press.
давильн/ый *a.* press, pressing; **д. пресс** stamping machine; **д. штамп** coining die; **—я** *f.* press.
давин *m.* davyne.
давить *v.* press, squeeze; **—ся** *v.* choke.
давка *f.* crush.
давл. *abbr. see* **давление.**
давлен/ие *n.* pressure, compression; stress; thrust; **д. акустической радиации** sound pressure; **д. воздуха** atmospheric pressure; air pressure; **д. всасывания** suction pressure; **д. земли** thrust of earth; **д. избыточное** overpressure; **д. излучения** radiation pressure; **д. на поверхность** surface pressure; **д. пара** vapor pressure; **д. разрыва** bursting pressure; **сбрасывать д.** depressurize; **д. света** light

pressure; **котел высокого —ия** high-pressure boiler; **коэффициент —ия** pressure ratio; **линия —ия** line of pressure; line of action (in gears); **пар низкого —ия** low-pressure steam; **указатель —ия** pressure gauge.

давн/ий, —ишний *a.* old, long established; **с —их пор** for a long time.

давно *adv.* long ago; for a long time; **—сть** *f.* remoteness, antiquity.

Давосский фригориметр Davos frigorimeter.

давсонит *m.* dawsonite.

Даг АССР *abbr. see* **Дагестанская АССР.**

дагер/отип, —ротип *m.*, **—отипный** *a.* daguerreotype; **—отипия** *f.* daguerreotypy.

Дагестанская АССР Dagestan ASSR.

Даддела поющая дуга Duddel singing arc.

даже *adv.* even; **даже если** even though.

Дайка *see* **Дика.**

Дайка радиометр Dike radio telescope.

Дайнакон *m.* Dynacon (dynamic condenser electrometer).

Дайнса анемограф Dines anemograph.

Дайсон Dyson.

дакеит *m.* dakeite.

дакиардит *m.* dachiardite.

д'Аламбера принцип d'Alembert principle.

даламбер(т)иан *m.* d'Alembertian.

далее *comp. of* **далеко,** farther, later; **и так д.** et cetera, and so forth.

далек/ий *a.* distant, remote; **д. от резонанса** off-resonance; **—ое инфракрасное излучение** far-infrared radiation; **—ое соударение, —ое столкновение** distant collision, distant encounter; **—ое ультрафиолетовое излучение** far-ultraviolet radiation.

далеко *adv.* far; by far; **д. идущая реакция** far-reaching reaction; **д. не** far from being, not . . . by far; **д. расположенный** outlying.

даллит *m.* dahllite.

даль *abbr.* (**дальневосточный**) Far Eastern (used as prefix).

даль *f.* distance, remoteness, expanse; **—нейший** *a.* farther, subsequent, furthermost; **в. —нейшем** subsequently; henceforth; below (in text).

дальн/ий *a.* distant, remote, long-range, long-distance; **д. порядок** long-range order; **—яя инфракрасная область** far-infrared region; **—яя связь** long-distance (telephone) service; **—яя точка** far point (of eye); **—ее действие** remote operation, long-range action.

дально— *prefix* distance, tele—.

дальновидн/ость *f.* foresight; **—ый** *a.* far-sighted.

дальнодейств/ие *n.* long-range interaction (or force); action at a distance; **—ующая сила** long-range force.

дальнозорк/ий *a.* far-sighted, presbyopic; **—ость** *f.* far-sightedness; **старческая —ость** presbyopia.

дальноизмерение *n.* telemetry, telemetering.

дальномер *m.* range finder; **д.-высотомер** range-and-height finder; **—ная рейка** telemeter rod; **—ная точность** range accuracy.

дальностный импульс range pulse.

дальность *f.* distance, remoteness, range; **д. видимости** visible range, visibility; **д. действия, д. передачи, д. полета** transmission range; **предельная д.** critical range, range limit; **д. пробега частицы** range of particle.

дальноуправляемый *a.* remote-controlled.

Дальтона законы испарения Dalton law of evaporation; **Д. закон кратных отношений** D. law of multiple proportions; **Д. закон растворимости газов** D. law of solubility of gases; **Д. температурная шкала** D. temperature scale.

дальтонид *m.* daltonide.

дальтонизм *m.* daltonism, color blindness.

дальше *comp. of* **далеко,** farther, further, forward; beyond.

дамаск *see* **дамасская сталь.**

дамаскиров/ание *n.*, **—ка** *f.* (met) damasking; **—анный** *a.* damasked.

дамасская сталь damask steel, Damascus steel.

дамба *f.* dam, dike, levee.

Дамуазо Damoiseau (lunar crater).

дамурит *m.* damourite.

АН *abbr.* (**Доклады Академии наук**) Proceedings of the Academy of Sciences (Soviet Physics — Doklady).
аниеля элемент Daniell cell.
ания Denmark.
анков Dancoff.
анник *m.* tributary.
анн/ое *n.* datum; —**ые** *pl.* data, facts, findings; —**ые лабораторного исследования** laboratory findings; —**ые расчетные** design data, calculation data; —**ые сгруппированные** (stat.) classified data; —**ые справочные** reference data; —**ые технические** specifications; —**ые цифровые** numerical data, figures; —**ый** *a.* given, present, under consideration, in question; **в —ом случае** in this instance, in the present case.
ар *m.* gift, grant.
арбу интеграл Darboux integral; **Д. уравнение** D. equation.
арвина-Фаулера метод Darwin-Fowler method.
ар/ение *n.* donation, presentation; —**еный** *a.* donated, presented; —**итель** *m.* donor; —**ить** *v.* donate, grant, present.
аров/ание *n.* gift; talent; granting; —**анный** *a.* donated, granted, conferred; —**ать** *v.* donate, grant, confer.
аровит/ость *f.* ability; —**ый** *a.* gifted, talented.
аро/вой *a.* gratuitous; —**м** *adv.* gratis; in vain.
арсе металл d'Arcet metal (bismuth-lead-tin alloy).
арси *m.* darcy.
ат. *abbr.* (**датский**) Danish.
ата *f.* date.
атиров/ание *n.*, —**ка** *f.* dating; —**анный** *a.* dated; —**ать** *v.* date; —**очный** *a.* date, dating.
атский *a.* Danish.
атчик *m.* data unit, transmitter; pickup, feeler, detector, gauge, detecting (or sensing) element; transducer; **д. высоты** altitude data unit; **д.-измеритель** data unit, pickup; **д. обратной связи** follow-up (instrument); **д. положения** position detector; **д. угла** angle-data transmitter.

дать *see* **давать.**
Дау элемент Dow (electrolytic) cell.
дау-металл *m.* Dowmetal (magnesium alloy).
даунтонский век (geo.) Downtonian stage.
Даусона газ Dawson (producer) gas.
дауэкс (**смола**) Dowex (ion-exchange resin).
дацит *m.* dacite.
дача *f.* giving.
дающий потенциометр data potentiometer; **д. прибор** data unit, signaling device; **д. пульт** data panel.
дб *abbr.* (**децибел**) decibel (db).
дв. *abbr.* (**двойной**) double.
ДВ *abbr.* (**длинные волны**) long waves; **Д. В.** (**Дальний Восток**) Far East.
два (**две** *f.*) two.
двадцати— *prefix* icosa—, twenty.
двадцати/гранник *m.* icosahedron; —**гранный** *a.* icosahedral; —**летие** *n.* twenty-year period; —**летний** *a.* twenty-year; —**сторонний** *a.* icosalateral, icosahedral; —**угольник** *m.* icosagon; —**четырехгранник** *m.* icositetrahedron.
двадцат/ый *a.* twentieth; —**ь** twenty.
дважды *adv.* twice, twofold; **д. квантованный** *a.* doubly quantized; **д. логарифмическая шкала** log-log plot.
двенадцати— *prefix* dodeca—, twelve.
двенадцати/гранник *m.* dodecahedron; —**гранный** *a.* dodecahedral; —**ричный** *a.* duodecimal; —**сторонний** *a.* dodecalateral, dodecahedral; —**угольник** *m.* dodecagon; —**угольный** *a.* dodecagonal.
двенадцат/ый *a.* twelfth; —**ь** twelve.
двер/ной *a.* door, gate; —**ь** *f.* door.
двести two hundred.
двигатель *m.* engine, motor; motive power; **д.-анемометр** propeller anemometer; **д. внутреннего сгорания** internal combustion engine; **д.-генератор** motor-generator (set); **д. двойного действия** two-way engine; **д. первичный** prime mover; **д. термический** heat engine; **д. четырехтактный** four-cycle engine; —**ный** *a.* engine, motor; propellent, impellent, motive; —**ная сила** motive power,

moving force; **источник —ной силы** prime mover.

двиг/ать *v.* move, set in motion, propel, drive; **—аться** *v.* move, travel; (mach.) run, operate; **—ающий** *see* **движущий.**

движен/ие *n.* motion, movement, propulsion; traffic; **д. безвихревое** laminar flow; **д. вечное** perpetual motion; **д. вихревое** vortex motion; **воздушное д.** air traffic; **д. в направлении оси** x x-motion; **д. вперед** propulsion; **д. круговращательное** gyration; **д. ламинарное** laminar flow; **д. льдов** ice flow, ice drift; **д. невихревое, д. потенциальное** irrotational motion; **д. по спирали** helical motion, spiral path; **д. поступательное** forward motion; **приводить в д.** start, set in motion; **д. при помощи атомного (ядерного) двигателя** atomic propulsion, nuclear propulsion; **д. равномерно ускоренное** uniformly accelerated motion; **д. равномерное** uniform motion; **д. разрывное** discontinuous motion; **д. ракет на ядерной энергии** nuclear rocket propulsion; **д. реактивное** jet propulsion; **д. свободной поверхности** free surface motion; **затор в —ии** traffic congestion; **количество —ия** momentum; **начало —ия** start; **сила —ия** *see* **двигательная сила**; **скорость —ия** traveling speed.

движим/ость *f.* mobility; **—ый** *a.* movable, mobile; moved, propelled, actuated.

движитель *see* **двигатель.**

движок *m.* slide; runner; movable arm.

движущ/ий *a.* motive, driving, propelling; **д. агент** motivating agent; **д. газ** streaming gas; **д. механизм** operating mechanism; **—ая сила** driving force, propulsive force; propellent, impellent, motive power, impetus; **—ая точка** movable point; **—ее колесо** driving wheel; **—ийся** *a.* moving, running, operating.

двинут/ый *a.* moved, moving; **—ь** *see* **двигать.**

двое two; **—кратный** *a.* twofold; reiterated; **—ние** *n.* dividing; rectification, distillation; **—точие** *n.* colon.

двоить *v.* double; (chem.) rectify, distil.

двоичн/ый *a.* binary; dual; (math.) dyadic; **д. счетчик** scale-of-two counter, binary scaler; **—ая единица** binary unit; **—ая запятая** binary point; **—ая пересчетная схема** binary scaler; **—ая цифра** binary digit; **—ое число** binary number (or digit), bit.

двойка *f.* two; pair.

двойник *m.* twin, duplicate; **д. прорастания** penetration twin; **д. срастания** interpenetration (or contact) twin; **—ование** *n.* (cryst.) twinning

двойников/ый *a.* twin, twinned; **д кристалл** twin (crystal); **д. шо** composition face (of twins); **—а дислокация** twinning dislocation **—ая ось** twinning axis; **—ая плос кость** twinning plane; **—ое сраста ние** (cryst.) twinning.

двойникующая дислокация twinnin dislocation.

двойничн/ик *m.*, **—ый** *a.* twin.

двойн/ой *a.* double, duplex, twofold dual, binary; twin; two-ply; di— duo—; (meteor.) duplicatus; **д. бета распад** double beta-decay; **д. дио** twin diode, double diode; **д. импуль** double pulse; **д. кристалл-спектро метр** double crystal spectrometer; **логарифмический масштаб** log-lo scale; **д. лучевой пентод** twin-bea power pentode, duo-beam pentode **д. маятник** double pendulum; **спин-резонанс** spin double reso ance; **д. сплав** binary alloy; **тепловой цикл** binary thermal cycl **д. триод** dual triode, twin triode; **штрих** (math.) double prime; **электрический слой** electric doub layer.

двойн/ой *cont.*, **—ая амплитуда** doub amplitude; peak-to-peak value; — **вакансия** double vacancy; — **звезда** binary star; double star; — **ионизационная камера** double (back-to-back) ionization chambe **—ая подача** dual supply; — **связь** double bond; **—ая смесь** bi ary mixture; **—ая таблица част** (stat.) bivariate frequency tab **—ая точка** double point; — **фокусировка** double focusing.

двойн/ой *cont.*, **—ое векторное произведение** vector triple product; **—ое деление** binary fission; **—ое квантование** second quantization; **—ое лучепреломление** birefringence, double refraction; **—ое лучепреломление в потоке** streaming (or flow) birefringence; **—ое отражение** double reflection; **—ое питание** dual supply; **—ое преломление** double refraction, birefringence; **—ое пропускание** double transmission (effect); **—ое рассеяние** double scattering; **—ое соединение** binary compound; **—ое соударение** two-body collision; **—ое срастание** twinning; **—ое управление** dual control.

двойня *f.* twins.

двойственн/ость *f.* duality, doubling; ambiguity; **—ости принцип** principle of duality; **—ый** *a.* dual, double.

двойчат/ка *f.* double kernel; **—ый** *a.* double; binary.

двояк/ий *a.* double, twofold, duplex; **—о** *adv.* doubly, in two ways, bi—.

двояко/вогнутый *a.* biconcave, double concave; **—выпуклый** *a.* biconvex, double convex.

двоякокомпактн/ое пространство bicompact space; **—ость** *f.* bicompactness.

двояко/периодический *a.* doubly periodic, biperiodic; **—преломляющийся** *a.* birefringent, double-refracting; **—сть** *f.* doubleness, duplicity; ambiguity.

дву— *prefix* di—, bi—, duo—, two, double, *see also* **двух—**.

двуаммониевый *a.* diammonium.

двуанодная лампа double-anode tube.

двуатомн/ый *a.* diatomic, biatomic; **д. спирт** dihydric alcohol; **—ая молекула** diatomic molecule; **—ое основание** diacid base.

двубазовый диод double-base diode; **д. транзистор** double-base transistor.

двувалентн/ость *f.* bivalence, divalence; **—ый** *a.* bivalent, divalent.

дву/вариантный *a.* bivariant; **—видный** *a.* dimorphous; **—годовалый, —годовой** *a.* two-year, biennial; **—горбый** *a.* double-humped; **—горбая кривая** double-humped curve, double-peaked curve; **—горлый** *a.* two-necked.

двугранный угловой отражатель dihedral corner reflector; **д. угол** dihedral angle, dihedron.

дву/жильный *a.* twin, twin-core (cable); **—значный** *a.* (math.) two-place, two-digit; two-valued; ambiguous; **—кислотный, —кислый** *a.* diacid; **—кольчатый** *see* **двухкольчатый**; **—конусная антенна** biconical antenna; **—красочный** *a.* dichromatic.

двукратн/о запрещенный переход second-forbidden (beta) transition; **—ый** *a.* double, twofold, two-stage; reiterated; **—ый интеграл** double integral; **—ая схема** push-push circuit; **—ое прохождение** double transmission.

двукристалловый *a.* double-crystal; **д. детектор** combination-crystal detector.

дву/кружный гониометр two-circle goniometer; **—линейный** *a.* bilinear; **—мерный** *a.* two-dimensional; dimetric; bivariate; **—молекулярный** *a.* bimolecular.

двунаправленн/ый *a.* bidirectional; **—ая антенна** bilateral antenna.

двунитный *a.* bifilar.

двуокись *f.* dioxide; **д. кремния** silica; **д. углерода** carbon dioxide; **д. урана** uranium dioxide.

двуосн/овный *a.* dibasic; diatomic, dihydric; **—ость** *f.* biaxiality.

дву/первичный *a.* diprimary; **—пламенный** *a.* double-flame; **—плечий** *a.* double-arm (lever).

двуполостн/ый *a.* double-cavity, two-cavity; **д. гиперболоид** parted hyperboloid, hyperboloid of two sheets.

двуполярный *a.* ambipolar, bipolar.

двупреломл/ение *n.* birefringence, double refraction; **—яющий** *a.* double-refracting.

дву/прямоугольный треугольник birectangular; **—путный** *a.* two-way.

дву/салициловая кислота disalicylic acid; **—связная область** doubly connected region; **—сернистый уран** uranous sulfide; **—сеточный** *a.* double-grid, two-grid; **—сеточная лампа**

double-grid tube; —**слойный** *a.* two-layer, two-ply, double-layer.

двусмысленн/о *adv.* ambiguously; —**ость** *f.* ambiguity, doubtfulness; —**ый** *a.* ambiguous, equivocal.

двустворчатый *a.* folding; **д. клапан** wing valve.

двустенный *see* **двухстенный.**

двусторонн/е-согласованный bilaterally matched; —**ий** *a.* bilateral, two-sided, two-way; duplex; double-ended; —**ий (объемный) резонатор** duplex cavity; —**ий преобразователь** bilateral transducer; —**ий транзистор** double-surface transistor; —**яя оценка** estimate of upper and lower bounds; —**яя шкала** zero-center scale; —**ее управление** dual control.

дву/ступенчатый *a.* two-stage, two-step; —**тавровый профиль** I-beam shape; —**тавровая балка** I-beam; H-beam; —**трехокись урана** uranous-uranic oxide.

двуугольн/ик *m.* (math.) lune; —**ый** *a.* biangular.

двух— *prefix* bi—, di—, two, double; *see also* **дву—.**

двух/атомный *see* **двуатомный**; —**боевой** *a.* duplex, double-faced (hammer).

двухвалковый *a.* two-roll, two-high (rolling mill); **д. прокатный стан, д. стан** two-high rolling mill, duo mill.

двух/вариантный *a.* bivariant; —**витковый** *a.* double-coil, double-turn; —**годичный** *a.* two-year, biennial; —**групповая модель** two-group model; —**дневный** *a.* two-day; —**дорожечный** *a.* dual-track.

двух/желобчатый *a.* double-grooved; —**жидкостный** *a.* double-fluid, two-fluid; —**жидкостная модель** two-fluid model; —**жильный** *see* **двужильный**; —**замещенные** *pl.* di-substitution products, di-derivatives; —**зарядный ион** doubly charged ion; —**заходная резьба** double (screw) thread.

двухзон/альный, —**ный** *a.* two-region, two-zone; **д. реактор** two-region reactor.

двух/карбонатный *a.* bicarbonate; —**каскадный усилитель** two-stage amplifier; —**квантовая аннигиляция** two-quantum annihilation; —**коленчатый** *a.* double-knee, double-throw; —**кольчатый** *a.* dicyclic; binuclear.

двухкомпонентн/ый *a.* two-component, binary; —**ое нейтрино** two-component neutrino.

двухконечный *a.* double-end, double-pointed.

двухконтактн/ый *a.* double-contact; —**ая вилка** two-pin plug.

двух/кратное дифференцирование double differentiation; —**кулачковый** *a.* (mech.) double-jawed; —**ленточный** *a.* two-strand; —**летний** *a.* two-year; —**линейное преобразование** bilinear transformation; —**листный** *a.* (math.) two-sheeted, parted; —**лобный** *see* **двухбоевой**; —**лопастный ослабитель** double-vane attenuator.

двухлористый *a.* dichloride (of).

двухлучев/ой интерферометр twin-wave interferometer; **д. осциллограф** double oscillograph; **д. осциллоскоп** dual-beam oscilloscope; —**ая антенна** twin-wire antenna; —**ая звезда** (nucl.) two-pronged star.

двух/мерный *a.* two-dimensional; —**месячный** *a.* two-month, bimonthly; —**минеральная порода** binary rock; —**недельный** *a.* two-week, biweekly; —**ниточная резьба,** —**оборотная резьба** double (screw) thread; —**объективный** *a.* double-lens; —**опорный** *a.* double-beat (valve).

двухосн/ый *a.* biaxial; —**ая деформация** plane deformation.

двух/палубный *a.* double-deck; —**перекидная схема** double flip-flop circuit; —**плоскостный** *a.* biplanar; —**позиционное регулирование** on-off control; —**положенное действие** two-position action; —**полупериодный выпрямитель** full-wave rectifier.

двухполюсн/ик *m.* two-terminal network; —**ый** *a.* (elec.) bipolar, double-pole, two-pole; —**ый выключатель** double-pole switch; —**ая машина** bipolar machine.

двух/поточный *a.* double-flow; **—предельный** *a.* two-limit; double-range; either-or; **—проводный** *a.* two-conductor, two-wire; **—пролетный клистрон** double-transit klystron; **—проходный кран** two-way cock; **—путевой** *a.* double-track; **—путный** *a.* two-way; **—раздельный** *a.* two-part; **—резонаторный клистрон** two-cavity klystron; **—резцовый** *a.* duplex (lathe); **—рельсовый** *a.* double-track; double-rail; **—рядный** *a.* two-row, double-row.

двух/сотый *a.* two-hundredth; biserial; **—станинный пресс** double-sided press; **—статорный конденсатор** tandem capacitor; **—створчатый** *see* **двустворчатый**; **—стенный** *a.* double-walled; **—ступенный** *a.* two-stage; **—ступенчатый** *see* **двуступенчатый**; **—суставный** *a.* double-hinged.

двухтактн/ый *a.* push-pull, full-wave, two-stroke, two-cycle (engine); **—ая схема** push-pull circuit.

двухударное событие double-hit event.

двухузловой *a.* binodal.

двухфазн/ый *a.* two-phase, biphase, diphase; **д. сплав** two-phase alloy; **—ая система** two-phase system.

двух/фокусный *a.* bifocal; **—фотонный** *a.* two-photon; **—хлористый** *see* **двухлористый.**

двухходов/ой *a.* two-way; two-pass; double-thread (screw); **—ая активная зона** two-pass core (of reactor).

двухцветн/ость *f.* dichroism, dichromatism; **—ый** *a.* dichroic, dichromatic; **—ая фотометрическая система** two-color photometric system.

двух/целевой *a.* dual-purpose; **—цепной** *a.* double-chain; (elec.) double-circuit; **—цилиндровый** *a.* two-cylinder; **—цокольный магнетрон** double-ended magnetron.

двухчаст/ичный *a.* two-particle, two-body; **д. потенциал** two-body potential; **—ный** *a.* two-part.

двух/шарнирный *a.* double-hinged; **—шпиндельный** *a.* duplex; **—ъядерный** *a.* binuclear, dinuclear; **—ъярусный, —этажный** *a.* two-story, double-level; **—электродная лампа** diode; **—эмульсионная пленка** sandwich film.

двучлен *m.* (math.) binomial; **—ный** *a.* binomial, two-termed, two-place.

двушкальный *a.* double-scale, double-dial.

двущелев/ой реактор dual-purpose reactor; **—ая антенна** double-slot antenna.

двуякорное реле double-armature relay.

дг *abbr.* (**дециграмм**) decigram.

де— *prefix* de—, des—, *see also* **дез—.**

деазоти/зация *f.*, **—рование** *n.* denitration, denitriding; **—рованный** *a.* denitrated; **—ровать** *v.* denitrate, denitride.

деактивация *see* **дезактивирование.**

деаэр/атор *m.* deaerator; **—ация** *f.* deaeration; **—изационный** *a.* deaeration, deaerating; **—ированный** *a.* deaerated; **—ировать** *v.* deaerate.

дебаевск/ий параметр, —ая температура Debye temperature; **д. радиус экранирования** D. shielding or screening distance; **—ая длина, —ое расстояние** D. length, screening length (distance, thickness); **—ая кристаллограмма** *see* **Дебая кристаллограмма**; **—ая частота** D. frequency.

дебаеграмма *f.* (Debye) powder diagram.

дебай *m.* Debye unit, debye.

дебат/ировать *v.* debate, discuss; **—ы** *pl.* debate.

Дебая единица *see* **дебай**; **Д. кристаллограмма** Debye crystallogram; **метод Д.-Шеррера** D.-Sherrer method; **рентгенограмма Д.-Шеррера** D.-Sherrer powder pattern (or photograph); **уравнение Д.** D. equation; **уравнение Д.-Гюккеля** D. and Hückel equation.

Деберейнера триады Dobereiner triads.

дебит *m.* output; discharge, flow.

деблокир/ование *n.*, **—овка** *f.* clearing, releasing; **—ованный** *a.* cleared, released; **—овать** *v.* clear, release, unlock, unblock; **—ующий** *a.* releasing.

де Бройля теория слияния theory of fusion (of de Broglie).

Дева Virgo (Vir) (constellation).

де Ваарда спектрометр De Waard spectrometer.

девалькит *m.* dewalquite.
Деваля испытание Deval (attrition) test.
девейлит *m.* deweylite.
девиа/та *f.* (stat.) variance; **—тор напряжения** stress deviator; **—торный** *a.* deviatoric; **—ционный** *a.*, **—ция** *f.* deviation; **—ционная камера** compensating chamber (of compass).
девиз *m.* device, motto.
девиндтит *m.* dewindtite.
девиометр *m.* deviometer.
Девиса печь Davis furnace.
девитрификация *f.* devitrification.
девон *m.*, **—ский период** (geo.) Devonian period.
девственная кривая virgin curve (of magnetization).
девтеранопия *f.* deuteranopia, green blindness.
девулканизация *f.* devulcanization.
девяност/о ninety; **—ый** *a.* ninetieth.
девятер/ной *a.* ninefold; **—о** nine.
девяти/десятый *a.* ninetieth; **—кратный** *a.* ninefold; **—ричный** *a.* nonary; **—сотый** *a.* ninehundredth; **—угольник** *m.* nonagon; **—штырьковый цоколь** noval base.
девят/ка *f.* nine; **—надцатый** *a.* nineteenth; **—надцать** nineteen; **—ый** *a.* ninth; **—ь** nine; **—ьсот** nine hundred.
де Гааза-ван Альфена эффект de Haas-van Alphen effect.
дегаз/атор *m.* degasifier; **—ация** *f.* degassing, outgassing, decontamination; **—ер, —ификатор** *m.* degasifier, degasser; **—ированный** *a.* degasified, degassed; **—ировать** *v.* degasify, outgas.
дегенер/ативный *a.* degenerate; **—ация** *f.* degeneration; negative feedback; **—ированный** *a.*, **—ировать** *v.* degenerate.
дегереит *m.* degeröite.
дегидрат/ация *f.*, **—ационный** *a.* dehydration; **—ировать** *v.* dehydrate; **—ирующее вещество** dehydrating agent, dehydrant.
дегидрация *see* **дегидратация.**
дегидрир/ование *n.* dehydrogenation; **—ованный** *a.* dehydrogenated; **—овать** *v.* dehydrogenate, dehydrogenize; **—ующий** *a.* dehydrogenating.
дегидро— *prefix* dehydro—.
дегидрогениз/ация *f.*, **—ационный** *a.* dehydrogenation; **—овать** *v.* dehydrogenate.
деготь *m.* tar, pitch; **каменноугольный д., коксовый д.** coal tar.
деград/ация *f.* degradation; **—ировавший** *a.* degraded; **—ированное излучение** degraded radiation; **—ировать** *v.* degrade.
дегтярный *a.* tar, tarry.
дегумировать *v.* degum.
Дедекинд Dedekind.
дедлеит *m.* dudleyite.
дедуктивно равные interdeducible.
деду/ктивный *a.* deductive; **—кция** *f.* deduction; **—цировать** *v.* deduce.
деекеит *m.* deeckeite.
дееспособн/ость *f.* competence; **—ый** *a.* competent.
дежур/ить *v.* be on duty; **—ный** *a.* on duty; *m.* attendant; **—ный анод, —ный электрод** keep-alive electrode; **—ный поиск** raster scan; **—ная горелка** pilot burner; **—ство** *n.* attendance, watch; **метеорологическое —ство** meteorological watch.
дез— *prefix* des—, de—; dis—.
дез/агрегация *f.* disaggregation, breakdown, disintegration; **—аксиальный** *a.* off-axis.
дезактив/атор *m.* deactivator, decontaminating apparatus; **—ация** *f.* decontamination, deactivation; **—ирование** *n.* deactivation; **—ированный** *a.* deactivated; **—ировать** *v.* deactivate, decontaminate.
дезинтегр/атор *m.* disintegrator; **—ация** *f.* disintegration; **—ированный** *a.* disintegrator; **—ировать** *v.* disintegrate.
дезинфицировать *v.* disinfect.
дезинформация *f.* misinformation; neg-information.
дезоксирибонуклеиновая кислота desoxyribonucleic acid (DNA).
дезорганиз/ация *f.* disorganization, disorder; **—ованный** *a.* disorganized; **—овать, —овывать** *v.* disorganize; **—ующее действие** disordering effect.

дезориент/ация *f.* disorientation; confusion, loss of bearing; **—ированность** *f.* random orientation; **—ированный** *a.* disoriented; **—ировать** *v.* disorient.

деиониз/ационное время deionization time; **—ация** *f.* deionization; **—ировать** *v.* deionize.

Деймос *m.* Deimos (satellite of Mars).

действенн/ость *f.* efficiency, effectiveness; activity; **—ый** *a.* efficient, effective, operative.

действ/ие *n.* action, operation, performance; effect, influence; treatment; **д. ветра** wind action; **д. излучения** radiation effect; **д. капилярности** capillary action; **д. мешающее** interference; **д. на расстоянии** action at a distance; **д. обратное** retroaction; **оказывать д.** operate, take effect; **приведенный в д.** started, actuated; **приводить в д.** start, work, operate, actuate; **д. резонансного поглотителя** resonance absorber effect; **д. рычага** leverage; **химическое д.** chemical reaction; **—ием** by the action of, by means of; **интенсивность —ия, сила —ия** effective force, working power, efficiency; **коэффициент полезного —ия** efficiency; **поле —ия** domain, field of action; **способ —ия** mode of operation; kind of action.

действительно *adv.* actually, in fact, really; **—сть** *f.* reality, actuality; efficiency, effectiveness, practicality; validity; operation; **в —сти** actually, in reality, in fact.

действительн/ый *a.* real, true, actual, virtual; effective, valid; **д. ветер** true wind; **д. размер** actual size; **д. член Академии наук** Member of the Academy of Sciences; **—ая емкость** actual capacity; **—ая ось** real axis; transverse axis (of hyperbola); **—ая отдача** practical efficiency; **—ая производительность** effective capacity; **—ая яркость** intrinsic brightness; **—ое изображение** real image; **—ое число** real number; **делать —ым** validate.

действит. чл. *abbr.* (**действительный член**) (full, active) member.

действовать *v.* act, operate, function; attack, react, treat; affect; **начать д.** take effect, start; **не д.** fail, be out of order.

действующ/ий *a.* active, acting, actuating, operative; effective; virtual; **д. катод** virtual cathode; **д. от руки** manual; **д. реактор** going reactor; **д. фронт** (meteor.) active front; **—ая высота** virtual height, effective height; **—ая емкость** effective capacitance; **—ая масса** active material; active mass; **—ая сила** effective force, working power, efficiency; **—ая среда** agent; **—ее звуковое давление** effective sound pressure; **—ее значение** effective value; **—ее поле** field of action; **закон —их масс** law of mass action.

дейтер/ид *m.* deuteride; **—иевый** *a.*, **—ий** *m.* deuterium; **—изовать** *v.* deuterate.

дейтеро— *prefix* deutero—.

дейтеро/генный *a.* (geo.) deuterogenic; **—окись** *f.* deuteroxide, heavy water; **—соединение** *n.* deutero compound.

дей/тон, —трон *m.*, **—тронный** *a.* deuteron.

дек. *abbr.* (**декабрь**) December.

дека *f.* sounding board.

дека— *prefix* deca—, ten.

декабрь *m.* December.

декаграмм *m.* decagram.

декад/а *f.* decade; ten-day period; (dial telephone) level; **—ник** *m.* ten-day period; **—ный** *a.* decade; decimal; scale-of-ten; **—ный делитель** decade (voltage) divider; **—ный магазин сопротивлений** decade resistance box; **—ный мост** decade bridge; **—ный счетчик** scale-of-ten counter, decade counter; **—ная пересчетная схема** decade scaler.

декалесценция *f.* decalescence.

декалитр *m.* decaliter.

декальцифи/кация *f.* decalcification; **—ровать** *v.* decalcify.

декаметр *m.* decameter.

декан *m.* (chem.) decane; dean.

декант/атор *m.* settling basin; **—ация** *f.*, **—ирование** *n.* decantation; **—ированный** *a.* decanted; **—ировать** *v.* decant, pour off.

декапиров/ание *n.*, **—ка** *f.* (met.) pickling; **—ать** *v.* pickle.
декарбоксилиров/ание *n.* decarboxylizing; **—ать** *v.* decarboxylize.
декарбонизация *f.* decarbonization.
Декарт Descartes (lunar crater).
Декарта овал Cartesian oval; **Д. правило знаков** Descartes rule of signs.
декартов/ый *a.* Cartesian, Descartes; **д. лист** (math.) C. leaf (or folium); **—ые координаты** C. coordinates.
декатрон *m.* decatron.
декаэдр *m.* decahedron; **—ический** *a.* decahedral.
декларация *f.* declaration.
деклин/ация *f.* declination; **—ометр, —атор** *m.* (elec.) declinometer.
деклуазит *m.* descloizite.
декогерер *m.* (rad.) decoherer.
декодирование *n.* decoding.
деколориметр *m.* decolorimeter.
декомпресс/ия *f.* decompression; **—ор** *m.* decompressor.
декоративный *a.* decorative.
декохерер *see* **декогерер.**
декре/мент *m.* decrement, logarithmic decrement; **д. затухания** logarithmic decrement, damping constant; **д. энергии** energy decrement; **—метр** *m.* decremeter.
декрет *m.* decree, statute; **—ное время** standard (or legal) time.
декстро— *prefix* dextro—, to the right, clockwise.
декстро/за *f.* dextrose; **—соединение** *n.* dextro compound, dextrorotatory compound.
дел. *abbr.* (**деление**) division, graduation.
дела *pl.* business, things, proceedings.
делаварит *m.* delawarite.
Деламбр Delambre (lunar crater).
Деландра уравнение Deslandres equation.
делатинит *m.* delatynite.
делать *v.* make, produce; cause; do; render; **д. отметку** mark, score; **—ся** *v.* be made, be done; become; occur.
делен/ие *n.* division, graduation; indexing; (elec.) scaling (down); splitting, partition, nuclear fission; unit, interval; **асимметричное д.** asymmetric fission; **д. (вызванное) тепловыми нейтронами** thermal-neutron fission, thermal fission, thermofission; **д. источника** source fission; **д. круга** cyclotomy; **д. на блоки** lumping; **д. на быстрых нейтронах** fast-neutron fission, high-energy fission; **д. на медленных нейтронах** slow-neutron fission; **д. на участки** sectionalization; **д. плутония** plutonium fission; **д. тория** thorium fission; **д. урана** uranium fission.
делен/ие *cont.*, **д. фаз** phase splitting; **д. фотонами** photofission; **д. частоты импульсов** scaling-down (of pulses); **д. шкалы** scale division; **д. ядра** nuclear fission; **д. ядра (вызванное) нейтроном** neutron fission, neutron-induced fission; **д. ядра (вызванное) протоном** proton-induced fission; **д ядра на три части** ternary fission; **наносить —ия** divide, subdivide, graduate; index.
деликатн/о *adv.* delicately, cautiously, carefully; **—ость** *f.* delicacy, carefulness, precision; **—ый** *a.* delicate, considerate; careful, precise.
Делиль Delisle (lunar crater).
делим/ое *n.* (math.) dividend; **д. ядро** fissionable nucleus; **—ость** *f.* (nucl.) fissility; (cryst.) cleavability, cleavage; (math.) divisibility; **—ый** *a.* divisible; cleavable; fissionable.
делитель *m.* (math.) divisor, denominator; divider, separator; **д. напряжения** voltage divider; **общий наибольший д.** greatest common divisor.
делительн/ость *f.* divisibility; **—ый** *a.* dividing; fission; scaling, counting-down; index, indexing; **—ый диск, —ый круг** index dial; **—ый инструмент, —ая головка, —ое приспособление** indexing head, spacing attachment; graduator; **—ый кран** separator stopcock; **—ая воронка** separating funnel; **—ая камера** fission chamber; **—ая лампа** scaling tube; **—ая машина** ruling machine; **—ая схема** scaling circuit.
делить *v.* divide, share, apportion.
Деллинжера эффект Dellinger effect.
дел/о *n.* matter, business, affair; occupation; work, act; **вести д.** supervise, manage; **д. в том, что** the point is; **иметь д.** deal with; **д. не обстоит так**

such is not the case; **в самом —е** really; **к —у** to the point, directly; **на самом —е** in fact, in reality; **первым —ом** first of all.

делов/итость *f.* efficiency; **—ой** *a.* efficient, skilled; business.

Делоне Delaunay.

делоренцит *m.* delorenzite.

Дельбрюка рассеяние Delbrück scattering.

дельвоксит *m.* delvauxite.

дельн/о *adv.* efficiently; **—ость** *f.* capability, cleverness; **—ый** *a.* capable, sensible; (met.) raw.

дельта *f.* delta (Greek letter); delta (of river); **д.-железо** delta iron; **д.-луч** delta ray; **д.-металл** delta metal; **д.-образное взаимодействие** delta-function interaction; **д.-функция** delta function; **д.-электрон** delta-electron, knock-on electron.

дельтамакс *m.* Deltamax (iron-nickel alloy).

дельто/видный, —вый *a.* deltoid, deltaic; **—видное крыло** delta wing; **—иддодекаэдр, —эдр** *m.* (cryst.) deltoid dodecahedron, deltohedron.

Дельфин *m.* Delphinus (Del) (constellation).

дельфинит *m.* delphinite.

делящ/ийся *a.* fissionable, fissile; **д. дериват** fissionable derivative; **д. элемент** fissionable element, fissile element; **—еся вещество** fissionable material.

демагнетизатор *m.* demagnetizer.

демаркац/ия *f.*, **—ионный** *a.* demarcation; **—ионная линия** line of demarcation, dividing line.

дематериализация *f.* annihilation of matter.

деминерализ/атор *m.* demineralizer; **—ация** *f.* demineralization; **—овать** *v.* demineralize.

демографический *a.* demographic.

демодул/ировать *v.* demodulate; **—ятор** *m.* demodulator; **—яция** *f.* demodulation.

демонстр/ация *f.*, **—ирование** *n.* demonstration, showing; **—ированный** *a.* demonstrated; **—ировать** *v.* demonstrate.

демонт/аж *m.*, **—ирование** *n.* dismounting, dismantling, disassembly; **—ировать** *v.* dismount, dismantle, disassemble, strip.

демпфер *m.* damper, buffer; damper winding; **—ная обмотка** (elec.) damper winding, damper; **—ная цепь** damping circuit.

демпфиров/ание *n.* damping, shock absorption, buffer action; **—анный** *a.* damped; **—ать** *v.* damp.

демпфирующ/ий *a.* damping; (rad.) antihunt; **—ая цепь** damping circuit; antihunt circuit.

Демуавра *see* **Муавра.**

денатур/ат *m.* denatured alcohol; **—атор** *m.* denaturant; **—ация** *f.* denaturation; **—ирование** *n.* denaturation; **—ированный** *a.* denatured; **—ированное ядерное горючее** denatured nuclear fuel; **—ировать** *v.* denature; **—ирующее средство** denaturant.

дендрит *m.* dendrite; **—ный, —овый** *a.* dendritic, arborescent; **—ный кристалл** dendritic crystal; **—ное строение** dendritic structure.

дендроидный *a.* dendroid, dendritic.

Денеб Deneb.

денежный *a.* monetary, financial; **д. знак** paper money.

дензиметр *see* **денсиметр.**

денитр/ация *f.*, **—ирование, —ование** *n.* denitration; **—ировать, —овать** *v.* denitrate.

Деннштедта печь Dennstedt furnace (analysis).

денси/метр *m.* densimeter, hydrometer; **—тометр** *m.* (phot.) densitometer; opacity meter; **—тометрический** *a.* densitometric.

денудация *f.* (geo.) denudation, erosion.

день *m.* day; **через д.** on alternate days; **на днях** before long; lately.

деньги *pl.* money, currency; **бумажные д.** bank notes, bills; **наличные д.** cash.

деп. *abbr.* (**департамент**) department, division.

депарафинизация *f.* deparaffination.

департамент *m.* department, division; **—ский** *a.* departmental.

депланация *f.* warping.

депозит *m.* deposit.

деполимериз/ация *f.* depolymerization; **—овать** *v.* depolymerize.

деполяриз/атор *m.* depolarizer; **—ация** *f.* depolarization; **—овать** *v.* depolarize; **—ующий фактор** depolarization factor, demagnetization factor; **—ующее поле** depolarization field.

депонировать *v.* deposit.

Депре-д'Арсонваля гальванометр Deprez-d'Arsonval galvanometer.

депресс/ант, —ор *m.* (min.) depressor, depressing agent; **—иометр** *m.* depression meter; **—ионный** *a.* depression, depressor; **—ия** *f.* depression; (meteor.) low-pressure area, low; **—ия постоянная** permanent low; **—ия частная** secondary depression.

дер. *abbr.* **(деревня)** village.

дерг/ание, —анье *n.* twitching, jerking, pulling; (elec.) jitter; **—анный** *a.* jerked, pulled; **—ать** *v.* twitch, jerk, pull.

деревен/ение *n.* lignification; **—еть** *v.* lignify.

деревня *f.* village.

дерево *n.* tree; wood.

деревообделочн/ый *a.* wood-working; **д. станок, —ая машина** wood-working machine, wood-finishing machine; **д. цех, —ая мастерская** wood-working shop.

деревян/еть *v.* lignify; **—истый** *a.* ligneous; **—ный** *a.* wooden, wood; *see also* **древесный.**

деревянистая медь wood copper.

держава *f.* state, power.

державка *f.* holder, support, bracket.

держан/ие *n.* keeping, maintaining; **—ный** *a.* kept, maintained.

держат/ель *m.* holder; adapter; jaw; mount, base; **д. образцов** sample holder; **д. электрода** electrode support; **—ь** *v.* keep, hold, retain; **—ься** *v.* adhere; hold out; hold up; behave.

дерз/ать, —нуть *v.* dare; **—кий** *a.* daring, bold.

дерив/ат *m.* derivative; **—ация** *f.* derivation, source; (hyd.) diversion, diversion structure.

дериво/граф *m.* drift indicator; **—метр** *m.* derivometer, drift gauge.

дерн *m.* turf, sod, peat.

Дернера-Госкинса распределение Doerner-Hoskins distribution.

дернит *m.* dehrnite.

дерновый *a.* turf, sod; **д. торф** peat sod.

дернут/ый *see* **дерганный**; **—ь** *see* **дергать.**

деррик *m.* derrick; **д.-вышка** derrick (for drilling); **д.-кран** derrick crane, derrick.

десант *m.*, **—ный** *a.* descent, landing.

десенсибилиз/атор *m.* desensitizer; **—ация** *f.* desensitization.

десиликация *f.* desiliconization.

десинхронизация *f.* desynchronization.

десквамация *f.* desquamation.

десмотроп *m.* desmotrope; **—ия** *f.* desmotropism, allelomorphism.

десорбировать *v.* desorb.

десорбция *f.* desorption; **д. перегонкой** extractive distillation.

дестабилизирующий *a.* destabilizing; **д. момент** disturbing moment.

деструк/тивный *a.* destructive; **—тивная перегонка** destructive distillation; **—ция** *f.* destruction, decomposition, disordering.

десульф/ация *f.*, **—ирование** *n.*, **—урация** *f.* desulfuration, desulfurization **—уризатор** *m.* desulfurizer.

десятер/ичный *a.* **—ной** *a.* tenfold; — ten.

десяти— *prefix* deca—, ten.

десяти/бальная шкала ten-point scale **—водный** *a.* decahydrate; **—гранник** *m.* decahedron; **—гранный** *a* decahedral; **—дневка** *f.* ten-day period; **—кратный** *a.* tenfold; **—летие** *n.* decade, tenth anniversary; **—летний** *a.* ten-year, decennial; **—сторонний** *a.* decalateral, decahedral **—угольник** *m.* decagon; **—угольный** *a.* decagonal.

десятичн/ый *a.* decimal; **д. знак** decimal (place); **д. логарифм** common logarithm; **д. молярный коэффициент поглощения** molar extinction coefficient; **д. пересчет** decade scaling **д. фактор** decade factor; **—ая дробь** decimal (fraction); **—ая запятая** decimal point; **—ая система чисел** decimal number system.

десят/ка, —ок ten; **—ки** *pl.* tens; doz

ens, scores; **—ый** *a.* tenth; **—ые доли** tenths; **—ь** ten.

·тал/изация, **—ировка** *f.* detail, elaboration, particularization; **—изировать** *v.* detail.

·таль *f.* detail; part, member, component, element; **д. конструкции** design detail, structural member; **д. машин** machine part (element, compound); **д. парная** mate; **—но** *adv.* in detail; **—ный** *a.* detailed; **—ное равновесие** detailed balance, detailed balancing.

тандер *m.* gas-expansion machine.

тектиров/ание *n.* detection; (elec.) rectification; **—ания коэффициент** detection coefficient; **—анный сигнал** rectified signal; **—ать** *v.* detect; (elec.) rectify.

тектор *m.*, **—ный** *a.* detector; (elec.) rectifier; **д. быстрых нейтронов** fast neutron detector; **д. интегрирующий импульсы** pulse-integrating detector; **д. квадратичный** square law detector; **д. с линейной характеристикой** linear response detector.

тергент *m.* detergent.

термин/ант *m.* determinant; **—ированность** *f.* determinacy.

тон/атор *m.* detonator; **—ация** *f.*, **—ационный** *a.* detonation, explosion; knock (of motor); **—ационная волна** detonation wave; **степень —ации** knock rating (of fuel), octane number; **—ировать** *v.* detonate; knock; **—ирующий** *a.* detonating; knocking.

грит/овый *a.* detrital; **—ус** *m.* detritus, rock waste.

фазиров/анный *a.* out of phase; **—ка** *f.* dephasing.

фект *m.* defect, imperfection, flaw; **д. массы** mass defect; **д. решетки** lattice defect, crystal defect; **д. типа вакансия-внедрение** interstitial-vacancy pair; **—ы в твердых телах** imperfections in solids; **—ивный** *a.* defective, faulty; **—ный** *a.* defect; imperfect, faulty, defective; **—ная проводимость** defect conductivity; **—ное место** (sol.) defect; **—ное число** (math.) deficiency number.

фектоскоп *m.*, **—ический** *a.* flaw detector; **—ия** *f.* flaw detection, radiography.

дефинитный *a.* definite.

дефис *m.* hyphen.

дефицит *m.* deficiency, deficit, defect; **д. насыщения** (meteor.) saturation deficit; **д. нейтронов** neutron deficit; **д. скорости** (hyd.) velocity defect; **—ный** *a.* deficit, deficient; scarce.

дефлагра/тор *m.* deflagrator; **—ция** *f.* deflagration.

дефлегм/атор *m.* reflux condenser, fractionating column, dephlegmator; still head; **—ация** *f.* dephlegmation, fractionation; **—ации коэффициент** reflux ratio; **—ировать** *v.* dephlegmate, fractionate.

дефлект/ометр *m.* deflectometer; **—ор** *m.* deflector.

дефлок/кулирование, —улирование *n.*, **—уляция** *f.* deflocculation; **—улированный** *a.* deflocculated; **—улировать** *v.* deflocculate; **—улирующий реагент** deflocculating agent, deflocculant.

дефляция *f.* deflation; wind erosion.

дефокусиров/ание *n.*, **—ка** *f.* defocusing; **—ать, —аться** *v.* defocus.

деформационн/ый *see* **деформация; д. скачок** (plastic) deformation jerk; **—ое поле** (meteor.) deformation field; **—ое размытие** stress broadening; **—ое старение** strain aging; **—ые колебания** deformation vibrations.

деформац/ия *f.* deformation, strain; **д. воздушной массы** air-mass modification; **д. диэлектрика** dielectric strain; **д. изгибания** flexural strain; **исчезающая д.** elastic deformation **д. плоская** plane strain; **д. ползучести** creep flow; **д. при растяжении, д. растяжения** tensile strain; **д. сдвига** shearing strain, shear deformation; **—ии степень** strain percent; **энергия объемной —ии** strain energy of dilatation.

деформиров/ание *see* **деформация; —анный** *a.* deformed, warped, strained; **—анное состояние** state of strain; **—анное ядро** deformed nucleus; **—ать** *v.* deform, strain; **—аться** *v.* warp, buckle.

деформиру/емость *f.* deformability; **—емый** *a.* deformable; **—ющий** *a.* de-

forming, straining; —**ющая сила** deforming force, stress.
дехлорирование *n.* dechlorination.
децелер/ация *f.* deceleration; —**омер** *m.* decelerometer.
децентрализ/ация *f.* decentralization; —**овать** *v.* decentralize.
децентрировка *f.* decentering.
деци— *prefix* deci—.
децибел *m.* decibel (db); —**метр** *m.* decibel meter; —**ьный потенциометр** decibel potentiometer.
дециграмм *m.* decigram.
децил *m.*, —**овый** *a.* decyl.
децилитр *m.* deciliter.
дециль *m.* decile.
деци/льон *m.* decillion; —**ма** *f.* (mus.) tenth; —**мальный** *a.* decimal.
дециметр *m.*, —**овый** *a.* decimeter; —**овые волны** decimeter waves.
децимолярный *a.* decimolar.
децин *m.* decine, decyne.
деци/непер *m.* decineper; —**нормальный** *a.* decinormal; —**нормальный раствор** tenth-normal solution; —**эрстед** *m.* deci-oersted.
дешев/еть *v.* fall in price; —**о** *adv.* inexpensively; —**ый** *a.* inexpensive.
дешифр/атор *m.* decoder; selector, discriminator; —**ировать** *v.* decipher; —**ование** *n.* deciphering.
Дешмана формула Dushman equation, Richardson-Dushman equation.
дэлектризация газа de-ionization.
деэтилирование *n.* de-ethylation.
деятель *m.* worker, agent; **д. науки** scientist; —**но** *adv.* actively; —**ность** *f.* activity, work, action; practicality; —**ность оптическая** optical activity, opticity; —**ность фронта** (meteor.) frontal activity; —**ный** *a.* active; practical; —**ная поверхность** active surface.
деят-сть *abbr.* (**деятельность**) activity, work, action.
Дж. J (English or French initial).
дж *abbr.* (**джоуль**) joule.
Джакобиниды Giacobinids (meteors).
джалмаит *m.* djalmaite.
джатекс *m.* jatex (a rubber latex).
Джезебель Jezebel (critical assembly).
джек *m.* jack; (min.) jackhammer.
Джекоби сплав Jacoby metal (lead-antimony-tin alloy).
джемсонит *m.* jamesonite.
джеромит *m.* jeromite.
Джерса нагревательный колодец (met.) Gjer's soaking pit.
джеффери̇зит *m.* jefferisite.
джефферсонит *m.* jeffersonite.
Джеффрис Jeffreys.
джиллеспит *m.* gillespite.
джинорит *m.* ginorite.
Джинс Jeans.
Джиорджи система Giorgi system.
джиорджиозит *m.* giorgiosite.
джиразоль *f.* girasol.
джоакинит *m.* joaquinite.
Джодрелл Бэнк Jodrell Bank.
джозефинит *m.* josephinite.
Джолли весы Jolly balance.
джонит *m.* juanite.
Джонсона-Ларк-Горовица формула Johnson-Lark-Horowitz formula; **Д. шум** J. noise.
джонструпит *m.* johnstrupite.
Джордана гелиограф Jordan heliograph.
Джорджи *see* **Джиорджи.**
джорджиадезит *m.* georgiadesite.
джоул/ев эффект Joule effect; —**ева теплота,** —**ево тепло** Joule heat; —**евы потери** Joule (heat) loss, —**ометр** *m.* joulemeter; —**ь** *m.* joule
Джоуля закон Joule law; **Д.-Томсона коэффициент** J.-Thomson coefficient; **Д.-Томсона эффект** J.-Thomson effect; **Д. эффект** *see* **джоулев эффект.**
Джоши эффект Joshi effect.
джурупаит *m.* jurupaite.
джэк *see* **джек.**
дзета-функция *f.* zeta function.
ди— *prefix* di—, bi—.
диабаз *m.* diabase; —**овый** *a.* diabase diabasic; —**овый миндальный камень** (petr.) amygdaloidal greenstone.
диаген/ез *m.* diagenesis; —**етический** *a* diagenetic.
диагно/з *m.* diagnosis; —**стический** *a* diagnostic.
диагометр *m.* diagometer.
диагонализ/ация *f.* diagonalization —**ировать** *v.* diagonalize.

диагональ *f.* diagonal, diagonal line; **—ный** *a.* diagonal, oblique.

диагр. *abbr. see* **диаграмма.**

диаграм/ма *f.* diagram, graph, figure, plot, chart; pattern; **д. в полярных координатах** polar diagram; **д. изодоз** isodose chart; **д. нагрузка-удлинение** load-extension diagram; **д. направленности** directional diagram (of antenna); directivity pattern, polar diagram; **д. напряжение-деформация** stress-strain diagram; **д. обнаружения** (rad.) coverage diagram; **д. растяжения** (tensile) stress-strain diagram; **д. сжатия** compression stress-strain diagram; **д. состояния** phase diagram, constitution diagram; **д. фазового равновесия** phase diagram; **—ная бумага** graph (or plotting) paper; **—ная линия** (x-ray) diagram line.

диаграф *m.* diagraph.

диад/а *f.* dyad, dyadic; **—ный** *a.* dyadic; **—ное произведение** dyad.

диадохит *m.* diadochite.

диа/зен *m.* diazene; **—зотропия** *f.* (phot.) diazo process; **—каустика** *f.* diacaustic.

диакисдодекаэдр *m.* dyakisdodecahedron, diploid.

диа/клаза *f.* diaclase; **—клинальный** *a.* diaclinal; **—критический** *a.* (elec.) diacritical.

диактинический *a.* diactinic.

диакусти/ка *f.* diacoustics; **—ческий** *a.* diacoustic.

диализ *m.* dialysis; **—атор** *m.* dialyzer; dialyzator; **—ированный, —ованный** *a.* dialyzed; **—ировать, —овать** *v.* dialyze; **—ирующий** *a.* dialyzing.

диалит *m.* dialite (insulator); **—ический** *a.* dialytic.

диам. *abbr.* (**диаметр**) diameter.

диамагн/етизм, —итизм *m.*, **—итность** *f.* diamagnetism; **—итный** *a.* diamagnetic; **—итная восприимчивость** diamagnetic susceptibility.

диаметр *m.* diameter; bore, caliber; **д. в свету, внутренний д.** inner diameter, bore; **д. столкновения** collision diameter; **—ально** *adv.* diametrically, in diameter; **—альный** *a.* diameter, diametric, diametral; **—альная обмотка** full-pitch winding.

диапазон *m.*, **—ный** *a.* range; (rad.) band; diapason; **д. мощности** power range; **д. пропорциональности** proportional band; **д. частот связи** communication band; **д. чувствительности** range of sensitivity; **—ная антенна** wide-band antenna.

диапозитив *m.* diapositive, transparency, slide; **—ный** *a.* diapositive.

диарил *m.*, **—ьный** *a.* diaryl.

диаскоп *m.* diascope, slide projector; **—ическая проекция** diascopic projection; **—ия** *f.* diascopy.

диаста/з *m.* diastase; **—зиметрия** *f.* diastasimetry; **—зический** *a.* diastasic, diastatic; **—тический** *a.* (geo.) diastatic.

диастол/а *f.* (biol.) diastole; **—ический** *a.* diastolic.

диастрофизм *m.* (geo.) diastrophism.

диатерм/ический, —ичный *a.* diathermic, diathermal; **—ичность** *f.* diathermy, diathermance; **—ия** *f.* diathermy; **—ометр** *m.* diathermometer.

диатоническая гамма diatonic scale.

диатрема *f.* (geo.) diatreme, volcanic vent.

диафано/метр *m.* diaphanometer; **—скоп** *m.* diaphanoscope.

диафорит *m.* diaphorite.

диафрагм/а *f.*, **—овый** *a.* diaphragm, membrane, septum; aperture, slit; iris; (opt.) stop; baffle; (elec.) iris, window; **индуктивная д.** inductive iris; **—ирование** *n.* diaphragming, orificing, irising; **—ированный волновод** iris waveguide; **—ировать** *v.* diaphragm, iris; **—ирующая щель** defining slit.

диашистовый *a.* diaschistic.

диборан *m.* diborane.

дивариантный *a.* bivariant.

диверген/тный *a.* divergent; **—ция** *f.* divergence.

дивертор *m.* diverter.

дивизия *f.* division.

див/ный *a.* wonderful, marvelous; **—о** *n.* wonder, marvel.

дигедральный *a.* dihedral.

дигексагональный *a.* dihexagonal.

дигептальный цоколь diheptal base.

дигестор *m.* digester.
дигидр— *prefix* dihydr—, dihydro—.
дигидрат *m.* dihydrate.
дигидрит *m.* dihydrite.
дигидро— *prefix* dihydro—.
дигидрокси— *prefix* dihydroxy—.
дигидрол *m.* dihydrol.
дигир/а *f.* twofold axis of symmetry; **—ный** *a.* rhombic, orthorhombic.
дигональный *a.* digonal, digonous.
дидим *m.* didymium (Di).
дидимолит *m.* didymolite.
дидодекаэдр *m.* didodecahedron, diploid; **—ический** *a.* didodecahedral, diploid.
диез *m.* diesis; (mus.) sharp.
диен *m.* diene; **—овый ряд** diene series.
диефир *m.* diester.
диз— *see also* **дис—**.
дизамещенный *a.* (chem.) disubstituted.
дизаналит *m.* dysanalite.
дизел/ь, —ьмотор *m.*, **двигатель —я** diesel (engine); **—ьное топливо** diesel fuel.
дизинтрибит *m.* dysyntribite.
дизъюнктивный *a.* disjunctive.
диизопропиловый эфир diisopropyl ether.
Дика приемник Dicke receiver.
дикий *a.* wild, reckless; extravagant.
диккинсонит *m.* dickinsonite.
диккит *m.* dickite.
диклинический *a.* diclinic.
дико *adv.* wildly, recklessly; extravagantly; **—сть** *f.* wildness, recklessness; extravagance.
диксенит *m.* dixenite.
диктов/ание *n.*, **—ка** *f.* dictation; **—анный** *a.* dictated; **—ать** *v.* dictate.
дикто/граф *m.* dictograph; **—р** *m.* (rad.) announcer; speaker; **—фон** *m.* dictaphone.
дикция *f.* diction.
Дила процесс Diehl (cyanide) process.
дилатометр *m.* dilatometer; **—ический** *a.* dilatometric; **—ия** *f.* dilatometry.
дилемма *f.* dilemma.
дилетант *m.* amateur.
дилувиальный *see* **дилювиальный**.
дилюв/иальный *a.* diluvial; **—ий** *m.*, **д. нанос** diluvium.
дилюци/я *f.* dilution; **—и коэффициент** (astr.) dilution factor.
ДИМ *abbr.* (**Днепропетровский научно-исследовательский институт металлов**) Dnepropetrovsk Scientific Metals Research Institute.
димер *m.* dimer; **—изация** *f.* dimerization; **—ность** *f.* dimerism; **—ный** *a.* dimeric.
диметил *m.*, **—овый** *a.* dimethyl.
диморф/изм *m.* dimorphism; **—ный** *a.* dimorphous, dimorphic.
дина *f.* dyne (d, dyn).
динама *f.* dyname (one thousand kilogram-meters); (mech.) wrench; dynamic screw.
динаметр *m.* dynameter.
динам/изм *m.* dynamism; **—ик** *m.* dynamic loudspeaker; **—ика** *f.* dynamics; **—ика твердого тела** dynamics of rigid bodies; **—ит** *m.*, **—итный** *a.* dynamite.
динамическ/ий *a.* dynamic; **д. винт** (mech.) wrench; **д. диапазон** dynamic range; **д. конденсатор** vibrating condenser; **д. коэффициент вязкости** dynamic (coefficient of) viscosity; **д. напор** kinetic energy (or dynamic) head; **д. электрометр** vibrating-reed electrometer; **—ая нагрузка** impact load; **—ая сплюснутость** dynamical flattening; **—ое воздействие** impact.
динам/ный *a.*, **—о** *n.*, **—омашина** *f.* dynamo; **—ограф** *m.* dynamograph; **—одвигатель** *see* **динамотор**.
динамометр *m.* dynamometer; **—ический** *a.* dynamometric; **—ический тормоз** power brake.
динамооптиметр *m.* dynamo-optimeter (instrument for measurement of flow-birefringence).
динамотор *m.* dynamotor.
динамоэлектрический *a.* dynamoelectric.
динантский ярус (geo.) Dinantian series.
динатрон *m.* dynatron; **—ный генератор** dynatron oscillator; **—ный эффект** dynatron effect, dynatron characteristic.
динейтрон *m.* dineutron.
динерит *m.* dienerite.
Дини условие Dini condition.
динод *m.* dynode.
динуклон *m.* dinucleon.

диод *m.*, **—ный** *a.* diode.
диоза *f.* diose.
диоксид *m.* dioxide.
диоктаэдр *m.* dioctahedron.
диоктил *m.* dioctyl.
диол *m.* diol.
диоптаз *m.* dioptase.
диоптр *m.*, **—ия** *f.* diopter; **—ика** *f.* dioptrics; **—ический** *a.* dioptric; **—ы** *pl.* sight.
диорама *f.* diorama.
диорит *m.* diorite.
диорто— *prefix* diortho—.
диотрон *m.* dyotron.
Диофант Diophantus (lunar crater).
Диофанта уравнение Diophantine equation.
дипир *m.* dipyre.
дипирамида *f.* bipyramid.
диплекс *m.* diplex; **—ер** *m.* diplexer; **—ная радиопередача** diplex radio transmission.
диплоид *m.* diploid.
диплом *m.* diploma; **университетский д.** university degree; **—ант** *m.* candidate for higher degree (preparing thesis), graduate, graduate student; **—ированный** *a.* graduate; licensed (engineer); **—ная работа** thesis.
диплопия *f.* diplopia.
диплот *m.* sounding machine.
диплоэдр *m.* diplohedron.
диполь *m.* dipole, doublet, double source; **д.-дипольное взаимодействие** dipole-dipole interaction; **—ный момент** dipole moment; **—ный переход** dipole transition; **—ная поляризуемость** dipolar (or orientational) polarizability; **—ная релаксация** dipole (or dielectric) relaxation; **—ная решетка** dipole lattice; **—ное излучение** dipole radiation.
дипротон *m.* diproton.
дипсевдо— *prefix* dipseudo—.
дир. *abbr.* **(директор)** director, manager, head.
Дирака уравнение Dirac equation; **Д. электронная теория** D. electron theory; **дираковская частица** D. particle.

директ/ива *f.*, **—ивные указания** instructions, directions; **—ивный** *a.* directive; **—ор** *m.* director, manager, head; **—ор-распорядитель** managing director, executive director; **—риса** *f.* directrix.
дирекц/ионный *a.* directional; **д. магнитный угол** grid magnetic azimuth; **—ия** *f.* direction, management, board (of directors).
дирижабль *m.* dirigible; **жесткий д.** rigid airship.
дирижер *m.* regulator.
Дирихле граничные (краевые) условия Dirichlet boundary conditions.
дисбаланс *m.* imbalance, unbalance.
дисгармон/ировать *v.* clash, conflict; **—ирующий** *a.* conflicting, incongruous; **—ия** *f.* disharmony, conflict.
диск *m.* disk, disc, plate; **д. градуированный** dial; **д. с вырезами** slotted disk; **д. связи** coupling disk; **д. сцепления** clutch plate.
Дискаверер Discoverer (artificial satellite).
дисков/ание *n.* dialing (telephone); **—ый** *see* **диск**; **—ый источник** disk source; **—ый фрезер** cutting disk; **—ая развертка** disk scanning.
дискоидальный *see* **дискообразный.**
дисколит *m.* discolith.
дисконическая антенна discone antenna.
дискообразн/ый *a.* disk-shaped, discoidal; **—ое распределение** plateline distribution.
дискразит *m.* dyscrasite.
дискредит/ация *f.*, **—ирование** *n.* discrediting; **—ировать** *v.* discredit.
дискретн/ость *f.* discreteness; **—ый** *a.* discrete; **—ая структура промежуточного состояния** domain structure (of superconductor); **—ое поглощение** line absorption; **—ое состояние** discrete state.
дискриминант *m.* discriminant.
дискримин/атор *m.* discriminator, analyzer; **д. амплитуды импульсов** pulse-height discriminator; **—ационный** *a.* discriminatory.
диску/ссионный *a.* controversial; debatable; **—ссия** *f.* discussion, debate;

controversy; —**тировать** *v.* discuss, debate.

дислокационная линия dislocation line.

дисло/кация *f.* dislocation, disturbance; —**цированный** *a.* dislocated; —**цировать** *v.* dislocate, disturb.

дислюит *m.* dysluite.

дисмембратор *m.* crusher.

диспенсерный катод dispenser cathode.

дисперг/атор *m.* disperser, dispersing agent (or medium); —**ирование** *see* **дисперсия**; —**ированный** *a.* dispersed; —**ировать** *v.* disperse, scatter, diffuse; —**ирующий** *a.* dispersing, dispersive; —**ирующий реагент** dispersion reagent; —**ирующая способность** dispersive power; —**ирующая среда** dispersive medium.

дисперсионн/ый *a.* dispersion, dispersing; **д. анализ** analysis of variance; —**ая зависимость** dispersion formula; —**ая сила** dispersion force; —**ая среда** dispersion medium; —**ая теория** dispersion theory; —**ое соотношение** dispersion relation; —**ое средство** dispersion agent; —**ое твердение** precipitation hardening.

дисперс/ия *f.* dispersion; (stat.) variance, *sometimes* standard deviation; —**ии коэффициент** (opt.) Abbe number; —**ность** *f.* (degree of) dispersion, dispersity; —**ный** *a.* dispersed; —**ная система** disperse system; —**ное вещество** dispersed material, dispersed phase.

дисперсо/графия *f.* size-distribution analysis; —**ид** *m.* dispersoid.

диспетчер *m.* dispatcher.

диспрозий *m.* dysprosium (Dy).

диспропорц/ионирование *n.* disproportionation; —**ия** *f.* disproportion.

диспут *m.* dispute, debate.

диссектор *m.* dissector.

диссерт. докт. *abbr.* (**диссертация докторская**) doctoral dissertation.

диссерт. канд. *abbr.* (**диссертация кандидатская**) candidate's dissertation.

диссертация *f.* dissertation, thesis.

диссиметричный *a.* asymmetric.

диссимиляция *f.* dissimilation.

диссип/ативный *a.* dissipative, dissipation; —**ация** *f.* dissipation, dispersion; —**ировать** *v.* dissipate; (astr.) disperse.

дисснит *m.* dyssnite.

диссольвер *m.* dissolving tank.

диссон/анс *m.* dissonance, discord; —**ансный аккорд** discord; —**ирующий** *a.* discordant, dissonant.

диссоци/ативный *a.* dissociative; —**ация** *f.* dissociation; —**ация газа** gaseous dissociation; —**ированный** *a.* dissociated; —**ировать** *v.* dissociate, break up, break down, split up; —**ирующийся** *a.* dissociable.

дистанциометрирование *n.* ranging.

дистанционир/ование *n.* spacing; —**овать** *v.* space; —**ующий** *a.* spacing, spacer; —**ующий стержень** spacer rod.

дистанционно-временная запись range-time record; **д.-управляемый** remotely controlled; **д.-управляемый вентиль** remote valve.

дистанционн/ый *a.* distance, distant, remote; spacer; **д. запал** time fuse; **д. компас** telecompass, distant-reading compass; **д. метеорологический прибор** telemeteorograph; **д. перенос** remote transfer; **д. прибор** remote-acting device; telemeter; **д. психрометр** telepsychrometer; **д. термометр** telethermometer; **д. указатель** remote indicator; —**ая система** remote system; —**ая точность** range accuracy; —**ое действие** remote (or time) action; —**ое манипулирование** remote handling; —**ое ребро** spacer rib; —**ое управление** remote control.

дистанция *f.* distance, interval, range; **небольшая д.** close range, short range.

дистарная линза Distar lens.

дистект/ика *f.* dystectic point; —**ический** *a.* dystectic.

дистен *m.* disthène, kyanite.

дистилл/ат *m.* distillate; —**ер**, —**ятор** *m.* distiller, still; condenser; —**ирование** *n.*, —**яция** *f.* distillation, distilling; —**ированный** *a.* distilled; —**ировать** *v.* distil; —**яционный** *a.* distillation.

дистор/сия *f.*, —**ционный** *a.* distortion.

дистрибутивн/ость *f.* distributivity; **—ый** *a.* distributive.

дисциплин/а, —ированность *f.* discipline; **—арный** *a.* disciplinary; **—ированный** *a.* disciplined, trained; **—ировать** *v.* discipline, train.

Дитеричи уравнение Dieterici equation (of state).

дитетрагон *m.* ditetragon; **—альный** *a.* ditetragonal.

дитетраэдр *m.* ditetrahedron; **—ический** *a.* ditetrahedral.

дитригон *m.* ditrigon; **—альный** *a.* ditrigonal.

дитрихит *m.* dietrichite.

дитцеит *m.* dietzeïte.

диф— *see also* **дифф—**.

дифанит *m.* diphanite.

дифен— *prefix* diphen—, dipheno—.

дифенат *m.* diphenate.

дифенил *m.*, **—овый** *a.* diphenyl.

дифманометр *m.* differential manometer.

дифмотор *m.* differential motor.

дифрагиров/авший пучок diffracted beam; **—анный** *a.* diffracted, scattered; **—анный нейтрон** scattered neutron; **—ать** *v.* diffract.

дифрактометр *m.* diffractometer.

дифракционн/ый *a.* diffraction; **д. кружок** diffraction disc; **д. максимум** diffraction peak, diffraction maximum; **—ая картина** diffraction pattern; **—ая решетка** diffraction grating; **—ое рассеяние** diffraction scattering.

дифракция *f.* diffraction; **д. на кристалле** crystal diffraction; **д. на порошке** powder diffraction; **д. у острого края** knife-edge diffraction.

дифсельсин *m.* differential selsyn.

дифсхема *f.* (elec.) differentiator.

дифф— *see also* **диф—**.

диффер. *abbr.* (**дифференциальный**) differential.

дифференциал *m.* differential; differential gear; **вал —а** differential shaft; **—ьно-разностное уравнение** differential-difference equation.

дифференциальн/ый *a.* differential; **д. показатель восстановления** differential recovery rate; **д. усилитель** difference amplifier; **д. эффект** differential effect; **—ая закалка** differential (or selective) hardening; **—ая ионизационная камера** differential ionization chamber; **—ая откачка** differential pumping; **—ая проницаемость** differential permeability; **—ое исчисление** differential calculus; **—ое сечение** differential cross section; **—ое уравнение** differential equation; **—ое уравнение в частных производных** partial differential equation.

дифференц/иатор *m.* differentiator; **—иация** *f.*, **—ирование** *n.* differentiation; discrimination; **—ированный** *a.* differentiated; **—ировать** *v.* differentiate; distinguish; **—ировка** *f.* differentiation; **—ируемый** *a.* differentiable; **—ирующий усилитель** differentiator amplifier; **—ирующая цепь** differentiating circuit; **—ирующее устройство** differentiator.

диффузат *m.* diffusate.

диффуз/ивность *f.* diffusivity; **—ионно конденсационная камера** diffusion chamber, diffusion cloud chamber.

диффузионн/ый *a.* diffusion, diffusional, diffusive; **д. барьер** diffusion barrier; **д. насос** diffusion pump; **д. паромасляный насос** oil diffusion pump; **д. перенос** diffusive transfer; **д. переход** (semicond.) diffused junction; **д. термоэффект** diffusion thermoeffect; **д. ток** diffusion(al) current; **д. экран** diffusion barrier; **—ая волна тепловых нейтронов** thermal diffusion length; **—ая длина** diffusion length; **—ая камера Вильсона** diffusion cloud chamber; **—ая конвекция** diffuse convection; **—ая постоянная** diffusion constant; **—ая среда** diffusion medium; **—ая ширина** diffusion breadth; **—ое приближение** diffusion approximation; **—ое ядро** diffusion kernel.

диффуз/ия *f.* diffusion, scattering; **д. взаимная** interdiffusion; **д. вихревая** eddy diffusion; **д. в твердой фазе** solid diffusion; **д. газа** gaseous diffusion; **д. нейтронов** neutron diffusion; **д. тепла** diffusion of heat; **коэффициент —ии** diffusion coefficient; **коэффициент обратной**

—**ии** (x-ray) back-scattering factor; **постоянная —ии** diffusion constant.

диффузн/о *adv.* diffusely; **д. отражающая поверхность** diffusely reflecting surface; —**ость** *f.* diffusivity; —**ый** *a.* diffuse, diffusive; —**ая серия** diffuse series; —**ое движение** diffusive motion; —**ое освещение** diffuse illumination; —**ое отражение** diffuse reflection; —**ое рассеяние** diffuse scattering; —**ое связывание** diffusion bonding; **коэффициент —ого отражения** diffuse-reflection factor.

диффузо/метр *m.* diffusometer; —**р** *m.* exit cone.

диффундир/овать *v.* diffuse, scatter; —**уемый** *a.* diffusible; —**ующий** *a.* diffusing, diffusible; —**ующий индикатор** diffusing tracer.

дихлор— *prefix* dichlor—, dichloro—.

дихотический *a.* dichotic.

дихро/изм *m.*, —**ичность** *f.* dichroism; —**ит** *m.* dichroite; —**ичный** *a.* dichroic.

дихроматизм *m.* dichromatism.

дихроскоп *m.* dichroscope.

дихросоль *f.* dichroic salt.

дициклический *a.* dicyclic.

диэдр *m.* dihedron; —**ический** *a.* dihedral.

диэлектр/ик *m.* dielectric, insulator; —**ит** *m.* dielectrite (insulator).

диэлектрическ/ий *a.* dielectric; **д. коэффициент** dielectric constant; —**ая восприимчивость** dielectric susceptibility; —**ая жесткость** (elec.) elastance; —**ая постоянная,** —**ая проницаемость** dielectric constant, permittivity; —**ая прочность** dielectric strength; —**ие потери** dielectric loss; —**их потерь коэффициент** dielectric loss factor (or coefficient).

диэтил *m.* diethyl.

диэфир *m.* diester.

дк *abbr.* (**дека**) deca—.

дкг *abbr.* (**декаграмм**) decagram.

дкл *abbr.* (**декалитр**) decaliter.

дкм *abbr.* (**декаметр**) decameter.

дл *abbr.* (**децилитр**) deciliter; **дл.** (**длина**) length.

длин/а *f.* length; **д. волны** wavelength; **д. габаритная** over-all length; **д. диффузии быстрых нейтронов** fast diffusion length; **д. диффузии тепловых нейтронов** thermal diffusion length; **д. диффузионного смещения** diffusion length; **д. замедления** slowing-down length, moderation length; **д. затухания** attenuation distance; **д. коллиматора** collimator distance; **д. миграции** migration length; **д. молекулы** length of molecule; **д. нейтронной волны** neutron wavelength; **д. орбиты** orbit circumference; **д. ослабления** attenuation length; **д. переноса** transport mean free path; **д. поглощения** absorption path; (cosm.) absorption thickness.

длин/а *cont.* **д. пробега** track (path) length; range, mean free path; **д. пробега до захвата** capture length; **д. пути перемешивания** mixing length; **д. размножения** multiplication length; **д. распространения** propagation distance; **д. рассеяния** scattering length; scattering mean free path; **д. релаксации** relaxation length; **д. свободного пробега** mean free path; **д. связи** bond length; **д. собственная** proper length; **д. утончения** thin-down length; **д. экранировки** shielding distance; **д. экстраполяции** extrapolation distance; **в —у, по —е** longitudinally, lengthwise; endwise; **во всю —у** along the full length.

длинно *adv.* long, lengthily; —**ватый** *a.* longish; —**волновой** *a.* long-wave; —**временный** *a.* long-time; —**периодный** *a.* long-period, long-lived; —**пробежный** *a.* long-range.

длинноты *pl.* prolixities; tedious passages.

длиннофокусн/ый объектив long-distance objective; —**ая линза** long-focus lens.

длинн/ый *a.* long, lengthy; —**ые волны** long waves.

длительно *adv.* a long time.

длительность *f.* persistence, duration; **д. вспышки-светимость** (astr.) life-luminosity relation (of a nova); **д. жизни** lifetime, life span; **д. зрительного восприятия** duration of vision; **д. импульса** pulse duration (length, width); **д. инсоляции, д. солнечного сияния** duration of sunshine; **д. нарастания** response time, time of growth; **д. прохождения** transit time; **д. флуоресценции** fluorescence duration (or persistence).

длительн/ый *a.* persistent, prolonged, protracted, long, long-term; **—ая компонента затухания** slow decay component; **—ая нагрузка** constant load; **—ая работа** continuous duty; **—ое равновесие** secular equilibrium; **—ое разрушение** delayed fracture; **—ое свечение** afterglow; **—ое уравнение** secular equation.

длить *v.* protract, prolong; **—ся** *v.* last, continue.

для *prep. gen.* for, to; **д. того чтобы** in order that, so that.

длящийся *a.* lasting, permanent.

дм *abbr.* (**дециметр**) decimeter; **дм.** (**дюйм**) inch.

ДМВ *abbr.* (**дециметровые волны**) decimeter waves.

дн *abbr.* (**дина**) dyne (d, dyn).

дневник *m.* journal, diary.

дневн/ой *a.* day, daytime, diurnal; **д. градус** (meteor.) degree day; **д. свет** daylight; **—ая поверхность** (min.) day (surface of the ground); **—ая частота** (rad.) day frequency; **—ое время** daytime; **коэффициент —ого освещения** daylight factor.

днем *adv.* in the daytime.

днище *n.* bottom.

дно *n.* bottom; floor; ground; **д. океана** ocean floor; **д. цилиндра** cylinder head; **вверх —м** upside down.

до *prep. gen.* before, prior; until, to, up to, as far as; so; approximately; **до отказа** to capacity; as far as possible; tight (of fitted part); **до сих пор** hitherto; **до—** *prefix with verbs* to completion, to the end; to finish; until, as far as, up to, to the point of; sufficiently, far enough; *with adj.* before, prior to, pre—; **до тех пор, пока** (*or* **как**) till, until.

до— *prefix* pre—, sub—; as far as; *with verbs* finish.

добав/ить *v.* add, supplement, admix, fill up; boost (voltage); **—ка** *f.* addition, correction, contribution; admixture, impurity; accessory; instrument (range) multiplier.

добавлен/ие *n.* addition, addendum, insertion, supplement, appendix; **д. примеси** doping; **—ный** *a.* added, mixed with.

добавлять *see* **добавить.**

добавочн/ый *a.* additional, supplementary, accessory, auxiliary, extra; filler; admixed; added; after (effect, etc.); booster; extension (telephone); **д. агент** (elec.) addition agent; **—ая труба** extension pipe; **—ое сопротивление** instrument (range) multiplier.

добела *adv.* to white heat; **раскаленный д.** white hot.

добиваться *v.* strive for; achieve, obtain.

добираться *v.* attain, reach.

добиться *v.* obtain, achieve, attain, gain; **д. своего** succeed.

добреелит *m.* daubréelite.

добро *n.* good.

добро— *prefix* good, positive.

добровольный *a.* voluntary.

доброкачественн/ость *f.* high quality; figure of merit; **—ый** *a.* high-quality; **—ая опухоль** benign tumor.

добро/совестный *a.* conscientious, honest; **—тность** *f.* figure of merit, quality, Q; **—тный** *a.* good-quality, high-Q.

добр/ый *a.* good, kind; high-Q; **—ое имя** reputation.

добы/вание *n.* extraction, mining; procuring; **—вать, —ть** *v.* extract, mine; obtain, procure; **—вающая промышленность** extractive industry.

добыча *f.* yield, output, extraction; **д. нейтронов на деление** yield of neutrons per fission.

довар/ивать, —ить *v.* finish boiling, boil sufficiently.

Дове призма Dove prism.

доведен/ие *n.* reduction; bringing to; finishing; **—ный** *a.* brought, led to; finished.

доверенн/ость *f.* trust; confidence; warrant; **по —ости** by proxy, by attorney; **—ый** *a.* trusted.

доверие *n.* confidence, trust.

доверительн/ый *a.* confidential; **д. интервал** (stat.) confidence interval; **д. предел** confidence limit; **—ая вероятность** confidence coefficient; **—ая граница** confidence limit; **—ое распределение** fiducial distribution.

доверить *see* **доверять.**

доверху *adv.* up to the top, full.

доверш/ать, —ить *v.* complete; **—ение** *n.* completion, accomplishment; **—енный** *a.* completed, accomplished.

доверять *v.* trust, believe; entrust.

довести *see* **доводить.**

довод *m.* reason, argument.

довод/ить *v.* lead; finish; reduce; **д. до максимума** maximize; **д. до минимума** minimize; **—ка** *f.*, **—очный** *a.* finishing; final adjustment; sizing, lapping.

довоенный *a.* prewar.

довольн/о *adv.* enough, sufficiently; rather, quite; reasonably; **—ый** *a.* satisfied.

довольствовать *v.* supply; **—ся** *v.* be satisfied.

догад/аться, —ываться *v.* guess, suspect; **—ка** *f.* guess; **—ливость** *f.* acumen; **—ливый** *a.* shrewd, keen.

догиалиновый *a.* dohyaline.

догляд/еть, —ывать *v.* watch, see to the end.

догма *f.*, **—т** *m.* dogma; **—тический, —тичный** *a.* dogmatic.

догнать *see* **догонять.**

договариваться *v.* negotiate, arrange, come to an agreement.

договор *m.* agreement, contract; **—иться** *see* **договариваться**; **—ный** *a.* contractual, stipulated, agreed.

догон/ка *f.* overtaking; **—ять** *v.* overtake.

догор/ать, —еть *v.* burn down.

догру/жать, —живать, —зить *v.* finish loading, add; recharge; **—зка** *f.* additional charge.

дода/вать, —ть *v.* make up, add.

додекан *m.* dodecane.

додекаэдр *m.* dodecahedron; **—ический** *a.* dodecahedral.

додел/анный *a.* finished, completed; **—ать, —ывать** *v.* finish, complete, touch up; **—ка** *f.*, **—ывание** *n.* finishing, completion, debugging.

додеценал *m.* dodecenal.

додум/аться, —ываться *v.* come to a conclusion, hit upon an idea.

дождев/ание *n.* sprinkling, sprinkler irrigation; **—ой** *a.* rain, rainy, pluvial; **—ой экватор** hyetal equator; **—ые облака, —ые осадки** rainfall, precipitation; **—ые помехи** (radar) rain clutter.

дожде/мер *m.* rain gauge; **—мерное ведро** rain-gauge receiver; **—непроницаемый** *a.* raintight; **—носный** *a.* rainy, pluvial; **—писец** *m.* pluviograph.

дожд/ить *v.* rain; **—ливость** *f.* raininess; **—ливый** *a.* rainy; **—ливый период** rainy season; **—ливая область** rain field.

дождь *m.* rain, shower; **д. метеоров** meteoric shower.

дожечь *see* **дожигать.**

дожига/ние *n.* afterburning; **—ния камера** afterburner section; **—ть** *v.* burn up; **—ться** *v.* burn out.

доза *f.* dose, dosage; **д. внутреннего облучения** internal dose; **д. излучения** radiation dosage; **д. излучения допустимая для человеческого организма** human tolerance dose; **д. на выходе** exit dose; **д. ниже допустимой** sub-tolerance dose; **д. облучения** radiation dose, exposure dose; **д. облучения всего тела** whole body dose; **д. половинной выживаемости** median lethal dose.

дозатор *m.* batcher.

дозвездный *a.* prestellar.

дозвол/енный *a.* allowed, permitted; **—енная орбита** allowed orbit; **—ительный** *a.* permissible; **—ить, —ять** *v.* permit, allow, authorize, grant.

дозвуковой *a.* subsonic, near-sonic.

дозиметр *m.* dosimeter, radiation monitor, intensiometer; **д. альфа-излучения** alpha survey meter; **индивидуальный д.** personnel monitor, personnel dosimeter; **д. "карандашного" типа** pen-type dosimeter; **д. местности** area monitor; **д. на скорость счета** count-rate dosimeter. **д. рентгеновского излучения** roentgen chamber; **д.-светофор** go-no-go radiation detector.

дозиметрист *m.* health physicist, health physics officer, radiation supervisor.

дозиметрическ/ий *a.* dosimetric, radiation-monitoring, radiation-measuring; **д. пробник** dosimetry probe; **д. электроскоп** radioscope; **—ая служба, физика** health physics.

дозиметрия *f.* dosimetry, radiation monitoring; **д. для личного состава** personnel monitoring; **д. излучения** radiation dosimetry; **д. местности** area monitoring.

дозиров/ание *n.*, **—ка** *f.* dosage; monitoring; (chem.) batching; **—анный** *a.* measured out, proportioned; **—ать** *v.* dose; measure out; **—очный** *a.* dosing, dosage.

дозна/вание *n.* inquiring; **—ваться** *v.* inquire, ascertain, **—ние** *n.* inquiry, investigation.

дозре/вать, —ть *v.* ripen.

доиск/аться *v.* ascertain, discover, determine; **—ивание** *n.* finding out, inquiry; **—иваться** *v.* search, inquire.

доисторический *a.* prehistoric.

дойти *see* **доходить.**

док *m.* dock; **ставить в д.** dock.

докадмиевый *a.* sub-cadmium.

доказатель/ный *a.* demonstrative, convincing, conclusive; **—ство** *n.* demonstration, argument, proof, evidence; **—ство от противного** indirect proof, reductio ad absurdum; **—ство по выводу** deductive proof.

доказ/ать, —ывать *v.* demonstrate, argue, prove, substantiate; **что и требовалось —ать** which was to be proved (Q.E.D.); **—уемость** *f.* demonstrability, probability; **—уемый** *a.* demonstrable, provable.

доканчив/ание *n.* finishing, completing; **—ать** *v.* complete.

докапывать *v.* finish digging; **—ся** *v.* reach; get at; discover.

докембрийский *a.* (geo.) Pre-Cambrian.

докл. *abbr.* (**доклады**) proceedings.

доклад *m.* report, paper, address, lecture; **—ная записка** memorandum, report; **—чик** *m.* speaker, lecturer; reporter; **—ы** *pl.* proceedings; **—ывать** *v.* report, present (a paper); announce.

доконч/енный *a.* ended, completed; **—ить** *see* **доканчивать.**

докопать *see* **докапывать.**

докрасна *adv.* to red heat, **раскаленный д.** red hot.

докритический *a.* subcritical.

доктор *m.* doctor, physician; **—ант** *m.* predoctoral graduate student; **—антура** *f.* predoctoral training; **—ат** *m.*, **—ская степень** doctorate, doctor's degree.

доктрина *f.* doctrine.

документ *m.* document, deed; **—альный** *a.* documentary.

дол. *abbr.* (**долгота**) longitude.

долб/ить, —нуть *v.* chisel, hollow; **—ление** *n.* chiseling, slotting, mortising; **—ня** *f.* beater, ram; **—як** *m.* gear-wheel cutter.

долг *m.* debt; obligation, duty; **—и** *pl.* debts, liabilities.

долгий *a.* long, protracted.

долго *adv.* a long time; **—вато** *adv.*, **—ватый** *a.* rather long; **—вечность** *f.* longevity, durability; life; **—вечный** *a.* long-lived, lasting, permanent, enduring; **—вечная лампа** long-life tube.

долговременн/ость *f.* durability, longevity; **—ый** *a.* lasting, of long duration, permanent.

долго/денствие, —летие *n.* longevity, life expectancy; **—живущий** *a.* long-lived; **—играющая пластинка** long-playing record; **—летний** *a.* of many years' standing, long-established.

долгосрочн/ый *a.* long-term, long-range, of long duration; **д. прогноз** long-range forecast; **—ые изменения реактивности** long-term reactivity change.

долгот/а *f.* length; longitude; **—ный** *a.* longitudinal; **—ный эффект** longitude effect.

Долежалека электрометр Dolezalek electrometer.

долерофанит *m.* dolerophanite.

долет/ать, —еть *v.* reach.

долж/ен must, should, ought; owe; **—но** *adv.* it is necessary; **—но быть** probably; must have (with past tense).

должност/ной *a.* official; **—ная инструкция** service instructions; **—ь** *f.*

job, post, office, function; **исполняющий —ь** acting, acting for.

должн/ый *a.* due, proper, right, owing; **быть —ым** owe.

долив/ать *v.* add (by pouring), pour full; **—ка** *f.* addition, pouring full.

долин/а *f.*, **—ный** *a.* valley; trough; **д. волны** wave trough; **—ный ветер** valley breeze; **—ный ледник** valley glacier.

долит/ый *a.* added, poured full; **—ь** *see* **доливать.**

Доллонда призма Dollond prism.

долож/енный *a.* reported; **—ить** *see* **докладывать.**

доломит *m.* dolomite.

долот/ной, —чатый *a.* chisel; **—ная сталь** chisel steel; **—о** *n.* chisel, gouge; **—образный** *a.* chisel-shaped; **—чатая головка** chisel point.

доль/ка *f.* lobule; **—ный** *a.* lobate.

дольше *comp. of* **долго,** longer.

доля *f.* part, portion, fraction; quota; share, contribution; fate; **д. покрытия** fractional coverage; **д. реакции** branching ratio.

дом *m.* house, home; **вне —а** outdoors.

домат/ический, —овый *a.* (cryst.) domatic.

домашний *a.* domestic, home.

домейкит *m.* domeykite.

домен *m.* (ferromagnetic) domain; **д.-область** domain; **—ный** *a.* domain; (met.) blast furnace; **—ный чугун** pig iron; **—ная печь** blast furnace; **—ная структура** domain structure.

доминир/овать *v.* dominate, predominate; **—ующий** *a.* dominating, predominant.

домкрат *m.* **—ный** *a.* (lifting) jack.

домна *f.* blast furnace.

домо/вый *a.* house; **—й** *adv.* home, homeward.

домы/вать, —ть *v.* finish washing.

донатор *m.* donor; **—ная примесь** donor impurity.

донаучный *a.* prescientific.

донашивать *v.* wear out.

Донбасс *abbr.* (**Донецкий каменноугольный бассейн**) the Donets coal basin.

донес/ение *n.* report, message; **—ти** *see* **доносить.**

донизу *adv.* to the bottom.

Доннана равновесие Donnan (membrane) equilibrium.

донн/ый *a.* ground, bottom; **д. лед** bottom ice; **д. осадок** bottoms, residue, sludge; **—ые наносы** (hyd.) bed-load.

донор *m.* donor; **—ная примесь** *n*-type impurity.

доносить *v.* carry up to; report, denounce.

донять *see* **донимать.**

доопределение *n.* supplementing of a definition.

доохла/дитель *m.* recooler, secondary cooler; **—ждать** *v.* recool; **—ждение** *n.* after-cooling.

доп. *abbr.* (**дополненный**) enlarged.

допе/кать, —чь *v.* finish baking.

допис/ывать, —ать *v.* finish writing.

доплата *f.* additional payment.

доподлинн/о *adv.* for certain; **—ый** *a.* certain, authentic.

дополнен/ие *n.* addition, supplement, complement; (math.) complementary minor; **д. алгебраическое** (math.) signed minor, cofactor; **д. до** complement with respect to; **д. до широты** colatitude; **—ный** *a.* supplemented, added, complemented; completed; **—ная матрица** augmented matrix.

дополнитель *m.* complementer; **—но** *adv.* in addition; **—ность** *f.* complementarity.

дополнительн/ый *a.* supplementary, additional, subsidiary, secondary, extra, accessory, auxiliary; complementary; admixed; **д. вибратор** complementary dipole; **д. заряд** booster charge; **д. минор** complementary minor; **д. множитель** cofactor; **д. модуль** complementary modulus (of an elliptic function); **д. угол до 90°** complementary angle; **д. угол до 180°** supplementary angle; **д. угол до 360°** conjugate angle, explementary angle; **д. член** additive term; **—ая величина** (math.) complement; **—ая реакция** side reaction; **—ое напряжение** secondary stress; boosting voltage; **—ое расширение**

after-expansion; **—ое условие** subsidiary condition, supplementary condition; **—ые лучи** complementary beams; **—ые цвета** complementary colors.

дополн/ить, —ять *v.* supplement, complete, add, complement, fill up.

Доппельмайер Doppelmayer (lunar crater).

Допплера расширение Doppler broadening; **Д.-Физо эффект** D.-Fizeau effect; **Д. эффект, допплер-эффект** D. effect.

допплеровск/ий свист Doppler whistle; **д. сдвиг, —ое смещение** D. shift; **—ая радиолокация** D. radar system.

допробойный ток preconduction current.

допуск *m.* allowance; admission; tolerance, clearance; **д. на** allowance for; **единица —а** tolerance unit.

допускаем/ость *f.* admissibility; **—ый** *a.* admissible, safe, permissible; **—ый зазор** safe clearance.

допуск/ать *v.* allow, tolerate; postulate, suppose, assume; **д. ошибку** commit an error; **—ающий** *a.* permitting; accessible.

допустим/ость *f.* validity, admissibility; **—ый** *a.* admissible, permissible, allowable; safe, possible; **—ый ток** current-carrying capacity; **—ая глубина модуляции** modulation capability; **—ая доза** permissible dose, tolerance; **—ая доза облучения** radiation tolerance; **—ая концентрация** permissible concentration; **—ая мощность** power-carrying capacity; **—ая мощность дозы** tolerance rate; **—ая нагрузка** safe load; load capacity; **—ая утечка** leak tolerance; **—ое отклонение** permissible variation.

допустить *see* **допускать.**

допущен/ие *n.* assumption, allowance, tolerance; **—ный** *a.* allowed, tolerated; authorized; assumed.

допыт/аться *v.* find out, discover; **—ываться** *v.* question, investigate.

дор. *abbr.* (**дорожный**) road, highway.

дораб/атывать, —отать *v.* finish working; **—отка** *f.* further improvement.

дореволюционный *a.* prerevolutionary.

дорелятивистский *a.* prerelativistic.

Дорна эффект Dorn effect.

дорный *a.* split, fissured, cracked.

дорог/а *f.* road, way, path; **в —е** en route.

дорого *adv.* expensively; **—й** *a.* expensive.

дорож/е *comp. of* **дорого, дорогой,** more expensive; **—ить** *v.* value.

дорож/ка *f.* path, track, trail; **—ный** *a.* road, highway; **—ный барометр** portable barometer.

досад/а *f.* disappointment, annoyance; **—ный** *a.* disappointing, displeasing; **—ная опечатка** unfortunate misprint.

досветовой *a.* slower than light.

досинхронный *a.* hyposynchronous.

доск/а *f.* **—овый** *a.* board, panel; slab, plate; **грифельная д.** blackboard, slate; **классная д.** (classroom) blackboard; **д. лабораторной схемы** "breadboard"; **д. приборная** instrument panel.

дословн/о *adv.* literally, verbatim; **—ый** *a.* literal, verbatim.

досм/атривать —отреть *v.* watch; inspect, examine.

доспе/вание *n.* ripening, maturing; **—вать, —ть** *v.* ripen; **—лый** *a.* ripe, mature.

досрочный *a.* premature; ahead of schedule.

доставать *v.* get, obtain, procure, secure; reach; suffice.

достав/ить, —лять *v.* deliver, convey; furnish, yield; **—ка** *f.*, **—ление** *n.* delivery; transportation; furnishing; yield; **—ка с помощью переноски** liquid-liquid extraction; **—ленный, —ляемый** *a.* delivered, conveyed; supplied; **—очный** *a.* delivery.

достаточн/о *adv.* sufficiently, satisfactorily; it is sufficient; fairly; **—ость** *f.* adequacy; competence; **—ый** *a.* sufficient, adequate, satisfactory; competent; **—ое условие** sufficient condition.

достать *see* **доставать.**

достиг/аемость *see* **достижимость**; **—аемый** *see* **достижимый**; **—ать, —нуть** *v.* reach, attain; achieve; amount to; **—нутый** *a.* reached, attained; **—нуть высшей точки** culminate; reach a climax; **не —нуть** fail.

достиж/ение *n.* achievement, attainment, advance, progress; **—имость** *f.* attainability, accessibility, practicability; **—имый** *a.* attainable, accessible, achievable, practicable.

достичь *see* **достигать.**

достоверн/ость *f.* authenticity, certainty; reliability; **граница —ости** confidence limit; **—ый** *a.* authentic, reliable, certain, trustworthy; **—ый запас** positive reserve; **—ая руда** proved ore, positive ore; **—ое событие** certain event; **—ые запасы** proved resources.

досто/инство *n.* quality, worth, merit; **—йный** *a.* worthy, deserving, merited.

достопримечательн/ость *f.* curiosity, noteworthy sight; **—ый** *a.* notable, remarkable, prominent.

достояние *n.* property; acquisition.

достр/аивание *n.*, **—ойка** *f.* completion; **—аивать, —оить** *v.* finish building, add on (building).

доступ *m.* access, admission, inlet; **—но** *adv.* easily, simply, accessibly; **—ность** *f.* accessibility, intelligibility, availability; **—ный** *a.* accessible, available, intelligible; **легко —ный** easily attainable.

досуг *m.* leisure, spare time.

досу/ха *adv.* to dryness, dry; **—шивать, —шить** *v.* finish drying, dry sufficiently.

досып/анный *a.* filled, added; **—ать** *v.* fill up, add.

досяг/ать, —нуть *v.* attain, reach, accomplish; **—аемость** *f.* reach, range, attainability; **—аемый** *a.* attainable, approachable.

дотация *f.* subsidy, grant.

доте/кать, —чь *v.* flow up to.

дотла *adv.* completely.

дотр/агиваться, —онуться *v.* touch.

дотя/гивать, —нуть *v.* drag up to, draw out to; last out; **—гиваться, —нуться** *v.* reach (with difficulty), hold out, last.

доутиит *m.* doughtyite.

дохнуть *see* **дышать.**

доход *m.* income, revenue, profit; **—ить** *v.* reach, attain; amount to, total; ripen, develop; **—ность** *f.* profitableness; **—ный** *a.* profitable, remunerative.

доц. *abbr.* *see* **доцент.**

доцент *m.* assistant professor; docent.

дочерн/яя фракция daughter fraction; **—ее ядро** daughter nucleus.

дочиста *adv.* completely.

дочь *f.* daughter; *pl.* **дочери.**

дощ/атый *a.* board, plank; **—ечка** *f.* small plank; tablet, plate.

доэвтект/ический *a.* hypoeutectic; **—оидный** *a.* hypoeutectoid.

д-р, др. *abbr.* (**доктор**) doctor, Dr.; **др.** (**другие**) others.

драга *f.* dredge.

драг/ер *m.* dredger; **—ирование** *n.* dredging; **—ировать** *v.* dredge.

драгоценн/ость *f.* jewel, gem, precious stone; **—ый** *a.* precious; **—ый камень** precious stone, gem.

драек *m.* dowel.

дражное дело *see* **драгирование.**

дразн/ение *n.* exciting; (met.) poling; **—илка** *f.* pole, stirrer; **—ить** *v.* excite; pole, stir.

драйер *m.* dryer, drying machine.

Дракон Draco (Dra) (constellation).

Дракониды Draconids (meteors).

дран/ица, —ка, —ь *f.*, **—ичный** *a.* lath, shingle; shaving, chip; **—ый** *a.* torn, ragged.

драть *v.* tear, strip off.

драфт *m.* glass rod.

драчевый напильник bastard file.

дребезж/ание *n.* trembling; rattling, jarring; flutter; **—ать** *v.* rattle; tremble.

древесина *f.* wood; wood pulp.

древесноугольный *a.* charcoal; **д. чугун** (met.) charcoal iron.

древесн/ый *a.* wood, woody; **д. уголь** charcoal; **—ая замазка** putty; **—ая мука** sawdust; **—ая шерсть, —ое мочало** wood wool, wood fiber, excelsior.

древн/ий *a.* ancient; **—ость** *f.* antiquity.

древовидн/ость *f.* arborescence; **—ый** *a.* arborescent; dendritic; **—ая фигура** tree pattern.

дрейкантер *m.* (geo.) dreikanter; (cryst.) trihedron.

Дрейпера каталог (astr.) Draper catalogue; **Д. эффект** D. effect.

дрейф *m.*, **—овый** *a.* drift, drifting; **д. ведущего центра, д. направляющего центра** guiding center drift (in plasma); **д. нуля** zero drift, instrument drift; **д. прибора** instrument drift; **—овать** *v.* drift; **—овая подвижность** drift mobility; **—овая трубка** drift tube; **—ующий** *a.* drifting.

дрек *m.* boat anchor.

дрем/ать *v.* slumber; **—лющий** *a.* slumbering; inactive.

дренаж *m.*, **—ный** *a.* drainage, drain; **—ировать** *see* **дренировать**; **—ный канал** drain, gutter; **—ая сеть** drainage system.

дрениров/ание *n.* drainage, draining; **—анный** *a.* drained; **—ать** *v.* drain, draw off.

Дрепера *see* **Дрейпера.**

дресва *f.* gravel.

дрессиров/ка *f.*, **—очный** *a.* (met.) dressing.

дрешер *m.* thrasher.

дриттельзильбер *m.* tiers-argent (silver-aluminum alloy).

дробилка *f.* crusher, disintegrator.

дробильн/ый *a.* crushing; **д. прибор, —ая машина** crusher; **—ые вальцы** crusher rolls.

дроб/ина, —инка *f.* small shot, pellet; **—ить** *v.* crush, pulverize, grind, granulate; divide, split up; **—ление** *n.* crushing, grinding; granulation; breaking down, fractionation, fine subdivision; **—ление дозы** dose fractionation; **—леный** *a.* crushed, ground, granulated.

дробно/-дождевые облака fractonimbus; **д.-кучевые облака** fractocumulus; **д.-линейный** *a.* linear-fractional; **д.-слоистые облака** fracto-stratus; **—атомная частица** subatomic particle; **—кратный** *a.* submultiple; **—сть** *f.* divisibility; **—шаговая обмотка** fractional-pitch winding.

дробн/ый *a.* fractional; divided, broken; **д. выход** fractional yield; **—ая гармоника** fractional harmonic; **—ая ионизация** fractional ionization, degree of ionization; **—ая кристаллизация** fractional crystallization; **—ая перегонка** fractional distillation.

дробов/ой *a.* shot; **д. шум** shot noise; **д. эффект** shot effect; **—ая коронка** (min.) core bit; **—ое бурение** shot drilling.

дробь *f.* (math.) fraction; (met.) shot; **бесконечная непрерывная д.** nonterminating continued fraction; **конечная непрерывная д.** terminating (or finite) continued fraction; **неправильная д.** improper fraction; **несократимая д.** irreducible fraction; **периодическая д.** circulating (or repeating) decimal; **правильная д.** proper fraction; **простая д.** common fraction.

дробящий *a.* crushing.

дровокол *m.*, **—ка** *f.*, **—ьный станок** woodchopper, wood-splitting machine.

дрогнуть *see* **дрожать.**

дрож/ание *n.* tremor, vibration, jitter; flickering, scintillation; zitterbewegung; **—ать** *v.* vibrate, shake; flicker, jar; **—ащий** *a.* vibrating, quivering, flickering.

дрозофила *f.* drosophila.

дросс *m.* (met.) dross, slag.

дроссел/евать, —ировать *v.* throttle, choke; **—ирование** *n.* throttling, choking; **—ирующий** *a.* throttling.

дроссель *m.* throttle, choke; (elec.) choke coil; **д.-клапан** throttle, throttle valve; butterfly valve; **д.-эффект** Joule-Thomson effect; **—но-емкостная связь** impedance-capacitance coupling.

дроссельн/ый *see* **дроссель**; **д. клапан** *see* **дроссель-клапан**; **д. сросток** choke joint; **—ая заслонка** baffle plate; **—ая катушка** (elec.) choke coil; **—ая связь** impedance coupling, inductor coupling; **—ое давление** throttle pressure.

дроты *pl.* glass tubes.

друг *m.* friend; **д. —а** each other, mutually; **д. за —ом** in succession; **д. от —а** from each other; **д. с —ом** with each other.

друг/ие *pl.* others, the rest; **и д.** and others, et al.; **—ой** *a.* other, another, different; **ни тот ни —ой** neither; **тот и —ой** both.

другмансит *m.* droogmansite.

Друде теория проводимости Drude theory of conduction; **Д. уравнение** D. equation.

друж/ба *f.* friendship; **—елюбный, —еский, —ественный** *a.* friendly; **—но** *adv.* amicably; unanimously; in unison, together; **—ный** *a.* friendly, harmonious; unanimous.

друза *f.* (min.) druse; node, nodule.

друммондов свет Drummond limelight, limelight.

дрыг/ание *n.* jerking, twitching; **—ать, —нуть** *v.* jerk, twitch.

Дрэгон Dragon (reactor).

дряблый *a.* flaccid, limp.

дрян/ной *a.* worthless; **—ь** *f.* trash, rubbish.

ДС *abbr.* (**дневной свет**) daylight.

д.т. диаграмма *abbr.* (**диаграмма давление-температура**) pressure-temperature chart (P-T).

дуал/изм *m.* dualism, duality; **—истический** *a.* dualistic; **—ьный** *a.* dual.

Дуана и Хунта закон Duane and Hunt law.

дуант *m.* dee (of cyclotron, etc.).

дуб/ильный *a.* tanning, tannic; **—итель** *m.* tanning agent; **—ить** *v.* tan; **—ление** *n.* tanning; **—леный** *a.* tanned.

дубл/ет *m.* doublet; duplicate; **—етное расстояние** doublet separation; **—етность** *f.* doubling, duplicity; **—икат** *m.* duplicate, replica.

дублиров/ание *n.* doubling, duplication; **—анный** *a.* doubled; **—ать** *v.* double, duplicate; fold; **—очный** *a.* doubling, double.

Дубна Dubna.

дуг/а *f.* arc, arch, bow; **д. интенсивного горения** high-intensity arc; **д. окружности** circular arc; **д. при размыкании** break arc; **сводить —ой** arch, curve.

дугласит *m.* douglasite.

дугов/ой *a.* arc, arched, curved; **д. ионный источник** ion-producing arc; **д. источник** arc source; **д. разряд** arc discharge; **д. разрядник** arc gap, arc discharger; **д. спектр** arc spectrum; **д. фонарь** arc lamp; **—ая линия** arc line; **—ая минута** minute of arc; **—ая печь** arc furnace; **—ая угольная лампа** arc lamp; **—ая электросварка** electric arc welding.

дугообразный *a.* arched, curved; **д. шквал** arched squall.

дугостойкий *a.* non-arcing.

дужка *f.* small arc, bow, airfoil profile.

дуксит *m.* duxite.

дуктил/иметр, —ометр *m.* ductilimeter; **—ометрия** *f.* ductilimetry; **—ьность** *f.* ductility; **—ьный** *a.* ductile.

дул/о *n.*, **—ьный** *a.* bore, muzzle.

дума *f.* thought; council; **—ть** *v.* think; believe, surmise, suppose, imagine; intend, mean.

дуновение *n.* puff, blowing.

Дунрейский реактор Dounrey reactor.

дунуть *see* **дуть.**

дуо/граф *m.* duograph; **—децима** *f.* (mus.) twelfth.

дуплекс *m.*, **—ный** *a.* duplex, double, two-way; **—ер** *m.* duplexer; **—ная система радиосвязи** two-way radio-communication system.

дуплет *m. see* **дублет.**

дупл/истый *a.* hollow, empty; **—о** *n.* hollow, cavity.

дуралий *see* **дюралий.**

дуримет *m.* Durimet (ferrous alloy).

дурной *a.* bad, wrong.

дут/ый *a.* inflated; **—ь** *v.* blow, inflate; blast; **—ье** *n.* (air) blast; blowing; **магнитное —ье** magnetic blowout.

дух *m.* odor; spirit; breath; "ghost" (line, etc.); **—а** *f.* (met.) air hole (of casting mold).

духов/ой *a.* wind, air; **—ое отопление** hot-air heating.

духомер *m.* wind gauge; blast meter.

душа *f.* soul, mind, spirit.

душистый *a.* fragrant, aromatic.

душить *v.* stifle, suffocate.

душн/ик *m.* (air) vent, ventilator, aspirator; **—ый** *a.* oppressive, sultry.

дующийся *a.* (geo.) heaving.

д. чл. *abbr. see* **действит. чл.**

дым *m.* smoke, fume; **—ить, —иться** *v.* smoke, fume; **—ка** *f.* mist; (damp) haze; **—комер** *m.* hazemeter; **—ный**

a. smoky, fuming; **—ная мгла** smoke haze.

дымов/ой *a.* smoke; **д. газ** flue gas; **д. канал** (chimney) flue; **—ая заслонка** damper; **—ая мгла** smoke haze; **—ая труба** chimney, stack, flue; **—ое отражение** (rad.) smoke echo.

дымогарн/ый котел fire-tube boiler; **—ая коробка** firebox; **—ая трубка** fire tube.

дымо/непроницаемый *a.* smoketight, smokeproof; **—обнаружитель** *m.* smoke detector; **—сос** *m.* exhaust fan; **—стойкий, —упорный** *a.* fume-resistant; **—ход** *m.* flue, chimney; **—ходный поток** chimney current.

дымчат/ый *a.* smoked; **—ое стекло** smoked glass.

дымящий *a.* smoking, fuming.

дыр/а, —ка *f.* hole, vacancy, gap, perforation, aperture; **—ка положительного иона** positive-ion vacancy; **—кообразование** *n.* hole formation; **—копромежуточный пар, —окол** *m.* perforator, punch; **—омер** *m.* hole gauge.

дыропробивн/ой *a.* punching, perforating; **д. пресс, д. станок, д. штамп, —ая машина, дыропробиватель** *m.* punch, puncher, punching machine, punch press; perforator.

дыроч/ка *f.* small aperture; **—ный** *a.* hole, *p*-type; vacant; **—ный ток** hole current; **—ная зона** (semicond.) valence band; **—ная подвижность** hole mobility; **—ная проводимость** *p*-type conductivity; **—ное перемещение** hole migration.

дыр/чатый, —явый *a.* full of holes, perforated; **—явить** *v.* pierce, perforate.

дыхание *n.* respiration.

дыхательный *a.* respiratory; **д. аппарат** respirator; **д. клапан** breather valve.

дышать *v.* breathe, respire.

дьюар *m.*, **Дьюара сосуд** Dewar vessel.

Дэви Davy (lunar crater).

Дэвиссона-Джермера опыт Davisson-Germer experiment.

ДЭС *abbr.* (**дуговая электросварка**) electric arc welding.

Дэффина-Кеммера перестановочные соотношения Duffin-Kemmer commutation rules.

дюбель *m.*, **—ный** *a.* dowel.

Дюгема-Маргулеса уравнение (соотношение) Duhem-Margules equation.

дюжина *f.* dozen.

дюжонит *m.* dudgeonite.

дюз *m.*, **—а** *f.* nozzle.

дюйм *m.* inch; **—овка** *f.* inch plank; **—овый** *a.* inch, one-inch.

дюкер *m.* sag pipe, inverted siphon.

Дюлонга-Пти закон Dulong and Petit law.

Дюма способ Dumas method.

дюмонтит *m.* dumontite.

дюмортьерит *m.* dumortierite.

дюн/а *f.*, **—ный** *a.* dune.

дюпаркит *m.* duparcite.

Дюпена индикатриса Dupin indicatrix.

Дюпон du Pont.

Дюпре уравнение Dupré equation.

дюпрен *m.* Duprene.

дюрайрон *m.* Duriron (acid-resistant alloy).

дюрал/евый *a.*, **—ь** *m.* Dural; **—ий** *m.* Duralium; **—ой** *m.* Duraloy.

дюралюмин, —ий *m.*, **—иевый** *a.* Duralumin, Dural.

Дюринга правило Dühring rule.

дюрометр *m.* durometer.

дюссертит *m.* dussertite.

дюфрениберауниt *m.* dufreniberaunite.

дюфренит *m.* dufrenite.

дюфренуазит *m.* dufrenoysite.

Дюфура осциллограф Dufour oscillograph.

Е

ев— *see also under* **эв—, эй—.**

евген/ика *f.* eugenics; **—ический** *a.* eugenic.

евгеновый блеск polybasite.

Евдокс Eudoxus (lunar crater).

Евдокса теорема Eudoxus theorem.

евклидов *see* **эвклидов.**

Евратом *abbr.* (**Европейское сообщество по атомной энергии**) European Atomic Energy Community.

Европа *f*. Europe.

Европейская организация (Европейский совет) по ядерным исследованиям (ЦЕРН) Conseil Européen pour la Recherche Nucléaire (CERN); European Council for Nuclear Research.

Европейское агентство по ядерной энергии European Nuclear Energy Agency; **Е. общество по атомной энергии** European Atomic Energy Society.

европий *m*. europium (Eu).

евстахиева труба Eustachian tube.

егип. *abbr*. (**египетский**) Egyptian.

Египет Egypt.

египетский *a*. Egyptian.

его *gen. of* **он, оно,** his, its; *acc*., him, it.

Егорова теорема Egorov theorem.

ед *abbr*. (**единица допуска**) tolerance unit; **ед.** (**единица**) unit; unity, one.

едва *adv*. hardly, scarcely, barely; **е. заметный** barely perceptible; **е. не** almost, nearly; **е. разборчивый** barely legible, barely readable.

ед. изм. *abbr*. (**единица измерения**) unit of measurement.

един/ение *n*. unity, accord; **—ить** *v*. unite.

единиц/а *f*. unit, unity, one; (math.) identity, identity element; **е. атомной массы** atomic mass unit (amu); **е. группы** (math.) identity (element) of a group; **е. допуска** tolerance unit; **е. измерения** unit of measurement; **е. облучения** rad (unit); **е. объема** unit volume; **е. теплоты** unit of heat, thermal unit; **в —ах** in units (of); **весовой —ы** per unit weight; **за —у, на —у** per unit, each.

единичн/ость *f*. singleness; **—ый** *a*. single, unique; unit, unitary, one; isolated, individual; **—ый вектор** unit vector; **—ый круг, —ая окружность** unit circle; **—ая матрица** unit matrix; **—ая окружность** unit circle; **—ая ступенчатая функция** unit step function; **—ая ячейка** unit cell, single cell.

едино— *prefix* uni—, mono—.

едино/временный *a*. once only; simultaneous, synchronous; **—гласие, —душие** *n*. unanimity, accord; **—гласный, —душный** *a*. unanimous.

единомысл/енный *a*. unanimous, agreeing; **—ие** *n*. unanimity, concord.

единообраз/ие *n*. uniformity; **—ный** *a*. uniform.

Единорог Monoceros (Mon) (constellation).

единственн/о *adv*. uniquely, solely; **—ость** *f*. soleness, singleness; **—ости теорема** uniqueness theorem; **—ый** *a*. only, sole, unique, single; **—ое значение** unique value.

един/ство *n*. unity; **—ый** *a*. single; unique; united, common; indivisible; **—ая модель ядра** unified nuclear model; **—ая теория поля** (rel.) unified field theory; unitary field theory.

едк/ий *a*. caustic, corrosive; acrid; **е. газ** corrosive gas; **е. натр** sodium hydroxide; **—ое вещество, —ое средство** caustic, corrosive; **—ое кали** potassium hydroxide; **—ие щелочи** caustic alkalis.

ее *gen. and acc. of* **она,** her.

еж *m*. (rad.) hedgehog transformer.

еже- *prefix* every.

ежегодн/ик *m*. yearbook, almanac annual (publication); **—о** *adv* yearly, annually, per annum; **—ый** *a*. yearly, annual; anniversary.

ежедекадно *adv*. every ten days.

ежедн. *abbr*. (**ежедневный**) daily, diurnal.

ежедневн/о *adv*. daily, per diem; **—ый** *a* daily, diurnal; **—ое изменение** diurnal variation.

ежекит *m*. jezekite.

ежем. *abbr*. (**ежемесячный**) monthly.

ежемесячн/о *adv*., **—ый** *a*. monthly.

ежеминутн/о *adv*., **—ый** *a*. every minute every instant; incessant, continual.

еженед. *abbr*. (**еженедельный**) weekly.

еженедельн/ик *m*. weekly (publication) **—о** *adv*., **—ый** *a*. weekly.

ежесезонн/о *adv*., **—ый** *a*. seasonally.

ежечасн/о *adv*., **—ый** *a*. hourly.

ежовый трансформатор *see* **еж.**

ей *dat. of* **она,** her, to her.

ек— *see under* **эк—**.

еле *adv*. hardly, scarcely, narrowly.
елочн/ый *a*. arborescent, treelike; **—ая антенна** fishbone antenna, christmastree antenna.
емк. *abbr*. (**емкость**) capacity, capacitance, cubic content.
емкий *a*. capacious, large-capacity.
емкостн/о-резистивная связь capacitance-resistance coupling; **е.-связанный** *a*. capacitance-coupled; **—ый** *a*. capacitance, capacitive, capacity; **—ый делитель** capacity divider; **—ый пробник** capacitive probe; **—ый усилитель** capacity amplifier; **—ая нагрузка** capacitive load; **—ая настройка** capacitance (or condenser) tuning; **—ая проводимость** capacitive susceptance; **—ая связь** capacitive coupling; **—ое сопротивление** capacitive reactance.
емкость *f*. capacity, capacitance; cubic content; **е. анод-нить** plate-filament capacitance; **запасная е.** reserve capacity; **е. памяти** storage capacity (of computer); **е. рассеяния** stray capacitance; **е. собственная** self-capacitance; **е. тела** body capacitance.
ему *dat. of* **он, оно,** him, to him; it, to it.
еремеевит *m*. eremeyevite.
ерунда *f*. nonsense, absurdity; trifle.
ерунок *m*. bevel, bevel square.
ерш *m*. jag, ragbolt; broach; brush.
если *conj*. if, in case, when; while; **е. бы** if; **е. бы не** if not for; **е. не** unless; **е. только** if only, provided; **е. только вообще** if at all; **е. только не** unless; **е. уже** if anything.
ЕСП *abbr*. (**естественный синоптический период**) natural synoptic period.
ЕСР *abbr*. (**естественный синоптический район**) natural synoptic region.
естественн/ик *m*. scientist; science teacher; science student; **—о** *adv*. naturally, of course; it is natural; **—о радиоактивный** naturally radioactive; **—ость** *f*. naturalness.
естественн/ый *a*. natural, inherent; spontaneous; reasonable; **е. газ** natural gas; **е. магнетизм** spontaneous magnetism; **е. магнит** natural magnet; **е. элемент** natural element; **—ая ионизация** spontaneous ionization; **—ая конвекция** free convection; **—ая неустойчивость** inherent instability; **—ая радиоактивность** natural radioactivity; **—ая устойчивость** inherent stability, structural stability; **—ая ширина линии** natural line width; **—ое охлаждение** self-cooling; **—ое расщепление** natural disintegration; **—ые богатства** natural resources.
естество *n*. nature, substance; **—ведение** *n*. natural science.
естествозн. *abbr*. *see* **естествознание.**
естествознание *n*. natural science.
естествоиспыт. *abbr*. (**естествоиспытатель**) naturalist.
естествоиспыта/ние *n*. natural history; **—тель** *m*. naturalist.
есть *v*. eat; *present of* **быть,** is, there is.
ехать *v*. drive, ride, travel.
еще *adv*. still, more, again; as long ago as, as far back as; **е. не, нет е.** not yet; **е. недавно** until recently.
ею *instr. of* **она,** by her, with her.

Ж

ж., Ж. *abbr*. (**журнал**) journal, periodical.
жабий глаз toad's eye tin.
жад *m*. jade.
жадеит *m*. jadeite.
жажда *f*. thirst.
жакет *m*. jacket.
жалоба *f*. complaint.
жалова/ние *n*. grant, donation, conferring; **—нный** *a*. granted, presented; **—ть** *v*. grant, bestow; **—ться** *v*. complain.
жалюз/и *n*. jalousie; **—ный динод** louvered dynode.
Жамена интерферометр Jamin interferometer; **жаменовская свеча** J. candle.
жанр *m*. genus; genre.

жар *m.* heat, glow; —**а** *f.* heat, hot weather.

жаргон *m.* jargon.

жаркий *a.* hot, sultry; **ж. пояс** torrid zone.

жаров/ой *a.* heat, fire; —**ая труба** fire tube, furnace flue.

жаро/производительная способность heating power; —**стойкий** *see* **жароупорный.**

жаротрубный *a.* fire-tube, flue; **ж. котел** fire-tube boiler.

жароупорн/ость *f.* resistance to heat; —**ый** *a.* heatproof, fire-resistant, fireproof; —**ый сплав** heat-resistant alloy; —**ый элемент** heat resistor.

ЖАХ *abbr.* (**Журнал аналитической химии**) Journal of Analytical Chemistry.

жгут *m.* rope, plait; bunched conductor.

жгуч/есть *f.* causticity, corrosiveness; —**ий** *a.* caustic, corrosive, hot.

ж.д. *abbr.* (**железная дорога**) railroad, railway.

жд/ать *v.* await, expect; —**ущая развертка** driven sweep.

же *conj.* but; and; however; *also denotes emphasis or identity.*

жединский век (geo.) Gedinnian stage.

жедрит *m.* gedrite.

жезл *m.* rod, staff.

жел. *abbr.* (**железный**) iron.

желан/ие *n.* wish, desire; **по —ию** as desired, if desired, optional.

желательн/о *adv.* it is desirable; **если ж.** if desired; —**ость** *f.* desirability; —**ый** *a.* desirable, desired.

желатин *m.* gelatin; —**изация** *f.*, —**ирование** *n.* gelatinization; —**ированный** *a.* gelatinized, gelated; —**ировать** *v.* gelatinize, gelate, gel; —**ный,** —**овый** *a.* gelatin, gelatinous.

желатино/зный, —**образный,** —**подобный** *a.* gelatinous.

жел/ать *v.* wish, desire; —**ающий** *a.* wishing.

железа *f.* gland.

железисто— *prefix* iron, ferro—, ferrous.

железистосерый *a.* iron gray.

железистосинерод/истоводородная кислота, —**оводородная кислота** ferrocyanic acid; —**истый** *a.* ferrocyanide (of).

железист/ость *f.* ferruginosity; —**о-цианистый** *see* **железистосинеродистый;** —**ый** *a.* iron, ferrous, ferruginous, ferriferous; —**ый голыш** sinople; —**ая кислота** ferrous acid; **соль —ой кислоты** ferrite; —**ая соль** ferrous salt.

железнение *n.* iron plating.

железно— *prefix* iron, ferri—, ferric.

железнокисл/ый *a.* ferric acid, ferrate (of); —**ая соль** ferrate.

железн/ый *a.* iron, ferric; **ж. блеск** iron glance, hematite; **ж. колчедан** iron pyrite; **ж. лом** scrap iron; **ж. магнитопровод** iron circuit; **ж. сплав** ferroalloy; —**ая дорога** railroad; —**ая жесть** sheet iron; —**ая кислота** ferric acid; **соль —ой кислоты** ferrate; —**ая слюда** micaceous iron ore; —**ые потери** (elec.) iron loss; —**ые товары** hardware.

железняк *m.* iron ore; **красный ж.** hematite; **ж. магнитный** lodestone.

железо— *prefix* iron, ferro—; ferri—, ferric; *see also* **железно—.**

желез/о *n.* iron (Fe); **ванадиевое ж.** ferrovanadium; **вольфрамистое ж.** ferrotungsten; **ковкое ж., сварочное ж., тягучее ж.** wrought iron, malleable iron; **окисная соль —а, соль окиси —а** ferric salt; **окисное ж., трехвалентное ж.** ferric iron; **окись —а** ferric oxide; **соединение окиси —а** ferric compound; **углеродистое ж.** iron carbide.

железо/аммониевые квасцы ferric ammonium alum; —**бетон** *m.*, —**бетонный** *a.* ferroconcrete, reinforced concrete; —**делательный завод** iron works, iron mill; —**кремнистый сплав** silicon-iron; —**магнитный** *a.* ferromagnetic; —**никелевый аккумулятор** nickel-iron battery, Edison storage cell; —**никелевый колчедан** pentlandite; —**обрабатывающая промышленность** iron industry —**плавильный завод** iron foundry —**прокатный стан** iron rolling mill; —**скобяные изделия** hardware —**содержащий** *a.* iron-containing ferruginous; ferriferous.

железобразный *a.* gelatinous.

желкнуть *v.* turn yellow.

желоб *m.* groove, gutter, trough, channel; **наклонный ж., спускной ж.** chute; **—истый, —коватый** *a.* grooved, channeled; **—ить** *v.* groove, channel, flute; **—ление** *n.* grooving, channeling, fluting; **—оватый, —о-образный** *a.* U-shaped, trough-shaped; **—ок** *m.* groove, flute, slot.

желобчат/ый *a.* grooved, fluted, channeled, ribbed; **ж. транспортер** trough conveyer; **—ое железо** U-iron; corrugated iron; **—ое колесо** sheave, grooved pulley wheel.

желт/еть *see* **желкнуть**; **—изна** *f.* yellowness, yellowishness.

желтовато— *prefix* yellow, yellowish.

желтоват/ость *f.* yellowishness, yellowness; **—ый** *a.* yellowish.

желто/-зеленый *a.* yellowish green; **—зем** *m.* yellow ocher; **—калильный жар** yellow heat; **ж.-коричневый** *a.* yellowish brown, fawn-colored.

желт/ый *a.* yellow; **—ая медь** brass; **—ое каление** yellow heat; **—ое пятно** macula littea (yellow spot of retina).

желудевая лампа acorn tube.

жемчу/г *m.*, **—жина** *f.* pearl; (met.) bead; **—жный** *a.* pearl, pearly; **—жная корона** pearly corona; **—жная накипь** pearl sinter.

женевит *m.* genevite.

женевский *a.* Geneva, Genevan.

жеода *f.* geode.

Жерар Gérard (lunar crater).

жердь *f.* pole.

Жеребенок (Малый Конь) Equuleus (Equ) (constellation).

жерло *n.* mouth, orifice, crater, vent.

Жермена уравнение Germain equation.

Жертвенник Ara (Ara) (constellation).

жестк/ий *a.* hard, rigid, stiff, inflexible; stable, rugged; strict, rigorous, stringent; **ж. ливень** (cosm.) hard shower; **ж. металл** hard metal; **ж. сверхпроводник** hard (or nonideal) superconductor; **ж. шарик** rigid sphere; **—ая компонента космических лучей** hard component of cosmic rays; **—ая конструкция** rigid construction; **—ая лампа** (elec.) hard tube; **—ая модификация** stable modification; **—ая обратная связь** direct feedback; follow-up; **—ая фокусировка** strong focusing; **—ое возбуждение** hard excitation; **—ое вращение** rigid rotation; **—ое движение** rigid motion; **—ое излучение** hard radiation; **—ое требование** rigid condition; rigorous demand, strict requirement.

жестко *adv.* stiffly, rigidly; roughly; **ж. связанный** rigidly bound, tightly bound; **—ватый** *a.* stiff, somewhat hard; stringent.

жесткость *f.* hardness, rigidity, stiffness, tightness; **ж. мембраны** membrane tension; **ж. на кручение** torsional rigidity (or stiffness).

жестокий *a.* tough; severe; **ж. холод** severe cold; **ж. шторм** storm (Beaufort number 11).

жестче *comp. of* **жесткий, жестко**; **—ние** *n.* stiffening, hardening.

жесть *f.* tin plate, sheet metal; **белая ж.** tin plate; **черная ж.** sheet iron.

жестян/ик, —щик *m.* tinsmith; **—ицкая** *f.* tinning shop, plating shop; **—ка** *f.* tin, tin can; **—ой** *a.* tin; **—ой сосуд** tin container.

жечь *v.* burn.

жжен/ие *n.* burning, calcining; **—ный** *a.* burned, roasted, calcined, charred.

живетский век Givetian stage.

жив/ой *a.* alive, living; lively, vivid; **—ая сила** kinetic energy; **—ая тектоника** dynamic tectonics; **—ое сечение** (hyd.) cross section; useful cross section.

Живописец Pictor (Pic) (constellation).

животн/ый *a.* animal; **ж. воск** animal wax; **ж. уголь** animal charcoal, bone black; **—ая пленка** goldbeater's skin.

живучесть *f.* vitality; stability.

Жигмонди фильтр Zsigmondy filter.

жидк/ий *a.* liquid, fluid, watery; **ж. воздух** liquid air; **ж. металл** molten metal, liquid metal; **ж. цикл** fluid cycle; **—ая горячая смесь** fluid fuel mixture; **—ая фаза** liquid phase; **—ое состояние** liquid state; **—ое тело** liquid, fluid; **—ое топливо** liquid fuel; fuel oil; **—ие отходы**

liquid waste; **мера —их тел** liquid measure.

жидкометаллический *a.* liquid-metal; **ж. катод** pool cathode.

жидкоплавк/ий *a.* liquid, fluid; **—ость** *f.* fluidity.

жидкопродвижность *f.* fluidity.

жидкостн/ый *a.* liquid, fluid; **ж. затвор, —ое уплотнение** liquid seal; **ж. манометр** liquid-column manometer; **ж. насос** fluid-flow pump; **ж. термометр** liquid-expansion thermometer; **ж. элемент** wet cell; **—ая граница** liquid junction.

жидкость *f.* liquid, fluid; fluidity; **ж. теплообменника** heat-exchanger fluid; **ж. теплопередачи** heat-transfer fluid.

жидко/текучесть *see* **жидкоплавкость**; **—текущий** *a.* fluid; **—фазный** *a.* liquid-phase.

жиз/неописание *n.* biography; **—нь** *f.* life, lifetime.

жиклер *m.* jet, discharge nozzle, jet tube (of carburetor).

жила *f.* (geo.) vein, lode, seam; strand, core (of cable); **ж.-проводник** (geo.) lead vein, leader; **сложная ж.** (min.) lode.

жильбертит *m.* gilbertite.

жильн/ый *a.* vein, veiny; **ж. материал, —ая порода** (min.) vein-rock; **ж. минерал** gangue mineral; **ж. пояс, —ая полоса, —ая толща, —ое месторождение** (min.) vein, lode, seam.

жир *m.* grease, fat.

жираторный *a.* gyratory, gyrating.

Жираф Camelopardus (Cam) (constellation).

жирационный *see* **жираторный.**

жирно— *prefix* fat, fatty.

жирно/ароматический *a.* aliphatic-aromatic; **—кислый** *a.* fatty acid; **—сть** *f.* greasiness, oiliness.

жирн/ый *a.* greasy, oily; fatty; **ж. шрифт** boldface (type); **—ая кислота** fatty acid; **—ая линия** heavy line; **—ое соединение, —ое тело** fatty compound.

жиро— *prefix* fat, fatty; *see also* **гиро—**.

жировик *m.* steatite, soapstone; **китайский ж.** agalmatolite, pagodite.

жиров/ой *a.* fatty; **—ое вещество** fatty matter.

жиро/клинометр *m.* gyrolevel; **—компас** *m.* gyrocompass; **—метр** *m.* gyrometer.

жиронепроницаемый *a.* greaseproof.

Жиро печь (elec.) Girot furnace.

жирораствор/имый *a.* liposoluble; **—яющий** *a.* fat-dissolving; **—яющий реактив** fat solvent.

жирорасщепл/ение *n.* lipolysis; **—яющий** *a.* lipolytic.

жироректор *m.* (aero.) gyrorector.

жироскоп *m.* gyroscope, gyro; **—ический** *a.* gyroscopic, gyro—; **—ический компас** gyrocompass.

жиростат/ика *f.* gyrostatics; **—ический** *a.* gyrostatic.

жиро/удаляющий реагент fat extractant; **—уловитель** *m.* grease trap.

жисмондин *m.* gismondine.

житель *m.* inhabitant, dweller.

ЖНХ *abbr.* (**Журнал неорганической химии**) Journal of Inorganic Chemistry.

жозеит *m.* joseite.

Жоли фотометр Joly photometer.

Жолио-Кюри Joliot-Curie.

жолоб *see* **желоб**; **—чатый** *see* **желобчатый.**

жом *m.* press; squeezer.

Жордан Jordan.

ЖОС *abbr.* (**Оптика и спектроскопия**) Optics and Spectroscopy (journal).

ЖОХ *abbr.* (**Журнал общей химии**) Journal of General Chemistry.

ЖПХ *abbr.* (**Журнал прикладной химии**) Journal of Applied Chemistry

ЖРМО *abbr.* (**Журнал русского металлургического общества**) Journal of the Russian Metallurgical Society.

ЖРП *abbr.* (**Журнал резиновой промышленности**) Rubber Industry Journal.

ЖРФХО *abbr.* (**Журнал русского физико-химического общества**) Journal of the Russian Physicochemical Society.

ЖТФ *abbr.* (**Журнал технической физики**) Journal of Technical Physics (Soviet Physics — Technical Physics).

Жуге условие Jouguet rule.

жужж/ание *n.*, **—ать** *v.* hum, buzz.
Жуковского профиль Zhukovskii (Joukowski, Joukowsky) profile.
жур. *abbr.* (**журнал**) journal, periodical.
Журавль Grus (Gru) (constellation).
Журдена принцип (mech.) Jourdain principle.
журн. *see* **жур.**
журнал *m.*, **—ьный** *a.* journal, periodical; log.
ЖФХ *abbr.* (**Журнал физической химии**) Journal of Physical Chemistry.
ЖХО *abbr.* (**Журнал химического общества**) Journal of the Chemical Society.
ЖХП *abbr.* (**Журнал химической промышленности**) Journal of the Chemical Industry.
ЖЭТФ *abbr.* (**Журнал экспериментальной и теоретической физики**) Journal of Experimental and Theoretical Physics (Soviet Physics—JETP).
жюльенит *m.* julienite.
Жюрена правило (**закон**) Jurin law.

З

з. *abbr.* (**записки**) notes, memoirs, annals.
З. *abbr.* (**запад**) west
за *prep. acc. and instr.* after, behind; beyond, out of; for, as; per, during; **за и против** pro and con; **за исключением** with the exception of, except; **за неделю** during a week, per week; **за час** per hour; **идти за** follow.
за— *prefix with verbs* begin; *often forms perfective*; *with adj.* beyond, trans—.
за/атлантический *a.* transatlantic; **—атмосферный** *a.* beyond the atmosphere.
забив/ание *n.*, **—ка** *f.* driving in; stopping up, clogging; **—ать** *v.* drive in, hammer in; swamp, clog; **—аться** *v.* clog up.
забирать *v.* take, draw from.
забит/ый *a.* driven in, hammered; clogged, plugged up; **—ь** *see* **забивать.**
заблаговременн/о *adv.* beforehand, in time; **—ый** *a.* done in time, done in advance.
заблужд/аться *v.* go astray; err; **—ение** *n.* error, delusion.
забой *m.* face, end face; **з. загрузки** charging face.
забол/ачивание *n.* bogging, swamping; **—ачивать** *v.* bog, swamp; **—оченный** *a.* swampy.
заболтать *see* **болтать.**
забор *m.* fence, enclosure, partition; intake; **обнести —ом** fence in; **—ный** *a.* fence, partition; intake; **—щик** *m.* intake (pipe), scoop.
забортовка *f.* beading.
забот/а *f.* concern; **—иться** *v.* take care of, look after; see to it.
забраков/ание *n.*, **—ка** *f.* rejection; **—анный** *a.* rejected; **—ать, —ывать** *v.* reject.
забрасыв/ание *n.* throwing; abandonment; stoking; **з. на орбиту** launching into orbit; **—ать** *v.* throw; abandon, neglect; stoke; take, bring.
забро/с *see* **забрасывание**; **—санный, —шенный** *a.* thrown; abandoned, neglected; **—сать, —сить** *see* **забрасывать.**
забрыз/ганный *a.* splashed, spattered; **—гать, —гивать, —нуть** *v.* splash, spatter; **—гивание** *n.* splashing, spattering.
забурник *m.* drill, borer, bore.
забут *m.* packing; **—ить** *v.* fill in, pack; bank up; **—ка, —овка** *f.* filling-in work, packing material, rubble masonry.
забы/вать, —ть *v.* forget, omit; **—вчивый** *a.* forgetful, careless.
зав. *abbr.* (**заведующий**) manager, director.
завал *m.* steep drop; avalanche, pile-up; **—енный** *a.* heaped up, loaded, clogged up; **—ивание** *n.* heaping up, filling up, clogging up; **—ивать, —ить** *v.* heap up, load, encumber, clog; **—иваться** *v.* be misplaced;

—ка *f.* priming, charging, filling; (furnace) charge.

завар/енный *a.* welded, sealed; scalded, scoured; **з. в стекло** glass-sealed; **—ивать, —ить** *v.* weld, seal; brew; scald; **—ной** *a.* boiled.

заведение *n.* establishment, institution.

заведом/о *adv.* certainly, clearly; necessarily; knowingly, deliberately, admittedly; **—ый** *a.* intentional; known.

заведующий *m.* manager, director, chief, superintendent; *a.* directing.

заведыв/ание *n.* management; **—ать** *v.* manage, superintend, direct; **—ающий** *see* **заведующий.**

завер/ение *n.* assurance; **—ить** *v.* assure.

заверт/ка *f.* screw driver; wrapping up; knob, catch; **—ывание** *n.* wrapping up; involution; screwing up; **—ывать** *v.* wrap, envelop; screw on; turn off (faucet).

заверш/ать, —ить *v.* complete, conclude; **—ающий** *a.* concluding; **—ение** *n.* completion, accomplishment; **—енный** *a.* completed, accomplished.

заверять *see* **заверить.**

завес/а *f.*, **—очный** *a.* curtain, screen; **—ить** *see* **завешивать;** **—ка** *f.* rack.

завести *see* **заводить.**

завешив/ание *n.* screening; **—ать** *v.* screen.

завив/ание *n.*, **—ка** *f.* twisting, coiling, convolution; **—ать** *v.* twist, curl, crimp; **—ающийся** *a.* twisting, curling, winding.

завин/тить, —чивать *v.* screw up.

зависать *v.* (aero.) hover.

зависеть *v.* depend on.

зависимост/ь *f.* dependence, relation, variation, function, behavior, trend; **з. массы от скорости** relativistic mass equation; **з. от времени** time dependence, time variation; **з. от спина** spin dependence; **з. от частоты** frequency dependence, frequency response; **з. пробега от энергии** range-energy relationship; **взаимная з.** interdependency; **изображать з. от, откладывать в —и от** plot against (in graph); **быть в —и от** depend on; **в —и от** as a function of; **изменение в —и от** variation with; **изображенный в —и от** plotted against; **кривая —и давления от температуры** temperature-pressure curve.

зависим/ый *a.* dependent, subordinate; **—ая переменная** dependent variable.

зависящ/ий *see* **зависимый; з. от времени** time-dependent; **з. от спина** spin-dependent; **принять все —ие меры** take all possible precautions (or measures).

завит/ой, —ый *a.* twisted, curled; **—ок** *m.* curl, spiral; **—ь** *see* **завивать.**

завихрен/ие *n.* vortex; **з. воздуха** air eddy; **з. за задней кромкой** trailing-edge vortex; **—ное движение** eddying motion; **—ность** *v.* vorticity.

Зав. лаб. *abbr.* (**Заводская лаборатория**) Industrial Laboratory (journal).

завлад/евать, —еть *v.* take possession (of), capture.

завлечен/ие *n.* capture; **—ная комета** captured comet.

завод *m.* works, plant, factory, mill; (mech.) starter; **з. по разделению изотопов** isotope separation plant; **автоматический з.** *see* **автоматическая заводка.**

завод/ить *v.* wind up, start (motor); acquire; set up, establish; bring, take, lead in; **—ка** *f.* winding up, starting; **автоматическая —ка,** self-starter; **—ной** *a.* winding, cranking, starting; **—ная гиря** driving weight; **—ная ручка** (starting) crank.

заводоуправление *n.* plant management.

заводск/ий, —ой *a.* works, plant, mill, factory.

завоевание *n.* conquest.

заволакивать *v.* become cloudy.

завтра *adv.* tomorrow.

завуалиров/анный *a.* masked, obscured, veiled; **—ать** *v.* conceal, mask, obscure, veil.

завывание *n.* howl.

завысить *see* **завышать.**

завыш/ать *v.* overestimate, exaggerate; **—ение** *n.* overestimate, exaggeration; **—енный** *a.* overevaluated, overestimated, excessive, exaggerated, oversized.

завяз/анный *a.* tied, bound; **—ать, завязывать** *v.* tie, bind; **—ка** *f.* tie, band, bond; **—ной** *a.* tying; **—ывание** *n.* tying, binding.

завянуть *v.* fade.

загадать *see* **загадывать.**

загад/ка *f.* enigma, puzzle; **—очный** *a.* enigmatic, puzzling; **—ывать** *v.* conjecture.

зага/сать, —снуть *v.* die out; **—сить** *v.* extinguish; **—шенный луч** (telev.) blanked beam.

загиб *m.* bend, fold, kink, flange, edge; **з. волновода** waveguide bend (or elbow); **з. кривой** knee of curve; **—ание** *n.* bending, folding; recurvature; **—ание кромок** beading; **—ать** *v.* bend, fold; **—ной** *a.* folding, folded; **—очный** *a.* bending; **—очная машина** creasing machine; flanging machine.

загипсов/ание *n.* cementing, plastering; **—ать** *v.* cement, plaster.

загл. *abbr. see* **заглавие.**

заглав/ие *n.*, **—ный** *a.* title, heading; **—ный лист** title page; **—ные буквы** capital letters.

загла/дить, —живать *v.* smooth, even, level.

заглубление *see* **углубление.**

заглуш/ать, —ить *v.* jam, damp, suppress, muffle, drown out; **—ающий** *a.* damping, jamming; **—ение** *n.* damping, deadening; **—енная камера** anechoic sound chamber.

заглушенн/ый *a.* damped, suppressed, deadened; opacified; **з. бак** anechoic tank; **з. зал** (acous.) dead room; **—ая камера** anechoic chamber.

загнут/ый *a.* bent, folded; **—ь** *see* **загибать**; **—ая окклюзия** recurved (or bent-back) occlusion.

заголовок *m.* title, heading, headline.

загоражив/ание *n.* enclosure; **—ать** *v.* enclose; block, shut off.

загор/ание *n.* firing, triggering; **—аться, —еться** *v.* ignite; **—ающийся** *a.* igniting, inflammable; **—ающаяся смесь** ignition mixture.

загород/ить *see* **загораживать**; **—ка** *f.* partition, fence.

загороженн/ый *a.* enclosed; **—ое место** enclosure.

загот/авливать, —овить *v.* store; prepare; **—овительный** *a.* storing; preparing.

заготовка *f.* stock; procurement; preparation; intermediate product; (met.) blank, billet.

заготовлен/ие *n.* preparing; **—ный** *a.* prepared; stored; **—ные части** fabricated parts.

заготов/лять *see* **заготавливать**; **—очный** *see* **заготовительный.**

загр. *abbr.* (**заграницей**) abroad; (**заграничный**) foreign.

загра/дить, —ждать *v.* obstruct, enclose, dam.

загражд/ающий *a.* obstructing; **з. контур** blanking circuit; **з. слой** barrier layer; **з. фильтр** band-elimination filter; rejection filter; **—ение** *n.* obstruction, barrier; **—енный** *a.* obstructed, blocked.

загран/ица *f.* foreign countries; **—ичный** *a.* foreign.

загромо/ждать, —здить *v.* encumber, block; **—ждение** *n.* jam, blocking.

загрубение *n.* coarsening.

загру/жать, —зить *v.* charge, load; **з. топку, з. топливо** stoke; **—жающий стержень-пробка** loading plug; **—женный** *a.* charged, loaded; **—женная эмульсия** impregnated emulsion.

загрузк/а *f.* charge, charging, loading; batch; **коэффициент —и** load factor; duty factor (of electron tube).

загрузочн/ый *a.* charging, loading, feeding; **з. спускной желоб** charge chute; **—ая сторона** feed end, charging face, load face (of reactor); **—ая схема** loading pattern; **—ая трубка** charging tube.

загрунтов/анный *a.* sized, primed; **—ать, —ывать** *v.* size, prime; **—ка** *f.* sizing, priming.

загрязн/ение *n.* contamination, contaminant, impurity, poisoning; **химическое з.** chemical impurity; **—енный** *a.* impure, contaminated, polluted; **—ить, —ять** *v.* contaminate, pollute; **—яющий** *a.* contaminating; **—яющее вещество** contaminant.

загуст/евание *n.*, **—ка** *f.* thickening; **—евать, —еть** *v.* thicken, condense.

задавать *v.* set, assign, give, define; **—ся целью** set oneself a goal.

задав/ить, —ливать *v.* crush; **—ленный** *a.* crushed.

задан/ие *n.* task, assignment, setting; **наперед —ное** given number; **—ный** *a.* assigned, given, prescribed, specified, preset.

задатчик *m.* (elec.) controller, setter, master; **з. мощности** power controller; **сигнал —а** demand signal.

задать *see* **задавать.**

задач/а *f.* problem, task, undertaking; object, aim; **з. двух тел** two-body problem; **з. трех тел** three-body problem; **-ник** *m.* (book of) problems.

задающ/ий генератор master oscillator; **з. импульс** driving pulse; **з. каскад** master stage, driver stage; **з. сигнал** *see* **сигнал задатчика; —ая лампа** master oscillator tube; **—ее плечо** master arm (of manipulator).

задвигать *v.* bolt, push in, slide; move; **—ся** *v.* slide; begin to move.

задвиж/ка *f.* bolt, fastening; gate, slide gate, slide valve; **—ной** *a.* sliding.

задвинут/ый *a.* bolted, pushed in; **—ь** *see* **задвигать.**

задев/ание *n.* grazing, interference, catching; **—ать** *v.* catch, graze, brush against, interfere; **не —ать** clear.

задел/анный *a.* sealed, closed; built-in, embedded; **з. в капсулу** encapsulated; **—ать, —ывать** *v.* seal, close; fix, embed; **—ка** *f.*, **—ывание** *n.* stopping up, closing; seal; fixing in, building in.

задергивать *v.* draw, pull.

задерж/ание, —ивание *n.* delay, detention; inhibition, retardation; retention, holding back; trapping; **—анный** *a.* delayed, retarded; retained; **—анное совпадение** delayed coincidence; **—ать, —ивать** *v.* delay, retard, impede, moderate; check, arrest, block, suppress; retain, entrap; **—аться, —иваться** *v.* lag; be retained.

задерживающ/ий *a.* retarding, delaying, inhibiting; retaining; **з. клапан** check valve; **з. механизм, —ее приспособление** lock mechanism, locking device; **з. потенциал** retarding (stopping, counter) potential; **з. слой** blocking (restraining, trapping) layer; intercepting layer; **—ая напряженность** coercive force; **—ая способность глаза** visual persistence; **—ее действие** blocking action; **—ее поле** retarding field.

задержка *f.* delay, hindrance, lag, arrest, retardation; detention, halt, trapping; **з. пламени** flame arrest, flame check.

задернуть *see* **задергивать.**

задет/ый *a.* caught; grazed; **—ь** *see* **задевать.**

задн/ий *a.* back, rear, end, following; **з. конец, —яя часть** tail end, back; **з. контакт** back contact; **з. край** trailing edge; **з. план, з. фон** background; **з. фокус** back focus; **з. фронт** trailing edge (of pulse); **з. ход** backing, reverse movement; return movement, return stroke; **дать з. ход** back, reverse; **—яя кромка** rear edge, trailing edge (of a wing); **—яя стенка** end wall; **—яя сторона** reverse (side); **метод —их линий** (x-rays) back reflection (method).

задолго *adv.* long in advance.

задом *adv.* backwards.

задранный *a.* scratched, scored.

задубленный *a.* tanned.

задув/ание *n.*, **—ка** *f.* blowing out, extinguishing; blowing in, starting up (blast furnace); **—ать** *v.* blow out, extinguish; blow in.

задувочн/ый *a.* blowing; **з. кокс** bed charge; **—ая колоша** (met.) blow-in burden, starting-up charge.

задум/анный *a.* planned, conceived; **—ать, —ывать** *v.* plan, conceive, intend.

задут/ый *a.* blown out, extinguished; blown in (furnace); **—ь** *see* **задувать.**

задуш/ение *n.* suffocation, choking, throttling, stifling; **—енный** *a.* suffocated; **—ить** *v.* suffocate, throttle.

задым/ленность *f.* smoke content, **—ливание** *n.* filling with smoke screening with smoke; **—лять, —ить** *v.* screen with smoke, fume.

заед/ание *n.* catching, sticking, jamming; **—ать** *v.* grip, catch, stick, jam

заершенный *a.* jagged, ragged, **з. болт** ragbolt.

зажат/ие *n.* pressing, squeezing **—ый** *a.* pressed, squeezed, held; **—ь** *see* **зажимать.**

заж/ечь *see* **зажигать**; **—женный** *a.* ignited.

зажигалка *f.* lighter.

зажиг/ание *n.* firing, ignition, triggering; striking (arc or spark); **з. дуги** striking of an arc; **обратное з.** arcing back; **з. с опережением** advanced firing; advanced ignition; **искра —ания** ignition spark; **коэффициент управления —анием** control ratio (of electron tube); **—атель** *m.* igniter; firing electrode.

зажигательн/ый *a.* ignition, igniting, incendiary; **з. прибор** ignition device, firing device; **з. шнур, —ая трубка** fuse; **—ая свеча** spark plug; **—ое стекло** burning lens.

зажигать, —ся *v.* ignite

зажим *m.* clamp, clip, fastener, gripping device, clutch; (elec.) terminal, binding post; pinchcock (for rubber tubing); **з.-капельник** drip cock; **пружинный з.** clip; **—ание** *n.*, **—ающий** *a.* clamping; **—ать** *v.* clamp, fasten, clip, cramp, squeeze, press, pinch.

зажимн/ой, —ый *a.* clamping, binding; **з. винт** set screw, adjusting screw; clamping screw, terminal screw; **з. конденсатор** compression condenser; **з. конец** (elec.) terminal; **з. кулачок, —ая губа, —ая колодка, —ая щека** chuck jaw, gripping jaw; **—ая гайка** binding (grip, clamp) nut; **—ая доска** (elec.) terminal board; **—ое приспособление, —ое устройство** gripping device, clamping device, jaw, jig, clutch, chuck; **—ые клещи** clamp tongs; **—ые колодки** clamping blocks.

зажимчик *see* **зажим.**

зажор *m.*, **—а** *f.* accumulation of water under snow.

зазвуковой *a.* supersonic.

заземлен/ие *n.* (elec.) grounding, ground (connection); **провод —ия, —ный кабель** ground wire; **—ный** *a.* grounded, ground.

заземл/итель *m.* (elec.) ground, grounded electrode; **—ительный** *see* **заземляющий**; **—ять** *v.* (elec.) ground.

заземляющий *a.* (elec.) grounding, ground; **з. провод** ground wire.

зазор *m.* clearance, space, gap, margin; (free) play, backlash; **з. воздушный** air gap; **з. магнита** magnet gap; **з. поршня** piston clearance (or play); **з. продольный** end play; **з. энергии** energy gap.

зазубр/енный *a.* notched, jagged, toothed, indented, serrated; **—ивать, —ить** *v.* notch, indent, dent, serrate; **—ина** *f.* notch, indentation.

заил/ение, —ивание *n.* filling in.

заимствов/ание *n.* borrowing; **—анный** *a.* borrowed; **—ать** *v.* borrow, copy, quote; adopt.

заиндев/евший, —елый *a.* frost-covered, rimy; **—еть** *v.* be covered with hoar frost.

заиневение *n.* formation of frost covering, riming.

заинтересов/ать, —ывать *v.* interest.

зайгерование *see* **зейгерование.**

зайчик *m.* (movable) light spot.

закадмиевый *a.* epicadmium.

заказ *m.*, **—ать, —ывать** *v.* order.

закал *see* **закалка.**

закаленн/ый *a.* hardened, tempered, chilled, quenched; **—ая сталь** hardened (tempered, chilled) steel; **—ое стекло** hard glass.

закалив/аемость *f.* hardenability, hardening capacity; **—ание** *see* **закалка**; **—ать, закалить** *v.* harden, temper, chill, quench; **—ать по поверхности** (met.) caseharden; **—ающий** *a.* hardening, tempering; **—ающее средство** hardening agent.

закалка *f.* hardening, tempering, quenching, chilling; freezing (of a reaction); **з. в масле** oil hardening; **з. поверхности, поверхностная з.** (met.) casehardening.

закалочн/ый *a.* hardening, tempering; **з. порок** quenching defect; **—ая ванна** quenching bath; **—ая печь** hardening furnace, tempering furnace; **—ая среда, —ое средство** hardening agent, tempering agent; **—ая трещина** quenching (or hardening) crack; —**ое упрочнение** quench hardening.

закалять *see* **закаливать.**

закаменеть *see* **каменеть.**

заканчивать *v.* complete, conclude.

закапчив/ание *n.* blackening with smoke; —**ать** *v.* cover with soot.

закат *m.* setting, decline; **з. солнца** sunset.

закат/ать, —**ить,** —**ывать** *v.* roll up.

закип/ание *n.* start of boiling; —**ать,** —**еть** *v.* start to boil; bubble, simmer.

закированный песок brea.

закисн/ый *a.* (lower or —ous) oxide; —**ая соль** (lower or —ous) salt.

закись *f.* (lower or —ous) oxide; **з. меди** cuprous oxide.

заклад/ка *f.* laying (of foundation); backing; **пустая з.** rubbish; —**ывать** *v.* lay (foundation), establish; wall up.

закле/ивать, —**ить** *v.* paste, seal.

заклейм/енный *a.* branded, marked; —**ить** *v.* stamp, mark, brand.

заклеп/анный *a.* riveted; —**ать** *see* **заклепывать;** —**ка** *f.* rivet, clinch; —**ник** *m.* riveting hammer; —**ный,** —**очный** *a.* rivet, riveting; —**очный шов** riveted joint, riveting.

заклепыв/ание *n.* riveting; —**ать** *v.* rivet, clinch.

заклин/ение, —**ивание** *n.,* —**ка** *f.* wedging; —**енный** *a.* wedged, jammed; —**ивать,** —**ить** *v.* wedge; —**иваться** *v.* wedge, jam.

заключ/ать *v.* include, enclose, contain; confine; conclude, deduce, infer; **з. в оболочку** encase, sheathe; **з. в себе** include, comprise, comprehend, embody; imply; hold; —**аться** *v.* consist (of); end, result (in); —**аться в** involve; —**ается в том, что** (this) lies in the fact that.

заключен/ие *n.* inclusion; conclusion, inference, decision; confinement; closing; —**ный** *a.* enclosed, included; embedded; concluded; —**ная плазма** confined plasma.

заключит/ельный *a.* final, terminal, conclusive; **з. антициклон** blocking anticyclone; —**ь** *see* **заключать.**

закон *m.* law, rule, principle; **з. больших чисел** law of large numbers; **з. взаимозаместимости** (phot.) reciprocity law; **з. действующих масс** law of mass action; **з. запаздывающего действия** law of retarded action; **з. идеального газа** ideal gas law; **з. коммутативности** commutative law; **з. кратных отношений** law of multiple proportions; **з. обратимости** principle of reversibility; **з. обратных квадратов** inverse square law; **з. подобия** similitude relationship, scaling law; **з. постоянных отношений** law of constant proportions, law of definite proportions; **з. рациональных индексов** law of rational indices; **з. смещения** displacement law; **з. соответственных состояний** law of corresponding states; **з. состояния газов** gas law; **з. сохранения непрерывности** continuity condition; **з. сохранения энергии** conservation of energy law; **з. трех вторых** three halves power law.

законн/ость *f.* legitimacy, admissibility, validity; —**ый** *a.* valid, legitimate.

закономерн/ость *f.* regularity; conformity with a law, lawfulness, admissibility; relationship, rule, law; —**ый** *a.* regular; conforming to a rule; —**ое явление** natural phenomenon.

законопа/тить, —**чивать** *v.* calk up; —**ченный** *a.* calked.

законч/енность *f.* completeness; finish; —**енный** *a.* completed, finished, final; —**ить** *see* **заканчивать.**

закопт/елость *f.* smokiness, sootiness; —**елый** *a.* smoky, sooty; —**ить** *see* **закапчивать.**

закопченн/ость *see* **закоптелость;** —**ый** *a.* smoked, smoky, sooty; —**ое стекло** smoked glass.

закорачив/ание *n.* short circuiting; —**атель** *m.* short-circuiter; shorting plunger (of waveguide); —**ающий поршень** short-circuiting plunger; —**ающий шлейф** shorting stub.

закоренелый *a.* deep-rooted, ingrained.

закороченный кабель shorted cable.

закреп *m.,* —**а,** —**ка** *f.* catch, clip, fastening; —**итель** *m.* fixer, fixing agent; —**ить** *see* **закреплять.**

закрепл/ение *n.* securing, pinning, immobilization; binding, fastening, attaching; tightening; (phot.) fixing;

—**енный** *a.* secured, fixed, fastened, attached, mounted; —**ять** *v.* secure, fix, fasten, attach, mount, tighten.

закрепляющ/ий *a.* fixing, fastening, clamping; **з. состав, —ее средство** fixing agent, fixative; —**ая ванна** (phot.) fixing bath; —**ая среда** mounting medium.

закрепная гайка lock nut.

закристаллизовать *v.* crystallize.

закритический *a.* supercritical.

закругл/ение *n.* rounding (off); curvature, bend; —**енный** *a.* rounded, rounded off; —**ить,** —**ять** *v.* round (off).

закрутка *f.* twist.

закрученн/ый *a.* twisted; —**ое место** kink.

закручив/ание *n.* twisting, curling, involution; **угол —ания** angle of torsion; —**ать** *v.* twist, curl, crimp; —**ающийся** *a.* twisting, curling.

закрыв/ать *see* **закрыть;** —**ающий** *a.* cutting off; occulting.

закрылок *m.* (aero.) flap.

закрыт/ие *n.* closing, shutting, enclosure; —**ый** *a.* closed, locked; sealed-in, covered; enclosed, potted; —**ый топливный агрегат** sealed-in fuel unit; —**ый ящик** "black box"; —**ая система** closed system; —**ь** *v.* close, shut off, stop, cut off, occult, screen, enclose, cover.

Заксе-Мора теория Sachse-Mohr theory.

закупор/енный *a.* corked, stopped, clogged, plugged; —**ивание** *n.*, —**ка** *f.* stopping up, sealing; clogging, obstruction; —**ивать,** —**ить** *v.* cork, stop up, seal; clog, plug, choke, obstruct; pack.

зал. *abbr.* (**залив**) Bay.

зал *m.*, —**а** *f.* hall, room.

залег/ание *n.* (geo.) attitude, occurrence, seam, bed; **элементы —ания** (geo.) attitude; dip and strike; —**ать** *v.* (geo.) occur, be deposited; —**ать на** overlie; —**ать под,** —**ать ниже** underlie; —**ающий** *a.* lying; occurring, deposited, embedded.

залежь *f.* (geo.) deposit, bed, stratum, seam.

залеп/ить, —**лять** *v.* glue, seal.

залет/ать, —**еть** *v.* fly in, fly beyond; stop, land; start flying; fly off.

залечиван/ие *n.* curing, healing; **длина —ия** (nucl.) healing distance.

залечь *see* **залегать.**

залив *m.* gulf, bay, cove, inlet.

залив (лунный) Зноя (Волнений) Sinus Aestum (lunar); **з. Радуги** Sinus Iridum (lunar); **з. Росы** Sinus Roris (lunar); **з. Срединный** Sinus Medium (lunar).

залив/ание *n.*, —**ка** *f.* flooding, drenching; filling up, priming (engine); lining; —**ать** *v.* flood, drench, wet, flush; fill up, prime; fill in, line; —**ать наводнением** flood, inundate.

заливающий *a.* flooding, filling, lining; **з. свет** floodlight.

заливн/ой *see* **заливочный; з. лед** bay ice.

заливочн/ый *a.* pouring, flooding; —**ая масса** sealing compound; filling (or potting) compound.

залит/ый *a.* flooded, potted; —**ь** *see* **заливать.**

заложение *n.* laying (of foundation).

зам. *abbr.* (**заместитель**) substitute; deputy, assistant, acting (for); vice—.

замагниченный *see* **намагниченный.**

замаз/ать, —**ывать** *v.* cement, putty, paint over; —**ка** *f.* cement, putty, paste.

замар/ать, —**ывать** *v.* soil; blot out, efface.

замаскиров/анный *a.* masked, camouflaged; —**ать,** —**ывать** *v.* screen, mask, hide.

замасл/ивать, —**ить** *v.* oil, grease, lubricate.

заматывать *v.* wind, twist, roll up.

замачив/ание *n.* wetting; —**ать** *v.* wet, soak.

замащивать *v.* pave; cover.

Замбони столбик, замбониев столб Zamboni dry cell.

замедлен/ие *n.* slowing down, retardation, lag, deceleration, delay, moderation; **з. нейтронов** neutron moderation (or thermalization); **коэффициент —ия** moderating ratio; —**ный** *a.* slowed, retarded, delayed, decelerated, hindered; —**ный нейтрон** moderated neutron; —**ная развертка**

delayed sweep; **—ное действие** retarded (or delayed) action.

замедливать *see* **замедлить**; **—ся** *see* **замедлиться.**

замедлитель *m.* moderator; inhibitor, retarder; (phot.) restrainer; **з. коррозии** corrosion inhibitor; **з. нейтронов** neutron moderator; **з.-охладитель** moderator-coolant.

замедл/ить, —ять *v.* slow down, retard, delay, defer, prolong; moderate; inhibit; **з. до тепловой скорости** thermalize; **—иться, —яться** *v.* slow down, decelerate, slacken.

замедляющ/ий *a.* moderating, retarding, inhibiting, decelerating; **з. электрод** decelerating electrode; **—ая линия** delay line; **—ая способность** slowing-down power, moderating power; **—ая среда** moderating or slowing medium; **—ее вещество** moderator material.

замен/а *f.* substitution, replacement; substitute; change, interchanging; **з. горючего** refueling; **з. каучука** rubber substitute; **з. обозначений** transcription; **з. переменных** change of variables; **—имость, —яемость** *f.* interchangeability, exchangeability; **—имый, —яемый** *a.* interchangeable, replaceable; **—итель** *m.* substitute; **—ить, —ять** *v.* substitute, replace; exchange, interchange; **—яющий** *a.* substituting, replacing.

замер *m.* measurement; **з. дальности** (radar) ranging; **—енный** *a.* measured.

замереть *see* **замирать.**

замерзан/ие *n.* freezing; **температура —ия, точка —ия** freezing point; **понижение температуры —ия** depression of the freezing point.

замерз/ать, —нуть *v.* freeze; **—ающий** *a.* freezing; **—ший** *a.* frozen.

замерять *v.* measure, gauge.

замес *m.* batch, mix; **—ить** *see* **замешать.**

заместитель *m.* substitute; substituent; deputy, assistant, vice-; **—ный** *a.* substitute, substitutive; **—ство** *n.* substitution.

заместить *see* **замещать.**

заметать *v.* sweep (over), cover (up).

замет/ить *see* **замечать**; **—ка** *f.* note, mark.

заметн/о *adv.* it is noticeable (obvious, clear); one can see; noticeably; **з. выраженный** distinct; **—ый** *a.* noticeable, marked, appreciable, observable, notable, pronounced, sensible.

замеч/ание *n.* remark, observation, comment; **—ательный** *a.* remarkable, outstanding, striking, unusual; **—ать** *v.* remark, notice, observe, mark, note.

замеш/анный *a.* mixed; involved; **—ать, —ивать** *v.* mix; involve.

замещ/аемый *a.* replaceable, displaceable; **—ать** *v.* substitute, replace, displace; change; **—ающий** *a.* substituting, replacing; **—ающая группа** substituent group; **—ение** *n.* substitution, replacement; occupation, insertion; change, conversion, decomposition; **—енный** *a.* substituted, replaced, displaced, occupied; **—енное производное** substitution derivative.

замир/ание *n.* dying away; fading; **—ать** *v.* die down, fade.

замкнут/ость *f.* closure; **—ый** *a.* closed, isolated, inland (sea); **—ый контур, —ая цепь** closed circuit; **—ый многоугольник сил** closed-force polygon; **—ый накоротко** short-circuited; **—ый цикл** closed circuit (cycle, loop); **—ая антенна** loop (or closed) antenna; **—ая аэродинамическая труба** closed-return wind tunnel; **—ая линия дислокации** (sol.) dislocation ring; **—ая оболочка** closed shell; **—ая ортогональная система** complete orthogonal set; **—ая система** closed system; **—ое выражение** closed expression; **—ое измерение углов** (geod.) closure of horizon; **—ь** *see* **замыкать.**

замковый захват locking (or gripping) device.

замок *m.* lock, retainer, nut; cutoff; **висячий з.** padlock; **секретный з.** combination lock.

замонтировать *v.* build in.

заморажив/ание *n.* freezing, congealing,

refrigerating; **з. орбитальных моментов** quenching of orbital angular momenta; **—атель** *m.* freezer; refrigerant; **—ать** *v.* freeze, congeal, refrigerate; **—ающий** *a.* freezing; **—ающая смесь** freezing mixture; **—ающее средство** refrigerant.

замороженный *a.* frozen, congealed, chilled; **з. орбитальный момент** quenched orbital moment.

замороз/ить *see* **замораживать**; **—ки** *pl.* (spring or autumnal) frost.

заморский *a.* overseas, foreign.

замостить *see* **замащивать.**

замотать *see* **заматывать.**

замочить *see* **замачивать.**

замощенный *a.* paved.

замуров/анный *a.* walled-in; built-in, embedded; **—ать, —ывать** *v.* immure, wall in; build in; bank up.

замут/ить *v.* make turbid, disturb; **—ненный** *a.* turbid.

замыв/ание *n.* smearing, blurring; washing off; **—ать** *v.* wash off.

замык/ание *n.* locking, closing; (math.) closure; **з. кольца** ring formation, cyclization; **з. накоротко, короткое з.** short-circuiting, short circuit; **—атель** *m.* contractor; **—ать** *v.* lock, close; **—ать цепь** close a circuit, make contact; **—ающая** *f.* closing line; **—ающий** *a.* locking, closing; **—ающий домен** (mag.) domain of closure.

замыс/ел *m.* project, scheme, intention, design; **—лить** *v.* project, plan, design, devise.

замысловат/ость *f.* intricacy, ingenuity; **—ый** *a.* intricate, complicated, complex, involved.

замыть *see* **замывать.**

замычка *f.* bolt, catch, lock.

замышлять *see* **замыслить.**

ЗАН *abbr.* **(Записки Академии наук СССР)** Annals of the Academy of Sciences, USSR.

занаве/с *m.*, **—ска** *f.* curtain, screen; **—сить, —шивать** *v.* curtain, screen; **—шенный** *a.* curtained, screened.

зандбергерит *m.* sandbergerite.

занести *see* **заносить.**

занижен/ие *n.* understating; **—ный** *a.* understated, too low.

занимательн/ый *a.* interesting, entertaining; **—ая физика** recreational physics.

занимать *v.* borrow; occupy; engage; **—ся** *v.* study, work (at), be occupied (with).

заново *adv.* anew, re—; **наполнять з.** refill.

занос *m.* skid; snow drift; pile-up; **—ить** *v.* note down, register, enter; skid; **—ить снегом** block up with snow.

занумеров/ать, —ывать *v.* number, index.

занят/ие *n.* occupation, employment, business; **—ой** *a.* busy; **—ости коэффициент** duty factor; **—ый** *a.* occupied; busy; **—ый уровень** filled level; **—ь** *see* **занимать.**

заодно *adv.* in concert, at once; at the same time; together.

заокеанский *a.* transoceanic.

заостр/ение, —ивание *n.* sharpening, pointing; point, tip; **точка —ения** vertex, apex; cusp; **—енность** *f.* keenness, taper; **—енный** *a.* pointed, cusped, tapered; **—ить, —ять** *v.* sharpen, point, taper down; **—яющая схема** peaking circuit; **—яющийся** *a.* tapering.

заочн/о *adv.* in absentia; **—ый** *a.* in absence of; **—ый курс** correspondence course.

зап. *abbr.* **(западный)** west, western, westerly; **(записки)** notes, memoirs, annals.

запад *m.* west.

запад/ание *n.* attenuation; **—ать** *v.* fall in, fall behind.

западный *a.* west, western, westerly.

запаздыв/ание *n.* retardation, lag, delay, lateness; **з. фазы** phase lag; **угол —ания** angle of lag; **—ать** *v.* lag, be late, be retarded.

запаздывающ/е-критический *a.* delayed-critical; **—ий** *a.* lagging, retarded, delayed; **—ий нейтрон** delayed neutron; **—ий потенциал** retarded potential; **—ая реактивность** delayed reactivity; **—ая частица** delayed particle; **—ее совпадение** delayed coincidence.

запа/ивать *v.* solder, seal; **—йка** *f.* soldering, sealing.

запаков/ать, —ывать *v.* pack, wrap up.

запал *m.* fuse, primer, cap, blasting charge; ignition, firing; (reactor) seed; **—ивать, —ить** *v.* ignite; **—ьник** *m.* ignition device, igniter, blasting fuse.

запальн/ый *a.* ignition, firing; **з. прибор** igniter; **з. шар** ignition chamber; **—ая искра** ignition spark; **—ая область** (reactor) seed region; **—ая сборка** (reactor) seed unit, seed assembly; **—ая свеча** spark plug; **—ая топливная плита** seed fuel plate (of reactor).

запар/ивать *v.* steam; **—ный** *a.* steaming; **—ный аппарат** steam chamber.

запас *m.* stock, reserve, stockpile; allowance, margin; **—ы** *pl.* stock, supply; resources, reserves; **з. воды** water reserve (or supply); **з. воды в снеге** water equivalent of snow; **з. прочности** safety factor; **з. реактивности** reactivity margin, reactivity excess; **коэффициент —а** safety factor; **—ание** *n.* storage, accumulation; **—ание дырок** hole-storage effect; **—ать** *v.* store, accumulate, reserve; **—енный** *a.* stored, accumulated.

запасн/ой, —ый *a.* reserve, spare; **з. агрегат** reserve unit; **з. выход** emergency exit; **—ая часть** spare part.

запасти *see* **запасать.**

запасть *see* **западать.**

запатентованный *a.* patented.

запах *m.* odor.

запа/янный *a.* soldered, sealed; **—ять** *see* **запаивать.**

зап.-европ. *abbr.* (**западно-европейский**) western European.

запер/еть *see* **запирать**; **—тый** *a.* closed; (elec.) blocked, nonconducting, cutoff, ungated, blanked; **—тые виды колебаний** trapped modes.

запечат/анный *a.* sealed; **—ать** *see* **—ывать.**

запечатле/вать, —ть *v.* impress, imprint.

запечатыв/ание *n.* sealing; **—ать** *v.* seal, seal up.

запил *m.* notch; **—енный** *a.* notched.

запир/ание *n.* locking, shutting; blocking, cutoff; (rad.) blackout, blanking, wipe-out (of tube); **з. пучка** beam suppression (or blanking); **область —ания** stop region (for radiation); **период —ания** idle period; **—ать** *v.* close, shut, lock; block, cut off; suppress.

запирающ/ий *a.* locking; **з. генератор** blanking oscillator; **з. импульс** disabling (or blanking) pulse; **з. потенциал, —ее напряжение** cutoff voltage; **з. слой** barrier layer (or film); **—ее реле** locking relay.

запис/анный *a.* recorded, **—ать** *see* **записывать**; **—ка** *f.* note, memorandum, report; **—ки** *pl.* notes, memoirs, annals; **—ная книжка** notebook.

записыв/ание *n.* taking notes, recording; **—ать** *v.* note, record, register; **—аться** *v.* register, subscribe; **—ающий** *a.* recording.

запись *f.* entry, record, recording, trace; notation; **з. звука** sound recording; **з. корреляции** correlatogram; **з. суммирования** summation convention.

заплавлять *v.* close by melting, seal.

запланировать *v.* plan.

заплат/а *f.* patch, piece; **—анный** *a.* patched; **—ать** *v.* patch, mend; **—ить** *v.* pay.

запле/сти, —тать *v.* braid, plait; **—тенный** *a.* braided, linked.

заплечик *m.* shoulder, collar, bead.

заплывать *v.* swim (float, sail) in.

заподлицо *adv.* flush (with).

заподозрить *v.* suspect.

запозд/авший, —алый *a.* late, retarded, overdue; **—алость** *f.* lateness; **—ание** *see* **запаздывание**; **—ать** *see* **запаздывать.**

заполн/ение *n.* filling (in), occupation; population; (surface) coverage; **коэффициент —ения** space factor; duty cycle (of pulses); **—енный** *a.* filled, charged; **—енная зона** filled band; **—енная оболочка** closed shell; **—енное состояние** occupied state; **—итель** *m.* filler; **—ить, —ять** *v.* fill charge; **—яющий материал** filler.

запомин/ание *n.* memorization, storage **—ать** *v.* remember, bear in mind **—ающий элемент** (elec.) memory (or storage) element; **—ающее реле**

storage relay; **—ающее устройство** (elec.) memory.

запомнить *see* **запоминать.**

запор *m.* bolt, lock, stop, shut-off device.

запорн/ый *a.* locking, closing, shut-off; **з. клапан** shut-off valve, gate valve; **з. кран** stopcock; **з. слой** barrier (or exhaustion) layer; **з. ток** back current; **—ая жидкость** sealing fluid; **—ая зона** barrier region; **—ое приспособление** closing device, plug.

заправ/ить, —лять *v.* service, repair; refuel, charge, prime; dress, sharpen (instrument); **—ка** *f.*, **—очный** *a.* servicing, repairing; refueling, charging, priming; dressing, sharpening.

запрашивать *v.* inquire.

запрессов/анный конденсатор molded capacitor; **—ка** *f.* pressurizing.

запрет *m.* forbidding, exclusion, prohibition; **з. симметрии** symmetry selection rule; **коэффициент —а** forbiddenness parameter, hindrance factor (in alpha decay); **правило —а** exclusion principle; **степень —а** degree of forbiddenness; **—ительный** *a.* prohibitive, prohibitory; **—ить** *see* **запрещать; —ный** *a.* prohibited, forbidden; **—ная зона** exclusion area (of reactor); forbidden zone.

запрещ/ать *v.* prohibit, forbid; inhibit; **—ение** *see* **запрет.**

запрещенн/ость *f.* forbiddenness; **—ый** *a.* prohibited, forbidden; **—ый переход** forbidden transition; **—ая зона** forbidden band; **—ая область** excluded (or forbidden) region.

запрограммировать *v.* program.

запрос *m.* inquiry, interrogation; **—ить** *see* **запрашивать.**

запру/да *f.* dam; **—дить, —живать** *v.* dam (up); **—жение** *n.* damming; **—женный** *a.* dammed, impounded; **—женная вода** backwater.

запуск *m.* start-up, triggering; flight, ascent; launching; **—ать** *v.* start, trigger; launch; **—ающий импульс** starting pulse, trigger pulse.

запут/авшийся *a.* entangled; **—анность** *f.* complication; **—анный** *a.* complicated, intricate; tangled, confused; **—ать, —ывать** *v.* complicate; involve, tangle; **—ывание** *n.* complication; entanglement, trapping, capture.

запущенн/ость *f.* neglect; **—ый** *a.* neglected.

запылать *v.* flare up.

запыл/енность *f.* dust content, dustiness; **—ивать, —ить** *v.* cover with dust.

запястное сочленение wrist joint.

запятая *f.* comma; **отделяющая з.** decimal point.

запятнанн/ость *f.* spottedness, spottiness; **—ый** *a.* spotted, stained.

запятн/ать *v.* spot, stain; **—енность** *see* **запятнанность.**

заравнивать *v.* level, even, smooth.

зараж/ать *v.* infect, contaminate; inoculate; **—ение** *n.* infection, contamination; inoculation, seeding (of crystal); **—ение внешней среды** environmental contamination; **—енный** *a.* contaminated; inoculated; **—енная местность** contaminated area.

зараз/а *f.* infection, contamination; **—ительный** *a.* contaminating; **—ить** *see* **заражать.**

заранее *adv.* beforehand, a priori; **з. изготовленный** prefabricated; **з. предвиденный** foregone (conclusion); **з. установленный** preset.

зараст/ать, —и *v.* be overgrown.

зарево *n.* glow, redness.

зарегистриров/ание *n.* registration; **—анный** *a.* registered, recorded; **—анная заявка** patent claim; **—ать** *v.* register, record.

заржав/евший, —елый, —ленный *a.* rusted, corroded; **—еть** *v.* rust.

зарница *f.* summer lightning.

заровнять *see* **заравнивать.**

зарод/ить *see* **зарождать; —ыш** *m.* (cryst.) nucleus, nucleating (or nucleation) center; embryo; germ; **—ышевый** *a.* incipient, embryonic.

зарожд/ать *v.* produce, generate, conceive; **—ающийся** *a.* incipient, nascent; **—ение** *n.* conception, origin; (cryst.) nucleation; **—ение колебаний** onset of oscillations; **—ение фронта** (meteor.) frontogenesis; **—енный** *a.* produced.

заруб/ать *see* **зарубить.**

зарубежный *a.* foreign.
заруб/ина, —ка *f.* notch, cut; **—ить** *v.* notch, cut.
зарухание *n.* devitrification.
зары/вать, —ть *v.* bury; **—ваться, —ться** *v.* bury oneself; dig in.
заря *f.* glow, dawn, sunset; **з. вечерняя** sunset, evening glow, dusk; **з. утренняя** sunrise, dawn.
заряд *m.* charge, loading; **з. иона** ionic charge; **—ить** *see* **заряжать**; **—ка** *see* **заряжение**; **—ность** *f.* (size of) charge.
зарядн/ый *a.* charge, charging, loading; **з. блок** charging unit; **з. ремень, —ая лента** charging belt; **—ая игла** spray point; **—ая сопряженность** charge conjugation; **—ое устройство** charging unit.
зарядово/-инвариантный *a.* charge-invariant; **з.-независимый** *a.* charge-independent; **з.-симметричный** *a.* charge-symmetrical; **з.-сопряженный** *a.* charge-conjugate.
зарядов/ый *see* **зарядный**; **—ая инвариантность** charge invariance; charge independence; **—ая независимость ядерных сил** charge-independence of nuclear forces; **—ая симметрия** charge symmetry; **—ая четность** charge parity; **—ое равенство** charge equality; **—ое равновесие** charge equilibrium.
заряж/аемый *a.* chargeable, charged; **—атель буферный** trickle charger; **—ать** *v.* charge, load; **—ающий** *a.* charging, loading.
заряжен/ие *n.* charging, charge, loading; **—ность** *f.* charge; **—ный** *a.* charged, loaded; **—ная частица** charged particle.
засал/ивать, —ить *v.* soil, grease.
засаривать *see* **засорить.**
засасыв/ание *n.* suction; **—ать** *v.* suck in; **—ающий** *a.* sucking in, suction; **—ающий насос** suction pump.
засвет/ить *v.* illuminate, irradiate; **—ка** *f.* illumination, irradiation, exposure.
засвеч/енный *a.* illuminated; (phot.) light-struck; **—ивание** *n.* light, irradiation.
засвидетельствов/ание *n.* authentication, certification; **—ать** *v.* attest, certify.
засев облаков cloud seeding.
засевший *a.* stuck, caught.
засед/ание *n.* conference, meeting, session; **—ать** *v.* hold a conference or meeting; stick (fast).
засекать *v.* notch; intersect; mark; **з. направление** take a bearing, get a fix.
засекреч/енный *a.* secret; security-restricted, classified; **—ивать** *v.* make secret; restrict (classify) information.
засел/ение *n.* settlement; **—енность** *f.* **—енный** *a.* populated; **—ить, —ять** *v.* populate.
засеч/ка *f.* notch, cut, mark; intersection; cross bearing, fix; **з. времени** timing; **звуковая з.** sound ranging; **обратная з.** (surv.) resection; **—ь** *see* **засекать.**
засилье *n.* preponderance, dominance.
заслон/ение *n.* shielding, screening; **—ить, —ять** *v.* shield, screen, shade; hide; **—ка** *f.* **—очный** *a.* door, gate, slide, baffle, damper; shutter; **—очная теория** (meteor.) barrier theory.
заслуг/а *f.* merit; **—и** *pl.* merits; services.
заслуж/енный *a.* merited; honored, emeritus; **з. деятель науки** honored scientist; **—ивает внимания** noteworthy; **—ивать, —ить** *v.* deserve, merit; **—ивающий** *a.* deserving, worthy.
засмол/ение *n.* pitching, tarring; resinification; **—ить, засмаливать** *v.* pitch, tar; resinify.
заснят/ый *a.* photographed; **—ь** *v.* photograph.
засов *m.* bolt, bar; **—ать, —ывать** *v.* push in, thrust in.
засор *m.* dirt, impurity; **—ение** *n.* obstruction; soiling, contamination; **—енный** *a.* clogged; soiled, contaminated; **—ить, —ять** *v.* obstruct, soil.
засосанный *a.* sucked in; **з. воздух** induced air.
заст. *abbr.* (**застывание**) freezing, solidification.
заставить *v.* cause, force; obstruct.
заставл/енный *a.* compelled; blocked **—ять** *see* **заставить.**

застаив/ание *n.* stagnation; **—аться** *v.* stagnate.

засте/гивать, —гнуть *v.* fasten, hook, button; **—жка** *f.* fastening, clasp; **—жка-молния** zipper.

застекл/енный *a.* glazed, vitrified; **—ить, —овать** *v.* glaze, vitrify; glass in.

заст/илать, —лать *v.* cover, screen; cloud, overcast; **—илка** *f.* covering.

застой *m.* stagnation; **—ный** *a.* stagnant; **—ная точка** stagnation point.

застопор/ивание *n.* stopping, clogging; **—ивать, —ить** *v.* stop; clog; jam.

застоявшийся *a.* stagnant, sluggish.

застраивать *v.* build up.

застрев/ание *n.* sticking, jamming; **—ать** *v.* stick, jam.

застройка *f.* building up.

застря/нуть, —ть *see* **застревать**; **—вший** *a.* stuck, jammed, trapped.

застыв/ание *n.* freezing, congealing, solidification; **температура —ания** solidification point; **—ать** *v.* freeze, set, gel, solidify; **—ающий** *a.* congealing; **—ший** *a.* congealed, solidified.

засты/нуть, —ть *see* **застывать.**

засунуть *see* **засовывать.**

засуха *f.* drought.

засушлив/ость *f.* aridity; **—ый** *a.* arid; **—ый период** period of drought.

засчит/ать, —ывать *v.* take into account.

засып/ать *v.* cover, fill, charge; pour; **—ка, —ь** *f.* covering, filling; (met.) charge, burden; **—ной** *a.* charging; **—ной ковш, —ная воронка** feed hopper.

засыхать *v.* dry.

затабулировать *v.* tabulate.

затачивать *see* **заточить.**

затвердев/ание *n.* hardening, solidification, setting, congealing; **температура —ания, точка —ания** solidification point; freezing point; coagulation point; **—ать** *v.* harden, solidify, set, congeal; **—ший** *a.* hardened, solidified, congealed, consolidated.

затвердел/ость *f.* hardness; **—ый** *a.* hardened, firm, set.

затверд/ение *see* **затвердевание**; **з. нейтронов** neutron hardening; **—еть** *see* **затвердевать**; **—итель** *m.* hardener.

затвор *m.* bolt, lock, fastening; stop valve, shut-off device; seal; shutter; **вакуумный з.** vacuum lock; **герметический з.** hermetic seal; **з. гидравлического действия** automatic hydraulic gate; **з. у шлюза** flood gate, water gate; **—енный** *a.* shut, closed; **—ить, —ять** *v.* close, shut off.

затекать *v.* flow in.

затем *adv.* then, thereupon, subsequently.

затемн/ение *n.* darkening, blackout, eclipse; shading; **—енный** *a.* darkened, blacked out; **метод —енного поля** dark field method; **—итель** *m.* dimmer; **—ить, —ять** *v.* darken, obscure, black out; **—яющая заслонка** dark screening slide.

затен/ение *n.* shading, vignetting; **—енная зона** shadow zone; **—ивать, —ить, —ять** *v.* shade, darken; **—итель** *m.* shade.

затер/еть *see* **затирать**; **—тый льдами** icebound.

затечь *see* **затекать.**

затир/ание *n.*, **—ка** *f.* rubbing over, smoothing out; **—ать** *v.* rub over, smooth out.

затих/ать, —нуть *v.* abate, die down; dampen.

затишь/е *n.* calm; **временное з.** lull; **экваториальная зона (или пояс) —я** doldrums.

заткнут/ый *a.* plugged, stopped up; **—ь** *see* **затыкать.**

затм/евать, —ить *v.* eclipse, obscure, darken; **—евающий диск** occulting disk; **—ение** *n.* eclipse, occultation; **полное —ение** total eclipse.

затменн/о-двойные звезды (astr.) eclipsing binaries; **—ый** *a.* eclipse, eclipsed; **—ая переменная** (astr.) eclipsing variable.

зато *conj.* in return.

затон *m.* backwater, creek; **—уть** *v.* sink, submerge.

затопл/ение *n.* flooding, inundation;

—енный *a.* flooded, submerged; **—ять** *v.* inundate, submerge.

затор *m.* obstruction, congestion; **з. льда** ice jam.

затор/маживание *n.* retardation; **з. дислокацией** (sol.) pinning of dislocations; **—моженный** *a.* braked; slowed down, delayed; **—моженный переход** hindered transition; **—мозить** *v.* brake; slow down, retard.

заточ/ить *v.* sharpen, point; **—ка** *f.*, **—ный** *a.* sharpening, pointing.

затрав/ка *f.*, **—ливание** *n.* (cryst.) inoculation, seeding; seed crystal; seed, nucleus; primer, priming, fuse; **—лять** *v.* inoculate, seed; prime.

затравочн/ый заряд bare charge; **з. источник** (reactor) startup source; **з. кристалл** seed crystal; **—ая масса** bare mass.

затрагивать *v.* touch upon (a subject).

затра/та *f.* cost, expenditure; **—ченный** *a.* expended; consumed; **—чиваемая частица** consumed particle; **—чивать** *v.* expend; consume.

затронуть *see* **затрагивать.**

затропический *a.* extratropical.

затруднен/ие *n.* difficulty; inhibition; **—ный переход** unfavored transition; **—ное вращение** hindered rotation.

затрудн/ительность *f.* difficulty; **—ительный** *a.* difficult, inconvenient, intricate; **—ить, —ять** *v.* hinder, suppress, inhibit.

затуман/ивание *n.* fogging; **—ивать, —ить** *v.* cloud, fog, obscure.

затуп/ившийся, —ленный *a.* dulled, blunt; **—ить, —лять** *v.* dull, blunt; **—иться, —ляться** *v.* become blunt.

затух/ание *n.* fading, damping, attenuation, loss, decrement; **з. волны** wave attenuation; **з. излучения** radiation damping; **з. передачи** transmission loss; **коэффициент —ания** attenuation factor (or constant); damping factor, decay coefficient; **постоянная —ания** attenuation constant; **—ать, —нуть** *v.* damp, die down, attenuate; be extinguished; **—ающий** *a.* damping, damped, attenuated; **—ающая волна** damped wave; **—ающие колебания** damped oscillations.

затушев/ать, —ывать *v.* shade, tint.

затуш/енный *a.* extinguished; **—ить** *v.* extinguish, suppress.

заты/кать *v.* stop up; obstruct; **—чка** *f.* plug, stopper; spigot.

затягив/ание *n.* tightening; (elec.) pulling; persistence; **—ать** *v.* tighten; cover; protract; drag; involve.

затяжка *f.* tightening; tie, tie-beam; delay, prolongation.

затяжной *a.* tightening; **з. болт** draw bolt; **з. трос** stay wire.

затянут/ый *a.* tightened; delayed, prolonged; **—ь** *see* **затягивать.**

зауальпит *m.* saualpite.

заузленный *a.* knotted.

заурановый *a.* transuranium; **з. элемент** transuranium element.

заурядный *a.* ordinary, commonplace.

заусен/ец *m.*, **—ица** *f.*, **—ок** *m.* projecting edge; chip; burr.

зафиксировать *v.* fix, set; record, register.

заформовать *v.* mold, shape.

зафронтальный *a.* (meteor.) postfrontal, transfrontal.

Захариасен Zachariasen.

захват *m.* capture; pickup; holding device, clamp, grip; scope; tong (of manipulator); **з. *K*-электрона** *K*-electron capture; **з. (нейтрона) с делением** fission capture; **з. нейтронов** neutron capture; **—ить** *see* **захватывать; —ка** *f.* trapping; detainer, catch, checking device; **—ный** *see* **захватывающий; —ные гамма лучи** capture gamma rays; **—чик** *m.* (chem.) acceptor.

захватыв/ание *n.* gripping, catching, locking; trapping, entrapment; **з. частоты** forcing of oscillations; **—атель** *m.* grip, clamp, fastener; **—ать** *v.* grip, catch, capture, trap; include; enclose.

захватывающ/ий *a.* gripping, catching; trapping; **з. интерес** absorbing interest; **з. механизм** gripper mechanism; **—ее приспособление, —ее устройство** gripping device, clamp, jaw, catch.

захваченный *a.* gripped, entrained, entrapped.

захлебывание *n.* (chem.) flooding (of column).

захлопывание *n.* sudden closing, collapse.

заход *m.* setting; (aero.) approach; **з. солнца** sunset.

захолодить *v.* freeze, chill.

захоронение *n.* burial (of radioactive waste).

зацентровка *f.* centering, alignment.

зацеп *m.*, **—ка** *f.* catch, detent; hook; hitch, snag; **—ить** *see* **зацеплять.**

зацеплен/ие *n.* catching, hooking, linkage, meshing, engagement; **вводить в з.** throw in gear; **входить в з.** mesh, engage; **в —ии** in gear, engaged; **—ный** *a.* caught, hooked, engaged, linked.

зацепл/ять *v.* catch, hook, mesh, couple, link; **—яющийся** *a.* coupled, linked.

зачат/ие *n.* conception, beginning; **—ок** *m.* rudiment.

зачаточн/ый *a.* incipient; elementary, rudimentary; **—ая усадка** incipient shrinkage.

зачем *adv.* why, wherefore.

зачерк/ивание *n.* crossing out, cancellation, deletion; **—ивать, —нуть** *v.* cross out, delete, cancel.

зачерп/нуть, —ывать *v.* scoop, ladle; **—ывание** *n.* scooping, ladling.

зачер/тить, —чивать *v.* draft, draw, sketch, trace; **—ченный** *a.* drafted, sketched, traced.

зач/есть, —итывать *v.* take into account.

зачет *m.* examination; **сдать з.** pass an examination.

зачинить *v.* mend.

зачисл/ить, —ять *v.* include; enroll.

зачистка *f.* (met.) dressing, trimming.

зачищ/ать *v.* clean, dress, trim; **—енный** *a.* cleaned, trimmed.

зашедший *a.* set (sun).

зашифров/ать, —ывать *v.* encode; **—ывание** *n.* enciphering, encoding.

зашкал/ивание *n.* off-scale reading; **—ить** *v.* go off scale (of instrument).

зашлаковывание *n.* slagging.

заштамповка *f.* closing (in metal forming).

заштрихов/анный *a.* hatched, cross-hatched, shaded; **—ывать** *v.* hatch, crosshatch, shade.

зашунтиров/анный *a.* shunted, switched; **—ать** *v.* shunt, switch.

защелк/а *f.* catch, latch, pawl, detainer, stop, trip, arresting device; **—ивать, —нуть** *v.* latch.

защем/ить, —лять *v.* pinch, restrain; jam; **—ление** *n.* pinching, fastening, restraint; sticking, jamming; **—ленный** *a.* pinched, entrapped, jammed, restrained.

защит/а *f.* guard, shield, defense, protection; **з. от ветра** wind screen (or shelter); **з. от облучения** radiation protection; **—ить** *see* **защищать.**

защитн/ый *a.* shielding, protective, guard; **з. бак** seal tank; **з. кожух** (shielding) can, jacket, sheathing; **з. коллоид** protective colloid; **з. слой** protective layer; sheath; **з. слой от быстрых нейтронов** fast neutron shield; **—ая дамба** check dam; levee, floodwall; **—ая камера** protection cell; **—ая камера с перчатками** glove box; **—ая оболочка** protective coating, casing, "can"; **—ая одежда** protective clothing; **—ая плита** baffle; **—ая полоса** (rad.) guard band; **—ая сетка** (elec.) suppressor-grid; **—ая экранировка** protective screen; **—ое действие** screening effect; **—ое кольцо** guard ring; **—ое обследование** protection survey; **—ое покрытие** protective coating; **—ое приспособление** protective device; **—ое стекло** (micros.) cover glass.

защищ/аемый, —енный *a.* defended, protected, screened, shielded; **—ать** *v.* defend, protect, guard, screen, shield; **—енный от пыли** dustproof; **—енный счетчик** shielded counter.

заэвтект/ический *a.* hypereutectic; **—оидный** *a.* hypereutectoid.

заэкраниров/анный *a.* screened; **—ываться** *v.* be screened.

заяв/ить, —лять *v.* declare, announce, state, claim; **—ка** *f.* claim, order; declaration, statement; **—ление** *n.* declaration, statement; application.

Заяц Lepus (Lep) (constellation).

звание *n.* rank, title.

звезд/а *f.* star; (mach.) spider; **з.**

вызванная протоном proton-induced star; **з.-гигант** giant (star); **з. образованная мезоном** meson-induced star; **падающая з.** shooting star; **Полярная з.** North Star, Polaris; **з.-ядро** nuclear star (of planetary nebula); **соединение —ой** (elec.) star connection; **—но-суточный** sidereal-diurnal.

звездн/ый *a.* star, stellar, sidereal; stellate; **з. год** sidereal year; **з. дождь** meteoric storm; **з. параллакс** stellar parallax; **з. полдень** sidereal noon; **з. транспортир** star plotter; **—ая вспышка** (astr.) nova; **—ая карта** star chart, celestial map; **—ая энергия** stellar energy; **—ое время** sidereal time; **—ые сутки** sidereal day.

звездообраз/ный *a.* star-shaped, radial; **—ная опора** (mach.) spider; **—ование** *n.* (nucl.) star production; **—ующий** *a.* star-producing.

звездочка *f.* asterisk; star wheel, sprocket wheel; turnstile; spider.

звездчат/ость *f.* (min.) asterism; **—ый** *a.* star-shaped, stellate, asteriated; **—ый остов** (mach.) spider.

звенеть *v.* ring, jingle, clank.

звен/о *n.*, **—ьевой** *a.* link, unit, section, element, component; group; **з. фильтра** filter section.

звенящий *a.* ringing.

звон *m.*, **—ить** *v.* ring.

звонк/ий *a.* resounding, clear; **—овый** *a.* bell; **—ость** *f.* sonorousness, clearness.

звонок *m.* bell.

звук *m.* sound, tone; **гласный з.** vowel; **сложный з.** complex tone; **согласный з.** consonant; **измеритель —а** acoustimeter.

звуко— *prefix* phono—, phon—, sound.

звукоанализатор *m.* sound analyzer.

звуков/ой *a.* sound, sonic, acoustic; audio; audible; aural; *see also* **акустический**; **з. барьер** sound barrier; **з. ветер** acoustic streaming, quartz wind; **з. генератор** audio-frequency oscillator; **з. детектор** aural detector; **з. зонд** sound probe; **з. излучатель** acoustic radiator; **з. спектр** sound spectrum.

звуков/ой *cont.*, **—ая волна** acoustic wave; **—ая дорожка** sound track; **—ая катушка** voice coil; **—ая линза** acoustic lens; **—ая линия** sonic line; **—ая маскировка** aural masking; **—ая несущая** voice carrier; **—ая рябь** flutter effect; **—ая характеристика** sonic line; **—ая частота** audio frequency; **—ое давление** sound pressure; **—ое кино** sound motion pictures; **—ое колебание** sound vibration; **—ое поле** sound field; **—ое течение** *see* **звуковой ветер.**

звуко/воспроизведение *n.* audio reproduction; **—записыватель** *m.* sound recorder; **—запись** *f.* sound recording; **—зондаж** *m.* echo sounding.

звукоизлучатель *m.* acoustic generator; **—ный элемент** acoustic radiating element.

звукоизмерение дальности sound ranging.

звукоизоляц/ия *f.* soundproofing; **коэффициент —ии** acoustic reduction factor.

звуко/лента *f.* audio tape; **—локация** *f.* sonar; **—мер** *m.* phonometer; **—метрия** *f.* sound ranging; **—непроницаемый** *a.* soundproof; **—отражение** *n.* sound (or acoustic) reflection; **—ощущение** *n.* sound sensation; **—пеленегация и локация** Sound Fixing and Ranging (SOFAR).

звукопогло/титель *m.* silencer, sound absorber; **—щательный, —щающий** *a.* sound-absorbing, soundproof; **—щение** *n.* sound (or acoustic) absorption.

звуко/преломление *n.* acoustic refraction; **—приемная аппаратура** sound pickup equipment.

звукопровод *m.* acoustic line; **—ный** *a.* sound-conducting, sound-transmitting.

звуко/проекция *f.* sound projection; **—проницаемость** *f.* sound (or acoustic) transmission; **—сниматель** *m.* sound pickup, sound box.

звукосъемочн/ый аппарат sound (movie) camera; **—ая камера** sonic camera.

звуко/тень *f.* sound shadow; **—улавливатель** *m.* sound detector (locator).

звуч/ание *n.* sounding, resounding, vibration; **—ать** *v.* sound, resound; **—ность** *f.* sonority; **—ный** *a.* sonorous, resonant; **—ащая дуга** singing arc.

з-д *abbr.* (**завод**) works, plant, factory, mill.

з. д. *abbr.* (**западная долгота**) west longitude.

здание *n.* building, structure.

здесь *adv.* here.

здешний *a.* local.

здоров/ый *a.* healthy, sound; **—ая структура** sound structure.

здравомысл/ие *n.* common sense; **—ящий** *a.* sensible.

здравоохранен/ие *n.* public health; **физика —ия** health physics.

зев *m.* mouth, jaw, span.

Зевс Zeus.

Зегера конус Seger cone, pyrometric cone.

зеебахит *m.* seebachite.

Зеебека эффект (явление) Seebeck effect.

Зеелингера парадокс Seelinger paradox.

Зеемана квадратный эффект Zeeman quadratic effect; **З. обратный эффект** inverse Z. effect; **З. простой эффект** normal Z. effect; **З. сложный эффект** anomalous Z. effect; **З. эффект (явление)** Z. effect; **зеемановское смещение** Z. displacement.

зейбертит *m.* seybertite.

зейгерный *a.* liquation.

зейгеров/ание *n.* liquation; **—анный** *a.* liquated; **—ать** *v.* liquate; segregate.

Зейделя аберрация Seidel aberration.

Зейтц Seitz.

зелено— *prefix* green, greenish; **—вато—** *prefix* greenish.

зеленоватый *a.* greenish; **з.-желтый** *a.* greenish yellow.

зеленчак *m.* jade.

зелен/ый *a.* green; **з. луч, —ое мерцание** (astr.) green flash.

зелигманнит *m.* seligmannite.

Зельмейера формула Sellmeier formula.

земельн/ый *a.* land; **—ая площадь** land area.

земле— *prefix* earth, land.

землеведение *n.* geography.

землемер *m.* (land) surveyor; **—ный** *a.* surveying, geodetic; **—ный циркуль** surveyor's compass.

земле/сос *m.* suction dredge; **—трясение** *n.* earthquake.

землечерп/алка *f.* dredge; **—ание** *n.* excavation, dredging; **—ательный** *a.* dredging.

земли *pl. of* **земля**; **редкие з.** rare earths; **щелочные з.** alkaline earths.

землистый *a.* earthen.

Земля (планета) Earth (planet).

земля *f.* earth, ground, soil; country; **з.-воздух управляемый снаряд** surface-to-air guided missile; **з. затопляемая приливом** tideland; **з.-земля управляемый снаряд** surface-to-surface guided missile.

землян/ой *a.* earth, earthen; ground; **з. возврат** (elec.) ground return; **з. ток** (elec.) ground current; **—ая дамба** earth embankment; **—ая плотина** earth dam.

земноводный *a.* amphibian.

земн/ой *a.* terrestrial, earth, telluric; **з. вес** terrestrial weight; **з. зажим** (elec.) ground terminal; **з. луч** ground ray; **з. магнетизм** terrestrial magnetism; **з. меридиан** terrestrial meridian; **з. ток** earth (or telluric) current; **з. туман** ground mist, ground haze; **з. шар** globe, the earth; **—ая зрительная труба** terrestrial telescope; **—ая кора** earth's crust; **—ая ось** earth's axis; **—ая поверхность** earth's surface; **—ое излучение** terrestrial radiation; **—ое магнитное поле** geomagnetic field; **—ое притяжение** gravity; **—ое тяготение** gravity, gravitation; **—ое ядро** earth's core.

земснаряд *m.* dredge.

Зенгена формула обращения Söhngen inversion formula.

зенит *m.* zenith; **—ный** *a.* zenith, zenithal; anti-aircraft; **—ный угол** zenith angle; **—ное притяжение** (astr.) zenith attraction; **—ное расстояние** zenith distance.

зенков/ание *n.* countersinking; **—ать** *v.* countersink; **—ка** *f.* countersink bit.

зеркало *n.* mirror; speculum; **водное з.** (geo.) water table; **з. для подсветки**

illuminating mirror (of microscope); **з. заднего вида, з. задней обзорности** rear-view mirror; **з.-отражатель** mirror-reflector; **полировка под з.** mirror finish; **з.-прожектор** mirror searchlight; **з. цилиндра** cylinder face.

зеркально/-отраженная система mirror-image system; **з.-поворотная ось** rotoflection axis; **з.-полированный** *a.* mirror-finished.

зеркальн/ый *a.* mirror, specular; **з. гальванометр** mirror (or reflecting) galvanometer; **з. изомер** enantiomorph, enantiomer; mirror (or optical) isomer; **з. импеданс** image impedance; **з. металл** speculum metal; **з. переход** mirror transition; **з. перископ** mirror periscope; **з. прицел** mirror (or reflex) sight; **з. реактор** reflected reactor; **з. телескоп** reflecting telescope; **з. чугун** specular cast iron; **з. экстензометр** mirror extensometer; **—ая камера** reflex camera; **—ая переориентировка** mirror-image reorientation; **—ая симметрия** mirror symmetry, bilateral symmetry; **—ая частота** image frequency; **—ое затухание** image attenuation; **—ое изображение** mirror image; **—ое изображение источника** image source; **—ое отображение** mirror image; **—ое отражение** mirror image, reflected image, specular reflection; **—ое стекло** plate glass; **—ое ядро** mirror nucleus; **—ые антиподы** optical antipodes; **—ые помехи** image interference.

зернен/ие *n.* granulation; **—ый** *a.* granulated.

зернист/ость *f.* granularity, grain size, mesh; **—ый** *a.* granular, granulated; **—ый излом** granular fracture; **—ый перлит** spheroidized pearlite; **—ый снег** granular snow.

зерн/ить *v.* granulate; **—о** *n.* grain, granule, seed; **номер —а** grain size, mesh; **—овой** *a.* grain, granular, seed; **—ышко** *n.* small grain, granule.

зетов/ый *a.* Z, zee-, Z-shaped; **—ая балка** zee-beam; **—ое железо** Z-iron.

Зефир Zephyr (reactor).

Зигбана спектрограф Siegbahn spectrograph; **З. спектрометр** S. spectrometer.

зигбургит *m.* siegburgite.

зигенит *m.* siegenite.

зигзаг *m.* zigzag; **—ообразный** *a.* zigzag; serrated; **—ообразная молния** zigzag lightning.

Зильбершлаг Silberschlag (lunar crater).

зим/а *f.*, **—ний** *a.* winter; **—нее солнцестояние** winter solstice; **—ой, —ою** *adv.* in winter.

Зинера ток Zener current.

Зисинга фаза Sissingh phase.

ЗЛ *abbr. see* **Зав. лаб.**

зло *n.* evil, wrong, harm.

зловон/ие *n.* stink, stench; **—ный** *a.* malodorous, fetid.

злокачественн/ый *a.* malignant; **—ая опухоль** malignant tumor; **—ое малокровие** pernicious anemia.

злоупотребл/ение *n.*, **—ять** *v.* abuse, misuse.

змеевидный *a.* serpentine, sinuous.

змеевик *m.* coil (pipe); serpentine; **з.-холодильник** condenser coil, cooling coil; **—овый** *a.* coil, spiral.

Змееносец Ophiuchus (Oph) (constellation).

змей *m.*, **бумажный з., воздушный з., —ковый** *a.* kite; **—ковый аэростат** kite balloon; **—ковый метеорограф** kite meteorograph.

Змея Serpens (Ser) (constellation).

зн. *abbr. see* **знак.**

знак *m.* sign, symbol, mark, indication, signal; **з. атома, химический з.** atomic symbol, chemical symbol; **з. вопроса** question mark; **з. иона** ionic charge; **з. корня** radical sign; **з. опознавательный** identification mark; **з. после запятой** decimal place; **з. равенства** sign of equality; **з. секунды** (math.) double prime; **—овая функция** sign function.

знаком/ить *v.* acquaint, inform, familiarize; **—иться** *v.* get acquainted, study, investigate; **—ство** *n.* knowledge of; familiarity with; **—ый** *a.* acquainted with; familiar, known.

знакоопределенный *a.* of fixed sign.

знакопеременн/ый *a.* alternating; **з. градиент** alternating gradient; **з. множитель** alternating-sign factor

з. ряд alternating series; —**ая нагрузка** alternating load; —**ая фокусировка** alternating-gradient focusing.

знако/постоянный *a.* of constant sign; —**чередующийся ряд** alternating series.

знаменатель *m.* (math.) denominator, consequent; **общий з.** common denominator; **з. прогрессии** (common) ratio of a geometric progression; —**ный** *a.* denominative; significant, noteworthy, important; characteristic.

знаменит/ость *f.* celebrity; fame, eminence; —**ый** *a.* celebrated, famous, eminent; illustrious.

знаменовать *v.* signify, indicate, mark.

знамя облачное (meteor.) banner cloud.

знание *n.* knowledge, learning; science, skill.

знатн/ость *f.* eminence; —**ый** *a.* eminent, distinguished, notable.

знаток *m.* judge, expert.

знать *v.* know, be aware of, be acquainted with; be skilled in.

значащая цифра significant digit (or figure).

значение *n.* value; meaning, sense; importance, significance; **иметь з.** be important; **конечное з.** final value.

значим/ость *f.* (stat.) significance; —**ый** *a.* significant.

значительн/о *adv.* considerably, significantly; —**ость** *f.* significance, importance; —**ый** *a.* significant, important, considerable, notable, marked, substantial; —**ый дождь** heavy rain.

значить *v.* mean, signify.

—**значный** *suffix* —valued.

значок *m.* mark, emblem; index.

знающ/ий *a.* knowing; expert, skilled; learned; —**ее лицо** expert.

зной *m.* heat, sultriness; —**ный** *a.* hot, sultry, torrid.

зодиак *m.* zodiac; —**альный** *a.* zodiacal; —**альный свет** zodiacal light.

зол/а *f.* ash; —**истый** *a.* ash, ashen.

Золотая Рыба (Дорад) Dorado (Dor) (constellation).

золотисто— *prefix* gold, auro—, aurous.

золот/истый *a.* golden; gold, aurous.

золотник *m.*, —**овый** *a.* slide, valve; **плоский з.** slide valve; —**овый шток,** —**овая скалка** slide rod, slide valve stem; —**овое зеркало** slide valve face.

золото *n.* gold (Au); **листовое з.** gold leaf, gold foil; **новое з.** Mannheim gold.

золото— *prefix* gold, auri—, auric.

золот/ой *a.* gold, golden; —**ая середина** golden mean; —**ое сечение** (math.) golden section.

золотоносный *a.* gold-bearing, auriferous.

золочен/ие *n.* gilding, gold plating; —**ый** *a.* gilded, gilt, gold-plated.

золь *m.* sol.

зольн/ик *m.* ash pit; cinder box; —**ость** *f.* ash content; —**ый** *a.* ash, cinder.

Зоммеринг Soemmering (lunar crater).

Зоммерфельд Sommerfeld.

зона *f.* band, zone, belt, range, area; **з. видимости** visibility range; **з. волнений** undular zone; **з. воспроизводства** breeding blanket (of reactor); **з. восстановления** reduction zone; **з. дезактивации** decontamination area; **з. действия** coverage; range; **з. действия по углу места** (radar) vertical coverage; **з. загрузки топлива** charging area; **з. затвердевания** solidification range; **з. затишья** calm belt, doldrums; **з. избегания** zone of avoidance (of spiral nebulae); **з. облучения** radiation zone; **з. опасности** danger zone; **з. отчуждения** exclusion area; **з. пассатных ветров** trade-wind belt; **з. прихода** impact zone (of radio emission); **з. проводимости** conduction band; **з. прозрачности, з. пропускания** transmission band; **з. радиоактивности** radiation zone; **з. сегрегации** zone of segregation; **з. укрытия** shelter area.

зональн/ость *f.* zonality; —**ый** *a.* zonal; —**ая пластинка** (opt.) zone plate; —**ая функция** (math.) zonal harmonic.

зонд *m.* probe, sonde; thin beam; **з. связи** (coupling) probe; —**аж** *see* **зондирование.**

зондиров/ание *n.* sounding, probing; **метод —ания** (radar) echo method;

—**ать** *v.* sound, probe; —**очный** *a.* sounding, probing.

зондовый *a.* probe, sounding, sound-type; **з. метеорограф** sounding meteorograph.

зонированный *a.* zoned.

зонн/ый *a.* zone, band; —**ая модель** (semicond.) band model; —**ая плавка** zone refining; —**ая пластинка** (opt.) zone plate; —**ая теория** (semicond.) band theory; —**ое выравнивание** zone leveling.

зонт, —**ик** *m.* umbrella; hood (of furnace); —**ичный,** —**ообразный** *a.* umbrella-shaped; —**ичная антенна** umbrella antenna.

зоо— *prefix* zoo—.

зоо/генный *a.* zoogenic; —**лит** *m.* zoolith, zoolite; —**литовый** *a.* zoolithic.

зоолог *m.* zoologist; —**ический** *a.* zoological; —**ия** *f.* zoology.

зоохим/ический *a.* zoochemical; —**ия** *f.* zoochemistry.

зорк/ий *a.* sharp-sighted, far-sighted; —**ость** *f.* keen vision.

зрач/ковый рефлекс pupillary reflex; —**ок** *m.* pupil (of eye).

зрел/ость *f.* maturity; —**ый** *a.* ripe, mature.

зрен/ие *n.* eyesight, vision; **обман** —**ия** optical illusion; **поле** —**ия** field of view; range of vision; **точка** —**ия** point of view; viewpoint; **угол** —**ия** visual angle.

зреть *v.* ripen, mature.

зритель *m.* spectator.

зрительн/ый *a.* visual, optic, optical; **з. нерв** optical nerve; **з. пурпур** visual purple; **з. фотометр** visual photometer; —**ая труба** terrestrial telescope; —**ое впечатление** visual impression; —**ое стекло** (micros.) eyepiece.

зуб *m.* tooth; **вставной з.** (mach.) bit.

зубец *m.* tooth, cog, lug, cam, projection, spur; dent, nick, notch; jog; prong, tine; pinnacle; **съемный з.** bit.

зубил/о *n.*, —**ьный** *a.* chisel.

зубчат/ка *f.* gear, gear wheel; —**о-дисковый разрядник** toothed disk discharger; —**ость** *f.* serration.

зубчат/ый *a.* toothed, gear, geared, serrated, indented, dented, notched; hackly; **з. блок** sprocket; **з. импульс** serrated pulse; **з. перебор,** —**ое зацепление** (transmission) gear; **сложный з. перебор** gear train assembly;—**ая передача** gear transmission (train, drive); —**ая полоса,** —**ая рейка** gear rack, toothed rack; —**ое колесо** gear, toothed wheel, gear wheel, sprocket; —**ое кольцо** ring gear.

зубчики *pl.* serration.

зуммер *m.* buzzer; —**ный** *a.* buzzer, humming.

зумф, зумпф *m.*, —**овый** *a.* sump.

зуниит *m.* zunyite.

зыб/кий *a.* vacillating, unsteady, unstable; —**кость** *f.*, —**ление** *n.* fluctuation.

зыбучий *a.* shifting, unsteady; **з. песок** quicksand.

зыбь *f.* spongy ground; swell; ripple.

зюйд *m.* south; —**овый** *a.* south, southerly.

И

и *conj.* and, also, too; but, although; both; even, as well as; **и тот и другой** both.

и [*in steel mark* (**инструментальная**)] instrument steel.

и. *abbr.* (**институт**) institute.

И *abbr.* (**иностранная литература**) foreign literature (in library cataloguing).

ИА *abbr.* (**истинный азимут**) true azimuth.

ИАН *abbr.* (**Известия Академии наук СССР**) Bulletin of the Academy of Sciences, USSR.

ИАН СССР, Сер. геол. *abbr.* (**Известия Академии наук СССР, Серия геологическая**) Bulletin of the Academy of Sciences, USSR, Geological Series.

ИАТ *abbr.* [**Институт автоматики и телемеханики** (**Академии наук СССР**)] Institute of Automation and

Remote Control (of the Academy of Sciences, USSR).

ИАЭ *abbr.* (**Институт атомной энергии**) Institute of Atomic Energy.

ибо *conj.* because, for, as.

ИБФ *abbr.* [**Институт биологической физики** (**Академии наук СССР**)] Institute of Biological Physics (of the Academy of Sciences, USSR).

ИВ *abbr.* (**индекс вязкости**) viscosity index.

ИВПИ *abbr.* [**Иваново-Вознесенский политехнический институт** (**им. М. Б. Фрунзе**)] M. B. Frunze Ivanovo-Voznesensk Polytechnic Institute.

ИГДАН *abbr.* (**Институт горного дела Академии наук СССР**) Mining Institute of the Academy of Sciences, USSR.

игельстремит *m.* igelströmite.

игл/а *f.* needle; spicule; pivot; **—истый, —овидный, —ообразный** *a.* needle-shaped, acicular; **—овидный кристалл** acicular crystal.

игнитрон *m.* ignitron.

игнорир/овать *v.* ignore, disregard, overlook, neglect; **—уемый** *a.* ignorable; **—уемая координата** ignorable coordinate.

игол/ка *see* **игла**; **—ьный** *a.* needle.

игольчат/ый *a.* needle, needle-shaped, acicular, spicular; **и. клапан** needle valve; **и. контакт** point contact; **и. кристалл** acicular crystal; **и. лед** needle ice; **и. разрядник** needle gap; **и. троостит** bainite.

игр/а *f.* game; (free) play; clearance, backlash; **и. валков** backlash; **и. осевая, и. продольная** (mach.) end play; **—ать** *v.* play; **—ать роль** play a part.

Игрек сплав Y alloy.

ИД *abbr.* (**Институт искусственного дождя**) Institute of Artificial Rain.

идеал *m.* ideal; **—изированный** *a.* idealized.

идеально *adv.* ideally, uniformly, perfectly, completely; **и. пластический** perfectly plastic; **—сть** *f.* ideality.

идеальн/ый *a.* ideal, perfect; **и. газ** ideal gas; **—ая жидкость** ideal fluid; **—ая разрешающая способность** infinite resolution.

идейный *a.* ideological.

идемпотентный *a.* idempotent.

идентифи/кация *f.*, **—кационный** *a.* identification; **—цировать** *v.* identify, determine; **—цируемый** *a.* identifiable, identified.

идентичн/ость *f.* identity; **—ый** *a.* identical.

идея *f.* idea, concept.

идио/морфный *a.* idiomorphic; **—синкразия** *f.* peculiarity; **—статический** *a.* idiostatic.

идиофан/изм *m.* idiophanism; **—ный** *a.* idiophanous.

идио/хроматический *a.* idiochromatic; **—электрический** *a.* idioelectric.

идокраз *m.* idocrase.

и др. *abbr.* (**и другие**) and others, et al.

ид/ти *v.* go, walk; operate, run, work; progress, proceed, occur; **и. на убыль** to decrease; **дождь идет** it is raining; **—ущий** *a.*, **—я** going, running, operating; **—ущий вверх** rising; **—ущий вниз** descending.

иенское стекло Jena glass.

из *prep. gen.* out of, from; **из-за** *prep. gen.* because of; from behind; **из-под** *prep.* from under.

ИЗ *abbr.* [**Исторические записки** (**Академии наук СССР**)] Historical Annals (of the Academy of Sciences, USSR) (serial publication).

из— *prefix* ex—; *see also* **изо—**.

изактина *f.* isactine.

изалея *f.* isalea.

изаллобар/а *f.* isallobar; **—ическая депрессия** isallobaric low.

изаллотерма *f.* isallotherm.

изанакатабара *f.* isanakatabar.

изанемона *f.* isanemone.

изаномал/а, —ь *f.* isanomal, isanomalous line.

изантезическая линия isanthesic line.

избав/ить, —лять *v.* rid (of); **—иться, —ляться** *v.* get rid (of); **—ление** *n.* release, riddance, liberation; **—ленный** *a.* rid, freed.

избе/гать, —гнуть, —жать *v.* avoid, evade, obviate, avert; **—жание** *n.* avoidance, averting; **—жание резонансного захвата** (nuclear reactor) resonance escape.

избирательн/ость *f.* selectivity, discrimination; **—ый** *a.* selective; **—ый**

растворитель selective solvent; **—ый фотоэффект** selective photoeffect; **—ая локализация** selective localization; **—ая ориентация** preferred orientation; **—ое отражение** selective reflection.

избирать *v.* choose, select.

избр/ание *n.* selection; **—анный** *a.* selected; **—ать** *see* **избирать.**

избыток *m.* surplus, excess; **и. нейтронов** neutron excess; **сферический и.** (math.) spherical excess; **и. цвета** color excess.

избыточн/о-нейтронный neutron-rich; **—ый** *a.* surplus, excess, excessive, extra; **—ый коэффициент размножения** excess multiplication factor (or constant); **—ый электрон** excess electron; **—ая реактивность** excess reactivity; **—ая энергия** excess energy; **—ое давление** overpressure; gauge pressure; (acoust.) excess pressure.

Изв. *abbr.* (**Известия**) Bulletin.

изверг/ать, —нуть *v.* erupt, eject; **—нутый** *see* **изверженный.**

извержен/ие *n.* eruption, ejection; excretion; **—ный** *a.* ejected, emitted; (geo.) eruptive, volcanic, igneous; **—ные породы** eruptive rocks, volcanic rocks; igneous rocks.

извест/ие *n.* news, information; **—ить** *see* **извещать**; **—ия** *pl.* news, information; bulletin.

известк/а *see* **известь**; **—ование** *n.* liming, chalking; **—овистый** *a.* calcareous, lime-like, lime-containing.

известковый *a.* lime, calcareous, calciferous, calcium; **и. уранит** autunite; **и. шпат** calcite.

известн/о *adv.* it is known; **—ость** *f.* reputation, fame; **поставить в —ость** inform; **—ый** *a.* famous, noted, (well-) known; certain; **в —ой мере** to a certain degree (extent); **в —ых случаях** in certain cases.

извест/няк *m.* limestone; **—няковый** *a.* limestone, calcareous, calciferous; **—ь** *f.* lime.

извещ/ать *v.* inform, notify; communicate, announce; **—ение** *n.* information, notification, notice.

извив *m.* winding, coil; **—ание** *n.* meandering, winding, coiling; **—аться** *v.* wind, coil; twist, meander.

извил/ина *f.* bend, crook, curve, convolution; **—истость** *f.* crookedness, sinuosity; **—истый** *a.* winding, sinuous, serpentine, twisting.

извин/ение *n.* apology, excuse; **—ить, —ять** *v.* excuse, forgive, pardon; **—ите (меня)** I beg your pardon.

извит/ость *f.* winding, twisting, **—ься** *see* **извиваться.**

извлек/ание *see* **извлечение**; **—ать** *v.* extract, derive, draw, recover; **—ающий** *a.* extracting.

извлеч/ение *n.* extraction, removal, withdrawal; recovery, stripping; abstract, summary; **и. корня** (math.) evolution; **и. растворителем** solvent extraction; **—енный** *a.* extracted, drawn off; derived; **—ь** *see* **извлекать.**

извне *adv.* outside, externally.

из-во *abbr.* (**издательство**) press.

извра/тить, —щать *v.* distort, misinterpret; **—щение** *n.* distortion, misinterpretation; **—щенный** *a.* distorted.

изгар/ина, —ь *f.* scale, scoria.

изгиб *m.* bend, deflection, kink, wriggle, curvature, flexure; (geo.) fold; elbow (of pipe); **и. волновода** waveguide bend; **испытание на и.** bending test, flexing; **продольный и.** buckling; **линия —а** curvature; **момент —а** *see* **изгибающий момент.**

изгиб/аемость *f.* deflectivity; **—ание** *n.* bending, deflection, kink, wriggle, curving, buckling; deformation; **—ать** *v.* bend, deflect, curve; **—аться** *v.* buckle, sag; **—ающий момент** bending moment; **—ающая сила** deflecting force; **—ающее возмущение** kinking perturbation (of plasma), **—ная волна** flexural wave; **—ное колебательное движение** bending vibrational motion.

изгла/дить, —живать *v.* efface, erase; **—живание** *n.* smoothing out.

изгородь *f.* enclosure, fence.

изгот/авливать, —овить *v.* prepare, produce, manufacture; **—овитель** *m* producer, manufacturer.

изготовлен/ие *n.* preparation, production, fabrication, manufacture; **промышленное и.** manufacture; **—ный** *a.* prepared, produced, manufactured.

изготовлять *see* **изготавливать.**

изд. *abbr.* (**издание**) edition, issue, publication; (**издательство**) press.

издав/ание *n.* emission; publication; **—ать** *v.* emit; publish, issue.

издан/ие *n.* edition, issue, publication; **—ный** *a.* published, issued.

издатель *m.* publisher; **—ство** *n.* press, publisher, publishing house.

Издатинлит *abbr.* (**Издательство иностранной литературы**) Foreign Literature Press.

изд/ать *see* **издавать**; **—ающий** *a.* emitting, giving off; issuing.

издел/ие *n.* manufactured article, product; **промышленные —ия** industrial goods.

издержка *f.* expense, cost, expenditure.

изентроп/а *f.* isentrope; **—ный, —ический** *a.* isentropic.

изерин *m.* iserine.

из-за *prep.* because of; from behind.

изинговская модель ферромагнетика Ising ferromagnetic model.

излагат/ельный *a.* expository; **—ь** *v.* state, give an account of, expound.

изламывать *v.* break, fracture.

излившийся *a.* effusive, extrusive.

излиш/ек *m.* surplus, excess; **—ество** *n.* excess; **—не** *adv.* superfluously; it is unnecessary; **—ний** *a.* excessive, unnecessary, redundant.

излияние *n.* outflow, effusion, eruption.

излож/ение *n.* account, statement, discussion, exposition; **краткое и.** summary; **—енный** *a.* discussed, expounded; **—ить** *see* **излагать.**

изложница *f.* (casting) mold.

излом *m.* break, rupture, fracture; discontinuity; kink, sharp bend, deflection; **листоватый и.** foliated fracture; **и. при отрыве** cleavage fracture; **и. усталости** fatigue fracture, endurance failure; **плоскость —а** fracture plane; **—анный, —ленный** *a.* fractured, broken; **—ать, —ить** *see* **изламывать**; **—ная неустойчивость** kink instability (of plasma pinch effect); **—ное возмущение** kinking perturbation (of plasma).

излучаем/ость *f.* emissivity, emittance; **—ый** *a.* radiated, emitted.

излучатель *m.* emitter, transmitter; radiator; **и. позитронов** positron emitter; **—ность** *f.* radiant emittance; **—ный** *a.* emitting, emissive, radiative; **—ный пирометр** radiation pyrometer; **—ная способность** emittance, emissive (or radiating) power; **—ное равновесие** radiation equilibrium.

излуч/ать, —ить *v.* emit, radiate; **—аться, —иться** *v.* radiate, emanate (from); **—ающий** *a.* radiative, emissive, emitting; radiant.

излучен/ие *n.* emission, radiation; **и. абсолютно черного тела** black-body radiation; **земное и.** terrestrial radiation; **космическое и.** cosmic radiation; **ночное и.** nocturnal radiation; **и. остановки** bremsstrahlung; **тяжелое и.** heavily ionizing radiation; **и. флуоресценции** fluorescent radiation; **коэффициент —ия** emission coefficient; **плотность —ия** *see* **излучательность**; **—ный** *a.* emitted, radiated.

излуч/ина *f.* curve, bend, winding; **—истый** *a.* bent, winding, tortuous.

измалывать *v.* grind, crush, break up.

измельч/ание, —ение *n.* grinding, crushing, size reduction; **—ать, —ить** *v.* grind, crush, pulverize; reduce to fragments; **—ающий** *a.* grinding, crushing; **—енный** *a.* finely divided, crushed, ground, pulverized; deflocculated; **—итель** *m.* crusher, pulverizer.

изменен/ие *n.* change, alteration, variation; fluctuation, drift; **и. интенсивности с высотой** intensity-height distribution; **и. нормировки** renormalization; **и. ориентации спина** spin flip; **и. температуры** temperature shift; **и. чувствительности** sensitivity drift; **—ный** *a.* changed, transformed, altered.

измен/имый *see* **изменяемый**; **—ить** *see* **изменять.**

изменчив/ость *f.* variability, mutability; **—ый** *a.* variable, changeable, irregular, unsettled.

измен/яемость *f.* variability, changeability; **—яемый** *a.* variable, changeable, mutable; **—ять** *v.* change, modify, vary, alternate; **—яться** *v.* change; fluctuate; **—яющийся** *a.* variable; **—яющееся сопротивление** varistor.

измер/ение *n.* measurement; survey; dimension, size; **и. дальности** ranging, sounding; **и. глубины эхолотом** echo sounding (or ranging); **—енный** *a.* measured; **—имость** *f.* measurability; **—имый** *a.* measurable.

измерит. *abbr.* (**измерительный**) measuring.

измеритель *m.* meter, gauge; pickup; **и. бета-интенсивности** beta gauge; **и. видимости** visibility meter; **и. влажности** hygrometer; **и. гамма-излучения** gamma-ray meter; **и. интенсивности** rate meter; **и. испарения** evaporimeter; **и. магнитного потока** fluxmeter; **и. натяжения** tensiometer; **и. непрозрачности, и. почернения** densitometer; **и. порывистости** gust meter; **и. скорости потока** flow meter.

измерительн/ый *a.* measuring; **и. зонд** measuring probe; **и. прибор** measuring instrument, gauge; meter; **и. сосуд** measuring vessel, graduate; **и. цилиндр** measuring cylinder, graduated cylinder; **и. шунт** instrument shunt; **—ая длина** gauge length; **—ая катушка** search coil, pickup loop; **—ая машина** gauging machine; **—ая плитка** gauge block; **—ая труба** measuring tube.

измер/ить, —ять *v.* measure, gauge, survey.

Измер. тех. *abbr.* (**Измерительная техника**) Measurement Techniques (journal).

измеряемый *a.* measurable, detectable.

измолот/ый *a.* ground; **—ь** *see* **измалывать.**

изморозь *f.* rime.

изморось *f.* drizzle, drizzling rain; sleet.

измочал/ивать, —ить *v.* shred.

изнанка *f.* reverse, inside, back.

изнашив/аемость *f.* wearability; **—ание** *n.* wear, wear and tear; **—ание от трения** abrasive wear, attrition; **—ать, —аться** *v.* wear out, erode.

износ *m.* wear, abrasion; depletion; **—ить** *see* **изнашивать.**

износо/стойкий, —упорный *a.* wear-resistant, durable; **—стойкость, —упорность** *f.* resistance to wear, durability.

изношенный *a.* worn out; eroded; used up, exhausted.

изнутри *adv.* from within; inside.

изо— *prefix* iso—, equal-, constant-.

изо/аврора *f.* isoaurore; **—амплитуда** *f.* isoamplitude; **—анормаль** *f.* isoabnormal (line); **—атмическая линия** isoatmic line, isothyme; **—база** *f.* isobase.

изобар *m.* (nucl.) isobar; **—а** *f.* (meteor.) isobar; **—ический, —ный** *a.* isobaric; **—ическая карта** (meteor.) pressure chart; **—ноизотермический потенциал, —ный потенциал** Gibbs free energy, Gibbs function, thermodynamic potential; **—ная теплоемкость** specific heat at constant pressure; **—ная триада** isobaric triplet; **—ометрический** *a.* isobarometric, isobaric.

изобат/а *f.* isobath; **—итерма** *f.* isobathytherm; **—ический** *a.* isobathic.

изобил/ие *n.* abundance; **—овать** *v.* abound (in); **—ующий** *a.* abundant, rich (in); **—ьный** *a.* abundant.

изображ/аемый *a.* represented; **—ать** *v.* represent, depict; **—ающий** *a.* representing, representative; **—ение** *n.* image, representation; transform; **метод —ений** (elec.) method of images; **—енный** *a.* represented, mapped.

изобразит/ельный *a.* descriptive, imitative; graphic; **—ь** *see* **изображать.**

изобрести *see* **изобретать.**

изобретатель *m.* inventor; **—ность** *f.* inventiveness, resourcefulness, ingenuity; **—ный** *a.* inventive, resourceful, ingenious; **—ство** *n.* invention.

изобрет/ать *v.* invent, devise; **—ение** *n.* invention, device; **—енный** *a.* invented, devised.

изобронта *f.* isobront.
изовектор *m.*, **—ный** *a.* isotopic spin vector.
изовола *f.* (geo.) isovol.
изога/ла *f.* isogal; **—лина** *f.* isohaline, isohalsine.
изогамма *f.* isogam.
изогелия *f.* isohel.
изогеотерм/а *f.* isogeotherm; **—ический** *a.* isogeothermal, geoisothermal.
изогидр/ический, —ичный *a.* isohydric; **—ометрическая линия** isohydrometric line.
изогиет/а *f.*, **—ная линия** isohyet, isohyetal line.
изогипса *f.* isohypse.
изогира *f.* isogyre.
изогнут/ость *f.* curvature, camber; **—ый** *a.* curved, bent; **—ый кристалл** bent (or curved) crystal; **—ая балка** camber beam; **—ь** *see* **изгибать.**
изогон/а *f.* isogon, isogonic line; **—альный** *a.* isogonal; **—ический** *a.* isogonic.
изоградиент *m.* isogradient; **—ный** *a.* isograde.
изограмма *f.* isogram.
Изода копер Izod impact machine.
изоденса *f.* isodense, isopycnic line.
изодиафер *m.* isodiaphere; **—ный** *a.* isodiapheric.
изодиморфизм *m.* isodimorphism.
изодинам/а *f.* isodynam; **—ический** *a.* isodynamic.
изодоз/а *f.* isodose; **—ограф** *m.* isodosograph.
изоерала *f.* isoeral.
изокатанабара *f.* isokatanabar.
изоклазит *m.* isoclasite.
изоклиматический *a.* isoclimatic.
изоклин/а *f.* isocline, isoclinic line; **—аль** *f.* **—альная складка** (geo.) isocline; **—альный, —ический** *a.* isoclinal, isoclinic.
изокозма *f.* isocosm.
изокотидальный *a.* isocotidal.
изокрима *f.* isocryme, isocrymal, isocrymic line.
изолиния *f.* isoline; **и. потока** isoflux curve (or contour).
изолирован/ие *see* **изоляция**; **—ный** *a.* isolated; insulated; free; segregated, quarantined; **—ный всплеск** (rad. astr.) isolated burst; **—ный уровень** single level; **—ная плазма** confined plasma.
изолиров/ать *v.* insulate, seal; isolate; segregate, quarantine; **герметически и.** seal off; **—ка** *see* **изоляция.**
изолировочн/ый *a.* insulation, insulating; **—ое вещество, —ое средство** *see* **изолирующее вещество.**
изолир/уемый *a.* insulated; segregated, quarantined; **—ующий** *a.* insulating, insulation; isolating; **—ующее вещество, —ующее средство** insulator; **—ующее свойство** insulating power.
изолита *f.* isolith.
изолог *m.* isolog; **—ический, —ичный** *a.* isologous; **—ический ряд** isologous series.
изолюкса *f.* isolux.
изолятор *m.*, **—ный** *a.* insulator.
изоляц/ионный *a.* insulation, insulating; **—ионная лента** (elec.) insulation tape; **—ия** *f.* insulation, sealing; isolation; segregation, quarantine; **—ия плазмы** confinement (or containment) of plasma.
изомагнитный *a.* isomagnetic.
изоменаль *m.* isomenal.
изомер *m.* isomer; **—изация** *f.* isomerization; **—изм** *m.*, **—ия** *f.* isomerism; **—изовать** *v.* isomerize; **—ия боковой цепи** chain isomerism; **—ия положения** place isomerism, position isomerism; **—ный** *a.* isomeric; **—ный переход** isomeric transition; **—ное разветвление** isomeric branching.
изометабола *f.* isometabole.
изометамерный *a.* isometameric.
изометеорическая линия isometeoric line.
изометеорограда *f.* isometeorograde.
изометопорала *f.* isometoporal.
изометрический *a.* isometric.
изоморф/изм *m.*, **—ность** *f.* isomorphism; **—ный** *a.* isomorphous, isomorphic, isostructural.
изонефа *f.* isoneph, isonephelic line.
изооктан *m.* isooctane.
изоортотерма *f.* isoorthotherm.
изоосмотический *see* **изосмотический.**

изопага *f.* isopag.
изопараллага *f.* isoparallage.
изопараметрический *a.* isoparametric.
изопахита *f.* isopach, isopachous line, isopachyte.
изопекта *f.* isopectic.
изопентан *m.* isopentane.
изоперм *m.* isoperm.
изопикн/а *f.*, **—ическая линия** isopycnic line, isopyc.
изопический *a.* isopical.
изоплера *f.* isoplere.
изоплета *f.* isopleth.
изоплоид *m.* isoploid.
изоповерхность *f.* isosurface.
изопора *f.* isopor.
изопотенциальный *a.* isopotential.
изопрен *m.* isoprene; **—овый каучук** isoprene rubber.
изопространство *n.* isospace.
изопье/за *f.*, **—стическая линия** isopiestic line.
изорванные облака ragged clouds, fractus.
изоротац/ионный *a.* isorotational; **—ия** *f.* isorotation.
изортоклаз *m.* isorthoclase.
ИЗОС *abbr.* [**Изюмский завод оптических стекол (им. Дзержинского)**] Dzerzhinskii Izyum Optical Glass Plant.
изосейсм/а *f.* isoseismal, isoseismic line, isoseism; **—ический** *a.* isoseismic, isoseismal.
изосияние *n.* isoaurora.
изосмотический *a.* isosmotic, isotonic.
изоспин *m.* isospin.
изостазия *f.* isostasy.
изостат/а *f.* isostatic curve, equal-pressure curve; **—ический** *a.* isostatic.
изостер/а *f.* isostere; **—ический** *a.* isosteric; **—ия** *f.* isosterism.
изоструктурный *a.* isostructural.
изотака *f.* isotac.
изотаха *f.* isotach, isovel.
изотера *f.* isothere, isotheral line.
изотерм/а *f.* isotherm; **—ический** *a.* isothermic, isothermal; **—ическая закалка** isothermal hardening, austempering; **—ическое равновесие** isothermal equilibrium; **—ичность** *f.* isothermality; **—ия** *f.* isothermy; **—ный** *a.* isothermal.
изотермо/бата *f.* isothermobath; **—гипса** *f.* isothermohyps.
изотеромброза *f.* isotherombrose.
изотима *f.* isothyme.
изотон *m.* isotone; **—ический** *a.* isotonic.
изотоп *m.* isotope; **и. с избыточным числом нейтронов** neutron-rich isotope; **и. с недостатком нейтронов** neutron-deficient isotope.
изотопическ/ий *a.* isotopic; **и. спин** isotopic spin; **и. эффект** isotope effect; **—ое изобилие** isotopic abundance; **—ое пространство** isotopic space; **—ое смещение** isotope shift; **—ое число** isotopic number, neutron excess.
изотопия *f.* isotopy.
изотопн/ый *see* **изотопический; и. индикатор** isotopic tracer; **и. мультиплет** isotopic multiplet; **и. обмен** isotopic exchange; **и. сдвиг** isotope shift; **и. состав** isotopic composition; **—ая масса** isotopic mass; **—ое отношение** isotopic ratio; **—ое равновесие** isotopic equilibrium; **—ое разбавление** isotopic dilution.
изотрон *m.* isotron.
изотроп/ический, —ный *a.* isotropic; **—ия, —ность** *f.* isotropy.
изофаза *f.* isophasm, isophasal line.
изофациальный *a.* isofacial.
изофена *f.* isophene, isophenological line.
изофот/а *f.* isophot, isophote; **—ный** *a.* isophotic, isophotal; **—ометр** *m.* isophotometer.
изофтора *f.* isophtor.
изохазма *f.* isochasm.
изохалина *f.* isohalsine, isohaline.
изохимена *f.* isocheim, isochimene.
изохиона *f.* isochion.
изохлора *f.* isochlor.
изохор/а *f.* isochor; **—ный** *a.* isochoric; **—ноизотермический потенциал, —ный потенциал** Helmholtz free energy, work function; **—ная теплоемкость** specific heat at constant volume.
изохром/ата *f.* isochromatic curve; **—атический, —атичный, —ный** *a.* isochromatic.

изохрон/а *f.* isochrone; **—изированный** *a.* isochronous; **—изм** *m.*, **—ность** *f.* isochronism; **—ический, —ный** *a.* isochronous, isochronal; **—ная поверхность** (geo.) equivalent time horizon.

изо/центр *m.* isocenter; **—циклический** *a.* isocyclic; **—эдрический** *a.* isohedral.

изоэлектрическая точка isoelectric point.

изоэлектронный ион isoelectronic ion; **и. ряд** isoelectronic sequence.

изоэн— *see also* **изэн—**.

изоэнергетический *a.* isoenergetic, isenergic, constant-energy.

изоэнтропический *a.* isentropic.

изразец *m.* tile.

израсходованный *a.* consumed, used.

изредка *adv.* occasionally.

изрез/анный *a.* cut, dissected; **—ать, —ывать** *v.* cut (into pieces), dissect.

изруб/ать, —ить *v.* chop up; **—ленный** *a.* chopped.

изры/вать, —ть *v.* dig up; **—тый** *a.* dug up.

изумлять *v.* surprise, amaze.

изумруд *m.*, **—ный** *a.* emerald.

изуч/ать, —ивать, —ить *v.* study, investigate, learn; **—ение** *n.*, **—енность** *f.* study, investigation; **—енный** *a.* studied, investigated, learned.

изъед/ать, изъесть *v.* corrode; **—енный** *a.* corroded.

изъяв/ить, —лять *v.* express; **—ление** *n.* expression.

изъян *m.* defect, flaw; shortcoming.

изъясн/ить, —ять *see* **объяснять.**

изъят/ие *n.* exception, exclusion, elimination, withdrawal; **—ый** *a.* excepted, excluded, omitted; **—ь** *v.* except, exclude; remove.

изымать *v.* eliminate, withdraw.

изыск/ание *n.* investigation, research; exploration, prospecting, survey; **делать —ания, производить —ания** survey; prospect; **—ать, —ивать** *v.* investigate, search for.

изэн— *see also* **изоэн—**.

изэнерга *f.* isoenergetic curve.

изэнтропа *f.* isentrope.

ИИЛ *abbr.* (**Издательство иностранной литературы**) Foreign Literature Press.

ИК *abbr.* (**инфракрасный**) infrared.

ИКМ *abbr.* (**импульсно-кодовая модуляция**) pulse code modulation (p.c.m.).

иконо/метр *m.* iconometer; **—скоп** *m.* iconoscope.

икосаэдр *m.* icosahedron; **—ический** *a.* icosahedral.

икоситетраэдр *m.* icositetrahedron.

икс *m.* x; **и.-единица** *f.* x-unit (xu); **и.-лучи** *pl.* x-rays.

иксиолит *m.* ixiolite.

иксо/бразный *a.* X-shaped; **—вая составляющая** x-component.

ИЛ *see* **ИИЛ.**

ил *m.* silt, mud, sludge.

илезит *m.* ilesite.

илеит *m.* ihleite.

илем *m.* (astr.) ylem.

или *conj.* or; **или . . . или** either . . . or.

илистый *a.* silty.

илл. *abbr.* (**иллюстратор**) illustrator; (**иллюстрация**) illustration.

иллиний *m.* illinium (Il).

иллиум *m.* illium.

иллюз/ия *f.* illusion; **—орный** *a.* illusory.

иллюмин/атор *m.* illuminator; **—ация** *f.* illumination; **—ированный** *a.* illuminated; **—ировать, —овать** *v.* illuminate; **—ометр** *m.* illuminometer.

иллюстр/атор *m.* illustrator; **—ация** *f.* illustration; **—ированный** *a.* illustrated; **—ировать** *v.* illustrate; **—ирующий** *a.* illustrative; illustrating.

ильменит *m.* ilmenite.

им. *abbr.* (**имени**) named after (*best rendered in translations by putting the name before the Institute, e.g., Baikov Institute of Metallurgy*).

ИМ *abbr.* (**Институт металлов**) Institute of Metals; (**импульсная модуляция**) pulse modulation.

им *instr. of* **он, оно,** (by) him, (with) it; *dat. of* **они,** (to) them.

ИМЕН *abbr.* (**Известия математических и естественных наук**) Bulletin of Mathematical and Natural Sciences.

именно *adv.* namely, to wit, that is, precisely, just; **а и.** notably; **и. когда** just when; **и. тогда** just then; **—й** *a.* nominal, name.

именов/ание *n.* naming, name, nomenclature; **—анный** *a.* named, called; **—анное число** denominate number; **—ать** *v.* name, call; designate.

ИМЕТ *abbr.* (**Институт металлургии**) Institute of Metallurgy.

иметь *v.* have, possess; **и. в виду** bear in mind; **и. дело с** be concerned with; **и. место** take place; **—ся** *v.* be, have, exist; **здесь имеется** here there is, here is; **у него имеется** he has.

имеющий *a.* having; **—ся** *a.* available, at hand.

ими *instr. of* **они,** (by) them.

имид *m.*, **—ный** *a.* imide.

имин *m.* imine.

имит/атор *m.* imitator, simulator; **и. реактора** pile simulator; **—ация** *f.*, **—ационный** *a.* imitation; **—ировать** *v.* imitate, copy.

имманентн/ость *f.* immanence; **—ый** *a.* immanent, inherent.

иммельман *m.* (aero.) Immelman turn.

иммерс/ионный *a.*, **—ия** *f.* immersion; **и. объектив** immersion objective; **—ионная линза** immersion lens.

иммобилиз/ация *f.* immobilization; **—ировать** *v.* immobilize; freeze (solution).

иммун/изация *f.*, **—изирование** *n.* immunization; **—изировать** *v.* immunize; **—итет** *m.* immunity; **—нентный** *a.* immune.

имп. *abbr.* (**импульс**) momentum, pulse, impulse.

импедан/с, —ц *m.* impedance; **и. излучения** radiation impedance.

импеллер *m.* impeller.

императив *m.*, **—ный** *a.* imperative.

импликац/ионный *a.* implication, implicational, implicative; **—ия** *f.* implication.

имплозия *f.* implosion.

импорт *m.* import, importation; **—ировать** *v.* import; **—ный** *a.* imported, import.

импульс *m.* momentum, pulse, impulse, surge; **и. напряжения** voltage (or potential) pulse; **и. отдачи** recoil momentum; **и. отметки** marking pulse, pip; **и. последствия** delayed pulse, afterpulse; **и. совпадения** coincidence pulse; **и. тока** current pulse; **и. управляющий пропусканием сигналов** gating pulse.

импульсивный *a.* impulsive.

импульсно *see also* **импульсо—; и.-модулированный** pulse-modulated.

импульсн/ый *a.* pulse, pulsed, impulsive; impulse, momentum; sampled (data); **и. генератор** pulse generator; **и. масс-спектрометр** pulse mass spectrometer; **—ая ионизационная камера** pulse ionization chamber; **—ая лампа** flash bulb (or lamp); **—ое освещение** intermittent light; **—ое представление** (quant.) momentum representation; **и. осциллоскоп** synchroscope; **и. разряд** impulsive discharge; **—ая газоразрядная лампа** flash-discharge tube; **—ое приближение** impulse approximation; **коэффициент —ого цикла** pulse duty factor.

импульсо/ванный *a.* pulsed; **—видный** *a.* pulselike, pulsed; **—заостряющий** *a.* pulse-sharpening; **—образующая схема** pulse-forming network, pulse shaper.

имуществ/енный *a.* property; **—о** *n* property, stock, goods; **опись —а** inventory.

им/я *n.* name; **и. числительное** numeral; **от —ени** on behalf (of).

ин. *abbr.* (**иностранный**) foreign.

инактивация *f.* inactivation.

иначе *adv.* otherwise, differently; alternatively, or else; **так или и.** in any case; in some way or other.

инвар Invar.

инвариант *m.* invariant; **—ная сумма** summational invariant; **—ность** *f.* invariance.

инверсионн/ый *a.* inversion; **и. барьер** inversion barrier; **и. слой** inversion layer; **и. спектр** inversion spectrum **—ая дымка** inversion mist; **—ая ось** rotation-inversion (or rotoinversion) axis; **—ое удвоение** inversion doubling.

инверс/ия *f.* inversion; **и. верхняя**

(meteor.) upper inversion; **и. влажности** humidity inversion; **и. времени** time inversion; **и. осадков** inversion of rainfall; **и. оседания** subsidence inversion; **и. приземная** ground inversion; **и. температуры** temperature inversion; **—ии оператор** space inversion (or parity) operator.

инверсн/о *adv.* inversely; **—ый** *a.* inverse.

инвертиров/ание *n.* inversion, inverting; **температура —ания** inversion point; **—анный** *a.* inverted; **—ать** *v.* invert.

инвертор *m.* inverter.

инволют/а *f.*, **—ный** *a.* involute.

ингибитор *m.* inhibitor.

Ингирами Inghirami (lunar crater).

ингредиент *m.* ingredient.

ингресс/ивный *a.* ingressive, entering; **—ия** *f.* ingression, entrance.

инд. *abbr.* (**индустрия**) industry; (**индустриальный**) industrial.

индаллой *m.* Indalloy.

Индеец Indus (Ind) (constellation).

индекс *m.* index, affix, subscript, superscript; **и. вверху** superscript; **и. внизу** subscript; **—ация** *f.* indexing; **—ный цикл** (meteor.) index cycle.

индентор *m.* indenter, indentor.

индетерминизм *m.* indeterminism.

индефинитная метрика indefinite metric.

индивид, —уум *m.* individual; **—уальность** *f.* individuality; **—уальный** *a.* individual, peculiar; independent; **—уальная производная** individual derivative.

индий *m.* indium (In).

индийский *a.* Indian.

индикатор *m.* indicator, display, gauge; (nucl.) tracer; **и. кругового обзора** (radar) plan position indicator (PPI); **химический и.** (chemical) tracer.

индикаторн/ый *a.* indicator, indicating; indicated; **и. механизм** indicating instrument, indicator; **—ая бумага** indicator paper, test paper; **—ая мощность** indicated power; **—ая трубка** indicator tube, display tube; **—ое количество** tracer amount, trace amount; **—ые часы** dial indicator.

индикатриса *f.* indicatrix; (characteristic) curve.

индикация *f.* indication, presentation.

индицирование *n.* indexing.

Индия India.

индукт/анц *m.*, **—ивность** *f.* inductance.

индуктивн/ый *a.* inductive; **—ое острие** (elec.) spray point; **—ое сопротивление** (elec.) inductive reactance; (hyd.) induced drag; **—ое сопротивление рассеяния** leakage reactance; **—ое торможение** (mag.) induction drag.

индуктир/ование *see* **индукция**; **—ованный** *a.* induced; **—овать** *v.* induce; **—ующий** *a.* inducing, inductive.

индукто— *prefix* inducto—, induction.

индукто/метр *m.* induction meter; **—р** *m.*, **—рный** *a.* inductor; magneto.

индукционн/ый *a.* induction, inductive; **и. ток** induced current; **и. ускоритель** induction accelerator; **—ая катушка** induction coil; **—ая электропечь** induction furnace; **—ые весы** induction balance.

индукциров/анный *see* **индуктированный**; **—ать** *see* **индуктировать.**

индукция *f.* induction; **и. движением** motional induction (of plasma); **и. насыщения** saturation induction; **и. на частном цикле** (mag.) incremental induction.

индустр. *abbr.* (**индустриальный**) industrial.

индустри/ализация *f.* industrialization; **—альный** *a.* industrial; **—я** *f.* industry.

инезит *m.* inesite.

иней *m.* hoarfrost.

инертн/ость *f.* inertia, inertness, inertance, sluggishness; **—ый** *a.* inert, inertial, inactive, passive; **—ый газ** inert gas; **—ый индикатор** nonradioactive tracer; **—ая масса** inert mass.

инерционн/ость *f.* inertia, time lag, rise time; time constant (of); **и. изображения** image persistence; **—ый** *a.* inertial; **—ая масса** inertial mass; **—ое свойство** inertial property.

инерц/ия *f.* inertia, inertness, lag; **и. зрительного восприятия** persistence of vision; **световая и.** afterglow; **момент —ии** moment of inertia; **снла —ии** inertia; **центь —ии** center of inertia, center of mass.

инж. *abbr.* (**инженер**) engineer; (**инженерный**) engineering.

инжектиров/анный *a.* injected.

инжек/тор *m.* injector; **и. струйный** jet injector; **—ционная оптика** injection optics; **—ция** *f.* injection; **—ция дырок** (semicond.) hole injection.

инженер *m.* engineer; **и.-геолог** geological engineer; **и.-гидравлик** hydraulic engineer; **и.-испытатель, и.-экспериментатор** testing engineer; **и.-исследователь** research engineer; **и.-конструктор** design engineer; **и.-консультант** consulting engineer; **и.-металлург** metallurgical engineer; **и.-механик** mechanical engineer; **и.-практик** practical engineer; **и.-радист** radio engineer; **и.-строитель** civil engineer; **и.-технолог** technological engineer; **и.-химик** chemical engineer; **и.-электрик** electrical engineer; **и.-энергетик** power engineer; **и.-ядерщик** nuclear engineer.

инженерн/ый *a.*, **—ое дело** engineering.

инж.-м. *abbr.* (**инженер-механик**) mechanical engineer.

инж.-т. *abbr.* (**инженер-технолог**) technological engineer.

инж.-х. *abbr.* (**инженер-химик**) chemical engineer.

инж.-эл. *abbr.* (**инженер-электрик**) electrical engineer.

иниоит *m.* inyoite.

инициал *m.* initial (letter).

инициат/ива *f.*, **—ивный** *a.* initiative; **—ор** *m.* initiator, pioneer.

инициирова/ние *n.* initiation; **—анный** *a.* initiated; **—ать** *v.* initiate; trigger; ignite.

инклин/атор *m.* dipping compass, dip needle, inclinometer; **—ометр** *m.* inclinometer.

инклюзия *f.* inclusion.

инконгруентный *a.* incongruent.

инкорпорация *f.* incorporation.

инкремент *m.* increment.

инкруст/ация *f.*, **—ирование** *n.* incrustation, scale, crust; inlay; **—ированный** *a.* incrusted; inlaid; **—ировать** *v.* incrust; inlay.

инкубац/ионный *a.*, **—ия** *f.* incubation.

ИННОРС *abbr.* (**Институт норм и стандартов строительной промышленности**) Institute of Norms and Standards for the Building Industry.

иновидный *a.* different.

иногда *adv.* sometimes.

иной *a.* different, other; some; **и. раз** *see* **иногда.**

инокул/ировать *v.* inoculate; **—яция** *f.* inoculation.

инообразный *see* **иновидный.**

инородный *a.* of different nature, foreign.

иностран/ец *m.* foreigner; **—ный** *a.* foreign.

инсеквентный *a.* insequent.

инсоляция *f.* insolation, solarization.

инспек/тирование *n.*, **—ция** *f.* inspection; **—тировать** *v.* inspect; **—тор** *m.* inspector; **—торский** *a.* inspectorial, inspection.

инспир/атор *m.* inspirator; respirator; **—ированный** *a.* inspired; **—ировать** *v.* inspire.

инсталляция *f.* installation.

инстинкт *m.* instinct; **—ивно** *adv.* instinctively; **—ивный** *a.* instinctive.

институт *m.* institute, institution.

инстр. *abbr.* (**инструктор**) instructor.

инструк/таж *m.* instructing; **—тировать** *v.* instruct, advise; **—тор** *m.* instructor; **—ционный** *a.* instruction; **—ция** *f.* instructions.

инструмент *m.* instrument, tool; set of tools; **комплект —ов, набор —ов** tool kit, set of tools.

инструментальн/ый *a.* instrumental, instrument, tool; **—ая доска** instrument board, dashboard; **—ая погрешность** instrumental error, index error; **—ая сталь** tool steel.

инструмент/альщик *m.* tool maker; **—одержатель** *m.* tool holder.

инст-т, ин-т *abbr.* (**институт**) institute.

интегр. *abbr.* (**интегральный**) integral, integrated.

интеграл *m.* integral; **и. действия** action integral; **общий и.** (math.) general solution; **и. ошибок** error function (or integral); **—ьно-показательная функция** exponential integral (function).

интегральн/ый *a.* integral, integrated; **и. свет** integrated light, white light; **и. фотометр** integrating photometer; **—ая величина** integral quantity; **—ая доза** integral dose; **—ая кривая** integral curve; **—ая показательная функция, —ая экспонента** exponential integral (function); **—ое исчисление** integral calculus; **—ое сечение** integrated cross section; **—ое уравнение** integral equation.

интегратор *m.* integrator; **и. ионного тока** ion current integrator; **—ный фотометр** *see* **интегральный фотометр.**

интеграф *m.* integraph.

интеграция *see* **интегрирование.**

интегрир/ование *n.* integration; **и. по частям** integration by parts; **—ованный** *a.* integrated; **—ованный поток** integrated neutron flux; **—овать** *v.* integrate; **—уемость** *f.* integrability; **—уемый** *a.* integrable; **—уемый в квадрате** quadratically integrable.

интегрирующ/ий *a.* integrating; **и. множитель** integrating factor; **—ая ионизационная камера** integrating ionization chamber; **—ая схема** integrating circuit.

интегродифференциальное уравнение integro-differential equation.

интеллигентный *a.* educated, cultured.

интенсивн/ость *f.* intensity, strength; rate; flux; **и. вихря** vortex strength; **и. деления** rate of fission; **и. дозы** dosage rate; **и. излучения** radiation intensity; **и. испускания** emission rate; **и. источника** source strength; **и. линии** (spect.) line strength; **и. нейтронов** neutron intensity; **и. потока излучения** radiation flux; **и. счета** counting rate; **и. трубки** (hyd.) tube strength; **и. частоты** frequency rate; **—ый** *a.* intensive, intense.

интенсиметр *m.* ratemeter.

интенсифи/катор *m.* intensifier; **—кация** *f.* intensification; **—цировать** *v.* intensify; **—цирующий экран** intensifying screen.

интервал *m.* interval, space, separation; range; **и. импульсов** momentum range; **и. повторения** recurrence interval; **и. пропорциональности** proportional region; **и. резонансной энергии** resonance energy region; **и. скоростей нейтронов** neutron velocity range; **и. тепловых энергий** thermal energy region; **и. экспозиций** range of exposures; **и. энергии** energy range; **правило —ов** interval rule; **—ометр** *m.* intervalometer.

интергранулярный *a.* intergranular.

интерес *m.*, **—овать** *v.* interest; **—но** *adv.* interestingly; it is interesting; **—но отметить** it is worth noting; **—ный** *a.* interesting, remarkable.

интеркомбинац/ионный переход intercombination transition; **—ионная линия** intercombination line; **—ия** *f.* intercombination.

интер/металлический *a.* intermetallic; **—миттирующий** *a.* intermittent; **—национальный** *a.* international.

интерпол/ирование *n.*, **—яция** *f.* interpolation; **и. назад** regressive interpolation; **—ировать** *v.* interpolate; **—яционный генератор** interpolation oscillator.

интерпрет/ация *f.* interpretation; **—ировать** *v.* interpret, explain.

интерсертальный *a.* (geo.) intersertal.

интерференц/иальный, —ионный, —ированный *a.* interference; **—ионный член** interference term; **—ионная полоса** interference fringe; **—ионное сопротивление** (hyd.) interference drag; **—ионные помехи** beat interference; **—ионные цвета** interference colors; **—ия** *f.* interference, interfering.

интерфер/ировать *v.* interfere; **—ограмма** *f.* interferogram, interference pattern.

интерферометр *m.* interferometer; **—ический** *a.* interferometer, interferometric.

интерцептор *m.* interceptor; (elec.) chopper.

интродукция *f.* introduction.
интру/дировать *v.* intrude; **—зивный** *a.* intrusive; **—зия** *f.* intrusion.
интуи/тивный *a.* intuitive, visualizable; **—ция** *f.* intuition.
инфильтр/ат *m.* infiltrate; **—ация** *f.* infiltration, seepage.
инфинитезимальный *a.* infinitesimal.
инфлектор *m.* inflector.
инфлюэнт/а *f.*, **—ная линия** influence line.
инфляция *f.* inflation.
информ. *abbr. see* **информационный.**
информационный *a.*, **—ия** *f.* information.
инфразвук *m.* subsonics; **—овой** *a.* infrasonic, subsonic, subaudio.
инфракрасн/ый *a.* infrared; **и. телескоп** infrared telescope; **—ая спектроскопия** infrared spectroscopy; **—ая часть спектра** infrared spectrum, dark heat; **—ое излучение** infrared radiation; **длинноволновая часть —ой области** far infrared; **—ые лучи** infrared rays.
инфрахроматический *a.* (phot.) infrared.
инфузия *f.* infusion.
инфундировать *v.* infuse.
инъ/екция *f.* injection; **—ецировать** *v.* inject.
ИОАН *abbr.* (**Институт океанологии Академии наук СССР**) Institute of Oceanography of the Academy of Sciences, USSR.
иоганнит *m.* johannite.
Иогансона плитки Johansson gauge blocks.
иод *m.* iodine (I).
иод— *prefix* iod—, iodo—.
иодат *m.* iodate.
иод/идный *a.* iodide; **—ирование** *n.* iodination, iodization.
иодирит *m.* iodyrite.
иодист/ый *a.* iodine, iodous, (lower or —ous) iodide (of); **и. литий** lithium iodide; **и. натрий** sodium iodide; **—ая медь** cuprous iodide.
иодный *a.* iodine, (higher or —ic) iodide (of).
иодо— *prefix* iodo—; iodoxy—.
иодозо— *prefix* iodoso—.
иодокси— *prefix* iodoxy—.
иодциан *m.* iodocyanogen.
ион *m.* ion; **и. молекулярный** ion ionized molecule; **и. отдачи** recoi ion; **передвижение —ов, перено —ов** ion migration; **—изатор** *m* ionizer.
ионизационн/ый *a.* ionization, ionizing **и. импульс** ionization pulse; **и манометр** ionization gauge, io gauge; **и. потенциал** ionization po tential; **и. спектрометр** ionizatio spectrometer; **и. счетчик** ionizatio counter; **и. ток** ionization current **и. ток насыщения** saturation io current; **и. толчок** ionization burst **—ая камера** ionization chamber **—ая камера с воздушной стенко** air-wall ionization chamber; **—а камера с сеткой** grid (or gridded ionization chamber; **—ая способ ность** ionizing power; **—ая энерги** ionizing energy; **—ое давление** ion ization pressure; **—ое усиление** ga amplification; **—ые потери** ionizatio loss.
ионизац/ия *f.* ionization; **и. излуче нием** radiation ionization; **и. колон нами** columnar ionization; **и. столк новением** ionization by collisio **коэффициент —ии** ionization c efficient; **линейный коэффициен —ии** specific ionization coefficien **постоянная —ии** ionization co stant; **теплота —ии** heat of ioniz tion.
ионизир/ованный *a.* ionized; **и. ато** ionized atom, atomic ion; **—овать** ionize; **—уемый** *a.* ionizable.
ионизирующ/ий *a.* ionizing; **—ая сп собность** ionizing capacity; **—а частица** ionizing particle; **— столкновение** ionizing collisio **—ийся** *see* **ионизируемый.**
ионизующий *see* **ионизирующий.**
ионий *m.* ionium (Io).
ионит *m.* ion exchanger, ionite.
ионно/сть *f.* ionicity; **—фокусирова ный пучок** ion-focused beam.
ионн/ый *a.* ionic, ion; **и. заряд** ion charge; **и. источник** ion source; **и. микр кристалл** ionic crystal; **и. микр скоп** ion microscope; **и. насос** i pump; **и. обмен** ion exchange;

остов ion core; **и. пучок** ion beam; **и. смеситель** gas mixer; **и. ток** ion current; **и. фотоэлемент** gas phototube; **и. электровакуумный прибор** *see* **газоразрядный электровакуумный прибор.**

ионн/ый *cont.* **—ая колонка** ion column; **—ая ловушка** ion trap; **—ая оболочка** ion sheath; **—ая орбита** ion orbit; **—ая плазма** ion plasma; **—ая подвижность** ionic mobility; **—ая проводимость** ionic conductivity; **—ая связь** ionic link (or bond); **—ая сила** ionic strength; **—ое облако** ion cloud; **—ое пятно** ion spot (or burn); **—ое соединение** ionic compound; **—ое усиление** gas amplification.

ионоген *m.* ionogen.

ионо/колориметр *m.* ionocolorimeter; **—люминесценция** *f.* ionoluminescence; **—метр** *m.* ionometer.

ионообменн/ая колонна ion-exchange column; **и. смола** ion-exchange resin; **—ик** *m.* ion exchanger.

ионо/пауза *f.* ionopause; **—ракета** *f.* ion rocket; **—собирающий** *a.* ion-collecting.

ионосфер/а *f.* ionosphere; **—ный** *a.* ionospheric; **—ная волна** ionospheric wave, sky wave.

ионотрон *m.* ionotron.

ионофон *m.* ionophone.

Йонсена правило Jönsson rule (x-rays).

ионструпит *m.* johnstrupite.

ионтофорез *m.* iontophoresis.

ИОНХ *abbr.* [**Институт общей и неорганической химии (им. Н. С. Курнакова)**] N. S. Kurnakov Institute of General and Inorganic Chemistry.

Иоос Joos.

иорданит *m.* jordanite.

иорданская вязкость (mag.) Jordan lag.

ИОХАН *abbr.* (**Институт органической химии Академии наук СССР**) Institute of Organic Chemistry of the Academy of Sciences, USSR.

ИПГ *abbr.* (**Институт прикладной геофизики**) Institute of Applied Geophysics.

и пр. *abbr.* (**и прочее**) and so forth, etc.

ипсомская соль Epsom salts.

ИПФ *abbr.* (**Институт прикладной физики**) Institute of Applied Physics.

ИРЕА *abbr.* (**Институт химических реактивов**) Institute of Chemical Reagents.

иридесценция *f.* iridescence.

иридиевый *a.* iridium, iridic.

иридизация *see* **иридесценция.**

иридий *m.* iridium (Ir).

иридирующий *a.* iridescent.

иризация *f.* irisation; iridescence.

иринит *m.* irinite.

ирис *m.* iris; **—овая диафрагма** (phot.) iris diaphragm.

Ирншоу теорема Earnshaw theorem.

ИРПА *abbr.* (**Институт радиовещательного приема и акустики**) Institute of Radio Broadcasting and Acoustics.

ирради/ация, —яция *f.* irradiation.

иррациональный *a.* irrational.

иррегулярный *a.* irregular, uneven.

ирриг/атор *m.* irrigator; **—ация** *f.*, **—ационный** *a.* irrigation; **—ированный** *a.* irrigated; **—ировать** *v.* irrigate.

ируптивный *a.* irruptive.

ИСЗ *abbr.* (**искусственный спутник Земли**) artificial earth satellite.

Исидор Isidorus (lunar crater).

искаж/ать *v.* distort, deform, spoil; **—ающий** *a.* distorting.

искажен/ие *n.*, **—ность** *f.* distortion, deformation; **и. поля** field distortion; **коэффициент —ия** distortion factor; **поверхность наименьшего —ия** (opt.) surface of least confusion; **—ный** *a.* distorted; **—ный спектр** distorted spectrum.

исказить *see* **искажать.**

искатель *m.* probe, searcher; selector, locator, finder; view finder; scanner; **—ный** *a.* searching; **—ная катушка** search coil; **—ная трубка** (opt.) object finder.

искать *v.* search, seek, hunt.

исключ/ать *v.* exclude, except, deduct; eliminate; **—ающий** *a.* excluding; **взаимно —ающий** conflicting; **—ая** except, excluding.

исключен/ие *n.* exclusion, exception; elimination; **и. фона** background cancellation; **за —ием** with the exception of; **принцип —ия** exclusion principle; **—ный** *a.* excluded, excepted; eliminated.

исключительн/о *adv.* exceptionally; exclusively, solely; remarkably; **—ый** *a.* exceptional, unusual, excellent; exclusive; **—ая видимость** excellent visibility.

исключить *see* **исключать.**

иском/ый *a.* sought, desired, required, unknown; **—ая величина, —ое число** unknown (or sought) quantity.

ископаем/ое *n.*, **—ый** *a.* mineral, fossil; **полезное и.** mineral; **—ый лед** fossil ice.

ископать *v.* dig up.

искорен/ение *n.* uprooting, eradication; **—ить, —ять** *v.* uproot, eradicate.

искорка *f.* scintillation.

искр/а *f.* spark, flash; **зажигание —ой** spark ignition; **зажигательная и.** ignition spark; **—ение** *n.* sparking, flashing; arcing.

искренн/ий, —ый *a.* sincere.

искрив/ившийся *see* **искривленный**; **—ить** *see* **искривлять.**

искривл/ение *n.* bend, curve, flexure; twisting, warpage, distortion, deformation; **коэффициент —ения рупора** flare factor; **—енный** *a.* bent, curved; twisted, distorted; **—енный кристалл** curved crystal; **—ять** *v.* bend, curve; twist.

искр/истый *a.* scintillating; **—ить, —иться** *v.* spark; flash, scintillate.

искров/ой *a.* spark; **и. промежуток** spark gap; **и. разряд** spark discharge; **и. разрядник** spark gap; **и. спектр** spark spectrum; **и. счетчик** spark counter; **—ое перекрытие** sparkover.

искрогаситель *m.*, **—ное устройство** spark arrester; spark killer, blow-out; **—ный** *a.* spark-extinguishing, blow-out; **—ная катушка** (elec.) blow-out coil.

искро/гашение, —тушение *n.* spark extinguishing, blow-out; **—мер** *m.* scintillometer; **—образование** *n.* spark formation, sparking; **—стойкий** *a.* nonsparking, nonarcing; **—тушитель** *see* **—гаситель**; **—удержатель** *m.* spark arrester; **—указатель** *m.* spark detector.

искряк *m.* aventurine.

искрящий *a.* sparking; **—ся** *a.* sparkling, scintillating.

искусный *a.* expert, skillful, clever, ingenious.

искусственн/о созданные условия simulated conditions; **—ый** *a.* artificial; synthetic; **—ый изотоп** artificial isotope; **—ый каучук** synthetic rubber; **—ый спутник** artificial satellite; **—ая линия** (elec.) artificial line; **—ая радиоактивность** artificial radioactivity, induced radioactivity; **—ое воздействие на погоду** weather control; **—ое превращение** artificial transmutation.

искусство *n.* art, craft; skill, proficiency adaptness, craftsmanship.

ИСЛ *abbr.* (**искусственный спутник Луны**) artificial moon satellite.

исландск/ий шпат Iceland spar, calcite **—ая депрессия** Icelandic low.

испан. *abbr.* (**испанский**) Spanish.

Испания Spain.

испанский *a.* Spanish.

испарен/ие *n.* evaporation, vaporization; vapor, fume; **—ный** *a.* evaporated, vaporized, volatilized.

испаривать *see* **испарить.**

испаритель *m.* evaporator, vaporizer (meteor.) evaporimeter, atmometer **—ный** *a.* evaporative; **—ная способность** evaporative capacity, volatility; **—ная центрифуга** evaporative centrifuge.

испар/ить, —иться, —ять, —яться *v* evaporate, vaporize, volatilize, fume **—яемость** *f.* evaporability, vaporizability, volatility; **—яемый** *a.* volatile; **—яющий** *a.* evaporating, vaporizing.

испепел/ение *n.* incineration; **—ить —ять** *v.* incinerate.

испещренный *a.* speckled, mottled.

исподволь *adv.* gradually.

исполн/ение *n.* accomplishment, fulfillment, execution, observance, completion; **—енный** *a.* accomplished fulfilled, complete; **—имость** *f.* feasibility, practicability; **—имый** *a* feasible, practicable.

исполнитель *m.* performer, executor; **—ный** *a.* performing, operating; **—ный механизм** slave mechanism (of manipulator); **—ный элемент системы управления** final control element, actuator.

исполн/ить, —ять *v.* execute, fulfill, carry out, perform; **—яющий** *a.* fulfilling, carrying out; deputy.

использов/ание *n.* utilization, use, employment; recovery, salvaging (of waste); **и. атомной энергии в мирных целях** peaceful uses of atomic energy; **коэффициент —ания тепловых нейтронов** thermal utilization factor; **коэффициент полезного —ания нейтронов** neutron economy; **процент —ания** recovery; efficiency; **—анный** *a.* used, utilized, consumed, spent; **—анное тепло** absorbed heat; **—ать** *v.* use, utilize; take advantage of.

испорошковывать *v.* pulverize, reduce to a powder.

испор/тить *v.* spoil, injure, damage; **—ченность** *f.* defectiveness; **—ченный** *a.* spoiled; injured, damaged, faulty.

испр. *abbr.* [**исправленное (издание)**] revised (edition).

исправ/имый *a.* remediable, rectifiable, corrigible; **—ительный** *a.* corrective; **—ить, —лять** *v.* correct, adjust, rectify, repair, amend, revise; **—иться, —ляться** *v.* improve; **—ление** *n.* correction, adjustment, rectification, fixing, revision; improvement; **—ленный** *a.* corrected, adjusted, fixed, repaired, revised; improved.

исправляющ/ий *a.* correcting; **и. пульсатор** regenerative pulser; **и. строб** regenerative gate; **—ая линза** correcting lens; **—ая пусковая схема** regenerative trigger circuit.

исправн/ость *f.* exactness; soundness, working order; **в полной —ости** in good working order; **—ый** *a.* exact, accurate; serviceable, in good working order; **—ое состояние** working order.

испр. и доп. изд. *abbr.* (**исправленное и дополненное издание**) revised and enlarged edition.

испробовать *v.* try, test.

испускаемый *a.* ejected, emitted.

испускание *n.* emission, emanation, ejection; emergence; **и. альфа-частиц** alpha-particle emission; **и. бета-лучей** beta-ray emission; **и. пары** pair emission; **и. позитронов** positron emission; **и. термоэлектронов** thermionic emission.

испуск/атель *m.* emitter; **—ательная способность** radiative capacity, emissive power; **—ать** *v.* emit, eject; **—аться** *v.* emerge; emanate; **—ающий** *a.* emitting, emissive, radiating.

испустить *see* **испускать.**

испыл/енный *a.* pulverized, pulverulent; **—ять** *v.* pulverize.

испытание *n.* test, checking; sampling; trial, experiment; assay; examination; **и. без разрушения** nondestructive testing; **и. в работе, и. в эксплоатации** field test, plant test; **и. в рабочих условиях** performance test; **и. длительное** endurance test; **летное и.** flight test; **и. массы, и. на объем** bulk test (of reactor shielding); **наземное и.** ground test; **и. на износ** abrasion test; **и. на модели** model test; **и. на разрыв, и. на растяжение** tensile test; **и. на скалывание, и. на срез** shearing test; **и. на скручивание** torsional test; **и. на усталость при колебательных усилиях** repeated stress test; **и. на усталость при повторных ударах** repeated impact test; **и. трением** friction test.

испыт/анный *a.* tested, tried, examined; **—атель** *m.* tester.

испытательн/ый *a.* test, testing, experimental; **и. кран** try cock; **и. полигон** proving ground; **и. прибор** tester, testing device; **и. реактор** test reactor; **и. стол** laboratory bench; **и. центр** testing center; **—ая катушка** exploring coil, test coil; **—ая таблица** test chart; **—ая установка** experimental plant, pilot plant.

испыт/ать *see* **испытывать**; **—уемый, —ующий** *see* **испытательный.**

испытыв/аемый *a.* test, tested, under test; **—ать** *v.* test, try; investigate, examine; assay; undergo; experience; **—ать на** test for.

исслед. *abbr.* (**исследовательский**) research, investigation.

исследован/ие *n.* investigation, research, study, survey; exploration; examination, analysis; **и. методом меченых атомов** tracer study; **производить и.** investigate; survey; **—ный** *a.* investigated, studied, examined, tested.

исследователь *m.* investigator, researcher; explorer; **—ский** *a.* research, investigation, exploratory; **—ский реактор** research reactor.

исслед/овать *v.* investigate, examine, study, analyze; search, explore; try, test; (met.) assay; **—уемый** *a.* in question; **—уемое вещество** experimental material.

иссуш/ать, —ить *v.* dry out, shrink, scorch.

иссякать *v.* dry up, exhaust, run dry, run low.

истекать *v.* elapse; flow out.

истер/еть *see* **истирать**; **—тый** *a.* worn, abraded.

истеч/ение *n.* outflow, efflux, discharge; emanation, emission, escape (of gas); expiration; **и. времени** lapse of time; **диаграмма —ения** effluogram; **—ь** *see* **истекать.**

истина *f.* truth.

истинн/ый *a.* true, actual; **и. горизонт** true (or celestial) horizon; **—ая аномалия** true anomaly; **—ая масса ядра** true nuclear mass; **—ая светимость** intrinsic luminosity; **—ое время** apparent (or true) solar time; **—ое поглощение** true absorption; **—ые сутки** apparent (or true) solar day.

истир/аемость *f.* wearability; **—ание** *n.* pulverizing; wear, attrition, abrasion; erosion; **—атель** *m.* pulverizer; abrasive; **—ать** *v.* crush, pulverize; wear down, abrade; erode; **—ающий** *a.*, **—ающее вещество** abrasive.

Истмэна фильм Eastman film.

исток *m.* outflow, source, headwater.

истолков/ание *n.* interpretation; **—атель** *m.* interpreter; **—ательный** *a.* explanatory; **—ать, —ывать** *v.* interpret.

истол/очь *v.* pound, crush; **—ченный** *a.* pounded, crushed.

истонит *m.* eastonite.

истопить *v.* melt, smelt; heat.

истор/ик *m.* historian; **—ический** *a.* historic, historical; **—ия** *f.* history.

источ/ать, —ить *v.* shed; spill.

источник *m.* source, origin; spring; principle; **и. движения** prime mover; **отрицательный и.** negative source; **и.-пара** doublet, double source; **и. питания** power supply; **положительный и.** positive source; **и. света** light source; **и. сеточного смещения** grid-voltage supply; **и. тепла** heat source; **и. энергии** source of energy, power source.

истощ/ать *v.* exhaust, deplete; **—ение** *n.* exhaustion, depletion; **—енный** *a.* exhausted, depleted; **—енное вещество** depleted material.

истреб/ить, —лять *v.* destroy, annihilate; **—ление** *n.* destruction, annihilation.

истый *a.* true, thorough.

ИСФХА АН СССР *abbr.* (**Известия сектора физико-химического анализа Академии наук СССР**) Bulletin of the Division of Physico-Chemical Analysis of the Academy of Sciences, USSR.

исход *m.* outcome, result; end; **—ить** *v.* issue, proceed from, originate; **—я из** on the basis of, in terms of; **—я из этого** hence.

исходн/ый *a.* original, initial, parent; reference; **и. материал, —ое сырье** charge material; starting material, raw material, source material; **и. меридиан** first (or prime) meridian; **и. продукт** original substance, starting (raw, feed) material; **и. пункт, —ая точка** reference point, starting point, point of departure; **и. элемент** parent element; **—ая координата** reference coordinate; **—ая линия** reference line, datum line, line of departure; **—ая ось** reference axis; **—ая плоскость** reference plane; **—ая частица** progenitor; **—ая фракция** parent fraction; **—ое вещество**

initial product, raw material, parent substance; **—ое деление** original fission; **—ое направление** reference direction; **—ое положение** initial position, starting point; **—ое состояние** initial state; **—ое ядро** original nucleus, parent nucleus; **—ые данные** initial (or input) data.

исходящий *a.* issuing, emergent, outgoing; **и. номер** reference number; **и. поток жидкости** effluent.

исчез/ать, —нуть *v.* disappear, vanish, fade away; **—ающий** *a.* disappearing, vanishing; **—ающая деформация** elastic deformation; **—новение** *n.* disappearance, fade-out, loss.

исчерп/ание *n.* exhaustion; **—ывать** *v.* exhaust; **—ывающий** *a.* exhaustive, comprehensive.

исчер/тить, —чивать *v.* streak, cover with lines; **—ченный** *a.* streaked, striated.

исчисл/ение *n.* calculation, computation; calculus; **и. бесконечно малых** infinitesimal calculus; **дифференциальное и.** differential calculus; **—енный** *a.* calculated, estimated; **—ить, —ять** *v.* calculate, compute.

исштрихованный *a.* streaked, striated.

и-т *see* **инст-т.**

ит. *abbr.* (**итальянский**) Italian.

ИТА *abbr.* (**Институт теоретической астрономии Академии наук СССР**) Institute of Theoretical Astronomy of the Academy of Sciences, USSR.

итак *conj.* thus, so.

Италия Italy.

итальянский *a.* Italian.

и т. д. *abbr.* (**и так далее**) and so forth, etc.

итер/ационный *a.* iteration, iterational; **и. метод** iteration method; **—ация** *f.* iteration; **—ированный** *a.* iterated.

итог *m.* sum, total; **в —е** to sum up, finally, ultimately; **в конечном —е** finally, as the final result; **—и** *pl.* results, returns; **подводить —и** sum up; **—о** *adv.* altogether, total; **—овый** *a.* total, resultant; concluding.

и т. п. *abbr.* (**и тому подобное**) and so forth, and the like.

итр *abbr.* (**инженерно-технический работник**) technician.

ИТС *abbr.* (**Инженерно-техническая секция**) Engineering-Technical Section; (**Инженерно-техническая служба**) Engineering-Technical Service.

иттербий *m.* ytterbium (Yb).

итти *see* **идти.**

иттр/иалит *m.* yttrialite; **—иевый шпат** xenotime; **—ий** *m.* yttrium (Y or Yt).

иттро/гуммит *m.* yttrogummite; **—кразит** *m.* yttrocrasite; **—сфен** *m.* yttrosphene; **—танталит** *m.* yttrotantalite; **—эрзит** *m.* yttroersite.

ИТЭФ *abbr.* (**Институт теоретической и экспериментальной физики**) Institute of Theoretical and Experimental Physics.

ИФ *abbr.* (**Институт физики**) Institute of physics.

ИФАК *abbr.* (**Международная федерация по автоматическому управлению**) International Federation of Automatic Control.

ИФП *abbr.* (**Институт физических проблем**) Institute for Physical Problems.

ИФХА *abbr.* (**Институт физико-химического анализа**) Institute of Physico-Chemical Analysis.

ИФХИ *abbr.* (**Институт физических и химических исследований**) Institute of Physical and Chemical Research.

их *gen. and acc. of* **они,** their, them.

ИХС *abbr.* (**Институт химии силикатов**) Institute of Silicate Chemistry.

ИХФ *abbr.* (**Институт химической физики**) Institute of Chemical Physics.

ишикаваит *m.* ishikawaite.

июль *m.* July.

июнь *m.* June.

К

к *prep. dat.* to; toward; by; for; **к тому времени** by then; **к тому же** besides, moreover.

к *abbr.* (**кило**) kilo—; (**кулон**) coulomb; **к.** (**копейка**) kopeck.

К [*in steel mark* (**кобальт**)] cobalt (Co).

К *abbr.* (**Каучук**) Caoutchouc (journal).

К° *abbr.* (**компания**) company (Co.).

ка *abbr.* (**килоампер**) kiloampere (ka).

Кабанн Cabannes.

кабанчик *m.* cabane.

Кабардино-Балкарская АССР Kabardinian-Balkar ASSR.

кабель *m.*, **—ный** *a.* cable; **—тов** *m.* cable length (608 ft.); hawser.

кабин/а, —ка *f.* cabin, cab, booth, cage, car.

кабл/ировать *v.* cable; **—ограмма** *f.* cablegram, cable.

кабрерит *m.* cabrerite.

кабрирование *n.* (aero.) pitching.

Кавалерий Cavalerius (lunar crater).

Кавендиш Cavendish (lunar crater).

Кавендиша опыт Cavendish experiment.

каверн/а *f.* cavern; vesicle, pocket; cavity; **—озный** *a.* cavernous, porous, vesicular; **—озная вода** (geo.) interstitial water.

кавитац/ионный *a.*, **—ия** *f.* cavitation; **к. взрыв** cavitation burst; **коэффициент —ии** (reactor) void coefficient.

кавычки *pl.* quotation marks.

кадастр *m.* cadastre, cadastral survey, inventory; **к. водный** inventory of water resources; **—овый** *a.* cadastral.

кадмиев/ый *a.* cadmium; **к. затвор** cadmium shutter; **к. коэффициент, —ое отношение** cadmium ratio; **к. регулятор** cadmium regulator; **к. стержень** cadmium rod; **—ая обманка** greenockite; **—ая полоса** cadmium strip.

кадмий *m.* cadmium (Cd).

кадмиров/ание *n.* cadmium plating; **—анный** *a.* cadmium-plated; **—ать** *v.* plate with cadmium.

кадр *m.* (phot., telev.) frame; **к. изображения** (telev.) picture area; **—овый период** frame period; **—овая синхронизация** vertical synchronization; **—овая частота** frame frequency.

кадры *pl.* personnel.

каем/ка *see* **кайма**; **—чатый** *a.* bordered.

каждо/годно *adv.* annually, every year; **—дневно** *adv.*, **—дневный** *a.* daily.

каждый *a.* each, every; *pron.* everyone.

кажется it seems, it appears; *see also* **казаться.**

кажущ/ийся *a.* seeming, apparent; **к. период полураспада** apparent half-life; **—аяся звездная величина** apparent stellar magnitude; **—аяся магнитная проницаемость** apparent permeability; **—аяся мощность** apparent power; **—ееся сопротивление** impedance; **—ееся удельное сопротивление** apparent resistivity.

казалось бы it would appear.

Казат Casatus (lunar crater).

казаться *v.* seem, appear.

Казахская ССР Kazakh SSR.

казенный *a.* government, state, public; fiscal.

Казимир Casimir.

казна *f.* treasury.

казолит *m.* kasolite.

Каз ССР *abbr. see* **Казахская ССР.**

Кайетэ/-Матиаса закон Cailletet and Mathias law; **К. трубка** C. tube.

кайзер *m.* kayser (cm^{-1}).

кайзерит *m.* kayserite.

кайл/а *f.*, **—овый** *a.* pick, pickax, hack.

кайма *f.* border, edge, rim.

кайнозит *m.* kainosite.

кайнозой *m.* (geo.) Cenozoic era; **—ский** *a.* Cenozoic.

как *adv. and conj.* how, as, like, as well as; **к. будто, к. бы** as if, as though; **к. бы ни** however, no matter how; **к. видно** as is evident; **к. если бы** as if; **к. известно** as is well known; **к. и следовало ожидать** as was to be expected; **к. например** as, such as, for instance; **к. ни** however; **к.-нибудь** somehow; **к. правило** as a rule; **к.-раз** exactly, just; **к. . . ., так и** both . . . and; **к. таковой** as such

к.-то somehow; once; **к. только** as soon as.

каков *pron. and a.* what kind of(?) what(?)

какой *a.* what(?) which(?); **к.-либо, к.-нибудь** some, any; **к.-то** some kind of.

какоксенит *m.* cacoxenite.

кал *abbr.* (**калория**) calorie.

калаверит *m.* calaverite.

каландр *m.*, **—овый** *a.* calender.

каледонит *m.* caledonite.

калейдоскоп *m.* kaleidoscope; **—ический** *a.* kaleidoscopic.

календар/ь *m.*, **—ный** *a.* calendar; **—ное число** date.

кален/ие *n.* incandescence, heating; **белое к.** white heat; **красное к.** red heat; **—ый** *a.* red hot, heated to redness.

калесценция *f.* calescence.

калибер *see* **калибр**; **—ный** *a.* caliber, gauge; **—ная дощечка** template; **—ная плитка** gauge block.

калибр *m.* caliber, gauge, bore; **выдвижной к., раздвижной к.** slide gauge, vernier caliper; **к.-кольцо** ring gauge, plug gauge; **к.-пробка** internal gauge, plug gauge; **к.-скоба** caliper gauge.

калибр/атор *m.* calibrator, calibrating source; **—ирование** *n.*, **—ировка** *f.*, **—ование** *n.*, **—овка** *f.* calibration, standardization; gauge, gauging; **—ированный, —ованный** *a.* calibrated, gauged, graduated, standardized; **—ировать, —овать** *v.* calibrate, gauge, graduate, standardize; **—ирующий** *a.* calibrating.

калибровочн/о-инвариантный gauge-invariant; **—ый** *a.* caliber, calibration; **—ая инвариантность** gauge invariance; **—ая кривая** calibration plot; **—ая отметка** marker pip; **—ое преобразование** (math.) gauge transformation.

калибромер *m.* gauge.

калиев/ый *a.* potassium, potash; **к. маргарит** potash margarite; **к. полевой шпат, к. шпат** potash feldspar, orthoclase; **—ая слюда** potash mica.

калий *m.* potassium (K); **двухромовокислый к.** potassium bichromate; **железистосинеродистый к.** potassium ferricyanide; **иодистый к.** potassium iodide; **марганцевокислый к.** potassium permanganate; **метабисульфит к.** potassium metabisulfite; **углекислый к.** potassium carbonate.

калильн/ый *a.* incandescent, glowing; heating; **к. жар** red heat, glowing heat; **к. катод** hot cathode; **к. свет** incandescent light; **к. ящик** annealing box; **—ая головка** ignition chamber; **—ая лампа** incandescent lamp; **—ая печь** annealing furnace; **—ая сетка** incandescent mantle; **—ое свечение** candoluminescence.

калиофилит *m.* kaliophilite.

Калипп Calippus (lunar crater).

калитомсонит *m.* kalithompsonite.

калить *v.* incandesce, heat up.

калифорн/ий *m.* californium (Cf); **—ит** *m.* californite.

каллаинит *m.* callainite.

каллиротрон *m.* kallirotron.

Каллье коэффициент Callier quotient.

калмаллой *m.* Calmalloy (nickel-copper-iron alloy).

Калмыцкая АССР Kalmuck ASSR.

каломель *f.* calomel, mercurous chloride.

калоресценция *f.* caloresсence.

калориз/атор *m.* calorizer; **—ация** *f.*, **—ирование** *n.* calorization; **—ировать** *v.* calorize.

калорийн/ое топливо caloric fuel; **—ость** *f.* caloricity.

калориметр *m.* calorimeter; **—ирование** *n.* calorimetric measurement; **—ический** *a.* calorimetric, calorific; **—ическая бомба** calorimetric bomb; **—ия** *f.* calorimetry.

калорифер *m.* air heater.

калорическ/ий *a.* caloric, calorific; **к. двигатель** hot-air engine; **—ое значение** calorific value.

калория *f.* calorie; **большая к., техническая к.** large calorie, kilocalorie; **малая к.** small calorie.

калушит *m.* kaluszite.

кальвонигрид *m.* calvonigrite.

кальдера *f.* (geo.) caldera.

кальдерит *m.* calderite.

калька *f.* tracing cloth, tracing paper; **бумажная к.** tracing paper; **полотняная к.** tracing cloth.

калькиров/ание *n.* tracing; calking; **—анный** *a.* traced; calked; **—ать** *v.* trace; calk.

калько— *see* **халько—**.

кальковскин *m.* kalkowskyn, kalkowskite.

калькул/ировать *v.* calculate, estimate; **—ятор** *m.* calculator; **—яционный** *a.* calculation, calculating; **—яция** *f.* calculation.

кальци— *prefix* calci—.

кальций *m.* calcium (Ca).

кальциметр *m.* calcimeter.

кальцин/ация *f.*, **—ирование** *n.* calcination, roasting; **—ированный** *a.* calcined, roasted; **—ировать** *v.* calcine, roast.

кальцио— *prefix* calcio—.

кальци/оторит *m.* calciothorite; **—т** *m.* calcite, Iceland spar; **—фикация** *f.* calcification.

калютрон *m.* calutron.

камарецит *m.* kamarezite.

камасит *m.* kamacite.

камедь *f.* gum.

камен/еть *v.* petrify, harden; **—истый** *a.* stony, rocky.

каменноугольн/ый *a.* coal, carboniferous; *see also* **угольный**; **к. газ** coal gas; **к. деготь, —ая смола** coal tar.

каменн/ый *a.* stone, stony, lithoidal; **к. метеорит** stony meteorite; **к. мозг** lithomarge; **к. подшипник** jewel bearing; **к. уголь** (bituminous) coal, *see also* **уголь**; **—ая кладка** masonry; **—ая соль** sodium chloride, rock salt.

камено— *see* **камне—**; **—ломня** *f.* quarry.

камень *m.* stone; jewel.

камера *f.* chamber, cell, compartment; cavity; room, office; (phot.) camera; inner tube (of tire); **к. давления** pressure vessel; **к. деления** fission chamber; **к. искусственного климата** climatic chamber; **конденсационная к.** cloud chamber; **к. магнита** magnet chamber; **к. облучения** exposure cell, radiation chamber; **к.-обскура** pinhole camera, camera obscura; **перчаточная к.** glove box; **к.-регистратор** monitor chamber; **к. сжатия** compression chamber; **к. слива** overflow chamber; **спаренная к.** twin chamber; **к. с плоскими параллельными электродами** parallel-plate chamber; **к. столкновений** collision chamber, target gas chamber; **к. уноса** entrainment chamber; **к. шлюза** lock chamber; **экспериментальная к.** (reactor) experimental cavity.

камеральная обработка office studies.

Камерлинг-Оннес Kammerlingh-Onnes.

камерный *a.* chamber, compartment.

камертон *m.*, **—ный** *a.* tuning fork; **—ный вибратор** (rad.) tuning fork oscillator.

камне/бурильный *a.* rock drilling; **—видный** *a.* stony, lithoidal; **—дробилка** *f.* stone crusher, rock crusher; **—печатание** *n.* lithography; **—печатный** *a.* lithographed, lithographic.

камора *f.* chamber; **зарядная к.** charge chamber.

Кампан Campanus (lunar crater).

кампания *f.* operating period, run; campaign.

Кампанский век Campanian stage.

кампилит *m.* campylite.

камселлит *m.* camsellite.

кам.-уг. *abbr.* (**каменноугольный**) coal, carboniferous.

камуфляж *m.* camouflage.

камфо— *prefix* campho—.

канаанит *m.* canaanite.

канава *f.* ditch, trench, gutter.

Канаверал (мыс) Cape Canaveral.

канавка *f.* groove, slot; ruling (of diffraction grating).

канад. *abbr.* (**канадский**) Canadian.

Канада Canada.

канадский *a.* Canadian; **к. бальзам** Canada balsam.

канал *m.* channel, canal, hole, pass; conduit, duct; bore (of gun); (astr.) lane; **к. выключения** shutdown channel; **к. для горючего** fuel channel; **к. для облучения** exposure hole; **к. звукового сопровождения** sound channel; **обводный к.** bypass (channel); **к. остановки** shutdown channel; **к. реактора** reactor channel; **к. реакции** reaction channel.

канализационн/ый *a.* sewage, waste; canalization; **—ая вода** sewage, waste water; **—ая сеть** sewer system;

—ая труба sewage pipe, sewer; water pipe, gas pipe, electric conduit.

каналов/ый *see* **канальный; к. спин** channel spin; **к. усилитель** window amplifier; **к. эффект** channeling; **коэффициент —ого эффекта** (reactor) channeling effect factor; **—ые лучи** canal rays.

каналь/ный *a.* canal, channel; **к. импульс** channel pulse; **к. спектр** channel spectrum; **—ная (газовая) сажа** channel black; **—чатый** *a.* channeled, grooved.

канат *m.*, **—ный** *a.* cable, rope.

канбарит *m.* kanbaraite.

канбиит *m.* canbyite.

кандидат *m.* candidate, applicant; **к. наук** candidate of science (academic degree); **—ская диссертация** candidate's dissertation.

кандолюминесценция *f.* candoluminescence.

канд. техн. наук *abbr.* (**кандидат технических наук**) candidate of technical sciences.

канелюра *f.* flute.

каникулы *pl.* vacation, holidays.

канит *m.* cahnite.

канифоль *f.*, **—ный** *a.* rosin.

канкринит *m.* cancrinite.

канниццарит *m.* cannizzarite.

Канниццаро реакция Cannizzaro reaction.

канонизировать *v.* reduce to canonical form.

каноническ/ий *a.* canonical; **—ое преобразование** canonical transformation.

кант *m.* edge, border.

Кант Kant (lunar crater).

кантонит *m.* cantonite.

канфильдит *m.* canfieldite.

канцеляр/ист *m.* clerk; **—ия** *f.* office.

КАО *abbr.* (**Крымская астрофизическая обсерватория**) Crimean Astrophysical Observatory.

каолин *m.*, **—овый** *a.* kaolin.

КАП *abbr.* (**Комиссия астрономических приборов**) Commission on Astronomical Equipment.

кап/ание *n.* dropping, dripping; **—ать** *v.* drop, drip; **—ающий** *a.* dripping; **—еж** *m.* drip.

Капелла Capella (star; lunar crater).

капель *f.* thaw; dripping; **—ка** *f.* droplet; **—ница** *f.* dropper, dropping glass (tube, bottle); dripcock; **—но-жидкий** *a.* liquid; **—но-жидкое облако** water cloud.

капельн/ый *a.* drop, dropping; trickling; **к. анализ** spot testing; **к. кран** dripcock; **к. способ** drop method, spot method; **к. фильтр** trickling filter; **к. электрод** dropping (mercury) electrode; **—ая воронка** dropping funnel; **—ая жидкость** liquid; dropping liquid; **—ая конденсация** dropwise condensation; **—ая модель ядра** (liquid-) drop nuclear model; **—ая подзарядка** trickle charging; **—ая проба, —ое испытание** drop test, spot test; **—ая смазка** drip lubrication; **—ое облако** *see* **капельно-жидкое облако.**

капельчатый *see* **капельный.**

капилляр *m.* capillary, pore; **—иметр** *m.* capillarimeter; **—но-дуговой источник** capillary-arc source; **—ность** *f.* capillarity.

капиллярн/ый *a.* capillary; **—ая трубка** capillary (tube); **—ая фильтрация** capillary penetration; **—ое поднятие** capillary rise; **—ое притяжение** capillary attraction; **—ое просачивание** capillary penetration.

капитал *m.* capital; **—овложение** *n.* investment.

капитальн/ый *a.* capital; main; thorough, fundamental; **к. ремонт** overhaul, overhauling; **—ая стена** main wall; **—ое вложение** *see* **капиталовложение.**

Капица Kapitsa (Kapitza).

капкан *m.* trap.

капле/заборник *m.* cloud drop (or raindrop) sampler; **—защищенный, —непроницаемый** *a.* drip-proof, driptight; **—образный** *a.* drop (-shaped); dropwise; **—стойкий** *a.* drip-proof; **—указатель** *m.* sight glass; **—упорный** *a.* drip-proof.

капля *f.* drop; blob; **к. холодного воздуха** (meteor.) cold-air drop, cold pool.

капницит *m.* kapnicite.
капнуть *see* **капать.**
капорчианит *m.* caporcianite.
капот *m.* (mach.) hood, cowling.
Каппа коэффициент Kapp coefficient; **линия К.** K. line.
каппеленит *m.* cappelenite.
капризный *a.* freakish; capricious.
капрон *m.*, **—овый** *a.* Kapron (nylon-like synthetic fiber); (chem.) caprone.
капсула *see* **капсюль.**
капсюл/ь *m.*, **—я** *f.* capsule; percussion cap; **—ьный** *a.* capsule; percussion cap; enclosed; **—ьный микрофон** button microphone.
каптаж *m.* capping (of well).
Капуан Capuanus (lunar crater).
капюшон *m.* hood.
карабин *m.*, **—ный** *a.* carbine; snap hook, latch hook; **—ный крючок** swivel.
карадокский ярус Carodocian stage.
Кара-Калпакская АССР Kara-Kalpak ASSR.
караколит *m.* caracolite.
карактрон *m.* charactron.
карандаш *m.*, **—ный** *a.* pencil; **—еобразный** *a.* pencil-shaped; **—ный триод** pencil-type triode.
карат *m.* carat.
Каратеодори Carathéodory.
каратный *see* **карат.**
карб— *prefix* carb—, carbo—.
карбазол *m.* carbazole.
карбид *m.*, **—ный, —овый** *a.* carbide; **к. кремния** silicon carbide; **—ированный катод** carbonized cathode; **—окремниевый варистор** silicon-carbide varistor.
карбо— *prefix* carbo—.
карбодавин *m.* carbodavynite.
карболовая кислота carbolic acid.
карболой *m.* Carboloy (tungsten-carbon-cobalt alloy).
карболон *m.* Carbolon.
карбонадо *m.* carbonado.
карбонат *m.* carbonate; **—ит** *m.* carbonatite.
карбониз/атор *m.* carbonizer; **—ация** *f.*, **—ационный** *a.*, **—ирование, —ование** *n.* carbonization, carbonation; **—ированный, —ованный** *a.* carbonized; **—ировать, —овать** *v.* carbonize.
карбонил *m.*, **—ьный** *a.* carbonyl; **—ьное железо** carbonyl iron.
карбоно/вый *a.* carbonaceous; **—метр** *m.* carbonometer.
карборунд *m.*, **—овый** *a.* carborundum.
карбоцер *m.* carbocer.
карбоциклическое соединение carbocyclic compound.
карбро-процесс carbro-process.
карбуран *m.* carburan.
карбюр/атор *m.* carburetor; **—ация** *f.*, **—ирование** *n.* carburation, carburetion; carburization; **—изатор** *m.* carbonizer; carburizer; **—ированный** *a.* carbureted; carburized; **—ировать** *v.* carburet; carburize.
кардан *m.*, **шарнир Кардана, —ный подвес, —ный шарнир** Cardan joint, universal joint; **—ный вал** C. shaft; **Кардана формула** C. solution.
кардинальн/ый *a.* cardinal; **—ая плоскость** cardinal plane; **—ая точка** cardinal point; **—ое число** cardinal number.
кардиоид/а *f.*, **—ный** *a.* cardioid; **—ная диаграмма** cardioid pattern.
Карельская АССР Karelian ASSR.
каретка *f.* (mech.) carriage.
кариинит *m.* caryinite.
карио/пилит *m.* caryopilite; **—церит** *m.* caryocerite.
Кариуса метод (chem.) Carius method.
каркас *m.* carcass, framework, shell, hull, skeleton, frame; housing, casing; **к. катушки** coil form; **к. ракеты** rocket body (or structure); **—ный тубус** (astr.) skeleton tube (of reflector).
карлик *m.* dwarf; **—овый** *a.* dwarf, dwarfish, stunted, diminutive.
карлозит *m.* carlosite.
карлсбадская соль Carlsbad salt.
карман *see* **карманный.**
Кармана вихревая дорожка Kármán vortex street.
карманн/ый *a.* pocket, box, container; **к. дозиметр** pocket meter; **—ая ионизационная камера** pocket ion chamber.
карминит *m.* carminite.
карналлит *m.* carnallite.

карнегиит *m.* carnegieite.

карнеол *m.* carnelian.

карниз *m.* cornice, eave.

карнийский век Carnian stage.

Карно круговой процесс, К. цикл Carnot cycle; **К. теорема** C. theorem.

карнотит *m.* carnotite.

каротаж *m.* logging, coring.

каротин *m.* carotin, carotene.

кароттаж *see* **каротаж.**

карролит *m.* carrollite.

карсель *m.* carcel unit; **—ская лампа** carcel lamp.

карсинотрон *m.* carcinotron.

карст *m.* cave.

карт/а *f.* map, chart; card; **к. в горизонталях** contour map; **к. излучений** (geo.) isorad map; **к. изобар** isobaric chart; **к. магнитных склонений** magnetic chart (or map); **к. очертаний** outline map; **к. погоды** weather map; **к. распределения дождей** rain chart; **к. с координатной сеткой** gridded map; lattice chart; **чертить —у** map, plot, chart.

картезианск/ий *a.* Cartesian; **—ие координаты** Cartesian coordinates.

картер *m.* crankcase, gear box, gear case, housing.

картин/а *f.* picture, pattern; **к. шумов** noise pattern; **—ный** *a.* picture, pictorial; **—ная плоскость** plane of a figure.

картиров/ание *n.* mapping, charting; **—ать** *v.* map, chart.

картограмма *f.* recorder chart.

картограф *m.* cartographer; **—ирование** *n.* mapping; **—ический** *a.* cartographic; **—ия** *f.* cartography.

картон *m.*, **—ный** *a.* cardboard, pasteboard; **прессовый к.** pressboard; **—аж** *m.* cardboard articles.

карто/тека *f.* card index, card catalog; **—чка** *f.*, **—чный** *a.* card.

картуш/ечный компас card compass; **—ка** *f.* compass card.

карфо/лит *m.* carpholite; **—сидерит** *m.* carphosiderite.

карциноген *m.* carcinogen; **—ный** *a.* carcinogenic.

карцинома *f.* carcinoma.

карьер *m.* (open) pit; **разработка —ами** open-cut mining.

карьера *f.* career.

карьерный *see* **карьер.**

касан/ие *n.* contact, tangency; **линия —ия** line of contact, tangent; **поверхность —ия** contact surface; **точка —ия** point of contact, point of tangency.

касатель/ная *f.*, **—ная линия** tangent; **к. составляющая** tangential component; **—но** *prep. gen.* relative to; concerning; **—ный** *a.* concerning, touching; tangent, tangential; **—ный модуль** (plast.) tangent modulus; **—ное напряжение** shearing stress; **—ное соударение** grazing collision; **—ство** *n.* relation, connection.

кас/аться *v.* concern, touch (upon); touch, be in contact (with); **что —ается** as regards, regarding, as to, as for; **—ающийся** *a.* concerning, touching (upon); tangent.

касвеллит *m.* caswellite.

каска *f.* helmet.

каскад *m.* cascade; stage; tandem; **к. промежуточной частоты** intermediate frequency (i.f.) stage; **к. разделительных установок** cascade of separating units; **—ирование** *n.* cascading, cascade operation; **—ировать** *v.* run in cascade.

каскадн/ый *a.* cascade, successive, successively emitted; **к. генератор** cascade generator; **к. ливень** cascade shower; ***n*-к.** *n*-stage; **—ая кривая** shower curve; **—ая лавина** cascade shower; **—ая теория** cascade theory; **—ое включение** cascading; **—ое устройство** cascading unit; **—ые гамма-лучи** cascade gamma rays, successive gamma rays; **—ые переходы** successive transitions.

Кассегрена рефлектор Cassegrainian reflector.

кассельская печь (cer.) pottery kiln.

кассета *f.* cassette, film (or plate) holder; **к. тепловыделяющих элементов** fuel assembly.

Кассини Cassini (lunar crater).

Кассини овал Cassinian oval.

кассинит *m.* cassinite.

Кассиопея Cassiopeia (Cas) (constellation).

кассиопий *m.* cassiopeium (lutecium) (Cp).
касситерит *m.* cassiterite.
кастанит *m.* castanite.
Кастильяно теорема Castigliano theorem.
Кастор Castor.
касторит *m.* castorite.
ката— *prefix* cata—, kata—.
катабатический *a.* katabatic, descending.
катадиоптрический рефрактор catadioptric refractor.
катакластический *a.* cataclastic.
катализ *m.* catalysis; **—атор** *m.* catalyst; **—овать** *v.* catalyze.
каталитический *a.* catalytic; **к. обмен** catalytic exchange.
катало/г *m.*, **—жный** *a.* catalog; **—гизировать** *v.* catalog.
катаморф/изм *m.* katamorphism; **—ный** *a.* katamorphic.
катан/ие *n.* rolling; **—ка** *f.* rolled wire; **—ый** *a.* rolled.
катаплеит *m.* catapleiite.
катапульта *f.* catapult.
катаракт *m.* cataract; damper; **—а** *f* (med.) cataract; **—ный** *a.* cataract.
Катарина Catharina (lunar crater).
катарометр *m.* katharometer.
катаспилит *m.* cataspilite.
катастроф/а *f.* catastrophe, disaster; **—ический** *a.* catastrophic, disastrous.
кататермометр *m.* katathermometer.
катать *v.* roll.
катафорез *m.* cataphoresis; **—ное покрытие** cataphoretic coating.
катафорит *m.* kataphorite.
катафронт *m.* katafront, subsidiary front.
категор/ический *a.* categorical; **—ия** *f.* category.
катенарный *a.* catenary.
катеноид *m.* catenoid.
катет *m.* cathetus, leg of right triangle; **прилежащий к.** adjacent side; **противолежащий к.** opposite side; **—рометр** *m.* cathetrometer.
катетрон *m.* cathetron.
катион *m.* cation; **—ит** *m.* cation exchange resin, cationite; **—ный дефект** cation defect; **—обменная смола** cation exchange resin; **—обменник** *m.* cation exchanger.
катить *see* **катать.**
каткинит *m.* cathkinite.
катковый плоский затвор (hyd.) stoney gate.
катлинит *m.* catlinite.
катод *m.* cathode; **к. жидкометаллический** pool cathode; **к. прямого накала** filamentary cathode.
катодн/ый *a.* cathode, cathodic, cathode-ray; **к. осциллограф** cathode-ray oscillograph; **к. повторитель** cathode follower; **вторая —ая темная область, темное —ое пространство** cathode (Crookes, Hittorf) dark space; **—ая граница** cathode border (between cathode dark space and negative glow); **—ая линза** cathode lens; **первая —ая темная область** Aston dark space; **—ая светящаяся пленка, первое —ое свечение** cathode glow; **—ое восстановление** cathodic reduction; **второе —ое свечение** negative glow; **—ое падение потенциала** cathode drop; **—ое покрытие** cathodic deposition; cathodic coating; **—ое пятно** cathode spot; **—ое распыление** cathode sputtering; **—ые лучи** cathode rays.
катодо/люминесценция *f.* cathodoluminescence; **—фосфоресценция** *f.* cathodophosphorescence.
каток *m.* roller, roll; **паровой к.** steam roller.
католит *m.* catholyte.
катоптри/ка *f.* catoptrics; **—т** *m.* catoptrite; **—ческий** *a.* catoptric.
катучий *a.* rolling; **к. кран** traveling crane.
катуш/ка *f.*, **—ечный** *a.* spool, bobbin, reel, roll; coil; **антенная удлинительная к.** antenna loading coil; **к. возбуждения** exciting (or field) coil; **к. индуктивности, индукционная к.** induction coil; **к. перемещения орбиты** orbit-shift coil; **к. самоиндукции** self-inductor; **к. связи** coupling coil; **к. сжатия** (elec.) collapse coil; **сотовая к.** honeycomb coil; **к. электромагнита** magnet coil.
катящийся *a.* rolling.
каузальный *a.* causal.

Каулса печь Cowles furnace.

каупер *m.*, **Каупера нагреватель** Cowper blast air heater.

кауст/ик *m.* (chem.) caustic; **—ика** *f.* caustic (curve); **—ификация** *f.*, **—ицирование** *n.* causticizing, causticization; **—ицировать** *v.* causticize.

каустич/еский *a.* caustic; **—еская кривая** caustic (curve); **—еская поверхность** caustic surface; **—еская сода** caustic soda; **—ность** *f.* causticity.

Кауч. и рез. *abbr.* (**Каучук и резина**) Caoutchouc and Rubber (journal).

каучук *m.* rubber, caoutchouc; **искусственный к.** synthetic rubber.

каучуков/ый *a.* rubber; **к. сок, —ое молоко** rubber latex; **—ая замазка** rubber cement; **—ая трубка** rubber tubing, rubber hose.

каучуко/образный, —подобный *a.* rubbery.

кафедр/а *f.* (university) department, faculty, chair; **заведывать —ой** head a department, hold a chair.

кахолонг *m.* cacholong.

кач/алка *f.* rocking device, rocker; **—ание** *n.* rocking, swinging; oscillation, fluctuation, wobbling; pumping; hunting (by a regulator); **—ание луча** beam swinging; **—ательно-сочлененный** *a.* hinged; **—ательный** *see* **качающийся**; **—ать** *v.* rock, swing, sway, shake; oscillate; pump; **—аться** *v.* rock, swing; oscillate, fluctuate; shake, wobble; **—ающий кристалл** oscillating crystal.

качающ/ийся *a.* rocking, swinging, oscillating, reciprocating, oscillatory, vibrating; shaking; tilting; fluctuating; **—аяся диаграмма** (radar) scanning pattern; **—аяся лепестковая диаграмма** swept-lobe diagram (of antenna).

качеств. *abbr. see* **качественный.**

качественн/ый *a.* qualitative; high-grade; **к. анализ** qualitative analysis; **—ые показатели** performance figures.

качеств/о *n.* quality, grade; **повышение —а, улучшение —а** refinement, improvement; **в —е** as, in the capacity of.

качка *f.* tossing; **бокова к.** rolling; **килевая к.** pitching.

качнуть *see* **качать.**

каша *f.* (rad.) random noise.

каш/еобразный *a.* pasty, viscous; **—ица, —ка** *f.* pulp.

кбм *abbr.* (**кубический метр**) cubic meter.

кв *abbr.* (**кванты**) quanta; (**киловольт**) kilovolt (kv); **кв.** (**квадратный**) square.

КВ *abbr.* (**короткие волны**) short waves.

ква *abbr.* (**киловольтампер**) kilovolt-ampere (kva).

квадрант *m.* quadrant.

Квадрантиды Quadrantid meteors.

квадрантн/ый *a.* quadrant, quadrantal; **к. угол** quadrantal angle; **к. электрометр** quadrant electrometer; **—ая антенна** quadrant antenna; **—ая погрешность** quadrantal error.

квадрат *m.* square; **возводить в к., возвышать в к.** (math.) square; **метод наименьших —ов** method of least squares; **—ический** *a.* quadratic, square, square-law; **—ическое отклонение** standard deviation.

квадратичн/о интегрируемый quadratically integrable; **к.-косекансная антенна** cosecant-squared antenna; **—ость** *f.* squareness; **—ый радиус** root-mean-square radius; **—ая зависимость** square-law variation; **—ая флуктуация** (mean) square fluctuation; **—ая форма** quadratic form; **—ое детектирование** square-law detection.

квадратно интегрируемый *see* **квадратично интегрируемый.**

квадратн/ый *a.* square, quadratic, quadric; tetragonal; **к. дециметр** square decimeter; **к. каскад** square cascade; **к. километр** square kilometer; **к. корень** square root; **к. метр** square meter; **к. миллиметр** square millimeter; **к. сантиметр** square centimeter; **—ая матрица** square matrix; **—ая система** (cryst.) tetragonal system; **—ое уравнение** quadratic equation; **—ые скобки** square brackets.

квадратор *m.* squarer, square-law function generator.

квадрат/рикса *f.* quadratrix; **—рон** *m.* quadratron.

квадратур/а *f.* quadrature, squaring; square area; **—ный прилив** neap tide; **—ная лампа** quadrature tube.

квадрика *f.* quadric.

квадрильон *m.* quadrillion.

квадрир/ование *n.* quadrature; **—овать** *v.* quadrate; **—уемость** *f.* integrability, squarability; **—уемый** *a.* integrable, squarable.

квадрупл/екс *m.* quadruplex; **—етность** *f.* quadruplicity.

квадруполь *m.*, **—ный** *a.* quadrupole; **—ный момент** quadrupole moment; **—ное взаимодействие** quadrupole interaction; **—ное излучение** quadrupole radiation; **—ное электрическое излучение** electric quadrupole radiation.

квази— *prefix* quasi—, quasi.

квази/геострофический *a.* quasi-geostrophic; **—гомогенный реактор** quasi-homogeneous reactor.

квазидейтрон *m.* quasi deuteron.

квазидиффузионное распространение quasi-diffusion propagation.

квази/импульс *m.* quasi momentum, crystal momentum; **—классический** *a.* semiclassical, quasi-classical; **—кристаллический** *a.* quasi-crystalline; **—локальный** *a.* quasi-localizable.

квазипостоянная депрессия quasi-permanent low.

квази/стабильный *a.* metastable; **—статический** *a.* quasi-static; **—стационарный уровень** quasi-stationary level; **—твердый** *a.* quasi-solid; **—упругое рассеяние** quasi-elastic scattering; **—установившийся** *a.* quasi-stationary; **—частица** *f.* quasi particle.

квазиэргодическая гипотеза quasi-ergodic hypothesis.

квалиметр *m.* qualimeter.

квалифи/кация *f.* qualification; skill; **—цированный** *a.* qualified; skilled, trained; **—цированный труд** skilled labor; **—цировать** *v.* qualify; **—цирующий** *a.* qualifying.

квант *m.* quantum; photon; **к. действия** quantum of action; **к. света** light quantum; **к. энергии** energy quantum; **—ы** *pl.* quanta; **—ов теория** quantum theory.

квантов/ание *n.* quantization; **к. интенсивности** intensity (or second) quantization; **—анный** *a.* quantized, quantizable; **—анное электромагнитное поле** quantized electromagnetic field; **—ать** *v.* quantize.

квантово/механический *a.* quantum mechanical; **—статистический** *a.* quantum statistical.

квантов/ый *a.* quantum, quantized; photon; **к. выход** quantum yield (or efficiency); **к. переход** quantum transition; **к. скачок** quantum jump; **—ая механика** quantum mechanics; **—ая отдача** quantum efficiency; **—ая статистика** quantum statistics; **—ая статистическая механика** quantum statistical mechanics; **—ая теория** quantum theory; **—ая теория поля** quantum field theory; **—ая функция распределения** quantum mechanical distribution law; **—ая электродинамика** quantum electrodynamics; **—ое взаимодействие** quantized interaction; **—ое излучение** quantum radiation; **—ое ограничение** quantum restriction; **—ое поле** quantized field; **—ое прохождение** (reactor) quantum leakage; **—ое состояние** quantum state; **—ое условие** quantum condition; **—ое число** quantum number; **—ое число изотопического спина** isotopic spin quantum number.

квантомеханический *see* **квантовомеханический.**

квар *abbr.* (**киловольтампер реактивный**) reactive kilovolt-ampere.

кварта *f.* quart; (mus.) fourth.

квартал *m.* quarter (of year); (city) block; **—ьный** *a.* quarterly; block.

квартет *m.* quartet.

квартиль *m.* quartile; **—ное отклонение** quartile deviation.

кварто *n.* quarto.

квартование *n.* (met.) quartation.

кварц *m.* quartz.

кварцев/ый *a.* quartz, quartzose; **к. генератор** quartz-crystal oscillator; **к. песчаник** quartzose sandstone; **к. сланец** quartz schist; **—ая лампа**

quartz lamp; **—ая нить** quartz fiber; **—ые часы** quartz-crystal clock.

кварц/еносный *a.* quartziferous, quartzose; **—ин** *m.* quartzine; **—ит** *m.* quartzite; **—итовый** *a.* quartzitic, quartzose; **—ованный генератор** quartz crystal oscillator.

квасц/овый *a.* alum, aluminous; **—ы** *pl.* alum; **алюмокалиевые —ы** potassium alum; **хромокалиевые —ы** potassium chrome alum.

кватернион *m.*, **—ный** *a.* quaternion.

кватерфенил *m.* quaterphenyl.

кв. дм *abbr.* (**квадратный дециметр**) square decimeter.

квенселит *m.* quenselite.

квенштедтит *m.* quenstedtite.

кверху *adv.* up, upwards.

кветенит *m.* quetenite.

квинкви— *prefix* quinqui—, quinque—.

квинквильон *m.* quinquillion.

Квинке метод Quincke method.

квинта *f.* (mus.) fifth.

квинтет *m.* quintet.

квинтильон *m.* quintillion.

квинтуплекс *m.* quintuplex.

квинтэссенция *f.* quintessence.

квитанция *f.* receipt, acknowledgment.

кв. км *abbr.* (**квадратный километр**) square kilometer.

кв. м *abbr.* (**квадратный метр**) square meter.

кв. мм *abbr.* (**квадратный миллиметр**) square millimeter.

к-во *abbr.* (**количество**) quantity.

кв. см *abbr.* (**квадратный сантиметр**) square centimeter.

квт *abbr.* (**киловатт**) kilowatt (kw).

квт-ч, квтч *abbr.* (**киловатт-час**) kilowatt-hour (kwhr).

кг *abbr.* (**килограмм**) kilogram (kg); **кГ** [**килограмм(-сила)**] kilogram (force).

кгм, кГм *abbr.* (**килограммометр**) kilogram-meter (kg-m).

кг-моль *abbr.* (**килограмм-молекула**) kilogram-molecule, kilomole.

кгс *see* **кГ.**

кгсм *abbr.* (**килограммосантиметр**) kilogram-centimeter.

КГУ *abbr.* (**Казанский государственный университет**) Kazan' State University; [**Киевский государственный университет (им. Т. Г. Шевченко**)] T. G. Shevchenko Kiev State University.

КГФТИ *abbr.* (**Комбинат государственных физико-технических институтов**) Complex of State Institutes of Physics and Technology.

кгц *abbr.* (**килогерц**) kilocycle (kc).

КД *abbr.* (**карманный дозиметр**) pocket dosimeter (PD).

кдж *abbr.* (**килоджоуль**) kilojoule, large joule.

кегоеит *m.* kehoeite.

Кейли Cayley.

кейльгауит *m.* keilhauite.

Кейпенхерст Capenhurst.

кейпер *m.* (geo.) Keuper.

Кейса уравнение Keyes equation (of state).

келифит *m.* kelyphite.

Келлога правило Kellogg rule.

келоид *m.* keloid.

Кельвина мост Kelvin bridge; **К. шкала** K. scale; **К. эффект** K. effect.

кель/ма, —ня *f.* trowel.

кельсаджиит *m.* culsageeite.

кем *instr. of* **кто,** by whom.

кеммererит *m.* kämmererite.

Кемпбелла-Стокса гелиограф Campbell-Stokes heliograph; **К. формула** C. formula.

кененит *m.* koenenite.

Кениг-Мартенса спектрофотометр Koenig-Martens spectrophotometer.

кенигин *m.* koenigine.

Кеннеди теорема Kennedy theorem.

Кеннелли-Хевисайда слой Kennelly-Heaviside layer, Heaviside layer.

кеннельский уголь cannel coal.

кеноплиотрон *m.* kenopliotron.

кенотрон *m.* kenotron.

Кеплер Kepler (lunar crater).

Кеплера закон Kepler law; **кеплеровское движение** Keplerian motion.

Кепселя аппарат Koepsel permeameter.

керамет *see* **кермет.**

керам/ика *f.* ceramics; **—иковый** *a.* ceramic, clay; **—иковые изделия** pottery, earthenware; **—ический** *a.* ceramic.

керамогалит *m.* keramohalite.

кераргирит *m.* cerargyrite.

керит *m.* kerite.

кермезит *m.* kermesite.

кермет *m.* cermet.
керн *m.* core; core sample; kernel; **к. катода** cathode base.
Керна дуга Kern arc.
кернер *m.* punch, prick punch, center punch.
керно *n.* prick punch; mark; **—вать** *v.* punch, prick.
керновый *a.* core; **к. режим кипения** nucleate boiling.
керосин *m.*, **—овый** *a.* kerosene.
Керра постоянная Kerr constant; **К. элемент** K. cell; **К. явление** K. effect.
керромаг *m.* Cerromag.
Керстена теория включений Kersten foreign body theory.
керсутит *m.* kaersutite.
Кертиса диск Curtis disk.
кертисит *m.* curtisite.
керченит *m.* kertschinite.
кессон *m.*, **—ный** *a.* caisson.
кетазин *m.* ketazin.
кето— *prefix* keto—.
кето/л *m.* ketol; **—н** *m.* ketone; **—форма** *f.* keto-form.
Кеттелера-Гельмгольца формула Ketteler-Helmholtz formula.
кефлахит *m.* köflachite.
кехлинит *m.* koechlinite.
кианит *m.* kyanite.
кибернетика *f.* cybernetics.
киватин *m.* (geo.) Keewatin.
Киви Kiwi (reactor).
кид/ание *n.* throwing; abandoning; **—анный** *a.* thrown; abandoned; **—ать** *v.* throw, fling, cast; abandon, drop.
кизерит *m.* kieserite.
килейит *m.* keeleyite.
килиндрит *m.* cylindrite.
кило— *prefix* kilo—.
кило/ампер *m.* kiloampere (ka); **—барн** *m.* kilobarn; **—вар** *m.* kilovar.
киловатт *m.* kilowatt (kw); **к. установленной мощности** installed kilowatt; **к.-час** kilowatt-hour (kwhr).
киловольт *m.* kilovolt (kv); **к.-ампер** *m.* kilovolt-ampere (kva); **—метр пиковый** peak-reading kilovoltmeter.
кило/гаусс *m.* kilogauss; **—герц** *m.* kilocycle (kc).
килограмм *m.* kilogram (kg); **к.-калория** kilocalorie (kcal); **к.-метр, —етр** *m.* kilogram-meter.
кило/джоуль *m.* kilojoule, large joule (kj); **—дина** *f.* kilodyne; **—икс (кх)** *m.* kx unit; **—калория** *see* **килограмм-калория**; **—кюри** *n.* kilocurie (kC); **—литр** *m.* kiloliter (kl); **—люмен** *m.* kilolumen; **—люмен-час** kilolumen-hour; **—мегагерц** *m.* kilomegacycle.
километр *m.* kilometer (km); **—аж** *m.* distance in kilometers; **—ическое затухание** attenuation in kilometers; **—овые волны** kilometer waves.
кило/моль *m.* kilomole; **—ом** *m.* kilohm (kohm); **—парсек** *m.* kiloparsec; **—тонна** *f.* kiloton; **—уатт** *see* **киловатт**; **—цикл** *m.* kilocycle; **—электронвольт** *m.* kiloelectron volt (kev).
киль *m.* keel; (aero.) fin.
Киль Carina (Car) (constellation).
кильбрикенит *m.* kilbriekenite.
кильватер *m.* ship's wake.
киматология *f.* kymatology.
Кина испытатель Keen tester; **К. цемент** Keene cement.
кингстон *m.* Kingston valve.
кинемат/ика *f.* kinematics; **—ический** *a.* kinematic; **—ический коэффициент вязкости** kinematic modulus of viscosity.
кинематограф *m.* motion picture theater; **—ический** *a.* cinematographic, motion picture; **—ия** *f.* cinematography, motion pictures.
кинемометр *m.* kinemometer.
кинескоп *m.* kinescope.
кинетика *f.* kinetics.
кинетическ/ий *a.* kinetic; **к. импеданс** motional impedance; **к. момент** angular momentum, moment of momentum; **—ая теория газов** kinetic theory of gases.
кинето/скоп *m.* kinetoscope; **—фон** *m.* kinetophone.
кинжал *m.* dagger.
кино *n.* movie theater; motion picture; **звуковое к.** talking picture.
киноаппарат *m.* motion picture camera.
киноварь *m.* cinnabar.
кино/кадр *m.* motion picture exposure (or frame); **—картина** *f.* motion picture; **—проектор** *m.*, **—проекцион-**

ный аппарат motion picture projector; —**проекция** *f.* motion picture projection; —**радиография** *f.* ciné-radiography.

киносъем/ка *f.* filming; (**покадровая**) **замедленная к.** time-lapse photography; —**очный аппарат** motion picture camera.

кино/фильм *m.* motion picture (film); —**хроника** *f.* newsreel.

кинут/ый *a.* thrown; —**ь** *see* **кидать.**

киоск *m.* booth.

кип. *abbr.* (**кипение**) boiling; (**контрольно-измерительный прибор**) control and measuring instrument.

кипа *f.* stack, pile.

кип/ение *n.* boiling; gassing; **температура** —**ения, точка** —**ения** boiling point; —**еть** *v.* boil; bubble.

Киппа аппарат Kipp generator.

кипп-реле *n.* kipp relay.

кипучий *a.* boiling; bubbling.

кипя/тильник *m.* boiler; —**тильный** *a.* boiling; —**тить** *v.* boil; —**ток** *m.* boiling water; —**чение** *n.* boiling; —**ченый** *a.* boiled.

кипящий *a.* boiling; bubbling; **к. слой** fluidized bed; **к. ядерный котел** boiling water reactor.

К и Р *see* **Кауч. и рез.**

Киргизская ССР, Кирг ССР Kirghiz SSR.

Кирилл Cyrillus (lunar crater).

кирка *f.* pick, pickax.

Кирквуда теория Kirkwood (approximation) theory (for liquids).

Киркендаля эффект Kirkendall effect.

Киропулоса метод Kyropoulos procedure.

кирпич *m.*, —**ный** *a.* brick; —**ная кладка** brick masonry.

киртолит *see* **циртолит.**

Кирхгофа закон Kirchhoff law; **К. уравнение** K. equation.

Кирхер Kircher (lunar crater).

Кис Kies (lunar crater).

кискеит *m.* quisqueite.

кисловат/ость *f.* sourness; —**ый** *a.* sourish; acidulous.

кислород *m.* oxygen (O); **к. воздуха** atmospheric oxygen.

кислородно— *see* **кислородо**—; **к.-цезиевый катод** cesium oxide cathode.

кислородн/ый *a.* oxygen, oxygenous; —**ая бомба** oxygen cylinder; —**ая кислота** oxy acid, oxygen acid; —**ая соль** oxy salt.

кислородо/ацетиленовая сварка oxyacetylene welding; —**водородная горелка** oxyhydrogen torch; —**содержащий** *a.* oxygen-containing, oxy—.

кислот/а *f.* acid; **азотная к.** nitric acid; **ангидрид** —**ы, безводная к.** acid anhydride.

кислотн/ость *f.* acidity; **коэффициент** —**ости** acid number; —**ый** *a.* acid; sour; —**ое число** acid number; —**ые пары** acid fumes.

кислото/измерение *n.* acidimetry; —**мер** *m.* acidometer, acidimeter; —**обработанный** *a.* acid-treated; —**образование** *n.* acid formation, —**стойкий,** —**упорный,** —**устойчивый** *a.* acidproof, acid-resisting; —**упорность** *f.* acid resistance.

кис/лый *a.* acid; sour; —**нуть** *v.* sour, turn sour, become acid.

КИСО *abbr.* (**Комиссия по исследованию солнца**) Solar Research Commission.

кист/евой *a.*, —**ь** *f.* brush; wrist; **к. разряд** brush discharge; **к. элемент** grip end (of manipulator).

кит. *abbr.* (**китайский**) Chinese.

Кит Cetus (Cet) (constellation).

Китай China.

Китайская Народная Республика, КНР People's Republic of China.

кишечный камень tripestone.

кишка *f.* hose.

кишцелит *m.* kiscellite.

киютин *see* **киватин.**

ккал *abbr.* (**килокалория**) kilocalorie (kcal).

ккюри *abbr.* (**килокюри**) kilocurie (kC).

кл *abbr.* (**килолитр**) kiloliter (kl).

к.-л. *abbr.* (**какой-либо**) any, some.

клавиатура *f.* keyboard.

Клавий Clavius (lunar crater).

клавиш *m.*, —**а** *f.*, —**ный** *a.* key; —**ная машина** key-actuated machine.

кладка *f.* laying; stack; **каменная к.** masonry.

кладовая *f.* storeroom.

кладь *f.* load.

Клайдена явление (эффект) Clayden effect.

Клайзена колба Claisen flask.

клапан *m.*, **—ный** *a.* valve, vent; **к. бабочка** butterfly valve; **впускной к.** inlet (or intake) valve; **выхлопной к.** exhaust valve; **контрольный к.** check valve; **прыгающий к.** poppet valve; **к. расцепления** trip valve; **к. управляемый поплавком** float check valve; **—ная камера, —ная коробка** valve chest (or box).

Клапейрона закон (Clapeyron) ideal gas law; **К. уравнение** C. equation; **К. уравнение состояния** C. equation of state; **К. уравнение состояния газов** (C.) ideal gas law.

Клаппа генератор Clapp oscillator.

Клапрот Klaproth (lunar crater).

клапротолит *m.* klaprotholite.

кларит *m.* clarite.

Кларка элемент Clark cell.

кларкеит *m.* clarkeite.

класс *m.* class; classroom.

классифи/катор *m.* classifier; **—кация** *f.* classification, sorting, sizing; **—цированный** *a.* classified, sorted, graded; **—цировать** *v.* classify, class, sort, grade, size; specify.

классическ/ий *a.* classic, classical; **—ая механика** classical mechanics; **—ая модель** classical model; **—ая физика** classical physics.

классичность *f.* classical character.

класс/ный *a.* classroom; class; **—овый** *a.* class.

кластическ/ий *a.* (geo.) clastic, fragmental, detrital; **—ие породы** clastic rocks.

класто— *prefix* clasto—.

класть *v.* lay, put, place, set.

клатрат *m.* clathrate compound.

клаудетит *m.* claudetite.

Клаузиуса - Клапейрона уравнение Clausius-Clapeyron equation; **К.-Моссотти формула** C.-Mossotti equation; **К. уравнение** C. equation.

клаусталит *m.* clausthalite.

Клебша - Гордана коэффициенты Clebsch-Gordan coefficients.

клевеит *m.* cleveite.

клевеландит *m.* cleavelandite.

клее/вой *a.* glue, adhesive; **—вое вещество** sizing material; **—ние** *n.* gluing, pasting, cementing.

клеен/ка *f.*, **—очный** *a.* oilcloth, oilskin; **половая к.** linoleum.

кле/еный *a.* glued, pasted, cemented; **—ильный** *a.* gluing, pasting.

клеиофан *m.* cleiophane.

кле/ить *v.* glue, paste, gum, cement; **—й** *m.* adhesive, glue, cement; size; **резиновый —й** rubber cement.

клейк/ий *a.* sticky; glue, adhesive; **—ое вещество** adhesive; sizing; **—ость** *f.* adhesiveness, stickiness.

клейм/ение *n.* branding, stamping, marking; **—еный** *a.* branded, stamped, marked; **—ить** *v.*, **—о** *n.* brand, stamp, mark; **—о фабричное** trademark.

клейн-нишиновское сечение Klein-Nishina cross section.

Клейна бутылка (math.) Klein bottle; **К.-Гордона уравнение** K.-Gordon equation; **К. и Нишина формула** K.-Nishina (scattering) formula.

клейнит *m.* kleinite.

Клейста банка Kleistian jar, Leyden jar.

клейстер *m.* filling, sizing.

Клемана-Дезорма метод Clément and Désormes method.

клемма *f.* (elec.) terminal.

Клеомед Cleomedes (lunar crater).

клеп/альный *a.* riveting; **к. молот, к. молоток** riveting hammer; **—анный** *a.* riveted; **—ать** *v.* rivet; **—ка** *f.* riveting; stave.

клепсидра *f.* clepsydra.

Клеро (дифференциальное) уравнение Clairaut (differential) equation.

клеровать *v.* clarify, refine.

клетевой *see* **клеточный.**

клет/ка *f.* box, square, place (in periodic table); cell; cage; **беличья к.** squirrel cage; **эффект —ки** (nucl.) cage effect; **—очный** *a.* cage; cell, cellular; **—очный магнетрон** squirrel-cage magnetron.

клетчат/ка *f.* cellulose; **—ый** *a.* squared, checkered; meshed; cellulose; cellular; **—ая бумага** graph paper.

клеть *f.* cage, housing.

клешневидное соединение chelate compound.

клещ/и *pl.*, **—евой** *a.* tongs, pliers, pincers; vise.

клиахит *m.* cliachite.

кливаж *m.* cleavage.

клидонограф *m.* klydonograph, Lichtenburg figure camera, surge voltage recorder.

климаграмма *f.* climagram.

климат *m.* climate; **—изатор** *m.* climatizer; **—изация** *f.* acclimatization; **—ический** *a.* climatic; **—ическая обработка** climatic conditioning.

климатолог *m.* climatologist; **—ический** *a.* climatological; **—ия** *f.* climatology.

клин *m.* wedge, key, cotter; cleat; **вбивать к.** wedge, wedge in; **сходить на к.** taper.

клингманит *m.* clingmanite.

клини/ка *f.* clinic; **—ческий** *a.* clinical.

клинкер *m.*, **—ный** *a.* clinker, cinder.

клиновидн/ый *see* **клинообразный**; **к. домен** tapered domain; **—ая изобара** wedge isobar.

клиновой *a.* wedge, cotter; tapered, wedge-shaped, V-shaped; **к. тон** edge tone.

клиногедрит *m.* clinohedrite.

клинок *m.* blade.

клиноклаз, —ит *m.* clinoclase.

клинометр *m.* clinometer, incline level.

клинообразный *a.* wedge-shaped, wedge, sphenic, sphenoid, tapered, V-shaped; **к. интрузив** (geo.) sphenolith.

клино/ось *f.* (cryst.) clino-axis; **—пирамида** *f.* clinopyramid; **—ромбический** *a.* clinorhombic, monoclinic; **—ромбоэдрический** *a.* clinorhomboidal, triclinic.

клинтонит *m.* clintonite.

клинчатый *a.* wedge, wedge-shaped, tapered.

клиренс *m.* clearance.

клирфактор *m.* nonlinear distortion factor.

клистрон *m.* klystron; **к. бегущей волны** traveling wave klystron; **к. с двойным пролетом** (reflex) klystron; **—ный генератор** klystron oscillator; **—ный отражатель** klystron repeller.

клифтонит *m.* cliftonite.

клица *f.* cleat.

клм *abbr.* (**килолюмен**) kilolumen.

Клода метод Claude process.

клокманнит *m.* klockmannite.

клокотать *v.* bubble.

клонить *v.* lean, incline; **—ся** *v.* lean, incline; decline; tend.

клопфер *m.* (telegraphy) sounder.

клочков/ание *n.* flocculation; **—атость** *f.* patchiness; **—атый** *a.* flocculent; ragged.

клочок *m.* flake, patch, shred, scrap; **к. облака** cloud patch.

клуб *m.* club; puff (of smoke), cloud (of dust); **—иться** *v.* curl, wreathe, swirl; **—ный** *a.* club.

клуб/оватый *a.* ball-like; **—ок** *m.* ball, tangle; (chem.) coil; **молекулярный —ок** coiled molecule.

Клузиуса колонна Clusius column.

клупп *m.* tap wrench, die stock.

Клэра преобразователь St. Clair transducer.

ключ *m.*, **—евой** *a.* key; wrench; spring, fountain; switch; **английский к., французский к.** monkey wrench; **гаечный к.** wrench; **к.-ползун** sliding-contact key.

клямера *f.* cramp iron.

км *abbr.* (**километр**) kilometer (km).

КМА *abbr.* (**Курская магнитная аномалия**) Kursk magnetic anomaly.

кМгц *abbr.* (**киломегагерц**) kilomegacycle (kMc).

КМПВ *abbr.* (**корреляционный метод преломления волн**) correlation method of wave refraction.

кн. *abbr.* (**книга**) book, volume.

к.-н. *abbr.* (**какой-нибудь**) some, any.

кн-во *abbr.* (**книгоиздательство**) press, publishing house.

к.н.д. *abbr.* (**коэффициент направленного действия**) directive gain (of antenna).

книга *f.* book, volume.

кн. изд. *see* **кн-во.**

книго/издательство *n.* press, publishing house; **—печатание** *n.* book printing; **—хранилище** *n.* library.

книж/ечка, —ка *f.* small book; notebook; **—ный** *a.* book.

книзу *adv.* down, downwards.

кноксвиллит *m.* knoxvillite.

кноп/ка *f.*, **—очный, —чатый** *a.* button, pushbutton, knob; snap fastener; **—очное управление** pushbutton control.

Кнудсена закон косинусов Knudsen cosine law; **поток К., кнудсеновский поток, кнудсеновское течение** K. flow.

ко *prep. see* **к**; *prefix* co—.

коагулир/ование *n.* coagulation; **—ованный** *a.* coagulated; **—овать** *v.* coagulate; **—уемость** *f.* coagulability; **—уемый** *a.* coagulable; **—ующий** *a.* coagulating; **—ующий реагент** coagulant.

коагул/янт *m.* coagulant, coagulating agent; **—ят** *m.* coagulate; **—ятор** *m.* coagulator; coagulant; **—яция** *f.*, **—яционный** *a.* coagulation, coagulating; coalescence; agglomeration, flocculation; **—яция капель** coalescence of drops.

коаксиальный *a.* coaxial.

коактиватор *m.* coactivator.

коалесценция *f.* coalescence.

коалиция *f.* coalition.

Коанда эффект Coanda effect.

коацерв/ат *m.* coacervate; **—ация** *f.* coacervation.

кобальт *m.* cobalt (Co); **—ин** *m.* cobaltite; **—ирование** *n.* cobalt plating; **—ированный** *a.* cobalt-plated; **—истый** *a.* cobaltous, cobalto—, cobalt.

кобальто— *prefix* cobalti—, cobaltic.

кобальтов/ый *a.* cobaltic, cobalti—, cobalt, cobaltiferous; **к. халькантит** cobalt chalcanthite; **—ая бомба** cobalt bomb; **—ые цветы** cobalt bloom.

Ковалевская Mme. Kowalevski.

ковалентн/ость *f.* covalence; **—ый** *a.* covalent; **—ая связь** covalent bond.

кованый *a.* forged, hammered; wrought (iron).

ковар *m.* Kovar.

ковари/антность, —ация *f.* covariance, covariation; **—антный** *a.* covariant.

коваровый *see* **ковар.**

ковать *v.* forge, hammer, work; **к. вхолодную** hammer-harden.

ковеллин *m.* covellite.

коверсинус *m.* coversed sine.

ковк/а *f.* forging, hammering; swaging; **—ий** *a.* malleable, forgeable, ductile; **—ое (сыродутное) железо** wrought iron; **—ость** *f.* malleability, forgeability, ductility.

коволюм *m.* covolume.

ковочн/ый *a.* forging; **к. пресс, к. штамп, —ая машина** forging machine, forging press; **—ая работа** forged work.

ковш *m.*, **—евой** *a.* ladle, scoop; bucket; **литейный к.** casting ladle.

когда *adv.* when; *conj.* when, whenever; **к.-либо, к.-нибудь** sometime; ever; **к.-так** if so, in that case; **к.-то** formerly, once.

когенит *m.* cohenite.

когер. *abbr.* (**когерентный**) coherent.

когерентн/ость *f.* coherence; **—ый** *a.* coherent, coherence; **—ое рассеяние** coherent scattering.

когер/ер *m.* coherer; **—ирование** *see* **когерентность**; **—ировать** *v.* cohere.

кого *acc. and gen. of* **кто,** whom.

когомология *f.* cohomology group.

код *m.* code.

кодаццит *m.* codazzite.

кодекс *m.* code.

код/ирование *n.* encoding; **—ированный** *a.* coded, encoded; **—ировать** *v.* code, encode; **—ифицировать** *v.* codify; **—овый** *a.* code.

кое *pron. n.* which, that; **к.-где** *adv.* here and there; **к.-как** *adv.* with difficulty, somehow; **к.-какой** *a.* some, any; **к.-кто** *pron.* someone; **к.-куда** *adv.* somewhere; **к.-что** *pron.* something, a little.

кож/а *f.* skin; hide, leather; **—аный** *a.* leather; **—ица** *f.* film, pellicle, thin skin; **—ный** *a.* skin, cutaneous; **—ная доза** skin dose.

кожух *m.* jacket, case, casing, mantle, sheath, housing, shell.

козалит *m.* cosalite.

Козерог Capricornus (Cap) (constellation); **—а тропик** tropic of Capricorn.

козл/овой *a.* trestle, gantry; **к. кран** gantry crane; **—ы** *pl.* support, saw horse; gantry, trestle; jack.

козырек *m.* visor; deflector, baffle plate; (aero.) windshield.

кокил/ь *m.*, **—ьный** *a.* (foundry) chill-mold, chill; **отливать в —ях** cast cold; **отливка в —ях, —ьная отливка, —ьное литье** chill casting; **—ьноотлитый** *a.* chill-cast.

кокимбит *m.* coquimbite.

кокинерит *m.* cocinerite.

кокколит *m.* coccolite.

Кокрофта-Уолтона ускоритель Cockcroft-Walton accelerator.

кокс *m.* coke; **доменный к.** metallurgical coke; **—ик** *m.* fine coke.

коксовальн/ый *a.* coke, coking; **—ая печь** *see* **коксовая печь.**

коксов/ание *n.* coking; **—ать** *v.*, **—ый** *a.* coke; **—ый газ** coke oven gas; **—ая печь** coke oven.

кол *m.* stake, picket, pole.

кол. *abbr.* (**колебание**) oscillation, fluctuation, variation, range, vibration, swinging.

колба *f.* flask; envelope, bulb; **к. без носика** pipeless bulb; **к.-приемник** collecting flask.

колбасная антенна sausage antenna.

колбочка *f.* small flask; (elec.) bulb; cone (of retina).

кол-во *abbr.* (**количество**) quantity.

Колдер-Холл Calder-Hall.

колебан/ие *n.* oscillation, fluctuation, variation, vacillation; range; vibration, swinging, hunting (by regulator); **к. захватывания** forced vibration (or oscillation); **к. изгиба** flexural vibration; **к. кристаллической решетки** lattice vibration; **к. плазмы** plasma oscillation; **к. полюса** mutation of the pole; **к. по толщине** transverse oscillation; **к. почвы** earth tremor; **к. скелета** skeletal vibration; **к. тропопаузы** tropopause variation (or oscillation); **плоскость —ия** plane of vibration.

колебательный *a.* oscillatory, vibrational, vibratory; fluctuating; **к. контур** oscillatory circuit, tank, circuit; **к. переход** vibrational transition; **к. спектр** vibrational spectrum.

колебать *v.* shake, agitate, vibrate; swing; **—ся** *v.* vibrate, oscillate, fluctuate; vary, range; hesitate; wobble, sway; **—ся в пределах** fluctuate, vary, range.

колеблющийся *a.* oscillatory, oscillating, fluctuating, variable; vibrating, vibratory; unsteady, wavering; flickering (flame); **к. ряд** oscillating series.

колеманит *m.* colemanite.

коленно-рычажн/ый механизм toggle; **—ое соединение** toggle joint, knee joint.

колен/о *n.*, **—ный** *a.* knee; elbow, bend; offset; (geo.) limb (of fold); **к. волновода** waveguide elbow.

коленчат/ый *a.* elbow-shaped, bent; crank, cranked; jointed, articulate; **к. микроскоп** elbow microscope; **к. рычаг** crank; **к. телескоп** elbow telescope; **—ая труба** elbow (pipe); **—ое соединение** elbow joint.

колер *m.* color, tint.

колеренит *m.* colerainite.

колес/ико *n.* small wheel, caster; **—ный** *a.* wheel, wheeled; **—ный механизм** clockwork; **—ная руда** wheel ore.

колесо *n.* wheel; **лопастное к.** impeller; **—видный** *a.* wheel-shaped.

колеч/ко *n.* small ring; **—ный** *a.* ring.

колея *f.* rut, track; (rail) gauge; **узкая к.** narrow gauge.

колиит *m.* collieite.

колинеарный *see* **коллинеарный.**

количеств. *abbr. see* **количественный.**

количественн/ый *a.* quantitative; **к. анализ** quantitative analysis; **к. анализ руд** assay; **—ое числительное** cardinal number.

количество *n.* quantity, amount, number; output; **к. движения** momentum; **к. информации** information content; **к. облаков** cloudiness, sky cover; **к. освещения** (phot.) exposure.

колк/а *m.* splitting, cleaving, chopping; **—ий** *a.* split; cleavable.

Коллара треугольник сил Collar force triangle.

коллатеральный *a.* collateral.

коллбранит *m.* collbranite.

коллег/а *m.* colleague, associate; **—ия** *f.* board.

колледж *m.* college.

коллектив *m.* association, staff; collective body; collective, aggregate; **к.**

сотрудников staff, team; —**изация** *f*. collectivization.

коллективизиров/анный *a*. collective; collectivized; —**анные электроны** collective electrons; —**ать** *v*. collectivize, form an aggregate.

коллективн/ый *a*. collective, cooperative; —**ая антенна** master (or community) antenna; —**ая модель** collective model; —**ое хозяйство** collective farm; —**ые колебания** collective (or cooperative) oscillations.

коллектирование *n*. storing.

коллектор *m*. collector, receiver, catcher; manifold, header; (elec.) commutator; —**ный** *a*. collecting, collector; commutator; —**ный двигатель** commutator motor; —**ный переход** (semicond.) collector junction; —**ный ток** collector current.

коллекци/онировать *v*. collect; —**я** *f*. collection, set.

Колл. жур. *abbr*. (**Коллоидный журнал**) Colloid Journal.

коллигативный *a*. colligative.

коллизия *f*. collision.

коллима/тор *m*. collimator; —**ция** *f*., —**ционный** *a*. collimation.

коллимир/ованный *a*. collimated; —**овать** *v*. collimate; —**ующий конус** collimating cone.

коллинеарн/ый *a*. collinear; —**ая (антенная) решетка** collinear array; —**ые плоскости** collinear (or coaxial) planes.

коллинеац/ионный *a*. collineatory; —**ия** *f*. collineation.

коллинсит *m*. collinsite.

коллирит *m*. collyrite.

коллод/иевый, —**ийный** *a*., —**ий** *m*. collodion.

коллоид *m*., —**ное вещество** colloid; —**альный,** —**ный** *a*. colloid, colloidal; —**альное подвешивание** colloidal suspension.

коллоксилин *see* **коллодий.**

коллофанит *m*. collophanite.

коллюв/ий *m*., —**иальное отложение** colluvial deposit, colluvial soil.

колматаж *m*. settling.

коловорот *m*. brace.

коловратн/ый *a*. rotary, rotative; **к. насос** rotary pump; —**ое движени** gyration.

коловращение *n*. rotation.

кологарифм *m*. cologarithm.

колода *f*. block; pack (of playing cards

колодезн/ый *a*. well; —**ая вода** we water.

колодец *m*. well, pit, sump; **отстойны к.** drain, sewer.

колод/ка *f*., —**очный** *a*. (mech.) sho block; **тормозная к.** brake shoe.

колок *m*. peg, pin.

колокол *m*. bell; bell jar; —**образны** —**оподобный** *a*. bell-shaped; —**о образная кривая** bell-shaped curv

колоколь/ный *a*. bell; **к. металл,** —**на бронза** bell metal; —**ная руда** sta nite; —**чик** *m*. small bell.

колонк/а *f*., —**овый** *a*. column; cor core sample; **к. ионов** column ionization; —**овое бурение** co drilling; —**ообразный** *a*. columnar.

колонн/а *f*. column, pillar; tower; **к капель** band of drops; **к. с тарел ками** plate column; —**ообразны** *see* **колонкообразный**; —**ообразны вихрь** columnar vortex.

колорадоит *m*. coloradoite.

колориметр *m*. colorimeter; —**ически** *a*. colorimetric; —**ия** *f*. colorimetry

колортрон *m*. colortron.

колоссальный *a*. colossal, huge.

колот/ило *n*., —**ушка** *f*. mallet; —**ить** beat, knock.

колоть *v*. split, cleave; pierce.

колофонит *m*. colophonite.

колош/а *f*. (met.) charge; —**ник** *n* furnace top (or throat); —**никовы газ** blast furnace gas.

колпак *m*. cap, cover, cowl, hood, bel cupola; dome (of furnace); lamp shade; **к. астрономического люк** astrodome; **воздушный к.** air cham ber (of pump); **колесный к.** hub cap **паровой к.** steam collector; **стекля нный к.** bell jar.

колпач/ковый, —**ный** *see* **колпак**; **к метод** (chem.) hood method; —**ко вая колонна** bubble-cap column —**ковая тарелка** (chem.) bubbl plate.

колпачок *m*. cap; **к. колонны** (chem bubble cap.

Колпица генератор Colpitts oscillator.

кол/сек *abbr.* (**колебания в секунду**) oscillations per second.

Колумб Colombo (lunar crater).

колумб/иевый *a.* columbic, columbium, niobium; **—ий** *m.* columbium (Cb); niobium (Nb); **—ит** *m.* columbite, niobite.

колусит *m.* colusite.

колчедан *m.* pyrite, pyrites; **железный к., серный к.** iron pyrites, pyrite; **лучистый к.** marcasite. **—ный, —овый** *a.* pyrite, pyritic.

колых/ание *n.* rocking, swaying, swinging, fluctuation; **—ать, —нуть** *v.* rock, sway, swing; **—аться, —нуться** *v.* rock, sway, swing; fluctuate; wave, flutter.

колышек *m.* peg.

кольбек/ин *m.* kolbeckine; **—ит** *m.* kolbeckite.

Кольби печь Colby furnace.

кольнуть *see* **колоть.**

Кольрауш Kohlrausch; **—а закон (независимого движения ионов)** K. law (of independent migration of ions).

Кольский (полуостров) Kola (peninsula).

кольцевание *n.* cyclization; (elec.) completion of circuit, interconnection.

кольцев/ой *a.* ring, ring-shaped, annular, circular; cyclic; **к. анод** orificed anode; **к. десятичный счетчик импульсов** ring-of-ten counter; **к. зазор** (mach.) radial clearance; **к. коллектор** ring header; **к. пленочный дозиметр** film ring (monitor); **к. подпятник** collar bearing, collar-step bearing; **к. разряд** ring discharge; **к. счетчик** annular counter; ring counter; **к. тензиметр** ring tensimeter; **к. трансформатор** toroidal transformer; **к. троечный счетчик импульсов** ring-of-three counter; **к. фокус** ring focus.

кольцев/ой *cont.*, **—ая дислокация** (cryst.) ring dislocation; **—ая заварка** ring seal; **—ая обмотка** (elec.) ring winding; **—ая пересчетная схема** ring scaler; **—ая (ускоряющая) трубка** doughnut (accelerator tube); **—ая цепь** link chain; **—ая щель, —ое пространство** annulus; **—ое соединение** ring compound, cyclic compound; **—ое уплотнение** O-ring seal.

кольцеобразный *a.* ring-shaped, annular, circular, collar-shaped; cyclic.

кольц/о *n.* ring, annulus, collar; coil; link; washer; ball race; **к. вычетов** (math.) residue class ring; **к. диполей** (hyd.) doublet ring; **к. дислокаций** dislocation ring; **к. источников** source ring; **контактное к.** (elec.) slip ring; **замыкание —а** ring closure, cyclization; **разрыв —а, расщепление —а** ring cleavage, cyclic cleavage.

кольчат/ый *a.* ring, ring-shaped, annular; cyclic; **—ое соединение** ring compound, cyclic compound.

ком *abbr.* (**килоом**) kilohm (kohm).

ком *m.* clot, lump, ball, clod; *prepositional of* **кто.**

кома *f.* coma.

комагматический *a.* comagmatic.

команд/а *f.* command; crew, party, team; **к. управления** steering command; **—ировать** *v.* send on a mission; **—ировка** *f.* mission.

командн/ый *a.* control, command; **к. прибор** control device; **к. рычаг** master arm (of manipulator); **—ая система (телеуправления)** command-guidance system; **—ое реле** control relay.

комбайн *m.* combine.

комбинат *m.* combine, complex; **—орика** *f.* combinational analysis; **—орный** *a.* combinatorial.

комбинац/ионный *a.* combination; (spect.) Raman; **к. принцип (Ритца)** (Ritz) combination principle; **к. тон** combination tone; **—ионная частота** combination frequency; **—ионное рассеяние** Raman scattering; combination scattering; **—ия** *f.* combination.

комбинезон *m.* overalls, coveralls.

комбинирован/ие *n.* combination; **—ный** *a.* combined, combination; composite; **—ный поглотитель** composite absorber; **—ная инверсия** combined inversion; **—ная лампа,**

—**ная электронная лампа** multiple-unit tube; —**ная четность** combined parity.

комель *f.* butt.

комета *f.* comet.

Коми АССР Komi ASSR.

комис. *abbr.* (**комиссия**) commission, committee.

коммиссар *m.* commissar; —**иат** *m.* commissariat.

комиссионер *m.* agent, broker.

комисс/ия *f.*, —**ионный** *a.* commission, committee; **междуведомственная к.** joint committee.

Комиссия по атомной энергии Atomic Energy Commission.

комитет *m.* committee.

комкать *v.* crumple.

комков/ание *n.* (met.) nodulizing; —**атый** *a.* clotted, lumped, lumpy.

комма *f.* (mus.) comma.

коммеморативный *a.* commemorative.

коммент/арий *m.* comment, commentary, remarks; —**ировать** *v.* comment.

коммер/сант *m.* business man, merchant —**ция** *f.* commerce, trade; —**ческий** *a.* commercial, business.

коммуна *f.* commune.

коммунальн/ый *a.* communal, public, municipal; —**ая техника** municipal engineering; —**ые предприятия** public utilities.

коммуника/тор *m.* communicator; —**ция** *f.* communication.

коммутативн/ость *f.* commutativity, commutability; **соотношение —ости** commutation relation; —**ый** *a.* commutative, commutation, commutable.

коммутатор *m.* switchboard, commutator; **выпрямляющий к.** commutator rectifier.

коммутац/ионный *a.*, —**ия** *f.* commutation, switching; **к. прибор** switch; —**ионная доска** switchboard; —**ионная скобка** commutator.

коммутир/ование *see* **коммутация**; —**ованный** *a.* (elec.) commutated, commuted; —**овать** *v.* commutate, commute, switch, reverse; —**ующий** *a.* commuting, commutative; —**ующий оператор** commutative operator.

комнат/а *f.* room; —**ный** *a.* room, indoor.

ком/овой *a.* ball, lump, clot; —**ок** *m.* lump, clump, clot; —**ками, в —ках** in lumps, lumpy, clotted; **осадок —ками** nodular deposit.

комол *m.* Comol (Remalloy) (iron-molybdenum-cobalt alloy).

комоч/ек *m.* small clump; **образовать —ки** clot.

компактн/ость *f.* compactness, density compaction; —**ый** *a.* compact, dense solid.

компандор *m.* (rad.) compander.

компан/ия *f.* company; party; —**ьон** *m* partner, companion.

компар/атор *m.* (elec.) comparator —**ирование** *n.* comparison, standardization.

Компас Pyxis (Pyx) (constellation).

компас *m.*, —**ный** *a.* compass; **горный к.** surveying compass; **небесный к** astrocompass; —**ный пеленг** compass bearing; —**ный румб** compass point; —**ная рама** gimbal suspension; —**ная стрелка** compass needle

компаунд *m.* compound; **к.-машина** (elec.) compound generator; **к.-обмотка** compound winding; **турбина к.** compound turbine.

компаундиров/ание *n.* compounding —**анный** *a.* compounded, compound compound-wound; —**ать** *v.* compound.

компаунд/ирующий *a.* compounding —**ный** *a.* compound, compound wound.

компендиум *m.* compendium, digest.

компенсатор *m.* compensator, balancer equalizer; —**ный сплав** compensator alloy.

компенсационн/ый *a.* compensation balance, equalizing; **к. пиргелиометр** compensating pyrheliometer **к. провод** compensating lead; —**ая камера** compensation chamber; —**ая катушка** compensating coil; —**ая часть** expansion piece.

компенсация *f.* compensation, balance equalizing; **к. аэродинамическая** aerodynamic balance.

компенсиров/ание *see* **компенсация**

—**анный** *a.* compensated, compensation, balanced; —**ать** *v.* compensate, cancel; neutralize; balance.

компенсирующ/ий *a.* compensating, equalizing; balancing; **к. стержень** shim rod; —**ая способность** (reactor) reactivity equivalent (of regulating rod); —**ее устройство** equalizer, compensator, balancer.

компетен/тность, —**ция** *f.* competence, ability; —**тный** *a.* competent.

компил/ировать *v.* compile; —**яция** *f.* compilation.

компланарн/ость *f.* coplanarity; —**ый** *a.* coplanar; —**ая схема** coplanar network.

комплекс *m.* complex; (chem.) group; aggregate, cluster, combination; **к. условий** set of conditions; **в** —**е с** combined with; —**но-сопряженный** *a.* complex conjugate; —**ность** *f.* complexity.

комплексн/ый *a.* (math.) complex; composite, combined, total; all-round; **к. институт** institute for comprehensive study; **к. ион** complex ion; **к. потенциал** complex potential; —**ая плоскость** complex plane; —**ая проводимость** (elec.) complex (or vector) admittance; —**ое сопротивление** (elec.) complex (or vector) impedance.

комплексообраз/ование *n.* (chem.) complexing; —**ующее вещество** complexing agent; —**ующее действие** complexing action.

комплект *m.* set, assembly; **к. активной зоны** (reactor) core assembly; **к. горючего** fuel assembly; —**ный** *a.* complete; —**ование** *n.* acquisition, completing; occupying, replacing; staffing; —**овать** *v.* complete (a set); staff; replenish.

композ/итный *a.* composite; —**иция** *f.* composition.

компонент *m.* component, constituent, ingredient.

компонента *f.* component; **к. высокой энергии** high-energy component; **к. деформации** strain component; **к. напряжения** stress component; **к. тензора деформации** strain (tensor) component.

компонов/ать *v.* arrange, group; —**ка** *f.* layout, installation, arrangement, grouping.

компресс/ия *f.*, —**ионный** *a.* compression; —**ометр** *m.* compressometer; —**ор** *m.*, —**орный** *a.* compressor.

компримирование *n.* compression.

компром/етировать *v.*, —**исс** *m.*, —**иссный** *a.* compromise; **не идущий на** —**исс** uncompromising.

комптометр *m.* comptometer.

комптон-эффект, Комптона эффект (**явление**) Compton effect.

комптонит *m.* comptonite.

комптоновск/ий электрон Compton electron; —**ая длина волны** C. wavelength; —**ое рассеяние** C. scattering.

ком-т *abbr.* (**комитет**) committee.

кому *dat. of* **кто,** to whom.

комучит *m.* comuccite.

комья *pl. of* **ком.**

конвейер *m.*, —**ный** *a.* conveyer; —**ная работа** assembly line work.

конвективн/ый *a.* convective, convection, convectional; —**ая зона** convective zone; —**ая оболочка** convective shell; —**ая ячейка** convection cell.

конвекционн/ый *see* **конвективный; к. потенциал** convective potential; **к. ток** convection current; —**ая потеря** convection loss; —**ое поле** convective field; —**ое преломление** convective refraction.

конвекция *f.* convection.

конвенция *f.* convention.

конверген/тный *a.* convergent; —**ция** *f.* convergence.

конверсионн/ый *a.* conversion; **к. электрон** conversion electron; —**ая линия** conversion line.

конверс/ия *f.* conversion; **к. на** ***K*-оболочке** *K*-conversion; **к. на** ***L*-оболочке** *L*-conversion; **коэффициент** —**ии** (internal) conversion coefficient; conversion ratio (or fraction).

конверт *m.* envelope, cover.

конверт/ер, —**ор** *m.*, —**ерный** *a.* converter; —**ирование** *n.* conversion; —**ированный** *a.* converted; —**ировать** *v.* convert.

конгломер/ат *m.* agglomeration, cluster,

blob; (geo.) conglomerate; **—ация** *f.* conglomeration.

конгруентн/ость *f.* congruence; **—ый** *a.* congruent; **—ое преобразование** congruent transformation.

Кондамин Condamine (lunar crater).

конденсат *m.* condensate; condensation; condensed water.

конденсатор *m.* capacitor; condenser; **к. добавочный** aftercondenser; **к. настройки** (elec.) tuning capacitor; **к. предварительный** precondenser; **к. связи** coupling capacitor, cross-coupling condenser; **струйный к.** spray condenser.

конденсаторн/ый *a.* capacitor; condenser; **к. агрегат** multiple condenser; **к. горшок** steam trap; **к. дозиметр** condenser dosimeter; **к. микрофон** capacitor microphone; **—ая антенна** condenser antenna; **—ая линза** condensing lens; **—ая связь** capacitor coupling.

конденсационн/ый *a.* condensation, condensing; **к. аппарат** condensing apparatus, condenser; **к. горшок** *see* **конденсаторный горшок**; **к. змеевик** condenser coil; **к. насос** diffusion pump; **—ая вода** condensation water, condensed water; **—ая камера** condensing chamber, cloud chamber; **—ая точка** condensation point.

конденсация *f.* condensation; **к. колец** (chem.) fusion of rings; **к. на ионах** ion condensation.

конденсиров/ание *n.* condensation; **—анный** *a.* condensed; **—анное кольцо** (chem.) fused ring; **—ать** *v.* condense.

конденсирующий *a.* condensing; **—ся** *a.* condensing, condensable; **—ся пар** condensable vapor.

конденсит *m.* condensite.

конденсор *m.* (opt.) condenser; **—ная система** condensing system.

кондиционер *m.* conditioner.

кондициониров/ание *n.* conditioning; **к. воздуха** air conditioning; **—анный** *a.* conditioned; **—ать** *v.* condition.

кондиц/ионный *a.* conditional; **—ия** *f.* condition.

Кондорсе Condorcet (lunar crater).

кондуктивн/ость *f.* conductivity; **—ый** *a.* conductive.

кондуктор *m.*, **—ный** *a.* conductor; (mach.) jig.

кондукц/ионный *a.* conduction, conductive; **—ия** *f.* conduction.

конель *m.* Konel metal.

кон/ец *m.* end, close; end point; extremity, tip; terminal; purpose; lead; **—цом** end on; **в —це —цов** finally, ultimately; in the long run; **вид с —ца** end view.

конечно *adv.* of course, certainly, surely.

конечно— *prefix* finite, finitely.

конечно/мерный *a.* finite-dimensional; **—разностная формула** finite-difference formula; **—сть** *f.* finiteness, finitude.

—конечный *suffix* pointed.

конечн/ый *a.* final, ultimate, residual, terminal, end; finite; **к. момент, —ая точка** end point; **к. предел колебания** amplitude of vibration; **к. продукт** end product, final product; **к. радиус** terminal radius; **к. результат** end result; **к. ряд** finite series; **в —ом итоге, в —ом счете** eventually, in the final analysis; **—ая длина** finite length; **—ая реакция** end reaction; **—ая скорость** final (or terminal) velocity; **—ое множество** finite set; **—ое ядро** product nucleus, residual nucleus.

кониметр *m.* (min.) konimeter (for measuring dust); **—ический** *a.* konimetric.

конинкит *m.* koninckite.

кониской *m.* koniscope.

конихальцит *m.* conichalcite.

коническ/ий *a.* conic, conical, cone; bevel; tapered; **к. клапан** cone valve; **к. подпятник** conical bearing; **—ая колба** Erlenmeyer flask; **—ое зубчатое колесо** bevel gear; **—ое сечение** conic section.

коничность *f.* conicity, angle of taper.

конкрет/изация *f.* concrete (or specific) definition; **—изировать** *v.* specify; **—ность** *f.* concreteness; **—ный** *a.* concrete, specific.

конкрец/ионный *a.* concretionary, nodular; **—ия** *f.* concretion, nodule.

конкур/ент *m.* competitor; **—ентный** *a.* competing; concurrent; **—енция** *f.* competition; **—ирующий** *a.* competing, competitive; **—ирующие схемы** competitive modes.

конкурс *m.* competition; **—ный** *a.* competing.

коннарит *m.* connarite.

Коновалова закон Konovalov (Konowaloff) rule.

коноид *m.*, **—альный** *a.* conoid.

коноп/атить *v.* calk; **—атка** *f.* calking; calking iron; **—атный** *a.*, **—ачение** *n.* calking.

коноскоп *m.* conoscope; **—ический** *a.* conoscopic.

конперник *m.* Conpernic (iron-nickel alloy).

консекутивный *a.* consecutive.

консерв/ативный *a.* conservative; **—атизм** *m.* conservatism; **—ация** *f.* conservation.

консертальный *a.* consertal.

консист/ентный *a.* consistent; **—енция** *f.* consistence; consistency; **—ометр** *m.* consistometer.

Конская голова Horsehead (nebula).

конские широты horse latitudes.

консолид/ация *f.* consolidation; **—ированный** *a.* consolidated; **—ировать** *v.* consolidate.

консоль *f.*, **—ный** *a.* console, cantilever, angle bracket, arm; **—ный кран** cantilever crane, bracket crane; **—ный подшипник** bracket bearing; **—ная балка, —ная ферма** cantilever.

консонанс *m.* consonance.

конспект *m.*, **—ивный** *a.* abstract, synopsis, summary; **—ивность** *f.* summarization; sketchiness; **—ировать** *v.* abstract, summarize.

константа *f.* constant; *see also* **постоянная**; **к. взаимодействия** coupling constant; **к. распада** decay constant (or coefficient); disintegration constant (or coefficient); **к. связи** coupling constant; **к. скорости** reaction rate.

константан *m.*, **—овый** *a.* constantan.

констатировать *v.* state; ascertain.

конститутивный *a.* constitutive, constitutional.

конституционн/ый *a.* constitutional, constitution; **—ая вода** constitution water; **—ая формула** constitutional formula.

конституция *f.* constitution.

конструиров/ание *n.* construction, designing; **—ать** *v.* construct, design, organize.

конструктивн/ость *f.* designability; **—ый** *a.* constructive, constructional, structural; **—ый шов** structural joint; **—ая переменная** design variable; **—ая черта** design feature.

конструктор *m.* constructor, designer; **—ский** *a.* constructor; structural.

конструкционн/ый *a.* construction, structural design; **к. материал** structural material; **—ая сталь** structural steel.

конструкц/ия *f.* construction; design; **последней —ии** of recent design.

консульт/ант *m.* consultant; tutor; **—ативный** *a.* consultative, consulting, advisory; **—ация** *f.* consultation; (meteor.) analysis; **—ировать** *v.* consult.

консумптивное составляющее (mag.) dissipative component.

контакт *m.* contact; **к. неплотный** loose contact; **к. плотный** close contact; **—ировать** *v.* make contact; **—ирующий** *a.* contiguous; **—но-разрывной механизм** (elec.) make-and-break mechanism.

контактн/ый *a.* contact; **к. микрофон** contact microphone; **к. термометр** contact thermometer; **—ая камера** catalyst chamber; **—ая радиоавтография** contact radioautography; **—ая разность потенциалов** contact potential (difference); **—ое вещество, —ое средство** contact agent, catalyst.

контакт/овый *see* **контактный**; **—ор** *m.* contactor.

контейнер *m.* container.

контекст *m.* context.

контингент *m.* contingent, quota.

континент *m.* continent; **—альный** *a.* continental.

контину/альный *a.* continuous; **—ум** *m.* continuum; **—умное обтекание** continuous streamline flow.

контор/а *f.* office, bureau; **—ка** *f.* writing desk.

контр(а)— *prefix* counter—, contra—.

контравалентность *f.* contravalence.

контравариант *m.*, **—ный** *a.* contravariant.

контрагент *m.* contractor.

контрагир/ование *n.* contraction, constriction; **—овать** *v.* contract, constrict; **—ующий** *a.* contracting, constraining.

контрагредиентный *a.* contragredient.

контракт *m.* contract, agreement; **—ант** *m.* contractor.

контракц/ионная гипотеза (Fitzgerald-Lorentz) contraction hypothesis; **—ия** *f.* contraction, constriction.

контрапрош *m.* counterapproach.

контраст *m.* contrast; **—ировать** *v.* contrast, compare; **—ность** *f.* (degree of) contrast; **коэффициент —ности** (phot.) gamma; **—ный** *a.* contrast, contrasting; **—ное изображение** (telev.) high-contrast (or hard) image.

контр/гайка *f.* lock (check, retainer, safety) nut; keeper; **—груз** *m.* counterweight, counterbalance; **—калибр** *m.* countergauge, standard (control, master) gauge; **—клин** *m.* counterwedge; gib, tightening key; **—мера** *f.* countermeasure.

контролер *m.* controller, inspector; monitor.

контролир/ование *n.*, **—овка** *f.* control, supervision; **—ованный** *a.* controlled, control; **—овать** *v.* check, monitor, control; **—уемая реакция** controlled reaction; **—ующий** *a.* controlling, supervisory; **—ующее устройство** monitor.

контроллер *m.* (elec.) controller; **ведущий к.** master switch.

контроль *m.* control, monitoring, checking; inspection, supervision; standardization; **к. радиоактивности** radiation monitoring; **—но-измерительные приборы** instrumentation.

контрольн/ый *a.* control, regulating, supervisory; check, test; pilot; monitor, monitoring; reference; **к. анализ** check analysis; **к. импульс** control pulse, reference pulse; **к. калибр** check gauge, master gauge, reference gauge; **к. канал** monitoring channel, pilot channel; **к. клапан** check valve; **к. монитор** monitor counter; **к. прибор** monitoring instrument; **к. сигнал** pilot signal; **к. стержень** control rod; **к. счетчик** monitor counter; **к. уровень** reference level; **к. щиток, —ая доска** dashboard, instrument board; **—ая ионизационная камера** monitor ionization chamber; **—ая лампа** pilot light (or lamp); **—ая линия** guide line; **—ая отметка** reference (or fiducial) mark; **—ая точка** reference (or check) point; **—ая фольга** monitoring foil; **—ая цепь** test (pilot, control, supervisory) circuit; **—ая частота** pilot frequency; **—ое определение** control determination; **—ые характеристики работы** reference performance.

контр/пар *m.* countersteam, back steam; **—поршень** *m.* counterpiston.

контрпривод *m.*, **—ный вал** countershaft.

контр/рельс *m.* guard rail, guide rail. **—ток** *m.* countercurrent, counterflow; **—фланец** *m.* counterflange.

контрфорс *m.* buttress; **—ная плотина** buttress dam.

контрчлен *m.* counterterm.

контур *m.* contour, outline; loop, path, circuit; (elec.) mesh; **набрасывать к.** outline; **к.-резервуар** tank circuit; **к. сместителя** (rad.) injection circuit; **линия —а** contour (line); **—ный** *a.* contour, outline; **—ный интеграл** contour integral; **—ный чертеж** outline drawing; **—ная диаграмма** contour diagram, topological plot; **—ная сила** (elast.) boundary force; **—ное условие** boundary condition.

конус *m.* cone; **ветровой к.** wind sleeve; **к. равных моментов инерции** equimomental cone; **к. скорости** velocity cone; **усеченный к.** frustum; **угол раствора —а** angle of taper.

конусн/о-цилиндрический *a.* cylindroconic; **—ость** *f.* conicity, (angle of) taper; **угол —ости** angle of taper; **—ый** *a.* cone, conic, conical; bevel; tapered, wedge-type; **—ое облу-**

...чение (rad.) gable illumination; —ое уплотнение wedge-type seal.

...нусо/видность, —образность *f.* conicity, taper; —видный, —образный *a.* cone-shaped, conoid, conical; tapered.

...нференция *f.* conference.

...нфигурац/ионный *a.* configuration, configurational; —ия *f.* configuration; —ия электронов electronic configuration.

...нфиденциальный *a.* confidential, private.

...нфликт *m.* conflict.

...нфлюэн/тный гипергеометрический ряд confluent hypergeometric series; —ция *f.* confluence.

...нфокальный *a.* confocal.

...нфоленсит *m.* confolensite.

...нформн/о-инвариантый *a.* conformally invariant; —ость *f.* conformability; —ый *a.* conformal; —ая связность (Вейля) (Weill's) affine connection; —ое отображение conformal mapping (or representation); —ое преобразование conformal transformation.

...нфузор *m.* convergent channel, nozzle.

...нхит *m.* conchite.

...нхоида *f.* conchoid; —льный *a.* conchoidal.

...нцевой *a.* end, terminal, *see also* конечный; к. эффект end effect.

...нцентрат *m.* concentrate; —ор *m.* concentrator.

...нцентрационн/ый *a.* concentration; к. аппарат concentrator; к. элемент concentration cell; —ое тушение concentration quenching.

...нцентрация *f.* concentration, abundance, density; атомная к. atomic percentage; к. по массе mass concentration; к. по объему volume concentration.

...нцентрир/ование *n.* concentration; —ованный *a.* concentrated; —овать *v.* concentrate; —ующий *a.* concentrating.

...нцентрич/еский *a.* concentric; —еская разделительная колонна coaxial-tube separating column; —ность *f.* concentricity.

...нцепция *f.* conception, idea.

концессия *f.* concession.

конц-ия *abbr.* (концентрация) concentration.

конч/ать, —ить *v.* finish, end, complete; —аться *v.* end, expire, lapse; —енный *a.* finished, completed.

кончик *m.* tip.

конъюгирован/ие *n.* conjugation; —ный *a.* conjugated, conjugate; —ные двойные связи conjugated double bonds.

конъюнктура *f.* conjuncture, juncture; situation.

кооп. *abbr.* (кооперативный) cooperative.

коопер/атив *m.*, —ативный *a.* cooperative; —ация *f.*, —ирование *n.* cooperation; —ированный *a.* affiliated; —ировать *v.* cooperate.

кооптировать *v.* coopt.

координат/а *f.* (math.) coordinate; —ы вращения rotational coordinates; —ный *a.* coordinate, coordinated; —ная сетка coordinate system (or network); reference grid; —ор цели (radar) homing coordinator.

координационн/ый *a.* coordination; —ая изомерия coordination isomerism; —ая связь coordination bond (or link); —ая сфера coordination sphere; —ое соединение coordination compound; —ое число coordination number.

координация *f.* coordination.

координиров/анный *a.* coordinated, coordinate; —ать *v.* coordinate.

коп. *abbr.* (копейка) kopeck.

копалит *m.* copalite.

коп/ание *n.* digging; —ать *v.* dig.

копараллел/изм *m.* coparallelism; —ьный *a.* coparallel.

копейка *f.* kopeck.

копер *m.* pile driver, ram impact machine, drop hammer.

Коперник Copernicus (lunar crater).

Коперника система Copernican system.

копиапит *m.* copiapite.

копильник *m.* (met.) forehearth, receiver.

копир *m.* master form; —ный *a.* copy.

копировальн/ый *a.* copying, duplicating; к. аппарат, —ое приспособление duplicator, duplicating device; к.

станок copying machine; —**ая бумага** carbon paper; tracing paper; —**ая краска** transfer color; —**ая рамка** printing frame.

копиров/ание *n.* copying, tracing; (phot.) printing; —**ать** *v.* copy, duplicate; trace.

копирующ/ий *a.* copying, duplicating; **к. запястный сустав** slave wrist joint (of manipulator); **к. манипулятор** master-slave manipulator; —**ее сочленение** slave joint (of manipulator).

копить *v.* store, accumulate, collect.

коп/ия *f.*, **снимать** —**ию** copy, duplicate.

копланарный *see* **компланарный.**

кополимер *see* **сополимер.**

копотливый *a.* sluggish, slow; tedious.

копоть *f.* lampblack, soot.

Коппа(-Неймана) правило Kopp law (for molar specific heat).

копровый *a.* pile-driver.

копролит *m.* coprolite.

копунктальный *a.* copunctal.

копь *f.* mine, pit.

кора *f.* cortex; crust; (casting) skin; **земная к.** (geo.) crust.

кораб/ельный *a.* ship, marine; —**ельная метеостанция** stationary weather ship; —**лестроение** *n.* shipbuilding; —**ль** *m.* ship, vessel.

коралловый *a.* coral.

корацит *m.* coracite.

Корбино диск Corbino disk.

корвусит *m.* corvusite.

корд *m.*, —**а** *f.* cord.

кордиерит *m.* cordierite.

кордилит *m.* cordylite.

кордит *m.* cordite.

корекс *m.* Corex.

корен/астый *a.* thickset, stumpy, stocky; —**иться** *v.* be founded on, have roots in, lie in.

коренн/ой *a.* root; radical, fundamental, basic, original; native; main; thorough; **к. вал** crankshaft; **к. подшипник** main bearing; —**ым образом** radically; —**ая свая** foundation pile.

кор/ень *m.* root; radical; **квадратный к.** square root; **кубический к.** cube root; **в —не** radically, fundamentally; **знак —ня** radical sign; **показатель —ня** root index, index of radical.

корзин/а, —**ка** *f.* basket; —**очная к**
тушка basket coil, Lorenz coil.

коридор *m.* corridor, passage; —**н**
порядок straight-line order.

коринит *m.* corynite.

Кориолиса коэффициент Coriolis c
efficient; **К. сила** C. force.

коричневый *a.* brown.

коричный камень cinnamon stone.

корка *f.* crust; (casting) skin.

коркит *m.* corkite.

Корма Puppis (Pup) (constellation).

корм/а *f.* stern; —**овой** *a.* stern; fee
intake; —**овая волна** stern wav
—**овая часть** afterbody; intake pa
feed end.

корнваллит *m.* cornwallite.

корневой *a.* root, radical; *see al*
коренной; **к. знак** radical sign.

корнетит *m.* cornetite.

Корнинга стекло Corning glass.

корнуит *m.* cornuite.

Корню спираль Cornu spiral; **К.-Гар**
мана формула C.-Hartmann formu

коробить, —**ся** *v.* warp.

коробка *f.* box, case, casing, che
housing; **к. передач, к. скорост**
transmission.

коробление *n.* warping, buckling.

короб/очка *f.* small box; —**очный**
box, case; —**чатый** *a.* box, box-lik
—**чатая балка** shell beam.

коровальт *m.* Corowalt.

короизотерма *m.* choroisotherm.

королек *m.* (met.) regulus.

коромысло *n.* yoke, balance bea
balance arm, rocker.

корона *f.* corona; crown.

коронадит *m.* coronadite.

корональн/ый луч coronal ray; —
дуга coronal arch; —**ая пусто**
(astr.) coronal cavity.

коронен *m.* coronene.

короний *m.* coronium.

корониров/ание *n.* corona, corona d
charge; —**ать** *v.* (elec.) displ
corona.

коронирующ/ий разряд corona, coro
discharge; **к. стабилизатор напр**
жения corona-tube voltage regulato
к. электрод corona electrode; —
лампа corona tube; —**ее остр**
corona point.

корон/ка *f.* crown; (min.) bit; —**ный** *a.* crown, corona; —**ный разряд** *see* **коронирующий разряд**; —**ная шестерня** crown wheel.

короно/визор *m.* (astr.) coronavisor; —**граф** *m.* coronagraph.

корончатый *see* **коронный**; **к. бур** crown drill.

коросил *m.* Koroseal.

коротк/ий *a.* short, brief; **к. импульс** short burst; (elec.) narrow pulse; —**ая волна** short wave; —**ое замыкание** short circuit; —**о** *adv.* briefly.

коротко— *prefix* short.

коротко/волновой *a.* short-wave; —**волокнистый** *a.* short-fibered; —**действие** *n.* short-range interaction (or force); —**действующая сила** short-range force; —**живущий** *a.* short-lived; —**замкнутый** *a.* (elec.) short-circuited, short-circuit; —**замыкатель** *m.* short-circuiting device; —**замыкающий** *a.* short-circuiting; —**периодный** *a.* short-period, short-range; —**плечий** *a.* short-arm (balance); —**пробежная частица** short-range particle; —**сть** *f.* shortness, brevity; —**фокусный** *a.* short-focus.

короче *comp. of* **короткий, коротко,** shorter.

корочка *f.* crust, skin, thin layer.

корпоидальный *a.* field, fieldlike.

корпора/тивный *a.* corporate; —**ция** *f.* corporation, body.

корпус *m.* body, carcass, frame; hull; housing, case, casing; building; (math.) field; **к. двигателя** engine block; **к. облачной системы** body of cloud system; **к. реактора** reactor vessel.

корпускула *f.* corpuscle; **солнечная к.** solar particle.

корпускулярн/о-волновой дуализм particle-wave dualism; —**ый** *a.* corpuscular; —**ый поток** corpuscular stream; —**ая теория света** corpuscular theory of light; **земное —ое излучение** (Van Allen) earth radiation belt.

корразия *f.* corrasion.

корректив *m.* correction, amendment; corrective.

корректиров/анный *a.* corrected, compensated; —**ать** *v.* correct, adjust; —**ка** *f.* correction; —**очно-предохранительный стержень** shim-safety rod; —**очный** *a.* corrective; —**очный стержень** (reactor) shim rod.

коррект/ирующий *a.* correcting, adjusting; —**ность** *f.* correctness; —**ный** *a.* correct, proper; —**ор** *m.* corrector; proofreader; —**ура** *f.* correction; proof (page); proofreading; —**урный лист** proof sheet.

коррекц/ионный *a.* correction; **к. множитель** correction factor; —**ия** *f.* correction, compensation.

коррел/ат, —**ят** *m.* correlate, correlative; —**ированность** *f.* correlation; —**ированный** *a.* correlated; —**ограмма** *f.* correlogram, correlation table; —**ятивный** *a.* correlative.

корреляц/ионный *a.* correlation, correlating; **к. момент** (stat.) covariance; —**ионная связь** correlation; —**ионное детектирование** correlation detection; —**ия** *f.* correlation; —**ии коэффициент** correlation coefficient.

корреспонден/т *m.* correspondent; —**ция** *f.* correspondence; report.

корродир/ованный *a.* corroded; —**овать** *v.* corrode; —**ующий** *a.* corroding, corrosive.

коррозие/стойкий, —**устойчивый** *a.* corrosion-resistant, noncorroding, rustproof; stainless (steel); —**стойкость,** —**устойчивость** *f.* corrosion resistance.

коррозийный *a.* corrosion; corrosive.

коррозионн/ость *f.* corrosiveness; —**ый** *see* **коррозийный**; —**ая активность** corrosivity; —**ая устойчивость** *see* **коррозиеустойчивость**; —**ое растрескивание** corrosion cracking.

коррозия *f.* corrosion; **местная к., точечная к.** pitting.

Корта сопло Kort nozzle.

Корти орган organ of Corti.

корубин *m.* Corubin.

корунд *m.* corundum; —**еллит** *m.* corundellite; —**офилит** *m.* corundophilite.

корытн/ый *a.* trough, U-shaped, trough-shaped; —**ое железо** U-iron, channel iron.

корыто *n.* trough, pan; —**образный** *see* **корытный;** —**образный отражатель** (rad.) snow-shovel reflector.

коса *f.* scythe; braid; **намывная к.** (geo.) spit; neck, point.

косвенн/ый *a.* indirect; oblique; circumstantial (evidence); **к. накал** indirect heating; **к. обмен** (sol.) superexchange, indirect exchange; —**ым образом** indirectly; —**ое возбуждение** indirect excitation; —**ое обменное взаимодействие** superexchange (interaction).

косейс/мический *a.* coseismal; —**та** *f.* coseismal curve (or line).

косеканс *m.* cosecant; —**но-квадратичный** *a.* cosecant-squared.

косинус *m.* cosine; —**оида** *f.*, —**оидальная кривая** cosine curve; —**оидальный** *a.* cosinusoidal.

косить, —**ся** *v.* slope, slant.

космическ/ий *a.* cosmic, (outer) space; **к. корабль** spaceship; **к. шум** cosmic noise; —**ая постоянная** (rel.) cosmological constant; —**ая ракета** space rocket (or probe); —**ое излучение** cosmic radiation; —**ое поглощение** interstellar absorption; —**ое пространство** outer space; —**ое расширение** cosmic expansion; —**ие лучи** cosmic rays; —**ие помехи** star static, cosmic jamming, Jansky noise.

космогония *f.* cosmogony.

космолог/ический *a.* cosmological; —**ия** *f.* cosmology.

космонавт *m.* astronaut; —**ика** *f.* astronautics, interplanetary navigation.

космос *m.* cosmos, outer space.

космотрон *m.* cosmotron.

косн/еть *v.* stagnate; —**ость** *f.* inertia, stagnation, sluggishness.

коснуться *see* **касаться.**

косный *a.* inert, stagnant, sluggish.

косо *adv.* obliquely, skew; —**ватость** *f.* obliquity; —**гор** *m.* incline, slope.

кос/ой *a.* slanting, sloping, oblique, diagonal, skew; **к. крестик** X (figure); **к. луч** skew ray; **к. удар** glancing collision; —**ая конгруэнция** (opt.) skew congruence; —**ая кривая** skew curve; —**ое преломление** oblique refraction.

косо/прицельный *a.* (mil.) oblique; —**симметрический,** —**симметричный** *a.* skew-symmetric, antisymmetric; —**слоистый** *a.* (geo.) cross-bedded; —**сть** *f.* obliquity, bias; —**угольный** *a.* oblique-angled; beveled; —**угольный треугольник** oblique triangle; —**усеченный** *a.* truncated.

коссаит *m.* cossaite.

Косселя теория Kossel theory.

коссирит *m.* cossyrite.

Коста-Рибейро эффект *see* **термодиэлектрический эффект.**

костенеть *v.* ossify.

Костинского явление Kostinskii effect.

кост/ный *a.* bone, osseous; —**ная проводимость** bone conduction; —**очка** *f.* small bone.

костыль *m.*, —**ный** *a.* spike.

кость *f.* bone; **игральная к.** die; —**як** *m.* skeleton, framework.

костян/ой *a.* bone; **к. уголь,** —**ая чернь** bone black, animal charcoal.

косынка *f.* corner plate.

косяк *m.* jamb; (door) post.

котангенс *m.* cotangent.

котел *m.* boiler; (nuclear) reactor, pile; **к. малой мощности** low-power reactor; **паровой к.** steam boiler; **к. с графитовым замедлителем** graphite-moderated reactor; **к. с мгновенным парообразованием** flash-type boiler; **к. с тяжелой водой** heavy-water reactor; **к.-утилизатор** waste-heat boiler; —**ьная** *f.* boiler room, boiler house.

котельн/ый *a.* boiler; reactor; **к. спектр нейтронов** reactor neutron spectrum; —**ое железо** boiler plate.

котидальный *a.* cotidal.

котиров/ать *v.* quote, cite; —**ка** *f.* quotation.

котло/ван *m.* foundation pit; —**вина** *f.* basin, pot hole, trough, syncline; —**вой осциллятор** (reactor) pile oscillator; —**образный провал** (geo.) cauldron, pot hole.

который *a. and pron.* which? what; which, that, who.

котрель *m.* Cottrell precipitator; **Котреля процесс** C. process, C. precipitation; **Котреля фильтр** C. gas cleaner.

коттигит *m.* köttigite.

Коттон-Мутона постоянная Cotton-Mouton magnetic birefringence constant.

Коттрелла облако Cottrell atmosphere.

котуннит *m.* cotunnite.

коук *m.* coking coal.

Коулинг Cowling.

кофункция *f.* cofunction.

коффинит *m.* coffinite.

Коха колба Koch flask.

кохез/ионная сила cohesive force; **—ия** *f.* cohesion.

кохерер *see* **когерер.**

кочубеит *m.* kotschubeite.

кошачий глаз cat's eye.

Коши задача Cauchy (boundary) problem; **интеграл К.** C. integral formula; **признак сходимости К.** C. convergence test; **К.-Римана условие** C.-Riemann condition (equation); **К. соотношения** C. relations; **К. теорема жесткости** C. rigidity theorem; **К. формула** C. formula.

кошка *f.* grapnel; drag; car (of crane).

коэнзим *m.* coenzyme.

коэрцит/ивность *f.* coercivity; **—ивный** *a.* coercive; **—ивная сила** coercive force; **—иметр** *m.* coercimeter.

коэрц. сила *abbr.* (**коэрцитивная сила**) coercive force.

коэфициент *see* **коэффициент.**

коэфф. *abbr. see* **коэффициент.**

коэффициент *m.* coefficient, factor, ratio, constant, number; **к. асимметрии** asymmetry parameter; **к. в уравнении трех-вторых** (elec.) perveance; **к. конформной связности** (rel.) component of affine connection; **к. полезного действия** efficiency (ratio); **к. при** (math.) coefficient of; **к. прозрачности** transmission coefficient; **к. расширения** coefficient of expansion; **к. стоячей волны напряжения** standing-wave ratio (swr); **к. теплопередачи** coefficient of heat transfer.

коядро *n.* cokernel.

кп [*in steel mark* (**кипящая**)] rimming, rimmed.

КП *abbr.* (**кислородный потенциал**) oxygen potential; (**коммунистическая партия**) Communist Party.

к.п.д. *abbr.* (**коэффициент полезного действия**) efficiency.

КПИ *abbr.* (**Киевский политехнический институт**) Kiev Polytechnic Institute.

КПСС *abbr.* (**Коммунистическая партия Советского Союза**) Communist Party of the Soviet Union.

краев/ой *a.* boundary, edge; region, district; **к. слой** boundary layer, outer zone; **к. угол** contact angle; **к. эффект** fringe effect, edge effect; **—ая дислокация** edge dislocation; **—ая задача** boundary value problem; **—ая люминесценция** edge emission; **—ое столкновение** grazing collision; **—ое условие** boundary condition.

краеугольный камень cornerstone.

край *m.* edge, rim, limit, boundary, border; end, tip; region; **главный к. поглощения** chief (x-ray) absorption edge; **к. линии поглощения** *K* *K* absorption edge; **к. (полосы) поглощения** absorption edge; **к. солнца** solar limb.

крайне *adv.* extremely.

крайн/ий *a.* extreme, outmost; last, end, outer, outside; **к. случай** limiting case, limit; **к. член пропорции** (math.) extreme; **—яя необходимость** emergency; **—ее значение** limiting value; **в —ем случае** as a last resort; **по —ей мере** at least.

крайност/ь *f.* extreme, extremity; emergency; excess; **впадать в —и** run to extremes; **до —и** to excess.

Крамера правило Cramer rule.

Крамерсов дублет Kramers doublet.

кран *m.* cock, stopcock, tap, faucet, valve; crane; **водомерный к.** gauge cock; **подъемный к.** crane.

крандаллит *m.* crandallite.

краник *m.* petcock.

крантцит *m.* krantzite.

крап/ать *v.* spot, speckle; **—чатый** *a.* spotted, speckled, mottled, marbled.

краруп/изация *f.* (elec.) Krarup loading, continuous loading; **—изированный** *a.* continuously loaded; **—изировать**

v. load continuously; **—овский кабель** Krarup cable.
красивый *a.* beautiful, fine.
красильн/ый *a.* dye; **к. камень** dyestone; **—ое вещество** dyestuff, dye.
красит/ель *m.* dye, dyestuff; pigment; **—ь** *v.* dye, color, stain, paint.
краска *f.* paint, dye, color, pigment; dyeing, painting.
краснеть *v.* redden.
красно/бурый *a.* reddish brown; **—ватый** *a.* reddish; **—зем** *m.* terra rossa, red earth.
краснокалильный *a.* red-hot; **к. жар** red heat.
красноломк/ий, —остный *a.* (met.) red-short, hot-short, hot-brittle; **—ость** *f.* red-shortness, hot-brittleness.
красностойкость *f.* (met.) red hardness.
красн/ый *a.* red; **к. железняк** red hematite; **к. накал** red heat; **—ая граница фотоэффекта** photoelectric threshold; **—ая медь** pure copper; **—ая охра** red ocher; **—ое каление** red heat; **—ое смещение** red shift.
красота *f.* beauty, fineness.
красть *v.* steal.
красящее вещество dyestuff.
кратер *m.* crater; **—ная лампа** crater lamp; **—ная чаша** crater bowl.
кратк/ий *a.* short, brief, concise; **—ое содержание** summary, abstract.
кратковременн/ый *a.* short, short-lived, short-duration, transient, temporary; ephemeral; **—ая вспышка** short burst; **—ое облучение** brief irradiation.
краткосрочн/ый *a.* short, short-term, short-range; **к. прогноз, —ое предсказание** short-range forecast.
краткость *f.* shortness, brevity.
кратно— *prefix* multiply, multi—.
кратн/ое *n.*, **—ое число** (math.) multiple; **общее к.** common multiple; **общее наименьшее к.** least common multiple; **—ость** *f.* multiplicity; **—ый** *a.* multiple; **—ый интеграл** multiple (or iterated) integral; **—ый корень** multiple root; ***n*-кратный** *n*-tuple, *n*-fold; **—ая частота** multiple frequency; **—ое образование** multiple production; **—ое пространство, —ое рассеяние** plural scattering; **—ые звезды** multiple stars; **закон —ых отношений** law of multiple proportions.
кратчайший *a.* shortest.
краузит *m.* krausite.
Крафта правило Craft rule.
крах *m.* break-up, failure.
крахмал *m.*, **—ьный** *a.* starch.
крашен/ие *n.* dyeing, coloring, painting; **—ный** *a.* dyed, colored, stained, painted.
креднерит *m.* crednerite.
крезол *m.*, **—овый —ьный** *a.* cresol.
крейсерский *a.* cruising.
крейцбергит *m.* kreuzbergite.
крек/инг *m.*, **—ирование** *n.* cracking (of petroleum); **—ированный** *a.* cracked; **—ировать** *v.* crack.
кремальера *f.* rack.
кремень *m.* flint.
кремерзит *m.* kremersite.
кремне— *prefix* silico—.
кремневокарбидный кирпич silicon carbide brick.
кремне/зем *m.* silica; **—органический** *a.*, **—органическое соединение** silicone, **—содержащий** *a.* siliceous.
кремниевый *a.* silicon, silicic, siliceous.
кремн/ий *m.* silicon (Si); **—ий органический** *a.* organosilicon, silicone; **двуокись —ия** silicon dioxide, silica; **карбид —ия, углеродистый к.** silicon carbide, carborundum.
кремнист/ый *a.* siliceous, flinty; silicide (of); **к. туф** siliceous sinter; **—ая сталь** silicon steel; **—ое железо** silicon iron.
Кремона диаграмма Cremona diagram.
крен *m.* (aero.) bank, list, tilt; heeling.
кренить, —ся *v.* heel, list; (aero.) bank.
кренкит *m.* kröhnkite.
кренометр *m.* bank indicator, lateral inclinometer.
креозот *m.*, **—овый** *a.* creosote.
крепежный *a.* fastening, mounting; reinforcing; **к. болт** fixing bolt.
крепит/ель *m.* binder, brace; **—ельный** *a.* strengthening, reinforcing; **—ь** *v.* strengthen, brace, prop, make fast.
крепк/ий *a.* strong, solid, fast, firm; **к. ветер** strong breeze (Beaufort

number 6); **к. закал** dead-cold chilling; **очень к. ветер** fresh gale (Beaufort number 8); **к. припай** hard solder; **—ая плавка, —ое расплавление** high melt; **—о** *adv.* firmly, tightly.

креп/ление *n.* mounting, fastening; strengthening, bracing; **прочность —ления** holding power; **—нуть** *v.* become stronger, strengthen.

крепость *f.* strength, firmness, rigidity; hardness; **к. на разрыв** breaking strength, rupture strength.

крепь *f.* (min.) timbering.

крепящий *a.* strengthening, fastening, bracing.

кресло *n.* (chem.) chair configuration.

крест *m.* cross; **к. нитей** cross wire.

крестморит *m.* crestmoreite.

крестовидн/ый *a.* cross-shaped, cruciform; **—ая муфта** four-way connection, crossing box.

крестовин/а, —ка *f.* cross, cross piece, cross connection; spider; turnstile; **связывающая к.** cross bond, cross brace; **к. якоря** armature spider.

крестов/ый *a.* cross; **—ая связь** cross bond, cross brace.

крестообразный *see* **крестовидный.**

Кри диаграмма (geo.) Chree diagram.

кривая *f.* curve, line; **к. блеска** (astr.) light curve; **к. верности воспроизведения** fidelity curve; **к. выхода продуктов деления** fission yield curve; **к. жизни частицы** (rel.) world line of a particle; **к. зависимости *A* от *B*** *A* versus *B* curve; **к. изменения яркости** (astr.) light curve; **к. коммутирования** (mag.) commutation curve; **к. намагничивания** magnetization curve; **к. напряжение-деформация** stress-strain curve; **к. нарастания** growth curve, rise curve; **к. ошибок** error function; **к. повторяемости** frequency curve; **рабочая к.** characteristic curve; **к. разгорания** rise curve; **к. распада** decay curve; **к. (распределения) нагрузки** load distribution line; load diagram; **к. роста** curve of growth.

кривизн/а *f.* curvature, camber; crookedness, warping; **коэффициент —ы** (math.) curvature; **линия —ы** line of curvature; **—ы параметр** (reactor theory) buckling.

кривить, —ся *v.* curve, bend.

крив/о *adv.* crookedly; **—обокий** *a.* lopsided; **—ой** *a.* crooked, curved, curve, bent; **—ая линия** curve.

криволинейн/ость *f.* curvilinearity; **—ый** *a.* curvilinear, curved.

кривошип *m.*, **—ный** *a.* crank; **ось —а, —ный вал** crankshaft; **плечо —а** crank arm; **—ная камера** crankcase; **—ная передача, —ношатунный механизм** crankgear.

кридит *m.* creedite.

кризис *m.* crisis; **к. сопротивления, к. обтекания** (hyd.) critical region of Reynolds number.

кризо— *see* **хризо—.**

кризувигит *m.* krisuvigite.

крио— *prefix* cryo—.

криогалит *m.* cryohalite.

криоген/ика *f.* cryogenics; **—ный** *a.* cryogenic.

криогидрат *m.* cryohydrate; **—ная точка** cryohydratic point.

криолит *m.* cryolite; **—ионит** *m.* cryolithionite.

крио/магнитный *a.* cryomagnetic; **—метр** *m.* cryometer.

криосар *m.* cryosar.

криоскоп *m.* cryoscope; **—ический** *a.* cryoscopic; **—ия** *f.* cryoscopy.

крио/стат *m.* cryostat; **—трон** *m.* cryotron.

криофиллит *m.* cryophyllite.

крип *m.* creep.

крипоустойчив/ость *f.* creep resistance (or strength); **—ый** *a.* creep-resistant.

крипто— *prefix* crypto—.

крипто/валентность *f.* cryptovalence; **—кластический** *a.* cryptoclastic; **—кристаллический** *a.* cryptocrystalline, microcrystalline.

криптон *m.* krypton (Kr).

криптоскоп *m.* cryptoscope, fluoroscope.

кристалл *m.* crystal; **плоскость —а** crystal plane.

кристаллиз/атор *m.* crystallizer, crystallizing tank (or pan); **—ация** *f.*, **—ационный** *a.* crystallization, crystallizing; **—ационная вода** water of crystallization; **—ированный, —ованный** *a.* crystallized; **—ировать,**

—овать, —ироваться *v.* crystallize; **—уемость** *f.* crystallizability; **—ующийся** *a.* crystallizing, crystallizable.

кристалл/ик *m.* small crystal, crystalline particle; **—ит** *m.* crystallite.

кристаллич/еский *a.* crystalline, crystal; **неясно к., скрытно к.** cryptocrystalline; **к. триод** transistor; **—еская ось** *n***-ого порядка** *n*-fold crystallographic axis; **—еская решетка** crystal lattice; **—еское состояние** crystalline state; **—ность** *f.* crystallinity.

кристалло/бластический *a.* (geo.) crystalloblastic; **—генезис** *m.*, **—гения** *f.* crystallogeny; **—генический** *a.* crystallogenic; **—гидрат** *m.* crystalline hydrate; **—гия** *f.* crystallogy; **—грамма** *f.* crystallogram.

кристаллограф *m.* crystallographer; **—ический** *a.* crystallographic; **—ическая (магнитная) анизотропия** crystalline anisotropy; **—ия** *f.* crystallography.

кристаллоид *m.*, **—альный** *a.* crystalloid.

кристаллой *m.* Crystalloy (iron-silicon alloy).

кристалло/логия *f.* crystallology; **—люминесценция** *f.* crystalloluminescence.

кристаллометр/ический *a.* crystallometric; **—ия** *f.* crystallometry.

кристалло/носный, —содержащий *a.* containing crystals, crystalliferous; **—образный, —подобный** *a.* crystallike, crystalloid, crystalline; **—оптика** *f.* crystal optics; **—физика** *f.* crystal physics; **—фосфор** *m.* phosphor crystal; **—химия** *f.* crystal chemistry.

кристальн/о *adv.*, **—ый** *a.* crystal; **к. чистый** crystal clear.

кристобалит *m.* cristobalite.

кристолон *m.* Crystolon (silicon carbide abrasive).

кристофит *m.* cristophite.

Кристоффел/ь Christoffel; **символы (скобки) —я** C. symbols.

крит. *abbr.* **(критический)** critical.

крит *m.* crit (critical mass).

критериальный *a.* criterial; (hyd.) dimensionless.

критерий *m.* criterion, condition; test; (hyd.) dimensionless number; **к. выбора** test of acceptance; **к. гравитационного подобия** Froude number; **к. подобия** (hyd.) dimensionless number; **к. режима движения** Reynolds number; **к. согласованности** goodness-of-fit test.

критик *m.* critic, reviewer; **—а** *f.* criticism, censure; review (of book); **—овать** *v.* criticize, censure; comment, review.

критическ/и *adv.* critically; **—ий** *a.* critical, crucial; **—ий реактор** critical reactor; **—ий угол скольжения** critical glancing angle; **—ая деформация** critical deformation, yield strain; **—ая масса** critical mass; **—ая нагрузка** ultimate load; **—ая опалесценция** critical opalescence; **—ая температура** critical temperature; **—ая точка** critical point; **—ая энергия** critical energy; cutoff; **—ая энергия деления** critical fission energy; **—ое поле сверхпроводника** threshold field curve of superconductor; **—ие размеры** critical size.

критичность *f.* criticality.

критмасса *abbr.* **(критическая масса)** critical mass.

критрадиус *abbr.* **(критический радиус)** critical radius.

критразмер *abbr.* **(критический размер)** critical size.

крица *f.* (met.) bloom, ball, bar.

кричный *a.* (met.) refinery; bloomery, bloom; **к. горн** refinery (hearth); bloomery.

кричтонит *m.* crichtonite.

кровавый *a.* bloody, blood; **к. дождь** blood rain, red rain; **к. железняк** hematite; **к. камень** bloodstone.

кров/оизлияние, —отечение *n.* hemorrhage; **—ь** *f.* blood; **—яное тельце** blood cell.

кро/ить *v.* cut out, cut (by pattern); **—йка** *f.* cutting out.

кроки *n.* sketch.

крокидолит *m.* crocidolite.

крокировка *f.* sketching, outlining.

крокодильчик *m.* crocodile clip.

крокоит *m.* crocoite.

крокус *m.* (mineral) crocus, rouge.

кромаг *m.* cromag.

кроме *prep. gen.* except; besides; **к. того** moreover, furthermore.

кром/ка *f.* edge, border, rim, bead, shoulder, lip; **задняя к.** trailing edge; **передняя к.** leading edge; **—очный** *a.* edge.

крон, —глас *m.* crown glass.

Кронекера символ Kronecker symbol; **кронекеровское произведение** K. product.

Кронига-Пенни модель Kronig-Penney model.

кронстедтит *m.* cronstedtite.

кронциркуль *m.* caliper.

кронштейн *m.* (angle) bracket, corbel, arm, holder.

кросс-модуляция *f.* cross-modulation.

кроссит *m.* crossite.

кроссовер *m.* (elec.) crossover.

кротоновая кислота crotonic acid.

крош/ащийся *a.* crumbling, friable; **—енный** *a.* crumbled; chopped up; **—ечный** *a.* tiny, minute; **—ить** *v.* crumble; chop up.

кроющий материал covering material, coating.

круг *m.* circle, disk, wheel, reel; period, cycle; range, scope; (meteor.) halo; **к. вокруг луны** lunar halo; **к. действия** circle of influence; **к. качания** (math.) rolling circle; **к. кривизны** circle of curvature; **поворотный к.** turntable; **к. склонения** (astr.) hour circle, declination circle; **к. сходимости** circle of convergence; **к. цели** target disk.

круг/леть *v.* become round; **—лить** *v.* make round, round off.

кругло— *prefix* round.

кругло/годовой *a.* all-year-round; **—суточный** *a.* day and night (continuously), 24-hour; **—сть** *f.* roundness.

кругл/ый *a.* round, circular, globular, spherical; **к. год** the year round; **—ая шкала** dial; **—ые скобки** round brackets, parentheses.

кругов/ой *a.* circular, round, cyclic, rotary; all-round; **к. двуугольник** lune, crescent; **к. конвейер** endless conveyer; **к. нониус** dial; **к. поиск** circular scanning; **к. процесс** cycle; **к. ток** ring current; **—ая векторная диаграмма** clock diagram; **—ая координата** angular coordinate; **—ая передача** continuous drive; **—ая перестановка** cyclic (or circular) permutation; **—ая поляризация** circular polarization; **—ая симметрия** circular symmetry; **—ая скорость** circular velocity, angular velocity; **—ая частота** angular frequency, circular frequency; **—ое движение** circular motion, rotary motion; **—ое обращение** circulation; circuit.

круго/ворот *m.* rotation, turnover; cycle; **к. азота** nitrogen cycle; **к. водяного пара** water cycle; **к. вращательный** rotary, gyrating, circulatory; **к. углерода** carbon cycle; **—вращение** *n.* rotation, circular motion; circulation; **—зор** *m.* horizon, view, outlook.

кругом *adv.* round, around, about; in a circle.

круго/обзорный *a.* omnidirectional; **—оборот** *m.* circuit, cycle; circulation.

кругообразн/ость *f.* roundness, circularity; **—ый** *a.* circular.

круго/обращение *n.* rotation; circulation; **—светный полет** round-the-world flight; **—суточный** *a.* 24-hour.

круж/ение *n.* turning, spinning; **—ить, —иться** *v.* turn, spin, gyrate, rotate; **—ный** *a.* circuitous, roundabout.

кружок *m.* small circle; disk; **к. наименьшего рассеяния** (opt.) least circle of aberration; **к. рассеяния (размытости, нерезкости)** (phot.) circle of confusion.

крукесит *m.* crookesite.

Крукса радиометр Crookes radiometer; **круксова трубка** C. tube; **круксово темное пространство** C. dark space.

круп/а *f.* soft hail, graupel; **ледяная к.** ice pellets; **снежная к.** snow pellets; **—инка** *f.* grain, granule; **—ичатый** *a.* granular.

крупнеть *v.* grow larger.

крупно *adv.* coarsely; **—габаритный** *a.* large-scale, bulk; **—зернистый** *a.* coarse-grained; **—кристаллический** *a.* macrocrystalline; **—масштабный** *a.* large-scale; **—сортный** *a.* large-size.

крупн/ость *f.* size, coarseness; **—ый** *a.* large, big, coarse; great, prominent; large-scale; **—ый план** (phot.) close-up.

крупчатый *a.* grainy, coarse.

крустифи/кация *f.* crustification; **—цированный** *a.* crustified.

крутая спираль tight spiral, fast spiral.

крутизна *f.* steepness, slope; (elec.) transconductance; **к. кривой** slope of a curve; **к. нарезки** height of screw thread; **к. преобразования** conversion transconductance; **к. ската** gradient.

крутильн/ый *a.* twisting, torsion, torsional; **к. гальванометр** torsion galvanometer; **к. магнитометр** torque magnetometer; **к. подвес** torsion suspension; **—ая головка** torsion head; **—ое колебание** torsional vibration; **—ые весы** torsion balance.

крут/ить, —иться *v.* turn, twist, revolve, spin, eddy; **—ка** *f.* twist.

крут/о *adv.* steeply, abruptly, sharply; **—ой** *a.* steep; **—ой импульс** steep pulse; **—ой поворот** sharp turn; **—ой слив** abrupt discharge.

круто/падающий *a.* steep, steep-dipping; **—сть** *f.* steepness, slope, (stat.) kurtosis, peakedness.

крутящ/ий *a.* twisting, turning, torsion, torsional; **к. момент** torque; **—ее усилие** torsional force.

круч/а *f.* steep slope; **—е** *comp. of* **круто, крутой,** steeper, more abrupt.

кручен/ие *n.* twisting, torsion; **момент —ия** *see* **крутящий момент**; **—ый** *a.* twisted.

круш/ение *n.* wreck; breakdown; **—ить** *v.* shatter, destroy, wreck.

к-рый *abbr.* (**который**) which, that, who.

крылат/ка *f.* vane; **—ый** *a.* winged.

крыло *n.* wing; airfoil; vane, impeller; fender; (geo.) leg, wall, side, limb, slope; **к. бесконечного размаха** airfoil of infinite span; **—видный, —образный** *a.* wing-shaped.

крылышко *n.* small wing, flap; vane; **к. гидропланирующее** hydrofoil.

крыль/евая антенна skid-fin antenna; **—ный** *a.* wing.

крыльчат/ка *f.*, **—ое колесо** vane wheel, blade wheel, impeller; **—ый** *a.* wing, vane; **—ая гайка** wing nut.

крыт/ый *a.* covered; **—ь** *v.* cover, conceal; roof.

крыш/а *f.* roof; **—ка** *f.*, **—ечный** *a.* cover, lid, cap.

крэк/инг, —ирование *see* **крекинг.**

крюк *m.* hook; **метод —ов** hook method (Haken-Methode).

Крюсса микрофотометр Krüss microphotometer.

крючко/ватый *a.* hooked, jagged; **—образный** *a.* hook-like, hooked.

крючок *m.* hook, catch.

кряж *m.* ridge, crest.

к.с. *abbr.* (**комплексно-сопряженный**) complex conjugate.

ксалостокит *m.* xalostocite.

ксанто— *prefix* xantho—.

ксанто/конит *m.* xanthoconite; **—ксенит** *m.* xanthoxenite; **—хроит** *m.* xanthocroite.

КСВН *abbr.* (**коэффициент стоячей волны напряжения**) voltage standing-wave ratio (vswr).

ксенолит *m.* xenolite.

ксенон *m.* xenon (Xe).

ксенотермальная зона xenothermal zone.

ксенотим *m.* xenotime.

ксерогель *m.* xerogel.

ксерография *f.* xerography.

ксилол *m.* xylene.

ксилометр *m.* xylometer.

ксилон *m.* xylon; **—ит** *m.* xylonite.

ксилоретинит *m.* xyloretinite.

ксонотлит *m.* xenotlite.

кстати *adv.* to the point; opportunely; incidentally.

к-та *abbr.* (**кислота**) acid.

ктипеит *m.* ktypeite.

кто *pron,* who, who?; **к. бы ни** whoever; **к.-либо, к.-нибудь** someone, anybody; **к.-то** somebody.

к.т.п. *abbr.* (**коэффициент теплопередачи** coefficient of heat transfer.

куб *m.* (math.) cube; vat; **возводить в к.** cube, raise to the third power; **перегонный к.** still, still pot; **закон —а** cube law.

кубанит *m.* cubanite.

кубатур/а *f.* cubic content; **—ная формула** cubature formula.

куб. дм *abbr.* **(кубический дециметр)** cubic decimeter.
кубик *m.* (small) cube, block.
кубическ/ий *a.* cubic, cubical; voluminal; **к. корень** cube root; **—ая парабола** cubical parabola; **—ая решетка** cubic lattice; **—ое уравнение** cubic equation.
кубичный *see* **кубический.**
куб. м *abbr.* **(кубический метр)** cubic meter.
куб. мм *abbr.* **(кубический миллиметр)** cubic millimeter.
кубо/видный *a.* cubiform; **—вый** *a.* cube; vat; **—идальный** *a.* cuboidal.
кубок *m.* beaker.
кубометр *m.* cubic meter.
кубообразный *see* **кубовидный.**
куб. см *abbr.* **(кубический сантиметр)** cubic centimeter.
кувалда *f.* sledge hammer.
куда *adv.* where? in what direction?; **к. бы ни** wherever; **к.-либо, к.-нибудь** somewhere, anywhere; **к.-то** somewhere.
Куетта течение Couette flow.
кузеранит *m.* couseranite.
кузн/ец *m.* blacksmith, smith; **к.-инструментальщик** toolsmith; **—ечный** *a.* forging, forge.
кузн/ица, —я *f.* smithy, forge.
кузов *m.* basket; body (of vehicle).
кукеит *m.* cookeite.
кукла *f.* doll.
кул. *abbr.* **(кулон)** coulomb.
кулак *see* **кулачок.**
кулачко/вый *see* **кулачок; к. вал** camshaft; **к. механизм, —вое распределение** cam gear; **к. привод** cam drive; **—образный** *a.* cam-shaped, jaw-shaped.
кулачн/ый *see* **кулачок; к. патрон** jaw chuck; **—ая муфта** jaw clutch.
кулачок *m.* cam, lobe, pin; jaw (of chuck); pawl, catch, detent, checking device; tappet; **приводной к., рабочий к.** actuating cam.
Кулиджа трубка Coolidge tube.
кулис/а *f.*, **—ный** *a.* link; guide slot, slot, slideway; **—ный камень** slide block; guide shoe; **—ный механизм, —ный привод** link gear.
кулон *m.* coulomb.
Кулона весы Coulomb torsion balance.
кулонметр *m.* coulometer.
кулоновск/ий *a.* Coulomb; **к. барьер** C. barrier; **—ая сила** C. force; **—ое возбуждение** C. excitation.
кульмин/ационный *a.* culmination, culminating; **—ация** *f.* culmination; **—ировать** *v.* culminate.
культура *f.* culture, cultivation.
куменгит *m.* cumengite.
куметр *m.* Q-meter.
Куммера преобразование Kummer transformation.
куммингтонит *m.* cummingtonite.
кумулированные связи cumulative bonds.
кумулянта *f.* cumulant.
кумулятивный *a.* cumulative; **к. импульс** cumulative pulse, pile-up pulse.
Кундта правило (закон) Kundt rule; **К. трубка** K. tube.
кунико *m.* Cunico (cobalt-nickel-copper alloy).
кунифе *m.* Cunife (copper-nickel-iron alloy).
кунцит *m.* kunzite.
Купер-Юитта лампа Cooper-Hewitt lamp.
куперовские пары Cooper pairs.
купол *m.*, **—ьный** *a.* cupola, dome; **—овидный, —ообразный** *a.* dome-shaped, humped, domal.
купорос *m.* vitriol.
куприт *m.* cuprite.
купро— *prefix* cupro—.
купроксный *a.* cuprous oxide, copper oxide.
купро/никель *m.* cupronickel; **—отунит** *m.* cuproautunite; **—склодовскит** *m.* cuprosklodowskite; **—уранит** *m.* cuprouranite.
купюра *f.* line segment, distance, interval; abbreviation, cutting off.
Курант Courant.
курвиметр *m.* curvometer, map measurer.
куронгит *m.* coorongite.
курс *m.* course; track, path; **держать к. на** head for, hold a course.
курсив *m.* italics; **—ом** in italics; **—ный** *a.* italic, italicized; **—ный шрифт** italic type.

Курская магнитная аномалия Kursk magnetic anomaly.

курсо/вой *a.* course; **—указатель** *m.* course indicator.

курьер *m.* messenger.

кусачки *pl.* cutting pliers.

куски *pl. of* **кусок.**

кусков/атый, —ой *a.* lump, lumpy.

кус/ок *m.* piece, lump, portion, fragment; length; **—ками, в —ках** in pieces, lumpy, clotted; **по —кам** piecemeal; **разбить на —ки** shatter; **—очек** *m.* small piece, fragment, patch.

кусочно *adv.* piecewise; **к.-гладкий** *a.* piecewise smooth (or continuous); **к.-линейный** *a.* piecewise linear; **к.-постоянная функция** step function.

куспидин *m.* cuspidine.

куст *m.* bunch; group, cluster; **к. точек** point cluster.

кустован/ие *n.* interconnection; **—ный** *a.* interconnected.

Кутта-Жуковского теорема Kutta-Joukowski theorem.

куч/а *f.* pile, heap; **в —е** in a pile, collectively, as a group.

кучев/ой *a.* cumulus; **—ое облако** cumulus (cloud); **—ые дождевые облака** cumulonimbus (clouds); **—ые средние облака** cumulus mediocris.

кучевообразные облака cumuliform clouds.

куч/ка *f.* small heap, small group; **—ной** *a.* heap, mound.

кучность *f.* grouping, compactness; **к. стрельбы** accuracy of fire.

Куэтта течение Couette flow.

КФ *abbr.* (**Казахстанский филиал**) Kazakh Branch; (**Киевский филиал**) Kiev Branch.

кыштым-паризит kyshtymo-parisite.

Кьелдаля колба Kjeldahl flask.

Кьеллина печь Kjellin (electric) furnace.

кьерульфин *m.* kjerulfine.

кэв *abbr.* (**килоэлектронвольт**) kilo-electron-volt (kev).

кэватрон *m.* kevatron.

Кэвендиш *see* **Кавендиш.**

Кэйли *see* **Кэли.**

кэк *m.* (sinter) cake.

Кэли Cayley; **теорема К.-Гамильтона** C.-Hamilton theorem. **К.-Клейна параметр** C.-Klein parameter.

кэррингтоновский оборот Carrington rotation (of sun).

кэт-вектор (Dirac) ket vector.

кэтрон *m.* ketron (beta-ray spectrometer).

кювет *m.* cell, vessel; bulb; ditch; **к. многократного прохождения** multiple-pass cell.

кюинавит *m.* keweenawite.

Кюкамбер Cucumber (thermonuclear device).

Кюри Curie; Kurie; **закон Кюри** C. law; **К.-Шевено весы** C.-Cheveneau balance.

кюри *n.* curie, Curie unit (c); **к. график** Kurie plot; **к. температура, к. точка** Curie point; **—грамма** *f.* curiegram; **—граф** *m.* (phot.) curiegraph; **—евый** *a.* curium.

кюрий *m.* curium (Cm).

кюри/т *m.* curite; **—терапия** *f.* radiotherapy.

кюстелит *m.* küstelite.

кюстерит *m.* custerite.

Л

л *abbr.* (**литр**) liter; **л.** (**левый**) left, left-hand, counterclockwise; (**лист, листы**) printer's sheets, folios.

Л. *abbr.* (**Ленинград**) Leningrad.

лаб. *abbr.* (**лаборант**) laboratory technician; (**лаборатория**) laboratory.

лабильный *a.* labile, unstable.

лабиринт *m.*, **—ный, —овый** *a.* labyrinth, maze; **—ное уплотнение** labyrinth seal.

лаб-ия *abbr.* (**лаборатория**) laboratory.

лабор. *abbr.* (**лаборант**) laboratory technician; (**лаборатория, лабораторный**) laboratory.

лаборант *m.*, **—ка** *f.* laboratory assistant (or technician).

лаборатор/ия *f.* laboratory; **л. высокорадиоактивных материалов** "hot" laboratory; **л. излучений** radiation laboratory; **—ный** *a.* laboratory; **—ная система координат** laboratory coordinate system; laboratory frame of reference; **—ная схема** (elec.) "breadboard" hookup.

лава *f.* lava, lava flow.

Лаваля сопло Laval nozzle.

ЛАВД *abbr.* [**Лаборатория высоких давлений и температур** (**Академии наук СССР**)] Laboratory of High Pressures and Temperatures (of the Academy of Sciences, USSR).

лавин/а *f.*, **—ный** *a.* avalanche, cascade; **л. дислокаций** dislocation avalanche; **л.-родоначальница** primary avalanche; **—ный лед** avalanche ice; **—ная единица** (cosm.) shower unit; **—ная ионизация** cumulative ionization; **—ная частица** cascade particle; **—ообразный** *a.* avalanche-type.

лавренсит *m.* lawrencite.

лаврентьевский *a.* Laurentian.

лавсонит *m.* lawsonite.

Лавуазье Lavoisier.

лаг *m.* log (nautical instrument).

Лагерра многочлен (**полином**) Laguerre polynomial.

Ла Гир La Hire (lunar crater).

Лагранж Lagrange (lunar crater).

Лагранжа-Гельмгольца теорема (Lagrange-) Helmholtz equation, L. (or Smith-Helmholtz) law; **Л. неопределенные множители** Lagrangian multipliers; **Л. функция** L. function, Lagrangian.

лагранж/ев, —евский *a.* Lagrangian; **—иан** *m.* Lagrangian (function).

лагун/а *f.* lagoon; **—ный** *a.* lagoonal.

Ладенбурга закон Ladenburg law.

ладинский век Ladinian stage.

ладожский *a.* Ladogian.

лаз *m.* access, opening, manhole; **—ейка** *f.* loophole, gap, opening; manhole.

лазер *m.* laser.

лазур/-апатит *m.* lazur-apatite; **—евый камень, —ик** *m.* lapis lazuli.

Лаймана серия Lyman series.

лайманов/а граница Lyman limit; **—ский непрерывный спектр** Lyman continuum; **—ское излучение** Lyman emission.

лайнер *m.* liner.

лак *m.* varnish; lacquer.

Лакайль Lacaille (lunar crater).

лакиров/ание *n.*, **—ка** *f.* lacquering; varnishing; **—анный** *a.* lacquered; varnished; **—ать** *v.* lacquer; varnish.

лакмус *m.* litmus; **—овая** (**реактивная**) **бумага** litmus paper.

лаковый *a.* lacquer, lacquered; varnish, varnished.

лакоткань *f.* varnished insulating cloth.

лакруаит *m.* lacroixite.

лактаза *f.* lactase.

лакто— *prefix* lacto—.

Лаланд Lalande (lunar crater).

Лаланда элемент Lalande cell.

ламбда-удвоение lambda-type doubling (in molecular spectra).

Ламберт Lambert (lunar crater).

ламберт *m.* lambert (unit).

Ламберта закон (**поглощения света**) Lambert law (of absorption).

ламбертит *m.* lambertite.

Ламе *see* **Ламэ.**

ламеллярный *a.* lamellar, lamellate.

ламель *m.* lamella, lamina; (elec.) commutator bar (or segment); **—ный** *see* **ламеллярный.**

ламинарн/ый *a.* laminar, streamline; **—ое течение** laminar flow, streamline flow.

ламиниров/ание *n.* lamination; **—анный** *a.* laminated; **—ать** *v.* laminate.

Ламона (**Ламонта**) **закон** (**формула**) Lamont law.

лампа *f.* lamp; (elec.) bulb, tube; **л. бегущей волны** traveling-wave tube; **л. бесшумной регулировки усиления** squelch tube; **л.-вспышка** flash bulb; **двухсеточная л.** space-charge tetrode; **л.-делитель частоты** frequency-divider tube; **л. дневного света** daylight lamp; **жесткая л.** hard tube; **л.-жолудь** acorn tube; **комбинированная л.** multiple tube; **мягкая л.** soft tube; **л. накаливания** incandescent lamp; **л. обратной волны** backward-wave tube, carcinotron.

лампа переменной крутизны variable-mu tube; **л. прямого накала** directly heated tube, filament-type tube; **л.**

с дрейфовым пространством drift tube; **л. с ионно-нагревным катодом** ion-heated cathode tube; **л. смещения** bias tube; **л. со вторичной электронной эмиссией** secondary-emission tube; **л. с отклоняемым лучом** beam-deflection tube; **л. с переменной крутизной** variable-mu tube; **л. с плоскими электродами** planar-electrode tube; **л. с поперечным управлением** balitron tube; **л. с совмещенными сетками** aligned-grid tube; **л. со стробированным лучом** gated-beam tube; **л.-стабилизатор** voltage-regulator tube; **л. тлеющего разряда** glow (or glow-discharge) tube or lamp.

лампов/ый *a.* lamp; **л. вольтметр** vacuum (or electronic) voltmeter; **л. выпрямитель** vacuum-tube rectifier; **л. генератор** vacuum-tube oscillator; **л. шум** tube noise; **л. электрометр** vacuum-tube electrometer; **—ая копоть, —ая сажа, —ая чернь** lampblack; **—ая схема** tube circuit.

лампо/испытатель *m.* tube tester; **—чка** *f.* small lamp; (elec.) bulb.

лампрофиллит *m.* lamprophyllite.

Ламэ коэффициент Lamé coefficient, scale factor; **Л.-Навье теория** L.-Navier theory; **Л. функции** L. functions.

лангбейнит *m.* langbeinite.

ланглей *m.* langley (ly).

Лангмюра *see* **Ленгмюра.**

Лангрен Langrenus (lunar crater).

Ландау-Лифшица формула Landau-Lifshits (Lifschitz) equation.

Ланде множитель Landé factor; **фактор (коэффициент) расщепления Л.** L. splitting factor.

ландезит *m.* landesite.

Ландольта черная полоса Landholdt fringe.

Ландсберг Landsberg (lunar crater).

Ланжевена ион Langevin ion.

Ланкзос Lanczos.

лантан *m.* lanthanum (La); **—ид, —оид** *m.* lanthanide; **—ит** *m.* lanthanite.

лап/а *f.* foot, claw, grip, lap; **—ка** *f.* claw, clutch, lug, pawl, tab, tenon.

Лапласа оператор Laplacian (operator); **Л. преобразование, лаплас-образ** Laplace transform (or transformation); **Л. уравнение (для скорости звука)** Laplace (sound velocity) equation.

лапласиан *m.* (math.) Laplacian; (reactor) buckling.

Лапорта правило четности Laporte parity rule.

ларамийский *a.* (geo.) Laramie, Laramide (sands).

ларингофон *m.* throat microphone.

Лармора прецессия, ларморова прецессия Larmor precession; **Л. формула** L. formula.

ласточкин хвост swallowtail, dovetail (joint).

лат. *abbr.* **(латинский)** Latin.

латв. *abbr.* **(латвийский)** Latvian.

Латвийская ССР, Латв ССР Latvian SSR.

латекс *m.* latex.

латенсификация *f.* latensification.

латентн/ый *a.* latent; **—ое изображение** latent image; **—ое состояние** latent state; **—ость** *f.* latency.

латеральный *a.* lateral.

латероид *m.* fish-paper.

латинский *a.* Latin.

л-атм *abbr.* **(литро-атмосфера)** liter-atmosphere.

латун/ирование *n.* brass plating; **—ировать** *v.* brass-plate; **—ный** *a.* brass.

латунь *f.* brass.

лаудербекит *m.* louderbackite.

лаузенит *m.* lausenite.

Лауритсена электроскоп Lauritsen electroscope.

лауро— *prefix* lauro—.

лауталь *m.* Lautal.

Лауэ рентгенограмма, лауэграмма Laue diffraction pattern.

ЛАФОКИ *abbr* [**Лаборатория научно-прикладной фотографии и кинематографии (Академии наук СССР)**] Laboratory of Scientific and Applied Photography and Cinematography (of the Academy of Sciences, USSR).

лацканный микрофон lapel microphone.

ЛБВ *abbr.* **(лампа с бегущей волной)** traveling-wave tube (TWT).

ЛГМИ *abbr.* (**Ленинградский гидрометеорологический институт**) Leningrad Hydrometeorological Institute.

ЛГУ *abbr.* (**Ленинградский государственный университет**) Leningrad State University.

ЛДНТП *abbr.* (**Ленинградский дом научно-технической пропаганды**) Leningrad House of Scientific and Technical Propaganda.

Лебег/а-Фубини теорема Lebesgue-Fubini theorem; **—ова площадь поверхности** L. measure.

лебед/ка *f.*, **—очный** *a.* winch, windlass.

Лебедь Cygnus (Cyg) (constellation).

Лебеля-Вант-Гоффа закон Le Bel-van't Hoff law.

Леблана способ Le Blanc process; **леблановская сода** Le Blanc soda.

Лев Leo (Leo) (constellation).

лев. *abbr.* (**левый**) left, left-hand, counterclockwise.

левее *comp. of* **лево,** (more) to the left of.

левеит *m.* loeweite.

леверрьерит *m.* leverrierite.

Леви-Чивита символ Levi-Civita symbol.

левигит *m.* loewigite.

левинит *m.* levynite.

левко— *see* **лейко—**.

лево, на л. *adv.* left, to the left.

лево— *prefix* levo—, left.

левобережный *a.* left-bank.

левовращающ/ий *a.* levorotatory, left-handed, counterclockwise; **л. электрон** left-polarized electron; **—аяся система координат** left-handed coordinate system.

левоинвариантный *a.* left-invariant.

лев/ый *a.* left, left-hand, left-handed; counterclockwise, levogyrate; levo—; **л. борт** (naut.) port(side); **л. кварц** left-handed quartz; **л. кристалл** left-handed crystal; **—ая кривая** left-handed curve, sinistrorse curve; **—ая (круговая) поляризация** left-hand circular polarization, counterclockwise polarization; **—ая нарезка** left-hand thread; **—ая система** left-handed system; **—ая сторона** left side; reverse side (of material); **—ая часть уравнения** left member of equation; **—ое вращение** levorotation, counterclockwise rotation; backing (of wind); **—ое вращение круга** (meteor.) counterclockwise rotation (or backing) of wind; **с —ым ходом** left-handed (screw, etc.).

легир/ование *n.* alloying, alloyage; **—ованный** *a.* alloyed, alloy; **—овать** *v.* alloy; **—ующий** *a.* alloying, alloy; **—ующий элемент** alloy component.

легк/ий *a.* light, lightweight; easy, simple; slight; **л. ветер** light breeze (Beaufort number 2); **л. водород** *see under* **водород**; **—ая вода** *see under* **вода**; **—ая дырка** light hole, high-mobility hole; **—ое масло** light oil; **—ое ядро** light nucleus.

легко *adv.* lightly, slightly, easily; it is easy.

легковесн/ость *f.* lightness, light weight; **—ый** *a.* light, lightweight.

легко/водный *a.* light-water; **—воспламеняющийся** *a.* readily inflammable; **—восстановимый** *a.* easily reducible; **—доступный** *a.* easily accessible, readily available; **—зольный** *a.* giving light ash; **—кипящий** *a.* low-boiling; **—летучий** *a.* highly volatile.

легкоплавк/ий *a.* (easily) fusible, low-melting; **л. металл** low-melting metal; **л. припой** quick solder; **л. сплав** fusible alloy; **—ая вставка** (elec.) fuse.

легко/подвижный *a.* mobile; **—растворимый** *a.* readily soluble; very soluble; **—сть** *f.* lightness; ease; **—ходовой** *a.* smoothly operating.

легче *comp. of* **легкий, легко,** lighter; easier.

лед *m.* ice; **блинчатый л.** pancake (or plate) ice; **грунтовый л., донный л., почвенный л.** ground ice, anchor ice; **редкий л.** open pack (or drift) ice, disappearing ice.

ледгиллит *m.* leadhillite.

ледебурит *m.* ledeburite.

леден/еть *v.* freeze, congeal; **—ец** *m.* crystallized sucrose, sucrose crystal; **—еющий, —ящий** *a.* freezing; **—ить** *v.* freeze, chill, ice.

ледник *m.* refrigerator; (geo.) glacier; **—овый** *a.* refrigerator; (geo.) glacial, glacier, ice; **—овый период** glacial period, ice age.

ледо/кол, —рез *m.* ice breaker; **—пад, —скат, —спуск** *m.* ice chute; **—ход** *m.* ice motion, debacle.
ледуксит *m.* ledouxite.
Ледюка-Риги эффект Leduc-Righi effect; **Л. ток** L. current.
ледян/ой *a.* ice, icy; glacial; *see also* **ледниковый**; **л. дождь** glazed rain, ice pellets; **л. затор** ice gorge (or jam); **л. отблеск** iceblink; **л. покров** icecap, ice sheet; **л. торос** ice hummock; **л. туман** ice fog; **л. шпат** ice spar; **—ая ванна** ice bath; **—ая гора** iceberg; **—ая зона** frigid zone; **—ая крупа** small hail; **—ое небо** iceblink.
Лежандра многочлен Legendre polynomial.
лежать *v.* lie, rest.
лежачий *a.* lying, horizontal; **л. бок** underside; (geo.) footwall.
лежащий *see* **лежачий**; **л. в** embedded; **л. между** interjacent; **л. ниже** underlying.
Лежен-Дирихле теорема Lejeune-Dirichlet theorem.
лежень *m.* foundation beam; sleeper.
лезвие *n.* knife edge, blade.
лезть *v.* get into; intrude, interfere.
леикавгит *m.* leucaugite.
лейас *m.* Lias.
Лейбница теорема Leibniz theorem.
лейденская банка Leyden jar.
лейк— *prefix* leuc—.
лейкемия *f.* (med.) leukemia.
лейко— *prefix* leuco—.
лейкоксен *m.* leucoxene.
лейко/основание *n.* leuco base; **—скоп** *m.* leucoscope.
лейко/фанит *m.* leucophanite; **—феницит** *m.* leucophoenicite; **—фосфит** *m.* leucophosphite. **—хальцит** *m.* leucochalcite.
лейкоцит *m.* leucocyte; **—оз** *m.* leucocytosis.
лейнер *m.* liner.
Лейтца микроскоп Leitz microscope.
лейфит *m.* leifite.
лейхтенбергит *m.* leuchtenbergite.
лейцит *m.* leucite; **—оид** *m.* leucitoid.
лекал/о *n.* curve, French curve; mold, pattern, template; **—ьный** *a.* curve, mold.
Лекланше элемент Leclanché cell.
леконтит *m.* lecontite.
лектор *m.* lecturer.
Ле-Кутера теория (nucl.) Le Couteur theory.
лекц/ия *f.* lecture; **л. памяти** memorial lecture; **читать —ии** lecture.
леллингит *m.* löllingite.
лембовск/ий сдвиг, —ое смещение Lamb shift.
лемма *f.* (math.) lemma.
лемниската *f.* lemniscate.
Лемуан Lemoine.
Ленарда лучи Lenard rays.
ленгенбахит *m.* lengenbachite.
Ленгзип *abbr.* (**Ленинградский завод измерительных приборов**) Leningrad Measuring Instruments Plant.
Ленгирд *abbr.* (**Ленинградская группа по изучению реактивного движения**) Leningrad Group for the Study of Jet Propulsion.
Ленгмюра закон Langmuir law; **Л. изотерма адсорбции** L. adsorption isotherm; **Л. темное пространство** L. dark space.
ленерит *m.* lehnerite.
ЛЕНЗОС *abbr.* (**Ленинградский завод оптического стекла**) Leningrad Optical Glass Plant.
леникс *m.* idler, idle wheel.
Ленинград Leningrad.
ЛенНИИ *abbr.* (**Ленинградский научно-исследовательский институт**) Leningrad Scientific Research Institute.
Леннито *abbr.* (**Ленинградское научное инженерно-техническое общество**) Leningrad Scientific, Technical and Engineering Society.
лента *f.* band, strip, tape, ribbon; belt; (motion picture) film; **зарядная л.** charging belt; **фрикционная л.** friction tape.
ленто/образный *a.* ribbon, band-shaped; **—протяжный механизм** tape winder (or transport).
ленточн/ый *a.* ribbon, tape, band, belt, strip; **л. громкоговоритель** ribbon loudspeaker; **л. конвейер, л. транспортер** belt (or band) conveyer; **л. микрофон** ribbon microphone; **л. регистратор** tape recorder; **л. тормоз** band brake; **—ая глина** varved clay;

—**ая лампа** ribbon-filament lamp; —**ая линия** flat-conductor line; —**ая молния** ribbon lightning; —**ая муфта** belt coupling; —**ая пила** band saw; —**ая подача** belt feed; —**ая яшма** riband jasper; —**ое сканирование** (radio astr.) stripwise scanning; —**ое сопротивление** tape-wound resistor.
Ленца правило Lenz law.
леонгардит *m.* leonhardite.
Леониды Leonids (meteors).
лепесток *m.* platelet, leaf (of crystal); fringe, lobe (of antenna pattern); tab, lug.
лепешкообразный *a.* oblate.
лепидо/крокит *m.* lepidocrocite; —**лит** *m.* lepidolite.
лептометр *m.* leptometer.
лептон *m.*, —**ный** *a.* lepton.
лептохлорит *m.* leptochlorite.
лербахит *m.* lehrbachite.
лерз/ит *m.* (petr.) lherzite; —**олит** *m.* lherzolite.
лерка *f.* screw-cutting die; gauge.
лес *m.* woods, forest; timber; —**а** *pl.* forests; scaffolding; —**истый** *a.* wooded, timbered.
леслейит *m.* lesleyite.
Лесли кубик Leslie's cube.
лесни/к, —**чий** *m.* forester; —**чество** *n.* forestry.
лесной *a.* wood, forest; lumber, timber; **л. склад** lumber yard.
лесо— *prefix* wood, forest.
лесо/водство *n.* forestry; —**материал** *m.* lumber, timber; —**пилка** *f.* sawmill.
Лесохим. пром. *abbr.* (**лесохимическая промышленность**) wood chemical industry.
лесс *m.* (geo.) loess.
лестни/ца *f.*, —**чный** *a.* staircase; ladder; scale; **движущаяся л.** escalator; **складная л.** stepladder; —**чная диаграмма** ladder diagram; —**чное приближение** ladder approximation.
лет *m.* flight; **на** —**у** in flight.
лета *pl.* years.
летальный *a.* lethal.
летание *n.* flight, flying.
летарг/ический *a.* lethargic; —**ия** *f.* lethargy.
летательный *a.* flying; **л. аппарат** aircraft.
лет/ать, —**еть** *v.* fly.
летка *f.* (met.) tap, tap hole.
летний *a.* summer.
летн/о-технические данные mechanical and flying characteristics; —**ый** *a.* flight, flying, aeronautics; —**ое дело** flying, aeronautics.
лето *n.* summer; *pl.* years.
летовицит *m.* letovicite.
летопись *f.* chronicle, annals, yearbook.
Летрон Letronne (lunar crater).
Летучая Рыба Volans (Vol) (constellation).
летуч/есть *f.* volatility; fugacity; —**ий** *a.* volatile; flying; —**ая зола** light ashes; —**ее соединение** volatile compound.
летчик *m.* aviator, flyer, pilot.
летящий *a.* flying.
Лехера система Lecher system (or wires); **лехеровская линия** L. wires.
лехиит *m.* lehiite.
лечебн/ица *f.* hospital; —**ый** *a.* medical, medicinal, medicine, healing, therapeutic.
леч/ение *n.* medical treatment; **л. облучением** radiation treatment; —**ить** *v.* treat, cure.
Ле-Шателье принцип Le Chatelier principle.
лешательерит *m.* lechatelierite.
лещадь *m.* slab, hearth bottom.
ли *interrogative particle* whether, if (not translated).
Ли алгебра Lie algebra.
либетенит *m.* libethenite.
Либига охладитель Liebig condenser.
либигит *m.* liebigite.
либо *adv.* or; **л. . . л.** either . . . or.
либрация *f.* libration.
ЛИВД *abbr.* (**Ленинградский научно-исследовательский институт высоких давлений**) Leningrad Scientific Research Institute of High Pressures.
ливейнгит *m.* liveingite.
ливень *m.* (cosm., meteor.) shower; **л. космического излучения** cosmic-ray shower; **л. с градом** hail shower.
ливер *m.*, —**ный** *a.* siphon; crane.
ливнев/ой, —**ый** *a.* shower, showery; **л. дождь** rain shower; downpour, cloudburst; **л. снег** snow shower; —**ая**

частица shower particle; —**ое облако** shower cloud.

ливнеобразование *n.* shower production.

ЛИВЫ *abbr.* (**приливы и отливы**) high and low tides.

лигатур/а *f.* alloy; —**ный** *a.* alloyed.

лигнит *m.* lignite.

лигноза *f.* lignose.

лидер *m.* leader.

лиева алгебра *see* **Ли.**

Лизеганга кольцо Liesegang ring.

лизиметр *m.* lysimeter.

ЛИИ *abbr.* (**Ленинградский индустриальный институт**) Leningrad Industrial Institute; (**Летно-испытательный институт**) Flight-Testing Institute; [**Летно-исследовательский институт** (**Министерства авиационной промышленности**)] Flight Research Institute (of the Ministry of the Aircraft Industry).

лик *m.* face.

ликвация *f.* liquefaction; (met.) liquation.

ликвид/ация *f.*, —**ирование** *n.* liquidation, elimination; —**ировать** *v.* liquidate.

ликвидус *m.* liquidus (line or curve).

Лилиенфельда трубка Lilienfeld (x-ray) tube.

ЛИМ *abbr.* (**Ленинградский институт металлов**) Leningrad Institute of Metals.

лимб *m.* graduated circle, dial; limb.

лимит *m.* limit; —**ационный** *a.* critical, limiting, threshold; —**ировать** *v.* limit, restrict.

лимни/граф *m.* limnograph; —**логия** *f.* limnology.

лимонит *m.* limonite.

лимонн/окислый *a.* citrate (of); —**ый** *a.* citric; —**ая кислота** citric acid; —**ое масло** lemon oil.

линдакерит *m.* lindackerite.

Линде способ Linde process.

Линдемана стекло Lindemann glass; **Л. электрометр** L. electrometer.

линдзейит *m.* lindsayite.

линдокит *m.* lyndochite.

линдстремит *m.* lindströmite.

линеариз/ация *f.* linearization; —**ованный** *a.* linearized; —**овать** *v.* linearize.

линеатура *f.* line ruling.

линев/ание *n.* ruling; —**анный** *a.* ruled —**ать** *v.* rule, make lines.

линейка *f.* ruler, rule, straightedge **логарифмическая л., расчетная л. счетная л.** slide rule.

линейно *adv.* linearly; **л.-поляризованный** *a.* plane-polarized, linearly polarized; **л.-упорядоченный** *a.* linearly ordered, simply ordered.

линейность *f.* linearity; **л. отклонения** deflection linearity.

линейн/ый *a.* linear, line; **л. диполь** line dipole; **л. интеграл** line integral **л. источник** line source; **л. коэффициент поглощения** linear absorption coefficient; **л. размер** linear dimension; **л. спектр** line spectrum **л. трансформатор** line transformer **л. усилитель** linear amplifier; **л. ускоритель** linear accelerator; **л. ускоритель с бегущей волной** traveling-wave linear accelerator; **л. элемент** line element, linear element.

линейн/ый *cont.*, —**ая антенна** line source antenna; —**ая дислокация** (cryst.) edge dislocation; —**ая дисперсия** linear dispersion; —**ая длина пробега** linear range; —**ая задерживающая способность** linear stopping power; —**ая индикация** (radar) conventional display; —**ая мера** linear measure; —**ая молния** streak lightning; —**ая поляризация** plane polarization; —**ая скорость горения** burning rate, speed of flame propagation; —**ая цепочка** linear array; —**ое расширение** linear expansion; —**ое соотношение** linear relationship —**ое увеличение** (opt.) linear magnification; —**ое усиление** linear amplification.

линейчат/ый спектр line spectrum —**ая поверхность** ruled surface **косая —ая поверхность** skew (or nondevelopable) ruled surface; —**ая структура** line structure.

линза *f.* lens; **л.-мениск** meniscus lens.

линзо/видный, —**образный** *a.* lenticular; —**вый барабан** lens drum —**вый спектрометр** lens spectrometer; —**вый телескоп** refracting telescope.

линия *f.* line, curve; **л. апсид** line of apsides; **л. большого круга** geodetic line; **л. ветвления** (math.) branch line; **л. визирования** line of sight (or sighting); **л. времени** time base; **л. горизонта** skyline; **л. даты** date line; **л. движения** trajectory; **л. действия ударного импульса** line of percussion; **л. дислокации** dislocation (line); **л. задержки** delay line; **л. изгиба** curvature; **л. касания** line of contact, tangent; **л. нулевого склонения** agonic line; **л. оси** center line; **л. отсчета** reference line.

линия передачи transmission line; **л. поля** field line; **л. равного объема** isoplere, isometric line; **л. развертки** sweep trace; **л. раздела** boundary; **л. разреза** (math.) branch cut; **л. сверхструктуры** superstructure line; **л. связи** communication line; **л. ската** (math.) line of steepest descent; **л. скольжения** slip (or glide) line; **л. сложной формы** irregular line; **л. солидус** solidus (curve); **л. спектра** spectral line; **л. спектра испускания** emission line; **л. сравнения** reference line; **л. тока** line of flow; (hyd.) streamline; **л. условного уровня** datum level; **л. фокусов** focal line.

линнеит *m.* linnaeite.

Линней Linné (lunar crater).

линовальная машина ruling engine.

линозит *m.* linosite.

лио/гель *m.* lyogel; **—металлургия** *f.* lyometallurgy.

лио/сорбция *f.* lyosorption; **—тропный** *a.* lyotropic; **—фильный** *a.* lyophilic; **—фобный** *a.* lyophobic.

липк/ий *a.* adhesive; sticky; **—ая лента** adhesive tape; **—ость** *f.* adhesiveness; stickiness.

липнуть *v.* adhere, stick.

липофильность *f.* lipophily, oleophily.

Липпман Lippmann.

Липшица условие Lipschitz condition.

Лира Lyra (Lyr) (constellation).

Лириды Lyrids (meteors).

лироконит *m.* liroconite.

Лисичка Vulpecula (Vul) (constellation).

лискирдит *m.* liskeardite.

Лиссажу картина, Л. фигура Lisssajou figure.

лист *m.* leaf; blade; sheet, lamina, lamination; foil; plate; **заглавный л., титульный л.** title page.

Листера способ Lyster flotation process.

листик *m.* leaflet, small sheet.

листов/альный *a.*, **—ание** *n.* sheeting; **—атый** *a.* foliate, laminated; **—атая структура** (geo.) book structure.

листовка *f.* leaflet.

листов/ой *a.* sheet; plate; leaf; **л. асбест** asbestos sheet; **л. металл** sheet metal; metal foil; **—ая рессора** leaf spring; **—ая сталь** steel plate, sheet steel; **—ая фибра** fiberboard; **—ое железо** sheet iron; **—ое золото** gold foil; **—ое стекло** sheet glass.

листок *m.* leaflet; **магнитный л.** magnetic shell.

листопрокатный валок (met.) plate roll; **л. стан** plate mill.

лит. *abbr.* (**литература**) literature; (**литературный**) literature, literary; (**литовский**) Lithuanian.

литейная *f.* foundry.

литейный *a.* foundry, casting; **л. завод, л. цех** *see* **литейная.**

литера *f.* letter, type.

литератур/а *f.* literature; **—ный** *a.* literature, literary; **—ный указатель** bibliography; **—ная собственность** copyright.

лит/иевый *a.* lithium; **—иевая слюда** lithia mica; **—ий** *m.* lithium (Li).

литио/амфибол *m.* lithium amphibole; **—филит** *m.* lithiophilite.

Литл Джо Little Joe (rocket).

ЛИТМО *abbr.* (**Ленинградский институт точной механики и оптики**) Leningrad Institute of Precision Mechanics and Optics.

лито— *prefix* litho—.

Литовская ССР Lithuanian SSR.

литогене/зис *m.* lithogenesis; **—тический** *a.* lithogenetic.

литограф/ический, —ский *a.* lithographic; **—ия** *f.* lithography.

лит/ой *a.* cast, poured, molten, fused; **л. бетон** poured concrete; **—ая соль** fused salt; **—ая сталь** cast steel.

литолог/ический *a.* lithologic; **—ия** *f.* lithology.

литосфера *f.* lithosphere.
литр *m.* liter (l).
лит-ра *abbr.* (**литература**) literature.
литраж *m.* displacement capacity.
литроатмосфера *f.* liter-atmosphere.
литров/ание *n.* refining, purifying; **—анный** *a.* refined, purified; **—ать** *v.* refine, purify.
литров/ый *a.* liter; volumetric; **—ая тяга** volumetric thrust.
Лит ССР *abbr. see* **Литовская ССР.**
Литтров Litthrow (lunar crater).
литцендрат *m.* Litz wire, litzendraht.
лить *v.* pour; found, cast; **—е** *n.* founding, casting; cast; **стальное —е** cast steel; steel casting.
Лиувилля теорема Liouville theorem.
лифт *m.*, **—овый** *a.* elevator.
Лихтенберг Lichtenberg (lunar crater).
Лихтенберга фигура, лихтенбергова фигура Lichtenberg figure.
ЛИХФ *abbr.* (**Ленинградский институт химической физики**) Leningrad Institute of Chemical Physics.
лицев/ой *a.* face, front; **—ая поверхность** face; **—ая сторона** face, front; right side (of material).
лиценз/ионный *a.*, **—ия** *f.* license; **—ионное удостоверение** certificate, license.
Лицет Licetus (lunar crater).
лицо *n.* face, side.
лично *adv.* personally, in person.
личн/ость *f.* personality; person; **—ый** *a.* personal, individual, private; **—ый состав** personnel; **—ая ошибка** personal error; **—ое уравнение** personal equation.
лиш/ать, —ить *v.* deprive (of), remove, eliminate; **—аться** *v.* be deprived (of), lose; **—ение** *n.* deprivation, loss; **—енный** *a.* deprived, stripped.
лишний *a.* superfluous, extraneous, excessive; spare, odd; **л. корень** (math.) extraneous root; **л. раз** once more.
лишь *adv.* only; as soon as; **л. бы** provided; **л. только** as soon as.
ЛИЭМ *abbr.* (**Ленинградский институт экспериментальной метеорологии**) Leningrad Institute of Experimental Meteorology.
лк *abbr.* (**люкс**) lux (lx).
ЛКАО метод *abbr.* (**метод линейных комбинаций атомных орбит**) method of linear combination of atomic orbitals.
Ллойда зеркало Lloyd mirror; **Л.-Фишера аппарат** L.-Fisher apparatus.
ЛЛТД *abbr.* (**Ленинградская лаборатория тепловых двигателей**) Leningrad Heat Engine Laboratory.
лм *abbr.* (**люмен**) lumen (lu).
лм-с, лм-сек *abbr.* (**люмен-секунда**) lumen-second (lu-sec).
лм-ч *abbr.* (**люмен-час**) lumen-hour (lu-hr).
лн *abbr.* (**линия**) line.
Лобачевский Lobachevskii (Lobatschewski).
лобный *a.* frontal; **л. гребень** frontal crest.
лобов/ой *a.* front, frontal, face; head-on; **—ая поверхность** frontal surface, face; **—ое давление** ram pressure; **—ое сопротивление** (aero.) head resistance, drag; **—ое сопротивление воздуха** air drag; **—ое столкновение** head-on (knock-on, central) collision; **коэффициент —ого сопротивления** drag coefficient.
ловенит *m.* låvenite.
ловильный *a.* catching, catch; **л. колокол** bell socket.
ловит/ель *m.* catcher; **—ь** *v.* catch, trap.
Ловица дуга Lowitz arc.
ловк/ий *a.* clever, skilful; **—ость** *f.* cleverness, skill, dexterity.
ловушка *f.* trap, collector, catcher; **л. пучка** beam catcher.
логарифм *m.* logarithm, log; **десятичный л.** common logarithm, Briggs logarithm; **таблица —ов** logarithmic table; **—ика** *f.* logarithmic curve.
логарифмиров/ание *n.* logarithmic operation; **—анный** *a.* in logarithmic form; **—ать** *v.* take the logarithm (of).
логарифмически-нормальный (stat.) logarithmic-normal, lognormal.
логарифмическ/ий *a.* logarithmic; **л. декремент затухания** logarithmic decrement; **л. измеритель скорости, л. интенсиметр** log-counting ratemeter; **—ая анаморфоза** logarithmic

plot; **—ая бумага** logarithmic coordinate paper; **—ая линейка** slide rule; *see also* **линейка**; **—ая производная** logarithmic derivative; **—ая сетка** logarithmic coordinate.

логи/ка *f.* logic; **—чески, —чно** *adv.* logically; **—ческий, —чный** *a.* logical; **—ческая цепь** logical net.

логометр *m.* (elec.) logometer, ratiometer.

Лоде параметр деформации Lode strain parameter.

Лодж-Мюиргеда когерер Lodge-Muirhead coherer.

лод/ка *f.*, **—очный** *a.* boat; **—очка** *f.* boat; debitense (in glass manufacturing).

ложбина *f.* trough; hollow.

ложе *n.* bed, channel; **л. океана** ocean floor (or bed).

ложка *f.* spoon; ladle.

ложно *adv.* falsely; **—кристаллический** *a.* pseudocrystalline; **—эвтектический** *a.* pseudoeutectic.

ложно— *prefix* pseudo—; *see also* **псевдо—**.

ложн/ый *a.* false, erroneous, spurious; pseudo—; **л. вывод** fallacy; **л. отсчет** spurious count; **л. пик** ghost peak; **л. сигнал** ghost signal, spurious signal; **л. туман** mock fog; **—ая корона** false corona; **—ая луна** mock moon, paraselene; **—ое горючее** dummy fuel; **—ое отражение** (radar) false echo; **—ое солнечное кольцо** parhelic circle; **—ое солнце** mock sun, parhelion; **—ое срабатывание** false response; misfiring; **—ые перистые облака** false cirrus.

ложь *f.* falsehood.

лозейит *m.* loseyite.

ЛОИ *abbr.* (**Ленинградский оптический институт**) Leningrad Optical Institute.

ЛОИАТ *abbr.* (**Ленинградское отделение института автоматики и телемеханики Академии наук СССР**) Leningrad Branch of the Institute of Automation and Remote Control of the Academy of Sciences, USSR.

Лоидиса вехи Loidis poles.

локализ/ация *f.* localization, trapping; **—ировать, —овать** *v.* localize, capture, trap; **—ованный** *a.* localized; **—уемость** *f.* localizability.

локально/-галилеев locally Galilean; **—сть** *see* **локализуемость.**

локальн/ый *a.* local, localized, localizable; **—ая доза** local dosage; **—ое поле** local field; **—ое уравнение поля** equation of a localizable field.

локация звуковая sonar.

локомотив *m.* locomotive.

локонообразный *a.* curled.

локсодромия *f.* loxodrome, loxodromic curve, rhumb line.

локсоклаз *m.* loxoclase.

локтальный цоколь loctal (loktal) base.

локтев/ой *a.* elbow; **—ое движение** elbow action.

локус *m.* locus.

лом *m.* crowbar; scrap, fragments; **железный л.** scrap iron; **металлический л.** scrap metal.

ломан/ая *f.* broken line; **—ие** *n.* breaking, fracturing; **—ый** *a.* broken, fractured, ragged; **—ый путь** broken path.

ломать *v.* break, fracture; quarry.

ЛОМЗ *abbr.* (**Ленинградский оптико-механический завод**) Leningrad Optical Equipment Plant.

лом/ик *m.* small crowbar, forcer; **—ка** *f.* breaking, demolishing; quarry; **—кий** *a.* brittle, friable, fragile; (met.) short.

ломкость *f.* brittleness, friability, fragility; **л. в холодном состоянии** cold shortness.

Ломоносова-Гершеля рефлектор Herschelian reflecting telescope.

ломонтит *m.* laumontite.

лонгбанит *m.* långbanite.

Лонгомонтан Longomontanus (lunar crater).

Лондона уравнение London equation.

лонжерон *m.* (aero.) longeron, wing spar.

ЛОНИИС *abbr.* (**Ленинградский областной научно-исследовательский институт связи**) Leningrad Regional Communications Research Institute.

ЛОНИТОМАШ *abbr.* (**Ленинградское отделение научно-инженерно-технического, общество машиностроителей**) Leningrad Branch of the

Scientific, Engineering and Technical Society of Mechanical Engineers.

ЛООНТИ *abbr.* (**Ленинградское отделение Объединенного научно-технического издательства**) Leningrad Branch of the United Scientific and Technical Press.

лопание *n.* bursting, cracking, breaking.

лопастн/ый *a.* blade, vane, paddle; **л. водомер** vane water meter; **л. насос** wing pump; —**ое колесо** impeller.

лопасть *f.* blade, vane, paddle.

лопат/а *f.* shovel, spade; rabble; —**ка** *f.* small shovel, trowel; blade, paddle, vane; —**очка** *f.* trowel; spatula.

лопаться *v.* burst, break, split.

Лопиталя правило (теорема) (math.) l'Hôpital rule.

лопнуть *see* **лопаться.**

Лорана разложение (ряд) Laurent expansion.

Лорентц, лорентцов Lorentz (usually **Лоренц, лоренцов**).

Лоренц/а преобразование Lorentz transformation; **Л.-Лорентца формула** Lorenz-Lorentz equation.

лоренценит *m.* lorenzenite.

лоренцов множитель Lorentz factor; —**а сила** Lorentz force; —**о сокращение** Lorentz contraction; —**ский** *a.* Lorentz, Lorentzian.

Лорина труба Lorin duct.

Лорман Lohrmann (lunar crater).

Лос-Аламос Los Alamos.

лоск *m.* gloss, luster.

лосн/истый *a.* glossy; —**иться** *v.* be glossy, lustrous; shine; —**ящийся** *a.* glossy, shiny.

лот *m.* plumb bob, sounding lead, sinker, sea gauge.

лотарингский ярус Lotharingian stage.

лотерея *f.* lottery.

ЛОТИ *abbr.* (**Ленинградский областной теплотехнический институт**) Leningrad Regional Heat Engineering Institute.

лот/кообразный *a.* trough-shaped; —**ок** *m.* flume, chute, gutter.

Лоу теория рассеяния Low scattering theory.

лоция *f.* pilotage, navigation instructions.

лоцман *m.*, —**ский** *a.* pilot.

Лошадиная Голова Horse Head nebula.

лошадиная сила horsepower (hp).

Лошмидта число Loschmidt number.

лощен/ие *n.* polishing; glazing; —**ый** *a.* glossy, polished; glazed.

лощина *f.* hollow, depression; ravine.

л.с. *abbr.* (**лошадиная сила**) horsepower (hp).

Л.-система *abbr.* (**лабораторная система**) laboratory system.

л. с.-ч. *abbr.* (**лошадиная сила-час**) horsepower-hour (hp-hr).

лубрикатор *m.* lubricator.

лудербакит *m.* louderbackite.

луд/ильный *a.* tinning; —**ить** *v.* tin.

лудловский ярус Ludlow stage.

лужен/ие *n.* (met.) tinning, tinplating; —**ый** *a.* tinned, tinplated; —**ое листовое железо** tinplate.

лузитанский *a.* Lusitanian.

лука *f.* bend, meander.

лум— *see* **люм—.**

луна *f.* moon.

лунка *f.* hole; lune.

лунно/-приливный *a.* lunitidal; **л.-солнечный** *a.* lunisolar.

лунн/ый *a.* lunar, moon; **л. камень** moonstone; **л. промежуток** lunitidal interval; **л. свет** moonlight; —**ое затмение** lunar eclipse.

луночка *f.* lune.

лупа *f.* magnifying glass; (math.) loop.

луч *m.* ray, beam; radius, radial line; (math.) half-line; (nucl.) prong (of a star); (astr.) streamer (of corona); **зеленый л.** (astr.) green flash; **л. зрения** line of sight; **л. регулируемый по углу места** (radar) variable-elevation beam; **испускать —и** radiate; **пучек —ей** beam, pencil.

лучев/ой *a.* ray, radiation; radial; **л. катод** beam cathode; **л. синдром** radiation syndrome; —**ая болезнь** radiation sickness; —**ая оптика** geometrical optics; —**ая скорость** (astr.) radial velocity; —**ое давление** radiation pressure; —**ое заболевание** radiation illness.

лучеиспускание *n.* radiation, emission.

лучеиспускательн/ый *a.* radiating, emitting; —**ая отдача экрана** screen radiant efficiency; —**ая способность** emittance.

лучеиспускающ/ий *see* **лучеиспускательный**; —**ая поверхность** emitting surface.

луче/образный *a.* raylike, radial; —**образующее устройство** beam-forming device; —**ограничивающий электрод** beam-confining electrode; **коэффициент** —**поглощения** absorption coefficient, immissivity.

лучепреломл/ение *n.* refraction; *see also* **преломление**; —**яющий** *a.* refractive.

лучисто/-волокнистый radiating columnar; —**сть** *f.* radiance.

лучист/ый *a.* radiant, radiative; light; ray, rayed, radial; **л. перенос** radiative transport; **л. поток** radiant flux; **л. разряд** (elec.) brush and spray discharge; **коэффициент** —**ого отражения** (coefficient of) radiant reflectivity (or reflectance); —**ая вязкость** (astr.) radiative viscosity; —**ая руда** clinoclase; —**ая структура** (astr.) ray structure; —**ая теплота** radiant heat; —**ая энергия** radiant energy; —**ое давление** radiation pressure; —**ое равновесие** radiative equilibrium, radiation equilibrium.

лучш/е *comp. of* **хороший, хорошо,** better; **как можно л.** as well as possible; **тем л.** so much the better; —**ий** *a.* best; better; **в** —**ем случае** at most.

ЛФМУ *abbr.* (**Ленинградская фабрика механизированного учета**) Leningrad Computing-Machine Factory.

ЛФТИ *abbr.* (**Ленинградский физико-технический институт**) Leningrad Physico-Technical Institute.

ЛФТЛ *abbr.* (**Ленинградская физико-техническая лаборатория**) Leningrad Physico-Technical Laboratory.

ЛХТИ *abbr.* (**Ленинградский химико-технологический институт**) Leningrad Institute of Chemical Technology.

лыж/а *f.*, —**ный** *a.* (elec.) shoe.

ЛьвГУ [**Львовский государственный университет** (**им. Ивана Франко**)] Ivan Franko L'vov State University.

льгота *f.* privilege, exemption, advantage.

льди/на *f.* ice floe; **коэффициент** —**стости** (geo.) ice ratio —**стый** *a.* icy.

льдо— *prefix* ice.

Льенара-Вихерта потенциал Liénard-Wiechert potential.

льнянокислый *a.* linoleic acid, linoleate (of).

Льюиса теория Lewis theory; **Л.-Рендалла правило** L.-Randall rule.

льюисит *m.* lewisite.

льюистонит *m.* lewistonite.

лэмбовский *see* **лембовский.**

Лэнгмюра *see* **Ленгмюра.**

ЛЭТЗ *abbr.* (**Ленинградский электротехнический завод**) Leningrad Electrotechnical Plant.

ЛЭТИ *abbr.* (**Ленинградский электротехнический институт**) Leningrad Electrotechnical Institute.

ЛЭФИ *abbr.* (**Ленинградский электрофизический институт**) Leningrad Institute of Electrical Physics.

ЛЭЭЛ *abbr.* (**Ленинградская экспериментальная электротехническая лаборатория**) Leningrad Experimental Electrical Engineering Laboratory.

любезн/ость *f.* kindness, courtesy; —**ый** *a.* courteous, obliging, polite; **будьте** —**ы** please, be so kind (as to).

любецкит *m.* lubeckite.

Любинецкий Lubinetzky (lunar crater).

любитель *m.* amateur; —**ская станция** (rad.) amateur station.

люблинит *m.* lublinite.

любознательн/ость *f.* curiosity, inquisitiveness; —**ый** *a.* curious, inquiring, inquisitive.

люб/ой *a.* any; every; *m.* either (of two); **в** —**ое время** at any time; —**ой ценой** at any price.

любопыт/ный *a.* curious, inquisitive; interesting; —**ство** *n.* curiosity.

людвигит *m.* ludwigite.

Людерса линии Lüders lines (slip bands).

люди *pl.* people.

людийский ярус Ludian stage.

люд/ный *a.* crowded; —**ской** *a.* human.

Люиса *see* **Льюиса.**

люк *m.* port, manhole, hatch; **входной л.** (opt.) entrance port; **выходной л.** (opt.) exit port.

люкит *m.* luckite.
люковый *a.* port, manhole, hatch.
люкс *m.* lux (lx).
Люкса газовые весы Lux gas balance.
Люксембург-Горьковский эффект Luxembourg effect.
люксметр *m.* luxmeter, luxometer.
люлька *f.* cradle.
люмахель *m.* lumachel (marble).
люмен *m.* lumen (lu); **л.-секунда** lumen-second (lu-sec); **л.-час** lumen-hour (lu-hr); **—метр** *m.* lumen meter, lumeter.
люминесц/ентный, —ирующий *a.* luminescent; **л. анализ** luminescent analysis; **л. спектрометр** scintillation spectrometer; **—енция** *f.* luminescence.
люмино/ген *m.* luminogen; **—скоп** *m.* luminoscope; **—фор** *m.* luminophor, phosphor, scintillator.
Люммера-Бродхуна фотометр Lummer-Brodhun photometer; **Л.-Герке пластинка** L.-Gehrcke plate.
люмнит *m.* lumnite.
люнебургит *m.* lüneburgite.
люнет *m.* lunette; support, rest; collar plate.
люсакит *m.* lusakite.
люсек *m.* lusec.
люсит *see* **люцит.**
люссатит *m.* lussatite.
лютетский ярус Lutetian stage.
лютец/ий *m.* lutecium (Lu); **—ит** *m.* lutecite.
люфт *m.* clearance; free play.
люцинит *m.* lucinite.
люцит *m.* lucite.
люцонит *m.* luzonite.
лючианит *m.* lucianite.
Лява волна Love wave.
лям/ка *f.*, **—очный** *a.* strap.
ляпис *m.* silver nitrate.
Ляпунова неравенство Lyapunov (Liapounoff) inequality.

M

м *abbr.* (**месяц**) month; (**метр**) meter (m); **м.** (**минута**) minute (min).
м- *see* **мета—**.
М [*in steel mark* (**молибден**)] molybdenum (Mo).
М *abbr.* (**мега**) mega (M); (**число Маха**) Mach number; **М.** (**Москва**) Moscow.
ма *abbr.* (**миллиампер**) milliampere (ma).
маар *m.* (geo.) maar.
Мааса компас Maas compass.
МААЭ *abbr.* (**Международное агентство по атомной энергии**) International Atomic Energy Agency.
Мавролик Maurolycus (lunar crater).
магазин *m.*, **—ный** *a.* store; magazine; **м. емкостей** capacitor box; **м. затухания** attenuation box; **м. сопротивлений** (elec.) resistance box.
МАГАТЭ *abbr. see* **МААЭ.**
Магеллановы Облака (astr.) Magellanic Clouds.
Магин Maginus (lunar crater).
магистр *m.* master (degree); **м. наук** Master of Science, M.S.
магистраль *f.*, **—ный** *a.* main line, main route; main; **—ный провод** (elec.) main; **—ная труба** main.
магистрант *m.* master's degree candidate.
магическ/ий *a.* magic; **м. глаз** tuning ("magic") eye; **—ое число** magic number.
магма *f.* magma; **—тический** *a.* magma, magmatic.
магн. *abbr.* (**магнитный**) magnetic.
магнал/ий, —иум *m.* magnalium.
магналит *m.* magnalite (aluminum-magnesium alloy).
магнальный цоколь magnal base.
магнезиальный *a.* magnesia, magnesian.
магнезио *prefix* magnesio—.
магнез/ит *m.* magnesite; **—ия** *f.* magnesia, magnesium oxide.
магнесин *m.* magnesyn.
магнетизм *m.* magnetism; **земной м.** terrestrial magnetism.
магнет/ит *m.*, **—итовый** *a.* magnetite; **—ический** *a.* magnetic.
магнето— *see also* **магнито—**.
магнето *n.* magneto; **м. пусковое** starting magneto.

магнетон *m.* magneton.

магнетор *m.* magnettor (magnetic modulator).

магнетофлекс *m.* Magnetoflex (copper-iron-nickel alloy).

магнето/форез *m.* magnetophoresis; **—электрический** *a.* magnetoelectric.

магнетрон *m.* magnetron; **двухразрезной м.** split-anode magnetron; **м. непрерывной генерации** continuous-wave magnetron; **м. с вмонтированными полюсами** packaged magnetron; **м. со связками** strapped magnetron; **м. с подстройкой частоты** tunable magnetron; **—ная частота** magnetron frequency.

магн/иевый *a.* magnesium, magnesia, magnesian; **—ий** *m.* magnesium (Mg).

магнико *m.* Magnico.

магнит *m.* magnet; **брусковый м.** bar magnet; **естественный м.** natural magnet, lodestone; **м. отбоя** release magnet; **постоянный м.** permanent magnet.

магнит/изм *m.* magnetism; **остаточный м.** residual magnetism; **—ик** *m.* small (or elementary) magnet; **—ить** *v.* magnetize.

магнитно/активный *a.* magnetically active, magnetic; **—гидродинамический** *a.* magnetohydrodynamic, hydromagnetic; **м.-гидромеханическая неустойчивость** hydromagnetic (or magnetohydrostatic) instability; **—дипольный** *a.* magnetic-dipole; **—жесткий** *a.* hard-magnetic, permanent-magnet; **—ограниченный** *a.* magnetically confined; **м.-спиновый момент** spin magnetic moment; **м.-удерживаемая плазма** magnetically confined plasma.

магнитн/ый *a.* magnetic, magnet; **м. анализатор** magnetic analyzer, analyzing magnet; **м. гистерезис** magnetic hysteresis; **м. дефлектор** magnetic deflector; **м. диполь** magnetic dipole; **м. железняк** magnetite, magnetic iron ore; **м. колчедан** magnetic pyrite; pyrrhotite; **м. листок** magnetic shell; **м. момент** magnetic moment; **м. полюс** magnetic pole; **м. поток** magnetic flux; **м. поток сцепления** magnetic flux linkage; **м. резонанс** magnetic resonance; **м. спектрометр** magnetic spectrometer; **м. ток** magnetic current; **м. усилитель** magnetic amplifier; **м. экран** (magnetic) induction screen.

магнитн/ый *cont.*, **—ая восприимчивость** magnetic susceptibility; **—ая вязкость** magnetic viscosity (time lag, after-effect); **—ая газодинамика** magnetohydrodynamics, hydromagnetics; **—ая жесткость** magnetic rigidity; magnetic hardness; **—ая индукция** magnetic induction; **—ая лента** magnetic tape; **—ая линза** magnetic lens; **—ая напряженность** magnetic field strength; **—ая проводимость** permeance; **—ая проницаемость** permeability; **—ая проницаемость на частном цикле** incremental permeability; **—ая сила** magnetic force; **—ая силовая линия** magnetic line of force; **—ая сопротивляемость** reluctivity; **—ая сталь** magnet steel; **—ая стрелка** magnetic (or dipping) needle; **—ая усталость** magnetic fatigue; **—ая фокусировка** magnetic focusing; **—ая цепь** magnetic circuit; **—ая широта** magnetic latitude.

магнитн/ый *cont.*, **—ое взаимодействие** magnetic interaction; **—ое возмущение** magnetic disturbance (or perturbation); **—ое запаздывание** magnetic lag; **—ое зеркало** magnetic mirror; **—ое квантовое число** magnetic quantum number; **—ое колебание** magnetic fluctuation (or variation); **—ое мультипольное излучение** magnetic multipole radiation; **—ое наклонение** magnetic inclination (or dip); **—ое поле** magnetic field; **—ое поле Земли** terrestrial magnetic field; geomagnetic field; **—ое поле старта** starting field; **—ое последствие** magnetic lag (or after-effect); **—ое превращение** magnetic transition, Curie point; **—ое притяжение** magnetic attraction; **—ое пространство** magnet space; **—ое рассеяние** magnetic scattering; magnetic dispersion; magnetic leakage; **—ое рассеяние нейтронов** magnetic neutron scattering; **—ое сжатие**

magnetic constriction (or pinch); **—ое склонение** magnetic declination; **—ое смещение** magnetic displacement; **—ое сокращение** magnetic foreshortening (of sunspots); **—ое сопротивление** reluctance; **—ое старение** magnetic aging; **—ое удерживание** magnetic confinement (or containment); **—ое экранирование** magnetic shielding; **—ые весы** magnetic balance.

магнито— *prefix* magneto—; *see also* **магнитно.**

магнито/аэродинамика *f.* magneto-aerodynamics; **—газодинамика** *f.* magnetohydrodynamics, hydromagnetics; **—гидродинамическая волна** magnetohydrodynamic wave; **—грамма** *f.* magnetogram; **—граф** *m.* magnetograph; **—движущая сила** magnetomotive force; **—держатель** *m.* magnet support; **—звуковая волна** magneto-sonic wave; **—ионное расщепление** magneto-ionic splitting; **—калорический эффект** magnetocaloric effect.

магнитометр *m.* magnetometer; **—ический** *a.* magnetometric; **—ия** *f.* magnetometry.

магнитомеханическ/ий фактор magnetomechanical factor; **—ое отношение** magnetomechanical (or gyromagnetic) ratio.

магнитомягкий *a.* soft-magnetic, high-permeability.

магнитоопт/ика *f.* magneto-optics; **—ическая экзальтация** magneto-optical exaltation; **—ическое явление** magneto-optical effect.

магнито/остаренный *a.* magnetically aged; **—провод** *m.* magnetic circuit; **—скоп** *m.* magnetoscope; **—статика** *f.* magnetostatics; **—статический** *a.* magnetostatic.

магнитострикц/ионный *a.* magnetostrictive, magnetostriction; **м. генератор** magnetostriction oscillator; **м. резонатор** magnetostrictive resonator; **—ия** *f.* magnetostriction.

магнитотепловой эффект magnetocaloric effect.

магнитоупруг/ий *a.* magnetoelastic; **—ая энергия** magnetic strain energy, magnetostriction energy; **константа —ой связи** magnetoelastic coupling constant.

магнито/фон *m.* magnetic recorder; magnetophone; **—химия** *f.* magnetochemistry.

магнитоэлектрическ/ий *a.* magnetoelectric, permanent-magnet; **м. прибор** moving-coil instrument; **—ая машина** permanent-magnet machine, magneto.

магнитоякорный громкоговоритель magnetic-armature loudspeaker.

Магнуса эффект Magnus effect.

Маделунга константа (постоянная) Madelung constant.

Маджи-Риги-Ледюка эффект Maggi-Righi-Leduc effect.

мажор/анта *f.* (math.) majorant, upper bound; **—антный** *a.* majorant; **—ировать** *v.* majorize; **—ный** *a.* (mus.) major.

Маза счетчик Maze counter.

маз/анный *a.* greased; **—ать, —нуть** *v.* grease, lubricate; **—еобразный, —еподобный** *a.* greasy.

Мазон Mason (lunar crater).

мазонит *see* **мезонит.**

мазурий *m.* masurium (Ma).

мазут *m.* mazut, black oil, petroleum residue.

мазь *f.* grease, lubricant.

май *m.* May.

Майевского число Maievskii (or Mach) number.

Майер T. Mayer (lunar crater).

Майера кривая атомных объемов Meyer atomic volume curve.

майерсит *m.* miersite.

Майкельсона эшелон Michelson echelon.

Майорана обменная сила Majorana exchange force.

Майран Mairan (lunar crater).

Майснер *see* **Мейснер.**

майтландит *m.* maitlandite.

Майя Maia.

макадам *m.* macadam (road).

макан/ие *n.* dipping; **—ный** *a.* dipped.

макароны *pl.* macaroni.

макат/ельный *a.* dipping; **—ельная смесь** dipping compound; **—ь** *v.* dip.

макет *m.* model, dummy, mock-up; blank; —**ный** *a.* simulated.

макинтошит *m.* mackintoshite.

маккенсит *m.* mackensite.

Мак-Леода манометр McLeod gauge; **М.-Л. уравнение** McLeod equation.

Маклорена теорема (ряд) Maclaurin theorem.

Мак Мас-Халбарт обсерватория Mc-Math-Hulbert Observatory.

макнуть *see* **макать.**

маконит *m.* maconite.

макро— *prefix* macro—, macroscopic.

Макробий Macrobius (lunar crater).

макро/вихревые токи macro eddy currents; —**вязкость** *f.* macroviscosity; —**графия** *f.* macrography; —**зерно** *n.* macrograin; —**изотропный** *a.* macroscopically isotropic; —**климат** *m.* macroclimate; —**климатология** *f.* macroclimatology; —**компонент** *m.*, —**компснента** *f.* macrocomponent; —**концентрация** *f.* macroscopic concentration; —**коррозия** *f.* macrocorrosion; —**метеорология** *f.* macrometeorology.

макромолекул/а *f.* macromolecule; —**ярный** *a.* macromolecular.

макро/напряжение *n.* macrostress; —**ось** *f.* (cryst.) macroaxis; —**погода** *f.* large-scale weather; —**процесс** *m.* large-scale process; —**радиография** *f.* macroradiography; macroradiograph; —**сегрегация** *f.* macrosegregation; —**сейсм** *m.* macroseism; —**синоптический** *a.* macrosynoptic; —**система** *f.* macrosystem.

макроскоп/ический *a.* macroscopic, gross; (petr.) megascopic; —**ия** *f.* macroscopy.

макро/структура *f.* macrostructure; —**турбулентный** *a.* large-scale turbulent; —**фотография** *f.* macrophotography, enlarging; —**фотоснимок** *m.* macrograph; macrophotograph, enlargement; —**шлиф** *m.* (met.) macrograph; large section.

макс. *abbr.* **(максимум)** maximum (max).

максвелл *m.* maxwell (mx).

Максвелла демон Maxwell demon; **уравнения М.** M. equations.

максвелл/метр *m.* fluxmeter; —**овское распределение** Maxwellian distribution.

максимальн/о *adv.* maximum; —**ый** *a.* maximal, maximum, peak; —**ый ток** peak current; —**ая валентность** absolute (or maximum) valence; —**ая скорость падения** terminal velocity of fall; —**ое значение** maximum, peak; —**ое реле** overload relay.

максимум *m.* maximum, peak.

максит *m.* maxite.

малаколит *m.* malacolite.

малакон *m.* malacon.

малахит *m.* malachite.

Малая Медведица Ursa Minor (UMi) (constellation).

малеиновый *a.* maleic.

мал/ейший *a.* least; —**енький** *a.* small.

малиновскит *m.* malinowskite.

малк/а *f.* bevel, bevel square; **в —у** askew, obliquely.

Малларда генератор Mullard (ultrasonic) generator.

мало *adv.* little, few, slightly, not enough; **м. вероятно** it is unlikely; **м. где** in few places, rarely; **м. по малу** gradually; **м. того** moreover; **м. того что** it is not enough that.

мало/активные отходы low-activity waste, "cold" waste; —**важность** *f.* insignificance, unimportance; —**важный** *a.* insignificant, unimportant; —**ваттный** *a.* (elec.) low-watt; —**вероятный** *a.* unlikely, of low probability; —**возбужденный** *a.* weakly excited; —**вязкий** *a.* low-viscosity.

малогабаритн/ый *a.* small-size, small-volume, small-dimensioned, small-scale, compact, miniature, midget; **м. дозиметр** small-volume dosimeter; **м. реактор** small-scale reactor; —**ая батарея** compact battery; —**ая лампа** miniature tube.

малограмотный *a.* semi-illiterate, uneducated, unskilled.

малогрупповой анализ few-group analysis.

мал/ое *n.* little; **без —ого** almost; **в —ом** in the small; in a small region.

Малое Магелланово Облако Small Magellanic Cloud.

малоемкостный *a.* small-capacitance,

anticapacitance; **м. кабель** small-capacity cable; **м. переключатель** (rad.) anticapacitance switch.

малозаметный *a.* barely noticeable.

малознач/ащий, —ительный, —ущий *a.* insignificant, unimportant; **—ительность** *f.* insignificance, unimportance.

мало/известный *a.* little-known; **—инерционный** *a.* low-inertia, quick-response; **—интенсивный** *a.* low-intensity; weak; **—калиберный** *a.* small-gauge, small-bore.

малокров/ие *n.* anemia; **—ный** *a.* anemic.

малолегированн/ый *a.* low-alloy; **—ая сталь** low-alloy steel.

мало/мерный *a.* scanty, short; **—мощный** *a.* low-power, low-powered, low-capacity; **—облученный** *a.* slightly irradiated; **—обогащенный уран** low-enriched uranium; **—омный** *a.* low-resistance; **—опасный** *a.* low-hazard; **—опытный** *a.* inexperienced; **—понятный** *a.* abstruse, difficult to understand; **—продуктивный** *a.* inefficient, unproductive; **—процентный** *a.* low-grade; **—радиоактивный** *a.* slightly (weakly, low-level) radioactive; **—сильный** *a.* weak, low-powered.

малоуглеродист/ый *a.* low-carbon; **—ая сталь** low-carbon (or mild) steel.

мало/употребительный *a.* rarely used; **—форматный** *a.* miniature, small-sized; **—фосфористый** *a.* low-phosphorus; **—ценный** *a.* of little value, poor, inferior.

малочисленн/ость *f.* scantiness, small number; **—ый** *a.* scanty, few.

мало/чувствительный *a.* insensitive, low-sensitivity; **—шумный** *a.* low-noise; **—щелочной** *a.* low-alkali, containing little alkali.

мал/ый *a.* little, small, low, minor; **бесконечно м.** infinitesimal; **весьма м.** minute; **м. ход** low speed; **м. элемент** trace element; **—ого увеличения** low power; **—ая вода** low water, low tide; **—ая инерционность** rapid response; **—ая калория** small calorie; **—ая ось** minor axis; **—ая связь** weak coupling; **—ая энергия** low energy; **—ое давление** low pressure; **—ое пересыщение** low supersaturation.

Малый Лев Leo Minor (LMi) (constellation).

Малый Пес Canis Minor (CMi) (constellation).

мальта *f.* maltha.

мальтийский крест Maltese cross.

Малюса закон Malus law; **М.-Дюпена теорема** M.-Dupin theorem.

манган/андалузит *m.* manganandalusite; **—брусит** *m.* manganbrucite; **—геденбергит** *m.* manganhedenbergite.

манганин *m.* manganin.

мангано/зит *m.* manganosite; **—кальцит** *m.* manganocalcite; **—колумбит** *m.* manganocolumbite; **—сферит** *m.* manganospherite; **—филлит** *m.* manganophyllite.

манган/пектолит *m.* manganopectolite; **—хлорит** *m.* manganchlorite.

мангеймское золото (met.) Mannheim gold.

мандат *m.* mandate, warrant.

манебахское двойникование Manebach twinning.

маневр *m.*, **—енный** *a.* maneuver; **—енность** *f.* maneuverability, adjustability; **—енная способность** maneuverability; **—ирование** *n.* maneuvering; switching; **—ировать** *v.* maneuver; switch, shunt; **—овый** *a.* maneuvering; shunting.

манекен *m.* dummy, mock-up.

манжета *f.* cuff; pump cup; (elec.) baffle.

Манзин Manzinus (lunar crater).

Манилий Manillius (lunar crater).

манипул/ирование *n.*, **—яция** *f.* manipulation, handling, keying; operation; **—ировать** *v.* manipulate, handle; operate; **—ятор** *m.* manipulator; operator; **—ятор ближнего действия** (reactor) handler.

манифест/ация *f.* manifestation, demonstration; **—ировать** *v.* manifest, demonstrate.

Маннинга формула Manning formula.

манодетандер *m.* reducing valve.

манометр *m.* manometer, pressu

gauge; —**ический** *a.* manometric, manometer, pressure.

мантисса *f.* mantissa.

манускрипт *m.* manuscript.

маншеит *m.* mansjöite.

маньяк *m.* manjak.

Маральди Maraldi (lunar crater).

марган/ец *m.* manganese (Mn); —**цевый** *see* **марганцовый.**

марганцов/истый *a.* manganous, manganese; —**ый** *a.* manganic, manganese; —**ый апатит** manganapatite; —**ый везувианит** manganvesuvianite; —**ый людвигит** manganludwigite; —**ый мусковит** manganmuscovite; —**ый нептунит** manganneptunite; —**ая сталь** manganese steel.

маргиналии *pl.* marginal notes.

Маргулеса (Маргулиса) уравнение (условие) Margules equation.

марево *n.* mirage, haze.

мареогр/амма *f.* marigram; —**аф** *m.* tide gauge.

Марий Marius (lunar crater).

Марийская АССР Mari ASSR.

мариньякит *m.* marignacite.

Мариотта закон Mariotte law.

марипозит *m.* mariposite.

марка *f.* mark, stamp, brand; quality, sort; **фабричная м.** trademark.

марказит *m.* marcasite.

маркер *m.*, —**ный** *a.* marker; —**ный импульс** reference pulse.

маркир/ованный *a.* marked, stamped, labeled; —**овать** *v.* mark, stamp; —**овка** *f.* marking, stamping, numbering; —**овочный** *a.* marker, reference; —**ующий** *a.* marking; —**ующий горизонт** (geo.) marker bed (or horizon), indicator horizon.

Маркова преобразование Markov transformation; **М. цепь** M. chain; **марковский случайный процесс** Markovian process.

Маркони когерер Marconi coherer.

маркшейд. *abbr.* (**маркшейдерский**) surveyor's, surveying.

маркшейдер *m.* mine surveyor; —**ский** *a.* surveyor's, surveying; —**ская съемка** mine surveying.

марочный *a.* stamp, mark.

Марс Mars.

марселин *m.* marceline.

марсианский *a.* Martian.

март *m.* March.

мартенов/ание *n.* open-hearth refining; —**ский** *a.* Martin, Siemens-Martin, open-hearth; —**ская печь** open-hearth furnace; —**ская сталь** open-hearth steel.

Мартенс-Гейн: твердость по —у Martens-Heyn hardness.

мартенсит *m.* martensite; —**ное превращение** martensite transformation; —**овый** *a.* martensite, martensitic.

мартурит *m.* martourite.

МАРУ *abbr.* (**мгновенная автоматическая регулировка усиления**) instantaneous automatic volume control (IAVC).

маршрут *m.*, —**ный** *a.* route, itinerary, run, course; —**ная фотосъемка** strip (aerial) photography.

МАС *abbr.* (**Международный астрономический союз**) International Astronomical Union (IAU).

маска *f.* mask; face guard.

масканьит *m.* mascagnite.

Маскелайн Maskelyne (lunar crater).

маскелинит *m.* maskelynite.

маскир/ование *n.* masking; —**ованный** *a.* masked, camouflaged; concealed; —**овать** *v.* mask, camouflage; conceal; —**овка** *f.* masking, camouflage; concealment; —**овочный,** —**ующий** *a.* masking, camouflage; concealing.

маслен/ка *f.* lubricator, oil can; oil cup, grease cup; —**ый** *see* **масляный.**

маслить *v.* oil, grease, lubricate.

масло *n.* oil; **густое м.** heavy oil; **жидкое м.** light oil, thin oil.

масломер *m.*, —**ное стекло** oil gauge.

масло/непроницаемый *a.* oilproof; —**образный** *a.* oily, greasy; —**образующий** *a.* oil-forming, olefiant; —**отделитель** *m.* oil separator; —**отражатель** *m.* oil seal (for shaft), oil thrower; —**очиститель** *m.* oil purifier; —**провод** *m.* oil pipeline, oil line; —**пропитанная бумага** oil-impregnated paper; —**растворимый** *a.* oil-soluble; —**сборник** *m.* oil pan, drip pan; —**указатель** *m.* oil gauge;

—**уловитель** *m.* drip pan, oil catcher; —**фильтр** *m.* oil filter.

маслянист/ость *f.* oiliness; lubricity; —**ый** *a.* oily; —**ая смола** oleoresin.

маслян/ый *a.* oil, oily, greasy; butyric; **м. газ** oil gas; **м. диффузионный насос** oil-diffusion pump; **м. конденсатор** oil-filled capacitor; **м. лак** oil varnish; —**ое пятно** grease spot; —**ое уплотнение** oil seal.

масс. ед. *abbr.* (**массовая единица**) mass unit.

масс/-сепаратор mass separator; **м.-спектр** mass spectrum; **м.-спектрограмма** mass spectrogram; **м.-спектрограф** mass spectrograph; **м.-спектрометр** mass spectrometer; **м.-спектрометр с двойной фокусировкой** double-focusing mass spectrometer; **м.-спектрометрический метод** mass spectrometric method; **м.-спектрометрия** mass spectrometry; **закон действия м.** law of mass action.

масс/а *f.* mass, bulk; particle; (paper) pulp; paste; **м. атома** atomic mass; **м. покоя** rest mass; **м. струи** flow mass; **в —е** as a whole, in the mass; in the bulk (of); **единица —ы** unit of mass.

массив *m.* massif; large mass; block; large tract; —**ноконтрфорсная плотина** massive-buttress dam; —**ность** *f.* massiveness, solidity; —**ный** *a.* massive, bulky, bulk, solid, heavy, compact, thick.

массикот *m.* massicot.

массов/ый *a.* mass, bulk; **м. излучатель** mass radiator; **м. коэффициент ослабления** mass absorption coefficient; **м. коэффициент поглощения** mass absorption coefficient; **м. расход** mass flow, mass velocity; **м. спектр** mass spectrum; —**ая единица** mass unit; —**ая передача** mass transfer; —**ая сила** body force, mass force; —**ая тормозная способность** mass stopping power; —**ая цепочка** mass chain; **коэффициент —ой передачи** mass transfer coefficient; —**ое производство** mass production; —**ое уничтожение** mass destruction; —**ое число** mass number.

массопроводность *f.* mass transfer.

мастер *m.* expert; foreman; —**ок** *m* trowel.

мастерск/ая *f.* workshop, shop; —**ие** *pl* shops; —**ой** *a.* skilful, masterly.

мастерство *n.* skill.

мастика *f.* mastic, mastic gum; putty —**тор** *m.* (rubber) masticator; —**ци** *f.* mastication.

масти/ковый, —**чный** *a.* mastic.

масштаб *m.* scale, measure; scalin ratio; **натуральный м.** full-scale **складной м.** folding rule; **большог —а** large-scale; **в маленьком —е** o a small scale; **по —у** to scale **чертить в —е** draw to scale.

масштабн/ый *a.* scale, scaling; **м. ко эффициент** scale factor; —**ая ламп** (elec.) scaling tube; —**ая линейк** scale, (measuring) rule; —**ая модел** scale model; —**ое приближени** scaling approximation.

мат *m.* mat, matte, mat finish; **наво дить м.** mat, frost (glass).

мат. *abbr.* (**математика**) mathematic (**математический**) mathematical.

математика *f.* mathematics.

математическ/ий *a.* mathematical; **м анализ** mathematical analysis; —**о действие** mathematical operatio —**ое ожидание** mathematical expe tation.

материал *m.* material; (*pl.*) data; **сыро м.** raw material; —**изация** *f.* mater alization, creation; —**оведение** study of materials.

материальн/ый *a.* material; **м. пар метр кривизны** (reactor) materi buckling; —**ая волна** matter wav —**ая точка** (material) particle; — **поле** material field.

материк *m.* continent, mainland; — **вый** *a.* continental, land; —**овы бриз** land breeze; —**овая поро** bedrock.

материнск/ий *a.* maternal, mothe parent; **м. элемент** parent elemen —**ая порода** mother (native, sourc rock; —**ая фракция** parent fraction

матер/ия *f.* matter, subject; fabri —**чатый** *a.* fabric, cloth.

матиров/ание *n.*, —**ка** *f.* (producin dull finish; frosting (glass); —**а**

ный *a.* mat, matte, dull; frosted; **—ать** *v.* dull, mat, matte; frost.

Матиссена правило Matthiessen rule.

матка *f.* master (or mother) batch.

матлокит *m.* matlockite.

матов/ость *f.* dullness; **—ый** *a.* dull; mat, matte; frosted; **—ый блеск** dull (or mat) finish.

маточн/ый *a.* mother; **м. раствор** mother solution (or liquor); **—ая смесь** mother (or master) batch.

матрикуляция *f.* matriculation.

матриц/а *f.* matrix; (met.) die; starting sheet (in electrodeposition); **м. коэффициентов корреляции** correlation matrix; **м.-образец** master die; **м. приспособления** adaptation matrix; ***N*-рядная матрица** $N \times N$ matrix; **м. столкновений** collision matrix; **—ирование** *n.* matrixing.

матричн/ый *a.* matrix; (met.) die; **м. коэффициент, м. элемент** matrix element; **—ая алгебра** matrix algebra; **—ая механика** matrix mechanics.

мать *f.* mother.

Матье функция Mathieu function.

маухерит *m.* maucherite.

мауцелиит *m.* mauzeliite.

мафи/ты *pl.* (geo.) mafites; **—ческий** *a.* mafic.

мах *m.* motion, stroke.

Маха конус Mach cone; **М. критерий** M. criterion, Mach number; **М. угол** M. angle; **М. число** M. number; **М.-Цендера интерферометр** M.-Zehnder interferometer.

мах/альный *a.*, **—ание** *n.* waving, signaling; **—ать** *v.* wave, signal.

махнуть *see* **махать.**

маховик *m.* flywheel; **м.-регулятор** flywheel governor; **сплошной м.** disk (or one-piece) flywheel; **привод от —а** flywheel drive.

маховичок *m.* pilot wheel; hand wheel; knob.

махов/ой *a.* flywheel; **м. момент** moment of inertia, moment of gyration; **—ое колесо** flywheel.

мацапилит *m.* mazapilite.

мацер/атор *m.* macerator; **—ация** *f.*, **—ирование** *n.* maceration; **—ировать** *v.* macerate.

мачт/а *f.*, **—овый** *a.* mast; column, post, pole, tower; **—овая антенна** mast antenna.

машин/а *f.* machine, engine; **—ы** *pl.* machines, machinery; **м.-аналог** analog computer; **м. двигатель** (driving) engine; **м. открытого исполнения** open-type machine; **м. параллельного действия** parallel machine; **паровая м.** steam engine; **м. с внутренним самовозбуждением** machine with inherent self-excitation; **составная м.** compound engine.

машинальный *a.* mechanical, automatic.

машин/изация *f.* mechanization; **—ист** *m.* machinist; (railroad) engineer; **—истка** *f.* typist; **—ка** *f.* small machine; typewriter.

машинн/ый *a.* machine, engine; power (driven); mechanical; **м. зал, —ое отделение** machine room, engine room; **—ое оборудование** machinery, mechanical equipment; **—ое черчение** mechanical drawing; **обрабатывать —ым способом** machine.

машиностр. *abbr.* (**машиностроение**) machine construction; mechanical engineering; (**машиностроительный**) machine construction; mechanical engineering.

машиностро/ение *n.* machine construction; mechanical engineering; **—итель** *m.* mechanical engineer; **—ительный** *a.* machine construction; mechanical engineering.

маяк *m.* lighthouse, beacon.

маятник *m.* pendulum, (watch) balance; **м. с подвижной катящейся осью** rocking pendulum; **—овый** *a.* pendulum; **—овый магнетометр** pendulum magnetometer; **—овая твердость** pendulum hardness.

маячковая лампа (elec.) lighthouse tube.

мб *abbr.* (**миллибар**) millibar (mb); (**миллибарн**) millibarn (mb); **м.б.** (**может быть**) perhaps; possibly; it is possible.

м-б *abbr.* (**масштаб**) scale.

мбар *abbr.* (**миллибар**) millibar (mb).

мбарн, мбн *abbr.* (**миллибарн**) millibarn (mb).

МБР *abbr.* (**межконтинентальная баллистическая ракета**) intercontinental ballistic missile (ICBM).

мв *abbr.* (**милливольт**) millivolt (mv).

МВ *abbr.* (**метровые волны**) meter waves.

м-во *abbr.* (**министерство**) ministry; board, department.

мвт *abbr.* (**милливатт**) milliwatt (mw).

Мвт *abbr.* (**мегаватт**) megawatt (Mw).

Мвтч *abbr.* (**мегаватт-час**) megawatt-hour (Mwhr).

мг *abbr.* (**миллиграмм**) milligram (mg).

мгал *abbr.* (**миллигал**) milligal (mgal).

МГГ *abbr.* (**международный геофизический год**) International Geophysical Year (IGY).

МГИМИП *abbr.* (**Московский государственный институт механических и измерительных приборов**) Moscow State Institute of Mechanical and Measuring Instruments.

МГК *abbr.* (**Международный геологический конгресс**) International Geological Congress.

мгл/а *f.* haze; **сухая м.** dry haze; **—истый** *a* hazy.

МГМИ *abbr.* (**Московский гидрометеорологический институт**) Moscow Hydrometeorological Institute.

мгн *abbr.* (**миллигенри**) millihenry (mh).

мгновен/ие *n.* instant, moment; **—но** *adv.* instantaneously, instantly; momentarily; **—но-критический реактор, —но-критичный реактор** prompt critical reactor; **—ность** *f.* instantaneousness.

мгновенн/ый *a.* instantaneous, prompt; momentary, transitory, transient; **м. нейтрон** prompt neutron; **м. подогреватель** flashed heater; **м. центр вращения** instantaneous center of rotation; **—ая мощность** instantaneous power; **—ая ось вращения** instantaneous axis of rotation; **—ая реактивность** prompt reactivity; **—ое гамма-излучение** prompt gamma rays; **—ое давление звука** instantaneous sound pressure; **—ое значение** instantaneous value; **—ое намагничивание** flash magnetization; **—ое сближение** instantaneous assembly.

МГРИ *abbr.* (**Московский геологоразведочный институт**) Moscow Geological Prospecting Institute.

Мгц *abbr.* (**мегагерц**) megacycles (Mc).

Мдж *abbr.* (**мегаджоуль**) megajoule.

м.д.с. *abbr.* (**магнитодвижущая сила**) magnetomotive force (mmf).

МДУ *abbr.* (**Московский дом ученых**) Moscow House of Scientists.

меандр/а *f.* meander; **—ирующий** *a.* meandering.

Мебиуса лист Moebius strip.

мег—, мега— *prefix* mega—, meg—.

мегаварметр *m.* megavarmeter.

мегаватт *m.* megawatt; **м.-час** megawatt-hour.

мега/вольт *m.* megavolt; **—герц** *m.* megacycle per second; **—джоуль** *m.* megajoule; **—дина** *f.* megadyne; **—кюри** *n.* megacurie.

мегалосферический *a.* megalospheric.

мега/мегагерц *m.* megamegacycle per second; **—метр** *m.* megameter; **—парсек** *m.* megaparsec.

мегаперм *m.* Megaperm (nickel-iron-manganese alloy).

мега/рад *m.* megarad; **—резерфорд** *m.* megarutherford; **—рентген** *m.* megaroentgen.

мегасейсм *m.* megaseism.

мегаскоп *m.* megascope; **—ический** *a* megascopic.

мега/температура *f.* megatemperature; **—тепловой, —термический** *a.* megathermal; **—тонна** *f.* megaton; **—трон** *m.* megatron; **—фон** *m.* megaphone; **—цикл** *m.* megacycle; **—электронвольт** *m.* million electron volts (Mev).

мег/гер *m.* megger; **—ом** *m.* megohm (meg); **—омит** *m.* megohmite; **—омметр** *m.* megohmmeter, megger; **—эрг** *m.* megaerg.

мед. *abbr.* (**медицинский**) medical.

медаль *f.* medal.

меде— *prefix* copper.

меденосный *a.* copper-bearing, cupriferous.

меджитит *m.* medjidite.

медзянкит *m.* miedziankite.

медиальный *a.* medial.

медиан/а *f.*, **—ный** *a.* median.

медиатриса *f.* perpendicular bisector.

медик *m.* physician; medical student.
медисто— *prefix* cuprous, copper.
медист/ый *a.* cuprous, copper; **м. вад** lampadite; **—ое золото** copper gold; **—ое серебро** copper silver.
медиум *m.* medium.
медицин/а *f.* medicine; **—ский** *a.* medical, medicinal.
медленн/о *adv.* slowly; **—одействующий** *a.* slow, slow-acting; **м. потухающий экран** long-persistence screen; **—ость** *f.* slowness; **—ый** *a.* slow, low energy.
медлить *v.* be slow, delay.
меднен/ие *n.* copper plating; **—ый** *a.* copper-plated.
медно— *prefix* cupric, copper.
меднозакисный *a.* cuprous oxide; **м. выпрямитель** cuprous oxide (or copper oxide) rectifier.
меднокрасный *a.* copper-colored.
медн/ый *a.* cupric, copper; **м. блеск** chalcosite; **м. колчедан** chalcopyrite; **м. купорос** copper sulfate; **—ое число** copper number (or value).
медовый камень mellite.
Медонская обсерватория Meudon Observatory.
медь *f.* copper (Cu); **желтая м.** brass; **красная м.** industrial (or technical) copper; **самородная м.** native copper; **—содержащий** *a.* copper-bearing, cupriferous.
медянка *f.* verdigris.
меж *see* **между.**
меж— *prefix* inter—; *see also* **между—.**
межа *f.* boundary.
межгалактический *a.* intergalactic.
междоуз/ельный *a.* interstitial; **—лие** *n.* interstice.
между *prep. instr.* between, among, amidst; *prefix* inter—; *see also* **меж—**; **м. прочим** incidentally; in passing; **м. тем** meanwhile; **м. тем как** while, whereas.
между/антный *a.* interdee; **—атомный** *a.* interatomic; **—ведомственный** *a.* interdepartmental, joint; **—витковая емкость** inter-turn capacitance; **—гранулярный, —зернистый, —зерновой** *a.* intergranular.
междукаскадн/ый *a.* interstage; **—ая цепь связи** coupling circuit.
между/кристаллический *a.* intercrystalline; **—лежащий** *a.* intermediate; **—молекулярный** *a.* intermolecular.
Международная академия керамики International Academy of Ceramics; **М. ассоциация строительной и мостовой техники** I. Association for Bridge and Structural Engineering; **М. вулканологическая ассоциация** I. Association of Volcanology; **М. геодезическая ассоциация** I. Association of Geodesy; **М. конференция по вопросам крупных энергетических сетей** I. Conference on Large Electrical Systems; **М. конференция по мирному использованию атомной энергии** I. Conference on the Peaceful Uses of Atomic Energy; **М. оптическая комиссия** I. Commission for Optics; **М. организация по стандартизации** I. Organization for Standardization; **М. осветительная комиссия (МОК)** I. Commission on Illumination (ICI or CIE); **М. сейсмологическая ассоциация** I. Association of Seismology and Physics of the Earth's Interior; **М. федерация астронавтов** I. Astronautical Federation; **М. федерация аэронавигации** I. Aeronautic Federation; **М. электротехническая комиссия** I. Electrotechnical Commission.
Международное агентство по атомной энергии International Atomic Energy Agency; **М. бюро мер и весов** I. Bureau of Weights and Measures; **М. гидрографическое бюро** I. Hydrographic Bureau; **М. общество по механике грунтов и фундаментостроению** I. Society of Soil Mechanics and Foundation Engineering.
международн/ый *a.* international; **—ая свеча** international candle.
Международный астрономический союз International Astronomical Union; **М. научный радио (электротехнический) союз** Union radioscientifique internationale (URSI), I. Scientific Radio Union; **М. светотехнический комитет** I. Commission on Illumination; **М. совет научных обществ** I. Council of Scientific

Unions; **М. совет по исследованию морей** I. Council for the Exploration of the Sea; **М. союз кристаллографии** I. Union of Crystallography; **М. союз радиолюбителей** I. Amateur Radio Union; **М. союз теоретической и прикладной механики** I. Union of Theoretical and Applied Mechanics; **М. союз теоретической и прикладной физики** I. Union of Pure and Applied Physics; **М. союз теоретической и прикладной химии** I. Union of Pure and Applied Chemistry.

между/полюсный *a.* interpolar; **—проводная емкость** wire-to-wire capacitance; **—протекающий** *a.* interfluent; **—сезонный** *a.* interseasonal; **—строчный** *a.* interlinear; **—суточный** *a.* interdiurnal, day-to-day; **—тропический** *a.* intertropical; **—широтный** *a.* interlatitudinal; **—электродный** *a.* interelectrode; **—ядерный** *a.* internuclear.

межевание *n.* surveying.

межзвездн/ый *a.* interstellar; **—ое пространство** interstellar space.

меж/зеренный, —зернистый *a.* intergranular; **—зеренное разрушение** intergranular fracture; **—каскадный** *a.* interstage.

межконтинентальный баллистический снаряд intercontinental ballistic missile (ICBM).

межкристалл/итный, —ический *a.* intergranular, intercrystalline; **—итное разрушение** intercrystalline fracture.

меж/ледниковый *a.* interglacial; **—нуклонный** *a.* internucleonic.

межпланетн/ый *a.* interplanetary, space; **—ая медицина** space medicine; **—ое пространство** interplanetary space.

меж/плоскостное расстояние interplanar spacing; **—поверхностный** *a.* intersurface, interfacial **—полюсный** *a.* interpolar; **—решеточный** *a.* interlattice; **—узловый** *see* **междоузельный**; **—фазный** *a.* interphase; **—формационный** *a.* (geo.) interformational; **—цикловый** *a.* intercycle; **—частичный** *a.* interparticle; **—ъядерный** *a.* internuclear; **—электродная емкость** interelectrode capacity; **—электронный** *a.* interelectronic.

мезабит *m.* mesabite.

мезитит *m.* mesitite.

мезо— *prefix* meso—, mes—; meson mesic.

мезо/атом *m.* mesonic (or mesic) atom **—водород** *m.* mesic hydrogen; **—дейтерий** *m.* mesic deuterium; **—динамика** *f.* meson dynamics; **—зойский** *a.* Mesozoic.

мезоклимат *m.* mesoclimate; **—ология** *f.* mesoclimatology.

мезолит *m.* mesolite.

мезомер *m.* mesomer; **—ия** *f.* mesomerism; **—ный** *a.* mesomeric.

мезометеоролог/ический *a.* mesometeorological; **—ия** *f.* mesometeorology.

мезо/молекула *f.* mesic molecule **—морфный** *a.* mesomorphic.

мезон *m.* meson; **—ий** *m.* mesonium.

мезонит *m.* masonite.

мезонн/ый *a.* meson, mesic; **—ая теория** meson theory.

мезо/пауза *f.* mesopause; **—производное** *n.* (chem.) meso-derivative **—протон** *m.* mesic hydrogen atom **—стазис** *m.* mesostasis; **—сфера** *f.* mesosphere; **—термальный** *a.* mesothermal.

мезотип *m.* mesotype.

мезоторий *m.* mesothorium.

мезотрон *m.* mesotron (obs. for meson)

мезоформа *f.* meso-form.

мейергофферит *m.* meyerhofferite.

мейерсит *m.* meyersite.

меймакит *m.* meymacite.

мейонит *m.* meionite.

Мейснера эффект Meissner effect.

Мексика Mexico; **мексиканский** *a.* Mexican.

мел *m.* chalk; Cretaceous (period **верхний м.** Upper Cretaceous; **нижний м.** Lower Cretaceous.

мелаконит *m.* melaconite.

меламин *m.* melamine.

мелано/флогит *m.* melanophlogit **—хальцит** *m.* melanochalcite; **—хроит** *m.* melanocroite; **—церит** *m.* melanocerite.

мелиор/атор *m.* specialist in land r

clamation; —**ация** *f.* land reclamation, land improvement.

лифанит *m.* meliphanite.

лк/ий *a.* small, fine, finely divided, minute; shallow; —**ая пульсация** ripple; —**ое дробление** fine crushing (or grinding).

лко *adv.* fine, in small particles; —**вкрапленный** *a.* (geo.) disseminated; —**водье** *n.* low water.

лкодисперсн/ость *f.* fine dispersion; —**ый** *a.* finely divided.

лкозернист/ость *f.* fineness of grain; —**ый** *a.* finely granular, microgranular.

лко/калиберный *a.* small-bore; —**кристаллический** *a.* finely crystalline, microcrystalline; —**кусковой** *a.* small-sized, fine; —**масштабный** *a.* very small-scaled; —**пористый** *a.* finely porous; —**раздробленный** *a.* finely divided; —**размолотый** *a.* finely ground; —**распыленный** *a.* finely divided (or pulverized); —**серийное производство** small-scale production; —**сеточный** *a.* fine-mesh; —**слоистый** *a.* finely stratified; —**сть** *f.* smallness, fineness; —**ячеистый** *a.* fine-mesh, close-mesh.

ёллера рассеяние, мёллеровское рассеяние Møller scattering.

еллина преобразование, М. трансформация Mellin transform.

ловой *a.* chalk, chalky; **м. период** Cretaceous period.

лочь *f.* trifle, detail.

ль *f.* shallow water.

льк/ание *n.* flashing, flickering; —**ать,** —**нуть** *v.* flash, flicker.

льница *f.* mill.

льхиор *m.,* —**овый** *a.* German silver.

льч/айший *a.* smallest, finest, minute; —**ать** *v.* diminish in size; —**е** *comp. of* **мелкий, мелко,** finer, smaller; shallower; —**ить** *v.* pulverize, grind.

мбран/а *f.* membrane, diaphragm; —**ный** *a.* membrane, diaphragm; —**ный насос** diaphragm pump; —**ное усилие** (elast.) membrane force.

мноскоп *m.* memnoscope.

морандум *m.* memorandum.

муары *pl.* memoirs.

менакканит *m.* menaccanite.

Менделеева периодическая система элементов Mendeleev periodic table; **М. таблица** periodic table; **М. число** atomic number.

менделеев/ий *m.* mendelevium (Mv); —**ит** *m.* mendelyeevite.

Мендиуса реакция Mendius reaction.

мендоцит *m.* mendozite.

менегинит *m.* meneghinite.

менее *comp. of* **мало,** less; **м. всего** least of all; **тем не м.** nevertheless.

Менелай Menelaus (lunar crater).

мензул/а *f.* (surv.) plane table; —**ьная съемка** plane-table survey.

мензурка *f.* graduate, measuring glass.

Мени схема Mesny circuit.

менисков/ый *a.* meniscus; **м. телескоп** meniscus telescope; —**ая система** meniscus system.

меньш/е *comp. of* **мало, малый,** less, smaller; —**ий** *comp. of* **малый,** lesser, smaller, minor, least; —**ая ось** minor axis; **по** —**ей мере** at least, to say the least; —**инство** *n.* minority.

менять *v.* change, vary, alternate; exchange; **м. знак** reverse sign; **м. ориентацию спина** flip the spin; —**ся** *v.* change, vary, fluctuate.

меняющийся *a.* changing, varying, variable, fluctuating, alternating.

мер/а *f.* measure, dimension, size; standard; degree, extent; **м. дисперсии** measure of dispersion; **м. защиты, м. предосторожности** precaution; **м. точности** (stat.) modulus of precision; **в значительной** —**е** to a considerable degree, to a large extent; **в известной мере** to a certain extent; **в** —**у** reasonably, sufficiently; **не в** —**у, сверх** —**ы, через** —**у** excessively, immoderately; **ни в коей** —**е** to no extent; **по большей** —**е** at most; **по крайней** —**е, по меньшей** —**е** at least, at any rate; **по** —**е** in proportion to; **принимать** —**ы** take measures.

мервинит *m.* merwinite.

мергель *m.* marl.

мерзлость *f.* congealment.

мерзлот/а *f.,* **вечная м.** permafrost; —**оведение** *n.* cryopedology (study of frozen ground); —**омер** *m.* cryopedometer.

мерз/лый *a.* frozen, congealed; —**ляк** *m.* frozen turf; —**нуть** *v.* freeze, congeal.

меридиан *m.* meridian; **исходный м., начальный м., первый м.** prime meridian; —**ный** *a.* meridian, meridional; —**ное наблюдение** meridian circle observation.

меридиональн/ый *see* **меридианный**; —**ая плоскость** meridian plane; —**ая циркуляция** meridian circulation.

мерило *n.* standard, criterion.

мерит/ельный *a.* measuring, gauging; —**ь** *v.* measure, gauge.

мерка *f.* measure.

меркаллит *m.* mercallite.

Меркатор Mercator (lunar crater).

меркаторская проекция Mercator projection.

меркнуть *v.* darken, grow dim.

Меркурий Mercury.

меркурирован/ие *n.* mercuration; —**ный** *a.* mercurized, mercurated.

мерн/ик *m.* measuring tank; —**ость** *f.* regularity; —**ый** *a.* measuring; measured; *n*-**мерный** *a.* *n*-dimensional; —**ая колба** measuring flask; —**ая плитка** gauge block; —**ая цепь** surveyor's chain.

мерометр *m.* merometer.

мероморфная функция meromorphic function.

мероопределение *n.* metric, measure.

Мероп Merope.

мероприятие *n.* measure.

мероскоп *see* **мерометр.**

Мерсенн Mersenne (lunar crater).

Мерсера ядро (math.) Mercer kernel.

мертв/ый *a.* dead; **м. груз** dead weight (load, freight); **м. конус обзора** (aero.) blind angle; **м. ход** play, backlash, lost motion; —**ая зона** (rad.) blind spot (or zone); dead space; dead-water region; —**ая зыбь** ocean swell; —**ая точка** dead point, dead center; (rad.) dead spot; —**ое время** dead time; —**ое положение** dead point, dead center; —**ое пространство** dead space.

Мертена теорема Merten theorem.

мерц/ание *n.* flicker, scintillation, twi[nkling], blinking; —**ать** *v.* flick[er], scintillate, gleam, flash, blink.

мерцающий *a.* flickering, scintillati[ng]; **м. фотометр** flicker photometer.

мес. *abbr.* (**месяц**) month.

Мессала Messala (lunar crater).

мессдоза *f.* hydraulic dynamometer.

Месси Massey.

Мессье Messier (lunar crater).

мести *v.* sweep.

Местинг Moesting (lunar crater).

местн/ость *f.* locality, district; —**ый** local, regional; native; —**ый нагр[ев]** local heating; —**ый перегрев** h[ot] spot, thermal spike; —**ая концен[]трация** local concentration; —[**ая**] **скорость** local velocity; —**ое гра[ж]данское время** local civil (or mea[n]) time; —**ое нормальное время** lo[cal] standard time; —**ое солнечное вр[е]мя** apparent solar time, local a[p]parent time; —**ое среднее вре[мя]** local mean time.

мест/о *n.* place, location, site, locu[s], seat, position, point; space; jo[b]; **м. возникновения** place of origi[n]; **геометрическое м.** locus; **м. действ[ия]** scene of action; **м. для захоронен[ия] радиоактивных отходов** buri[al] ground (of radioactive waste pr[o]ducts); **м. захвата** trap, trappi[ng] center; **м. наблюдения** observati[on] point; **м. разрыва** point of ruptu[re]; —**ами** here and there; **занять** [м.] replace; **иметь м.** take place, occu[r]; **на вашем —е** in your place; [**не**] **имеет —а** does not occur; is not t[he] case; **трогаться с —а** move.

место/нахождение, —расположение location; —**положение** *n.* locatio[n], fix; situation; site; —**пребывание** residence; —**рождение** *n.* birthplac[e]; (geo.) bed, deposit; occurrence; **карт[а] —рождения** (geo.) field map.

меся/ц *m.*, month; moon; **молодой** [м.] new moon; —**чный** *a.* monthly.

мета— *prefix* meta—.

метабо/лизм *m.* metabolism; —**лон** *m.* metabolon.

мета/варисцит *m.* metavariscite; —**во[к]сит** *m.* metavauxite.

метагалакти/ка *f.* metagalaxy; **—ческий** *a.* metagalactic.
метагейландит *m.* metaheulandite.
метадин *m.* metadyne.
мета/-изомер *m.* meta-isomer; **—коллоид** *m.* metacolloid; **—кристалл** *m.* metacrystal; **—кремневый** *a.* metasilicic; **—криловый** *a.* methacrylic, methacrylate.
метаксит *m.* metaxite.
металл *m.* metal; **белый м.** white metal; **благородный м.** noble metal; **м. переходной группы** transition metal; **цветной м.** nonferrous metal; **черный м.** ferrous metal.
металлиз/ация *f.* metallization, metallizing; (rad.) bonding; **—ирование** *n.* metallization, metal plating; **—ированный, —ованный** *a.* metallized; **—ировать, —овать** *v.* metallize, plate; **—ованная схема** (elec.) printed circuit.
металлическ/ий *a.* metal, metallic; **м. лом** scrap metal; **м. ртутник** metal-tank mercury-arc rectifier; **м. уран** uranium metal; **—ая связь** metallic bond; **—ая сетка** wire gauze; **—ие изделия** hardware.
металличность *f.* metallicity.
металлмикроскоп *m.* metallurgical microscope.
металло— *prefix* metallo—, metal.
металловед/ение *n.* physical metallurgy, (general) metallography, metal research; **—ческий** *a.* metallographic, metallurgical.
металловидн/ость *f.* metallicity; **—ый** *a.* metallic, metalliform.
металлогенический *a.* metallogenic.
металлограф *m.* metallographer; **—ический** *a.* metallographic; **—ия** *f.* metallography.
металлоид *m.* metalloid.
металлокерами/ка *f.* metal ceramic, cermet; powder metallurgy; **—ческий** *a.* metal-ceramic, cermet; **—ческий сплав** powdered-metal alloy.
металлометр *m.* metallometer, metal tester, **—ический** *a.* metallometric.
металло/микроскоп *m.* metallographic microscope; **—носный** *a.* metalliferous.
металлообраб/атывающий *a.*, **—отка** *f.* metal working.
металло/органический *a.* organometallic; **—очистительный** *a.* metal-refining; **—плавильная печь** smelting furnace; **—подобный** *a.* metalline, metal-like; **—содержащий** *a.* metal-containing, metalliferous.
металло/физика *f.* physics of metals; **—химия** *f.* metal chemistry.
металлург *m.* metallurgist; **—ический** *a.* metallurgical; **—ия** *f.* metallurgy.
метамагнетик *m.* metamagnetic (substance).
метамер *m.* metamer; **—ия** *f.* metamerism.
метамикт/ный, —овый *a.* (geo.) metamict.
метаморф/изация *f.* metamorphization; **—изировать** *v.* metamorphize; **—изм** *m.* metamorphism; **—изованный** *a.* metamorphized; **—ический** *a.* metamorphic; **—оз** *m.*, **—оза** *f.* metamorphosis.
метан *m.* methane.
метание *n.* throwing.
мета/положение *n.* meta-position; **—производное, —соединение** *n.* meta-derivative, meta-compound.
метасомат/изм, —оз *m.* metasomatism; **—ический** *a.* metasomatic.
метастабильный *a.* metastable.
метастаз *m.* metastasis.
метательный *a.* projectile, missile; launching, propellant; **м. аппарат** launcher; **м. снаряд** projectile, missile.
мета/тенардит *m.* metathenardite; **—титанат** *m.* metatitanate; **—торбернит** *m.* metatorbernite.
метать *v.* throw, fling.
мета/устойчивость *f.* metastability; **—хальколит** *m.* metachalcolite; **—хроматический** *a.* metachromatic; **—хьюэттит** *m.* metahewettite.
мета/цейнерит *m.* metazeunerite; **—циннабарит** *m.* metacinnabarite; **—ярлит** *m.* metajarlite.
метацентр *m.* metacenter; **—ический** *a.* metacentric; **—ическая высота** metacentric height.
метель *f.* snowstorm.
метен *m.* methene.

метео/данные *pl.* meteorological data; —**донесение** *n.* weather report; —**информация** *f.* meteorological information; —**наблюдение** *n.* meteorological observation; —**обслуживание** *n.* weather service; —**обстановка** *f.* weather conditions; —**прибор** *m.* meteorological instrument.

метеор. *abbr.* (**метеорологический**) meteorological.

метеор *m.* meteor; —**ит** *m.* meteorite; —**итика** *f.* meteoritics; —**итный,** —**итовый** *a.* meteoritic; —**ический** *a.* meteoric.

метеорн/ый *see* **метеорический; м. поток** meteor stream (or shower); **м. рой** meteor shower; **м. след** meteor trail; —**ая ионизация** meteoric ionization.

метеорограмма *f.* meteorogram, aerogram.

метеорограф *m.* meteorograph, aerograph; —**ический** *a.* meteorographic; —**ия** *f.* meteorography.

метеороид *m.* meteoroid.

метеоролог *m.* meteorologist; —**ический** *a.* meteorological; —**ический элемент** meteorological element (or parameter); —**ическая будка** meteorological instrument shelter; —**ическая служба** weather service; —**ия** *f.* meteorology; **авиационная —ия** aeronautical meteorology.

метео/сводка *f.* weather report; —**станция** *f.* weather station; —**шар** *m.* meteorological balloon; —**элемент** *m.* meteorological element.

метил *m.*, —**овый** *a.* methyl; —**овый спирт** methyl alcohol, methanol.

метить *v.* label, tag, mark; aim at.

метка *f.* mark, marker; tag, label, sign; **м. времени** time marking (or trace); **м. частоты** frequency marker.

метк/ий *a.* well-aimed, accurate; —**ость** *f.* accuracy, precision.

метландит *m.* maitlandite.

метод *m.* method, process, procedure, technique; **м. вращающегося кристалла** (cryst.) rotation method; **м. времени пролета** time-of-flight method; **м. замещения** substitution method; **м. изображений** method of images; **м. минимальных квадратов, м. наименьших квадратов** method of least squares; **м. отбора проб** sampling system; **м. перевала** method of steepest descent; **м. подбора** trial-and-error method, method of successive approximations; **м. порошковых фигур** powder (diagram) method; **м. проб** trial-and-error method.

методика *f.* technique, procedure; methods; methodology; **м. измерений** measurement procedure; **м. работы** procedure.

методич/еский *a.* methodical, systematic; methodological; —**еские указания** operating instructions; —**ность** *f.* methodicalness; —**ный** *a.* methodical, systematic, orderly.

метр *m.* meter (m); **м.-свеча** meter-candle; —**аж** *m.* metric area; footage.

метризуемый *a.* metrizable.

метрика *f.* metric; metrics.

метрическ/ий *a.* metric; —**ая система** metric system.

Метровес *abbr.* (**Завод точных измерительных приборов и весов**) Weights and Precision Measuring Instruments Plant.

метровый *a.* meter.

метролог/ический *a.* metrological; —**ия** *f.* metrology.

метроном *m.* metronome.

метросвеча *f.* meter-candle, lux.

метчик *m.* tap, screw tap.

мех *m.* bellows.

механиз/ация *f.* mechanization; —**ированный** *a.* mechanized; —**ировать** *v.* mechanize.

механизм *m.* mechanism, gear; **м. включения и выключения** on-off mechanism; **часовой м.** clockwork; —**ы** *pl.* machinery.

механик *m.* mechanic; mechanician; —**а** *f.* mechanics.

механическ/ий *a.* mechanical, machine, power-driven; **м. момент** spin; **м. ом** mechanical ohm; **м. регистратор** mechanical recorder; **м. селектор нейтронов** fast neutron chopper; **м. селектор скоростей** mechanical velocity selector, chopper; **м. тормоз** power brake; **м. цех,** —**ая мастерская** machine shop; **м. эквивалент света** mechanical equivalent of light;

м. эквивалент тепла mechanical equivalent of heat; **—ая коррозия** stress corrosion; **—ая отдача** mechanical efficiency; **—ое напряжение** mechanical stress; **—ое оборудование** machinery; **—ое приспособление** mechanical device; **—ое старение** strain aging; **—ое упрочнение** strain hardening; **с —им приводом** power-driven.

механо/калорический эффект mechanocaloric effect; **—стрикция** *f.* mechanostriction; **—химия** *f.* mechanochemistry.

мехом *abbr.* (**механический ом**) mechanical ohm.

Меций Metius (lunar crater).

меч *m.* sword; **—евидный** *a.* sword-shaped.

мечен/ие *n.* labeling, tagging; **—ный, —ый** *a.* marked, labeled, tagged; **—ый атом** labeled atom; tracer; **—ый углерод** carbon tracer; **—ая молекула** labeled (or tagged) molecule; **—ое соединение** tracer compound.

мечта *f.*, **—ть** *v.* dream.

меш *m.* size of mesh.

мешалка *f.* mixer, agitator, stirrer; **стеклянная м.** stirring rod.

меш/альный *a.* mixing, stirring; **—ание** *n.* mixing, stirring, agitation; **—ать** *v.* mix, stir, agitate; hinder, impede, interfere, prevent.

мешающ/ий *a.* interfering, troublesome; inhibiting; mixing, stirring; **м. край полосы** interference fringe; **м. передатчик** (rad.) jamming transmitter; **—ее действие** interference; **—ее излучение** background radiation.

мешо/к *m.*, **—чный** *a.* bag, sack; pocket; **воздушный м.** air pocket; **—чная ткань** sacking.

МИ *abbr.* (**Математический институт**) Institute of Mathematics.

Ми теория Mie theory.

миазм/а *f.*, **—ы** *pl.* miasma; **—атический** *a.* miasmatic.

МИАН *abbr.* [**Математический институт Академии наук (им. В. А. Стеклова)**] V. A. Steklov Institute of Mathematics of the Academy of Sciences.

миаргирит *m.* miargyrite.

миг/ание *n.* flicker, twinkling, blinking; pulsation, ripple; **—ать** *v.* blink, flicker, twinkle.

мигающий *a.* blinking, flickering, twinkling; intermittent, pulsed; **м. пучок** pulsed (or intermittent) beam; **м. фотометр** flicker photometer; **м. циклотрон** pulsed cyclotron.

миграц/ия *f.*, **—ионный** *a.* migration; **длина —ии** migration length.

мигрировать *v.* migrate.

мидель *m.* midsection, center section; midship.

МИЗ *abbr.* (**Московский инструментальный завод**) Moscow Tool Plant.

мизенит *m.* misenite.

Мизес Mises.

мизи *m.* misy.

микалекс *m.* mycalex.

миканит *m.*, **—овый** *a.* micanite.

микарта *f.* micarta.

микро— *prefix* micro—.

микро/авторадиография *f.* microautoradiography; **—ампер** *m.* microampere; **—амперметр** *m.* microammeter; **—анализ** *m.* microanalysis; **—атмосфера** *f.* artificial atmosphere (in small space).

микроб *m.* microbe, bacterium.

микробар *m.* microbar; **—ограф** *m.* microbarograph.

микроб/иология *f.* microbiology; **—ный** *a.* microbe, microbic.

микро/бухта *f.* (geo.) bay; **—бюретка** *f.* microburet; **—вариограф** *m.* microvariograph.

микроватт *m.* microwatt; **—метр** *m.* microwattmeter.

микро/весы *pl.* microbalance; **—вибриограф** *m.* microvibriograph; **—винт** *m.* micrometer screw; **—вихревые токи** micro eddy currents.

микроволн/овой, —овый *a.* microwave; **—овая спектроскопия** microwave spectroscopy; **—ы** *pl.* microwaves.

микро/вольт *m.* microvolt; **—всплеск** *m.* (radio astr.) microburst; **—выключатель** *m.* microswitch; **—генри** *m.* microhenry; **—горелка** *f.* microburner; **—грамм** *m.* microgram.

микрограф *m.* micrograph; **—ический**

a. micrographic; —**ия** *f.* micrography.

микро/деформация *f.* microdeformation; —**дождемер** *m.* micropluviometer; —**измеритель** *m.* microgauge, probe; —**интерферометр** *m.* microinterferometer; —**исследование** *n.* microexamination, microanalysis.

микро/калориметр *m.* microcalorimeter; —**канонический** *a.* microcanonical; —**киносъемка** *f.* microcinematography, microfilming.

микроклимат *m.* microclimate; —**ический** *a.* microclimatic; —**ология** *f.* microclimatology.

микроклин *m.* microcline; **м.-альбит-пертит** *m.* micro-albite-perthite; **м.-пертит** *m.* microcline perthite.

микро/колебание *n.* microvariation; agitation; —**количество** *n.* microquantity, trace amount;—**компонента** *f.* microcomponent; —**копия** *f.* microcopy, microfilm; —**коррозия** *f.* microcorrosion.

микрокосм *m.* microcosm; —**ический** *a.* microcosmic.

микрокристалл/ический *a.* microcrystalline; —**ография** *f.* microcrystallography.

микро/кулон *m.* microcoulomb; —**кюри** *n.* microcurie.

микро/лит *m.* microlite, microlith; —**литр** *m.* microliter; —**люкс** *m.* microlux (0.000001 of lux); —**м** *m.* microhm.

микро/магнетометр *m.* micromagnetometer; —**манипулятор** *m.* micromanipulator; —**манометр** *m.* micromanometer; —**масштаб** *m.* microscale; —**меритный** *a.* micromeritic.

микрометеор/ит *m.* micrometeorite; —**ограф** *m.* micrometeorograph; —**ология** *f.* micrometeorology.

микрометод *m.* micromethod.

микрометр *m.* micrometer, micrometer gauge; —**ический** *a.* micrometer; —**ический винт** micrometer screw, micrometer; —**ия** *f.* micrometry.

микромехан/изм *m.* micromechanism; —**ический** *a.* micromechanical.

микромикро— *prefix* micromicro—.

микромикро/н *m.* micromicron; —**фарада** *f.* micromicrofarad.

микро/миллиметр *m.* micromillimeter, micron; —**минералогия** *f.* micromineralogy; —**мир** *m.* microcosm; —**мо** *n.* micromho.

микро/н *m.* micron; —**напряжение** *n.* microstrain.

микро/объектив *m.* microscope objective; —**объемный** *a.* microvolumetric; —**определение** *n.* microdetermination; —**организм** *m.* microorganism, microbe.

микро/петрографический *a.* micropetrographic; —**печь** *f.* microfurnace; —**пипетка** *f.* micropipet; —**пленка** *f.* microfilm; —**плювиометр** *m.* micropluviometer; —**полость** *f.* microcavity; —**пористый** *a.* microporous; —**проекция** *f.* microprojection; photomicrograph; —**пуаз** *m.* micropoise; —**пульсация** *f.* micropulsation; —**пучок** *m.* microbeam.

микрорадио/автограф *m.* microautoradiograph, microautograph; —**волны** *pl.* microwaves; —**графия** *f.* microradiography; —**метр** *m.* microradiometer.

микро/реакция *f.* microreaction; —**резерфорд** *m.* microrutherford.

микрорентген *m.* microroentgen; —**ография** *f.* x-ray micrography.

микро/рисунок *m.* micrograph; —**рой** *m.* (liquid) microcrystal; —**сегрегация** *f.* microsegregation.

микросейсм/ический *a.* microseismic; microseism; —**ология** *f.* microseismology.

микро/секунда *f.* microsecond; —**система** *f.* microsystem.

Микроскоп Microscopium (Mic) (constellation).

микроскоп *m.* microscope; **м.-микрометр** micrometer microscope; **м. с бегущим лучом** flying-spot microscope; **м. сравнения** comparator; —**ический,** —**ичный** *a.* microscopic; —**ичность** *f.* microscopicity; —**ия** *f.* microscopy.

микро/скрытокристаллический *a.* microcryptocrystalline; —**состояние** *n.* microstate; —**спектроскоп** *m.* microspectroscope; —**структура** *f.* microstructure; —**сфера** *f.* microsphere; —**твердость** *f.* microhardness.

микротелефон *m.*, **—ная трубка** microtelephone; **—ный** *a.* microtelephone, microtelephonic.

микро/тепловой *a.* microthermal; **—термометр** *m.* microthermometer; **—том** *m.* microtome; **—трещина** *f.* microcrack.

микротрон *m.*, **—ный** *a.* microtron.

микрофарад/а *f.* microfarad; **—ометр** *m.* microfaradmeter.

микро/физика *f.* microphysics; **—фильм** *m.* microfilm; **—фильмирование** *n.* microfilming; **—фировый** *a.* microphyric; **—флюидальный** *a.* microfluidal; **—флюктуация** *f.* microfluctuation.

микрофон *m.*, **—ный** *a.* microphone, microphonic; **—ный эффект** microphonic effect (or disturbance), microphonics, microphonism.

микрофото/грамма *f.* microphotogram; **—графирование** *n.* photomicrography; **—графия** *f.* photomicrography, photomicrograph; **—метр** *m.* microphotometer, microdensitometer; **—метрирование** *n.* microphotometry; **—снимок** *m.* photomicrograph.

микрохим/ический *a.* microchemical; **—ия** *f.* microchemistry.

микро/циклон *m.* microcyclone; **—частица** *f.* microparticle; **—шлиф** *m.* microsection; **—штатив** *m.* microscope stand; **—электрофорез** *m.* microelectrophoresis; **—элемент** *m.* (chem.) trace element; (elec.) microcell; **—явление** *n.* microphenomenon, microeffect.

миксер *m.* mixer.

миксит *m.* mixite.

милл. *abbr.* (**миллион**) million.

Миллера индексы, миллеровские индексы Miller indices; **М. эффект** M. effect.

милли— *prefix* milli—.

милли/ампер *m.* milliampere (ma); **—амперметр** *m.* milliammeter.

миллиард *m.* milliard, billion.

милли/бар *m.* millibar (mb); **—барн** *m.* millibarn (mb); **—ватт** *m.* milliwatt (mw).

милливолновая радиация millimeter microwaves.

милли/вольт *m.* millivolt (mv); **—гал** *m.* milligal; **—генри** *m.* millihenry (mh); **—грамм** *m.* milligram (mg); **—единица массы** millimass unit.

Милликена опыт Millikan (oil-drop) experiment.

милли/кулон *m.* millicoulomb; **—кюри** *n.* millicurie (mC); **—литр** *m.* milliliter (ml); **—масса** *f.* millimass (unit).

миллиметр *m.* millimeter (mm); **—овая бумага** millimeter graph paper.

милли/микрон *m.* millimicron (mμ); **—микросекунда** *f.* millimicrosecond; **—микрофарада** *f.* millimicrofarad; **—моль** *m.* millimole; **—ом** *m.* milliohm.

миллион *m.* million; **—ный** *a.* millionth.

милли/пуаз *m.* millipoise; **—радиация** *f.* millimeter microwaves; **—резерфорд** *m.* millirutherford; **—рентген** *m.* milliroentgen (mr).

миллисекунд/а *f.* millisecond (msec); **—омер** *m.* millisecond timer.

милли/стильб *m.* millistilb; **—фарада** *f.* millifarad (mf); **—фот** *m.* milliphot; **—эквивалент** *m.* milliequivalent.

миллозевичит *m.* millosevichite.

Милна задача Milne problem; **М. шкала времени** M. time scale.

милошит *m.* miloschite.

мильбарс *m.* (met.) mill bar.

миля *f.* mile; **авиационная м.** aeronautical (or air) mile; **морская м.** nautical mile.

мимеограф *m.*, **—ический** *a.* mimeograph.

миметезит *m.* mimetesite.

мимический *a.* mimic.

мимо *adv. and prep. gen.* past, by; **м. цели** wide of the mark.

мимолетн/ость *f.* transience; **—ый** *a.* transient, passing, short-lived.

мимоходом *adv.* in passing.

мин *abbr.* (**минимум**) minimum; **мин.** (**минерал**) mineral; (**министр**) minister; (**минута**) minute (min).

мина *f.* (mil.) mine.

мин-во *abbr. see* **м-во.**

Минас-Жераис Minas Geraïs.

мингетит *m.* minguetite.

миндале/видный, —образный *a.* amygdaloidal.

миндалина *f.* (geo.) amygdule.

минераграф/ический *a.* mineragraphic, mineralographic; **—ия** *f.* mineragraphy, mineralography.

минерал *m.* mineral.

минерализ/атор *m.* mineralizer; **—ация** *f.* mineralization; **—ирующая жидкость** ore-forming fluid; **—ованный** *a.* mineralized; **—овать** *v.* mineralize; **—ующий** *a.* mineralizing; **—ующийся** *a.* mineralizable.

минералог *m.* mineralogist; **—ический** *a.* mineralogical; **—ия** *f.* mineralogy.

минерало/графия *f.* mineralography; **—металлокерамика** *f.* cermet.

минеральн/ый *a.* mineral; **—ое сырье** mineral ore or resources.

миниатюрный *a.* miniature; **м. выключатель** microswitch.

минимакс *m.* minimax.

минимальн/ый *a.* minimum, minimal; **м. термометр** minimum thermometer; **—ое отклонение** minimum deviation; **—ое уравнение** minimal equation.

минимиз/ация *f.*, **—ирование** *n.* minimizing; **—ировать** *v.* minimize.

минимум *m.* minimum.

минировать *v.* mine.

минист/ерство *n.* ministry; office, board, department; **—р** *m.* minister.

миниюлит *m.* minyulite.

Минковского геометрия Minkowski geometry.

минный *a.* (mil.) mine.

миновать *v.* pass, elapse; escape, elude; omit.

миноискание *n.* mine detection.

минор *m.* (math.) minor, subdeterminant.

минувш/ее *n.* the past; **—ий** *a.* past.

минус *m.* minus, odd; defect, shortcoming; **—овый** *a.* minus; negative.

минут/а *f.* minute; **в данную —у** at the present moment.

минутн/ый *a.* minute; momentary; transient; **—ая стрелка** minute hand.

минуть *see* **миновать.**

миоцен *m.*, **—овый** *a.* Miocene.

миполам *m.* mipolam.

мир *m.* world, universe; peace.

Мира Кита (astr.) Mira Ceti.

Мир. Вр. *abbr.* (**мировое время**) universal time.

мираж *m.* mirage; **боковой м.** lateral mirage; **верхний м.** superior (or direct) mirage; **нижний м.** inferior mirage; **обратный м.** inverted mirage.

мириа— *prefix* myria— (denoting 10,000).

мириа/ватт *m.* myriawatt; **—литр** *m.* myrialiter; **—метр** *m.* myriameter.

мирить *v.* reconcile; **—ся** *v.* tolerate, accept.

мирно *adv.* peacefully, harmoniously.

Мирный Mirny (Antarctic station).

мирн/ый *a.* peace, peaceful; **—ое использование атомной энергии** peaceful use of atomic energy.

мировоззрение *n.* outlook, ideology.

миров/ой *a.* world, universal, global, cosmic; peace, peaceful; **м. вектор** world vector; **м. тензор** world tensor; **м. эфир** universal ether; **—ая линия** world line; **—ая точка** world point; **—ая трубка** world tube; **—ое время** universal time (UT); **—ое пространство** outer space; **—ое расстояние** (rel.) world distance, world interval.

мироздание *n.* the universe.

миропонимание *see* **мировоззрение.**

мисит *m.* miesite.

миспикель *m.* mispickel.

миссия *f.* mission.

мистраль *m.* mistral (wind).

митинг *m.* meeting.

Митчерлиха закон Mitscherlich law.

митчерлихит *m.* mitscherlichite.

миф *m.* myth.

МИФИ *abbr.* (**Московский инженерно-физический институт**) Moscow Engineering Physics Institute.

мифический *a.* mythical.

Мицар Mizar.

мицелл/а *f.* micelle; **—ярный** *a.* micellar.

миццонит *m.* mizzonite.

мишель-левит *m.* michel-levyte.

мишен/ь *f.*, **—ный** *a.* target.

Мишима сплав Mishima alloy.

мишура *f.* tinsel.

мк *abbr.* (**микро—, микрон**) micro—, micron (μ).

МК *abbr.* (**магнитный курс**) magnetic course.

мка *abbr.* (**микроампер**) microampere.

мкбар *abbr.* (**микробар**) microbar.
мкв *abbr.* (**микровольт**) microvolt.
мквт *abbr.* (**микроватт**) microwatt.
мкг *abbr.* (**микрограмм**) microgram.
мкгн *abbr.* (**микрогенри**) microhenry.
МКГСС система *abbr.* [**система метр-килограмм(сила)-секунда**] mk(force)s system.
мкк *abbr.* (**микрокулон**) microcoulomb.
мккюри *abbr.* (**микрокюри**) microcurie.
мкл *abbr.* (**микролитр**) microliter.
мкмк *abbr.* (**микромикро—, микромикрон**) micromicro—, micromicron ($\mu\mu$).
мкмкф *abbr.* (**микромикрофарада**) micromicrofarad.
мком *abbr.* (**микром**) microhm.
мкр *abbr.* (**микрорентген**) microroentgen.
МКРЕ *abbr.* (**Международная комиссия по радиологическим единицам и измерениям**) International Commission on Radiological Units and Measurements (ICRU).
МКРЗ *abbr.* (**Международная комиссия по радиологической защите**) International Commission on Radiological Protection (ICRP).
мкс *abbr.* (**максвелл**) maxwell (mx).
мксек *abbr.* (**микросекунда**) microsecond.
МКС система *abbr.* (**система метр-килограмм-секунда**) meter-kilogram-second system (mks).
мкф *abbr.* (**микрофарада**) microfarad.
Мкюри *abbr.* (**мегакюри**) megacurie (Mc).
мл *abbr.* (**миллилитр**) milliliter (ml).
младший *a.* younger, junior; *m.* the youngest; **м. научный сотрудник** junior scientific associate; **м. член** (math.) lowest term.
Млечный Путь Milky Way.
млн. *abbr. see* **милл.**
млрд. *abbr.* (**миллиард**) milliard, billion.
мм *abbr.* (**миллиметр**) millimeter (mm).
ММВ *abbr.* (**миллиметровые волны**) millimeter waves.
мм вод. ст. *abbr.* (**миллиметры водяного столба**) millimeters of water column.
ммк *abbr.* (**миллимикрон**) millimicron.
ммксек *abbr.* (**миллимикросекунда**) millimicrosecond.
ммкф *abbr.* (**миллимикрофарада**) millimicrofarad.
ммоль *abbr.* (**миллимоль**) millimole.
мм рт. ст. *abbr.* (**миллиметры ртутного столба**) millimeters of mercury (mm Hg).
мм/сек *abbr.* (**миллиметры в секунду**) millimeters per second.
мн. *abbr.* (**минута**) minute (min); (**многие**) many; — **др.** many others.
мнемонический *a.* mnemonic.
мнение *n.* opinion.
МНИ *abbr.* (**Московский нефтяной институт**) Moscow Petroleum Institute.
мним/ый *a.* imaginary; virtual; apparent; alleged, sham, dummy; **—ый фронт** (meteor.) false front; **—ая антенна** image antenna; **—ая величина, —ое число** imaginary number; **—ая ось** imaginary axis, conjugate axis (of hyperbola); **—ая часть** imaginary part; **—ое горючее** dummy fuel; **—ое изображение** virtual image.
мн-к *abbr.* (**многоугольник**) polygon.
многие *pl.* many.
много *adv.* much, many; **на м.** by far, much.
много— *prefix* poly—, multi—, many, multiple.
многоактный *a.* multievent; **м. процесс** multiple process.
много/арочная плотина multiple-arch dam; **—атомный** *a.* multiatomic.
многовалентн/ость *f.* multivalence; **—ый** *a.* multivalent.
много/вариантный *a.* multivariant; **—вершинный** *a.* polyconic; **—витковый** *a.* multiturn; **—временный формализм** many-time formalism.
многогранн/ик *m.* polyhedron; **—ый** *a.* polyhedral.
многогруппов/ой *a.* multigroup; **—ая модель** multigroup model; **—ое приближение** multigroup approximation.
много/диапазонный *a.* multirange; **—доменный** *a.* polydomain; **—дырчатый** *a.* multiperforated.
мног/ое *n.* much; **во —ом** in many respects.

многожильный *a.* multiple-strand, multiple-cord; **м. кабель** multicore cable.

много/зарядный *a.* multiply charged; **—зазорный разрядник** multigap discharger; **—звенный фильтр** ladder filter, iterated filter; **—знаменательность** *f.* significance; **—знаменательный, —значительный** *a.* significant.

многозначн/ость *f.* multivaluedness; ambiguity; multivalence; **—ый** *a.* multiple-valued; multiple-digit, multidigit; **—ое число** multiple-digit number.

многозонн/ый *a.* multiregion; **—ая решетка** multiregion lattice.

много/камерный *a.* multicellular; multichamber, multiple-cavity; **—канальный** *a.* multichannel.

многокаскадный *a.* multistage; **м. усилитель** multistage (or cascade) amplifier.

много/кольчатый *a.* polycyclic; **—компонентный** *a.* multicomponent; **—контактный** *a.* multiple-contact; **—контурный двигатель** multistream engine; **—конфигурационный** *a.* multiconfigurational; **—красочный** *a.* polychromatic.

многократн/о *adv.* repeatedly, multiply; **м. наложившиеся (частицы)** pile-up (of particles); **—ость** *f.* recurrence, frequency; multiplicity.

многократн/ый *a.* frequent, multiple, reiterated, repeated, manifold, multi—; **м. отсчет** multimetering; **м. резонанс** multiple resonance; **—ая ионизация** multiple ionization; **—ая передача** multiplex transmission; **—ая связь** multiple bond; **—ая щель** multislit; **—ое отражение** multiple reflection; **—ое разделение** multiple separation; **—ое рассеяние** multiple scattering; plural scattering; **—ое рождение мезонов** plural meson production; **—столкновение** multiple collision; **—ое фракционирование** multiple fractionation.

многолегированная сталь complex steel.

многолетн/ий *a.* of many years, old, long-living; **—яя мерзлота** permafrost.

много/линейчатый спектр band spectrum; **—листная поверхность** multisheeted surface.

многолучев/ой интерферометр multiple-wave interferometer; **м. источник** multiple source; **—ая антенна** multiwire antenna; **—ая осциллоскопия** multitrace oscilloscopy.

многомерн/ый *a.* multidimensional; multivariate; **—ая регрессия** (stat.) multiple regression.

много/молекулярный *a.* multimolecular; **—моторный** *a.* multiple-motor, multiengine; **—направленный** *a.* multidirectional; **—нитный счетчик** multiwire counter; **—обещающий** *a.* promising.

многообраз/ие *n.* diversity, variety; (math.) manifold, set; **—ность** *f.* variety, manifold; **—ный** *a.* diverse, varied, multiform, manifold.

много/объективный фотоаппарат multilens camera; **—опорный клапан** multiple-seated valve.

многоосновн/ость *f.* polybasicity; **—ый** *a.* polybasic.

много/петлевой цикл compound cycle; **—пластинная камера Вильсона** multiplate cloud chamber; **—полосная развертка** (telev.) multiple scanning; **—полостный** *a.* multicavity; **—польное излучение** multipole radiation.

многополюсн/ик *m.* multiterminal network; **—ый** *a.* multipolar, multipole, multiterminal; **—ая машина** multipolar machine.

многопредельный *a.* multirange; **м. прибор** multirange instrument.

много/прожекторная труба multigun tube; **—разовый** *a.* frequent, repeated; **—разрезный магнетрон** multislot magnetron, multisegment magnetron; **—резонаторный магнетрон** multicavity magnetron.

многорядн/ый *a.* polyserial; **—ая вибраторная сеть** (rad.) stacked-dipole array; **—ая (синфазная) решетка** broadside (antenna) array.

многосвязн/ый *a.* multiply connected; **—ая область** multiply connected region.

многосернистый *a.* polysulfide.

многосеточн/ый *a.* multigrid; **—ая лампа** multigrid tube.

много/скоростной *a.* multiple-speed, multivelocity; **—сложный** *a.* complicated, complex.

многослойн/ый *a.* multilayer, laminated; **м. пакет** multiple sandwich; **—ая ионизационная камера** multiplate ionization chamber.

многосторонн/ий *a.* polygonal, multilateral; many-sided, versatile; **—ость** *f.* versatility, variety.

многоступенчат/ый multistage; **м. последовательный распад** multiple decay; **—ое разделение** multiple separation.

много/токовый *a.* multiple-current; **—томный** *a.* voluminous; **—точие** *n.* dotted line.

многоугольн/ик *m.* polygon; **м. сил** force polygon; **соединение —ом** (elec.) mesh connection (of polyphase circuit); **—ый** *a.* polygonal; multiangular; **—ая схема** mesh circuit.

многофазный *a.* polyphase, multiphase.

многоходов/ой *a.* multipass; **—ая резьба** multiple thread.

многоцветн/ость *f.* pleochroism, pleochromatism; polychromy; **—ый** *a.* pleochroitic, pleochromatic; polychrome, polychromatic; multicolored.

много/целевой реактор multipurpose reactor; **—частичный** *a.* many-particle; **—частотный** *a.* multifrequency.

многочисленн/ость *f.* multiplicity, plurality; **—ый** *a.* multiple, numerous.

многочлен *m.* polynomial; multinomial; **—ный** *a.* polynomial; multinomial; many-termed; many-place (logarithm).

многошкальный *a.* multiscale, multirange; **м. прибор** multimeter instrument; **м. усилитель** multirange amplifier.

много/электродная лампа multielectrode tube; **—электронный** *a.* many-electron; **—элементный** *a.* multielement; **—энергетический** *a.* polyenergetic; **—этажный** *a.* manystoried, multistage.

многоядерн/ый *a.* polynuclear, polynucleate; **—ое соединение** polycyclic compound.

многоярусный *a.* multistage.

многояч/еистый, —ейковый *a.* multicellular, multicell; **—ейный** *a.* multichambered.

множественн/ость *f.* multiplicity, plurality; **—ый** *a.* multiple, plural; multivariate; **—ое образование, —ое рождение** multiple production.

множество *n.* great number; multiplicity; (math.) set; **м. точек** (math.) set of points.

множимое *n.* multiplicand.

множит/ель *m.* multiplier, coefficient, factor; **м. асимметрии** asymmetry factor; **атомный м.** atomic (scattering) factor; **общий м.** common factor; **м. ортогональности** orthogonality factor; **переводный м.** conversion factor; **м. пропорциональности** proportionality factor **м. статистического веса** statistical weight factor; **—ельное устройство** multiplier, multiplying unit **—ь** *v.* multiply.

МНР *abbr. see* **Монгольская Народная Республика.**

мо *n.* mho.

мобилиз/ация *f.* **—ационный** *a.* mobilization; **—ировать** *v.* mobilize.

мобильн/ость *f.* mobility; **—ый** *a.* mobile.

могавкит *m.* mohawkite.

могильник *m.* burial ground.

могущество *n.* power, might.

модальность *f.* modality.

моделиров/ание *n.* modeling, model design, model operation; simulation; analog formation; **—ать** *v.* model, simulate.

моделирующ/ая машина analog computer; **м. система** analog; **—ее устройство** simulator; analog computer.

модель *f.* model, pattern, simulator; **м. в. разрезе** cut-away model; **м. независимых частиц** independent-particle model **м. оболочек** shell model; **м. одного тела** one-body model (of nuclear interactions); **м. реактора** reactor model; reactor simulator; **м. составного ядра** compound nucleus model; **м.-эталон** master pattern.

модельн/ый *a.* model, pattern; **—ое дело** pattern making; **—ое рассмотрение** model study.

модерниз/ация *f.* modernization; **—ировать** *v.* modernize.

модифи/катор *m.* modifier, modifying agent; (met.) inoculant; **—кация** *f.* modification, variant, version; **—цирование** *n.* modification; (met.) inoculation; **—цированный** *a.* modified; **—цировать** *v.* modify.

модулиров/ание *n.* modulation; **—анный** *a.* modulated; **—анный по частоте** frequency-modulated; **—ать** *v.* modulate.

модулиру/емость *f.* modulability **—ющая частота** modulating frequency.

модулометр *m.* modulation meter.

модул/ь *m.* modulus; module; **м. затухания** decay modulus; **м. изгиба** flexural modulus; **м. кручения** torsion modulus; **м. объемной упругости** bulk modulus (of elasticity); **м. разрыва** modulus of rupture; **м. распада** decay modulus (mean lifetime); **м. сдвига** shear modulus; modulus of rigidity; **м. скольжения** shear modulus; **м. сопротивления** resistance modulus; **м. среза** shear modulus, modulus of rigidity; **м. упругости** elastic modulus; elastic compliance coefficient; **по —ю** (math.) modulo; in absolute value; **—ный** *a.* module, modular.

модулятор *m.* modulator; **м. света** light chopper.

модуляционный *a.* modulation; **м. множитель** (math.) modulation factor; **м. радиометр** Dicke radiometer.

модуляц/ия *f.* modulation; **м. на большой мощности** high-level modulation; **м. по скорости** velocity modulation; **м. по Хисингу** Heising modulation; **м. прямоугольниками** square-wave modulation; **м. пучка по плотности** bunching; **м. смещением** grid-bias modulation; **коэффициент —ии** modulation index.

может *see* **мочь.**

можно *adv.* it is possible, one may, one can; **м. было ожидать** it might have been expected; **м. видеть** it will be seen; **м. думать, м. сделать вывод** it may be inferred; **если м.** if possible; **как м. скорее** as soon as possible.

мозаи/ка *f.* mosaic, mosaic structure; **—чность** *f.* mosaic (or block) structure; **угол —чности** mosaic angle; **—чный** *a.* mosaic.

мозандрит *m.* mosandrite.

мозг *m.* brain; cerebrum; marrow; **—овой** *a.* brain, cerebral.

мозезит *m.* mosesite.

мозжечок *m.* cerebellum.

Мозли закон Moseley law.

МОИМ *abbr.* (**Московское отделение Института Металлов**) Moscow Branch of the Institute of Metals.

МОИП *abbr.* (**Московское общество испытателей природы**) Moscow Society of Naturalists.

мой *pron.* my, mine.

МОК *abbr.* (**Международная осветительная комиссия**) International Commission on Illumination (ICI or CIE).

мокнуть *v.* become wet, get soaked; soak, steep.

мокр/ота *f.* wetness, moisture; **—ый** *a.* wet, moist; **—ый элемент** wet cell.

мол *m.* pier, jetty, breakwater.

мол. % *abbr.* (**молярный процент**) molar percent.

мол. вес *abbr.* (**молекулярный вес**) molecular weight (mol wt).

Молдавская ССР, Молд ССР Moldavian SSR.

молекул/а *f.* molecule; **—ярность** *f.* molecularity.

молекулярн/ый *a.* molecular, molar; **м. вес** molecular weight; **м. генератор** maser; **м. процент** mole percent; **—ая орбита** molecular orbital; **—ая теплоемкость** molecular heat; **—ая теплота соединения** molecular combining heat; **—ое поле** molecular (or Weiss) field.

молибдат *m.* molybdate.

молибден *m.* molybdenum (Mo); **—истый** *a.* molybdenum, molybdous

—ит *m.* molybdenite; **—овый** *a.* molybdenum, molybdic.

молибдит *m.* molybdite.

молибдо/менит *m.* molybdomenite; **—содалит** *m.* molybdosodalite; **—филлит** *m.* molybdophyllite.

молизация *f.* molecule formation from ions.

молизит *m.* molysite.

Молля микрофотометр Moll microphotometer.

молн/еотвод, —иеотвод *m.* lightning rod, lightning arrester.

молния *f.* lightning; **зигзагообразная м.** forked lightning; **ленточная м.** ribbon lightning; **сплошная м.** sheet lightning; **четочная м.** beaded (or pearl) lightning; **шаровая м., шаровидная м.** ball (or globe) lightning; **штриховая м.** streak lightning.

молод/ежь *f.* youth, young people; **—ой** *a.* young, youthful, new; **—ость** *f.* youth.

молоко *n.* milk.

молот *m.*, **—ковый** *a.* hammer; **—кообразный след** hammer track; **—ок** *m.* hammer; hammer track.

молот/ый *a.* milled, ground; **—ь** *v.* mill, grind, crush.

молочн. *abbr. see* **молочный.**

молочн/ый *a.* milk, lactic; milky; **м. кварц** milky quartz; **м. опал** milky opal; **—ая опалесценция** milky opalescence.

молча *adv.* silently, tacitly; **—ливый** *a.* silent, tacit; **—ние** *n.* silence; **—ть** *v.* be silent; **—щий** *a.* silent, quiescent, idle; **—щий микрофон** idle microphone.

моль *m.* mole, gram-molecule, g-mol.

Молье диаграмма Mollier diagram.

мольеровская функция Molière function.

мол/ьность *f.* molarity; **—ьный** *a.* mole, molar; **—ьная доля** mole fraction; **—ьная концентрация** mole concentration; **—ьная теплоемкость** molecular heat; **—яльность** *f.* molality (moles per 1000 g of solvent); **—ярность** *f.* molarity (moles per liter of solution).

молярный *a.* molar, gram-molecular; molal; **м. вес** gram-molecular weight, molar weight; **м. раствор** molar solution.

мом *abbr.* (**миллиом**) milliohm.

Мом *abbr.* (**мегом**) megohm.

момент *m.* moment; momentum, torque; spin; instant; factor, aspect; **м. вращения** angular momentum; torque; **м. высшего порядка** multipole moment; **м. диполя** dipole moment; **м. инерции** moment of inertia; **м. количества движения** angular momentum, moment of momentum; **м. кручения** torque; **м. махового колеса** moment of gyration; **м. силы** moment of force; **м. сопротивления** drag torque, moment of resistance; **м. сухого трения** dry friction torque; **м. центробежной пары** centrifugal couple; **м. ядра** nuclear moment.

моментальн/о *adv.* instantly; **—ый** *a.* instantaneous; momentary; **—ый фотографический снимок** snapshot; **—ого действия** instantaneous, immediate.

моментная функция (stat.) moment.

МО метод *abbr.* (**метод молекулярных орбиталей**) method of molecular orbitals.

монарный *a.* monic.

монауральный *a.* monaural.

монацит *m.*, **—овый** *a.* monazite.

монгеймит *m.* monheimite.

Монгольская Народная Республика Mongolian People's Republic.

монель (металл), Монеля сплав Monel metal.

монета *f.* coin.

Монжа-Ампера уравнение Monge-Ampere equation.

монимакс Monimax (iron-nickel-molybdenum alloy).

монитор *m.*, **—ный** *a.* monitor; **—ирование** *n.* monitoring.

моно— *prefix* mono—, single.

моно/атомный *a.* monatomic; **—вариантный** *a.* monovariant; **—генный** *a.* (math.) monogenic; **—гира** *f.* onefold rotation axis; **—гирный** *a.* monoclinic; **—графия** *f.* monograph.

моно/дисперсный *a.* monodisperse; **—замещенный** *a.* monosubstituted.

монокарбоновая кислота monocarboxylic acid.

монокинетический *a.* monoenergetic.

монокись *f.* monoxide.

монокл. *abbr.* (**моноклинный**) monoclinic.

моноклиналь *m.*, **—ная складка** monocline; **—ный** *a.* monoclinal.

моноклин/ический, —ный *a.* monoclinic.

монокок *m.* (aero.) monocoque.

монокристалл *m.* single crystal.

монокулярный *a.* monocular.

монолит *m.* monolith; **—ный** *a.* monolithic, monolith; **—овый** *a.* monolithic.

моном *m.* monomial.

мономер *m.* monomer; **—ный** *a.* monomeric.

монометаллический *a.* monometallic.

мономолекулярн/ый *a.* monomolecular; **—ая пленка** monomolecular film.

монопол/изация *f.* monopolization; **—изировать** *v.* monopolize; **—ия** *f.* monopoly; **—ь** *m.* monopole; **—ьный** *a.* monopolistic, exclusive.

монополярный *a.* monopolar.

моноскоп *m.* monoscope.

монослой *m.* monolayer, unilayer, monomolecular layer.

монотип *m.* monotype.

монотонн/о *adv.* monotonically, smoothly; **—ость** *f.* monotony; **—ый** *a.* monotonic, monotone; continual, continuous; monotonous.

моно/топливо *n.* monofuel; **—трон** *m.* monotron.

монотроп *m.*, **—ия** *f.* monotropy; **—ный** *a.* monotropic.

монохорд *m.* monochord.

монохромати/зация *f.* monochromatization; **—зировать** *v.* monochromate; **—зирующий кристалл** monochromatic crystal; **—ческий, —чный** *a.* monochromatic, monoenergetic.

монохроматор *m.* monochromator, monochromatic illuminator.

моноциклический *a.* monocyclic.

моноэдр *m.* hemihedron; (obs.) monohedron; **—ический** *a.* hemihedral; (obs.) monohedral.

моноэнергетич/еский *a.* monoenergetic, monochromatic; **—ность** *f.* energy homogeneity.

монтаж *m.* assembly, erection, installation, mounting; **—ный** *a.* assembling, erecting, mounting; **—ный каркас** mounting frame; **—ая схема** (elec.) wiring diagram, hook-up.

монтебразит *m.* montebrasite.

Монте-Карло метод Monte-Carlo method.

монтер *m.* assembler.

монтиров/ание *n.*, **—ка** *f.* assembly, erection, mounting; **—анный** *a.* assembled, erected, mounted; **—ать** *v.* assemble, erect, mount, install.

монтичеллит *m.* monticellite.

монтмориллонит *m.* montmorillonite.

монтроидит *m.* montroydite.

монумент *m.* monument; **—альный** *a.* monumental.

Мооса шкала *see* **Моса шкала.**

Моперти Maupertius (lunar crater).

Моперти принцип Maupertius principle.

Мора круг Mohr circle.

мораль *f.* morals, ethics; **—ный** *a.* moral, ethical; **—ное состояние** morale.

Мордовская АССР, Морд АССР Mordovian ASSR.

море *n.* sea; (astr.) mare, *pl.* maria; **м. глубоко возмущенное** very rough sea; **м. зеркальное** calm sea.

море лунное lunar mare; **м. Влажности** Mare Humorum; **м. Волн** Mare Undarum; **м. Восточное** Mare Orientalis; **м. Гумбольдта** Mare Humboldtianum; **м. Дождей** Mare Imbrium; **м. Изобилия** Mare Foecunditatis; **м. Краевое** Mare Marginis; **м. Кризисов (Опасностей)** Mare Crisium; **м. Нектара** Mare Nectaris; **м. Новое** Mare Novum; **м. Облаков** Mare Nubium **м. Паров** Mare Vaporum; **м. Пены** Mare Spumans; **м. Смита** Mare Smythii; **м. Спокойствия** Mare Tranquillitatis; **м. Холода** Mare Frigoris **м. Южное** Mare Australe; **м. Ясности** Mare Serenitatis.

море сильно возмущенное rough sea **м. слегка возмущенное** slight sea **м. спокойное** smooth sea; **м. умеренно возмущенное** moderate sea.

морена *f.* moraine.

моренозит *m.* morenosite.

моренсит *m.* morencite.
мореплав/ание *n.* navigation; **—атель** *m.* navigator; **—ательный** *a.* nautical.
Морера теорема Morera theorem.
Морет Moretus (lunar crater).
мореход/ность *f.* seaworthiness; **—ный** *a.* nautical; **—ство** *n.* navigation.
Морзе код Morse code; **М. потенциал** Morse potential; *see also* **Морса.**
мористый *a.* out at sea.
мороз *m.* frost; **—ить** *v.* freeze; **—ность** *f.* frigidity; **—ный** *a.* frosty, frost; **—обоина, —овина** *f.* frost cleft.
морозостойк/ий *a.* frostproof, antifreeze, nonfreezing; **—ость** *f.* resistance to frost.
мороксит *m.* moroxite.
морос/ить *v.*, **—ь** *f.* drizzle; **—ящий дождь** drizzling rain; **—ящий туман** drizzling (or wet) fog.
Морса уравнение Morse equation.
морск/ой *a.* sea, marine, maritime; nautical; naval; **м. радиоинтерферометр** cliff radio interferometer; **—ая миля** nautical mile; **—ая пенка** sea foam, meerschaum, sepiolite.
морфолог *m.* morphologist; **—ический** *a.* morphological; **—ия** *f.* morphology.
морфотроп/изм *m.* morphotropism; **—ия** *f.* morphotropy; **—ный** *a.* morphotropic.
морщ/ина *f.* wrinkle, crease; **—инистый** *a.* wrinkled, creased; **—ить** *v.* wrinkle.
морянка *f.* blister steel.
мос— *abbr.* (**московский**) Moscow (used as a prefix).
Моса шкала твердости Mohs hardness scale.
Мосгэс *abbr.* (**Московская гидроэлектрическая станция**) Moscow Hydroelectric Power Plant.
моск. *abbr.* (**московский**) Moscow.
Москва Moscow.
московский *a.* Moscow.
Мосметровес *abbr.* (**Московский завод точных весов и измерительных приборов**) Moscow Precision Weights and Measuring Instruments Plant.
Моссбауера эффект Mössbauer effect.
мост *m.* bridge; **висячий м.** suspension bridge; **м.-водовод** aqueduct; **м. малых сопротивлений** conductivity bridge; **м. переменного тока** alternating-current bridge; **подъемный м.** lift bridge.
мостик *m.*, **—овый** *a.* bridge.
мостов/ой *a.* bridge; pavement; **м. кран** traveling crane; **м. фильтр** differential filter; **—ая схема** bridge circuit; **—ые весы** weigh bridge.
мостостроение *n.* bridge building.
мот/алка *f.* reeler, reel, winder, machine; **—альный** *a.* reeling, winding; **—анный** *a.* wound, coiled; **—ать** *v.* reel, wind, coil; **—аться** *v.* dangle.
мотив *m.* motive, cause; **—ировать** *v.* motivate; **—ировка** *f.* motivation, reason, justification.
мотовил/о *n.* reel; **—ьный** *a.* reeling.
моток *m.* bundle.
мотор *m.* motor, engine; **м.-генератор** motor generator; **—изация** *f.* motorization; **—изованный** *a.* motorized; **—ный** *a.* motor; **—чик** *m.* fractional-horsepower motor.
Мотта-Шоттки теория Mott-Schottky theory.
мотыль *m.* crank.
моховой агат moss agate.
мохокэн *m.* Mohawkian series.
Мохоровичина поверхность Mohorovičić discontinuity.
мочен/ие *n.* wetting, soaking, steeping; **—ый** *a.* wetted, soaked.
мочильный *a.* wetting, soaking.
мочить *v.* wet, soak.
мочь *v.* be able; **может быть** perhaps, possibly; it is possible; **может встретиться** it may occur, it may be encountered; **не может быть** it is impossible.
мощностный *a.* power.
мощност/ь *f.* power; capacity, output; strength; (geo.) thickness, width; (math.) cardinality, cardinal number, power (of set); **входная м.** grid-driving power (of electron tube); **м. двигателя** engine power (capacity, thrust); **м. дозы** dose rate; **м. излучения** radiated power; **м. испускания** emissive power; **м. источника**

source strength; **м. на согласованной нагрузке** available power; **номинальная м.** rated power; **м. облучения** exposure rate; **отдаваемая м.** power output; **переданная м., подведенная м., поглощенная м., потребляемая м., сообщенная м.** power input; **м. питания** input power; **м. поглощения** absorptive power; absorbed power; **м. рассеяния** dissipated power; **большой —и** high-power; **коэффициент —и** power factor; **малой —и** low-power; **полной —ью** full power.

мощн/ый *a.* powerful; power, high-power, heavy-duty, heavy (machine); **м. каскад** power stage; **м. разряд** high-current (or high-power) discharge; **м. транзистор** power transistor; **—ая лампа** (rad.) power tube; **—ая лучевая лампа** (rad.) beam-power tube; **—ые кучевые облака** cumulus congestus.

мощь *f.* power; **воздушная м.** air power.

моющ/ий *a.* washing, detergent; **—ая способность** detergency; **—ее средство** detergent.

МП *abbr.* (**магнитный пеленг**) magnetic bearing.

мПВ *abbr.* (**морской полярный воздух**) polar maritime air.

МПГ *abbr.* (**Международный полярный год**) International Polar Year.

мпуаз *abbr.* (**миллипуаз**) millipoise.

мр *abbr.* (**миллирентген**) milliroentgen (mr).

мрак *m.* darkness, obscurity.

мрамор *m.*, **—ный** *a.* marble; **руинный м.** ruin marble; **—изованный** *a.* marbleized.

мрачный *a.* dark, dim.

мрезерфорд *abbr.* (**миллирезерфорд**) millirutherford.

МСА *abbr.* (**международная стандартная атмосфера**) International Standard Atmosphere (ISA).

мсб *abbr.* (**миллистильб**) millistilb.

м.св. *abbr.* (**международная свеча**) international candle.

м-свеча *abbr.* (**метр-свеча**) meter-candle.

мсек *abbr.* (**миллисекунда**) millisecond (msec).

МСт. *abbr.* (**мартеновская сталь**) open-hearth steel.

МСТ *abbr.* (**метеорологическая станция**) meteorological station.

МСЭ *abbr.* (**Малая Советская Энциклопедия**) Small Soviet Encyclopedia; (**Международный Союз Электросвязи**) International Telecommunications Union.

мТВ *abbr.* (**морской тропический воздух**) tropical maritime air.

МТС *abbr.* (**метр-тонна-секунда**) meter-ton-second (system).

МТЦ *abbr.* (**Московский телевизионный центр**) Moscow Television Center.

Муавра теорема De Moivre theorem; **М. формула** D. M. relation.

муар *m.* moiré.

муассанит *m.* moissanite.

мудрый *a.* wise.

муж/ской *a.* masculine, male; **—чина** *m.* man.

муза *f.* musa antenna.

музей *m.*, **—ный** *a.* museum; **—ная вещь** museum specimen.

музык/а *f.* music; **—альная искра** singing spark.

мукит *m.* muckite.

мулликит *m.* mullicite.

мульда *f.* (met.) mold, pan, basin (geo.) trough, syncline.

мульти— *prefix* multi—, poly—; *see also* **много—**.

мульти/валентный *a.* multivalent; **—вариантный** *a.* polyvariant, multivariant; **—вибратор** *m.* multivibrator; **—вибратор узких селекторных импульсов** narrow-gate multivibrator; **—плексный** *a.* multiplex.

мультиплет *m.* multiplet; **—ность** *f.* multiplicity; **—ный** *a.* multiplet multiple; **—ная структура** multiple structure.

мультиплика/тивный *a.* multiplicative factorized product; **—тор** *m.* multiplier; pressure booster; **—ция** *f.* **—ционный** *a.* multiplication.

мультиплицирующий *a.* multiplying.

мультипол/е *n.* multipole field. **—ь** *m.* multipole; **—ьность** *f.* multipole order.

ультипольн/ый *a.* multipole, multipolar; **—ый момент** multipole moment; **—ое излучение** multipole emission (or radiation); **—ое магнитное излучение** magnetic multipole radiation; **—ое электрическое излучение** electric multipole radiation.

ультиротация *f.* mutarotation, multirotation, birotation.

ультхоппа формула Multhopp formula.

уметалл *m.* mumetal.

ундшту/к *m.*, **—чный** *a.* mouthpiece.

униципальн/ый *a.* municipal; **—ые предприятия** public utilities.

унка газ Munk gas.

уон *m.* muon.

урав/а *f.*, **—ить** *v.* glaze; **—ление** *n.* glazing; **—леный** *a.* glazed.

уравьинокислый *a.* formic acid, formate (of); **м. уранил** uranyl formate.

уравьин/ый *a.* formic; **—ая кислота** formic acid.

урит *m.* mooreite; **м.-дельта** deltamooreite.

усковит *m.* muscovite.

усор *m.*, **—ный** *a.* debris, refuse; **—осжигатель** *m.* incinerator.

уссон *m.*, **—ный** *a.* monsoon.

утаротация *f.* mutarotation, birotation.

утация *f.* mutation.

утить *v.* disturb, make turbid, stir up; **—ся** *v.* become turbid.

утманнит *m.* muthmannite.

утн/оватость, —ость *f.* turbidity; **коэффициент —ости** turbidity factor; **—ый** *a.* turbid, muddy, cloudy; **—ый снимок** blurred photograph.

уть *f.* suspension, sludge, sediment.

уфель *m.*, **—ный** *a.* muffle; **—ная печь** muffle furnace.

уфт/а *f.*, **—овый** *a.* clutch; coupling, connecting piece, connector sleeve; **кабельная м.** cable box; **стяжная винтовая м.** turnbuckle; **—овое соединение** sleeve joint.

уха Musca (Mus) (constellation).

уч/ение *n.* suffering, pain; **—ить** *v.* worry, torment.

мушиный глаз fly's eye, compound eye.

мф *abbr.* (**миллифарада**) millifarad (mf); (**миллифот**) milliphot.

МФТИ *abbr.* (**Московский физико-технический институт**) Moscow Physics and Technology Institute.

м-ц *abbr. see* **мес.**

МЧ *abbr.* (**меридиональные части**) meridional parts.

мы *pron.* we.

мыл/енный *a.* soaped; **—ить** *v.* soap; **—кий** *a.* soapy; **—кость** *f.* soapiness; **—о** *n.* soap.

мыльн/ый *a.* soap, soapy, saponaceous; **—ая пена** soapsuds.

мыс *m.* (geo.) cape.

мысл/енный *a.* mental, conceptual; imaginary, assumed; **—енный эксперимент** thought experiment; **—имый** *a.* thinkable, conceivable; **—ить** *v.* think, conceive.

мысль *f.* thought, idea, notion, concept; **наводить на м., подавать м.** suggest; **основная м.** basic idea.

мыслящий *a.* thinking, intellectual.

мыть *v.* wash; **—е** *n.* washing.

мышьяк *m.* arsenic (As); **—овистый** *a.* arsenic, arsenous, arsenical, arsenide (of); **—овистый водород** hydrogen arsenide, arsine; **—овый** *a.* arsenic, arsenical.

МЭ *abbr.* (**магнитоэлектрические приборы**) magnetoelectric instruments.

Мэв *abbr.* (**мегаэлектронвольт**) million electron volts (Mev).

Мэв/с *abbr.* (**мегаэлектронвольт/скорость света**) million electron volts/velocity of light (Mev/c).

МЭИ *abbr.* (**Московский энергетический институт**) Moscow Power Institute.

МЭИЗ *abbr.* (**Московский электроизоляционный завод**) Moscow Electrical Insulation Plant.

МЭИС *abbr.* (**Московский электротехнический институт связи**) Moscow Communications Electrical Engineering Institute.

МЭК *abbr.* (**Международная электротехническая комиссия.**) International Electrotechnical Commission.

МЭКВ *abbr.* (**миллиэквивалент**) milliequivalent (meq).

МЭМЗ *abbr.* (**Московский электромеханический завод**) Moscow Electromechanical Plant.

МЭП *abbr.* (**Министерство электротехнической промышленности**) Ministry of the Electrotechnical Industry.

МЭСЭП *abbr.* (**Министерство электрических станций и электропромышленности**) Ministry of Electric Power Plants and the Electrical Industry.

МЭТИИСС *abbr.* (**Московский электротехнический институт инженеров сигнализации и связи**) Moscow Electrotechnical Institute of Signal and Communications Engineers.

мю *n.* mu; **м.-мезоатом** mu-mesic atom; **м.-мезон** mu-meson, muon.

мюллер/ит *m.* müllerite; **—ово стекло** Müller's glass.

мюон *m.* muon; **—ий** *m.* muonium.

мягк/ий *a.* soft, mild, weak; **м. климат** mild climate; **м. негатив** thin negative; **м. сверхпроводник** soft (or ideal) superconductor; **—ая вода** soft water; **—ая закалка** mild quench; **—ая компонента** soft component; **—ая лампа** soft vacuum tube; **—ая трубка** soft (x-ray) tube; **—ая фокусировка** weak focusing; **—ое излучение** soft radiation; **—ие рентгеновские лучи** soft x-rays.

мягко/рисующий *a.* soft-focus; **—сть** *f.* softness.

мягч/е *comp. of* **мягкий,** softer; **—ение** *n.* softening; **—итель** *m.* mollient, mollifier; **—ительный** *a.* softening, plasticizing; **—ить** *v.* soften.

мятина *f.* hollow, dent, nick.

мятый *a.* crumpled; crumbled; exhaust (steam).

мять *v.* crumple; knead; throttle (steam).

мяч *m.* ball.

Н

Н [*in steel mark* (**никель**)] nickel (Ni).

н. *abbr.* (**научный**) scientific; (**национальный**) national; (**нормальный раствор**) normal solution.

на *prep.* at, by; on, upon; in, into; for; per; over; to, toward; **на вес** by weight, in weight; **на единицу** per unit; **на запад** to the west; **на куски** into pieces; **на полном ходу** at full speed.

на— *prefix with verbs* sufficiently; directional action (on, to); *with nouns and adjectives* on, over, upon.

набав/ить, —лять *v.* add, increase; **—ка** *f.* increase; **—ленный** *a.* increased.

набат *m.* alarm, alarm bell; **—ный колокол** alarm bell, warning bell.

набег *m.* inroad; advance; **—ание** *n.* running against; **—ать** *v.* encounter, run against; advance; accumulate; **—ающий** *a.* leading; incoming, oncoming; accumulating; **—ающий край** leading edge; **—ающая лопасть** advancing blade.

набежать *see* **набегать.**

набело *adv.* clean, fair; **переписанное н.** clean copy.

набережная *f.* embankment.

набив/ание *n.*, **—ка** *f.* filling, stuffing, packing; padding; **—ать** *v.* fill, stuff, pack; ram; nail on; **—ной** *a.* tamped, rammed; **—очный** *a.* packing, stuffing; **—очный материал** packing.

набирать *v.* collect, gather; typeset, dial; **н. высоту** gain altitude.

набит/ый *a.* packed; **—ь** *see* **набивать.**

набла *f.* (math.) nabla, del.

наблюд/аемый *a.* observed, observable, experimental; **—атель** *m.* observer.

наблюдательн/ость *f.* power of observation; **—ый** *a.* viewing, observation, observational; **—ый отсек** viewer box; **—ый пункт** observation point.

наблюд/ать *v.* observe, view; supervise, control; **—ающий** *a.* observing, supervisory; **—ение** *n.* observation, supervision, viewing, tracking; **—енный** *a.* observed.

набок *adv.* on one side, sideways, awry.

набор *m.* set; bank, gang; kit; collection, typesetting; dialing; **н. программы** programming.

набрасыв/ание *n.* sketching; **—ать** *v.* sketch, outline, draft; throw.

набрать *see* **набирать.**

набрести *v.* come across, happen upon.

наброс/анный *a.* sketched, outlined; **—ать, —ить** *see* **набрасывать; —ная плотина** rock-fill dam; **—ок** *m.* draft, layout, sketch, outline.

набрызг *m.* sputtering.

набух/ание *n.* swelling; **вода —ания** gelation water; **—ать, —нуть** *v.* swell; **—ший** *a.* swollen.

навал *m.*, **—ка** *f.* loading, heaping; **—ивать, —ить** *v.* heap up, pile; charge, load; **—иваться, —иться** *v.* fall on, lean.

навальцованный *a.* rolled-on.

навар/енный *a.* welded (on); deposited; faced; **н. медью** copper-clad; **н. сталью** steel-faced; **—ивать, —ить** *v.* weld (on), overlay.

наведен/ие *n.* leading, guiding, homing; aiming; guidance; bringing (on); (elec.) induction; **н. справок** looking up references; making inquiries; **—ный** *a.* led, guided, directed; induced.

наверно *adv.* most likely; certainly; **знать н.** know for certain.

навернут/ый *a.* twisted-on; screwed-on; **—ь** *see* **навертывать.**

наверняка *adv.* surely, for certain.

наверст/ать, —ывать *v.* make up; compensate; **—ывание** *n.* recovery; compensation.

наверт/ка *f.* twisting, winding; **—ный** *a.* twist; screw (cap); **—ывать** *v.* twist around, wind; screw on.

наверх *adv.* upward, up; on top; **—у** *adv.* above.

навес *m.* shed; canopy.

навес/ить *see* **навешать; —ка** *f.* hanging; hinge; **—ный** *a.* hanging; downward; **—ная дверь** hinged door; **—ная петля** hinge; **—ная траектория** curved trajectory.

навести *see* **наводить.**

навесу *adv.* hanging; in suspension.

наветренный *a.* windward.

навеш/ать, —ивать *v.* hang, suspend; weigh (out); **—енный** *a.* suspended.

навзничь *adv.* backwards.

навив/альный, —ной, —очный *a.* winding, coiling; **—ание** *n.*, **—ка** *f.* winding on, spiraling, rolling on; **—ать** *v.* wind, roll on, reel, coil.

навига/тор *m.* navigator; **—ция** *f.* navigation; **—ция по небесным светилам** celestial navigation.

навин/тить, —чивать *v.* screw on; **—ченный** *a.* screwed-on; **—чивающийся** *a.* screw-on.

навис/ание *n.* hanging over; impendence; **—ать, —нуть** *v.* hang over, overhang; impend; **—ающий** *a.* overhanging; **—лый, —ший** *a.* overhanging; impending.

навит/ый *a.* wound-on, rolled-on; **—ь** *see* **навивать.**

навле/кать, —чь *v.* bring on, cause; incur.

наводимый снаряд guided projectile.

наводить *v.* direct, aim at, sight; set, adjust; lead; cover, apply; (elec.) induce; **н. на мысль** suggest; **н. на фокус** focus; **н. справку** make inquiries; look up.

наводка *f.* directing, sighting, focusing; induction; pickup.

наводн/ение *n.* flood, inundation; **—ить, —ять** *v.* flood.

наводороженный *a.* hydrogenated.

наводящий *a.* directing, aiming; (elec.) inducing.

навряд, —ли *adv.* hardly, scarcely.

навсегда *adv.* forever; **раз н.** once (and) for all.

навстречу *adv.* toward; counter; **включенные н.** bucking, connected in opposition; **н. друг другу** in opposition; **идти н.** meet.

навыворот *adv.* inside out.

навык *m.* skill; habit, practice, experience.

навылет *adv.* through.

Навье-Стокса уравнение Navier-Stokes equation.

навязывать *v.* fasten, tie on; impose, obtrude.

нагар *m.* scale, carbon deposit.

нагартов/анный *a.* cold-worked, hammered; **—ка** *f.* (met.) cold working.

нагель *m.* pin, dowel, peg.

нагиагит *m.* nagyagite.

нагиб/ание *n.* bending; **—ать** *v.* bend.

наглухо *adv.* hermetically, tightly; permanently.

наглядн/о *adv.* clearly; graphically; intuitively; **—ость** *f.* visualizability; visualization; clear representation; **—ый** *a.* clear, obvious; visual, pictorial, graphic; intuitive; visualizable; **—ый пример** obvious case; **—ое доказательство** visual proof; graphic demonstration; **—ые пособия** visual aids.

нагнетан/ие *n.* pressing, forcing, injection; **ход —ия** pressure stroke.

нагнетатель *m.* supercharger; blower; **н. волновода** waveguide pump.

нагнетательн/ый *a.* pressure, force; delivery; **н. вентилятор** blast fan; **н. клапан** pressure valve; delivery valve; **н. насос** forcing pump; **н. рукав** pressure hose; **н. трубопровод** pressure line; delivery conduit; **—ая камера** discharge chamber; plenum chamber; **—ая труба** discharge pipe, delivery pipe; **—ое сопло** discharge nozzle.

нагнет/ать *v.* force, press; deliver; pump; **—ающий** *a.* forcing, pressing, pressure; **—ающий вентилятор** *see* **нагнетательный вентилятор**; **—енный** *a.* forced, pressed.

нагнут/ый *a.* bent; **—ь** *see* **нагибать.**

нагон воды surge, wash, tide.

нагон/ять *v.* overtake; force together; **—яющий годограф** (seis.) overtaking travel-time curve.

нагораживать *v.* stack up; divide into compartments.

нагорный *a.* raised; mountainous.

нагородить *see* **нагораживать.**

наготове *adv.* ready, in readiness; **держать н.** keep in readiness.

наград/а *f.*, **—ной, —ный** *a.* reward; award; **—ить** *v.* reward.

награжд/ать *see* **наградить**; **—ение** *n.* reward; **—енный** *a.* rewarded.

нагрев *m.*, **—ание** *n.* heating; **поверхность —а** heating surface; **—аемость** *f.* heat absorption.

нагреватель *m.* heater; oven; **—ный** *a.* heating; preheating.

нагре/вать, —ть *v.* heat, warm; **—вающий** *a.* heating, warming; **—востойкость** *f.* thermal stability (or endurance), heat stability; **—тый** *a.* heated; **—тый магнетрон** hot magnetron.

нагромо/ждать, —здить *v.* pile up, accumulate; **—ждение** *n.* pile; piling; **—жденный** *a.* piled.

нагруж/аемость *f.* load capacity; **—ать** *v.* load, charge; burden; **—ающий** *a.* loading, charging; **—ение** *n.* loading; **—енный** *a.* loaded, charged.

нагрузить *see* **нагружать.**

нагрузк/а *f.* load, loading, charge; (math.) weight; **допускаемая н., допустимая н.** load capacity; permissible load; **н. на пучок** (elec.) beam load; **полная н.** full load; full-time job; **величина —и** load intensity; **коэффициент —и** load factor.

нагрузочн/ый *a.* load, loading, charge; **н. ток** load current; **—ая способность** load capacity; **—ое сопротивление** load resistance.

над *prep. instr.* above, over; on, upon; **работать н.** work at, work on.

над— *prefix* over—, super—, hyper—; above—; per— (acid, salt).

надав/ить, —ливать *v.* contract; press.

надатмосферное пространство outer space.

надбав/ить, —лять *v.* add; increase; **—ка** *f.* increase; **—ленный** *a.* increased; **—очный** *a.* additional.

надбарьерный *a.* above the barrier, exceeding barrier energy.

надвесный *a.* overhung, overhanging.

надвиг *m.* thrust; (geo.) thrust, thrust fault.

надви/гать, —нуть *v.* move up, thrust; **—гаться** *v.* approach, impend; **—гающийся** *a.* approaching, advancing, impending, imminent; **—жение** *n.* approach.

надводный *a.* above-water, surface.

надвое *adv.* in two, in half.

надгибать *see* **нагибать.**

надда/вать, —ть *v.* add, increase.

наддув *m.* supercharge.

надевать *v.* put on; invest.

надежда *f.* hope; reliance; expectation.

надежн/ость *f.* reliability, security, safety; (stat.) accuracy; **—ый** *a.* safe, reliable, dependable, trustworthy; (stat.) accurate.

надел/ение *n.* allotment; **—ить, —ять** *v.* allot; provide.

надеяться *v.* hope for, look forward to; rely upon, have confidence in.

надзвуковой *a.* ultrasonic, supersonic.

надземный *a.* above-ground; overhead; elevated (railroad).

надзиратель *m.* supervisor; **—ство** *n.* supervision.

над/зирать *v.* supervise, inspect; **—зор** *m.* supervision, inspection, surveillance.

надир *m.* nadir.

надкадмиевый *a.* epicadmium.

надкалывать *v.* pierce slightly; split slightly.

надкислота *f.* peracid.

надколоть *see* **надкалывать.**

надкритич/еский, —ный *a.* supercritical, above-critical; **—ность** *f.* supercriticality.

надламывать *v.* crack.

надлеж/аще *adv.* appropriately, suitably, properly; **—ащий** *a.* appropriate, proper; **—ащий размер** correct size; **—ащим образом** properly, duly; thoroughly; **—ит** it is necessary, one should.

надлом *m.* fracture, break; **—ать, —ить** *see* **надламывать; —ленный** *a.* cracked.

надмножество *n.* inclusive set.

надо it is necessary; *prep. see* **над; ему н.** he must, he needs.

надобн/ость *f.* necessity, requirement, need; **нет —ости** there is no need; **—ый** *a.* necessary, requisite.

надолго *adv.* for a long time.

надорвать *see* **надрывать.**

надосновный *a.* superbasic.

надпил *m.*, **—ивать, —ить** *v.* notch.

надпис/анный *a.* inscribed; **—ать, —ывать** *v.* inscribe, superscribe; **—ывание** *n.* inscribing; **—ь** *f.* inscription, superscription.

надполе *n.* (math.) extension field.

надрез *m.* cut, incision, notch; **эффект —а** notch effect; **—анный** *a.* cut, notched; **—ать** *v.* cut into, incise, notch.

надрезывать *see* **надрезать.**

надруб/ать, —ить *v.* notch, chip.

надрыв *m.* slight tear, strain; **—ать** *v.* begin to tear.

надсе/кать, —чь *v.* notch.

надсинхронный *a.* hypersynchronous.

надслуховой *a.* ultrasonic.

надсмотр *m.* control, inspection, supervision.

надсоль *f.* (chem.) persalt.

надстав/ить, —лять *v.* extend; **—ка** *f.* adapter; extension; **кольцевая —ка** extension ring; **—ленный** *a.* added-on, lengthened, extended.

надстр/аивать, —оить *v.* build on; **—ойка** *f.* superstructure.

надстрочный *a.* superlinear; interlinear; **н. индекс** superscript.

надтепловой нейтрон epithermal neutron.

надтональный *a.* supersonic.

надув/ание *n.* inflation; **—ать** *v.* inflate, distend; **—аться** *v.* inflate; **—ная подушка** air cushion.

надум/анный *a.* exaggerated; **—ать, —ывать** *v.* devise; **—аться, —ываться** *v.* make up one's mind, decide.

над ур. м. *abbr.* (**над уровнем моря**) above sea level.

надут/ый *a.* inflated; **—ь** *see* **надувать.**

надфронтальные облака frontal clouds.

надфункция *f.* majorant.

наедине *adv.* in private.

наем *m.* hire, employment; **—ный** *a.* hired.

нажат/ие *n.* pressure; **—ь** *see* **нажимать.**

нажда/к *m.*, **—чный** *a.* emery; **—чный круг, —чное точило** emery wheel (or disk).

нажим *m.* pressure; clamp, pinchcock; **—ать** *v.* push, press; clamp, pinch; **—ающее усилие** pressure; **—ной** *a.* pressure; clamp, clamping; **—ной валик** pressure roll; **—ной винт** clamping (or adjusting) screw; **—ная кнопка** push button.

наз. *abbr.* (**называемый**) called, named; (**называется**) is called.

назад *adv.* back, backwards; **взгляд н.** retrospect; **взять свои слова н.** retract; **год тому н.** a year ago; **движение н.** backward movement, return; **ход н.** reverse running, backing; return stroke.

назв. *abbr. see* **название.**

назв/ание *n.* name, designation; title; **—анный** *a.* named; **—ать** *see* **называть.**

наземн/ый *a.* ground, surface, ground-level; land, terrestrial; **н. воздух** surface air; **—ая вода** surface water; **—ая съемка** ground survey; **—ое давление** surface pressure.

назначать *v.* appoint, designate, set; prescribe.

назначен/ие *n.* appointment, assignment; designation; purpose, destination; **двойного —ия** dual-purpose; **место —ия** destination; **общего —ия** general-purpose; **отвечать своему —ию** serve the purpose; **—ный** *a.* appointed, assigned, set; **—ная отметка** marker pip; **—ная частота** assigned frequency.

назначить *see* **назначать.**

назонит *m.* nasonite.

назре/вать, —ть *v.* ripen, mature; be about to happen; **—вающий** *a.* ripening.

назубр/енный *a.* indented, notched; **—ивать, —ить** *v.* indent; notch.

назыв/аемый *a.* named, called; **так н.** so-called; **—ать** *v.* name, call, designate, term.

наи— *superlative prefix* the most.

наиб. н. г. *abbr.* (**наибольшая нижняя грань**) greatest lower bound.

наиболее *adv.* the most; **н. вероятный** most probable; **н. глубокий** innermost; **н. удаленный электрон** outermost electron.

наибольш/ий *a.* the greatest, maximum, extreme; **н. общий делитель** greatest common divisor; **—ая дальность** extreme range.

наивыгоднейший *a.* most advantageous, most favorable, optimized, optimum.

наивысше— *prefix* highest.

наивысший *a.* highest, utmost.

наизнанку *adv.* inside out.

наизусть *adv.* by rote.

наилучший *a.* the best, optimum.

наим. в. г. *abbr.* (**наименьшая верхняя грань**) least upper bound.

наименее *adv.* the least.

наименов/ание *n.* name, denomination; **привести к одному —анию** (math.) reduce to one denomination; **—ать** *v.* name, denominate, designate.

наименьш/ий *a.* the least, minimum; **—ее общее кратное** least common multiple; **—ее расстояние (сближения)** distance of closest approach, collision diameter.

наинизший *a.* lowest.

наискорейший *a.* the quickest.

наискось *adv.* obliquely.

наихудший *a.* the worst.

найд. *abbr. see* **найденный.**

найденный *a.* found.

Найквиста теорема Nyquist theorem.

найлон *m.*, **—овый** *a.* nylon.

Найта смещение (сдвиг) Knight shift; **найтевский** *a.* Knight.

найти *see* **находить.**

накал *m.* (elec.) heater, filament; heating, glow, incandescence; heater current; **белый н.** white heat; **напряжение —а** filament voltage; **нить —а** filament; **ток —а** heater (or filament) current.

накаленн/ость *f.* heat, incandescence; **—ый** *a.* incandescent, heated, glowing.

накаливан/ие *n.* heating, incandescence; **н. добела** incandescence, white heat; **н. докрасна** red heat; **лампа —ия** incandescent lamp.

накаливать *v.* heat; **н. добела** bring to white heat; **н. докрасна** bring to red heat; **—ся** *v.* incandesce, become hot.

накал/ивающийся *a.* incandescent; **—ить** *see* **накаливать.**

накалывать *v.* prick; split, break.

накал/ьный *a.* heater, filament; **—ять** *see* **накаливать.**

накануне *adv.* the day before, on the eve (of).

накапать *see* **накапывать.**

накаплив/ание *n.* storage; **—ать** *see* **накоплять.**

накапывать *v.* pour by drops; spill on.

накат *m.* subflooring; **—анный** *a.* rolled-on; **—ать, —ить** *see* **накатывать.**

накатина *f.* joist.

накат/ка *f.* knurl; **—ывание** *n.* rolling on; knurling; **—ывать** *v.* roll, roll on, smooth; knurl, mill.

накач/ать, —ивать *v.* pump up, inflate; **—енный** *a.* pumped up, inflated; **туго —енный** fully inflated; **—ивание** *n.* pumping up, inflation; **—ка** *f.* pumping.

накид/ать, —ывать *v.* throw on.

накип/ийный *a.*, **—ь** *f.* scum; scale, incrustation.

накладка *f.* cover plate, covering, cap; patch; **стыковая н.** fishplate; joint bar.

накладн/ой *a.* laid-on, superposed, applied; **н. металл** metal plating; **—ые расходы** overhead (cost).

накладыв/ание *n.* superimposing; plating, coating; **—ать** *v.* put on, superimpose, superpose, apply, coat, plate; apply (tool); **—ать сверху** superimpose; **—ающийся** *a.* superposable.

наклеи/вание *n.* gluing; **—вать, —ть** *v.* glue on.

наклейка *f.* patch; label.

наклеп *m.* (met.) cold hardening (or working); **н. при обработке** work hardening; **—ывать** *v.* rivet.

наклон *m.* slope, inclination, slant, tilt, pitch, dip (angle); **н. эклиптики** (astr.) obliquity (of ecliptic).

наклонен/ие *n.* inclination, dip, tilting, slant, pitch; **магнитное н.** magnetic dip (or inclination); **угол —ия** angle of dip (or inclination); **—ный** *a.* inclined, dip.

наклонить *see* **наклонять.**

наклонн/о *adv.* obliquely; **—ость** *f.* inclination, tendency; obliquity; **—ый** *a.* oblique, inclined, sloping, tilted, slant; **—ый вход** oblique entry; **—ая координата** oblique coordinate; **—ая плоскость** inclined plane; **—ая поляризация** oblique polarization; **—ая производная** directional derivative; **—ая съемка** (phot.) inclined exposure; **—ое распространение** oblique transmission.

наклономер *m.* tiltmeter.

наклон/яемый, —яющийся *a.* inclinable; **—ять** *v.* incline, slope, tilt; decline; **—яться** *v.* slope, incline, lean.

наковаль/нообразные облака anvil clouds; **—ня** *f.* anvil; (meteor.) incus, anvil cloud.

наков/анный *a.* forged-on; **—ать, —ывать** *v.* forge on.

накожный *a.* cutaneous, skin.

наколоть *see* **накалывать.**

наконец *adv.* at last, finally.

наконечник *m.* tip, point; nozzle, nosepiece, mouth, mouthpiece; adapter; head, cap; terminal; tag; ferrule; tailpiece.

накопитель *m.* storage element (or device); accumulator; register; **н. информации** (elec.) memory; **—ный** *a.* cumulative, storage; **н. конденсатор** reservoir capacitor.

накопить *see* **накоплять.**

накоплен/ие *n.* accumulation, buildup, storage, pileup; **н. запасов** stockpiling; **точка —ия** (math.) limit (cluster, accumulation) point; **—ный** *a.* accumulated, stored; cumulative; **—ная энергия** stored energy; **—ные связи** cumulative bonds.

накопл/ять *v.* accumulate, heap up, store; **—яющийся** *a.* cumulative.

накрепко *adv.* firmly, tightly.

накрест *adv.* crosswise; **—лежащие углы** alternate angles.

накрой *m.* lap (joint), overlap.

накры/вание, —тие *n.* covering; **—вать, —ть** *v.* cover; **—тый** *a.* covered.

нактоуз *m.* binnacle.

налаг/ать *v.* impose, lay on, superimpose; overlap; **—ающийся** *a.* superposed; concurrent.

налад/ить *v.* align; adjust; repair; **—ка** *f.* alignment; adjustment; repairing.

налаж/енный *a.* repaired; adjusted, set; aligned; **—ивание** *see* **наладка**; **—ивать** *see* **наладить.**

налево *adv.* to the left, on the left.

налега/ние *n.* superposition; congruence, coincidence; **—ть** *v.* rest on, overlie; overlap; make an effort.

наледен/елый *a.* iced; **—еть** *v.* freeze over.

налеп/ить, —лять *v.* glue on.

налет *m.* deposit, thin coating, film; **—ать** *v.* fly; fly upon; **—ающая частица** incoming (incident, impinging) particle.

налету *adv.* in flight.

налив *m.*, **—ка** *f.* pouring in, infusion; **—ание** *n.* pouring in, filling; **—ать**

v. pour in, fill; **—ной** *a.* pouring, filling.

налип/ать, —нуть *v.* stick, adhere.

налит/ый *a.* poured-in, filled; **—ь** *see* **наливать.**

налицо *adv.* present, available.

наличие *n.* presence, availability, existence.

наличн/ость *f.* presence, availability; **—ый** *a.* available, present, on hand; **—ый состав** personnel staff; **—ая мощность** available capacity.

налог *m.*, **—овый** *a.* tax.

наложен/ие *n.* application, superposition, overlapping; coincidence; covering; **н. импульсов** pulse pile-up; **н. резонансов** resonance overlap; **—ный** *a.* superposed, superimposed; covered.

наложить *see* **налагать, накладывать.**

нам *dat. of* **мы,** us, to us, for us.

намагни/тить *see* **намагничивать; —чение** *see* **намагничивание.**

намагниченн/ость *f.* (intensity of) magnetization; **н. насыщения** saturation magnetization (or induction); **—ый** *a.* magnetized.

намагничив/аемость *f.* magnetizability; **—аемый** *a.* magnetizable; **—ание** *n.* magnetization, magnetizing; **—ать** *v.* magnetize.

намагничивающ/ий *a.* magnetizing, magnetization; **—ая сила** magnetizing force; **—ее поле** magnetizing field; **—ийся** *a.* magnetizable.

намаз/анный *a.* smeared, coated; **—ать, —ывать** *v.* smear, coat.

намасл/енный *a.* greased, oiled; **—ивание** *n.* greasing, oiling, lubrication; **—ивать, —ить** *v.* grease, oil, lubricate.

наматыв/ание *n.* winding, reeling; **—ать** *v.* wind, reel, coil; **—ающий** *a.* coiling, reeling, winding.

намачив/ание *n.* wetting, moistening; soaking; **—ать** *v.* wet, moisten; soak.

намек *m.*, **—ать, —нуть** *v.* hint.

намер/еваться *v.* intend, propose; **—ение** *n.* intention, purpose; **—енный** *a.* intentional, deliberate.

наметать *v.* drift; sweep together.

наме/тить, —чать *v.* mark; contemplate, plan; designate; **—ченный** *a.* marked; planned, projected; designated.

наметка *f.* rough draft, first outline.

нами *instr. of* **мы,** by us, us.

НАМИ *abbr.* **(Государственный союзный ордена Трудового Красного Знамени научно-исследовательский автомобильный и автомоторный институт)** State All-Union "Order of Red Banner of Labor" Automobile and Automobile Engine Scientific Research Institute.

намного *adv.* by far.

намок/ать, —нуть *v.* become wet; **—ший** *a.* wet; soaked.

намот/анный *a.* wound, coiled; **—ать** *see* **наматывать; —ка** *f.* winding, coil; **—очный** *a.* winding.

намоч/енный *a.* wet, wetted; soaked; **—ить** *see* **намачивать.**

намыв *m.* alluvium; **—ание** *n.* alluviation, deposition; **—ной** *a.* alluvial; **—ная земляная плотина** hydraulic-fill dam.

намыл/енный *a.* soaped, lathered; **—ивать, —ить** *v.* soap, lather.

нанес/ение *n.* drawing, plotting; deposition; **—енный** *a.* drawn, plotted, applied; **—ти** *see* **наносить.**

нанизывать *v.* thread, string.

нанимать *v.* hire, employ; rent; **—ся** *v.* apply for work; be hired.

нано— *prefix* nano—, millimicro— (10^{-9}).

наноампер *m.* nanoampere.

нанос *m.* alluvium, deposit; **—ы** *pl* detritus; sediment; **—ить** *v.* bring deposit; apply, coat; plot, draw map; **—ный** *a.* alluvial; superficial.

нанофарада *f.* nanofarad.

наоборот *adv.* contrary, inversely, the wrong way; on the contrary, on the other hand; **и н.** and vice versa.

наоткос *adv.* obliquely.

наощупь *adv.* to the touch.

напад/ать *v.* criticize, attack, assail; **—ение** *n.* attack.

напаивать *v.* solder (on).

напаковка *f.* filling, packing.

напасть *see* **нападать.**

напая/нный *a.* soldered (-on); **—ть** *see* **напаивать.**

наперерез *adv.* across (path).

напереть *see* **напирать.**

наперст/ковая ионизационная камера thimble chamber; **—ок** *m.* thimble.

напечат/анный *a.* printed, published; **—ать** *v.* print, publish.

напил/енный *a.* filed; **—ок, —ьник** *m.* file.

напирать *v.* press, depress.

напис/ание *n.* writing (down); spelling; graphic representation; **—анный** *a.* written; **—ать** *v.* write (down).

напит/анный *a.* impregnated, saturated; **—ать** *see* **напитывать.**

напитыв/ание *n.* saturation, impregnation; **—ать** *v.* saturate, impregnate.

наплав/ить, —ливать, —лять *v.* fuse, melt; **—ленный** *a.* fused-on; **—ленный металл** weld metal.

наплав/ной, —очный *a.* fused; floating; **н. материал** (welding) filler; **н. металл** (welding) filler metal.

напластов/ание *n.* (geo.) stratification, bedding; **—ания** *pl.* strata, rock beds; **—анный** *a.* stratified; **—ывать, —ываться** *v.* stratify.

наплыв *m.* overflow, excess; deposit; influx.

наподобие *prep. gen.* like.

наполнен/ие *n.* filling, loading; impregnation; **—ность** *f.* fullness; **—ный** *a.* filled, loaded.

наполнитель *m.* filler, filling; **—ный** *a.* filling; feeding.

наполн/ить, —ять *v.* fill; impregnate; inflate (with gas); **—яющий** *a.* filling.

наполовину *adv.* half, semi—.

напом/инание *n.* reminding, reminder; **—инать, —нить** *v.* remind, recall, resemble, suggest; **—инающий** *a.* reminding, reminiscent.

напор *m.* pressure, thrust, head, pressure head; **полный н.** total thrust; total head.

напорн/ый *a.* pressure, force; delivery, **н. водяной реактор** pressurized water reactor; **н. корпус** pressurized casing; **н. поток** confined flow; **н. резервуар** pressurized reservoir; **н. трубопровод** closed delivery conduit; **—ая камера** pressure chamber; **—ая плита** flat slab (of buttress dam); **—ая труба** delivery pipe; **—ое давление** total head.

напр. *abbr.* (**например**) for instance, e.g., for example.

направ/ить *see* **направлять**; **—ка** *f.* adjustment, setting.

направлен/ие *n.* direction, sign, sense; trend, tendency; bearing, set; course, route; **н. вектора** sense of a vector; **н. вперед** forward direction; **н. к центру** centering; **н. падения** incident direction; **н. спина** spin alignment, spin orientation; **в —ии на** in the direction of; **в —ии течения** streamwise; **изменение —ия** change of direction, reversal; **по —ию** in the direction of, toward; **—ность** *f.* directivity, directional effect, direction.

направленн/ый *a.* guided, directed, oriented, directional; **н. геттер** directional getter; **н. наружу** outward; **н. под прямым углом** normal; **—ая антенна** directional antenna; **—ая валентность** directed valence; **—ая корреляция** directional correlation; **—ая производная** directional derivative; **—ое движение** ordered motion; **—ое действие** directional effect; **—ое охлаждение** directional cooling; **коэффициент —ого действия** (antenna) directive gain.

направлять *v.* direct, guide, orientate; aim; set, adjust; refer; **—ся** *v.* head (for).

направляющая *f.* guide, track, jig; (math.) directrix.

направляющ/ий *a.* guiding, guide, direction, directing; control, controlling, regulating; leading; pilot; idling; **н. брус** guide bar; **н. конус** director cone; **н. косинус** direction cosine; **н. луч** guide (directing, controlling) beam; **н. паз** track; **н. ролик** guide roller; **н. стержень** guide bar; **н. угол** direction angle; **н. центр** guiding center; **н. шкив** guide, guide pulley, idle pulley, idler; **—ая колодка** guide shoe; **—ая кривая** directrix; **—ая лопасть** guide vane; **—ая ножка** positioning pin; **—ая плита** guide plate; **—ая сила** guiding force; **—ая труба** guide tube; **—ее колесо** guide wheel, idler; **—ее поле** guide field.

направо *adv.* to the right, on the right.

напрасн/о *adv.* in vain, uselessly; **не н.** to some purpose, not in vain; **—ый** *a.* useless, purposeless.

напрашиваться *v.* suggest itself.

например *adv.* for example, e.g., for instance.

напрол/ет, —ом *adv.* through, through and through.

напротив *prep.* opposite, facing; *conj.* on the contrary; conversely.

напрягать *v.* strain; span.

напряжен/ие *n.* tension, strain, traction, stress; effort; (elec.) voltage potential; **н. блокировки** sticking voltage (of luminescent screen); **н. ветра** wind stress; **н. вихревой нити** strength of vortex tube; **н. вихря** vortex strength; **н. зажигания** firing (starting, striking, sparking, breakdown) voltage or potential; **н. искрения** arcing (sparking, spark-over) voltage; **н. накала** filament (or heater) voltage; **н. на поверхности** surface tension; **н. питания** supply voltage; **н. подсветки** intensifier potential; **н. при кручении** torsional stress; **н. при продольном изгибе** buckling stress; **н. при разрыве** breaking stress; **н. при сдвиге, н. сдвига** shear (or shearing) stress; **н. при срезе** shear stress; **н. разрушения** fracture strength; **н. растяжения** tensile stress; **н. сети** line voltage, mains input; **н. сжатия** compressive stress; **сложное н.** complex stress; **н. течения** flow stress; **н. тока** voltage; **высокого —ия** high-voltage.

напряженн/ость *f.* tension; intensity, strength; **н. вихря** vorticity; **н. поля** field intensity (or strength); **—ый** *a.* stressed; tense, strained; intense, strenuous; **—ое состояние** stressed state.

напуск *m.* admission, admitting; lap, lapping, overlapping; **—ать** *v.* admit, fill (with); lap, overlap; **—ной** *a.* admitted; overlapping.

напустить *see* **напускать.**

напущенный *a.* admitted; overlapped.

напыл/ение *n.* deposition, vaporized coating; **—енный** *a.* sprayed, vaporized-on; **—ивать, —ить** *v.* spray, sputter; coat (with dust, particles).

нар. *abbr.* (**народный**) popular, people's, national, public.

наравне *adv.* on a level with, flush with; on a par with, on an equal footing; **идти н. с** keep pace with.

нараст/ание *n.* growth, rise, increase, buildup; accumulation, accretion; **—ать, —и** *v.* intensify, increase, accumulate; **—ающий режим реактора** rise of reactor; **—ить** *see* **наращивать.**

наращ/ение, —ивание *n.* increment accretion, accumulation; building up **—енный** *a.* accumulated; **—ивать** *v* accumulate; build up.

нарегулированный *a.* regulated.

нарез *see* **нарезка; —ание** *n.* cutting **—анный** *a.* cut; threaded; **—ать** *se* **нарезывать.**

нарезк/а *f.* cut; cutting; thread (o screw); rifling; **винт с правой —ой** right-handed screw.

нарез/ной *a.* cut; threaded; rifled **—ывать** *v.* cut; thread (screw); rifle

нарисов/анный *a.* drawn, sketched **—ать, —ывать** *v.* draw, sketch.

нарицательный *a.* nominal.

народ *m.* people, nation.

Народная Республика Албания People' Republic of Albania.

Народная Республика Болгария Peo ple's Republic of Bulgaria.

народ/ный *a.* popular, people's, nationa public; **—ное хозяйство** nationa economy; **—онаселение** *n.* popula tion.

нарост *m.* outgrowth, excrescence; ove growth; nose; **—ить** *see* **наращиват**

нарочно *adv.* purposely, intentionally

наруб/ать, —ить *v.* cut; **—ка** *f.* cu notch.

наружн/о *adv.* externally; apparentl **—ость** *f.* exterior, appearance; **—ы** *a.* external, exterior, periphera outer, outside; surface; extraneou outdoor; **—ая резьба** male (or ou side) thread; **—ые размеры** extern dimensions.

наружу *adv.* outside, outwards.

наруш/ать *v.* break, break down, destroy; violate; disturb, disrupt; impair; disarrange; **не —ая общности** without loss of generality.

нарушен/ие *n.* disturbance; breakdown; impairment; disarrangement; dislocation; deviation; violation; damage; **н. кристалла** crystal imperfection (or defect); **н. непрерывности** discontinuity; **н. общности** loss of generality; **н. правила** breaking (or violation) of a rule; **н. (правильности) решетки** lattice imperfection; **н. структуры** disarrangement of the structure, imperfection, dislocation; **н. укладки** (cryst.) stacking fault; **—ный** *a.* broken, violated; disturbed, disrupted; affected.

арушит/ель *m.* violator; **—ь** *see* **нарушать.**

ар. х-во *abbr.* (**народное хозяйство**) national economy.

аряду *adv.* together with, alongside, side by side, on a level with; besides.

ас *gen., prep., acc. of* **мы,** us.

ас. *abbr.* (**население**) population.

асад/ить *see* **насаждать, насаживать;** **—ка** *f.* adapter, nozzle, cap, head, mouthpiece; fitting on; (chem.) column packing; **—ка полного напора** total-head tube (Pitot tube); **—очная колонка** packed column.

асажд/ать *v.* spread, propagate; cultivate; **—ение** *n.* propagation; **—енный** *a.* cultivated.

асаж/енный *a.* put-on, set; planted; **—ивать** *v.* put on, fit on, mount; pack.

асекаль/ный *a.* cutting, incising; **—щик** *m.* cutter.

асек/ание *n.* notching, slotting; hatching; **—ать** *v.* notch; hatch.

асекомое *n.* insect.

асел/ение *n.* population; **—ить, —ять** *v.* populate; inhabit.

асеч/енный *a.* cut, incised; hatched; **—ка** *f.* incision, notch.

асильно *adv.* by force.

аскак/ать, —ивать *v.* run against, collide with.

асквозь *adv.* through, right through; **проходить н.** penetrate, pierce.

насколько *adv.* how much; as far as; **н. нам известно** as far as we know.

наскоро *adv.* hastily, hurriedly.

наскочить *see* **наскакивать.**

наслаив/ание *n.* stratification; superposition; **—ать** *v.* stratify, laminate; superpose.

наслед/ие *n.* heritage, inheritance; **—овать** *v.* inherit; **—ственный** *a.* hereditary.

наслоен/ие *n.* stratification, lamination; interleaving; (geo.) stratum, layer, bedding; **—ный** *a.* stratified, laminated.

Насос (Воздушный) Antlia (Pneumatica) (Ant) (constellation).

насос *m.*, **—ный** *a.* pump; **н. для откачки газа** off-gas pump; **питательный н., н. подпитки** feed pump; **—ный агрегат** vacuum system; **—ная станция** pumping station.

наспех *adv.* hurriedly.

наст *m.* frozen snow crust.

наст. *abbr.* (**настоящий**) present, current; real.

наставать *v.* begin, start; come.

настав/ить *v.* extend; join; aim; **—ка** *f.* extension.

наставл/ение *n.* directions, instructions; **—ять** *see* **наставить.**

наставн/ой *a.* added; **—ая труба** extension pipe; adapter.

настаив/ание *n.* infusion; persistence; **—ать** *v.* infuse; persist; **—ать на том, что** insist that; **—ающий** *a.* insistent.

настал/енный *a.* steeled, steel-faced; **—ивание** *n.* steeling, steel facing; **—ивать** *v.* steel.

настать *see* **наставать.**

настенный *a.* wall, wall-type.

настиг/ать, —нуть *v.* reach, overtake.

настил *m.* floor, flooring; **—ать** *v.* lay, pave; **—ка** *f.*, **—очный** *a.* laying; flooring.

настильн/ый *a.* grazing; flat; **—ая траектория** flat trajectory.

настичь *see* **настигать.**

настлать *see* **настилать.**

насто/енный *a.* infused; **—й** *m.* infusion.

настойчив/ость *f.* persistence, insistence; urgency; **—ый** *a.* persistent; urgent, pressing.

настолько *adv.* so; so far, so much; **н., насколько** as much as.
настольн/ый *a.* table, desk, bench; **—ая книга** reference book, manual.
настороже *adv.* on the alert, on the look-out.
настоян/ие *n.* insistence; **по его —ию** at his urgent request.
настоятельн/ость *f.* urgency; **—ый** *a.* urgent, pressing, imperative.
настоять *see* **настаивать.**
настоящ/ий *a.* real, actual, genuine, true; present, current; **в —ее время** at present, now.
настраив/аемый *a.* tunable, adjustable; **—ание** *see* **настройка**; **—ать** *v.* adjust, tune; build (on); incite; **—ающий** *a.* adjusting, tuning.
настроенн/ый *a.* adjusted, tuned, resonant; built (-on), added (-on); **н. виток** resonance loop; **—ая антенна** tuned antenna.
настро/ечный *a.* tuning, aligning; **—ить** *see* **настраивать.**
настройка *f.* adjustment, tuning; superstructure; **острая н.** sharp tuning.
наступ/ать, —ить *v.* come, approach, advance; begin; **—ающий** *a.* approaching, advancing; **—ление** *n.* coming, approach, advance, advent, onset.
настуран *m.* uraninite, pitchblende.
настыль *f.* crust, incrustation.
насухо *adv.* dry.
насущный *a.* daily; urgent.
насчет *prep.* of, about, concerning, with regard to.
насчит/ать, —ывать *v.* count, number.
насып/ать *v.* put, fill; **—ка** *f.* filling; **—ной** *a.* filled, poured; bulk; **—ной вес** bulk density; **—ь** *f.* embankment; dam, dike; fill.
насыт/имый *a.* saturable; **—итель** *m.* saturator; **—ить** *see* **насыщать.**
насыщаем/ость *f.* saturability; **—ый** *see* **насытимый.**
насыщать *v.* saturate; **н. тритием** tritiate.
насыщающ/ий *a.* saturating; **—ее средство** saturator; **—ийся** *a.* saturable.
насыщен/ие *n.* saturation, impregnation; **давление —ия** saturation pressure; **предел —ия, точка —ия** saturation point.
насыщенн/ость *f.* saturation; **предел —ости** saturation value; **—ый** *a.* saturated; **—ый раствор** saturated solution; **—ое обратное рассеяние** saturation backscattering.
наталкиваться *v.* encounter.
натапливать *v.* heat intensely; melt.
натачивать *v.* sharpen.
натек *m.* (geo.) sinter, incrustation; **—ание** *n.* inleakage; overflowing **—ать** *v.* flow into, flow over; accumulate; **—ающий** *a.* leaking-in, leaked-in.
натер/еть *see* **натирать**; **—тый** *a* rubbed.
натеч/ка *f.* fine-calibrated orifice; **—ные отложения** (geo.) sinter; **—ь** *see* **натекать.**
натир/ание *n.* rubbing; **—ать** *v.* rub.
натиск *m.* onset; impact; impression.
наткнут/ый *a.* driven-in; **—ь** *see* **натыкать.**
натолкнуться *see* **наталкиваться.**
натопить *see* **натапливать.**
наточить *see* **натачивать.**
натр *m.* soda; **—иево-графитовый реактор** sodium-graphite reactor.
натриев/ый *a.* sodium, soda; **—ая лампа** sodium-vapor lamp; **—ая селитра** Chile saltpeter, sodium nitrate; **—ое растворимое стекло** water glass, sodium silicate.
натрий *m.* sodium (Na).
натро— *prefix* natro—.
натроборокальцит *m.* natroborocalcite
натрово— *prefix* sodium.
натровый *see* **натриевый.**
натронный *a.* sodium, soda.
нату/га *f.* effort, strain; **—женный** *a.* strained; **—живать, —жить** strain; **—живаться, —житься** make an effort, strain.
натура *f.* nature, character.
натуральн/о *adv.* naturally; **—ость** naturalness; **—ый** *a.* natural; **—ый масштаб** full-scale.
натурный *a.* natural.
натыкать *v.* drive in, stick in; **—ся** encounter.
натяг *m.* tightness; interference, obstruction; clearance (of roll).

натягив/ать *v.* stretch, strain, tighten, draw, pull; **—ающий** *a.* tightening, pulling, drawing; **—ающее усилие** tensile stress.
натяжен/ие *n.* pull, tension, strain, tautness; **поверхностное н.** surface tension; **сила —ия** tensile strength.
натяжка *f.* tension.
натяж/ной *a.* tightening; tension; stretching; **н. болт** adjuster bolt; **н. винт** tightening screw; **н. зажим** strain clamp; **н. прибор, —ное приспособление** tightening device; stretcher, stretching device; **н. ролик, н. шкив** tension pulley.
натянут/ость *f.* tension, tenseness; **—ый** *a.* tense, tight, drawn; **—ь** *see* **натягивать.**
наугад *adv.* at random; at a guess, presumably.
науглерож/енный *a.* carbonized; carburized; **—ивание** *n.* carbonization; carburization; **—иватель** *m.* carburizer; (met.) cement; **—ивать** *v.* carbonize; carburize; **—ивающий** *a.* carbonizing; carburizing.
наугольник Norma (Nor) (constellation).
наугольн/ик *m.* angle rule, square; level; **—ый** *a.* angular; corner.
наудачу *adv.* haphazardly, at random.
наука *f.* science; knowledge; **прикладная н.** applied science; **точная н.** exact science; **академия наук** Academy of Sciences.
науч. *abbr. see* **научный.**
науч/ать, —ить *v.* teach, instruct; **—аться, —иться** *v.* learn.
научно *adv.* scientifically; **н.-популярная литература** popular science literature; **н.-фантастическая литература** science fiction.
научно-исследовательск/ий институт research institute; **—ая работа** scientific research work, research.
научный *a.* scientific; **н. работник, н. сотрудник** scientific worker (or collaborator); **старший н. сотрудник** senior scientist.
науч. сотр. *abbr.* (**научный сотрудник**) scientific worker (or collaborator).
наушник *m.* earphone, headphone.
нафт— *prefix* naphth—, naphtho—.
нафталин *m.* naphthalene.
нафтоиды *pl.* naphthenes.
Нахичеванская АССР, Нах АССР Nakhichevan ASSR.
нахколит *m.* nahcolite.
нахлестк/а *f.* lap, overlap; **в —у** *adv.* overlapping.
нахлестыв/ание *n.* lapping, overlapping; **—ать** *v.* lap, overlap.
находить *v.* find, locate, discover; determine; **—ся** *v.* be, exist, occur; be found; **—ся в согласии** agree.
находка *f.* find, finding.
находчив/ость *f.* resourcefulness, presence of mind, readiness; **—ый** *a.* resourceful.
находящий *a.* finding; **—ся** *a.* being, occurring.
нахождение *n.* finding, locating, detecting; being, occurrence; calculation, deriving; **н. повреждений** troubleshooting.
нац. *abbr.* (**национальный**) national.
наце/дить, —живать *v.* decant.
нацел/ивание *n.* aiming, pointing; **—ивать, —ить** *v.* aim, point; align.
нацело *adv.* entirely; evenly; totally.
национал/изация *f.* nationalization; **—изировать** *v.* nationalize; **—ьность** *f.* nationality; **—ьный** *a.* national.
нация *f.* nation, people.
нач. *abbr.* (**начало**) beginning, origin; (**начальник**) head, chief, superior; (**начальный**) initial, first.
начал/о *n.* beginning, commencement, start, outset, onset, origin, inception; principle, law; **брать н.** rise from, originate; **вести н., давать н.** originate; **н. координат** (math.) origin; **н. отсчета** reference point; (math.) origin; **положить н.** initiate; **н. термодинамики** law of thermodynamics; **в —е** in the beginning; early in; **с самого —а** from the start; **—а** *pl.* principles, elements, fundamentals.
начальник *m.* head, chief, superior.
начальн/ый *a.* initial, inceptive, opening, first; reference; initiating; elementary; **н. вихрь** starting vortex; **н. меридиан** prime (or first) meridian; **н. момент** (stat.) moment (about the origin); **н. момент времени** zero

time; **—ая ось** initial axis, reference axis; **—ая точка** origin, source; starting point; **—ое пластическое течение** incipient (or impending) plastic flow; **—ое условие** initial condition.

начальство *n.* authorities, superiors; command; **—вать** *v.* command.

начат/ой, —ый *a.* started; **—ь** *see* **начинать.**

начерно *adv.* rough, roughly, coarse, coarsely; in draft form.

начертание *n.* sketch, outline; tracing.

начертательн/ый *a.* graphic; **—ая геометрия** descriptive geometry.

начер/тить, —чивать *v.* draw, trace, outline; draft; **—ченный** *a.* traced, outlined.

начин/ание *n.* beginning; undertaking; **—атель** *m.* originator, initiator; **—ать** *v.* begin, start, initiate; undertake; **—ать действия** start operations; **успешно —ать** make a good start; **—ающий** *m.* beginner; *a.* beginning, initiating; **—ающийся** *a.* incipient.

начист/ить *see* **начищать; —о** *adv.* cleanly; thoroughly.

начищать *v.* clean; polish.

нач. ск. *abbr.* (**начальная скорость**) initial velocity, starting speed.

наш *pron.* our, ours; **по —ему мнению** in our opinion.

нашатырь *m.* sal ammoniac, ammonium chloride.

нашел *past of* **найти.**

нашествие *n.* invasion, inroad.

наэгит *m.* naëgite.

наэлектризов/ание *n.*, **—анность** *f.* electrification; **—анный** *a.* electrified; **—ать, —ывать** *v.* electrify.

н.в.э. *abbr.* (**нормальный водородный эквивалент**) normal hydrogen equivalent.

НГК *abbr.* (**нейтронный гамма-каротаж**) neutron gamma-ray logging.

не *adv.* no, not, none.

не— *prefix* un—, in—, non—, ir—, mis—, dis—, a—.

неавтоматический *a.* nonautomatic, manual.

неаддитивн/ость *f.* nonadditivity; **—ый** *a.* nonadditive.

неадекватный *a.* inadequate.

неадиабатич/еский *a.* nonadiabatic **—ность** *f.* nonadiabaticity.

неактивированный *a.* nonactivated.

неактивн/ость *f.* inactivity, passivity **—ый** *a.* inactive, passive, inert; idle **—ое тело** inactive substance (o body).

неактиничный свет nonactinic light.

неаналитический *a.* not analytic, non analytic.

Неандр Neander (lunar crater).

Неарх Nearchus (lunar crater).

неассоциированная жидкость unasso ciated (or nonassociated) liquid.

небезынтересный *a.* not without in terest.

небеса *pl.* sky.

небесн/ый *a.* celestial, sky; **н. компа** astrocompass; **н. меридиан** celestia meridian; **н. объект** celestial (o astronomical) object; **н. полюс** celes tial pole; **н. свод** sky, firmament; **н экватор** celestial equator; **—ая меха ника** celestial mechanics; **—ая нави гация** celestial (or astronomical navigation; **—ая сфера** celestia sphere; **—ое светило** heavenly body

небесполезный *a.* of some use.

неблагоприятный *a.* adverse, unfavo able, disadvantageous.

неблагородный *a.* ignoble, base; **н металл** base metal.

неблендированный *a.* unblended.

небо *n.* sky, heaven; crown (of furnace

небольш/ой *a.* small, meager; low; **сто —им** one-hundred-odd.

небосвод *see* **небесный свод; кривизн —а** sky profile curvature.

небосклон *m.* horizon.

небрежн/ость *f.* carelessness, negligenc **—ый** *a.* careless, negligent, slipsho

небулий *m.* nebulium.

небулярн/ый *a.* nebular; **—ая гипоте** nebular hypothesis.

небывалый *a.* unprecedented.

небытие *n.* nonexistence.

небьющийся *a.* shatterproof.

неважн/о *adv.* insignificantly; poor indifferently; it is not importar **это н.** it does not matter; **—ый** unimportant, insignificant; poor; i different.

невед/ение *n.* ignorance; **—омый** *a.* unknown, unfamiliar.

невеликий *a.* small, meager.

неверн/о *adv.* incorrectly; **—ость** *f.* inaccuracy; **—ый** *a.* inaccurate, incorrect, invalid, wrong; untrue, false.

невероятн/о *adv.* incredibly; it is improbable; **—ость** *f.* incredibility; improbability; **—ый** *a.* incredible, inconceivable; improbable, unlikely.

невесом/ость *f.* weightlessness, zero gravity; imponderability; **—ый** *a.* imponderable; weightless.

невещественный *a.* nonreal, complex.

невзаимо/действующий *a.* noninteracting; **—заместимость** *f.* noninterchangeability.

невзирая *see* **несмотря.**

невзрыв/аемый, —чатый *a.* nonexplosive.

невидимый *a.* invisible, unseen, unobservable.

невихревой *a.* irrotational.

невнимательный *a.* careless, inattentive.

невнятн/ость *f.* inaudibility, indistinctness; **—ый** *a.* inaudible, indistinct.

невод/ный *a.* nonaqueous; **—остойкий** *a.* hydrolabile.

невозбужденный *a.* unexcited.

невозделанный *a.* raw, crude, untreated.

невозможн/о *adv.* impossibly; it is impossible; **—ость** *f.* impossibility; **—ый** *a.* impossible.

невозмущенный *a.* unperturbed, undisturbed; nonturbulent.

невольно *adv.* involuntarily; automatically; unintentionally.

невоспламеняющийся *a.* incombustible, nonflammable, flameproof, nonignitable.

невоспри/имчивость *f.* nonsusceptibility; **—имчивый, —нимающий** *a.* unsusceptible, nonsusceptible.

невосстан/авливающийся, —овимый *a.* unreducible; **—овленный** *a.* unreduced.

невсецелый *a.* incomplete.

невставленный *a.* unmounted, loose.

невыгод/а *f.* disadvantage; **коэффициент —ы** disadvantage factor; **—но** *adv.* disadvantageously, unprofitably; it is unprofitable; **—ный** *a.* disadvantageous, unprofitable, uneconomical; **ставить в —ное положение** place at a disadvantage.

невыделанный *a.* raw, crude, unfinished.

невыдыхающийся *a.* nonvolatile.

невыполн/ение *n.* failure, nonperformance, nonfulfillment; **—имость** *f.* impracticability; **—имый** *a.* impracticable.

невырожденный *a.* nondegenerate, undegenerate, nonsingular.

невысокий *a.* low.

невычет *m.* (math.) nonresidue.

невыясненный *a.* unexplained, obscure.

невьянскит *m.* nevyanskite.

невязк/а *f.* discrepancy; **—ий** *a.* nonviscous, inviscid.

негасимый *a.* unquenchable.

негатив *m.* negative; **—ность** *f.* negativeness; **—ный** *a.* negative; **—ное изображение** negative image.

негатрон *m.* negatron.

негде *adv.* there is no place.

негеострофический *a.* ageostrophic.

негерметический *a.* nonhermetic, unsealed.

негибк/ий *a.* inflexible, stiff, rigid; **—ость** *f.* inflexibility, stiffness, rigidity.

негигиенический *a.* unsanitary.

негигроскопичный *a.* nonhygroscopic.

негидростатический *a.* nonhydrostatic.

негладкий *a.* uneven, rough.

неглубок/ий *a.* shallow, superficial; **—ая ловушка** shallow trap; **—ое выгорание** low burnup; **—ое землетрясение** shallow earthquake.

негнущийся *a.* unbending, inflexible, rigid.

негодн/ость *f.* unfitness, unsuitability; worthlessness; **—ый** *a.* unsuitable, improper; invalid; useless, worthless; refuse, waste.

неголономн/ость *f.* nonholonomic state; **—ый** *a.* nonholonomic.

негомогенный *a.* inhomogeneous.

негорюч/есть *f.* incombustibility; **—ий** *a.* noncombustible.

неготовый *a.* unprepared.

неградиентная связь direct (or nonderivative) coupling.

негэнтропия *f.* negentropy.

недавн/ий *a.* recent, late, new; **—о** *adv.*

recently, lately; **—ость** *f.* newness, recentness.

недалек/ий *a.* near; **—о** *adv.* near, near at hand.

недаром *adv.* not in vain, not without reason.

недвижим/ость *f.* immobility; **—ый** *a.* immobile, motionless.

недвусмысленный *a.* unambiguous.

недействительн/ость *f.* ineffectiveness, inefficiency; invalidity; **—ый** *a.* ineffective, inefficient, inoperative; invalid; **делать —ым** invalidate, nullify; cancel; neutralize.

недействующий *a.* inactive, passive, inert; idle, inoperative.

неделим/ость *f.* indivisibility; **—ый** *a.* indivisible.

неделовой *a.* unbusinesslike.

недел/ьный *a.* week, weekly; **—я** *f.* week.

неделящийся *a.* nonfissionable.

недетонирующий *a.* antiknock (gasoline).

недеформированный *a.* unstrained, undeformed.

недеятельный *a.* inactive, passive; inoperative, idle; unreactive.

недиагональный матричный элемент off-diagonal matrix element.

недиаграммная линия nondiagram line (x-rays).

недиссипативный *a.* nondissipative.

недо— *prefix* under—, incompletely.

недоволь/ный *a.* dissatisfied; **—ство** *n.* dissatisfaction.

недовыполнение *n.* underfulfillment.

недовыработка *f.* underproduction.

недоглядеть *v.* overlook, neglect.

недогр/ев *m.* underheating; **—етый** *a.* underheated.

недогру/женный *a.* underloaded; **—зка** *f.* underloading.

недодача *f.* deficiency in delivery.

недоделанный *a.* unfinished, incomplete.

недодержка *f.* (phot.) underexposure.

недожженный *a.* underfired.

недоказанный *a.* unproved, undemonstrated.

недокал *m.* underheating.

недокись *f.* suboxide.

недокомпенсация *f.* undercompensation.

недоконченный *a.* unfinished, incomplete.

недолго *adv.* for a short period, briefly; **—вечный** *a.* short-lived, transient, ephemeral.

недолет *m.* undershot.

недонапряжение *n.* undervoltage.

недоокисленный *a.* incompletely oxidized.

недоопределенный *a.* subdefinite.

недоохлаждение *n.* underquenching, undercooling.

недооцен/ивать *v.* underestimate, underrate, undervalue; **—ка** *f.* underestimation.

недопроизводство *n.* underproduction.

недопроявление *n.* (phot.) underdevelopment.

недопустим/ость *f.* inadmissibility; **—ый** *a.* inadmissible, intolerable, objectionable.

недопущение *n.* prohibition; nonadmission.

недоразви/вшийся *a.* immature; underdeveloped; **—тый** *a.* underdeveloped, rudimentary.

недоразумение *n.* misunderstanding, confusion; ambiguity.

недосмотр *m.* oversight; **—еть** *see* **недоглядеть.**

недоставать *v.* lack, miss.

недостат/ок *m.* deficiency, shortage, lack; defect, fault; disadvantage, shortcoming; **иметь н.** be faulty, have a defect; lack, need; **н. нейтронов** neutron deficiency; **из-за —ка** for lack of, for want of.

недостаточн/о *adv.* insufficiently; under—; it is insufficient; **н. замедленный** undermoderated; **н.-нейтронный** neutron-deficient; **н. устойчивый** understable; **—ость** *f.* insufficiency; inadequacy; defectiveness; imperfection; **—ый** *a.* insufficient, inadequate, deficient; defective, imperfect; inefficient.

недост/ать *see* **недоставать**; **—ающий** *a.* deficient, lacking.

недостижим/ость *f.* inaccessibility; **—ый** *a.* inaccessible, unattainable.

недостоверный *a.* doubtful, uncertain; unreliable, unauthentic.

недостроенн/ость *f.* incompleteness; **—ый уровень** incomplete level.

недоступн/ость *f.* inaccessibility; **—ый** *a.* inaccessible, impervious; unavailable; prohibitive (cost); unattainable; difficult.

недосыщенный *a.* undersaturated.

недосягаем/ость *f.* unattainability; **—ый** *a.* unattainable; unrivaled, unequaled.

недоум/евать *v.* be perplexed; **—ение** *n.* perplexity, quandary.

недоучет *m.* shortage.

недофокусировка *f.* underfocusing.

недохват *m.*, **—ка** *f.* shortage, deficiency.

недочет *m.* shortage, deficit; shortcoming, defect.

недра *pl.* interior, depths; mineral resources.

недюжинный *a.* remarkable, unusual, extraordinary.

Неера-Харпера схема гашения Neher-Harper quenching circuit.

неестественный *a.* unnatural, abnormal.

нежелательн/ость *f.* undesirability; **—ый** *a.* undesirable, objectionable.

нежелезный *a.* nonferrous.

нежестк/ий *a.* flexible, nonrigid; soft (water); **—о соединенный** loosely connected.

незавершенный *a.* incomplete.

независим/о *adv.* independently; **н. от** irrespective of; **—ость** *f.* independence; **—ый** *a.* independent, individual, separate; **—ая переменная** independent variable; **—ая частица** independent particle.

независящий от спина spin-independent.

незавихренное движение irrotational motion.

незагруженный *a.* unloaded, uncharged; idle (machine).

незагрязненн/ость *f.* noncontamination, purity; **—ый** *a.* uncontaminated, pure.

незадолго *adv.* **н. до** shortly before.

незаземленный *a.* ungrounded.

незакаленный *a.* (met.) untempered, soft.

незаконн/ость *f.* illegality; **—ый** *a.* illegal, illegitimate.

незакономерн/ость *f.* irregularity; **—ый** *a.* irregular.

незаконченный *a.* unfinished, incomplete.

незакрепленный *a.* loose, unfastened, unrestrained.

незамедл/енный *a.* unretarded, undelayed; (nucl.) unmoderated; **н. переход** unhindered transition; **—яющее вещество** nonmoderator.

незамерзающий *a.* nonfreezing, frostproof.

незаметн/о *adv.* unnoticeably, imperceptibly; it is not noticeable; **—ый** *a.* imperceptible; insignificant.

незамкнут/ость *f.* openness, open-circuit state; **—ый** *a.* open, open-circuited; **—ый цикл** open cycle; **—ая цепь** open circuit.

незанят/ый *a.* unoccupied, empty, vacant; idle; **—ое состояние** empty state.

незапаздывающий нейтрон prompt neutron.

незаполненн/ый *a.* unfilled, vacant, blank; **н. уровень** vacant level; **—ая оболочка** unfilled shell.

незаряженный *a.* uncharged.

незасекреченный *a.* nonsecret, unclassified.

незатвердевший *a.* unconsolidated.

незатухающ/ий *a.* continuous, sustained, undamped; **—ая реакция** sustained reaction; **—ие волны** continuous (or undamped) waves; **—ие колебания** continuous (or sustained) oscillations.

незаурядный *a.* superior, outstanding.

незахватывающее столкновение noncapture collision.

незачем *adv.* unnecessarily; there is no need.

неза́щищенный *a.* unprotected, unshielded, unguarded.

незеркальное отражение nonspecular reflection.

незнакомый *a.* unknown, unfamiliar.

незнание *n.* ignorance.

незначимость *f.* insignificance.

незначительн/ость *f.* insignificance; **—ый** *a.* insignificant, negligible, small, slight, minor.

незрелость *f.* immaturity.

незыблемый *a.* fixed, firm, stable, immovable, unshakable.
неидеальный *a.* nonideal, imperfect; **н. сверхпроводник** nonideal (or hard) superconductor.
неидорфит *m.* neudorfite.
неизбежн/о *adv.* inevitably; **—ость** *f.* inevitability, imminence; **—ый** *a.* inevitable, imminent, unavoidable.
неизв. *abbr.* (**неизвестный**) unknown.
неизведанный *a.* unknown; unexplored.
неизвестн/о *adv.* it is unknown; **—ое** *n.* the unknown; **—ость** *f.* uncertainty; ignorance; obscurity; **—ый** *a.* unknown, uncertain, indeterminate, obscure.
неизгибаемый *a.* inflexible, rigid.
неизгладим/ость *f.* indelibility; **—ый** *a.* indelible, ineffaceable.
неизданный *a.* unpublished.
неизлечимый *a.* incurable.
неизменн/ость *f.* invariability; continuity; **—ый** *a.* invariable, invariant, unalterable, immutable; constant, permanent, stable, fixed. **—ое напряжение** constant voltage.
неизменяем/ость *f.* inalterability; permanency; **—ый** *a.* unalterable, immutable; permanent, constant.
неизмерим/ость *f.* immeasurability; immensity, vastness; **—ый** *a.* immeasurable, vast.
неизолированный *a.* uninsulated.
неизомерный *a.* nonisometric.
неизотермичность *f.* nonisothermicity.
неизотопный *a.* nonisotopic.
неизотропн/ость *f.* anisotropy; **—ый** *a.* anisotropic.
неимение *n.* lack, want.
неименованный *a.* unnamed; (math.) abstract.
неинвариантность *f.* noninvariance.
неиндуктивный *a.* noninductive.
неион/изующий *a.* nonionizing; **—ный, —огенный** *a.* nonionic.
неискаженный *a.* undistorted; unbiased.
неискрящий *a.* nonarcing, nonsparking.
неисполн/ение *n.* nonperformance, nonfulfillment; fault; violation; **—енный** *a.* unfulfilled, unrealized, unsatisfied; **—имость** *f.* impracticability; **—имый** *a.* impracticable.
неисправимый *a.* irreparable, irremediable; incorrigible.
неисправн/ость *f.* inaccuracy; disrepair, inoperable condition; faultiness, failure; **—ый** *a.* inaccurate, improper, unsatisfactory; unrepaired, out of order, defective; **—ое действие** malfunction, maloperation.
неиспытанный *a.* untested, untried.
неисследованный *a.* uninvestigated, unexplored.
неиссякаемый *a.* inexhaustible.
неистощим/ость *f.* inexhaustibility; **—ый** *a.* inexhaustible.
неисчезающий *a.* nonvanishing, nonzero.
неисчерпаем/ость *f.* inexhaustibility; **—ый** *a.* inexhaustible.
неисчислимый *a.* innumerable, incalculable.
нейзильбер *m.*, **—овый** *a.* German silver.
нейлон, —овый *see* **найлон, найлоновый.**
Неймана граничные условия Neumann boundary conditions; **Н. закон** N. law; **Н. формула** N. formula; **Н. функция** N. function.
нейтрализ/ация *f.* neutralization; **—ованный** *a.* neutralized; **—овать** *v.* neutralize; counteract; **—ующий** *a.* neutralizing; **—ующее средство** neutralizing agent, neutralizer.
нейтралитет *m.* neutrality.
нейтраль *f.* (elec.) neutral (wire, point, plane).
нейтральн/о *adv.* neutrally; **—ость** *f.* neutrality; **—ый** *a.* neutral, nonselective; indifferent, inert.
нейтрин/ный *a.*, **—о** *n.* neutrino.
нейтродин *m.*, **—ный, —овый** *a.* neutrodyne.
нейтрон *m.* neutron; **н. деления** fission neutron; **н. не испытавший столкновения** virgin neutron; **н.-протонное взаимодействие** neutron-proton interaction; **—ика** *f.* neutronics.
нейтронн/ый *a.* neutron, neutronic; **н. каротаж** neutron logging; **н. селектор** neutron-velocity selector; **—ая оптика** neutron optics; **—ая экономия** neutron economy.

ейтронограмма *f.* neutron-diffraction pattern.

ейтронограф *m.* neutron-diffraction camera (apparatus); **—ический** *a.* neutron-diffraction; **—ия** *f.* neutron-diffraction study.

ейтроно-дефицитный *a.* neutron-deficient; **н.-избыточный** *a.* neutron-rich; **н.-непроницаемый** *a.* neutron-tight.

ейтро/пауза *f.* neutropause; **—сфера** *f.* neutrosphere.

екаль *m.* Nekal (detergent).

екасательный *a.* nontangential.

еквалифицированный *a.* unqualified; unskilled.

еквантов/анный, —ый *a.* unquantized.

екий *a.* some, a certain.

екогда *adv.* formerly; there is no time.

екогерентн/ость *f.* incoherence; **—ый** *a.* incoherent, noncoherent; **—ое рассеяние** incoherent scattering.

еколебание *n.* nonoscillation, stability.

еколебательный *a.* nonoscillatory.

еколлимированный *a.* uncollimated.

екоммутирующий (между собой) non-commuting.

екомпенсированный *a.* uncompensated.

екомпетентн/ость *f.* incompetence; **—ый** *a.* incompetent.

екомпланарн/ость *f.* noncoplanarity; **—ый** *a.* noncoplanar.

екомплексные ионы unclustered ions.

екомплект *m.* shortage, deficiency; **—ный** *a.* incomplete; odd, extra.

екондиционный *a.* nonstandard, substandard.

еконтактный взрыватель proximity fuse.

еконтрастное изображение soft image.

еконтролируемый *a.* uncontrolled.

екоптящий *a.* sootless, smokeless.

екоррект/ированный *a.* uncorrected, uncompensated; **—ность** *f.* fallacy, error, incorrectness; tactlessness.

екоррелированный *a.* uncorrelated.

екорродир/уемый, —ующий *a.* noncorrosive.

екотор/ый *a.* some, certain; **—ым образом** to a certain extent; somehow.

екристалли/зованный *a.* uncrystallized; **—зующийся** *a.* noncrystallizable; **—ческий** *a.* noncrystalline, amorphous.

некритич/еский ядерный реактор noncritical reactor; **—ность** *f.* noncriticality.

некролог *m.* obituary.

некруг/лый, —овой *a.* noncircular.

нек-рый *abbr.* **(некоторый)** some, certain.

некстати *adv.* inopportunely; irrelevantly.

некто *pron.* someone.

некуда *adv.* nowhere.

нелегированный *a.* unalloyed.

нелеп/ица, —ость *f.* absurdity; **—ый** *a.* absurd.

нелетучий *a.* nonvolatile.

нелинейн/ость *f.* nonlinearity; **—ый** *a.* nonlinear.

неловкий *a.* awkward.

нелокал/изованный *a.* nonlocalized; **—изуемое поле, —ьное поле** nonlocal field; **—ьная теория поля** nonlocal field theory.

неломкий *a.* (met.) tenacious; tough; unbreakable.

нельзя *adv.* impossible; it is impossible, it is forbidden.

нем. *abbr.* **(немецкий)** German.

немагическое ядро nonmagic nucleus.

немагнитный *a.* nonmagnetic.

немал/о *adv.* much, many; **—оважный** *a.* important; **—ый** *a.* fairly large, sizable.

немафиллит *m.* nemaphyllite.

немедленн/о *adv.* immediately, directly, at once; **—ый** *a.* immediate, instantaneous, prompt, fast.

неметалл *m.* nonmetal; **—ический** *a.* nonmetallic.

немецк/ий *a.* German; **—ое серебро** German silver.

немеченый *a.* unlabeled, untagged.

неминуем/ость *f.* inevitability, unavoidability; **—ый** *a.* inevitable, unavoidable.

немног/ие *pl.* few, not many; **—о** *adv.* little, somewhat; some, few; **—ое** *n.* little.

немногочисленн/ость *f.* fewness, scarcity; **—ый** *a.* few, meager, scanty, scarce.

немодулированный *a.* unmodulated.

нем/ой *a.* silent, dumb; dummy, blank; **н. индекс** dummy index; **—ая карта** outline map; **—ая лампа** dummy tube; **—ая точка** silent point.

немолекулярный *a.* nonmolecular.

немонотонная функция nonmonotonic function.

немонохроматич/еский, —ный *a.* nonmonochromatic; heterogeneous; polychromatic; **—ность** *f.* nonmonochromaticity.

немоноэнергетич/еский *a.* nonmonoenergetic, polyenergetic; **—ность** *f.* energy inhomogeneity.

немонтированный *a.* unmounted; unassembled.

немыслимый *a.* unthinkable, inconceivable, impossible.

ненаблюдаемый *a.* unobservable.

ненагретый *a.* unheated.

ненагруженный *a.* unloaded, idle.

ненадежн/ость *f.* unreliability, insecurity; **—ый** *a.* unreliable, insecure, unsafe.

ненадкевит *m.* nenadkevite.

ненадлежащий *a.* improper.

ненадобн/ость *f.* uselessness; **за —остью** as unnecessary; **—ый** *a.* useless.

ненадолго *adv.* for a short time.

ненамагниченный *a.* unmagnetized.

ненаправленный *a.* nondirectional, undirected.

ненапряженный *a.* unstressed.

ненарушенный *a.* undisturbed, unbroken.

ненастоящий *a.* not genuine, pseudo—, false.

ненастроенный *a.* untuned, unadjusted.

ненастье *n.* bad (inclement, rough) weather.

ненасыщ/ающийся *a.* nonsaturating, unsaturable; **—ение** *n.*, **—енность** *f.* nonsaturation; **—енный** *a.* unsaturated.

ненатянут/ость *f.* looseness, slack; **—ый** *a.* loose, slack.

ненормальн/ость *f.* abnormality, anomaly; **—ый** *a.* abnormal, nonstandard.

ненужно *adv.* unnecessarily, uselessly.

ненулев/ой *a.* nonzero, nontrivial; **—ое решение** nontrivial solution.

неньютоновский *a.* non-Newtonian.

нео— *prefix* neo—.

необделанный *a.* unfinished, rough.

необедненный *a.* undepleted.

необитаемый *a.* uninhabited, vacant; unmanned.

необлученный *a.* nonirradiated, unirradiated, unexposed.

необменный *a.* nonexchange.

необнаруживаемая концентрация undetectably low concentration.

необогащенный уран unenriched uranium.

необожженный *a.* unburnt, unroasted, unbaked.

необозначенный *a.* not indicated.

необоснованн/ость *f.* groundlessness, **—ый** *a.* groundless, baseless, un founded, unjustified.

необработанн/ый *a.* untreated, un refined, unprocessed, crude, un finished, rough; **н. материал** rough stock; raw material; **—ая эмульсия** unprocessed emulsion.

необратим/ость *f.* irreversibility; **—ый** *a.* irreversible.

необученный *a.* untrained.

необходим/о *adv.* necessarily; it is neces sary; one should; **н. и достаточн** necessary and sufficient; **—ость** necessity; **вызвать —ость** necessi tate; **—ый** *a.* necessary, requisite indispensable, essential; **—ое усло вие** necessary condition.

необъясним/о *adv.* unexplicably; it i inexplicable; **—ость** *f.* unexplicabil ty; **—ый** *a.* inexplicable, unaccounta ble.

необыкновенн/о *adv.* unusually; it unusual; **—ость** *f.* unusualnes singularity; **—ый** *a.* unusual, singu lar, uncommon, extraordinary; **—а волна** extraordinary wave; **—а составляющая** extraordinary com ponent.

необыч/айный, —ный *see* **необыкн венный.**

необязательный *a.* not obligatory, o tional.

неоген *m.* Neogen (copper-base alloy).

неограненный *a.* unfaceted.

неограниченн/о *adv.* without restri tion, indefinitely; **н. долго** indefinit ly; **—ый** *a.* unrestricted, indefinit unlimited, unbounded.

неодим *m.* neodymium (Nd).
неодинаковый *a.* unequal, unlike, unidentical, uneven.
неодновременный *a.* nonsimultaneous; noncontemporary.
неоднозначн/о *adv.* nonuniquely, in more than one way; **—ость** *f.* ambiguity, indeterminacy; **—ый** *a.* nonunique, ambiguous.
неодноименный *a.* unlike, opposite, dissimilar.
неоднократн/о *adv.* repeatedly; **—ый** *a.* repeated, reiterated; manifold, multiple.
неоднолистное отображение multivalent mapping.
неоднообразный *a.* irregular.
неоднородн/ость *f.* inhomogeneity, heterogeneity, nonuniformity; discontinuity; **—ый** *a.* heterogeneous, inhomogeneous, nonhomogeneous, nonuniform; **—ая жидкость** inhomogeneous fluid; **—ая смесь** heterogeneous mixture; **—ая среда** heterogeneous medium; **—ое дифференциальное уравнение** nonhomogeneous differential equation; **—ое поле** inhomogeneous (or nonuniform) field.
неодносвязная область multiply connected domain.
неожиданн/о *adv.* unexpectedly, suddenly; **—ость** *f.* suddenness; **—ый** *a.* sudden, unexpected.
неокисл/яемость *f.* nonoxidizability, inoxidizability; **—яемый, —яющийся** *a.* nonoxidizable, inoxidizable; **—яющий** *a.* nonoxidizing.
неоколеманит *m.* neocolemanite.
неоком *m.* Neocomian stage.
неокончательный *a.* inconclusive.
неоконченный *a.* unfinished, incomplete, imperfect.
неокрашенный *a.* colorless; unfinished.
неолит *m.*, **—ический век** Neolithic stage; **—ический** *a.* Neolithic, Stone-Age.
неон *m.* neon (Ne); **—овая лампа** neon lamp.
неопалеозойский *a.* Neopaleozoic.
неопознанный *a.* unidentified.
неоправданный *a.* unjustified; unsound.
неопределенн/о *adv.* indefinitely; it is not definite; **—ость** *f.* indeterminancy, uncertainty, vagueness, indefiniteness; (math.) indeterminate form; **принцип —ости** uncertainty principle; **соотношение —остей** uncertainty relation; **—ый** *a.* indeterminate, indefinite, undefined, vague, undetermined, ambiguous; **—ый (диафантов) анализ** Diophantine analysis; **—ый интеграл** indefinite integral; **—ые коэффициенты** undetermined coefficients; **—ые множители** undetermined multipliers.
неопредел/имый *a.* indeterminate; undefinable; **—яющий** *a.* indeterminate.
неопрен *m.*, **—овый** *a.* neoprene.
неопробованный *a.* untested, untried.
неопровержим/ость *f.* irrefutability; **—ый** *a.* irrefutable, indisputable, incontrovertible.
неоптический *a.* nonoptical; invisible.
неопытн/ость *f.* inexperience; **—ый** *a.* inexperienced.
неорбитальный *a.* nonorbital.
неорганизованн/ость *f.* disorganization; **—ый** *a.* disorganized.
неорганический *a.* inorganic.
неосведомленность *f.* lack of information, scanty information.
неосвещенный *a.* dark; unexplored.
неосевой *a.* nonaxial, off-axis.
неослабный *a.* unremitting.
неосновательн/о *adv.* groundlessly, without foundation; **—ость** *f.* groundlessness; **—ый** *a.* groundless, unfounded; superficial.
неосновной носитель minority carrier; **н. член** nondominant term.
неособенный *a.* nonsingular, ordinary, regular.
неоспоримый *see* **неопровержимый.**
неосторожн/о *adv.* carelessly; **—ость** *f.* carelessness, negligence; **—ый** *a.* careless, negligent.
неосуществим/ость *f.* impracticability; **—ый** *a.* impracticable, unfeasible, unrealizable.
неосязаем/ость *f.* intangibility; **—ый** *a.* intangible, imperceptible, impalpable.
неотвратимый *a.* inevitable.
неотделанный *a.* unfinished, rough.

неотделимый *a.* inseparable.
неотклоненный *a.* undeflected.
неоткуда *adv.* from nowhere.
неотличимый *a.* indistinguishable.
неотложн/ость *f.* urgency; **—ый** *a.* urgent, imperative.
неотлучный *a.* ever-present, continuous.
неотокит *m.* neotocite.
неотпущенный *a.* unannealed, untempered.
неотражающий *a.* nonreflective.
неотразимый *a.* irrefutable.
неотрицательн/ость *f.* nonnegative character; **—ый** *a.* nonnegative, positive.
неотрон *m.* neotron.
неотстоявшийся *a.* turbid.
неотступный *a.* persistent.
неотчетливый *a.* indistinct, vague.
неотъемлем/ый *a.* inalienable, inseparable, inherent, integral; **—ая часть** integral part.
неоцен *m.* Neocene.
неоценимый *a.* inestimable, invaluable.
неочищенный *a.* unpurified, unrefined, crude, raw.
неощутимый *a.* imperceptible.
непараллельность *f.* nonparallelism; misalignment.
непарный *a.* odd, unpaired, unmatched.
непахучий *a.* odorless.
непер *m.* neper.
непереводимый *a.* untranslatable.
неперенормируемый *a.* unrenormalizable.
непереносный *a.* nonportable, stationary.
непересекающий *a.* nonintersecting, nonoverlapping.
неперестановочный *a.* noncommutative.
непериодич/еский, —ный *a.* nonperiodic, aperiodic; **—ность** *f.* aperiodicity.
неперов логарифм Napierian (or natural) logarithm.
неплав/кий, —ящийся *a.* infusible; **—кость** *f.* infusibility.
неплотн/ость *f.* looseness; leakiness; **—ый** *a.* loose, not compact; leaky; unsound; (math.) nondense.
неплохой *a.* fair; quite good.
неповрежденный *a.* unimpaired, intact.
непогло/тительный, —щающий *a.* nonabsorbing, nonabsorptive; **—щающая среда** nonabsorbing medium.
непогода *f.* bad weather.
неподвижн/о *adv.* motionlessly; immovably, securely; **—ость** *f.* immobility; **—ый** *a.* immobile, immovable, stationary, fixed, rigid; motionless, stagnant; static; **—ый ледник** inactive glacier; **—ая мишень** fixed target; **—ая решетка** rigid lattice; **—ая точка** fixed point; **—ое ядро** stationary nucleus.
неподеленные пары unshared pairs.
неподлежащий *a.* not subject to.
неподменим/ость *f.* noninterchangeability; **—ый** *a.* noninterchangeable.
неподоб/ие *n.* dissimilarity, nonsimilarity; **—ный** *a.* unlike, dissimilar.
неподражаемый *a.* inimitable.
неподходящий *a.* inadequate; unsuitable, inappropriate.
непозволительный *a.* improper, inadmissible.
непоколебим/ость *f.* firmness; **—ый** *a.* firm.
непокрытый *a.* uncoated, uncovered.
неполадка *f.* maladjustment, trouble.
неполно *adv.* incompletely; **—мерный** *a.* short, undersized; **—та** *f.* incompleteness, imperfection; **—ценность** *f.* inferiority, unreliability.
неполн/ый *a.* incomplete, partial; short; imperfect, defective; **—ая гамма-функция** incomplete gamma function; **—ая мощность** subpower; **—ая нагрузка** light (or fractional) load; **—ое квадратное уравнение** pure quadratic equation; **—ое частное** partial quotient (or continued fraction).
неполяр/изованный *a.* unpolarized; **—ный** *a.* nonpolar; **—ное соединение** nonpolar compound.
непомерный *a.* exorbitant, excessive.
непомеченный *a.* unmarked.
непонят/но *adv.* incomprehensibly; it is incomprehensible; **—ность** *f.* incomprehensibility; **—ный** *a.* incomprehensible, obscure; **—ый** *a.* misunderstood.
непоправ/имый *a.* irreparable; **—ленный** *a.* uncorrected.

непорядок *m.* disorder.
непоследовательн/о *adv.* inconsistently, not in order; **—ость** *f.* inconsistency; **—ый** *a.* inconsistent; irrelevant; irregular, nonconsecutive.
непосредственн/о *adv.* immediately, directly, just; **н. присоединенный** directly connected; **—ость** *f.* immediateness; **—ый** *a.* immediate, direct; **—ый отсчет** direct reading; **—ый продукт распада** immediate decay product; **—ый эффект** immediate effect; **—ая близость** immediate vicinity, close proximity; **—ая связь** direct coupling.
непостижим/ость *f.* incomprehensibility; **—ый** *a.* incomprehensible.
непостоян/ный *a.* variable, inconstant, nonuniform, unsteady; **н. ветер** variable wind; **—ная скорость** nonuniform velocity; **—ство** *n.* inconstancy; instability, variability, impermanence.
непотопляем/ость *f.* unsinkability; **—ый** *a.* insubmersible.
непохожий *a.* dissimilar.
непоявление *n.* nonappearance.
неправдоподобный *a.* unlikely.
неправильно *adv.* incorrectly; it is incorrect; **—сть** *f.* incorrectness, inaccuracy; irregularity.
неправильн/ый *a.* incorrect, inaccurate, wrong, untrue; irregular, defective; unsound; anomalous, abnormal; mis—; **н. подход** wrong approach; **—ая дробь** improper fraction; **—ая регулировка** maladjustment; **—ая форма** irregular shape; **—ое обращение** mishandling; **—ое применение** misapplication; **—ое употребление** misuse; **—ое употребление термина** misnomer; **—ые величины** erratic values.
неправомерн/ость *f.* illegitimacy, inadmissibility; **—ый** *a.* illegitimate, inadmissible.
неправоспособн/ость *f.* legal incompetence, disability; **—ый** *a.* incompetent, disqualified.
непрактичн/ость *f.* impracticability; **—ый** *a.* impracticable.
непревзойденный *a.* unsurpassed, supreme.
непредвиденный *a.* unforeseen.
непредельный *a.* unlimited, unbounded; (chem.) unsaturated.
непредохраненный *a.* unprotected.
непреклонный *a.* rigid, inflexible.
непреложн/ость *f.* immutability; **—ый** *a.* immutable, unalterable.
непременн/о *adv.* necessarily; certainly; **—ый** *a.* certain; unconditional; necessary.
непреодолимый *a.* insurmountable; irresistible.
непрерывно *adv.* uninterruptedly, continuously; **—сть** *f.* continuity; **уравнение —сти** equation of continuity.
непрерывн/ый *a.* uninterrupted, continuous, unbroken, constant, steady; **н. анализ** continuous analysis; **н. обмен** continuous exchange; **н. пучок** steady beam; **н. спектр** continuous spectrum; **—ая дробь** continued fraction; **—ая пропорция** continued proportion; **—ое множество** continuum; **—ое распределение** continuous distribution; **—ого действия** continuous.
непрестанный *a.* unceasing.
непреходящий *a.* permanent.
неприветлив/ость *f.* unfriendliness; inclemency; **—ый** *a.* unfriendly; inclement.
неприводим/ость *f.* (math.) irreducibility; **—ый** *a.* irreducible.
непривычный *a.* unaccustomed, unusual.
непригодный *a.* unfit, ineffective, unsuitable, useless.
неприемлемый *a.* unacceptable, inadmissible, unsuitable.
неприкрепленный *a.* unattached.
неприкрытый *a.* uncovered, unprotected.
неприменим/ость *f.* inapplicability; irrelevance; **—ый** *a.* inapplicable; impracticable; irrelevant.
непринужденный *a.* unconstrained, free.
непринятие *n.* nonacceptance, rejection.
неприродный *a.* nonnatural.
неприсоединенный *a.* detached.
неприспособляем/ость *f.* inadaptability; inapplicability; impracticability; **—ый** *a.* inadaptable; inapplicable; impracticable.

неприступн/ость *f.* inaccessibility; **—ый** *a.* inaccessible.
неприученный *a.* untrained.
неприятный *a.* unpleasant, troublesome.
непробиваемый *a.* punctureproof.
непробитый искровой промежуток nonarcing gap.
непроверенный *a.* unreliable, unverified, unproved.
непровзаимодействовавший *a.* noninteracted.
непровод/ник *m.* nonconductor, insulator; **—ящий** *a.* nonconducting, nonconductive.
непродолжительн/ый *a.* brief; **в —ом времени** shortly, soon.
непродуктивный *a.* nonproductive.
непрозрачн/ость *f.* opacity; **коэффициент —ости** (coefficient of) opacity; **—ый** *a.* opaque, nontransparent.
непроизводительн/ость *f.* unproductiveness, barrenness; **—ый** *a.* unproductive.
непроизвольн/о *adv.* involuntarily, unintentionally; **—ый** *a.* involuntary, unintentional.
непромокаем/ость *f.* impermeability, imperviousness; **—ый** *a.* impermeable, waterproof.
непромышленный *a.* nonindustrial, noncommercial.
непроникающая частица nonpenetrating particle.
непроницаем/ость *f.* impermeability, impenetrability; **н. для излучения** radiopacity; **—ый** *a.* impervious, impermeable, impenetrable, hard; opaque; **—ый для излучения** radiopaque.
непропаянный сросток solderless joint.
непропитанный *a.* unimpregnated.
непропорциональн/о *adv.* disproportionately; **—ость** *f.* disproportion; **—ый** *a.* disproportionate.
непропуска/емый *a.* untransmitted; **—емая полоса** suppressed band; **—ющий** *a.* nontransmitting; tight; impervious.
непрореагировавший *a.* unreacted.
непросвечивающ/ий *a.* opaque; **—ие (плотные) облака** opacus clouds.
непростительный *a.* unpardonable, unjustifiable.
непросушенный *a.* unseasoned, undried.
непротекающий *a.* vacuumtight, sealed.
непротивление *n.* nonresistance.
непротиворeч/ивость *f.* consistency; **—ивый** *a.* noncontradictory, consistent.
непрофессиональный *a.* nonoccupational, nonprofessional.
непроходим/ость *f.* impassability, impenetrability; **—ый** *a.* impassable, impenetrable, impervious.
непрочный *a.* fragile, unstable; labile; loose, insecure.
непроявление *n.* (phot.) nondevelopment.
непрямой *a.* indirect.
Нептун Neptune.
нептун/иевый *a.* neptunium; **—изм** *m.* neptunism; **—ий** *m.* neptunium (Np).
непуит *m.* nepouite.
неработа/вший реактор clean reactor; **—ющий** *a.* idle, inoperative.
нерабоч/ий *a.* idle, inoperative; **—ее положение** off position.
неравенство *n.* inequality, disparity.
неравнобокий *a.* unequal-sided, scalene; **н. угол** L, L-shape.
неравновес/ие *n.* nonequilibrium, unbalance; **—ный** *a.* unbalanced, nonequilibrium; **—ное состояние** nonequilibrium state.
неравногранн/ик *m.* scalenohedron; **—ый** *a.* scalenohedral.
неравнозернистый *a.* inequigranular.
неравномерн/о *adv.* irregularly, nonuniformly; **—ость** *f.* irregularity, unevenness, nonuniformity, variation inconsistency; jerkiness; inequality **—ый** *a.* nonuniform, inhomogeneous uneven, irregular; unequal; **—ое отражение** irregular reflection.
неравноправность *f.* disparity.
неравносвойственный *a.* anisotropic.
неравносторонний *a.* scalene, inequiangular.
неравный *a.* unequal, uneven, irregular **н. нулю** nonvanishing, nonzero.
нерадиационный переход nonradiativ (or radiationless) transition.
нерадиоактивный *a.* nonradioactive.
неразбавленный *a.* undiluted.

неразборчив/ость *f.* unintelligibility, illegibility; **—ый** *a.* illegible, indecipherable, unintelligible; undiscriminating; **—ый шум** babble.

неразветвленный *a.* nonbranching.

неразви/вшийся, —тый *a.* undeveloped.

нераздел/имый *a.* indivisible, unseparable; **—ьность** *f.* inseparability, indivisibility; **—ьный** *a.* inseparable; unseparated, undivided; **—ьная часть** integral part; **—яющая смесь** inextricable mixture.

неразлагаемый *a.* undecomposable, simple; indivisible.

неразличим/ость *f.* indistinguishability; **—ый** *a.* indiscernible, indistinguishable.

неразлож/енный, —ившийся *a.* undecomposed; **—имый** *see* **неразлагаемый.**

неразрезной *a.* continuous, solid.

неразреш/енный *a.* forbidden; unsolved; **—имый** *a.* insoluble.

неразрушим/ость *f.* indestructibility; **—ый** *a.* indestructible.

неразрывн/ость *f.* continuity; **уравнение —ости** equation of discontinuity; **—ый** *a.* continuous, inseparable.

неразъед/аемый, —ающийся *a.* noncorroding.

неразъемн/ый *a.* nondetachable, one-piece, permanent; **—ое соединение** permanent connection.

нераскисленный *a.* unreduced.

нераспавшийся *a.* undecomposed.

нерасплавленный *a.* unfused, unmelted.

нераспознаваемый *a.* undecipherable, undistinguishable.

нерастворенный *a.* undissolved; **—имость** *f.* insolubility; **—имый** *a.* insoluble; **—яющийся** *a.* indissoluble, insoluble.

нерастяж/имость *f.* inextensibility; **—ной** *a.* nonexpandable.

нерасшифрованный *a.* undeciphered, uninterpreted.

нерасщепляемый *a.* nonsplitting, nonfissile.

нерациональный *a.* irrational, impractical.

нервюра *f.* rib (of airplane).

нереактивный *a.* nonreactive, unreactive.

нереальный *a.* unreal.

нереверс/ивный *a.* nonreversing; **—ируемый** *a.* irreversible.

нерегенеративный *a.* nonregenerative, nonbreeding.

нерегул/ируемый *a.* uncontrolled, unregulated; **—яризируемый** *a.* unregularizable; **—ярность** *f.* irregularity; **—ярный** *a.* irregular, sporadic.

нередко *adv.* often.

нерезкий *a.* poorly defined, blurred, fuzzy.

нерезонансн/ый *a.* nonresonant, nonresonance; **н. процесс** nonresonance process; **—ая теория** continuum theory (of compound nucleus).

нерелятивистский *a.* nonrelativistic.

нерешенный *a.* unsolved, undecided.

нерешительн/ость *f.* indecision, hesitation; **—ый** *a.* undecided, indecisive, hesitating.

нержавеющ/ий *a.* nonrusting, rustproof, rust-resistant, noncorroding; **—ая сталь** stainless steel.

Нернста лампа, Н. штифт Nernst lamp (or glower); **Н. теорема** N. heat theorem; **Н. явление** N. effect; **Н.-Томсона правило** N.-Thompson rule.

неровн/о *adv.* unevenly, roughly, irregularly; **—ость** *f.* unevenness, roughness, irregularity, ruggedness; inequality; **—ый** *a.* uneven, rough irregular, rugged, jagged; unequal; odd (number).

нерудный *a.* nonmetalliferous.

неряшливый *a.* careless, negligent, slovenly.

несамовоспламеняющееся топливо diergolic propellant.

несамо/гасящий *a.* non-self-quenching; **—сопряженный** *a.* non-self-adjoint.

несамостоятельный разряд semi-self-maintained discharge; **н. термический дуговой разряд** externally heated arc.

несбалансированная разница unbalance.

несбыточный *a.* unrealizable, unachievable.

несведущий *a.* inexpert, unskilled, ignorant.
несвежий *a.* not fresh.
несвертыва/емый, —ющийся *a.* incoagulable.
несветящийся *a.* nonluminous.
несвободный *a.* restricted, bound.
несводимый *a.* irreducible.
несвоевременн/ость *f.* inopportuneness; **—ый** *a.* inopportune, untimely; tardy.
несвойственный *a.* uncharacteristic, unnatural, inappropriate, unusual.
несвязанн/ый *a.* free, disconnected, uncombined, unbound; (stat.) uncorrelated; **—ая вода** free water; **—ая частица** unbound particle; **—ое состояние** unbound state.
несвязн/ость *f.* incoherence; **—ый** *a.* incoherent, noncohesive, cohesionless; unconnected, disconnected; **—ое рассеяние** incoherent scattering.
несгибающийся *a.* inflexible.
несгор/аемость *f.* incombustibility; **—аемый** *a.* incombustible, fireproof, refractory; **—ающий** *a.* incombustible; **—евший** *a.* unburned.
несгущаемый *a.* incondensable.
несдавливаемый *see* **несжимаемый.**
несекретный *a.* nonsecret, unclassified.
неселективный *a.* nonselective, unselective.
несение *n.* performance.
несерое вещество nongray material.
несжимаем/ость *f.* incompressibility; **—ый** *a.* incompressible; **—ый поток** incompressible flow.
несильный *a.* moderate.
несимметр/ический, —ичный *a.* unsymmetric, nonsymmetric, asymmetric; **—ичная линия** unbalanced line; **—ичное деление** asymmetric fission; **—ичность** *f.*, **—ия** *f.* asymmetry, dissymmetry.
несинусоидальный *a.* nonsinusoidal.
несинхронный *a.* nonsynchronous, asynchronous.
неск. *abbr.* (**несколько**) somewhat, slightly; some, few, several.
несквегонит *m.* nesquehonite.
несквозн/ой *a.* not through; **—ое отверстие** blind hole.
нескользящий *a.* nongliding; nonskidding, nonslipping.
несколько *adv.* somewhat, slightly; some, few, several; **н. раз** severalfold, by a considerable factor.
нескомпенсированный *a.* uncompensated.
нескончаемый *a.* endless, interminable.
несложн/о *adv.* simply; **—ость** *f.* simplicity; **—ый** *a.* simple.
неслоистый *a.* unstratified.
неслы/ханный *a.* unheard-of, unprecedented; **—шный** *a.* inaudible.
несмачива/емый *a.* nonwettable; **—ющий** *a.* nonwetting.
несменяемый *a.* nonremovable, nondetachable.
несмесимость *see* **несмешиваемость.**
несмеш/анный *a.* unmixed; **—иваемость** *f.* immiscibility; **—иваемый, —ивающийся** *a.* immiscible.
несмещенн/ый *a.* unbiased; **—ая оценка** (stat.) unbiased estimate.
несмонтированный *a.* unmounted.
несмотря на in spite of, notwithstanding, regardless of; **н. на это** in spite of this, nevertheless.
несмываемый *a.* indelible.
несоблюдение *n.* nonobservance, infringement.
несобранный *a.* unassembled, dismantled; uncollected.
несобственный *a.* improper, singular; **н. интеграл** improper integral.
несовершен/ный *a.* imperfect, incomplete; **н. кристалл** imperfect crystal; **—ство** *n.* imperfection.
несовместим/ость *f.* incompatibility, inconsistency; **принцип —ости** exclusion principle; **—ый** *a.* incompatible, mutually exclusive.
несовпадение *n.* noncoincidence, anticoincidence; discrepancy, variance; incongruency; mismatch, misalignment; **н. осей** misalignment of axes.
несоглас/ие *n.* disagreement, variance, discrepancy, nonconformity; **—но** *adv.* at variance, in disagreement with; **—ность** *f.* disagreement; **—ный** *a.* disagreeing, inconsistent; (geo.) unconforming, unconformable.
несоглас/ованность *f.* inconsistency, uncoordination, maladjustment; non-

conformity; mismatching; —**ующийся** *a.* incompatible, mismatched.

есодержащий *a.* free from, not containing.

есоизмеримый *a.* incommensurable.

есокра/тимый, —щаемый *a.* irreducible.

есокрушимый *a.* firm, steady; indestructible.

есомненн/о *adv.* undoubtedly, certainly; —**ый** *a.* doubtless, indubitable; obvious.

есообразн/ость *f.* incompatibility, incongruity, absurdity; —**ый** *a.* incompatible, incongruous with, absurd.

есоосный *a.* off-axial.

есоответств/енный, —ующий *a.* conflicting, incongruous, incongruent; inadequate, inexpedient; undue; —**ие** *n.* noncorrespondence, nonconformity, discrepancy, disparity, incompatibility; inadequacy; incongruity; mismatch.

есопряженн/ый *a.* disconnected; —**ая связь** nonconjugated bond.

есоразмерн/ость *f.* disproportion, inadequacy; —**ый** *a.* disproportionate, inadequate.

есортированный *a.* unsorted.

есостоявшийся *a.* nonoccurring.

есостоятельн/ость *f.* untenability, groundlessness, unsoundness; —**ый** *a.* untenable, groundless, unsound.

есохранение *n.* nonconservation; **н. четности** parity nonconservation; **н. энергии** nonconservation of energy.

еспаренный *a.* unpaired, uncoupled.

еспекающийся *a.* noncaking, nonsintering.

еспециал/ист *m.* layman; —**ьный** *a.* general-purpose, unspecialized, universal.

еспиновый магнитный момент extraspin magnetic moment.

еспокойный *a.* erratic.

еспособн/ость *f.* incapacity, inability, ineptitude, failure; —**ый** *a.* incapable, unable, incompetent, unfit, inadequate.

есправедливый *a.* unfair, unjust.

есраб/атывание *n.* malfunction; —**отавший счетчик** undischarged counter.

несравнимый *a.* incongruent, incomparable.

несродный *a.* heterogeneous.

нестабилизованный *a.* unstabilized.

нестабильн/ость *f.* instability; —**ый** *a.* unstable; —**ая частица** decaying particle.

нестандартный *a.* nonstandard, nontypical, off-gauge.

нестареющий *a.* nonaging.

нестационарный *a.* nonstationary, transient, unsteady; (astr.) variable.

нести *v.* carry, bear; —**сь** *v.* rush (along); drift.

нестираемый *a.* indelible.

нестойк/ий *a.* unstable; —**ость** *f.* instability.

нестробный *a.* (elec.) ungated.

несущественный *a.* unessential, unimportant, immaterial.

несущ/ий *a.* carrying, carrier; bearing, supporting, load-carrying; **н. ток** carrier current; **н. элемент** carrier; —**ая волна** carrier wave; —**ая кривая** (math.) supporting curve; —**ая линия** (aero.) lifting line; —**ая ось** supporting axle; —**ая поверхность** supporting (bearing, lifting) surface; —**ая способность** supporting power; carrying capacity; competence; —**ая (частота)** carrier (frequency); —**ее напряжение** carrier voltage; —**ее соединение** carrier compound.

несферич/еский, —ный *a.* nonspherical, aspherical.

несход/имость *f.* nonconvergence, divergence; —**ный** *a.* dissimilar, unlike, diverse; —**ство** *n.* dissimilarity, difference, discrepancy, disparity; —**ящий** *a.* divergent.

несчаст/ливый, —ный *a.* unlucky, unfortunate; —**ный случай** accident, mishap; —**ье** *n.* misfortune, accident; **к —ью** unfortunately.

несчетн/ый *a.* innumerable; —**ая последовательность** nondenumerable sequence; —**ое множество** nondenumerable set.

несяк *m.* floeberg.

нет no; *adv.* not, no, not any; **вовсе н.**

not at all; **сойти (сводиться) на н.** come to nothing.

нетвердый *a.* unsteady, shaky, insecure, soft.

нетекучий *a.* stagnant.

нетепловой *a.* nonthermal.

Нетер теорема Noether theorem; **нетерово кольцо** (math.) Noetherian ring.

нетерпение *n.* impatience.

нетоксичн/ость *f.* nontoxicity; **—ый** *a.* nontoxic.

неточечн/ость *f.* astigmatism; **—ый источник** extended source.

неточн/о *adv.* inaccurately; **—ость** *f.* inaccuracy, error, discrepancy, uncertainty; **—ый** *a.* inexact, inaccurate.

нетребовательный *a.* nonexacting, tolerant.

нетривиальный *a.* nontrivial.

нетронутый *a.* untouched, intact.

нетрудно *adv.* without difficulty, easily.

нетурбулентный *a.* nonturbulent.

неубедительный *a.* unconvincing, inconclusive.

неубывающий *a.* nondecreasing.

неуверенн/ость *f.* uncertainty; **—ый** *a.* uncertain.

неувязка *f.* maladjustment, noncoordination, disorganization.

неугасимый *a.* inextinguishable, unquenchable.

неудач/а *f.* failure; **—но** *adv.* unsuccessfully; **—ный** *a.* unsuccessful, unfortunate, infelicitous (expression).

неудобн/о *adv.* inconveniently; it is inconvenient; **—ый** *a.* inconvenient, awkward.

неудобо/исполнимый *a.* impracticable; **—понятный** *a.* unintelligible; **—проходимый** *a.* impassable; **—читаемый** *a.* illegible.

неудобство *n.* inconvenience, defect, drawback, difficulty, disadvantage.

неудовлетвор/енность *f.* dissatisfaction; **—енный** *a.* dissatisfied; **—ительность** *f.* inadequacy, insufficiency; **—ительный** *a.* unsatisfactory, imperfect, insufficient, inadequate; **—яющий стандартам** substandard.

неужели *adv.* is it possible?

неузнаваемый *a.* unrecognizable.

неуклонный *a.* steady, undeviating.

неулавливаемый *a.* imperceptible.

неулетучивающийся *a.* nonvolatile.

неуловимый *a.* elusive, imperceptible.

неуме/лый *a.* unskillful; **—ние** *n.* lack of skill.

неумеренн/о *adv.* immoderately, in excess; **—ый** *a.* immoderate, excessive.

неуместный *a.* misplaced, irrelevant, inappropriate.

неумышленный *a.* unintentional, inadvertent.

неуничтожаем/ость *f.* indestructibility; **—ый** *a.* indestructible.

неуплотн/енный *a.* unconsolidated; **—яемость** *f.* incompressibility; **—яемый** *a.* incompressible, uncondensable.

неупорядоченн/ый *a.* disordered; **н. сплав** disordered alloy; **—ая полоса** disordered (spectral) band.

неупотреб/ительный *a.* not in use, unused, unpracticed; unusual; **—ление** *n.* disuse.

неуправляем/ый *a.* unguided, uncontrolled; **н. снаряд, —ая ракета** unguided rocket; **—ое возрастание мощности** (reactor) runaway; **—ое расширение** random expansion (of cloud chamber).

неупруг/ий *a.* inelastic, stiff, rigid; **—ое рассеяние** inelastic scattering; **—ое столкновение** inelastic collision; **—ость** *f.* anelasticity, inelasticity.

неуравновешенн/ый *a.* unbalanced, unstable; **н. мост** unbalanced bridge; **—ое напряжение** unrelieved stress.

неурочный *a.* inopportune.

неусиленный *a.* nonreinforced.

неуспе/х *m.* failure; **—шный** *a.* unsuccessful.

неустанов/ившийся *a.* unsteady, nonsteady, nonstationary; variable, unbalanced, unsettled, irregular; transient, transitional; **н. режим** nonsteady state; **—ившееся движение** unsteady motion; **—ившееся течение** unsteady flow; **—ленный** *a.* unestablished; unmounted.

неустойчив/ость *f.* instability, inbalance, unsteadiness; **—ый** *a.* unstable, labile, unsteady, fluctuating, shifting; **—ая частица** unstabl particle; **—ое колебание** unstable oscillation, flutter; **—ое равновесие** unstable equilibrium.

еустранимый *a.* nonremovable.

еустройство *n.* disorder, disorganization.

еутечка *f.* nonleakage.

еутолимый *a.* unquenchable, insatiable.

еутомляемый *a.* fatigueproof.

еучет *m.* neglect.

еучитываемый *a.* negligible.

ефелин *m.* nepheline.

ефелометр *m.* nephelometer, turbidimeter; **—ический** *a.* nephelometric, turbidimetric.

ефиксированный *a.* unfixed, varying.

ефо/логия *f.* nephology; **—метр** *m.* nephometer; **—скоп** *m.* nephoscope.

ефотоактивный *a.* nonphotostimulated.

ефракционированный *a.* unfractionated.

ефрит *m.* nephrite; **—оид** *m.* nephritoid.

ефт. *abbr.* (**нефтяной**) petroleum, oil.

ефте— *prefix* petroleum, oil.

ефтегазовый *a.* oil and gas.

ефтепер. *abbr.* (**нефтеперегонный**) petroleum refining.

ефтепромысел *m.* oil field.

ефт. хоз. *abbr.* (**Нефтяное хозяйство**) Petroleum Economy (journal).

ефт/ь *f.*, **—яной** *a.* petroleum, oil.

ехарактерный *a.* nonrepresentative.

ехват/ать *see* **недоставать**; **—ка** *f.* shortage, scarcity.

ехороший *a.* bad, poor, low (yield).

ецелесообразный *a.* inexpedient, inadvisable.

ецелый *a.* noninteger, fractional.

ецентральн/ый *a.* noncentral, off-center; **—ая сила** noncentral force.

ецентрированн/ость *f.* eccentricity; **—ый** *a.* eccentric.

ециклический *a.* acyclic.

еч. *abbr.* (**нечетный**) odd (number).

ечаянный *a.* unexpected, unintentional, accidental, inadvertent.

ечего *pron.* nothing; there is no need to; **н. и говорить, что** it goes without saying that; **больше н.** nothing more, no more.

нечерное тело nonblack body.

нечеткий *a.* undecipherable, indistinct; illegible; slipshod.

нечетнократный *a.* odd-multiple.

нечетно/-нечетное ядро odd-odd nucleus; **н.-четное ядро** odd-even nucleus.

нечетн/ый *a.* odd, of odd parity; **—ое состояние** odd parity; **—ое число** odd number; **—ое ядро** odd-mass nucleus.

нечист/ота *f.* impurity; **—ый** *a.* unclean, impure; defective.

нечленораздельный *a.* inarticulate.

нечто *pron.* something, somewhat.

нечувствительн/ость *f.* insensitivity; **зона —ости** (elec.) dead zone; **—ый** *a.* insensitive, insensible.

неэвклидова геометрия non-Euclidean geometry.

неэквидистантный *a.* nonequidistant, unequally spaced.

неэконом/ичный, —ный *a.* uneconomical.

неэкранированный *a.* unshielded.

неэкспоненциальный *a.* nonexponential.

неэластичн/ость *f.* inelasticity; **—ый** *a.* inelastic.

неэлектрический *a.* nonelectric.

неэрмитов/ость *f.* non-Hermiticity; **—ый** *a.* non-Hermitian.

неэффективный *a.* ineffective, inefficient; insensitive; **н. объем** insensitive volume.

неяв/ка *f.* nonappearance, absence; **—ный** *a.* tacit, implicit; unclear; **—ная функция** implicit function.

неядовитый *a.* nontoxic, nonpoisonous.

неясн/о *adv.* vaguely; it is not clear; **н. кристаллический** cryptocrystalline; **—ость** *f.* vagueness, obscurity, confusion; **—ый** *a.* vague, obscure, indistinct, unclear.

ни *conj.* neither, nor; not; **ни . . . ни** neither . . . nor; **ни один** not one, not a single.

н.-и. *abbr.* (**научно-исследовательский**) scientific research.

НИА *abbr.* (**Научно-исследовательская ассоциация**) Scientific Research Association.

НИАИ *abbr.* (**Научно-исследовательский аэро-институт**) Scientific Research Aviation Institute.

НИАМАШ *abbr.* (**Научно-исследовательская ассоциация машиностроения**) Scientific Research Association of Mechanical Engineering.

НИАФИЗ *abbr.* (**Научно-исследовательская физическая ассоциация**) Physical Scientific Research Association.

НИБ *abbr.* (**Научно-исследовательское бюро**) Scientific Research Office.

НИБТН *abbr.* (**Научно-исследовательское бюро технических нормативов**) Scientific Research Office of Technical Standards.

нивелир *m.* level, leveling instrument, gradienter; **—ная рейка** *see* **—овочная рейка**; **—ование** *n.*, **—овка** *f.* leveling, grading; **—овать** *v.* level, grade; **—оваться** *v.* be leveled, be counterbalanced.

нивелировочн/ый *a.* leveling, level; **—ая марка, —ая точка** bench mark; **—ая рейка** leveling rod.

нивелирующий *a.* leveling.

нивенит *m.* nivenite.

нигде *adv.* nowhere.

нидер. *abbr.* (**нидерландский**) Netherland.

Нидерланды the Netherlands.

ниже *comp. of* **низкий, низко** lower; *prep. gen.* below, beneath, under; **—изложенный** *a.* given below; **—лежащий** *a.* underlying; **—лежащий слой** underlayer, sublayer; **—означенный** *see* **нижеупомянутый**; **—подписавшийся** *a.* the undersigned; **—приведенный** *a.* stated below, cited below.

нижеследующ/ий *a.* following, next; **сказал —ее** said as follows.

нижеупомянутый *a.* mentioned below.

нижнепропускающий фильтр low-pass filter.

нижн/ий *a.* lower, bottom, inferior, under; lowest; **н. бьеф** tailwater; **н. значок** subscript; **н. мираж** inferior mirage; **н. слой** substratum, bottom layer; **—яя кромка облаков** cloud base; **—яя ступень ракеты** first-stage rocket; **—яя тяга** downdraft; **—яя часть** bottom (part); **—ие частоты** lower frequencies.

низ *m.* bottom, base.

низать *v.* string, thread.

низведение *n.* bringing down.

низвер/гать, —гнуть *v.* precipitate; **—жение** *n.* precipitation.

низ/вести, —водить *v.* bring down.

низк/ий *a.* low; inferior; deep (sound); **н. вакуум** low (or rough) vacuum; **н. циклон** low-level cyclone; **—ая частота** audio frequency; low frequency; **—ое напряжение** low voltage.

низко *adv.* low; **—вольтный** *a.* low-voltage; **—вязкий** *a.* low-viscosity; **—калорийный** *a.* low-calorie; **—кипящий** *a.* low-boiling; **—легированный** *a.* low-alloy; **—лежащий** *a.* low-lying; **—молекулярный** *a.* low-molecular.

низкоомн/ый *a.* low-resistance, low-impedance; **—ое сопротивление** low ohmic resistance.

низкопробн/ость *f.* inferior quality; **—ый** *a.* poor-quality, base.

низко/проходный фильтр (elec.) low-pass filter; **—процентный** *a.* low-percentage; low-grade; **—радиоактивный** *a.* weakly radioactive; **—сортный** *a.* poor-quality, low-grade; **—температурный** *a.* low-temperature; **—точный** *a.* low-current; **—углеродистый** *a.* low-carbon; **—частотный** *a.* low-frequency; **—широтный** *a.* low-latitude.

низменн/ость *f.* lowness; lowland; **—ый** *a.* low.

низов/ой *a.* downstream; **—ая грань** downstream face (of dam).

низш/ий *comp. of* **низкий** lower, inferior; lowest; low-lying; **н. полимер** low polymer; **—ее состояние** lower state.

НИИ *abbr.* (**Научно-исследовательский институт**) Scientific Research Institute.

НИИВЕСПРОМ *abbr.* (**Научно-исследовательский институт весов и приборов**) Scientific Research Institute of Weights and Instruments.

НИИГ *abbr.* (**Научно-исследовательский институт гидротехники**

Scientific Research Institute of Hydroengineering.

НИИГГР *abbr.* (**Научно-исследовательский институт геофизических и геохимических методов разведки**) Scientific Research Institute of Geophysical and Geochemical Prospecting Methods.

НИИГМП *abbr.* (**Научно-исследовательский институт гидро-метеорологического приборостроения**) Scientific Research Institute of Hydrometeorological Instruments.

НИИГР *abbr.* (**Научно-исследовательский институт геофизических методов разведки**) Scientific Research Institute of Geophysical Prospecting Methods.

НИИЗМ *abbr.* (**Научно-исследовательский институт земного магнетизма**) Scientific Research Institute of Terrestrial Magnetism.

НИИЗМИР *abbr.* (**Научно-исследовательский институт земного магнетизма, ионосферы и распространения радиоволн**) Scientific Research Institute of Terrestrial Magnetism, the Ionosphere and Radio Waves.

НИИИАМ *abbr.* (**Научно-исследовательский испытательный институт авиационной медицины**) Scientific Research Testing Institute of Aviation Medicine.

НИИМ *abbr.* (**Научно-исследовательский институт математики**) Scientific Research Institute of Mathematics.

НИИММ *abbr.* (**Научно-исследовательский институт математики и механики**) Scientific Research Institute of Mathematics and Mechanics.

НИИМРТП *abbr.* (**Научно-исследовательский институт Министерства радиотехнической промышленности**) Scientific Research Institute of the Ministry of the Radio-Engineering Industry.

НИИПГ *abbr.* (**Научно-исследовательский институт прикладной геофизики**) Scientific Research Institute of Applied Geophysics.

НИИПМ *abbr.* (**Научно-исследовательский институт пластических масс**) Scientific Research Institute of Plastics.

НИИПТ *abbr.* (**Научно-исследовательский институт постоянного тока**) Direct Current Scientific Research Institute.

НИИРТ *abbr.* (**Научно-исследовательский институт радиовещания и телевидения**) Scientific Research Institute of Radio and Television.

Ниистройкерамика *abbr.* (**Общесоюзный научно-исследовательский институт строительной керамики**) All-Union Scientific Research Institute of Structural Ceramics.

НИИТ *abbr.* (**Научно-исследовательский институт телемеханики**) Scientific Research Institute of Remote Control.

НИИТН *abbr.* (**Научно-исследовательский институт технического нормирования**) Scientific Research Institute of Technical Standards.

Ниичермет *abbr.* (**Научно-исследовательский институт черной металлургии**) (Scientific Research Institute of Ferrous Metallurgy.

НИИЭЗ *abbr.* (**Научно-исследовательский институт и экспериментальный завод им. Фрунзе**) Frunze Scientific Research Institute and Pilot Plant.

НИИЭЭ *abbr.* (**Научно-исследовательский институт энергетики и электрификации**) Scientific Research Institute of Power Engineering and Electrification.

никак *adv.* by no means, in no way; **—ой** *a.* no, not any, none.

никалой *m.* Nicaloi (iron-nickel alloy).

никелев/ый *a.* nickel; **—ое железо** ferronickel.

никелин *m.*, **—овый** *a.* nickeline (copper-zinc-nickel alloy); (mineral) *see* **никколит.**

никелиров/ание *n.*, **—ка** *f.* nickel plating; **—анный** *a.* nickel-plated; **—ать** *v.* nickel plate.

никелисто— *prefix* nickelo—, nickelous, nickel.

никель *m.* nickel (Ni).

никкел/евый *see* **никелевый**; **—ь** *see* **никель.**

никколит *m.* niccolite.

никогда *adv.* never.

никоим образом *adv.* by no means, in no way; not at all.

николаит *m.* nicolayite.

николь-анализатор *see* **Николя призма.**

Никольсона интеграл Nicholson integral.

Николя призма Nicol prism.

никр/ал *m.* Nicral; **—ом** *m.* Nichrome; **—осилал** *m.* Nicrosilal.

никто *pron.* nobody, no one, none.

никуда *adv.* nowhere.

НИКФИ *abbr.* (**Научно-исследовательский кино-фото институт**) Motion Picture and Photography Scientific Research Institute.

НИЛ *abbr.* (**Государственный научный институт им. П. Ф. Лесгафта**) P. F. Lesgaft State Scientific Institute.

нилас *m.* ice crust (or skin), glass ice.

НИЛФА *abbr.* (**Научно-исследовательская лаборатория фотоэлектронной автоматики для станков**) Scientific Research Laboratory of Photoelectronic Automatic Controls for Machine Tools.

ниль *m.* nil, null, zero.

ниль/потентный *a.* nilpotent; **—степенный** *a.* nilpotent.

нимало *see* **нисколько.**

нимб *m.* nimbus, aureole.

НИМГУ *abbr.* (**Научно-исследовательский институт Московского государственного университета**) Scientific Research Institute of Moscow State University.

НИМС *abbr.* (**Научно-исследовательская мерзлотная станция**) Permafrost Scientific Research Station.

ниобат *m.* niobate, columbate.

ниоб/иевый *a.* niobium; **—ий** *m.* niobium (Nb).

ниоткуда *adv.* from nowhere.

нипермаг *m.* Nipermag (iron-nickel-aluminum-titanium alloy).

Нипкова диск Nipkow disk.

ниппель *m.* nipple, fitting, union.

Нира масс-спектрометр Nier mass spectrometer.

НИРП *abbr.* (**Научно-исследовательский институт резиновой промышленности**) Scientific Research Institute of the Rubber Industry.

НИС *abbr.* (**научно-исследовательская станция**) scientific research station; (**научно-исследовательский сектор**) scientific research department.

нисколько *adv.* not at all, not in the least; **н. не меньше** nonetheless.

ниспадающий *a.* descending, katabatic.

ниспровержение *n.* subversion.

НИСС *abbr.* (**Научно-исследовательский институт судостроения и судовых стандартов**) Scientific Research Institute of Shipbuilding and Ship Specifications.

нисходящий *a.* descending, downward, katabatic; **н. ветер** katabatic (or fall) wind; **н. поток** descending (or downward) current.

нисхождение *n.* descent.

нит *m.* nit (unit of luminance).

НИТГЭО *abbr.* (**Научно-исследовательский институт теплогидроэнергетического оборудования**) Scientific Research Institute for Thermal and Hydro-Power Equipment.

ните/видный, —образный *a.* filamentary, filiform, filament; straight-chain; **н. катод** filamentary cathode; **н. кристалл** filamentary crystal, whisker; **—видные облака** fibratus, filosus (clouds).

НИТИНФ *abbr.* (**научная инженерная техническая информация**) Scientific Engineering and Technical Information.

нитка *f.* thread, fiber, filament.

НИТО *abbr.* (**Научное инженерно-техническое общество**) Scientific Engineering and Technical Society.

нитон *m.* niton (Nt), radon.

нитр— *prefix* nitr—, nitro—.

нитраллой *m.* Nitralloy (chromium aluminum steel).

нитрат *m.* nitrate; **н. уранила** urany nitrate.

нитрато— *prefix* nitrato—.

нитрид *m.* nitride.

нитрил *m.* nitrile; nitryl; **—ьный каучук** nitrile rubber.

нитриров/ание *n.* nitration; (met.) ni

triding; —**анный** *a.* nitrated; nitrided; —**ать** *v.* nitrate; nitride.

нитрит *m.* nitrite.

нитрицировать *v.* nitrify.

нитро— *prefix* nitro—.

нитров/альная смесь nitrating mixture; —**ание** *n.* nitrating; (met.) nitriding; —**анный** *a.* nitrated; nitrided; —**ать** *see* **нитрировать.**

нитроклетчат/ка *f.*, —**очный** *a.* nitrocellulose.

нитро/краски *pl.* nitro dyes; —**пленка** *f.* nitrate film; —**соединение** *n.* nitro compound.

нитроцеллюлоз/а *f.*, —**ный** *a.* nitrocellulose.

нитрующий *a.* nitrating.

НиТУ *abbr.* (**Нормы и технические условия**) Standards and Technical Requirements.

нит/ь *f.*, —**яный** *a.* filament, fiber, thread; **вихревая н.** vortex filament; **н. накала** (elec.) filament; —**яный крест** cross hairs.

нифе (geo.) Ni-Fe (nickel-iron core of earth).

Нифера защита Nipher shield.

НИФИ *abbr.* (**Научно-исследовательский физический институт**) Scientific Research Institute of Physics.

никольсонит *m.* nicholsonite.

нихром *m.* Nichrome (nickel-chromium-iron alloy).

ничего *gen. of* **ничто** nothing; **н. подобного** nothing of the kind.

ничей *a.* nobody's.

ничто *pron.* nothing; **н. иное как** nothing less than, nothing but.

ничтож/ество *n.* nonentity; —**ный** *a.* insignificant, negligible; worthless; —**ная концентрация** trace concentration; —**ное количество** trace amount.

ничья *f.* tie, draw (game).

ниша *f.* niche, recess.

НИЭИРП *abbr.* (**Научно-исследовательский экспериментальный институт радиопромышленности**) Scientific Research Experimental Institute of the Radio Industry.

НК *abbr.* (**Народный комиссариат**) People's Commissariat; (**натуральный каучук**) natural rubber; (**научный комитет**) scientific committee; (**нейтронный каротаж**) neutron logging; (**нуль карты**) datum level.

но *conj.* but.

но. *abbr.* (**номер**) number (in a series).

НО *abbr.* (**норд-ост**) northeast.

НОА *abbr.* (**научно-опытный аэродром**) scientific testing airfield.

Нобелевская премия Nobel prize.

нобелий *m.* nobelium (No).

нов. *abbr.* (**новый**) new.

новасекит *m.* novacekite.

новатор *m.* innovator; —**ство** *n.* innovation.

Новая Зеландия New Zealand.

новейший *a.* newest, modern, most recent, latest, up-to-date.

нов/изна *f.* novelty, newness; —**инка** *f.* novelty; —**ичок** *m.* novice, beginner.

ново— *prefix* new, newly.

нововведение *n.* innovation.

новоизобретенный *a.* newly invented.

новолуние *n.* new moon.

новоподобный *a.* novalike.

новостройка *f.* new (building) project.

новость *f.* news.

нов. ст. *abbr.* (**новый стиль**) new style (Gregorian calendar).

новшество *n.* innovation, novelty.

нов/ый *a.* new, novel, modern, recent; **н. стиль** new style (Gregorian calendar); —**ые достижения** recent advances.

нога *f.* leg; foot.

нож *m.* knife, blade.

ножев/ой *a.* knife; **н. клинок** knife blade; **н. контакт** knife-switch contact; **н. луч** knife-edge beam (of interferometer); (radar) beavertail beam; —**ая опора** knife edge, knife-edge bearing.

ножка *f.* foot; leg; mount; jaw (of measuring instrument); (elec.) pinch.

ножницы *pl.* scissors, shears.

ножной *a.* foot, pedal; **н. привод** foot drive; **н. рычаг** pedal.

ножовка *f.* hack saw; knife file; **машинная н.** jig saw.

ножовый *see* **ножевой.**

ноздреват/ость *f.* porosity, sponginess; —**ый** *a.* porous, spongy.

нозеан *m.* nosean.

нолит *m.* nohlite.

Ноллская атомно-энергетическая лаборатория Knolls Atomic Power Laboratory.
ноль *see* **нуль.**
номенклатур/а *f.* nomenclature; glossary; **—ная стоимость** list price.
номер *m.* number; issue; size, gauge, mesh; item; **—ный** *a.* number, numerical.
номинал *m.* rating; nominal (or face) value.
номинальн/ый *a.* nominal; rated; **—ая долговечность** rated life; **—ая мощность** rated power (or capacity), available power; **—ые параметры** rating.
номо/грамма *f.* nomogram, nomograph, alignment chart; **—графия** *f.* nomography.
нонвариантный *a.* nonvariant, invariant.
нониус *m.* vernier, nonius.
Нониус Nonius (lunar crater).
норв. *abbr.* (**норвежский**) Norwegian.
Норвегия Norway.
норвежский *a.* Norwegian.
норд *m.* north; **н.-вест** northwest; **н.-ост** northeast.
норденшильдит *m.* nordenskiöldine.
нория *f.* bucket conveyor.
норм. *abbr.* (**нормальный**) normal.
норма *f.* norm, standard; rate; quota.
нормали *pl. of* **нормаль.**
нормализ/атор *m.* normalizer; **—ация** *f.* standardization; **—ованный** *a.* normalized, standardized; **—овать** *v.* normalize, standardize.
нормаль *f.* normal; standard; **—но-упорядоченный** (math.) normally (or well) ordered; **—ность** *f.* normalization; normality.
нормальн/ый *a.* normal; standard, regular; rated; **н. вес** standard weight; **н. вид** normal mode, standard form; **н. делитель** normal divisor; **н. закон** normal (distribution) law; **н. порог** normal threshold; **н. раствор** normal solution; **н. термометр** standard thermometer; **н. тон** standard tone; **н. уровень** datum level; **н. элемент** (elec.) standard cell; **—ая величина** rating; **—ая ионизационная камера** free-air ionization chamber; **—ая производная** normal derivative, normal gradient; **—ое атмосферное давление** standard atmospheric pressure; **—ое произведение** normal product; **—ое сечение** (math.) right section; **—ое состояние** ground state; **—ое уравнение** standard equation; **—ые колебания** normal (oscillatory) mode; **—ые условия** standard condition.
норматив *m.*, **—ный** *a.* norm, standard.
норменный *a.* normed.
нормиров/ание *n.*, **—ка** *f.* normalization, standardization; setting up norms (rates); **—анный** *a.* normalized; **—ать** *v.* normalize, standardize; **—очный множитель** normalization factor (or constant); **—очная постоянная** normalization constant.
нормирующий интеграл normalization integral; **н. множитель** normalizing factor.
Нортона теорема Norton theorem.
нортупит *m.* northupite.
нос *m.* nose; point, forepart, tip; (geo.) headland, promontory; lip (for pouring); bow (of boat); **—ик** *m.* spout.
носильный *a.* carrying.
носител/ь *m.* carrier, bearer; **н. тока** current carrier; **н. удерживания** hold-back carrier; **без —я** carrier-free.
нос/ить *v.* carry, bear; **—ка** *f.* carrying, bearing; **н. с собой** imply.
ноский *a.* durable.
носный *suffix* bearing, containing, —iferous.
носов/ой *a.* nose, nasal; bow; forepart, **—ая антенна** forward antenna; **—ая часть** bow.
носок *m.* spout, nozzle; nose; point **сливной н.** pouring lip.
нота *f.* note.
ноцерит *m.* nocerite.
ночн/ой *a.* night, nighttime, nocturnal **—ое излучение** nocturnal radiation
ноч/ь *f.* night; **по —ам, —ью** at night.
ноябрь *m.* November.
НПИ *abbr.* (**Новочеркасский политехнический институт**) Novocherkassk Polytechnical Institute.
нр *abbr.* (**научный работник**) scientifi

worker, collaborator, scientist; **нр. (номер)** number (in a series).

нравиться *v.* please.

НСО *abbr.* (**научное студенческое общество**) student scientific society.

н. сотр. *abbr. see* **науч. сотр.**

н. ст. *abbr. see* **нов. ст.**

нт *abbr.* (**нит**) nit.

НТБ *abbr.* (**научно-техническая библиотека**) scientific and technical library.

НТК *abbr.* (**научно-технический комитет**) committee for science and technology.

ΙΤΟ *abbr.* (**научно-технический отдел**) scientific and technical division; (**научно-техническое общество**) scientific and technical society.

ΙΤΟЭΠ *abbr.* (**Научно-техническое общество энергетической промышленности**) Scientific and Technical Society of the Power Industry.

ΙΤC *abbr.* (**Научно-технический совет**) Council for Science and Technology.

ΙΤУ *abbr.* (**нормальные технические условия**) normal technical specifications.

ужд/а *f.* need, necessity; **без —ы** unnecessarily; **—аться** *v.* need, require, want; be in want of, lack; **—ающийся** *a.* needing, requiring.

ужный *a.* necessary, requisite, proper.

клео/протеид, —протеин *m.* nucleoprotein.

клид *m.* nuclide; **—ный** *a.* nuclidic.

кломезодинамика *f.* nucleomesodynamics.

клон *m.* nucleon; **н. выбивания** prompt nucleon; **н. -нуклонное рассеяние** nucleon-nucleon scattering; **н. отдачи** recoil nucleon.

клонн/ый *a.* nucleon, nucleonic; **н. изобар** nuclear isobar; **н. каскад** nucleonic cascade; **—ая компонента** nucleonic component; **—ое число** mass number.

лев/ой *a.* zero, zeroth, zeroth-order; zero-point, null, neutral; datum; trivial; **н. астатический магнетомер** null astatic magnetometer; **н. вектор** null vector; **н. детектор** null detector; **н. дифракционный максимум** central diffraction maximum; **н. заряд** zero charge; **н. меридиан** prime (or first) meridian; **н. метод** null method; **н. момент** zero moment; **н. отчет** zero reading; **н. прибор** null instrument (or detector); center-zero-meter; **н. провод** (elec.) neutral wire; **н. указатель** null indicator; **н. уровень** zero level; datum (or reference) level; **н. уровень энергии** zero-energy level.

нулев/ой *cont.*, **—ая валентность** null-valency; **—ая гипотеза** (stat.) null hypothesis; **—ая матрица** null matrix; **—ая мощность** zero power; **—ая отметка, —ая черта, —ое деление** zero mark; **—ая поверхность** (surv.) datum level; **—ая прямая** fiducial line; **—ая степень** zero degree; **—ая точка** zero point, zero; **—ая энергия** zero-point energy; **—ое значение** zero (value); **—ое положение** zero (or initial) position; origin; zero balance; **—ое приближение** zeroth(-order) approximation; **—ые колебания** zero-point vibrations (or oscillations).

нулик *m.* small circle.

нуль *m.* null, zero; origin; **н.-вектор** null vector; **н. высоты** datum (level); **н.-детектор** null detector; **н.-индикатор** null indicator; **—мерный** *a.* zero-dimensional; **—пункт** *m.* zero point.

нумеит *m.* noumeite.

нумер *see* **номер**; **—атор** *m.* indicator board, annunciator, register; numerator; recorder; **—ация** *f.*, **—ование** *n.* numeration, numbering; number system; **—ованный** *a.* numbered; **—овать** *v.* number; **—оскоп** *m.* numeroscope.

нуолаит *m.* nuolaite.

Нуссельта критерий, Н. число Nusselt number.

нут/ация *f.* nutation; **—ировать** *v.* nutate.

нутромер *m.*, **н.-калибр** inside calipers.

н. ч. *abbr.* (**научная часть**) scientific section.

НЧ *abbr.* (**низкочастотный**) low frequency (lf).

ныне *adv.* now, at present; **—шний** *a.* present, modern.

ныр/яло *n.* ram, plunger; **—яние** *n.*

diving, plunging; **—ять** *v.* dive, plunge.

ньюбериит *m.* newberyite.

Ньютон Newton (lunar crater).

Ньютона бином binomial series, binomial theorem; **Н. (интерференционные) кольца** Newton rings; **Н. теория излучения** N. theory of light.

ньютон/ианский *a.* Newtonian; **—ит** *m.* newtonite.

ньютонов, —ский *a.* Newtonian; **—ая механика** Newtonian mechanics; **—ский закон сопротивления** Newton law of resistance; **—ский потенциал** Newtonian potential.

н. э. *abbr.* (**нашей эры**) our era (A.D. or A.D., Anno Domini).

нюссиерит *m.* nussierite.

нюх *m.* sense of smell; **—ание** *n.* smelling; **—ать** *v.* smell.

O

о. *abbr.* (**область**) region, oblast; (**общество**) society, association; (**объединение**) association, union; (**объединенный**) associated, united; (**остров**) island; (**отдел**) section, division, branch, department; (**отделение**) compartment, partition.

о, об, обо *prep.* of, about, concerning, on, upon; over; against.

о—, об—, обо— *prefix with verbs* around; off.

об. *abbr.* (**область**) region, oblast.

об. % *abbr.* (**объемный процент**) percent by volume (vol. %).

оба both.

обвал *m.* crumbling, collapse; landslide, slide, avalanche; **—ивать, —ить** *v.* crumble, cave in; heap around; **—иваться, —иться** *v.* crumble, cave in; **—ившийся** *a.* caved-in, fallen.

обвар/ивать, —ить *v.* scald.

обведен/ие *n.* enclosing, surrounding; outline, contour; **—ный** *a.* surrounded.

обвер/нуть, —теть, —тывать *v.* wrap up, envelop.

обвести *see* **обводить.**

обветренный *a.* weather-beaten, weathered.

обви/вать, —ваться, —ть *v.* wind around, twist.

об-во *abbr.* (**общество**) society; company; community.

обвод *m.* bypass; enclosure; outline, contour; **—ить** *v.* lead around; surround; outline, contour; **—ка** *f.* enclosing, surrounding; outlining.

обводн/ение *n.* irrigation; **—ительная система** irrigation system; **—ить** *v* irrigate, supply with water.

обводн/ый *a.* encircling, surrounding **о. канал** bypass (channel); **о. провод** bypass conduit.

обвол/акивать, —очь *v.* envelop, en close, cover, coat; drag around.

обвяз/ать —ывать *v.* bind, tie; **—ка** *f* brace, framework; **—очный** *a.* binding, fastening.

обгар *m.* combustion loss.

обгонять *v.* outdistance, pass, overtake

обгор/ание *n.* burning; **—ать, —еть** be scorched; **—елый** *a.* burn scorched, charred.

обдел/ать, —ывать *v.* work, form finish; **—ка** *f.* working, shaping jacketing, lining.

обдир/ать *v.* strip; rough; **—ка** *f.* stripping; roughing; **—ный, —очный** stripping; abrasive.

обдув/ание *n.* blowing; **—ать** *v.* blow **—ка** *f.* steam-blast cleaning.

обдум/анно *adv.* deliberately; **—анн** *a.* well-planned, deliberate; **—ат** **—ывать** *v.* consider, think over.

обедн/евший, —елый *a.* impoverishe

обеднен/ие *n.* depletion, impoveris ment (of fuel), deficit; **—ный** depleted, stripped, impoverishe **—ный уран** depleted uranium; **—н фракция** depleted (or stripped) fra tion.

обедн/итель *m.* stripper; **—ить, —ять** deplete, impoverish; **—яющий** depleting, stripping.

обез— *prefix* de—, dis—, un—; —less

обезвоженный *a.* dehydrated.

обезвожив/ание *n.* dehydration; **—атель** *m.* dehydrator; **—ать** *v.* dehydrate; **—ающий** *a.* dehydrating; **—ающее средство** dehydrating agent, dehydrant.
обезврежив/ание *n.* decontamination; **—ать** *v.* decontaminate.
обезгаж/енный *a.* outgassed, degassed; **—ивание** *n.* outgassing, degassing; **—ивать** *v.* degas, outgas.
обезжириватель *m.* degreaser.
обеззаражив/ание *n.* decontamination; **—ать** *v.* decontaminate.
обезопасить *v.* free from danger, secure.
обезоруж/ение *n.* disarmament; **—ивать** *v.* disarm.
обезуглерож/енный *a.* decarbonized; decarburized; **—ивание** *n.* decarbonization; decarburization; **—ивать** *v.* decarbonize; decarburize.
обер/егать, —ечь *v.* guard, protect.
обернут/ый *a.* wrapped, enveloped; turned; **—ь** *see* **обертывать.**
обертка *f.* wrapper, envelope.
обертон *m.* overtone, harmonic; **—овый** *a.* overtone.
оберт/очный *a.* wrapping; **о. материал** packing material; **—ывать** *v.* wrap up, envelop.
обес— *prefix see* **обез—.**
обеспеч/ение *n.* security, guarantee, provision; **о. безопасности** safety control; **—енный** *a.* guaranteed, provided (for); **—ивать, —ить** *v.* secure, guarantee, ensure, provide; **—ивающий** *a.* guaranteeing.
обеспыливание *n.* dust removal.
обессер/ение, —ивание *n.* desulfurization; **—енный** *a.* desulfurized.
обесточ/енный *a.* (elec.) idle, de-energized; **—ивать, —ить** *v.* stop current, de-energize.
обесцве/тить *see* **обесцвечивать**; **—ченный** *a.* decolorized, bleached.
обесцвечив/ание *n.* discoloration; fading, bleaching; **—ать** *v.* decolorize, bleach; discolor; **—ающий** *a.* decolorizing; discoloring; **—ающее средство** decolorant, decolorizing agent.
обесцен/ение, —ивание *n.* depreciation; **—ивать, —ить** *v.* depreciate, invalidate.
обещ/ание *n.*, **—ать** *v.* promise.
обжат/ие *n.* squeezing, pressing; (rolling) reduction; **о. конца** nosing (in metal forming); **о. на конус** tapering; **о. шейки** necking (in metal forming); **—ый** *a.* squeezed, pressed, rolled; **—ь** *see* **обжимать.**
обжечь *see* **обжигать.**
обжиг *m.*, **—ание** *n.* burning, roasting, calcination; firing, annealing, kilning, baking; **—ательный** *a.* roasting; baking; annealing; **—ать** *v.* burn, burn off; roast, calcine; anneal, kiln; bake.
обжим *m.*, **—ка** *f.* squeezing, pressing, shortening; **—ать** *v.* squeeze, press, reduce.
обз. *abbr.* (**обзор**) survey, review; summary.
обзол/ивать, —ить *v.* calcine, incinerate; ash.
обзор *m.* survey, review; scanning; summary, compilation; field of view; **краткий о.** abstract, résumé; **—ный доклад** review (report, paper); **—ный прибор** survey instrument; **—ная статья** review article.
обилие *n.* abundance.
обильн/ость источника source strength; **—ый** *a.* abundant, fertile; **—ый дождь** heavy rain; **—ые осадки** heavy precipitation.
обит/аемый *a.* inhabited, habitable; manned; **—атель** *m.* inhabitant; **—ать** *v.* dwell, reside, live (in).
обиход *m.* custom, habit; **выйти из —а** become obsolete; **—ный** *a.* daily, everyday.
обкат/ание *n.*, **—ка** *f.* rolling; **—ать, —ывать** *v.* roll.
обклад/ка *f.*, **—ывание** *n.* facing, lining; casing, coating; **о. конденсатора** capacitor plate; **—ывать** *v.* face, line, coat, encase; edge.
обл. *abbr.* (**областной**) regional, oblast; (**область**) region, oblast; (**обложка**) wrapper; book jacket.
облагоражив/ание *n.* improvement; purification, refining; **—ать** *v.* improve; purify, refine.
облад/ание *n.* possession; **—атель** *m.* possessor, owner; **—ать** *v.* possess, own, have; **—ающий** *a.* possessing,

owning, having; —**ающий чувствительностью в . . .** with a sensitivity of . . .

облак/о *n.* cloud; cluster; —**а верхнего яруса** upper (or high-level) clouds; —**а нижнего яруса** low clouds; —**а среднего яруса** medium (or medium-level) clouds; —**омер** *m.* cloud-range meter; —**ообразование** *n.* cloud formation.

обламывать *v.* break (off).

областной *a.* regional, oblast.

область *f.* area, zone, field, domain, range; region, oblast; **о. больших энергий** high-energy region; **о. видимости** field of view; **о. действий** range (of action); **о. задания** region (range, domain) of definition; **о. интегрирования** integration range (interval, domain); **о. несмешиваемости** miscibility gap; **о. определенности** region (range, domain) of definition; **о. плато** plateau region; **о. применения** field (or range) of application; **о. пропорциональности** proportional band (in regulators), proportional region (in counters); **о. пропускания** transmission band (or region); **о. существования** existence domain; **о. тени** shadow, shadow zone; **о. течения** zone of flow.

облатка *f.* wafer.

облачн/ость *f.* cloudiness; —**ый** *a.* cloudy, clouded; —**ая вершина** cloud dome; —**ая шапка** cap cloud; —**ое знамя** banner cloud.

облег/ать *v.* encircle, encompass; —**ающий** *a.* encircling, encompassing; outlining.

облегч/ать, —**ить** *v.* relieve, alleviate, lighten, ease, facilitate; —**ающий** *a.* relieving, alleviating, lightening; —**ение** *n.* relief, alleviation, lightening, easing, facilitation; —**енный** *a.* relieved, alleviated, lightened, eased, facilitated; —**енный переход** favored transition.

обледен/ение *n.* icing, ice deposit; —**еть** *v.* ice over.

облез/ать, —**ть** *v.* peel.

облекать *v.* put on; invest.

облет *m.* flight around; —**ать,** —**еть** fly around.

облив *m.* glazing; —**ание** *n.* pourin over; —**ать** *v.* pour over; —**ной** glazed.

облик *m.* face, figure, appearanc (cryst.) habit.

облицевать *see* **облицовывать.**

облицов/анный *a.* faced, lined, cla —**ка** *f.*, —**очный** *a.* facing, linin jacketing, casing; —**ывать** *v.* fac line, coat.

обличать *v.* expose; reveal; display.

облический *a.* oblique.

обличить *see* **обличать.**

облож/енный *a.* faced; surrounde edged; —**ить** *see* **обкладывать.**

обложка *f.* wrapper; book jacket.

обложн/ой дождь steady rain; —**ы тучи** heavy overcast.

облом/анный *a.* broken-off; —**ать,** —**ит** *see* **обламывать;** —**ок** *m.* fragmen —**ки** *pl.* fragments, chips, debri (geo.) detritis; —**очный,** —**чатый** (geo.) clastic, detrital.

облуч/аемый *a.* irradiated, expose bombarded; —**атель** *m.* irradiato illuminator; (antenna) exciter; —**ат** *v.* irradiate.

облучен/ие *n.* irradiation, illuminatio exposure, bombardment; **о. радиацией** exposure to radiation; **рентгеновскими лучами** x-irradiation; —**ность** *f.* irradiance; —**ный** irradiated, exposed, bombarded.

обмаз/анный *a.* smeared, greased; —**ат** —**ывать** *v.* smear, grease; —**ка** —**ывание** *n.* smearing, greasing.

обмак/ивание *n.* dipping; —**иват** —**нуть** *v.* dip.

обман *m.* fraud; illusion; **о. зрени** optical illusion.

обманка *f.* (min.) blende; **бархатная** sammet blende; **роговая о.** hor blende.

обман/ный *a.* fraudulent; misleadin —**уть,** —**ывать** *v.* deceive, mislea —**чивость** *f.* fallacy, illusion; —**чивый** *a.* deceptive, delusive, illusory

обматыв/ание *see* **обмотка;** —**ать** wind (around), coil, wrap, sheathe

обмачивать *v.* dip, soak, wet.

обмен *m.*, **—а** *f.* exchange, interchange, change; **о. веществ** metabolism; **о. зарядами** charge exchange; **о. местами** interchange; **о. спинами** spin exchange; **о. теплоты** heat exchange; **о. электрона** electron transfer; **—ивать** *v.* exchange, interchange, replace.

обменн/ый *a.* exchange; **о. интеграл** exchange integral; **о. каталитический реактор** catalytic exchange reactor; **о. потенциал** exchange potential; **о. реактор** exchange reactor; **о. член** exchange term; **о. электронно-спиновый резонанс** exchange-frequency electron spin resonance; **—ая волна** (seis.) exchanged (or transformed) wave; **—ая реакция** exchange reaction; **—ая связь** exchange coupling; **—ая сила** exchange force; **—ая энергия** exchange energy; **—ое взаимодействие** exchange interaction; **—ое вырождение** exchange degeneracy; **—ое поле** exchange (Weiss, molecular) field; **—ое разложение** double decomposition; **—ое рассеяние** exchange scattering; **—ое столкновение** exchange collision.

обменять *see* **обменивать.**

обмер *m.* measurement.

обмерз/ать, —нуть *v.* ice over.

обмер/ивать, —ить, —ять *v.* measure.

об/мин. *abbr.* **(обороты в минуту)** revolutions per minute (rpm).

обмор/аживать, —озить *v.* freeze.

обмотанн/ый *a.* wound, coiled; **о. провод, —ая проволока** (elec.) covered wire, insulated wire.

бмот/ать *see* **обматывать; —ка** *f.* winding, wrapping, sheath, taping; **—ка возбуждения** excitation (or field) winding; magnet coil; **коэффициент —ки** (elec.) winding coefficient; **—очный** *a.* winding, wrapping, taping, covering.

бмочить *see* **обмачивать.**

бмуров/анный *a.* brick-lined; **—ка** *f.* brickwork, brick lining.

бмыв/ание *n.* washing; **—ать** *v.* wash.

бнадеж/ивать, —ить *v.* encourage.

бнаж/ать, —ить *v.* uncover; reveal; **—аться, —иться** *v.* appear, become exposed; **—ение** *n.* uncovering, exposure; erosion; outcrop; **—енный** *a.* bare, uncovered, exposed; outcropped; **—енная порода** (geo.) outcrop.

обнаруж/ение, —ивание *n.* detection, discovery; appearance; display; **о. атомных взрывов** atomic explosion detection; **—енный** *a.* discovered, located; **—ивать** *v.* detect, disclose, discover, locate; reveal; display; **—иваться** *v.* develop, appear; **—имость** *f.* detectability.

обнаружит/ель *m.* detector; **о. излучений** radiation detector; **—ельный** *a.* detecting; **—ельная антенна** search antenna; **—ь** *see* **обнаруживать.**

обнести *see* **обносить.**

обнов/ить, —лять *v.* restore, renovate, renew; **—ление** *n.* restoration, renovation, renewal; innovation; **—ленный** *a.* restored, renewed; **—ляемый** *a.* renewable.

обносить *v.* enclose.

обо *see* **о**; **обо—** *see* **о—.**

обобщ/ать *v.* generalize, draw inferences; **—ение** *n.* generalization, unification; extension.

обобщенн/ый *a.* generalized, unified; extended; **о.-однородный** *a.* (math.) of equal degree; **—ая величина** generalized quantity; **—ая модель** unified model; **—ая модель ядра** collective model of nucleus; **—ая теория поля** unified field theory; **—ые координаты** generalized coordinates.

обобществлен/ие *n.* collectivization; **—ный** *a.* collectivized, socialized.

обогатитель *m.* enricher; **—ный** *a.* enriching; (met.) concentration, dressing.

обога/тить, —щать *v.* enrich; (met.) concentrate, beneficiate; **—щать кислородом** oxygenize, oxygenate; **—щающая установка** enrichment plant.

обогащен/ие *n.* enriching, enrichment; (met.) concentration, beneficiation; **о. изотопов** isotopic enrichment; **коэффициент —ия** enrichment factor; **—ный** *a.* enriched, concentrated, beneficiated; **—ный уран** enriched uranium; **—ное ядерное горючее** enriched nuclear fuel.

обогн/анный *a.* outdistanced, passed; **—ать** *see* **обгонять.**

обогнуть *v.* bend around; round (off); fit (curve).

обогр/евание *n.* warming, heating; **—евать, —еть** *v.* warm, heat; **—евающая катушка** heating coil; **—етый** *a.* warmed, heated.

обод *m.*, **—ковый** *a.*, **—ок** *m.*, **—очный** *a.* rim, hoop.

ободр/анный атом stripped atom; **—ать** *v.* strip.

ободр/ить, —ять *v.* encourage; **—яющий** *a.* encouraging, promising.

обожженный *a.* burnt, calcined, roasted.

обозн. *abbr.* **(обозначение)** symbol, notation.

обозначать *v.* mark, denote, designate, characterize; **детально о.** specify.

обознач/ение *n.* mark, marking, designation, specification; sign, symbol; **(условное) о.** legend; **система —ений** notation, legend; **—енный** *a.* marked; designated, specified; **—ить** *see* **обозначать.**

обозр/еватель *m.* reviewer; **—евать, —еть** *v.* review, survey, inspect; **—ение** *n.* review, survey; (astr.) Durchmusterung; **—имый** *a.* visible; foreseeable.

обойденный *a.* bypassed, circumvented.

обойма *f.* (iron) ring, yoke, clip.

обой/ти *see* **обходить; —тись** *see* **обходиться.**

оболочечн/ый *a.* shell; **—ая волновая функция** orbital (wave function); **—ая модель ядра** shell model of nucleus; **—ое строение** shell structure.

оболочк/а *f.* envelope, shell; cover, casing, jacket, sheath, coating; **о. атома** atom shell; **газовая о.** gas blanket; **о. Земли** mantle of the earth; **о. из положительных ионов** positive ion sheath; **о. реактора** reactor envelope (or shell); **о. реактора-размножителя** breeder blanket; **о. топливного элемента** fuel-element jacket; **электронная о.** electron shell; electron cloud; **о. ядра** shell of nucleus; **покрываться —ой** film (over).

обон/яние *n.* sense of smell; **—ятельный** *a.* olfactory; **—ять** *v.* smell.

оборачив/ание фазы phase reversal; **—ать** *v.* turn; **—ающая линза** erecting lens.

оборв/анный *a.* broken; **—ать** *see* **обрывать.**

оборон/а *f.* defense; **—ительный** *a.* defense, defensive; **—ить, —ять** *v.* defend.

оборот *m.* revolution, rotation, turn; cycle, turnover; **на —е** on the reverse, on the back; **сбавить —ы** slow down (engine); **счетчик —ов** tachograph, tachometer.

оборотить *see* **оборачивать.**

оборотн/ый *a.* reverse, back; reversible; **о. маятник** reversible pendulum; **—ая призма** reversing prism; **—ая призма полного внутреннего отражения** Porro prism; **—ая сторона** reverse side; **—ое горючее** circulating fuel.

оборудов/ание *n.* equipment, outfit; instrumentation; plant; **—ать** *v.* equip, fit out.

обоснов/ание *n.* basis, reason, justification; evidence; demonstration, proof, substantiation; establishment; **—анный** *a.* substantiated, validated, valid, sound; **—ать, —ывать** *v.* substantiate, validate, justify, support, give grounds for.

обособ/ить, —лять *v.* isolate; **—ление** *n.* separation, isolation; **—ленность** *f.* individualization, individuality, isolation; **—ленный** *a.* individual, single; isolated, independent.

обостр/ение *n.* accentuation; aggravation; peaking; **—енный** *a.* aggravated; **—ить, —ять** *v.* aggravate, increase, accentuate; **—яющая схема** peaking circuit.

обоюдн/о *adv.* mutually, reciprocally, doubly; **—ость** *f.* mutuality, reciprocity; **—ый** *a.* mutual, reciprocal.

обр. *abbr.* **(образец)** sample.

обрабатываем/ость *f.* workability, processability; machinability; **—ый** *a.* workable, processable; machinable

—**ый предмет, —ое изделие** work-piece.

обрабатыв/ание *see* **обработка**; **—ать** *v.* work, process, treat; machine, tool, finish, mill; develop, elaborate; **—ающий** *a.* working, processing, treating; machining; **—ающая промышленность** processing industry.

обработ/анный *a.* worked, processed, treated; machined, tooled; finished; developed; **—ать** *see* **обрабатывать.**

обработка *f.* working, fabrication, processing, handling, treatment; machining, tooling, milling; manufacture, preparation; **о. данных** processing (analysis, interpretation, evaluation) of data; **о. измерений** interpretation of measurements.

обравн/ивать, —ять *v.* level.

образ *m.* shape, form; image; object; way; transform; **о. действия** behavior; procedure; **о. мыслей** viewpoint; **главным —ом** mainly, chiefly; **каким —ом** how, in what manner; **надлежащим —ом** properly, suitably; **некоторым —ом** to a certain extent, somewhat; **никоим —ом** by no means, not at all; **подобным —ом** similarly; **равным —ом** equally, similarly; **таким —ом** thus, in this way; **тем или иным —ом** somehow.

образ/ец *m.* specimen, sample, model, example; pattern; standard; **сделать по —цу** duplicate, pattern after.

образно *adv.* figuratively.

образн/ый *a.* figurative, graphic, descriptive, pictorial; *suffix* —shaped, —like, —formed, —form, —oid, —wise; **S-о.** S-shaped.

образовавш/ийся *see* **образованный**; **—еся ядро** product nucleus.

образован/ие *n.* formation, production, generation; marking, structure; education, instruction; **о. вихрей** vortex formation; **высшее о.** higher education, university education; **о. двойников** twinning; **о. дуги** arcing; **о. зародышей, о. центров кристаллизации** nucleation; **о. осадка** precipitation; **о. пар** pair production; **о. сгустков** clustering, bunching; **о. следов** track condensation (in cloud chamber); **среднее о.** secondary education; **о. шейки** necking down; **состояние —ия** nascent state.

образованн/ость *see* **образование**; **—ый** *a.* formed, produced; generated; educated.

образов/ательный *a.* educational; **—ать, —ывать** *v.* form, produce; evolve, generate; organize; constitute, make up; teach, educate; **—ать зародыши** nucleate.

образующ/ая *f.* generating line, generatrix; **—ий** *a.* forming, producing, generating; **—ий угол** generating angle.

образцов/ый *a.* sample, model, standard, master; **о. прибор** standard (or reference) instrument; **—ая мера** standard measure.

образчик *m.* specimen, pattern.

обрамл/ение *n.* framing; **—енный** *a.* framed; **—ивать, —ять** *v.* frame.

обраст/ание *n.* overgrowing; envelopment; **—ать, —и** *v.* overgrow with, accrete.

обратим/ость *f.* reversibility, convertibility; (math.) reciprocity, invertibility; **о. времени** time reversibility, time-reflection symmetry; **закон о.** (opt.) principle of reversibility; **—ый** *a.* reversible, invertible, convertible; **—ый процесс** reversible process; **—ая (магнитная) проницаемость** reversible permeability; **—ая система** bilateral system.

обратит/ель *m.* reverser, inverter; **—ь** *see* **обращать.**

обратно *adv.* back, inversely, conversely, reversibly, counter—, re—; **о. действующий** retroactive; **о. идущий** retrogressive, retrograde, returning; **идти о.** return; **о. пропорциональный** inversely proportional; **о. текущий** flowing back, returning, reflux.

обратн/ый *a.* reverse, return, back, backward; counter, opposite, converse, inverse, reciprocal, inverted; **о. квадратичный закон** inverse square law; **о. клапан** check valve; **о. ом** reciprocal ohm, mho; **о. оператор** inverse operator; **о. потенциал** reverse potential; **о. поток** reflux; **о. провод** return conductor; **о. процесс** inverse process; **о. ток** return current; reverse current, inverse current; **о. удар** kick, kickback, recoil; **о. фотоэлектрический эффект** inverse photoelectric effect; **о. ход** return (motion), reverse run; back stroke (of piston); **о. час** (reactor) inhour (reactivity unit).

обратн/ый *cont.*, **—ая бомбардировка** back bombardment; **—ая величина, —ая дробь** reciprocal, inverse; **—ая волна** backward wave, return wave; **—ая вспышка** backfire, flashback; **—ая гиперболическая функция** inverse hyperbolic function; **—ая диффузия** back diffusion; **—ая длина** reciprocal length; **—ая дуга** arcback; **—ая задача** inverse problem; **—ая крутизна** (elec.) transimpedance; **—ая матрица** inverse (or reciprocal) matrix; **—ая намагниченность** reverse magnetization; **—ая обмотка** return winding; **—ая операция** inverse operation; **—ая полярность** reversed polarity; **—ая пропорциональность** inverse proportionality; **—ая реакция** back (inverse, reverse) reaction; **—ая решетка** reciprocal lattice.

обратн/ый *cont.*, **—ая связь** feedback; **—ая связь по напряжению** voltage feedback; **—ая связь по току** current feedback; **—ая скорость** reciprocal velocity; **—ая спинель** inverse spinel; **—ая сторона** reverse, back; **—ая теорема** converse theorem; **—ая тригонометрическая функция** inverse trigonometric function; **—ая функция** inverse function; **—ая характеристика** (elec.) back characteristic; **—ая электродвижущая сила** back electromotive force; **—ое визирование** backsight, reverse bearing; **—ое включение** reversal; **—ое вращение** counterrotation; **—ое движение** return movement, back stroke; (astr.) retrograde motion; **—ое действие** reaction; **—ое зажигание** arcback, backfire; **—ое излучение** reradiation; **—ое изображение** inverted image; **имеющий —ое действие** retroactive.

обратн/ый *cont.*, **—ое направление** opposite (or reverse) direction; **—ое напряжение** inverse voltage, blocking potential, reverse voltage; **—ое отношение** inverse ratio; **—ое отображение** inverse representation (or image); inverse mapping; **—ое падение** falling back; **—ое преобразование** inverse transformation; **—ое пространство** reciprocal space; **—ое рассеяние** backscattering; **—ое смещение** reverse (or back) bias; **—ое соединение** recombination; **—ое соответствие** reciprocal coordination (or correspondence); **—ое сопротивление** back resistance; **—ое течение** reverse flow; reflux; **формула —ых часов** (reactor) inhour formula.

обращать *v.* turn, change, convert, transform; reverse, invert; circulate; **о. внимание на** pay attention to, draw attention to, turn attention to, point out; **о. на себя внимание** be noteworthy; attract attention; **не о. внимания** disregard, ignore.

обращаться *v.* turn, rotate; become; return; circulate; apply; appeal; handle; treat; **о. в бесконечность** become infinite; **о. в нуль** vanish, disappear, become zero; **о. в тождество** become identical.

обращающий *a.* reversing; **о. слой** reversing layer; **—ся** *a.* rotating, circulating.

обращен/ие *n.* revolution, rotation, turn, circulation; conversion, inversion, transformation; reversal, reversion, treatment, handling; appeal; **о. в нуль** vanishing, disappearing; **о. времени** time reversal (or inversion); **о. линий** reversal of lines; **о. спектральных линий** reversal of spectrum; **о. теоремы** converse theorem; **о. трезвучия** inversion of a triad; **о. функции** inversion of a function; **время —ия информации** access time.

обращенн/ый *a.* turned to, facing; reversed; inverse, inverted; **о. в времени** time reversed; **о. вогнутостью вверх** concave upward; **о. триод** inverted triode; **—ая лампа** inverted tube; **—ая решетка** reciprocal lattice; **—ая частота** inversion frequency.

обрез *m.* edge; **—ание** *n.*, **—ка** *f.* cutting, cutoff; **—атель импульсов** pulse chopper; **—ать** *v.* cut (off); **—ающий** *a.* cutoff, cutting, chipping; **—ной** *a.* cut, cutoff, trimming.

обрез/ок *m.* piece, cut, length; **—ки** *pl.* pieces, scraps, waste.

обрезыв/ание *see* **обрезание**; **—ать** *see* **обрезать.**

обремен/ение *n.* overloading, burdening; **—ительный** *a.* burdensome; **—ить, —ять** *v.* burden, overload.

обрет/ать, обрести *v.* find, discover; **—ение** *n.* finding, discovery; **—енный** *a.* found, discovered.

обрисов/ать, —ывать *v.* sketch, outline, delineate; **—ка** *f.* sketch, outline.

обруб/ать, —ить *v.* trim (off); chip off; **—ленный** *a.* cut, trimmed.

обруч *m.* band, collar.

обруш/ать, —ивать, —ить *v.* demolish; cave in; **—аться, —иваться, —иться** *v.* crumble, break down, collapse; attack; **—ение, —ивание** *n.* collapse; **—енный** *a.* fallen, collapsed.

обрыв *m.* break, breakoff, breakaway; steep decline; (abrupt) termination, cutoff; precipice; **—ание** *n.* breaking; **—ать** *v.* break; cut off.

обрывист/ость *f.* steepness, abruptness; **—ый** *a.* steep, abrupt.

обрыв/ок *m.* scrap; **о. облака** scud, patch of cloud; **—ки тумана** fog streaks.

обрызг/ать, —ивать *v.* spray, wet; **—ивание** *n.* spraying, wetting.

обсерв. *abbr. see* **обсерватория.**

обсерва/тория *f.* observatory; **—ционный** *a.* observation; observatory; **—ция** *f.* observation.

обсидиан *m.* obsidian.

обследов/ание *n.* inspection, examination, exploration, survey; **о. местности** area survey; **—ать** *v.* inspect, examine, explore.

обслужив/аемый *a.* attended, serviced; **о. вручную** manually operated; **—ание** *n.* servicing, maintenance, attendance; **—ать** *v.* service, maintain, attend; **—ающий** *a.* servicing, attending; **—ающий персонал** staff, personnel.

обсохнуть *see* **обсыхать.**

обстав/ить, —лять *v.* surround.

обстановка *f.* arrangement; circumstances, situation, environment.

обстоятель/ность *f.* circumstantiality; thoroughness; **—ный** *a.* circumstantial; detailed; thorough; **—ство** *n.* circumstance, case, fact.

обсто/ять *v.* be, get on; **все —ит благополучно** all is well; **дело —ит** the situation (matter, case) is.

обстраив/ание *n.* building; **—ать** *v.* build (around), construct.

обстрел *m.* fire, firing, bombardment; **—ивать** *v.* bombard.

обстроить *see* **обстраивать.**

обструг/ать, —ивать *v.* plane.

обструк/тивный *a.* obstructive; **—ция** *f.* obstruction, obstacle.

обсужд/ать, обсудить *v.* consider, discuss; **—ение** *n.* consideration, discussion; **предмет —ения** topic of discussion, issue.

обсуш/ивать, —ить *v.* dry.

обсчит/аться, —ываться *v.* miscalculate.

обсып/ать *v.* sprinkle, powder; **—ка** *f.* sprinkling.

обсыхать *v.* dry.

обтаивать *v.* thaw.

обтачив/ание *n.* turning, machining, rounding off; **—ать** *v.* turn, machine, round off.

обтаять *see* **обтаивать.**

обтекаем/ость *f.* streamlining; **—ый** *a.* streamlined; circumfluous; **—ый контур, —ая форма** streamline; **—ая поверхность** (aero.) fairing; **—ое течение** streamline flow.

обтека/ние *n.* streamline flow; flow around; **коническое о.** cone flow, cone-type streamlining; **линия —ния** streamline; **—тель** *m.* (aero.) fairing; **носовой —тель** (rocket) nose cone; **—ть** *v.* flow around; **—ющий** *a.* ambient, circumfluent.

обтереть *see* **обтирать.**

обтес/анный *a.* squared; trimmed; **—ать, —ывать** *v.* square; trim.

обтирать *v.* dry, wipe; polish, grind.

обточ/енный *a.* machined, rounded-off; **—ить** *see* **обтачивать**; **—ка** *f.* turning, machining, rounding off.

обтюратор *m.* obturator, shutter.

обтя/гивать, —нуть *v.* sheathe, jacket; **—жка** *f.* tight covering, skin; jacketing, sheath; **—нутый** *a.* sheathed, jacketed.

обугл/енный *a.* carbonized, charred; **—ивание** *n.* carbonization, charring; **—ивать, —ить** *v.* carbonize, char; **—ивающий** *a.* carbonizing.

обуж/ение *n.* narrowing, tightening; **—енный** *a.* narrowed, narrow, tight; **—ивать** *v.* narrow, tighten.

обузд/ание, —ывание *n.* restraint, checking; **—ать, —ывать** *v.* restrain, check.

обузить *see* **обуживать.**

обуславливать *see* **обусловить.**

обуслов/ить, —ливать *v.* cause; specify, stipulate; **—иться, —ливаться** *v.* be stipulated, depend upon; **—ленность** *f.* conditionality; **—ленный** *a.* due to, resulting from; specified, stipulated, assumed; conditional, dependent upon; **—ливающий** *a.* causing, responsible for.

обуч/ать, —ить *v.* teach, instruct, train; **—аться** *v.* learn; **—ение** *n.* teaching, instruction, training; **—енный** *a.* taught, trained.

обхаживать *see* **обходить.**

обхват *m.* circumference; clasp; **—ить, —ывать** *v.* include, clasp; surround, envelop.

обход *m.* bypass; circuit, revolution, rotation; circumvention, evasion; **в о.** indirectly; **—ить** *v.* go around; bypass, avoid; evade, circumvent; **—иться** *v.* treat, manage; **—иться без** manage without.

обходный *a.* roundabout, circuitous; bypass; **о. канал** bypass (channel); **о. конденсатор** bypass capacitor.

об. ц. тетраг. *abbr.* [**объемноцентрированная тетрагональная (решетка)**] body-centered rectangular (lattice) (bc rect.).

обчи/стить, —щать *v.* clean.

обшивание *see* **обшивка.**

обшив/ать *v.* face, sheathe; border, edge; **—ка** *f.*, **—очный** *a.* facing, sheathing, cladding, casing; edging; **—ка крыла** wing skin.

обширн/ость *f.* spaciousness, magnitude, vastness, expanse; **—ый** *a.* spacious, vast, voluminous, extensive.

обшит/ый *a.* faced, covered, lined; **—ь** *see* **обшивать.**

обшкур/ивать, —ить *v.* grind, polish.

общ. *abbr.* (**общество**) society; company; community; (**общий**) general.

общаться *v.* associate.

обще— *prefix* general, generally, widely.

общедоступн/ость *f.* accessibility; popularity; **—ый** *a.* accessible; popular.

обще/известный *a.* well-known, popular; well-understood; **—народный** *a.* general, public; **—ние** *n.* intercourse; contact; **—образовательный** *a.* general education.

общеполезн/ость *f.* universal utility; **—ый** *a.* generally useful, universally beneficial.

общепонятн/ость *f.* obviousness, clarity; **—ый** *a.* obvious, clear.

общепринятый *a.* universal, generally accepted, current, standard, conventional; **о. метод** standard method, usual procedure.

обществ/енный *a.* social, public; **—о** *n.* society; company; community.

общеупотребительный *a.* commonly used, customary, current.

общ/ий *a.* general, common, public; total, aggregate, cumulative, overall; joint, mutual; **о. вид** general (or overall) view; general form; **о. делитель** common divisor; **о. интеграл** (math.) general solution; **о. итог, —ая сумма** total; **о. коэффициент полезного действия** net efficiency; **о. коэффициент теплопередачи** overall heat-transfer coefficient; **о. множитель** common factor; **о. наибольший делитель** greatest common divisor; **—ая отдача** overall (or net) efficiency; **—ая стабильность** overall stability; **—ая теория относительности** general theory of relativity; **—ая циркуляция атмосферы** general circulation of the atmosphere; **—ее кратное** common multiple; **—ее назначение** general purpose; **—ее наименьшее кратное** least common multiple; **—ее решение** general solution; **—ее среднее**

grand average; —**ее уравнение реактора** general reactor equation; —**ее число** total number; —**ие лучи** white light; **в —ем** generally, in general, on the whole; **в —их чертах** roughly, in outline, in general.

общин/а *f.* community; —**ный** *a.* communal, common.

общность *f.* community, generality.

объединение *n.* union, interconnection, unification, amalgamation; society; **о. множеств** (math.) sum of sets.

Объединенные Нации United Nations.

объедин/енный *a.* united, unified, joint; —**енная модель ядра** collective model of nucleus; —**ить,** —**ять** *v.* unite, join, unify; combine.

Объединенный институт ядерных исследований Joint Institute for Nuclear Research (USSR); **О. норвежско-голландский центр ядерных исследований** Joint Establishment of Nuclear Energy Research (JENER).

объезжать *v.* drive, go around, travel over.

объект *m.* object, item; topic; unit; objective.

объектив *m.* objective (lens).

объективн/ость *f.* objectivity; —**ый** *a.* objective.

объем *m.* volume, size, bulk, space, extent, capacity; body; **о. граммолекулы** molar volume; **о. протекания реакции** reacting volume; **о. пустот** void content; **удельный о.** specific volume; **измеритель —а** volumenometer; —**истый** *a.* voluminous, bulky; —**лющий** *a.* enveloping, convolute.

объемно *adv.* volumetrically; in volume; **о.-резонаторная антенна** cavity antenna; —**сть** *f.* volumicity (relative density of polymer coil in solution); —**центрированный** *a.* body-centered.

объемн/ый *a.* volume, volumetric, bulk; three-dimensional; solid; space, spatial; **о. анализ** volumetric analysis; **о. вес** specific weight, weight density; **о. заряд** space charge; **о. интеграл** volume integral; **о. контур** (elec.) cavity circuit; **о. коэффициент вязкости** second coefficient of viscosity; **о. модуль упругости** bulk rigidity modulus; **о. процент** percent by volume; **о. резонатор** cavity resonator; **о. элемент** element of volume; **о. эффект** volume effect; **модуль —ого сжатия** bulk modulus; **коэффициент —ого расширения** volume expansion coefficient.

объемн/ый *cont.*, —**ая (сейсмическая) волна** body (seismic) wave; —**ая восприимчивость** volume susceptibility; —**ая вязкость** second (or dilatational) viscosity; —**ая деформация** volume (or cubic) strain; —**ая ионизация** volume ionization; —**ая концентрация** volume concentration; —**ая магнитострикция** volume magnetostriction; —**ая плотность** volume (or bulk) density; —**ая поправка** volume correction, finite size correction; —**ая производительность, полезное —ое действие** volumetric efficiency; —**ая производная** spatial derivative; —**ая рассеяния тепла** volume heat dissipation; —**ая рекомбинация** volume recombination; —**ая самолетная антенна** cavity aircraft antenna; —**ая сжигаемость** volume compressibility; —**ая сила** body force; —**ая скорость потока** volumetric flow rate; —**ая сферическая гармоническая функция** solid spherical harmonic; —**ая часть** part by volume; **модуль —ой упругости** bulk modulus; —**ое количество** volume; —**ое расширение** volume (or cubic) expansion, cubic dilatation.

объемометр *m.* volumenometer, volumeter.

объехать *see* **объезжать.**

объизвествл/ение *n.* calcification; —**енный** *a.* calcified; —**ять** *v.* calcify.

объяв/итель *m.* announcer; —**ить,** —**лять** *v.* announce; state, notify, declare; —**ление** *n.* announcement; statement; label; notice.

объясн/ение *n.* explanation, comment; legend (of diagram); —**имый** *a.* explicable; —**ительный** *a.* explanatory; —**ить,** —**ять** *v.* explain, elucidate, demonstrate, clear up, account for, interpret.

объять *v.* fill; envelop; comprehend.

обыденн/ость *f.* commonness, usualness; **—ый** *a.* common, usual, everyday.

обыкновен/ие *n.* habit, custom; **—но** *adv.* usually, habitually, ordinarily; **как —но** as usual.

обыкновенн/ый *a.* usual, habitual, customary, normal; ordinary; **о. волчок** common (spinning) top; **о. закон ошибок** normal error law; **—ая волна** ordinary wave; **—ая точка** regular point (of curve); **—ое дифференциальное уравнение** ordinary differential equation.

обычай *m.* custom, usage.

обычн/о *adv.* usually, generally, regularly, commonly; **—ый** *a.* usual, habitual, regular; routine, standard, conventional, ordinary, common; **—ый воздух** normal air; **—ая звезда** normal star; **—ое горючее** conventional fuel; **—ого типа** conventional (type).

обязанн/ость *f.* duty, obligation, responsibility; **—ый** *a.* obligated, indebted; due to.

обязатель/но *adv.* necessarily, surely, certainly; **—ный** *a.* obligatory, compulsory; **—ство** *n.* obligation, commitment, pledge.

обяз/ать, —ывать *v.* bind, oblige.

о-в *abbr.* (**остров**) island; *pl.* **о-ва.**

ОВ *abbr.* (**отравляющее вещество**) toxic material, poison gas.

овал *m.*, **—ьный** *a.* oval; **—изация** *f.* ovalization; **—ьность** *f.* ovality.

Овен Aries (Ari) (constellation).

Оверхаузера эффект Overhauser effect.

овихиит *m.* owyheeite.

овлад/евать, —еть *v.* seize, take possession of; master; **—ение** *n.* seizing; mastering.

о-во *abbr. see* **об-во.**

оводн/ение *n.* irrigation; soaking; **—ять** *v.* irrigate; soak.

ОВП *abbr.* (**окислительно-восстановительный потенциал**) oxidation-reduction potential.

огарок *m.* cinder.

огиб/ание *n.* bending; enveloping; passage around; rounding; **—ающая (кривая)** (math.) envelope (curve); **—ающая функция** envelope function.

огива *f.* ogive.

оглавление *n.* table of contents; **составлять о.** index, prepare the table of contents.

огла/сить, —шать *v.* publish, announce; **—ска** *f.* publicity; **—шение** *n.* publicizing.

оглуш/ать, —ить *v.* deafen; **—енный** *a.* deafened; **—ительный** *a.* deafening.

огля/деть, —дывать, —нуть *v.* look around, examine.

ОГМИ *abbr.* (**Одесский гидрометеорологический институт**) Odessa Institute of Hydrometeorology.

огне— *prefix* pyro—, fire.

огнев/ой *a.* fire; (geo.) pyrogenous; **о. ход, —ая труба** (flame) flue; **—ая камера, —ая коробка, —ое пространство** firebox.

огнегаситель *m.*, **—ный прибор** fire extinguisher; **—ный** *a.* fire-extinguishing.

огненный *a.* fire, igneous; **о. шар** fireball.

огнеопасн/ость *f.* inflammability; fire hazard; **—ый** *a.* inflammable.

огне/постоянный *a.* fire-resistant, heat-stable; **—родный** *a.* (geo.) pyrogenous, igneous.

огнестойк/ий *see* **огнеупорный; —ость** *see* **огнеупорность.**

огнетрубный котел fire-tube boiler.

огнетушитель *m.*, **—ный прибор, —ное средство** fire extinguisher; **—ный** *a.* fire-extinguishing.

огнеупор *m.* refractory (material); **—ность** *f.* refractoriness; **—ный** *a.* fireproof, fire-resistant, refractory; flameproof; **—ный кирпич** firebrick, refractory brick; **—ная глина** fire clay.

огни Святого Эльма St. Elmo's fire.

оговаривать *see* **оговорить.**

оговор/енный *a.* stipulated, specified; **если особо не —ено** unless otherwise stated; **—ить** *v.* reserve; stipulate; **—ка** *f.* reservation, stipulation, proviso.

огол/енный *a.* uncovered, stripped, exposed, naked, bare; **—ить** *v.* uncover, strip.

оголовок контрфорса haunch of buttress.
оголовье *n.* headband.
оголять *see* **оголить.**
огонь *m.* fire; light; **разводить о.** fire up.
огораживать *v.* enclose.
Огра Ogra (Soviet thermonuclear mirror machine).
ограда *f.* fence, enclosure.
оградитель *m.* protector, guard; breakwater; —**ный** *a.* protecting, guard; enclosing.
огражд/ать, оградить *v.* defend, guard; enclose; —**ающий** *a.* safety, security; enclosing; —**ающий вал** levee, floodwall; —**ение** *n.* guard, protection; enclosure, barrier.
огран/енный *a.* faceted; —**ить** *v.* facet.
ограничен/ие *n.* limitation; constraint; clipping; **без —ия общности** without loss of generality; **время —ия** clipping time.
ограниченн/о *adv.* conditionally, limited; —**ость** *f.* boundedness, limitedness, scantiness; narrow-mindedness; —**ый** *a.* limited, finite, restricted, confined, narrow, bounded; —**ый предел** close margin; —**ая плазма** confined plasma; —**ая пропорциональность** limited proportionality; —**ое горение** limited combustion; —**ое измерение** finite variation; —**ое множество** bounded (or finite) set.
ограничив/ание *n.* containment, confinement; —**ать** *v.* limit, bound, confine, restrict; terminate.
ограничивающ/ий *a.* limiting, bounding; collimating; **о. конус** collimating cone; **о. фактор** limiting factor; —**ая щель** collimating slit; —**ийся** *a.* confined, restricted.
ограничитель *m.* guard, stop, arresting device; limit, limiter; (elec.) clipper; **о. хода** guard, stop, arresting device; limit, limiter; —**ный** *a.* stopping, arresting; limiting.
ограничить *see* **ограничивать.**
огранка *f.* faceting.
огре/вать, —ть *see* **обогревать.**
огромн/ость *f.* vastness, hugeness; —**ый** *a.* enormous, vast, huge, immense, bulky, formidable.
огрубление *n.* coarsening, roughening; desensitization; rough approximation.
огульн/о *adv.* without grounds; without discrimination; —**ый** *a.* groundless, unfounded; indiscriminate.
одабривать *see* **одобрить.**
одаренный *a.* talented, gifted, accomplished.
одевать *v.* coat, cover, dress.
одежда *f.* jacket, lining; pavement; **о. канала** canal lining.
одет/ый *a.* dressed, coated; **о. нуклон** dressed nucleon; —**ь** *see* **одевать.**
од/ин *m., a., pron.*, —**на** *f.*, —**но** *n.* one; a certain; a, an; alone, only, single; same; **о. другого** one another, each other; **о. за другим** one after another, one by one; **о. и тот же** the same; one and the same; **о. или несколько** one or more; **ни о. из** neither of; —**ним словом** in a word, briefly; —**но и то же** one and the same thing; —**но лишь** merely; **по —ному** one by one, singly.
одинаков/о *adv.* in like manner, equally; —**ость** *f.* sameness, identity, equality; —**ый** *a.* same, identical, equal.
одинарн/ый *a.* unary; —**ая связь** single bond; —**ая функция** unary function.
одиннадцати/плоскостной, —плоскостный *a.* hendecahedral; —**угольник** *m.* hendecagon; —**угольный** *a.* hendecagonal.
одиннадцат/ый *a.* eleventh; —**ь** eleven.
одиноч/ество *n.* solitude, isolation; —**ник** *m.* singlet.
одиночн/ый *a.* single, individual, sole, isolated; **о. уровень** single level; —**ая точка** isolated point; —**ая электростатическая линза** univoltage (unipotential, symmetrical) electrostatic lens; —**ое попадание** single-hit (phenomenon).
одна *see* **один.**
однажды *adv.* once, at one time.
однако *conj.* but, however; nevertheless.
одно *see* **один.**
одно— *prefix* one, mono—, uni—, single.
одноатомный *a.* monatomic.
одновалентн/ость *f.* monovalence; —**ый** *a.* monovalent, univalent, monad.

одно/вариантный *a.* monovariant; univariant; **—вибратор** *m.* univibrator; **—витковый** *a.* single-turn, single-coil; **—водный гидрат** monohydrate.

одновременн/о *adv.* simultaneously; **существовать о.** coexist; **—ость** *f.* simultaneity, synchronism, coincidence; **—ый** *a.* simultaneous, synchronous, isochronous, contemporaneous; **—ое выделение** codeposition.

одногорбый *a.* single-humped.

одногруппов/ой *a.* one-group; **—ая теория** one-group theory; **—ое приближение** one-group approximation.

одно/дневный *a.* one-day; **—жильный** *a.* single (cable); **—замещенный** *a.* monosubstituted; **—зарядный** *a.* singly charged; **—звенный фильтр** single-section filter.

однознач/ащий *a.* synonymous; **—но** *adv.* uniquely; unambiguously, unequivocally; **—ный** *a.* single-valued, univalued; unambiguous; unique; equivalent; **взаимно —ный** one-to-one; **—ное число** digit.

однозонный реактор one-region reactor.

одноизотопный элемент monoisotopic element.

одноименн/о заряженный of like charge; **—ый** *a.* like, similar, of the same kind; **—ые полюсы** like poles.

одно/канальный *a.* single-channel; **—кислотный** *a.* monoacid.

однокомпонентн/ый *a.* one-component; **—ая система** one-component system; **—ое топливо** monofuel, monopropellant.

одноконтактный транзистор unijunction transistor.

одноконтурный *a.* single-circuit.

однократно *adv.* once; **о. запрещенный переход** first-forbidden transition; **о. заряженный** singly charged; **о. ионизированный** singly ionized.

однократн/ый *a.* single, simple, single-stage; unique; **о. ион** singly charged ion; **о. метод** batch method, once-through method; **о. урановотопливный цикл** once-through uranium fuel cycle; **—ая ионизация** single ionization; **—ое возбуждение** single excitation; **—ое прохождение** single transit (or transmission); **—ое рассеяние** single scattering; **—ое сжатие** single-stage compression; **—ого действия** single-acting.

одно/кристалловый *a.* single-crystal; **—кружный гониометр** one-circle goniometer; **—листный** *a.* (math.) one-sheeted; **—лопастный** *a.* unilobed, single-lobed; **—лучевое событие** one-pronged event; **—мерный** *a.* one-dimensional; univariate.

одномолекулярный *a.* monomolecular; **о. слой** monomolecular layer, monolayer.

одно/молярный *a.* unimolar; **—моторный** *a.* single-engine; **—направленный** *a.* monodirectional, unidirectional; **—натриевый** *a.* monosodium.

однонит/ный, —очный *a.* unifilar; **о. электрометр Вульфа** Wulf string electrometer.

однонуклонн/ый *a.* single-nucleon; **—ая модель** (nucl.) independent-particle (or single-particle) model.

однооборотный *a.* single-thread (screw).

однообраз/ие *n.* uniformity, monotony; **—но** *adv.* similarly, uniformly; **—ность** *f.* uniformity; **—ный** *a.* uniform, monotonous, alike.

однооднозначное соответствие one-to-one correspondence.

одноокись *f.* monooxide.

одноосновн/ый *a.* monobasic; **—ая кислота** monobasic acid.

одноосн/ость *f.* uniaxiality; **—ый** *a.* uniaxial.

однополосный *a.* single-band.

однополостный гиперболоид unparted hyperboloid, hyperboloid of one sheet; **о. клистрон** single-cavity klystron.

однополупериодн/ый выпрямитель half-wave rectifier; **—ое выпрямление** half-wave rectification.

однополюсн/ик *m.* unipole; **—ость** *f.* unipolarity; **—ый** *a.* unipolar, single-pole, monopolar, homopolar; **—ый транзистор** unipolar transistor.

одно/поточный *a.* single-flow; **—преломляющий** *a.* singly refracting.

однопроводн/ый *a.* single-wire; **—ая цепь** single-wire circuit.

одноразмерный *a.* one-dimensional.

одноразовый *a.* one-time, one-kick, single-shot, single-swing; **о. мультивибратор** one-shot (or single-kick) multivibrator.

однородн/ость *f.* homogeneity, uniformity, similarity; **—ый** *a.* homogeneous, uniform, similar; **—ый пучок** uniform beam; **—ая жидкость** homogeneous fluid; **—ая модель ядра** uniform model of nucleus; **—ая плоская волна** uniform plane wave; **—ая среда** homogeneous medium; **—ое дифференциальное уравнение** homogeneous differential equation; **—ое поле** homogeneous (or uniform) field; **—ое уширение** (spect.) homogeneous broadening.

одно/рядный *a.* single-row, single-layer; uniserial, unilinear; **—связная область** simply connected region; **—сернистый** *a.* monosulfide (of).

односкоростн/ый метод one-velocity method; **—ая модель** one-velocity (or one-group) model.

однослойный *a.* single-layer, single-ply, monolayer.

односторонн/ий *a.* unilateral, one-sided, one-way, unidirectional; linear, single-ended; **о. канал** one-way channel; **—яя проводимость** unidirectional (or unilateral) conductivity; **—яя производная** one-sided derivative; **—яя связь** one-way communication; **—ее давление, —ее сжатие** linear (or uniaxial) compression.

одноступен/ный, —чатый *a.* single-stage, single-step.

одно/суставный *a.* single-jointed; **—тактный** *a.* single-cycle, half-wave.

однотипн/ость *f.* uniformity; **—ый** *a.* uniform, of the same kind (or type).

одно/точечный *a.* single-point; **—ударный** *a.* single-stroke; **—узловой** *a.* uninodal.

однофазный *a.* single-phase, monophase, uniphase; **о. сплав** single-phase alloy.

однохлористый *a.* monochloride (of).

одноцветн/ый *a.* monochromatic, monochrome; **—ое телевидение** monochrome television.

одно/центровый *a.* concentric; **—цепный** *a.* single-chain; (elec.) single-circuit; **—цилиндровый** *a.* single-cylinder.

одно/частичная модель (nucl.) independent-particle (or single-particle) model; **—частотный** *a.* single-frequency.

одночлен *m.* monomial; **—ный** *a.* monomial, one-term; one-place, monadic.

одно/электронный *a.* one-electron, single-electron; **—элементный прибор** single-unit device; **—этажный** *a.* single-stage, single-deck, one-story; **—ядерный** *a.* mononuclear; **—якорный** *a.* single-armature; **—ярусный** *a.* single-stage, single-level; **—ячейковый** *a.* unicellular.

одобр/ение *n.* approval, clearance; **—енный** *a.* approved; **—ительный** *a.* approving; **—ить, —ять** *v.* approve, endorse.

одол/евать, —еть *v.* overcome, surmount, master.

одометр *m.* odometer.

одревеснение *n.* lignification.

одум/аться, —ываться *v.* reconsider, change one's mind.

оже-электрон Auger electron; **Оже эффект** A. effect.

ожечь *see* **обжигать.**

оживальный *a.* ogival.

оживленный *a.* revived, vitalized; lively.

ожигать *see* **обжигать.**

ожида/емый *a.* expected, anticipated; required; **—ние** *n.* expectation; **обмануть —ние** disappoint; **в —нии** pending; **—ть** *v.* expect; anticipate; believe.

ожиж/атель *m.* liquefier; **—ать** *v.* liquefy; **—ающийся** *a.* liquefiable; **—ение** *n.* liquefying, liquefaction, thinning; liquation.

ожог *m.* (skin) burn.

оз. *abbr.* (**озеро**) lake.

озабо/тить, —чивать *v.* cause concern; **—титься, —чиваться** *v.* attend to, take care of; **—ченность** *f.* anxiety, concern; **—ченный** *a.* preoccupied, anxious, concerned.

озаглав/ить, —ливать *v.* entitle; **—ленный** *a.* entitled.

озадач/енный *a.* perplexed, puzzled; **—ивать, —ить** *v.* perplex, puzzle.

озаннит *m.* osannite.
озар/ить, —ять *v.* illuminate.
озвученный фильм sound film.
оздор/авливать, —овить, —овлять *v.* improve sanitary conditions.
озер/ный *a.* lake, lacustrine; **—о** *n.* lake.
озеро Смерти Lacus Mortis (lunar); **о. Сновидений** Lacus Somniorum.
озеро холодного воздуха (meteor.) cold pool.
ознак/амливать, —омить *v.* acquaint with; **—амливаться, —омиться** *v.* become acquainted, become familiar with; **—омление** *n.* acquaintance, knowledge.
ознаменов/ание *n.* sign; **в о.** in honor (of), to mark the occasion; **—ать, —ывать** *v.* signalize, mark.
означ/ать *v.* designate, denote, indicate, imply; **—енный** *see* **вышеобъявленный.**
озокерит *m.* ozocerite.
озолять *see* **обзоливать.**
озон *m.* ozone; **—атор** *m.* ozonizer; **—ация** *f.* ozonization; **—ид** *m.* ozonide; **—идация** *f.* ozonidation.
озониз/атор *see* **озонатор; —ация** *see* **озонирование.**
озониров/ание *n.* ozonization; **—анный** *a.* ozonized; **—ать** *v.* ozonize.
озонная бумага ozone (test) paper.
озонолиз *m.* ozonolysis.
озонометр *m.* ozonometer; **—ический** *a.* ozonometric; **—ия** *f.* ozonometry.
озоно/пауза *f.* ozonopause; **—скоп** *m.* ozonoscope; **—стойкость** *f.* ozone resistance; **—сфера** *f.* ozonosphere.
озотипия *f.* ozotype.
ОИЗ *abbr.* (**общество изобретателей**) Society of Inventors.
ОИЯИ *abbr.* (**Объединенный институт ядерных исследований**) Joint Institute for Nuclear Research.
ок. *abbr.* (**океан**) ocean; (**около**) near; around, about, approximately.
ОК *abbr.* (**организационный комитет**) organizing committee.
оказ/ание *n.* showing, rendering; **—ать, —ывать** *v.* show, render; exert; **—ать влияние** influence, affect; **—аться** *v.* appear; prove to be; **—ывается** it appears that; it is found that; **—алось** it was found that.
окайм/ить, —лять *v.* border, edge, flange; **—ление** *n.* bordering, edging, flange; **—ление светлое** halo, halation; **—ленный** *a.* edged, bordered.
окалина *f.* cinder, clinker; scale.
окамен/евать, —еть, —ять *v.* petrify; harden, fossilize; **—елость** *f.* petrifaction; fossil; **—елый** *a.* petrified; fossil; **—ение** *n.* petrifaction; fossilization.
окантов/ать, —ывать *v.* frame, mount.
оканчивать, —ся *v.* finish, end, terminate.
окатанный *a.* rolled.
окварцевание *n.* quartzification.
океан *m.* ocean.
океан Бурь Oceanus Procellarum (lunar).
океанический *see* **океанский.**
океанограф *m.* oceanographer; **—ический** *a.* oceanographic; **—ия** *f.* oceanography.
океанология *f.* (physical) oceanography.
океанск/ий *a.* ocean, oceanic, maritime, marine; **—ое дно** ocean floor.
окерманит *m.* åkermanite.
окиленная складка (geo.) carinate (or isoclinal) fold.
окис/ать *v.* oxidize; **—ел, —ель** *see* **окись.**
окислен/ие *n.* oxidation; **—ность** *f.* degree of oxidation; **—ный** *a.* oxidized.
окислитель *m.* oxidant; **—но-восстановительный потенциал** oxidation-reduction potential, redox potential; **—но-восстановительный цикл** oxidation-reduction cycle; **—ный** *a.* oxidizing.
окисл/ить, —ять *v.* oxidize; **—яемость** *f.* oxidizability; **—яемый, —яющийся** *a.* oxidizable; **—яющий** *a.* oxidizing.
окисн/ый *a.* oxide; **—ая соль** —ic salt.
окись *f.* oxide (—ic oxide); **о. бериллия** beryllium oxide, beryllia; **о. дейтерия** deuterium oxide; **о.-закись урана** uranous-uranic oxide; **о. кадмия** cadmium oxide; **о. тория** thorium oxide, thoria; **о. урана** uranium

oxide; **красная о. цинка** red oxide of zinc.

окклюдиров/ание *see* **окклюзия**; **—анный** *a.* occluded; **—ать** *v.* occlude.

окклюзия *f.* occlusion; **загнутая о.** recurved occlusion; **о. типа теплого фронта** warm-front (type) occlusion; **о. типа холодного фронта** cold-front (type) occlusion.

оккуп/ация *f.* occupation; **—ированный** *a.* occupied; **—ировать** *v.* occupy.

оклеивать *v.* glue, paste.

окно *n.* window; opening, port; **атмосферное о.** (meteor.) water-vapor window; **о. в облаках** break (rift, hole) in clouds.

око *n.* eye.

оков/анный *a.* iron-bound; **—ать, —ывать** *v.* bind (with iron); **—ка** *f.* binding (with iron).

около *prep. gen.* near; around, about, approximately.

окологоризонтальный *a.* circumhorizontal.

околозвуков/ой *a.* transonic; **—ая скорость** transonic speed; **—ое течение** transonic flow.

околозенитный *a.* circumzenithal.

околокритический *a.* near-critical.

около/полюсный, —полярный *a.* circumpolar.

околосолнечное пространство space about the sun.

окольный *a.* roundabout, indirect; **о. путь** indirect route; detour.

оконечн/ость *f.* extremity, end, tip; **—ый** *a.* terminal, end, final; **—ая скорость** terminal velocity.

оконный *a.* window.

оконтур/ивание, —ирование *n.* mapping, delineation, outlining; **—ивать, —ировать** *v.* map, outline.

окончание *n.* end, ending, completion, termination, conclusion, closing, expiration.

окончательн/о *adv.* finally, definitely; **—ый** *a.* final, definitive; terminal; ultimate; **—ая отделка** finishing (work).

оконч/енный *a.* finished, completed; **—ить** *v.* finish, complete, terminate.

окоп *m.*, **—ный** *a.* trench.

окор/ачивать, —отить *v.* shorten, curtail.

окош/ечный *see* **оконный**; **—ко** *n.* (small) window; peephole.

окр. *abbr.* (**округ, окружной**) district.

окраина *f.* borderland, outskirts, margin.

окрас/ить *see* **окрашивать**; **—ка** *f.* color, coloration, tint; dyeing; painting.

окраш/енный *a.* colored, tinted; dyed; painted; **о. F-центр** color center, F-center; **—ивание** *see* **окраска**; **—ивать** *v.* color, tint; dye; paint.

окремн/евать *v.* silicify; **—ение** *n.* silicification; **—енный** *a.* silicified.

окрестн/ость *f.* neighborhood, vicinity, proximity, surroundings; **—ый** *a.* neighboring, surrounding.

Окридж Oak Ridge.

округ *m.* district; circuit.

округлен/ие *n.* rounding (off); **—но** *adv.* in round numbers; **—ность** *f.* roundness.

округленноугловат/ость *f.* subangularity; **—ый** *a.* subangular.

округл/енный *a.* rounded (off); **—ить, —ять** *v.* round (off); **—ость** *f.* roundness; curve; **—ый** *a.* round, rounded, curved.

окружать *v.* surround, encircle, enclose, encompass.

окружающ/ий *a.* surrounding, encircling, ambient, circumfluent; **—ая среда** environment, ambient; **—ая температура** ambient temperature; **—ие условия** environment, environment factors.

окруж/ение *n.* surrounding, encircling, enclosing; surroundings, environment; **—енный** *a.* surrounded; **—ить** *see* **окружать**.

окружн/ой, —ый *a.* circle, circular, circumferential, peripheral; surrounding, neighboring; **—ая деформация** tangential strain; **—ая скорость** circular velocity; peripheral velocity; **—ость** *f.* circle, circumference, periphery; neighborhood.

оксаммит *m.* oxammite.

окси— *prefix* hydroxy—; oxy—.

оксиацетиленовая сварка oxyacetylene welding.

оксидиров/ание *n.*, **—ка** *f.* oxidation; **—анный** *a.* oxidized; **—ать** *v.* oxidize.
оксидный *a.* oxide; **о. катод** oxide-coated cathode, oxide cathode.
оксифер *m.* a type of ferrite (magnetic core material).
оксонит *m.* (expl.) oxonite.
оксфордский ярус Oxfordian stage.
окт. *abbr.* (**октябрь**) October.
окт— *prefix* oct—.
октава *f.* octave.
октальная панель octal (tube) socket.
октан *m.* octane.
Октан Octans (Oct) (constellation).
октант *m.* octant.
октаэдр *m.* octahedron; **—ит** *m.* octahedrite; **—ический** *a.* octahedral.
октет *m.* octet.
октиббегит *m.* oktibbehite.
октил *m.*, **—овый** *a.* octyl.
октиль *m.* (stat.) octile.
окто— *prefix* octo—.
октогидрат *m.* octahydrate.
октод *m.* octode.
октуполь *m.* octupole; **—ный момент** octupole moment; **—ное излучение** octupole radiation.
октябрь *m.* October.
окулист *m.* oculist.
окуляр *m.* ocular, eyepiece; **о.-микрометр** micrometer eyepiece; **—ный** *a.* ocular; **—ный микрометр** ocular micrometer.
окун/ать, —уть *v.* dip, plunge, immerse.
окур/енный *a.* fumigated; **—ивание** *n.* fumigation; **—ивать, —ить** *v.* fumigate, disinfect; **—ивающий** *a.* fumigating; **—ивающее средство** fumigant.
окутанный *a.* blanketed.
Олдермастон Aldermaston.
оледен/елый *a.* frozen, iced; **—ение, —ие** *n.* freezing; (geo.) glaciation; **—еть** *v.* freeze; glaciate.
олео— *prefix* oleo—, oil.
олео/графия *f.* oleography; **—метр** *m.* oleometer; **—фильный** *a.* oleophilic.
олефин *m.* olefin; **—овый** *a.* olefinic.
оливин *m.* olivine.
олигоклаз *m.* oligoclase.
олигоцен *m.*, **—овый** *a.* Oligocene.
олимпиада *f.* All-Union student's problem-solving contest.
олов/о *n.* tin (Sn); **—янный** *a.* tin, stannic; **—янная чума** tin plague (or pest); **—янное дерево** dendritic tin crystals.
олометр *m.* holometer.
Ольберс Olbers (lunar crater).
ольдгамит *m.* oldhamite.
ом *m.* ohm; **Ома закон** Ohm's law.
омбилическая точка (math.) umbilical point.
омега *f.* omega; **—трон** *m.* omegatron.
омедн/ение *n.* copper coating, copper plating; **—енный** *a.* copper-plated, copper-clad; **—ивать, —ять** *v.* copper, copper plate.
ОМЕН *abbr.* (**Отделение математических и естественных наук Академии наук СССР**) Department of Mathematics and Natural Sciences of the Academy of Sciences, USSR.
ОМЗ *abbr.* (**Оптикомеханический завод**) Optical Equipment Plant.
омич/еский *a.* ohmic, resistive, resistance; **о. контакт** ohmic contact; **—еское сопротивление** (ohmic) resistance, d-c resistance; **—ность** *f.* ohmic character.
омметр *m.* ohmmeter.
омрач/ать, —ить *v.* obscure, darken, cloud; **—енный** *a.* obscured, darkened, clouded.
ОМС *abbr.* (**Отделение метеорологической службы**) Division of Meteorological Service.
омфацит *m.* omphacite.
омыв/аемый *a.* circumfluous; washed; **—ать** *v.* wash.
омыл/ение, —ивание *n.* saponification; **—ять, —яться** *v.* saponify.
он *pron.* he; **—а** she.
онгстрем *see* **ангстрем.**
о.н.д. *abbr.* (**общий наибольший делитель**) greatest common divisor (g.c.d.).
ондограф *m.* ondograph.
ондул/ировать *v.* undulate; **—ятор** *m.* undulator.
Онзагера теорема взаимности Onsager reciprocal relation; **О. уравнение для диэлектрической постоянной** O. equation for dielectric constant.

и *pron.* they.
икс *m.* onyx.
ихит *m.* onychite.
козиметр *m.* oncosimeter.
козин *m.* oncosine.
неродит *m.* ånnerödite.
о *pron.* it.
ІТИ *abbr.* (**Объединение научно-технических издательств**) United Scientific and Technical Presses.
лит *m.* oölite.
Н *abbr.* (**Организация Объединенных Наций**) United Nations (U.N.).
. *abbr.* (**опыт**) experiment.
ад/ать *v.* fall off; subside; **—ение** *n.* subsidence.
аздыв/ание *n.* delay, retardation; **—ать** *v.* be late.
аивать *see* **опаять.**
аковый *a.* opaque.
аленный *a.* singed, burned.
алесц/енция *f.* opalescence; **—ировать** *v.* opalesce; **—ирующий** *a.* opalescent.
ал/ивание *n.* burning; **—ивать, —ить** *v.* burn, scorch.
аловый *a.* opal, opaline.
алять *see* **опаливать.**
ас/аться *v.* fear, apprehend; **—ение** *n.* fear, apprehension, misgiving.
асн/о *adv.* dangerously; it is dangerous; **—ость** *f.* danger, risk, hazard; **—ый** *a.* dangerous, unsafe.
асть *see* **опадать.**
ахал/о *n.* fan; (astr.) plume; **—ьный луч** fan ray.
аять *v.* solder.
еративн/ый *a.* operative, operational; **—ая цепь** operating circuit (or loop).
ератор *m.* operator; **о. поглощения, о. уничтожения** annihilation operator; **—ный** *a.* operational, operator; **—ное равенство** operational equation.
ерац/ионный *a.* operation, operating, operational; **—ионное исчисление** operational calculus; **—ия** *f.* operation, procedure; **—ия множеств** set-theoretical operation.
ере/дить, —жать *v.* lead, advance, outstrip; anticipate.
ережающий *a.* leading; **о. потенциал** advanced potential; **о. ток** leading current; **о. угол** *see under* **опережение.**
опережен/ие *n.* leading, lead, outrunning; advance, advancing; anticipation; **угол —ия** advance angle; lead angle.
оперен/ие *n.* (aero.) tail, tail assembly, empennage; (rocket) fins; **—ный снаряд** finned missile.
опереться *see* **опираться.**
опериров/ание *n.* operation, operating; **—ать** *v.* operate.
опертый *a.* supported, depending (on).
опечат/ать, —ывать *v.* seal.
опечатка *f.* misprint, error.
опизометр *m.* opisometer.
опил/ивание *n.*, **—овка** *f.* filing; **—ивать, —ить** *v.* file; **—ки** *pl.* filings; sawdust; **—овочный** *a.* filing.
опир/ать *v.* rest; push; **—аться** *v.* rest on, be based on; **—аясь на** on the basis of.
опис/ание *n.* account, report, description; **—анный** *a.* described; circumscribed; **—ательный** *a.* descriptive; **—ать** *v.* describe, depict, give an account, report; circumscribe.
описка *f.* (clerical) error.
описывать *see* **описать.**
опись *f.* list, catalog; schedule; inventory.
оплавл/ение *n.* fusion, fusing; (welding) flashing off; **сварка с —ением** flash welding; **—ивать, —ять** *v.* fuse, fuse on.
оплат/а *f.* payment, remuneration; **—ить** *see* **оплачивать.**
оплач/енный *a.* paid; **—ивать** *v.* pay, remunerate.
оплет/ать, оплести *v.* braid; **—енный** *a.* braided.
оплошность *f.* negligence.
оплы/вать, —ть *v.* circumnavigate.
оповещ/ать *v.* inform, notify; **—ение** *n.* announcement, notification, message; information.
опозд/ание *n.* retardation; delay; tardiness; **—ать** *see* **опаздывать.**
опозна/вание, —ние *n.* identification; **—вать, —ть** *v.* identify, recognize.
ополаск/ать, —ивать *v.* rinse; **—ивание** *n.* rinsing.

ополз/ание *n.* creep, creeping, sliding; **—ать** *v.* creep, slide, slip; **—ень** *m.* landslide, slide, earth creep.

ополоснуть *see* **ополаскивать.**

опор/а *f.* bearing, support, mounting, bracket; fulcrum; **катковая о.** roller bearing; **клиновидная о., ножевая о., призматическая о.** knife edge; **точка —ы** fulcrum; point of support, bearing.

опоражнив/ание *n.* emptying; **—ать** *v.* empty, evacuate.

опорн/ый *a.* bearing, supporting, seating; reference; **о. изолятор** stand-off insulator; **о. импульс** pedestal pulse; **о. контур** index contour; **о. уровень** base level; **—ая балка** supporting beam; **—ая волна** (seis.) reference wave; **—ая линия** reference line; datum line; **—ая площадь, —ая поверхность** bearing surface (or area); **—ая подушка** support, cushioning; **—ая призма** knife edge, fulcrum; **—ая прямая** line of support; **—ая реакция** (static) reaction, reactive force; **—ая точка** reference point; **—ое давление** bearing pressure; counterpressure; **—ое лезвие** knife edge; **—ое направление** reference direction; **—ое напряжение** reference voltage; **—ое ребро** knife edge, fulcrum; **—ое трение** static friction.

опорожн/ение *see* **опоражнивание**; **—енный** *a.* emptied, evacuated; **—ить, —ять** *see* **опоражнивать.**

опояс/ать, —ывать *v.* encircle.

Оппенгеймера-Филлипса эффект Oppenheimer-Phillips effect.

оппо/зиция *f.* opposition; **—нировать** *v.* oppose.

оправа *f.* setting, mounting, rim; mandrel; **о. линзы** lens mount.

оправд/ание *n.* justification; **—анный** *a.* sound, justified, warranted; **—ать, —ывать** *v.* justify; confirm; **—ываемость** *f.* justification; correctness, accuracy.

оправить *see* **оправлять.**

оправ/ка *f.* mandrel; **—лять** *v.* set, mount; arrange; **—очный** *a.* setting, mounting; mandrel.

опрашив/ать *v.* question, inquire; **—ающий импульс** "search" pulse.

определен/ие *n.* determination; definition; appointment; attribute; **о. возраста** dating; **о. даты изотопами** isotopic dating; **о. даты радиоуглеродом** radiocarbon dating; **по —ию** by definition.

определенн/о *adv.* definitely, positively; **о.-отрицательный** *a.* (math.) negative definite; **о.-положительный** positive definite; **—ость** *f.* definiteness, determinacy; **—ый** *a.* determined, definite, fixed, specific; determinate; defined; **—ый интеграл** definite integral.

определ/имость *f.* determinability; **—имый** *a.* determinable, definable; **—итель** *m.* finder, locator, detector; (math.) determinant; **—ить, —ять** *v.* determine, establish, ascertain, define, distinguish; specify, fix; assign, appoint; **—яющий** *a.* decisive, determining, specifying; defining; controlling; governing; **—яющий фактор** controlling factor.

опресн/ение *n.* distillation (of salt water); **—итель** *m.* distiller; **—ить, —ять** *v.* distill.

опрессов/анный *a.* sheathed (under pressure), pressed; involved; **—ка** *f.* molding, pressing; **коэффициент —ки** bulk factor.

опрессовыв/ание *n.* pressurization; **—ать** *v.* pressurize.

опробов/ание *n.* sampling; testing; assay; **—атель** *m.* sampler; **—ательный** *a.* sampling; testing.

опровер/гать, —гнуть *v.* refute, disprove; **—жение** *n.* refutation, disproof, denial.

опрокидыв/ание *n.* reversing, inverting, flip; (elec.) flip-flop; overturning, upsetting, tipping, tilting; **о. гребней волн** breaking of waves; **—атель** *m.* dumper, tipper, inverter, tripper; **—ать** *v.* overthrow, overturn, flip, upset, tip, trip, tilt, invert; reverse; **—ающий момент** tilting moment, leverage.

опрокинут/ый *a.* overturned, upset, tipped, tilted, inverted; reversed; **—ь** *see* **опрокидывать.**

опрос *m.* interrogation; **—ный** *a.* i

terrogatory; —**ный лист** questionnaire.

опрыс/канный *a.* sprayed, sprinkled; —**кивание** *n.* spraying, sprinkling; —**киватель** *m.* sprayer, spray; —**кивать,** —**нуть** *v.* spray, sprinkle, wet, moisten; —**кивающий** *a.* spraying, spray.

оптик *m.* optician; opticist; —**а** *f.* optics; —**о-механическое трансформирование** (phot.) optical rectification.

оптимальный *a.* optimum, optimal.

оптимизация *f.* optimization.

оптимум *m.* optimum.

опт. и спектр. *abbr.* (**Оптика и спектроскопия**) Optics and Spectroscopy (journal).

оптически *adv.* optically; **о. деятельный** optically active; **о. недеятельный** optically inactive.

оптическ/ий *a.* optic, optical, visual, visible; **о. обман** optical illusion; **о. пирометр** optical (or absorption) pyrometer; **о. прицел** optical (or telescopic) sight; **о. спектр** optical spectrum; —**ая алидада** telescopic alidade; —**ая глубина** optical depth; —**ая деятельность** optical activity, optical rotation, opticity; —**ая длина пути** optical path; —**ая модель** optical model; —**ая ось** optic axis (of crystal); optical axis (of instrument); —**ая перекачка** optical pumping; —**ая плотность** (phot.) optical density; —**ая сила линзы** lens power; —**ая скамья** optical bench; —**ая толща** optical thickness; —**ая труба** telescope; —**ое имущество** optical equipment (or instruments); —**ое соединение** optical joint; —**ое сопровождение** optical tracking; —**ое стекло** optical glass; lens; —**ие антиподы** optical antipodes.

птичность *see* **оптическая деятельность.**

пто/техника *f.* optotechnics, optical technology; —**фон** *m.* optophone.

публ. *abbr.* (**опубликован**) published.

публиков/ание *n.* publication, promulgation; —**анный** *a.* published, issued; —**ать,** —**ывать** *v.* publish, make public, issue.

опудривание *n.* powdering, dusting.

опуск *m.* omission; —**ание** *n.* lowering, dropping, descent, sinking; downstroke; (geo.) subsidence; —**ать** *v.* lower, sink; drop, omit; —**аться** *v.* descend, sink, subside, drop down; —**ающий** *a.* lowering, descending; —**ной** *a.* lowering, drop.

опуст/евать, —**еть** *v.* become empty; —**евший,** —**елый** *a.* empty.

опуст/ившийся *a.* sunken, submerged; —**ить** *see* **опускать.**

опущен/ие *n.* omission; lowering; —**ный** *a.* omitting; lowered, dropped.

опыт *m.* experiment, test, trial; experience, practice; **о. эксплоатации** operating experience; **в пределах ошибок** —**а** within the limits of experimental error; **на** —**е** experimentally; in practice; **производить** —**ы** experiment, conduct experiments.

опытн/о *adv.* expertly; experimentally; —**ость** *f.* experience, proficiency; —**ый** *a.* experienced, expert, competent, skillful; experimental, test, pilot; empirical; —**ый образец** prototype; test-piece; —**ый реактор** pilot reactor, experimental reactor; —**ым путем** experimentally; —**ая установка** pilot plant; —**ая формула** empirical formula.

опытовый бассейн model basin.

опять *adv.* again; **о. же, о.-таки** besides.

оранжевый *a.* orange.

оранжер/ейный *a.*, —**ея** *f.* greenhouse; **о. эффект** greenhouse effect.

оранжит *m.* orangite.

орбита *f.* orbit, trajectory; orbital.

орбиталь *f.*, —**ный** *a.* orbital; —**ный момент** orbital moment; —**ный электрон** orbital electron.

орг. *abbr.* [**органическая (химия)**] organic (chemistry).

орган *m.* member, element, unit; organ; —**ы управления** controls; —**ы чувств** sensory organs.

организац/ионный *a.* organizational, organization; —**ия** *f.* organization.

организм *m.* organism; **в** —**е** in vivo.

организов/анность *f.* discipline; —**анный** *a.* organized, managed, arranged; —**ать,** —**ывать** *v.* organize, manage, arrange.

органика *f.* organic matter.
органическ/и *adv.* organically, inherently; **—ий** *a.* organic; **—ое стекло** plastic.
органные трубы organ pipes.
органолюминофор *m.* organic luminophor.
оргстекло *see* **органическое стекло.**
ординальный *a.* ordinal.
ординар *m.* normal (water) level; **—ный** *a.* ordinary, common.
ордината *f.* (math.) ordinate.
ордович *m.* Ordovician period.
Орел Aquila (Aql) (constellation).
ореол *m.* aureole, halo; halation; **о. рассеяния** (geo.) dispersion halo.
орех *m.* nut.
оригинал *m.* original; (math.) inverse transform.
оригинальн/о *adv.* originally; **—ость** *f.* originality; **—ый** *a.* original, unique.
ориентационн/ый *a.* orientation, orientational; **—ая поляризация** orientational polarization; **—ая поляризуемость** orientational (or dipolar) polarizability.
ориентация *f.* orientation, aligning; **о. спина** spin orientation; **о. ядер** nuclear orientation (or polarization).
ориентир *m.* reference point, guiding line; **о.-буссоль** declinometer.
ориентирован/ие *n.* orientation; **—ный** *a.* oriented; **—ное ядро** oriented (or polarized) nucleus.
ориентиров/ать *v.* orient, direct; **—ка** *see* **ориентирование**; **—очный** *a.* tentative, preliminary, provisional.
ориентирующая сила directive force.
Орион Orion (Ori) (constellation).
Ориониды Orionids (meteors).
орисканский ярус Oriskany stage.
орлец *m.* rhodonite.
орнитоптер *m.* orthopter, ornithopter.
ороген/езис *m.* orogenesis; **—ический** *a.* orogenic.
орограф/ический *a.* orographic; **—ия** *f.* orography.
орозеит *m.* oroseite.
орология *f.* orology, orography.
орометрия *f.* orometry.
оросит/ель *m.* irrigator, sprinkler; **—ельный** *a.* irrigating, irrigation, sprinkling, spray; **—ь** *see* **орошать.**
орош/атель *m.* irrigator; **—ать** *v.* irrigate, sprinkle, shower, spray; **—ающий** *a.* irrigating, sprinkling; **—ение** *n.* reflux (in column); trickling; (supplementary) irrigation; sprinkling, spraying; **—енный** *a.* irrigated, sprinkled.
орт *m.* unit vector; basis vector.
ортикон *m.* orthicon.
ортит *m.* orthite, allanite.
орто— *prefix* ortho—.
орто/водород *m.* orthohydrogen; **—гелий** *m.* orthohelium.
ортогонализировать *v.* orthogonalize.
ортогональн/ость *f.* orthogonality; **—ый** *a.* orthogonal.
ортодейтерий *m.* orthodeuterium.
ортодин *m.* orthodyne.
ортоклаз *m.*, **—овый** *a.* orthoclase.
орто/кластический *a.* orthoclastic; **—магнитный** *a.* orthomagnetic; **—метрический** *a.* orthometric.
ортоник *m.* Orthonic (iron-nickel alloy).
ортоноль *m.* Orthonol (iron-nickel alloy).
ортонорм/альная волновая функция orthonormal wave function; **—ированная система** (math.) orthonormal set; **—ируемость** *f.* orthonormality.
орто/ось *f.* ortho axis, ortho diagonal; **—-пара превращение** ortho-para conversion; **—позитронный** *a.* orthopositronium; **—положение** *n.* ortho position.
орторомбическ/ий *a.* orthorhombic, rhombic; **—ая структура** orthorhombic (or rhombic) structure.
ортоскоп *m.* orthoscope; **—ический** *a.* orthoscopic; **—ия** *f.* orthoscopy.
орто/соединение *n.* ortho compound; **—состояние** *n.* ortho state; **—тропизм** *m.* orthotropism; **—фонический** *a.* orthophonic; **—форма** *f.* orthoform.
ортохром Т *m.* orthochrome T; **—атический** *a.* orthochromatic.
ортохронный *a.* orthochronous.
оруден/елый *a.* mineralized; **—ение** *n.* mineralization.
орудие *n.* instrument, tool; gun.
оружие *n.* weapon, arms.

осадитель *m.* precipitator, precipitant; —**ный** *a.* precipitation, precipitating; settling.

осадить *see* **осаждать, осаживать.**

осадка *f.* settling, setting, set; sag; sedimentation.

осадко/мер *m.* precipitation gauge; —**образование** *n.* precipitation formation.

осад/ок *m.* residue; sediment, deposit, deposition, precipitate, precipitation; **выпадение —ка** precipitation; —**ки** *pl.* precipitation, rainfall, fallout.

осадочн/ый *a.* settling; precipitation; sedimentary; **о. бассейн** precipitation (sedimentation, settling) tank; —**ые породы** sedimentary rock.

осаждаем/ость *f.* precipitability; —**ый** *a.* precipitable.

осаждать *v.* precipitate, deposit, settle (out), separate (out); **о. вместе** coprecipitate; —**ся** *v.* precipitate (out), settle (out), be deposited.

осаждающ/ий *a.* precipitating, settling; —**ее вещество** precipitant, precipitator; —**ийся** *a.* precipitating, settling; precipitable.

сажден/ие *n.* precipitation, settling (out), deposition, sedimentation; precipitate, deposit, sediment; plating; **о. на электроде** electrodeposition; **о. носителем** carrier precipitation; —**ный** *a.* precipitated, settled, deposited; sedimentary.

саживать *v.* clinch.

сваив/ание *n.* familiarization; —**ать** *v.* familiarize, assimilate, master. —**аться** *v.* familiarize oneself, become familiar with.

сведомит/ель *m.* informer, informant; —**ельный** *a.* informative; —**ь** *v.* inform; —**ься** *v.* inquire.

сведомлен/ие *n.* inquiry; information; —**ность** *f.* information, knowledge, awareness; —**ный** *a.* informed, well-informed.

сведомлять *see* **осведомить**; —**ся** *see* **осведомиться.**

свеж/ать, —**ить** *v.* refresh, freshen; —**ающий,** —**ительный** *a.* refreshing; —**ение** *n.* refreshment; —**енный** *a.* refreshed.

осветитель *m.* illuminator; condenser (of microscope); —**ный** *a.* illuminating, illumination, lighting; —**ная ракета** flare; —**ная сеть** lighting system.

осветить *see* **освещать.**

осветл/ение *n.* clarification; —**енный** *a.* clarified, cleared; —**итель** *m.* clarifier, clarifying agent; —**ять** *v.* clarify, clear.

освещ/ать *v.* light, illuminate; elucidate; irradiate; expose (to light); —**ение** *n.* light, lighting, illumination; (phot.) exposure; elucidation, interpretation; —**енность** *f.* illumination, illuminance, irradiance; exposure.

освидетельствов/ание *n.* examination, inspection; —**ать** *v.* examine, inspect.

освинцов/ание *n.* lead plating, lead lining; —**анный** *a.* lead-plated, lead-lined, lead-coated; —**ать,** —**ывать** *v.* treat with lead, lead-plate.

освободит/ельный *a.* liberating, freeing; —**ь** *see* **освобождать.**

освобожд/ать *v.* free, release, liberate; disengage; rid; **о. энергию** release energy; —**ающий** *a.* liberating, releasing.

освобожден/ие *n.* liberation, release; elimination; exemption; —**ный** *a.* freed, liberated, released; exempt.

осво/ение *n.* appropriation, utilization, assimilation; mastering; conquest; —**иться** *see* **осваиваться.**

осев/ой *a.* axial; axle; central, center; **о. проводник** central wire (or conductor); —**ая линия** center line, axial line; —**ая нагрузка** axial load; —**ая окружность** circular axis (of torus); —**ое квантовое число** magnetic quantum number.

осевший *a.* precipitated, settled, deposited.

оседаем/ость *f.* precipitability; —**ый** *a.* precipitable.

осед/ание *n.* settling, lowering, subsidence; sagging; settling, precipitation; —**ать** *v.* settle, sink, subside; sag; set; precipitate; —**ающий** *a.* settling, sinking; sagging.

Осеена уравнение Oseen equation.

осел/ок *m.,* —**очный** *a.* whetstone, grindstone.

осен/ний *a.*, **—ь** *f.* autumn, fall; **золотая —ь** *see* **бабье лето.**

осесимметричный *a.* axisymmetric.

осили/вать, —ть *v.* overcome; master.

оскол/ок *m.*, **—очный** *a.* fragment, splinter, chip; **—ки деления** fission fragments.

оскорб/ительный *a.* offensive; **—ить, —лять** *v.* offend; **—ление** *n.* offense, insult; **—ленный** *a.* offended, insulted.

оскулаторный *a.* osculatory.

ослабе/вание *n.* weakening, slackening, relaxation, abatement; **—вать, —ть** *v.* weaken; decrease, fade away, decline, slacken; relax; **—вший, —лый** *a.* weakened, slackened.

ослабит/ель *m.* (phot.) reducer; optical wedge; (elec.) attenuator; weakener; **—ь** *see* **ослаблять.**

ослаблен/ие *n.* attenuation, suppression, extinction; reduction, weakening, slackening, relaxation; (phot.) clearing; **о. ветра** decrease (abating, slackening) of wind; **о. пучка** beam attenuation; **атомный коэффициент —ия** atomic absorption coefficient; **коэффициент —ия** attenuation factor, extinction coefficient.

ослабл/енный *a.* weakened; reduced; loose, relaxed; (phot.) reduced; **—ять** *v.* weaken, attenuate; reduce, decrease, abate; loosen; relax, slacken; (phot.) reduce.

ослабляющ/ий *a.* weakening; loosening; **о. раствор** (phot.) reducing solution; **—ая интерференция** destructive interference.

ослаб/нувший, —ший *a.* weakened, weak; loose, slack; **—нуть** *see* **ослабевать.**

ослеп/ительный *a.* blinding, glaring, dazzling; **—ить, —лять** *v.* blind, dazzle; **—ление** *n.* blinding; **—ленный** *a.* blinded, dazzled.

осложн/ение *n.* complication; **—енный** *a.* complicated, complex; **—ить, —ять** *v.* complicate.

О-слой *m.* O-shell.

ослышаться *v.* hear incorrectly.

осмалив/ание *n.* resinification; pitching, tarring; **—ать** *v.* resinify; pitch, tar; **—аться** *v.* resinify.

осматривать *v.* examine, scan, inspect, survey.

осм/иевый *a.* osmium, osmic; **—ий** *m.* osmium (Os); **—истый** *a.* osmious, osmium.

осмозировать *v.* osmose.

осмол/ение, —ка *see* **осмаливание; —енный** *a.* resinified; pitched, tarred; **—ять** *see* **осмаливать.**

осмометр *m.* osmometer.

осмос *m.* osmosis.

осмотическ/и *adv.* by osmosis; **—ий** *a.* osmotic; **—ое давление** osmotic pressure.

осмотр *m.* examination, inspection, survey, review.

осмотрительн/ость *f.* circumspection, caution, discretion; **—ый** *a.* circumspect, cautious.

осмотрщик *m.* examiner, inspector.

осмысл/енный *a.* intelligent, sensible; significant, meaningful; **—ить** *v.* comprehend; interpret.

осн. *abbr.* (**основа**) (chem.) base; (**основан, основанный**) founded.

осна/стить, —щать, —щивать *v.* equip, fit out; **—стка** *f.*, **—щение** *n.* fittings, equipment; **—стка приборами** instrumentation; **—щенный** *a.* equipped, fitted out.

основа *f.* base, basis, foundation, origin, principle, element, fundamental; (cryst.) base (material), host; starting sheet (in electrodeposition); **о. пленки** film backing.

основан/ие *n.* foundation, basis, base (chem.) base; bottom; end (of cylinder); founding; (math.) radix; reason, justification; **о. логарифмов** base of logarithms; **о. облака** cloud base; **лежать в —ии** underlie; **не без —ия** not without reason, with reason; **—ный** *a.* based; founded.

основатель *m.* founder, establisher; **—но** *adv.* fully, thoroughly, soundly, firmly; **—ность** *f.* soundness, judiciousness; **—ный** *a.* solid, well grounded, thorough, firm.

основать *see* **основывать.**

основн/ой *a.* fundamental, basic, principal, essential, base, main, primary, reference; sub— (salt); **в —ом** primarily, essentially, mainly, princi pally, basically, largely; **о. активатор** dominant activator; **о. вектор** basis vector; **о. вид колебаний** dominant mode of oscillations; **о. горизонт** reference (or datum) level; **о. закон** fundamental law; **о. импульс** (elec.) ground pulse; **о. лепесток** (antenna) major lobe; **о. металл** base (or parent) metal; **о. носитель** (semicond.) majority carrier; **о. период** fundamental period; **о. поток** main flow; **о. реактор** primary reactor; **о. резонанс** major (or main) resonance; **о. рентгеновский К-край поглощения** main K-absorption edge; **о. рентгеновский К-спектр поглощения** main K-absorption spectrum; **о. слой** base layer.

основн/ой *cont.*, **о. термодинамический цикл** Carnot cycle; **о. тон** fundamental tone; **о. уровень** (quant.) ground level; (rad.) base level; **о. фон** inherent background; **о. фронт** (meteor.) primary front; **о. цвет** primary color; **о. член** principal term; dominant term; **о. электрод** base (of transistor); **—ая гармоника** fundamental harmonic; **—ая единица** fundamental unit; **—ая кривая намагничивания** normal magnetization curve; **—ая линия** (spect.) principal line; base line; **—ая масса** great bulk, majority; matrix.

основн/ой *cont.*, **—ая область** (semicond.) base region; **—ая плита** base plate; **—ая плоскость** basal plane (or face); **—ая полоса** (semicond.) valence band; **—ая реакция** main reaction; **—ая решетка** base (or host) crystal; **—ая соль** basic salt, subsalt; **—ая структура** (geo.) basement structure; **—ая форма облаков** cloud genus; **—ая частица** fundamental particle; **—ая частота** fundamental frequency; **—ая часть** major portion.

основн/ой *cont.*, **—ое арифметическое действие** fundamental arithmetical operation; **—ое вещество** base (or host) material; **—ое значение** primary meaning; **—ое колебание** fundamental oscillation, normal mode; **—ое количество** bulk; **—ое правило** fundamental rule; **—ое состояние** ground state; principal state; **—ые ветры** cardinal winds; **—ые соотношения** fundamental principles.

основ/ность *f.* basicity; **—ополагающий** *a.* basic.

основоположник *m.* founder, initiator.

основыв/ать *v.* found, establish, base, erect; **—аться** *v.* be based on; **—аясь на** on the basis of.

особенно *adv.* especially, particularly, unusually; specifically, notably.

особенност/ь *f.* peculiarity, singularity, discontinuity, anomaly, distinctive feature; characteristic, nature, property; **главная о.** chief characteristic; **характерная о.** characteristic (property); **в —и** in particular, particularly, especially.

особенн/ый *a.* special, singular, peculiar, particular, specific, specialized; **—ая звезда** peculiar star.

особняк *m.* isolated object (or phenomenon).

особо *adv.* separately; especially.

особ/ый *a.* peculiar, particular, singular, special, specific; separate; **—ая оговорка** specification; **—ая точка** singular point, singularity; **сильная —ая точка** essential singular point; **слабая —ая точка** nonessential singular point; **—ая чистота** high purity; **—ое квантовое число** "strangeness" (quantum number); **—ое решение** singular solution.

осозн/авать, —ать *v.* realize, perceive.

оспа *f.* variola.

оспаривать *v.* dispute, contend, controvert.

осреднен/ие *n.* averaging, average; **—ный** *a.* average, mean.

ОСТ *abbr.* (**Общесоюзный стандарт**) All-Union Standard.

остав/аться *v.* remain; **—ить, —лять** *v.* leave, abandon; **—ить за собой** reserve; **—ить у себя** keep, retain; **—ление** *n.* leaving; **—ленный** *a.* left.

осталив/ание *n.* (met.) steeling; conversion into steel; **—ать** *v.* steel; convert to steel.

остальн/ой *a.* remaining, residual; **в**

—**ом** in other respects, otherwise; —**ые** *pl.* the rest.

останавливать *v.* stop, discontinue, shut down; check, arrest; —**ся** *v.* stop; —**ся на** dwell on, discuss.

останавливающий *a.* stopping, shutoff, arresting; **о. раствор** (phot.) stop bath.

останец *m.* (geo.) residual mountain, butte, mesa.

останов *m.* stop, checking device, detent; —**ившаяся частица** stopped particle; —**ить** *see* **останавливать**; —**иться** *see* **останавливаться**; —**ка** *f.* stopping, halt, cessation, stop; shutdown; interruption; **полная** —**ка** deadlock; —**ленный** *a.* stopped, standing; —**очный** *a.* stopping, stop, check.

остат/ок *m.* residue, remainder; surplus, balance; (chem.) radical; **атомный о.** atomic core; —**ки** *pl.* scraps, fragments, refuse, waste.

остаточн/ый *a.* residual, remanent; permanent; (geo.) detrital; after—; **о. импульс** afterpulse; **о. магнетизм** remanent magnetism, remanence; **о. накал** afterglow; **о. пробег** residual range; **о. ток** residual current; transient-decay current, aftercurrent; —**ая деформация** remanent strain; permanent set (or deformation); —**ая емкость** residual capacitance; —**ая (магнитная) индукция** remanence, residual magnetic induction; —**ая намагниченность** remanence, remanent magnetization; **обратная** —**ая намагниченность** reversed remanent magnetization; —**ая световая сумма** afterglow light sum; —**ая теплота,** —**ое тепло** afterheat; —**ое излучение** residual radiation; —**ое изменение** residual drift; —**ое изображение** afterimage; —**ое поле** remanent field; —**ое расширение** permanent expansion; —**ое сжатие** permanent contraction; —**ое ядро** residual (or final) nucleus; —**ые лучи** residual rays, reststrahlen; **коэффициент** —**ых потерь** residual loss constant.

остаться *see* **оставаться.**

остающийся *a.* residual, remaining; permanent, durable, stable; persistent.

Оствальда закон Ostwald law; **коэффициент растворимости О.** O. solubility coefficient.

остеклов/ание *n.* vitrification; —**анный** *a.* vitrified, glazed; —**ать,** —**ывать** *v.* vitrify, glaze.

остеклян/елый *a.* vitreous, glassy; —**еть** *v.* vitrify.

остео/саркома *f.* osteosarcoma; —**тропный** *a.* bone-seeking; —**фил** *m.* bone seeker.

остер/егание *n.* warning; —**егать,** —**ечь** *v.* warn, caution.

остов *m.* skeleton, framework, frame hull, body, casing; (nucl.) core; **о. катушки** reel; **о. снаряда** missile body (structure, frame).

осторожн/о *adv.* carefully, cautiously —**ость** *f.* care, caution, precaution —**ый** *a.* careful, cautious, delicate (adjustment).

острение *n.* pointing, sharpening.

остр/ие *n.* point; edge (of knife); spike peak, cusp; pivot; —**ийный счетчик** point counter tube; —**ить** *v.* sharpen whet; point; —**о** *adv.* sharply.

остров *m.* island.

островершинность *f.* (stat.) peakedness kurtosis; pointedness.

остров/ной *a.* isolated, insular, island **о. эффект** island effect; —**ок** *m.* islet.

острогать *v.* plane, pare down.

Остроградского/-Гаусса формула (теорема) Gauss divergence theorem **теорема О.-Грина** Green theorem.

острогубцы *pl.* cutting pliers.

остроконечн/ый *a.* cusped, cuspate, cuspidal; (fine-) pointed, peaked, ridged —**ая кривая** peaked curve; —**ое ребро** cuspidal edge.

остролучевая антенна pencil-beam antenna.

остронаправленный пучок pencil (beam).

остроносый *a.* pointed, sharp, tapered.

острота *f.* sharpness, acuteness, acuity keenness.

остроугольный *a.* acute-angled.

остроумный *a.* ingenious, clever.

острофокусн/ый *a.* fine-focus, sharp-focused; **—ая трубка** fine-focus (x-ray) tube.

остр/ый *a.* sharp, keen, edged, pointed; acute; **о. клин** narrow wedge; **о. конец** point; **о. лучевой синдром** acute radiation syndrome; **о. пар** live steam; **—ая настройка** fine tuning; **—ое положение** critical situation.

остудить *see* **остужать.**

остудневать *v.* gelate, gelatinize, gelatinate.

остуж/ать *v.* cool, chill; **—енный** *a.* cooled, chilled; **—ивание** *n.* cooling, chilling.

осты/вать, —нуть, —ть *v.* cool (off); **—вший** *a.* cooled, cold, congealed.

осу/дить, —ждать *v.* criticize, blame, censure; **—ждение** *n.* blame, censure.

осуш/аемый *a.* dried, dehumidified; drained; **—ать** *v.* drain; dry; **—ение** *n.* drying, desiccation; drainage, land reclamation.

осушитель *m.*, **—ное средство** drier, drying agent, desiccant; **—ный** *a.* drying, desiccating; draining, drainage; **—ный канал** drainage channel.

осуш/ить *see* **осушать**; **—ка** *f.* draining; drying.

осуществ/имость *f.* feasibility, realizability, practicability; **—имый** *a.* feasible, practicable, realizable; **—ить, —лять** *v.* realize, accomplish, achieve, carry out; **—иться, —ляться** *v.* occur, take place, be accomplished (or realized); be implemented; be effected; **—ление** *n.* realization, accomplishment; **—ленный** *a.* realized, accomplished.

осциллир/ование *n.* oscillation; **—ующий** *a.* oscillating.

осциллограмма *f.* oscillogram.

осциллограф *m.* oscillograph; **—ирование** *n.* oscillography; **—ическая трубка** oscillotron.

осциллоскоп *m.* oscilloscope.

осцилля/тор *m.* oscillator; **—ция** *f.* oscillation.

осып/ание *n.* falling down, crumbling; sprinkling, dusting; **—анный** *a.* fallen, crumbled; sprinkled, dusted, strewn; **—ать** *v.* sprinkle, dust, strew (with); **—ь** *f.* (geo.) talus, scree.

ос/ь *f.* axis; axle, shaft, spindle, pin, pivot; center line; **боковая о., побочная о.** secondary axis; **большая о.** major axis; **о. вращения** axis of rotation; **имеющий общую о., совпадающий —ями** coaxial; **о. качания** axis of oscillation; **о. легкого намагничивания** direction of easy magnetization; **меньшая о.** minor axis; **о. плавания** axis of buoyancy; **о. подвеса** axis of suspension; **о. растяжения** axis of dilatation, axis of tension; **о. сжатия** axis of contraction; **о. симметрии** ***n*-ого порядка** *n*-fold axis of symmetry; **о. синфазности** (seis.) axis of synchronous phases; **числовая о.** number scale (or axis); **на одной —и** in line with, in alignment (with), aligned; **по —и** axially, endwise.

осьми— *prefix* octa—.

осяз/аемость *f.* tangibility; **—аемый** *a.* tangible, tactile; **—ание** *n.* sensation (or sense) of touch; **—ательный** *a.* tactile, palpable; sensitive; **—ать** *v.* touch, feel.

от *prep. gen.* from, off, of; for; **время от времени** from time to time; **день ото дня** from day to day.

ОТ *abbr.* (**относительная топография**) relative topography, thickness pattern.

отаплив/ание *n.* heating; firing; **—ать** *v.* heat; fire.

отбав/ить, —лять *v.* decrease, diminish, take away, subtract; **—ка** *f.*, **—ление** *n.* decrease, diminution, taking away, subtraction.

отбел/енный *a.* whitened, bleached; blanched; **—ивание** *n.* whitening, bleaching; blanching; decolorizing; **—ивать, —ить** *v.* whiten, bleach; blanch; decolorize.

отбелка *see* **отбеливание.**

отбереговой ветер offshore wind.

отбив *m.*, **—ание** *n.*, **—ка** *f.* repelling, repulsion; **—ать** *v.* repel.

отбир/ание *n.* removal; selecting, sorting; **—ать** *v.* remove, withdraw; select, sort (out), sample; **—ающий** *a.* selective.

отбит/ие *see* **отбивание**; **—ь** *see* **отбивать.**

отблеск *m.* reflection, gleam, blink.

отбликовать *v.* tarnish.

отбой *m.* repulsion; stop; breaking off (connection); **—ный** *a.* repelling, recoil; guard; breaking.

отбор *m.* selection, choice, sample, sampling; (power) takeoff; **о. образцов, о. проб** sampling; **правило —а** selection rule; **—ный** *a.* choice, select; screened (ore).

отбортов/ка *f.*, **—ывать** *v.* flange, crimp.

отбрасыв/аемый *a.* rejected; thrust-back; **—ание** *n.* rejection, discarding; repulsion; kick; **—ать** *v.* reject, discard; repulse.

отброс *m.* residue, waste product; kick; **—ы** *pl.* waste, refuse; **—ать, —ить** *see* **отбрасывать**; **—ный** *a.* waste.

отброшенный *a.* rejected, discarded, dropped, neglected; **о. поток** slip stream.

отбытие *n.* departure.

отвал *m.* dump, dumping ground; **—ивание** *n.* heaping; dumping.

отваливать *v.* heap; dump; **—ся** *v.* fall off.

отвар/ивание *n.* boiling; unwelding; **—ивать, —ить** *v.* boil; unweld; **—ной, —ный** *a.* boiled.

отведен/ие *n.* removal, diversion; **—ный** *a.* removed, drained-off, diverted.

отвезти *see* **отвозить.**

отверг/ать, —нуть *v.* reject, refute, repudiate; **—нутый** *a.* rejected, discarded.

отверд/евание, —ение *n.* hardening, consolidation, setting, solidification; **—евать, —еть** *v.* harden, consolidate, solidify; **—елость** *f.* hardness; **—елый** *a.* solidified, consolidated; **—ить** *see* **отверждать.**

отвержд/ать *v.* consolidate, strengthen, harden; **—ение** *see* **отвердевание**; **—енный** *a.* consolidated, strengthened, hardened.

отвернуть *see* **отвертывать.**

отверст/ие *n.* hole, aperture, opening, gap, orifice, vent, port; (screen) mesh; **о. для пучка** beam hole; **сто —ий на 1 дм.** 100-mesh.

отверт/ка *f.* screw driver; **—ывать** *v.* unscrew; open (faucet, valve); turn back, avert.

отвес *m.* perpendicular, vertical, normal, plumb (line); **—ить** *see* **отвешивать.**

отвесн/о *adv.* sheer, plumb, perpendicular; **—ость** *f.* perpendicularity, verticality, steepness; **—ый** *a.* perpendicular, vertical, plumb; sheer, precipitous; **—ая доска** plumb rule.

отвести *see* **отводить.**

ответ *m.* answer, reply, response.

ответвит/ель *m.* (elec.) coupler; **—ельный** *a.* branching, branch, distributing; **—ь** *see* **ответвлять.**

ответвлен/ие *n.* branching, branch, tap arm; (elec.) shunting, shunt; **сделать о.** branch off; **—ный** *a.* branched branch; (elec.) shunt.

ответвл/ять *v.* branch off, derive, tap shunt; **—яться** *v.* branch, ramify bifurcate; **—яющий** *a.* branching shunting.

ответ/ить *see* **отвечать**; **—ный** *a.* reply answering.

ответственн/ость *f.* responsibility; **—ый** *a.* responsible; important; **—ый редактор** editor-in-chief; **—ый сотрудник** executive; **—ая часть** critical (or important) part; strength member.

ответчик *m.* responder (beacon).

отвечать *v.* answer, reply, respond; be responsible; **о. требованию** satisfy (or meet) a requirement.

отвеш/енный *a.* weighed (out); **—ивание** *n.* weighing (out); **—ивать** *v.* weigh (out).

отвин/тить, —чивать *v.* unscrew; **—ченный** *a.* unscrewed; **—чивание** *n.* unscrewing; loosening.

отвис/ать, —нуть *v.* hang down.

отвлек/ать *v.* distract, divert; abstract; **—аться** *v.* digress; **—ающий** *a.* distracting.

отвлеч. *abbr.* (**отвлеченный**) abstract.

отвлеч/ение *n.* distraction, digression; abstraction; discharge, removal; **—енный** *a.* abstract; **—енная величина** abstract quantity; **—ь** *see* **отвлекать.**

отвод *m.* branch, branch pipe, offtake; bend, elbow; tap, drain, runo tapping, withdrawal, removal; discharge; diversion; allotment, distribution; **делать о.** object, take exception (to). **о. тепла** heat removal (elimination, rejection, dissipation); **катушка с —ами** tapped coil.

отвод/имый *a.* outgoing, exit; withdrawable; **—итель** *m.* outlet; **—ить** *v.* lead off, carry off, draw off, drain (off), discharge; divert, deflect; shunt; assign; **—ка** *f.* shifter, shifting device.

отводн/ый *a.* branch; outlet, drain; **о. канал** offtake, spillway; **о. кран** drain (cock); **—ая труба** branch (outlet, drain, discharge) pipe.

отводящ/ий *a.* deflecting, diverting; discharge, outlet; **о. канал** offtake; **о. патрубок** outlet branch; **о. трубопровод** drain (pipe); **—ая труба** exhaust pipe, exhaust.

отвозить *v.* transport, take away.

отворачивать *see* **отвертывать, отворотить.**

отворить *see* **отворять.**

отворот *m.* flange, fold; **—ить** *v.* turn away; avert.

отворять *v.* open.

отв. ред. *abbr.* (**ответственный редактор**) editor-in-chief.

отв/см² *abbr.* (**отверстий в сите на 1 см²**) openings/cm² in screen or sieve.

отвяз/ать, —ывать *v.* untie, unfasten, loosen, disengage.

отгиб *m.* fold; **—ание** *n.* turning back, bending; unbending, straightening; **—ать** *v.* turn back, fold; unbend, straighten.

отгов/аривать, —орить *v.* dissuade; **—орка** *f.* pretext, excuse.

отгон *m.* distillate; **—ка** *f.* elimination; distillation; **—ять** *v.* drive off, eliminate; distill (off); repel.

отгор/аживать, —одить *v.* partition off, shut off; **—оженный** *a.* partitioned, shut (off); **—оженное место** enclosure.

отградуированный *a.* calibrated.

отгру/жать, —зить *v.* unload; **—зка** *f.* unloading.

отд. *abbr.* (**отдел, отделение**) section, division, branch, department; (**отдельный**) separate.

отдаваемая мощность power (or energy) output.

отдавать *v.* give away; deliver, yield; have the odor of; return, restore; recoil, rebound; loosen; **о. должное** do justice (to); **о. назад** return; recoil; **—ся** *v.* devote oneself (to); resound.

отдав/ить, —ливать *v.* squeeze, crush.

отдален/ие *n.*, **—ность** *f.* remoteness, distance; removal; **в —ии** at a distance, in the distance; **—ный** *a.* distant, remote; **—ные последствия облучения** late radiation effects.

отдал/ить, —ять *v.* move away, remove; postpone.

отданный *a.* returned; yielded, given off.

отдать *see* **отдавать.**

отдач/а *f.* efficiency, performance (of machine); delivery, output, yield; release; evolution; return; recoil, rebound, springiness; **о. флуоресценции** fluorescence yield; **о. ядра** nuclear recoil; **коэффициент —и** efficiency.

отдел *m.* section, division, branch, department; (geo.) series.

отдел/анный *a.* finished, dressed, trimmed; **—ать** *see* **отделывать.**

отделение *n.* division, branch, department, section, compartment, partition; separation, detachment, separating (out), segregation; evolution, emission, precipitation; recovery (from waste); isolation; **о. вихрей** vortex detachment; **о. переменных** separation of variables; **о. слоев** exfoliation.

отделенный *a.* separated, segregated, eliminated, isolated; detached; **о. осаждением** precipitated (out).

отдел/ившийся *a.* separated, loosened; **—имость** *f.* separability; **—имый** *a.* separable; detachable; **—итель** *m.* separator, eliminator; **—ительный** *a.* separating; **—ить** *see* **отделять.**

отдел/ка *f.* finishing, dressing, cleaning; structure; **—очный** *a.* finishing, cleaning; **—ывать** *v.* finish, dress, clean, trim.

отдельно *adv.* separately; **о. расположенный, о. стоящий** independent, separate, detached.

отдельност/ь *f.* individuality; (geo.) cleavage, jointing; structure; **в —и** separately, individually.

отдел/ьный *a.* separate, discrete, specific, individual; selected, detached, independent, isolated, single; partial, divided; particular; **о. рефлекс** (cryst.) isolated reflection; **о. уровень** discrete level; **—ять** *v.* separate; single out, isolate, segregate; divide; detach, disengage; eliminate, liberate, release; extract.

отдер/гивание *n.*, **—жка** *f.* drawing back; **—гивать, —нуть** *v.* draw back, withdraw.

отдир/ание *n.* stripping; **—ать** *v.* strip.

отдохнуть *see* **отдыхать.**

отд. тех. наук *abbr.* (**отделение технических наук**) division of technical sciences.

отдулина *f.* bulge.

отдушина *f.* (air) hole, vent.

отдых *m.* rest, relaxation; **—ать** *v.* rest.

отекать *v.* flow off.

отенит *m.* autunite.

отепленный *a.* coldproof, winterproof.

отереть *see* **отирать.**

оте/ц *m.* father; **—ческий** *a.* paternal.

отечественн/ый *a.* native, home; **—ое производство** domestic manufacture.

отечь *see* **отекать.**

отжат/ый *a.* squeezed-out; **—ь** *see* **отжимать.**

отжечь *see* **отжигать.**

отжиг *m.*, **—ание** *n.* annealing; **—ательный** *a.* annealing; **—ательная печь** annealing furnace; **—ать** *v.* anneal; burn off.

отжим/ание *n.* squeezing (out), pressing (out); **—ать** *v.* squeeze (out).

отзвук *m.* repercussion; echo; reverberation.

отзейгерованный *a.* (met.) liquated.

отзыв *m.* opinion, comment; review; testimonial, reference; **—ать** *v.* recall; **—аться** *v.* recall; echo; respond; comment; affect.

отирать *v.* wipe, dry.

отказ *m.* refusal, denial, rejection; (mach.) failure, breakdown; **до —а** to the limit.

отказ/ать, —ывать *v.* refuse, reject, deny; renounce; **—аться, —ываться** *v.* refuse; give up, renounce; **—аться действовать** fail, break down.

откалыв/ание *n.* breaking off, splitting off; **—ать** *v.* break off, split off; separate.

откат *m.* recoil; backwash; **—ать** *v.* roll back, roll away.

откат/ить *see* **откатывать**; **—ка** *f.* haulage.

откатыв/ание *n.* rolling away; **—ать** *v.* roll away; (min.) haul; **—аться** *v.* recoil.

откач/анный *a.* evacuated; **—ать, —ивать** *v.* pump out, evacuate, exhaust; **—ивающий насос** exhaust pump; **—ка** *f.* pumping, evacuation; **дифференциальная —ка** differential pumping; **—ной** *a.* pumping, exhaust; **—ное устройство** pump assembly.

отки/дной *a.* folding, collapsible; hinged; **—дывать, —нуть** *v.* throw off; throw away, omit, discard; tilt.

откисл/енный *a.* neutralized, deacidified; **—ить** *v.* deacidify, neutralize.

откладыв/ание *n.* postponing; putting aside; **—ать** *v.* plot (curve); postpone, defer; adjourn, call off; put aside, reserve; settle, deposit, precipitate.

отклеи/вать, —ть *v.* unglue.

отклик *m.* response; comment; **о. антенны** antenna response; **—аться** *v.* respond (to); comment (on).

отклонен/ие *n.* deflection, declination, divergence, diversion, digression, deviation, departure; refusal; variation, discrepancy, bias, error, aberration; **о. луча** beam deflection; **среднее арифметическое о.** (stat.) mean deviation; **среднее квадратическое о.** root-mean-square deviation; **коэффициент —ия** deflection coefficient; **угол —ия** angle of deviation (or displacement); **—ный** *a.* deflected, divergent, displaced.

отклонитель *m.* deflector.

отклон/ить, —ять *v.* decline, deflect, divert; **—иться, —яться** *v.* decline, deflect, deviate, digress, diverge; slant, tilt.

отклоняющ/ий *a.* deflecting, defocusing, diverting; **о. фронт** deflecting front;

—ая катушка deflecting coil; **—ая пластина** deflecting plate, deflector; **—ая сила** deflecting force; **—ее напряжение** deflection voltage; **—ийся** *a.* divergent, deviating.

отключ/аемый *a.* detachable; **—ать, —ить** *v.* detach, disconnect, trip; **—ение** *n.* detachment, disconnecting; **—енный** *a.* detached, disconnected.

откованный *a.* forged.

откол *m.* splitting off; **—отый** *a.* split-off, cleaved; **—оть** *see* **откалывать; —ьный** *a.* split-off.

откос *m.* slant, slope, incline, declivity; **с —ом** sloped.

откреп/ить, —лять *v.* unfasten, detach.

откровенн/ость *f.* frankness; **—ый** *a.* frank, outspoken.

откру/тить, —чивать *v.* untwist, unscrew.

открыв/аемый *a.* detectable; **—ание** *n.* opening; **—ать** *v.* open, uncover, reveal; (elec.) gate; discover, detect.

открытие *n.* opening; discovery, invention; detection; uncovering.

открыт/о *adv.* openly, publicly; **—ость** *f.* openness; **—ый** *a.* open, exposed, bare; (elec.) "on"; outspoken; **—ый пучок** open beam; **—ая литература** "unclassified" literature; **—ое множество** open set; **—ое скопление** (astr.) open cluster.

открыть *see* **открывать.**

откуда *adv.* from where; from which, whence, wherefrom; **о.-либо, о.-нибудь** from somewhere or other; **о. ни** wherever from; **о. следует** whence it appears, it follows.

откупор/енный *a.* uncorked, unstopped; **—ивать, —ить** *v.* uncork, unstop.

отлагат/ельство *n.* delay; **—ь** *v.* delay; (geo.) deposit; **—ься** *v.* separate, deposit.

отламывать *v.* break off, chip off.

отлеп/ить, —ливать, —лять *v.* unglue.

отлет *m.* flying away, takeoff; **—ать, —еть** *v.* fly off, take off; **—ающий** *a.* outgoing, emitted.

отлив *m.* reflux, return flow, discharge; ebb, low tide; **прилив и о.** ebb and flow; high tide and low tide.

отлив/ать *v.* cast; pour (off); ebb; **—ка** *f.* casting; cast; pouring off, decanting.

отливн/ой *a.* cast; founding, casting; decanting; **—ое течение** ebb.

отливо/к *m.* cast; casting; **—чный** *a.* casting.

отлип/ание *n.* ungluing, loosening; **—ать, —нуть** *v.* unglue, loosen.

отлит/ый *a.* cast, founded; poured-off; **—ь** *see* **отливать.**

отлич/ать *v.* distinguish, discriminate; **—аться** *v.* differ; be distinguished by, be characterized by; surpass, excel; **—ившийся** *a.* excellent, outstanding; **—ие** *n.* difference, distinction, diversity; **в —ии от** in contrast to, unlike; **—имый** *a.* distinguishable.

отличит/ельный *a.* distinctive, distinguishing, characteristic; **о. признак** distinguishing feature, characteristic; **—ь** *see* **отличать.**

отличный *a.* excellent, perfect; different, distinct (from); **о. от нуля** nonvanishing, nonzero.

отлог *m.* inclination, slope; **—ий** *a.* sloping, gentle, flat; **—о спускаться, —ость** *f.* slope.

отлож/ение *n.* precipitation, precipitate, sediment; deposit, deposition; postponing; **—енный** *a.* precipitated, deposited; plotted; postponed; **—ившийся** *a.* precipitated, deposited, settled; **—ить** *see* **откладывать, отлагать.**

отлом/ать, —ить *see* **отламывать.**

отматывать *v.* unwind.

отмачивать *v.* soak off.

отмель *f.* bank, shoal, shallow.

отмен/а *f.* abolition; revocation, cancellation; **—ить** *v.* abolish; revoke, annul, cancel.

отменн/ость *f.* superiority, excellence; **—ый** *a.* superior, excellent.

отменять *see* **отменить.**

отмерз/ать, —нуть *v.* thaw; **—лый** *a.* frozen; thawed out.

отмер/ивание *n.* measuring off; **—ивать, —ить, —ять** *v.* measure off, mark off.

отме/сти, —тать *v.* sweep away; reject.

отмет/ина *f.* mark, marking; **—ить** *see* **отмечать; —ка** *f.* mark, marker;

pip; datum; sign, indication, criterion; recording, registration; —**ка времени** time marking; timing; —**чик** *m.* marker, recorder.

отмеч/ать *v.* mention, remark, notice, stress, underline; mark, register, record; —**ающий** *a.* recording, registering; —**енный** *a.* marked, recorded, registered; plotted; distinguished.

отмор/аживание *n.* freezing; —**аживать,** —**озить** *v.* freeze; —**оженный** *a.* frozen.

отмотать *see* **отматывать.**

отмочить *see* **отмачивать.**

отмуч/енный *a.* elutriated; —**ивание** *n.* elutriation; —**ивать,** —**ить** *v.* elutriate.

отмыв/ание *n.*, —**ка** *f.* washing off; —**ать** *v.* wash off.

отмык/ание *n.* unlocking, opening; —**ать** *v.* unlock, open.

отмыт/ый *a.* washed (off); —**ь** *see* **отмывать.**

отмяк/лость *f.* softening; —**лый,** —**ший** *a.* softened, soft; —**нуть** *v.* soften.

ОТН *abbr. see* **отд. тех. наук.**

отн. ед. *abbr.* (**относительная единица**) relative unit.

отнесен/ие *n.* reference; assignment; —**ный** *a.* referred to, relative to, per; divided by; adjusted to; attributed, assigned.

отнести *see* **относить.**

отнимать *v.* take away, subtract.

относ *m.* deviation.

относит. *abbr.* (**относительный**) relative.

относительно *adv.* comparatively, relatively; *prep. gen.* concerning, about, with reference to; —**сть** *f.* relativity.

относительн/ый *a.* relative, comparative; **о. вес** specific gravity; **о. выход деления** fission yield; **о. размах** (aero.) aspect ratio (of wing); —**ая апертура** relative aperture; —**ая биологическая эффективность** (**излучения**) radiobiological effectiveness (factor); —**ая вероятность ветвей** branching ratio; —**ая влажность** relative humidity; —**ая дисперсия** dispersive power; —**ая единица** relative unit; —**ая полуширина линии** line width (%) (of mass spectrometer); —**ая потеря** fractional loss; —**ое отверстие** relative aperture, aperture ratio; —**ое содержание изотопа** relative isotopic abundance; —**ое увеличение объема** dilation; —**ое укорочение** compressive strain (or deformation).

относ/ить *v.* take, deliver; relate, refer, attribute, coordinate; carry away, transfer; —**иться** *v.* relate, concern, pertain; refer; apply; drift; —**ящийся** *a.* concerning, pertaining; acting.

отношен/ие *n.* ratio, proportion; relation; respect; attitude; **весовое о.** ratio by weight; **двойное о.** anharmonic (double, cross) ratio; **иметь о.** pertain to, concern, affect; **о. масс** mass ratio; **обратное о.** inverse ratio; **о. ответвления** branching ratio; **разностное о.** quotient of differences; **о. сигнала к шуму** signal-to-noise ratio; **о. смеси** mixing ratio; **закон кратных** —**ий** law of multiple proportions; **закон постоянства весовых** —**ий** law of definite proportions; **в** —**ии** with respect to, concerning; versus; **в других** —**иях** in every respect; **в этом** —**ии** in this respect; **не имеющий** —**ия** unrelated, not pertinent; **по** —**ию к** with respect to, concerning; as compared to, as a percentage of.

отныне *adv.* henceforth.

отнюдь *adv.* by no means, not at all.

отнят/ие *n.* taking away, removal, elimination; —**ый** *a.* taken away, removed, eliminated; —**ь** *see* **отнимать.**

ото *see* **от.**

отображ/ать *v.* reflect; represent, map; —**ение** *n.* image, representation, mapping, reflection.

отобразить *see* **отображать.**

отобр/анный *a.* selected; **о. пар** extracted steam; —**ать** *see* **отбирать.**

отовсюду *adv.* from everywhere.

отогн/анный *a.* driven off; distilled; —**ать** *see* **отгонять.**

отогнут/ый *a.* bent back; —**ь** *see* **отгибать.**

отогре/вание *n.* warming; —**вать,** —**ть** *v.* warm.

отодви/гание *n.* removing, drawing back; **—гать, —нуть** *v.* remove, shift, move aside, displace; **—гаться, —нуться** *v.* move aside, shift; **—нутый** *a.* shifted, displaced.

отодрать *see* **отдирать.**

отождеств/ить, —лять *v.* identify; **—ление** *n.* identification.

отожженный *a.* annealed.

отойти *see* **отходить.**

отомкнут/ый *a.* unlocked, open; **—ь** *see* **отмыкать.**

отопит/ельный *a.* heating; **—ь** *see* **отапливать.**

отоплен/ие *n.* heating; **—ный** *a.* heated.

оторв/анный *a.* torn, separated; **—ать** *see* **отрывать.**

отослать *see* **отсылать.**

отпад/ать *v.* fall off, drop out; **—ающий** *a.* falling, dropping; **—ение** *n.* falling off, dropping.

отпа/ечный *a.* sealing; **—ивать** *v.* seal (off); **—йка** *f.* sealing off.

отпалка *f.* firing, blasting.

отпар/ивание *n.* steaming; **—ивать, —ить** *v.* steam.

отпасть *see* **отпадать.**

отпа/янный *a.* sealed-off; **—ять** *see* **отпаивать.**

отпер/еть *see* **отпирать; —тый** *a.* unlocked, open; (elec.) conducting.

отпечат/ание, —ывание *n.* printing; impression; **—ать, —ывать** *v.* print; imprint, impress; **—ок** *m.* print; impression; replica.

отпилить *v.* saw off.

отпир/ание *n.* unlocking, opening; triggering; **—ать** *v.* unlock, open, unfasten; unblock, trigger; **—ающая схема** trigger circuit.

отпор *m.* rebuff, resistance.

отпот/евание *n.* sweating, sweat, dew, condensate; **—евать, —еть** *v.* sweat; **—елый** *a.* covered with sweat.

отправитель *m.* transmitter, sender; **—ный** *a.* transmitting, sending.

отправ/ить *see* **отправлять; —ка** *f.* sending; shipment; **—ление** *n.* sending, shipping; transmission; departure, start; performance, exercise; functioning, function; **место —ления, точка —ления** starting point; point of origin; **—ленный** *a.* sent, shipped.

отправлять *v.* send, forward; ship; perform, exercise; **—ся** *v.* depart, start, proceed.

отправн/ой *a.* starting; **—ая точка** starting point, origin.

отпрессованный *a.* pressed-out.

отпрыг/ивать, —нуть *v.* rebound, recoil, spring back.

отпуск *m.* tempering, annealing, bake; leave of absence, holiday; **высокий о.** high-temperature tempering; **низкий о.** low-temperature tempering.

отпуск/ание *n.* slackening, loosening; (met.) annealing, tempering; **—ать** *v.* slacken, loosen, ease; (met.) temper, draw; **—ающий** *a.* release, releasing; **—ной** *a.* releasing; tempering.

отпу/стить *see* **отпускать; —щенный** *a.* slackened, loosened; (met.) tempered.

отраб/атывать *v.* finish off; **—отавший** *see* **отработанный.**

отработанн/ый *a.* used-up, exhausted, depleted, spent, waste; **о. газ** waste gas, exhaust gas; **о. пар** spent steam; **—ое горючее** spent fuel.

отработать *see* **отрабатывать.**

отрав/а *f.* poison, poisoning; **—ить, —лять** *v.* contaminate, poison; **—ление** *n.* poisoning; **—ленный** *a.* poisoned; **—ляющий** *a.* poisonous; **—ляющая примесь** poison, killer.

отражаемый *a.* reflected; image.

отражатель *m.* reflector, repeller; (antenna) dish; deflector; **о. клистрона** klystron repeller plate; **о. нейтронов** neutron reflector.

отражательн/ый *a.* reflecting, reverberatory; deflecting; **о. гониометр** reflecting goniometer; **о. клистрон** reflex klystron; **о. телескоп** reflecting telescope; **о. эшелон** reflection echelon; **—ая доска** baffle; **—ая заслонка** deflector; **—ая печь** (met.) reverberatory furnace; **—ая решетка** reflection grating; **—ая способность** reflectivity, reflectance, albedo.

отражать *v.* reflect, reverberate; indicate; represent; repel; **о. эхо** reecho;

—**ся** *v.* reflect, reverberate; rebound; echo.

отражающий *a.* reflecting, reverberatory; deflecting; **о. слой** reflecting layer; **о. экран** sheet reflector (of antenna).

отражен/ие *n.* reflection, reverberation, echo; image; repercussion; repulsion; **о. первого порядка** first-order reflection; **коэффициент —ия** reflection coefficient (or factor).

отраженн/ый *a.* reflected, reverberated; **о. ветер** cross wind; **о. звук** echo; **о. импульс** echo pulse; **—ое рассеяние** back scattering.

отразить *see* **отражать.**

отрасль *f.* branch.

отраст/ать, —и *v.* grow.

отра/стить, —щивать *v.* grow; tap, branch off.

отрегулиров/ание *n.* adjustment, regulation; **—анный** *a.* adjusted, regulated; **—ать** *v.* adjust, regulate.

отрез *m.* cut; **—ание** *n.*, **—ка** *f.*, **—ывание** *n.* cutting (off); **—анный** *a.*, **—ать** *v.* cut (off); **—ной** *a.* cutoff, cutting.

отрез/ок *m.* piece, length, section, fragment; (math.) segment, intercept; **о. отсекаемый на оси** intercept on an axis; **о. следа** track segment; **—ки** *pl.* fragments, scrap; **—ывать** *see* **отрезать.**

отре/каться, —чься *v.* deny, renounce.

отрицание *n.* negation, denial.

отрицательно *adv.* negatively; **о. заряженный** negatively charged; **о. определенный** (math.) negative definite.

отрицательн/ый *a.* negative; deleterious, unfavorable; **о. импульс** negative (or negative-going) pulse; **о. источник** negative source; **о. катализатор** anticatalyst; **о. кристалл** negative crystal; **о. мениск** negative meniscus, convexo-concave lens; **—ая линза** diverging lens; **—ая обратная связь** (elec.) degeneration; **—ая проводимость** *n*-type conductivity; **—ая сторона** disadvantage, drawback; **—ое тлеющее свечение** negative glow; **—ое ускорение** deceleration.

отрицать *v.* negate, deny, contradict; exclude.

отрог *m.* spur, offshoot, extension.

отросток *m.* branch, branch piece; prolongation, extension; finger; spur; (geo.) apophysis.

отруб/ать, —ить *v.* chop off.

отрыв *m.*, **—ание** *n.* break, breaking away, tear; cleavage, separation; discontinuance; (aero.) takeoff; **в о. от** separately (or apart) from; **о. от Земли** escape from the Earth; **о. потока** flow separation; **—ать** *v.* break off, detach, tear away; interrupt; unearth, excavate; **—аться** *v.* break off, break away, tear away; (aero.) take off; **—ающая сила** pull.

отрывист/ость *f.* abruptness, suddenness, jerkiness; **—ый** *a.* abrupt, sudden, jerky.

отрыв/ной *a.* separating, tearing-away, breaking-away; **—ное обтекание** detached flow; **—ное приспособление** (elec.) contact-breaking device; **—ок** *m.* fragment; excerpt; **—очный** *a.* interrupted, fragmentary.

отрыть *v.* excavate.

отряд *m.* order.

отря/сать, —сти, —хивать, —хнуть *v.* shake off.

отсасыв/ание *n.* suction; **—ать** *v.* suck, draw off, exhaust; **—ающий** *a.* suction; exhaust; **—ающий трансформатор** draining transformer.

отсвет *m.* reflection.

отсвечив/ание *n.* reflection; brilliance; **—ать** *v.* reflect.

отсев *m.* selection, screening, sieve analysis; **—ать** *see* **отсеивать.**

отседать *v.* settle, precipitate.

отсеив/ание *n.* sifting, screening; **—ать** *v.* select; filter, pass; sift, screen.

отсек *m.* compartment, section; **—ание** *n.* splitting off; cutting off; **—ательный, —ающий** *a.* cutting-off; **—ательный клапан** cutoff valve; **—ать** *v.* split off, cut off; intercept, detach.

отсеч/ение *n.*, **—ка** *f.* cutting off; cutoff; **—енный** *a.* splitoff; cutoff; **—ь** *see* **отсекать.**

отсеять *see* **отсеивать.**

отсифонив/ание *n.* siphoning off; **—ать** *v.* siphon off.

отскакив/ание *n.* recoil, rebound; break

ing away; **—ать** *v.* recoil, rebound; break away.

отско/к *see* **отскакивание**; **—чить** *see* **отскакивать.**

отслаив/ание *n.* scaling, peeling, exfoliation; **—аться** *v.* scale (off), peel off, flake.

отсло/ение, —йка *see* **отслаивание**; **—иться** *see* **отслаиваться.**

отслуж/ивать, —ить *v.* finish time of service; be worn out.

отсоединен/ие *n.* disconnecting, isolation; **—ный** *a.* disconnected, detached; **—ный скачок** detached shock.

отсортиров/ание *n.*, **—ка** *f.* sorting; **—анный** *a.* sorted; **—ать, —ывать** *v.* sort.

отсос *m.* suction, pumping; **—анный** *a.* drawn-off, sucked-off; **—ать** *see* **отсасывать.**

отсохнуть *see* **отсыхать.**

отсроч/ивать, —ить *v.* postpone, delay, defer; **—ка** *f.* postponement, delay, deferment, adjournment.

отстав/ание *n.*, **—ать** *v.* lag; **—ать от** lag behind.

отстав/ить, —лять *v.* set aside; dismiss, discharge; **—ка** *f.*, **—ление** *n.* setting aside; dismissal; resignation, retirement; **в —ке** retired.

отстаив/ание *n.* standing, settling; **—ать** *v.* let stand, settle; defend; **—аться** *v.* settle, precipitate.

отстал/ость *f.* backwardness; **—ый** *a.* backward, retarded.

отст/ать *see* **отставать**; **—ающий** *a.* lagging, late.

отстег/ивать, —нуть *v.* unfasten.

отстой *m.* sediment, dregs, residue; **—ник** *m.* settling (sump, retention) tank; **—ный** *a.* settling.

отсто/ять *see* **отстаивать**; **—ящий** *a.* distant, remote; spaced.

отстраивать *v.* build (up); (rad.) tune out.

отстран/ение *n.* putting aside; removal, elimination; dismissal; **—ить, —ять** *v.* put aside, push aside; discharge, dismiss.

отстро/ить *see* **отстраивать**; **—йка** *f.* building up; (rad.) tuning out.

отступ/ать, —ить *v.* withdraw, recede; digress; **—ающий** *a.* deviating, digressing; receding, recoil; retrogressive; **—ление** *n.* withdrawal, recession; departure, deviation, divergence; **—ной** *a.* receding, retreating, retrograde.

отсутств/ие *n.* absence; deficiency; **—овать** *v.* be absent (lacking, missing); **—ующий** *a.* absent.

отсчет *m.* reading; count; (elec.) readout; **о. показаний** reading (of an instrument); **производить о., сделать о.** take a reading; **о. совпадений** coincidence counting; **поверхность —а** reference surface; **система —а** frame of reference.

отсчетн/ый *see* **отсчет**; **о. микроскоп** measuring microscope; **—ая линия** reference line.

отсчит/анный *a.* read-off; counted-off, reckoned; **—ать, —ывать** *v.* read (off), take a reading; count off, reckon; measure; **—ывание** *n.* reading (off); counting off, reckoning.

отсылать *v.* send off; refer to.

отсыпать *v.* pour out (dry material).

отсыр/евать, —еть *v.* dampen; **—елый** *a.* damp, dampened; **—ение** *n.* damping.

отсыхать *v.* dry out.

отсюда *adv.* from here; hence; **о. явствует** hence it appears, it follows.

оттаив/ание *n.* thawing; **—ать** *v.* thaw.

отталкив/ание *n.* repulsion; **—ать** *v.* repel, resist; reject; **—ающая сила** repulsive force.

оттачив/ание *n.* sharpening, whetting; **—ать** *v.* sharpen, whet, point.

отта/янный *a.* defrosted; **—ять** *see* **оттаивать.**

оттен/енный *a.* shadowed, preshadowed; **—ок** *m.* shade; **—ять** *v.* shade, tint, graduate.

оттепель *f.* thaw.

отт/ереть, —ирать *v.* rub away, abrade; wipe away.

оттиск *m.* impression; print, copy, reprint.

Отто цикл Otto cycle.

оттого *adv.* therefore, that is why; because; **о. что** because; **это случилось о., что** it happened because.

отток *m.* flowoff, runoff, outflow; leakage.
оттолкнуть *see* **отталкивать.**
оттопыр/ивать, —иваться, —ить, —иться *v.* protrude.
оттормаживать *v.* release brake.
отточ/енный *a.* sharpened, pointed; **—ие** *n.* dotted line; **—ить** *see* **оттачивать.**
оттренированный *a.* conditioned, trained; aged.
оттуда *adv.* therefrom, from there.
оттягив/ание *n.* drawing off; drawing out; delaying, prolonging; **—ать** *v.* draw off; draw out; delay, prolong; **—ать струну** pluck string; **—ающая пружина** restoring (back, pulloff) spring.
оттяж/ка *f.* delay, procrastination; drawing out; exhaust; guy, stay; **—ной** *a.* drawing-out.
оттянут/ый *a.* drawn (out); **—ь** *see* **оттягивать.**
отунит *m.* autunite.
отфейллит *m.* hautefeullite.
отфиксирование *n.* (phot.) fixing.
отфильтров/анный *a.* filtered; **—ать, —ывать** *v.* filter (out).
отформов/ать, —ывать *v.* mold, shape, form.
отход *m.* departure; withdrawal, removal; **—ы** *pl.* waste; **—ить** *v.* depart, withdraw; branch out.
отходящий *a.* outgoing, exit, waste; **о. газ** waste gas, exhaust gas.
отцеживать *v.* strain off, filter.
отцеп/ить, —лять *v.* unhook, uncouple, disengage; **—ка** *f.* uncoupling; **—ляемый** *a.* detachable.
отчасти *adv.* in part, partially.
отчего *adv.* why, for what reason.
отчерк/ивать, —нуть *v.* mark off.
отчет *m.* account, report.
отчетлив/ость *f.* clearness, distinctness; intelligibility; **—ый** *a.* clear, distinct, sharp.
отчетн/ость *f.* accounts; **—ый** *a.* report; **—ый год** current year; year under review; **—ый доклад** (summary) report.
отчисл/ение *n.* deduction; **—ить, —ять** *v.* deduct.
отчи/стить, —щать *v.* clean off; purify; **—щенный** *a.* cleaned; purified.
отшедший *a.* receding.
отшиб/ать, —ить *v.* strike off, knock off.
отшлифов/анный *a.* ground, polished; **—ать, —ывать** *v.* grind, polish.
отшнуров/ание, —ывание *n.* constriction, pinch; **—анный разряд** filamentary discharge; pinched discharge.
отщепить *v.* chip off, split off; detach.
отщепл/ение *n.* splitting, cleavage, spallation, cut; detaching, separation; **глубокое о.** spallation; **—енный** *a.* split-off; detached, separated; **—ять** *see* **отщепить.**
отъедин/ение *n.* disconnecting; **—ить, —ять** *v.* disconnect.
отъез/д *m.* departure; **—жать** *v.* depart.
отъемный *a.* removable, detachable.
отыск/ание *n.* search (for); detection, finding, localization; **—ать** *v.* find, discover; **—ивание** *n.* searching; **—ивать** *v.* search for; find, discover.
отяго/тительный *a.* burdensome; **—щать** *v.* burden, aggravate.
отяжел/евший *a.* heavy; **—ение** *n.* growing heavy; **—еть** *v.* become heavy; **—ить** *v.* increase weight of.
оулофолит *m.* oulopholite.
оуэнит *m.* owenite.
офиокальцит *m.* ophicalcite.
офиолит *m.* ophiolite.
офит *m.* ophite.
официальный *a.* official, formal.
официоз *m.* semiofficial publication; **—ный** *a.* semiofficial.
ОФМ *abbr.* (**отделение физико-математических наук**) Division of Physics and Mathematics.
оформл/ение *n.* formulation, design, layout; **—енный** *a.* formulated; **—ять** *v.* shape, design; formulate.
офорт *m.* etching.
офтальмо/логия *f.* ophthalmology **—скоп** *m.* ophthalmoscope.
охарактеризов/анный *a.* characterized described, specified; **—ать** *v.* characterize, describe, specify.
охват *m.* reach, range, scope; inclusion envelopment; coverage; girth; **—ить —ывать** *v.* envelop, loop, encompass comprise, involve, include, cover

subtend, span; —**ываемый** *a.* included, comprehended; subtended (angle); (mach.) male; —**ывающий** *a.* encompassing; subtending; looped with; (mach.) female.

охваченный *a.* enveloped, encompassed, involved, included, covered; spanned.

охлад/евать, —**еть** *v.* become cool.

охладитель *m.* cooler, refrigerator; radiation condenser; coolant, refrigerant; (met.) quenching medium; **обратный о.** reflux condenser; —**ный** *a.* cooling.

охладить *v.* cool, chill; quench; refrigerate; condense (steam).

охлаждаем/ый *a.* cooled; **о. воздухом** air-cooled; —**ая ловушка** cold trap.

охлаждать *see* **охладить.**

охлаждающ/ий *a.* cooling, chilling, freezing, refrigerant; condensing; **о. жидкий металл** liquid-metal coolant; **о. прибор** cooler, refrigerator; —**ая вода** water coolant; —**ая жидкость,** —**ая среда** coolant; —**ая колонна** cooling tower; —**ая смесь** freezing mixture; —**ее средство** coolant, refrigerant; (met.) quenching compound.

охлажден/ие *n.* cooling, chilling, refrigeration; condensation; **естественное о.** self-cooling; **искуственное о.** air conditioning; **поверхность** —**ия** cooling (or condensing) surface; —**ный** *a.* cooled, chilled, refrigerated; condensed; **резко** —**ный** quenched.

ОХН АН СССР *abbr.* (**Отделение химических наук Академии наук СССР**) Division of Chemical Sciences of the Academy of Sciences, USSR.

охотно *adv.* willingly.

охра *f.* ocher.

охран/а *f.* security, guard; conservation; **о. вод** water conservation; **о. здоровья** health care; —**ение** *n.* guarding, protection; —**ительный,** —**ный** *a.* protective, guard; —**ная пластина** guard plate; —**ное кольцо** guard ring; —**ить,** —**ять** *v.* guard, protect.

охр/истый, —**овый** *a.* ocherous, ocher-colored.

охролит *m.* ochrolite.

охрупчение *n.* embrittlement.

оцен/ивать, —**ить,** *v.* estimate, evaluate; delimit.

оцен/ка *f.* estimate; valuation, appraisal, rating; limit; **о. сверху** upper limit; **о. снизу** lower limit; **двусторонние** —**ки** upper and lower limits; —**очная функция** (stat.) estimator.

оцеп/ить, —**лять** *v.* surround, encompass; —**ление** *n.* surrounding, encompassing.

оцинков/ание *n.*, —**ка** *f.*, —**ывание** *n.* (met.) zinc plating, galvanizing; —**анный** *a.* zinc-plated, galvanized; —**ать,** —**ывать** *v.* zinc plate, galvanize.

оцк *abbr.* [**объемноцентрированная кубическая** (**решетка**)] body-centered cubic (lattice) (bcc).

ОЧ *abbr.* (**октановое число**) octane number.

очаг *m.* seat, focus, (place of) origin, center, source; region; hearth; **о. воздушной массы** air-mass source; **о. землетрясения** seismic center; **о. нарушения** seat of disturbance.

очевид/ец *m.* eyewitness; —**но** *adv.* evidently, obviously; it is obvious; —**ность** *f.* evidence, obviousness, manifestness; **с** —**ностью** obviously, clearly; —**ный** *a.* evident, obvious, apparent, manifest, clear.

очень *adv.* very, greatly, highly, much.

очеред/ной *a.* alternate, in turn; next, following; regular, usual, recurrent; —**ность** *f.* order, priority; —**ь** *f.* turn; **в первую** —**ь** in the first place, primarily; **по** —**и** in turn.

очерк *m.* outline, sketch; synopsis, abridgment; tabulation.

очер/тание *n.* outline, configuration, form, profile; —**тить,** —**чивать** *v.* trace, outline, describe; —**ченный** *a.* outlined, defined, sketched.

очехловка *f.* jacketing, canning.

очиститель *m.* purifier, cleaner, cleanser, (gas) scrubber; rectifier; —**ный** *a.* purifying, cleaning; clearing, sweeping.

очистить *v.* clean, cleanse; purify, refine; clarify, clear; decontaminate; rectify.

очист/ка *f.* cleaning, cleansing; decontamination; purification, refining; rectification; clarification, clearing; **о. газа** gas scrubbing; **зонная о.** zone refinement; **коэффициент —ки** decontamination factor; **—ной** *a.* cleaning.

очищать *see* **очистить.**

очищающ/ий *a.* purifying, cleaning; **—ее поле** clearing (or sweeping) field; **—ее расширение** cleaning expansion (of cloud chamber).

очищен/ие *see* **очистка**; **—ный** *a.* purified, cleaned; refined; rectified; clarified.

очки *pl.* eyeglasses; **защитные о., предохранительные о.** goggles.

очко *n.* point; hole; mesh (of screen); **—вые стекла** eyeglasses.

очувствлен/ие *n.* sensitization, activation; **—ный примесями** impurity sensitized, impurity activated.

ошиб/аться, —иться *v.* make a mistake, err.

ошиб/ка *f.* mistake, error, blunder; **о. в расчете** miscalculation; **о. на параллакс** parallactic error; **о. отсчета** reading error; **о. при установке** alignment error; **по —ке** by mistake, in error; **закон —ок** error function.

ошибочн/о *adv.* by mistake, erroneously; **—ость** *f.* fallibility; inaccuracy; **—ый** *a.* false, wrong, incorrect; erratic; **—ое направление** misalignment; **—ое поведение** erratic behavior.

ошлаков/ание *n.* slagging, scorification; **—анный** *a.* scorified; **—ать, —ывать** *v.* form slag, scorify.

ошпар/енный *a.* scalded; **—ивание** *n.* scalding; **—ивать, —ить** *v.* scald.

ощелачив/ание *n.* alkalizing; **—ать** *v.* alkalize.

ощуп/ание, —ывание *n.* feeling, probing; **—ывать** *v.* feel, probe.

ощупь *f.* touch, feel; **на о.** to the touch.

ощутимый *a.* sensible, perceptible, appreciable.

ощутительн/ость *f.* perceptibility; **—ый** *a.* perceptible, tangible, palpable, appreciable.

ощутить *see* **ощущать.**

ощущ/аемый *see* **ощутимый**; **—ать** *v.* feel, perceive; **—ение** *n.* sensation, feeling, perception.

ояманит *m.* oyamalite.

П

п. *abbr.* (**параграф**) paragraph, section, clause; (**патент**) patent; (**правый**) right, right-hand, clockwise; (**профессор**) professor; (**пуд**) pood.

***п*-** *see* **пара—.**

П. *abbr.* (**Петроград**) Petrograd; (**в переплете**) bound.

Павлин Pavo (Pav) (constellation).

паводок *m.* inundation, flood, high water.

пагоскоп *m.* pagoscope.

пагубный *a.* ruinous.

падать *v.* fall, drop; decrease; impinge.

падающ/ий *a.* falling, dropping; decreasing; incident; **п. ветер** fall wind; **п. пучок** incident beam; **—ая звезда** shooting (or falling) star; meteor; **—ее излучение** incident radiation.

паден/ие *n.* fall, decrease, reduction, depression, drop; incidence; dip; gradient, slope, inclination, grade; precipitation; collapse; **анодное п. напряжения** anode fall (or drop); **п. вакуума** breaking of vacuum; **п. давления** pressure drop; **п. напряжения, п. потенциала** potential drop; **п. по нормали** normal incidence; **свободное п.** free fall; **высота —ия** drop height; **сброс по —ию** (geo.) dip fault; **угол —ия** angle of incidence; (geo.) dip angle.

паевой *a.* portion, part; (chem.) equivalent, equivalent-weight.

паженый *a.* grooved.

ПАЗ *abbr.* (**противоатомная защита**) antiatomic defense.

паз *m.* slot, groove, mortise, channel, gap; **—ить, —овать** *v.* groove, mortise; **—овый** *a.* groove, mortise, slot.

па/й *m.* part, portion; interest; (chem.) equivalent, equivalent weight, combining weight; **вес —я** weight equivalent; **электрохимические —и** electrochemical equivalents.

пайгеит *m.* paigeite.

Пайерлс Peierls.

пайка *f.* soldering; **п. крепким припоем** brazing.

пайрекс *see* **пирекс.**

пайсбергит *m.* pajsbergite.

пак *m.* pack, pack ice.

пакгауз *m.* warehouse, storehouse.

пакет *m.* packet, package; stack; bunch; **волновой п.** wave packet.

пакетиров/ание *n.*, **—ка** *f.* packing; bunching; **—анный** *a.* packed; bunched; **—ать** *v.* pack; bunch.

пакетный *a.* package, packet; **п. магнетрон** packaged magnetron.

паков/ание *n.* packing; **—ать** *v.*, **—ый** *a.* pack.

палата *f.* chamber, board; **П. мер и весов** Bureau of Weights and Measures.

палевый *a.* pale-yellow, straw-colored.

пален/ие *n.* burning; blasting; **—ый** *a.* burned, scorched.

палео— *prefix* paleo—.

палео/ботаника *f.* paleobotany; **—ген** *m.* paleogene.

палеозой *m.*, **—ская эра** Paleozoic era; **—ский** *a.* Paleozoic.

палеоклиматология *f.* paleoclimatology.

палеолит *m.* paleolith; **—ический** *a.* Paleolithic.

палеомагнетизм *m.* paleomagnetism.

палеонтолог *m.* paleontologist; **—ия** *f.* paleontology.

палеоцен *m.*, **—овый период** (geo.) Paleocene period.

палет/ка *f.* (geo.) set of master curves, abacus; template, graticule; **—очная кривая** (geo.) master curve.

палец *m.* finger; pin, peg; stud, cam.

палильный *a.* burning; blasting.

палимпсестовая структура (geo.) palimpsest structure.

палить *v.* burn; blast.

палка *f.* stick.

паллад/иевый *a.* palladic, palladium; **п. фильтр** palladium thimble; **—ий** *m.* palladium (Pd); **—ированный** *a.* palladized, palladium-coated, palladium-plated; **—истый** *a.* palladous, palladium.

Паллас Pallas (lunar crater).

палласит *m.* pallasite.

паллионимбус *m.* pallionimbus.

паллиум *m.* pallium.

палочка *f.* rod; bacillus; **п. глаза** rod of the retina.

палуб/а *f.*, **—ный** *a.* deck.

пальмер, Пальмера толщиномер micrometer caliper; **Пальмера эффект** Palmer effect.

пальмьерит *m.* palmierite.

пальник *m.* blasting cap, cap.

пальцевый *a.* finger; pin; **п. захват** finger-action tool.

пальчиковая лампа bantam tube.

палящий *a.* burning, scorching.

памят/ник *m.* monument, memorial; **—ный** *a.* memorable; **—ная записка** memorandum; **—ь** *f.* memory, recollection; (computer) storage.

пандус *m.* ramp.

панель *f.*, **—ный** *a.* panel, board; pavement; **п. лабораторной схемы** (elec.) breadboard; **п. управления** control panel.

панорам/а *f.* panorama; **—ирование** *n.* scanning; **—ный** *a.* panorama, panoramic; **—ный перископ** scanning periscope; **—ное фотографирование** panoramic (or wide-angle) photography.

пантал *m.* Pantal (aluminum alloy).

пантеле/граф *m.* pantelegraph; **—графия** *f.* pantelegraphy; **—фон** *m.* pantelephone.

панто/граф *m.* pantograph; **—скоп** *m.* pantoscope.

панхроматический *a.* panchromatic.

панцырн/ый *a.* iron-encased, armored; **—ая плита** armor plate.

папирусный *a.* papyrus.

папка *f.* cardboard, pasteboard; portfolio.

папозит *m.* paposite.

Паппа теорема Pappus theorem.

Папперица уравнение Papperitz equation.

Паппуса *see* **Паппа.**

пар *m.* steam, vapor; **водяной п.** steam; water vapor; **давление —а** vapor pressure, steam pressure; **перегонка —ом** steam distillation; **плотность —а** vapor density; **полным —ом** full steam, full power; **расход —а** steam consumption; **температура образования —а** vaporization point; **упругость —а** vapor pressure.

пар/а *f*. pair, couple; **п. дырка-электрон** hole-electron pair; **п. ионов** ion pair; **п. сил** force couple; **плечо —ы сил** arm-of-force couple; **без —ы** unpaired, odd; **в —е с** paired with.

пара— *prefix* para—.

парааминофенол *m*. para-aminophenol.

парабол/а *f*. parabola; **п. второго порядка** parabola, second-order parabolic curve; **п. запирания** (elec.) cutoff parabola; **—ический** *a*. parabolic; **—оид** *m*. paraboloid; **—оидальный** *a*. paraboloidal.

пара/водород *m*. parahydrogen; **—гелий** *m*. parahelium; **—генезис** *m*. paragenesis.

параграф *m*. paragraph, section, clause.

пара/гумми *see* **паракаучук**; **—дейтерий** *m*. paradeuterium.

парадокс *m*. paradox; **п. часов** (rel.) clock paradox; **—альный** *a*. paradoxical.

парадоксит *m*. paradoxite.

паразит *m*. parasite; (mach.) idler; **—ический** *a*. parasitic.

паразитн/ый *a*. parasitic; extraneous; (mach.) idle, intermediate; (elec.) spurious, parasitic, stray; **п. захват** parasitic capture; **п. импульс** spurious pulse; **—ая емкость** stray capacitance; **—ая индуктивность** stray inductance; **—ая связь** stray coupling; **—ое колесо** idle (or intermediate) wheel (or gear), idler; **—ое сечение** parasitic cross section; **—ые колебания** parasitic oscillations; **—ые явления** parasitics, spurious effects.

пара/-изомер *m*. para-isomer; **—каучук** *m*. Para rubber.

паракокимбит *m*. paracoquimbite.

параксиальный луч paraxial ray.

парализов/анный *a*. paralyzed; **—ать** *v*. paralyze.

параллакс *m*. parallax; **п. по скоплению** cluster parallax.

параллактическ/ий *a*. parallactic; **п. угол** angle of parallax; **—ое смещение** parallactic displacement.

параллел/епипед *m*. parallelepiped; **прямой п.** right parallelepiped. **—изм** *m*. parallelism; **—изованный** *a*. collimated; **—ограм** *m*. parallelogram.

параллель *f*. parallel; **проводить п.** draw a parallel; **суточная п.** diurnal circle.

параллельно *adv*. parallel with, analogous to, concomitantly with; (elec.) in parallel; **п.-последовательное соединение** (elec.) multiple-series (or series-parallel) connection; **—сть** *f*. parallelism; **—точная центрифуга** concurrent (or parallel-flow) centrifuge.

параллельн/ый *a*. parallel; **п. контур, —ая цепь** parallel circuit; **п. перенос** (math.) translation; **п. поток** parallel flow; **п. резонанс** antiresonance, parallel resonance; **п. сброс** (geo.) strike fault; **—ое перемещение, —ое перенесение** parallel displacement; **—ое соединение** parallel coupling (or connection); **—ое сопротивление** shunt resistance.

парамагнет/изм *m*. paramagnetism; **—ик** *m*. paramagnetic (substance), paramagnet.

парамагнитн/ый *a*. paramagnetic; **—ое резонансное поглощение** paramagnetic resonance absorption.

параметр *m*. parameter, constant; **п. ближнего порядка** short-range order parameter; **п. дальнего порядка** long-range order parameter; **п. кривизны** (reactor) buckling; **п. малости** series expansion parameter; **п. решетки** lattice parameter (or constant); **п. состояния** state variable; **п. соударения, п. столкновения, п. удара** impact (or collision) parameter; **п. статистической флюктуации** straggling parameter; **—ический** *a*. parametric.

параморф/изм *m*. paramorphism; **—ный** *a*. paramorphic; **—оза** *f*. paramorph.

парантгелий *m*. paranthelion.

парантиселена *f*. parantiselena.

пара/-орто превращение para-ortho conversion; **—позитроний** *m*. parapositronium; **—положение** *n*. para position; **—процесс** *m.* para-process (true magnetization); **—селена** *f.* paraselena; **—состояние** *n.* para-state; **—фазный усилитель** para-phase amplifier; **—фенилендиамин** *m.* paraphenylene diamine.

парафин *m.* paraffin; **—ированный** *a.* paraffined; **—ировать** *v.* paraffin; **—оборный коллиматор** borax-paraffin collimator; **—овый** *a.* paraffin, paraffinic.

пара/хор *m.* parachor; **—центрический** *a.* paracentric.

парашют *m.* parachute; **—ист** *m.* parachutist.

паргел/ий *m.* parhelion; **—ический круг** parhelic circle.

парение *n.* soaring.

паризит *m.* parisite.

парировать *v.* parry.

паритет *m.* parity; **на —ных началах с** on a par with.

парить *v.* soar.

парк *m.* park, yard; **п. подвижного состава** rolling stock; **п. путей** switch yard.

паркеризация *f.* (met.) parkerization.

парковый *a.* park.

парламент *m.* parliament.

парниковый эффект greenhouse effect.

парн/ость *f.* pairing; **—ый** *a.* pair, paired; **—ый эффект** pair effect; **—ая конверсия** pair conversion; **—ая корреляция** pair correlation; **—ая сила** two-body force; **—ая энергия** pairing energy; **—ое образование** pair production; **—ое фоторождение мезонов** double meson photoproduction.

паро— *prefix* steam.

паровик *m.* boiler.

паро/водяная смесь steam-water mixture; **—воз** *m.*, **—возный** *a.* (steam) locomotive; **—воздушная смесь** steam-air mixture, vapor-air mixture.

паров/ой *a.* steam, steam-driven; vapor; **п. коллектор** steam collector (or header); **п. цилиндр** steam drum; **—ая машина** steam engine; **—ая полость** vapor pocket; **—ая сила** steam power; **—ая установка** steam plant.

паро/впуск *m.* steam admission (pipe); **—впускной клапан** steam inlet valve; **—выпускной клапан** steam exhaust valve.

парогенератор *m.* steam generator; **—ный цикл** steam power cycle.

паро/запорный *a.* steam cutoff; **—масляный насос** oil-vapor pump; **—мер** *m.* steam flow meter; **—непроницаемый** *a.* vaportight, steamtight.

паром *m.* ferry.

парообраз/ный *a.* vaporous; **—ование** *n.* steam generation; vaporization; **теплота —ования** heat of vaporization.

парообразователь *m.*, **—ный прибор** steam generator; evaporator, vaporizer; **—ный** *a.* steam-generating.

паро/отвод *m.*, **—отводная труба** steam discharge (or exhaust) pipe; **—отделитель** *m.* steam separator; **—перегреватель** *m.* steam superheater; **—подвод** *m.* steam supply; **—провод** *m.*, **—проводная труба** steam pipe.

паропроизводитель/ность котла boiler steam capacity (or rating); **—ный** *a.* steam-producing; evaporating.

парораспредел/ение *n.* steam distribution; **—итель** *m.* steam distributor, steam header.

паро/ртутный насос mercury-vapor pump; **—сборник, —собиратель** *m.* steam collector (or header); **—светная лампа** vapor-discharge lamp; **—силовая установка** steam power plant; **—содержание** *m.* steam content; vapor content; **—стойкий** *a.* vaporproof; **—струйный** *a.* steam-jet; **—фазный** *a.* vapor-phase.

парофит *m.* parophite.

пароход *m.*, **—ный** *a.* steamship.

Парро Parrot (lunar crater).

Парсеваля теорема Parseval theorem; **П. формула** P. formula.

парсек *m.* parsec.

парсонсит *m.* parsonsite.

партийный *a.* party.

партиний *m.* partinium (aluminum alloy).

партиция *f.* partition.

партия *f.* party, group; batch, lot; game.

Парус Vela (Vel) (constellation).

парус *m.* sail; **—ина** *f.*, **—инный, —и-**

новый *a.* canvas; tarpaulin; **—ный** *a.* sail.
парциальн/ый *a.* partial; **—ая доля** abundance; **—ое давление** partial pressure.
парчинит *m.* partschinite.
пар/ы *pl. of* **пар,** vapor; fumes; **п. ртути** mercury vapor; **очищать —ами** fumigate.
Паскаля закон Pascal law.
паскоит *m.* pascoite.
пасмурн/ость *f.* mist, haze; cloudiness; **—ый** *a.* overcast, cloudy, dull.
пасовать *v.* shirk.
паспорт *m.* passport; certificate, certification; **—ный** *a.* certified.
пассаж *m.* passage; **—ный инструмент** (astr.), transit instrument; **—ный инструмент с ломаной трубой** broken transit; **—ный интерферометр** (radio astr.) drift interferometer.
пассат *m.*, **—ный ветер** tradewind; **—ная инверсия** tradewind inversion.
пассив/атор *m.* passivator; **—ация, —изация** *f.*, **—ирование** *n.* passivation; **—ированный** *a.* passivated, passive; **—ировать** *v.* passivate.
пассивн/ость *f.*, **—ое состояние** passivity, inertness; **—ый** *a.* passive, inert; **—ый полет ракеты** rocket coasting; **—ый рефлектор** (rad.) passive reflector; **—ый элемент антенны** parasitic element (of antenna).
паста *f.* paste.
пастериз/ация *f.* pasteurization; **—овать** *v.* pasteurize.
пат. *abbr. see* **патент.**
патент *m.* patent; **заявлять п.** patent, apply for a patent; **описание —а** patent specification; **—ирование** *see* **патентование; —никель** *m.* copper-nickel alloy resembling constantan; **—ный** *a.* patent, patented; **—ное бюро** patent office.
патентов/ание *n.* patenting; **—анный** *a.* patented, patent; **—ать** *v.* patent.
Патерсона функция (cryst.) Patterson function.
патина *f.* patina.
патогенный *a.* pathogenic.
патологический *a.* pathologic.
патрон *m.* chuck, jig, socket, holder; lamp socket; cartridge; pattern; **плавкий п.** cartridge fuse; **—ник** *m.* cartridge chamber.
патронн/ый *see* **патрон; п. захват** socket tool (of manipulator); **п. станок, п. токарный станок** chucking lathe; **—ая муфта** sleeve coupling.
патрубок *m.* connecting piece (pipe, branch), spur, fitting; branch pipe; nipple, nozzle.
патруль *m.*, **—ный** *a.*, **—ная служба** patrol.
пауза *f.* pause, break, interval, space, rest.
паук *m.* spider.
Паули принцип (прецепт, запрет) исключения Pauli exclusion principle; **паулиевский** *a.* Pauli.
Паулинга правило Pauling rule.
паундаль *m.* poundal.
пау/тина *f.* web, gossamer; **—чок** *see* **паук.**
пахнолит *m.* pachnolite.
пах/нуть *v.* smell (of) ; **—учий** *a.* odorous.
пациент *m.* patient.
пачка *f.* pack, stack, bundle, parcel batch; bunch.
пачк/ание *n.* soiling, contamination **—ать** *v.* soil, contaminate.
Пашена/-Бака явление (эффект) Paschen-Back effect; **серия П.** P. series
паяльн/ик *m.* soldering iron (or bit) **—ый** *a.* soldering; **—ый свинец** lead solder; **—ая горелка, —ая лампа —ая трубка** blowpipe; blowtorch.
пая/льщик *m.* solderer; **—ние** *n.* soldering; **—ть** *v.* solder.
Пб. *abbr.* **(Петербург)** St. Petersburg.
пв *abbr.* **(полая вода)** high water.
ПВ *abbr.* **(полярный воздух)** polar air
ПВД *abbr.* **(прямоточный воздушно реактивный двигатель)** ramjet engine.
ПВО *abbr.* **(противовоздушная оборона)** antiaircraft defense.
ПВРД *abbr. see* **ПВД.**
пг *abbr.* [**пикограмм (микромикрограмм)**] picogram, micromicrogram
Пг. *abbr.* **(Петербург)** St. Petersburg **(Петроград)** Petrograd.
ПД *abbr.* **(поршневой двигатель)** piston engine.

Пегас Pegasus (Peg) (constellation).
пегель/мессер *m.*, **—ная установка** transmission level meter.
пегмат/изация *f.* pegmatization; **—ит** *m.* pegmatite; **—итовый** *a.* pegmatitic; **—оидный** *a.* pegmatoid.
пед., педаг. *abbr.* (**педагогика**) pedagogy; (**педагогический**) pedagogical, teacher's.
педагогический *a.* pedagogical, teacher's.
педаль *f.*, **—ный** *a.* pedal, treadle.
педантичный *a.* pedantic.
педвуз *abbr.* (**педагогическое высшее учебное заведение**) pedagogical higher educational institution.
педиальный *a.* pedial.
педин *abbr.* (**педагогический институт**) pedagogical institute, teachers college.
педометр *m.* (surv.) pedometer.
педучилище *abbr.* (**педагогическое училище**) pedagogical school.
пейзаж *m.* landscape.
пек *m.* pitch.
пекгамит *m.* peckhamite.
Пекле критерий Péclet number.
пектолит *m.* pectolite.
пелаг/ит *m.* pelagite; **—ический** *a.* pelagic.
Пеле волосы (geo.) Pélé's hair.
пелена *f.* (meteor.) veil, cover; sheet; **вихревая п.** (hyd.) vortex sheet; **облачная п.** cloud veil; (meteor.) fumulus, damp haze; **п. перистых облаков** cirrus veil; **п. тумана** fog cover.
пеленг *m.*, **—овый** *a.* bearing, direction; **—атор** *m.* direction finder; **—ация** *f.*, **—ирование** *n.* direction finding; **—овать** *v.* take a bearing, set a course.
пеликанит *m.* pelicanite.
пелит *m.* pelite (mudstone); **—овый** *a.* pelitic, argillaceous.
пелликула *f.* pellicle, film.
Пельтона колесо Pelton wheel.
Пельтье коэффициент Peltier coefficient; **П. явление (эффект)** P. effect.
пемз/а *f.*, **—овый** *a.* pumice (stone); **—овать** *v.* pumice.
пен/а *f.* foam, froth; bead.
пенвитит *m.* penwithite.
пенеплан *m.* peneplain.
пенетр/ация *f.* penetration; **—ометр** *m.* penetrometer.
пен/истость *f.* foaminess, frothiness; **—истый** *a.* foamy, frothy; **—истая резина** foam rubber; **—иться** *v.* foam, froth.
пенициллиновая кислота penicillic acid.
пенкатит *m.* pencatite.
Пеннинга эффект Penning effect.
пенн/ый *a.* foam, froth; **—ая флотация** froth flotation.
пено— *prefix* foam, froth.
пенобетон *m.* foam concrete.
пенообраз/ный *a.* foamy, frothy; **—ователь** *m.*, **—ующее вещество** foaming agent, frothing agent.
пено/пласт *m.* foam plastic; **—полистирол** *m.* foam polystyrene, polyfoam.
пенрозеит *m.* penroseite.
пенсильванский период Pennsylvanian period.
пента— *prefix* penta—.
пента/гон *m.* pentagon; **—гональный** *a.* pentagonal; **—грамма** *f.* pentagram; **—грид** *m.* pentagrid.
пентад/а *f.* **—ный** *a.* pentad, five-day period.
пента/диен *m.* pentadiene; **—замещенный** *a.* pentasubstituted; **—лен** *m.* pentalene.
пентан *m.* **—овый** *a.* pentane.
пента/призма *f.* pentaprism; **—циклический** *a.* pentacyclic.
пентаэдр *m.* pentahedron; **—ический** *a.* pentahedral.
пентод *m.* pentode.
пенфильдит *m.* penfieldite.
пенящийся *a.* frothing, foaming.
пепел *m.* ashes, cinders; **—ьный** *a.* ash, ashen; **—ьный свет** earthlight (on the moon).
пептид *m.* peptide.
пептиз/атор *m.* peptizing agent; **—ация** *f.* peptization; **—ировать** *v.* peptize; **—ованный** *a.* peptized.
пер. *abbr.* (**перевод**) translation; (**переводчик**) translator; (**переплет**) (book) binding, cover.
пер— *prefix* per—.
первейший *a.* first-rate; very first.
первенство *n.* priority, precedence, preeminence; **—вать** *v.* take precedence.

первично *adv.* primarily, initially, first; **—сть** *f.* priority, precedence.

первичн/ый *a.* primary, initial; **п. контур** primary circuit; **п. металл** virgin metal; **п. нейтрон** primary (virgin, uncollided) neutron; **п. реактор** primary reactor; **п. элемент** primary battery; **—ая волна** primary wave; **—ая обмотка** primary winding; **—ая радуга** primary rainbow; **—ая частица** initial particle, primary particle, precursor; **—ое космическое излучение** primary cosmic radiation; **—ое темное пространство** primary (or Aston) dark space.

перво— *prefix* first.

перво/бытный *a.* primitive, original; **—зданный** *a.* (geo.) primitive, primary; **—источник** *m.* primary source, origin; **—классный** *a.* first-class, first-rate; **—курсник** *m.* freshman.

первоначальн/ый *a.* original, initial; elementary, primary, primitive; incipient; **п. материал, —ое вещество** parent substance; raw material; **п. разгон** initial acceleration; **—ая ветвь** (astr.) zero-age branch; **—ое число** cardinal number; base; radix; **—ое ядро** parent nucleus; **—ые данные** raw data; **—ые цвета** primary colors.

первообраз *m.* original, prototype; (math.) primitive; inverse image; **—ный** *a.* original; (math.) primitive; **—ный корень** primitive root; **—ная функция** (math.) primitive; **—ование** *n.* inception, beginning.

перво/основа *f.* fundamental principle; **—очередной, —очередный** *a.* immediate, primary; **—причина** *f.* initial cause, origin; **—сортный** *a.* first-class, top-quality; **—степенный** *a.* paramount, foremost.

перв/ый *a.* first, former, earliest; foremost, best; **п. вертикал** (astr.) prime vertical; **п. звук** first sound; **п. материал** raw (or starting) material; **п. меридиан** prime (or first) meridian; **—ая помощь** first aid; **—ые соседи** nearest neighbors; **в п. раз** the first time; **во —ых** in the first place, first.

пергамент *m.*, **—ный** *a.* parchment.

пере— *prefix* again, anew, re—; over—; out—; inter—; trans—.

перебе/г *m.*, **—гание** *n.* running over (or across); overrunning; **—гать, —жать** *v.* run over, cross; **—гающий холодный фронт** overrunning cold front.

перебив/ать *v.* interrupt; **—ка** *f.* interruption.

перебирать *v.* sort, consider, look over.

перебить *see* **перебивать.**

переблокировать *v.* (elec.) interlock.

перебой *m.* interruption; stoppage, breakdown, failure; irregularity; misfiring.

перебор *m.* gear; gear train; **—ка** *f.* sorting; reassembly; bulkhead; partition.

перебрасывать *v.* throw over; transfer.

перебрать *see* **перебирать.**

переброс *m.*, **—очный** *a.* flip, flipping, flopover, changeover; **—ать, —ить** *see* **перебрасывать**; **—ка** *f.* throwing over; transfer.

переброшенный *a.* thrown-over; transferred; (geo.) overthrust.

перевал *m.* crossing, passing; pass, saddle point; **метод —а** (math.) method of steepest descents; **—ить** *v.* cross; **—ка** *f.* rolling; roll changing, transfer; **—ьный путь** (math.) path of steepest descent.

переве/денный *a.* transferred, shifted, converted; translated; **—зти** *see* **перевозить.**

перевер/нувшийся, —нутый *a.* inverted, reversed; **—нутое изображение** inverted image; **—нуть, —тывать** *v.* upset, invert; reverse, flip; stir; **—тывание** *n.* inverting, flipping; upsetting, shaking up; **—тывание спина** spin flipping.

перевес *m.* overweight, overbalance, preponderance; advantage; **иметь п.** overbalance; **—ить** *see* **перевешивать.**

перевести *see* **переводить.**

перевешив/ание *n.* overbalance, excess weight; **—ать** *v.* reweigh; outbalance, overbalance, outweigh; **—аться** *v.* overhang; **—ающий** *a.* preponderant; top-heavy.

перевив/ать *v.* reweave; interweave, intertwine; **—ной** *see* **перевитой.**

перевис/ать, —нуть *v.* overhang.

перевит/ой, —ый *a.* interwoven, intertwined; **—ь** *see* **перевивать.**

перевод *m.* transfer, changeover, shift; conversion; translation; **устный п.** interpreting; **множитель —а** conversion factor; **таблица для —а** conversion table; **—имый** *a.* transferable; convertible; translatable.

переводина *f.* joist.

переводить *v.* transfer, change over, switch over, shift; convey; convert; translate, interpret.

переводн/ой, —ый *a.* transfer, shifting, switch; conversion; translation; **п. множитель** conversion factor; **—ная бумага** carbon paper; **—ная таблица** conversion table; **—ое издание** (published) translation.

переводчик *m.* translator; change-lever; **устный п.** interpreter.

перевоз *see* **перевозка.**

перевозбужден/ие *n.* (elec.) overexcitation; **—ный** *a.* overexcited, overdriven.

перевоз/имый *a.* transportable; **—ить** *v.* move, transfer, transport; **—ка** *f.* conveyance, transfer, transport, transportation; **—ный, —очный** *a.* transporting.

перевор/ачивание *n.* (meteor.) subversion; **—ачивать, —отить** *see* **перевертывать; —ачивающий телескоп** inverting telescope; **—от** *m.* (geo.) cataclysm.

перевыполн/ение *n.* overfulfillment, surpassing; **—ять** *v.* surpass, exceed.

перевяз/ать, —ывать *v.* bind; **—ка** *f.* bond.

перегиб *m.* bend, bending (back and forth), twist; recurvature; kink (in dislocation); **п. кривой** inflection; **точка —а** bending point; (math.) point of inflection; **—ать** *v.* bend, twist, kink.

перегн/анный *a.* distilled; **—ать** *see* **перегонять.**

перегнуть *see* **перегибать.**

перегов/аривать, —орить *v.* discuss; **—орный** *a.* negotiatory; **—орный пункт** telephone call office; **—оры** *pl.* negotiations.

перегонка *f.* distillation; **п. в вакууме** vacuum distillation; **дробная п.** fractional distillation; **п. с водяным паром** steam distillation.

перегон/ный, —очный *a.* distillation, distilling; distilled; **п. куб** still; **п. прибор** distillation apparatus; **—яемый** *a.* distillable; **—ять** *v.* distill; surpass.

перегораживать *v.* partition (off).

перегор/ание *n.* combustion, burning out; **—ать, —еть** *v.* burn out; **—елый** *a.* burnt-out.

перегород/ить *see* **перегораживать; —ка** *f.* partition, diaphragm, membrane; baffle (plate); barrier; closure.

перградировка *f.* recalibration.

перегранич/ивать, —ить *v.* change the boundaries.

перегрев *m.* superheat, excess heat, superheating, overheating; **—ание** *n.* superheating, overheating; **—атель** *m.* superheater; **—ать** *v.* superheat, overheat; reheat.

перегрет/ый *a.* superheated, overheated; **п. пар** superheated steam; **—ая точка** hot spot; **—ь** *see* **перегревать.**

перегруж/аемость *f.* overload capacity; **—ать, —ивать** *v.* overload, overcharge; transfer a load; **—енный** *a.* overloaded.

перегруз/ить *see* **перегружать; —ка** *f.* overload, overcharge; reloading, recharging; transshipment; **—очный** *a.* overload; transfer; **—очная защита** overload protection.

перегруппиров/ание *n.*, **—ка** *f.* rearrangement, regrouping; **—анный** *a.* rearranged, regrouped; **—ывать** *v.* rearrange, regroup.

перед *prep. instr.* before, in front of, preceding; compared to; *m.* front, forepart.

передав/аемый *a.* transmitted; **—ать** *v.* transmit, transfer, impart; communicate; broadcast.

передавливание *n.* pressure transfer.

перед/анный *a.* transmitted, imparted; **—аточность** *f.* transmissibility.

передаточн/ый *a.* transmitting, transmission, transfer, conveying, carrier;

driving; intermediary; **п. вал** countershaft; **п. импеданс** transfer impedance; **п. механизм** transmission mechanism; **—ое отношение, —ое число** gear ratio, transmission ratio.

передат/чик *m.* transmitter; **—ь** *see* **передавать.**

передач/а *f.* transmission, transfer; broadcast, communication, sending; gear, drive; **винтовая п.** screw gear; **высокая п.** high gear; **п. звука** sound transmission; **п. изображений** facsimile transmission; **п. импульса** momentum transfer; **низкая п., первая п.** low gear; **п. тепла** heat transfer (or flow); **цепная п.** chain drive; **п. энергии** energy transfer; **коэффициент —и** transfer constant; transmission coefficient; **коэффициент —и по напряжению** voltage transmission coefficient.

передающ/ий *a.* transmitting; **—ая линия** transmission line; **—ая телевизионная трубка** camera tube; **—ее приспособление** gearing.

передвиг/ать *v.* move, shift; **—аться** *v.* move, travel, migrate; **—ающий** *a.* moving, shifting.

передвиж/ение *n.* movement, displacement, transfer, migration, shifting; **п. хромосом** chromosome translocation; **средства —ения** means of transportation; **—ной** *a.* mobile, traveling, portable; adjustable; shifting.

передвинуть *see* **передвигать.**

передел *m.* redivision, repartition; **—ать, —ывать** *v.* alter, remodel; convert; **—ка** *f.* alteration; vicissitude.

передемпфированный *a.* overdamped.

передерж/анный *a.* overexposed; **—ать, —ивать** *v.* hold over; (phot.) overexpose; **—ка** *f.* overexposure.

передн/ий *a.* front, fore, forward, preceding, leading; **п. план** foreground; **п. фронт** leading edge; **—яя камера** forechamber; **—яя кромка** leading edge; **—яя плоскость** faceplate (of cathode-ray tube); **—яя сторона, —яя часть** front, forepart; **—яя точка** tip.

передник *m.* apron.

передо *see* **перед.**

передовер/ить, —ять *v.* transfer (of responsibility).

передовица *see* **передовая статья.**

передов/ой *a.* front, advanced, forward; progressive, leading; **п. метод** advanced method; **п. хребет** (geo.) front range; **п. человек** progressive (-minded) person; **—ая статья** leading article; editorial.

передув/ать *v.* overblow; **—ка** *f.* overblowing; afterblow.

передум/ать, —ывать *v.* change one's mind; think over.

передутая сталь overblown steel.

передышка *f.* respite, rest.

пере/езд *m.* passage, crossing; removal; **—езжать, —ехать** *v.* cross; move.

пережать *see* **пережимать.**

переж/ечь *see* **пережигать; —женный** *a.* burnt.

пережив/ание *n.* experience; **—ать** *v.* experience; outlast.

пережиг/ание *n.* burning; **—ать** *v.* burn.

пережим *m.* narrowing; **—ать** *v.* pinch; press.

пережит/ок *m.* survival, vestige; **—ь** *see* **переживать.**

пережог *m.* overburning.

переза/гашенный *a.* overdamped; **—медленная решетка** overmoderated reactor; **—правка** *f.* refueling; **—пуск** *m.* restarting, refiring, retriggering.

перезаря/д *m.* recharge; overcharge; **—дить, —жать** *v.* overcharge; recharge; reload; **—дка** *f.* charge exchange; charge transfer; recharge; reloading; overcharging.

переза/тушенный *a.* overdamped; **—хват** *m.* recapture.

перезре/вать, —ть *v.* overripen; **—лый** *a.* overripe, overmature.

переизбыток *see* **избыток.**

переиздавать *v.* reprint, republish.

переизлуч/ать *v.* re-emit; **—ение** *n.* re-emission; **—енный** *a.* re-emitted.

переизмерить *v.* remeasure.

переименов/ать, —ывать *v.* rename.

перей/дем *imp. of* **переходить,** we shall proceed; let us proceed, let us turn (to); —**денный** *a.* passed-over; —**ти** *see* **переходить.**

перекал *m.* overheating; (met.) overtempering; —**енный** *a.* overheated; —**ивать,** —**ить** *v.* overheat; overtemper.

перекат *m.* sand bar (or bank); thunder reverberation; —**ить,** —**ывать** *v.* roll (over).

перекач/ать, —**ивать** *v.* pump (over); transfer; —**ивание** *n.* pumping (or piping) over; —**ка** *f.* pumping over; transfer; —**ка энергии** energy transfer.

перекашив/ание *n.* distortion, warping; —**ать,** —**аться** *v.* distort, warp.

перекид/ать *see* **перекидывать;** —**ка** *f.* throwing over; transfer; (elec.) jumper; —**ной** *a.* throw-over, flip-flop; toggle, reversible, tipping; —**ной механизм** tumbler.

переки/дывать, —**нуть** *v.* turn over, throw over, transfer.

перекисл/ение *n.* peroxidation; —**енный** *a.* peroxidized; —**ить,** —**ять** *v.* peroxidize.

перекись *f.* peroxide; **п. водорода** hydrogen peroxide.

переклад/ина *f.* crossbar, joist; slat, rung; spar; —**ка пассажного инструмента** reversal-of-passage instrument; —**ывать** *v.* interlay; reset, relay, shift.

переклассификация *f.* reclassification.

переклейка *f.* plywood; regluing.

переключаемый *a.* reversible; exchangeable.

переключатель *m.* switch; **п. диапазонов** band selector; range switch; **п. фазы** phase-reversing switch.

переключ/ать *v.* switch; shift; —**ающий,** —**ающийся** *a.* switching; shifting.

переключен/ие *n.* switching; shifting; reversing; **п. скоростей** gear shifting; —**ный** *a.* shifted; switched.

переключить *see* **переключать.**

перекомпаундирован/ие *n.* (elec.) overcompounding; —**ный** *a.* overcompounded.

перекомпенс/ация *f.* overcompensation; —**ировать** *v.* overcompensate.

перекос *m.* slant, skewness; sag; misalignment; —**ить** *see* **перекашивать.**

перекошенный *a.* crooked, skew, warped.

перекрасить *v.* recolor, color.

перекрест *m.* crossing over; —**нослоистый** *a.* cross-bedded.

перекрестн/ый *a.* cross, crossing, crossed; **п. переход** crossover transition; **п. ток** crosscurrent; —**ая модуляция** cross modulation; —**ая наводка,** —**ое искажение** (elec.) crosstalk; —**ая релаксация** cross relaxation; —**ые призмы** crossed prisms; —**ые члены** cross terms.

перекрест/ок *m.* crossing; —**ье** *n.* reticle, cross hairs, cross wires.

перекрещ/енный *a.* crossed; —**ивание** *n.* crossing, intersection; —**ивать,** —**иваться** *v.* cross, intersect; —**ивающийся** *a.* crossing, intersecting.

перекристаллиз/ация *f.* recrystallization; —**ованный** *a.* recrystallized; —**овать** *v.* recrystallize.

перекруч/енный *a.* twisted; —**ивание** *n.* twisting; —**ивать** *v.* twist.

перекрыв/ание *n.* overlapping, lap; —**ать** *v.* overlap, lap; span, bridge over; shut off; —**ающий** *a.* overlapping, covering; —**ающая расходимость** overlap divergence.

перекрыт/ие *n.* overlap, lap; duplication; closing, cover, ceiling; floor; span; (elec.) flashover, sparkover; **п. импульсов** pulse overlap; **п. нейтронного пучка** neutron beam shuttering; —**ый** *a.* overlapped; covered; bridged, spanned; closed.

перекрыш/а, —**ка** *f.* overlap, lap; ceiling, cover.

переламывать *v.* break (in two); fracture.

перелет *m.* flight; —**ать,** —**еть** *v.* fly (over).

перелив *m.* overflow; —**ание** *n.* overflow; pouring; transfusion; —**ать** *v.* pour over; transfuse; (foundry) recast; —**аться** *v.* overflow; iridesce; —**ка** *f.* (foundry) recasting; —**ной** *a.* pouring; overflow; (foundry) recasting; —**ная труба** overflow pipe; —**чатый** *a.* iridescent.

перелит/ый *a.* poured (over); (foundry) recast; **—ь** *see* **переливать.**

перелицованный *a.* turned-over, reversed.

переложение *n.* transposition; **—енный** *a.* transposed; **—ить** *see* **перекладывать.**

перелом *m.* break, discontinuity; abrupt change; fracture; **п. кривой** break (or knee) of a curve; **—ать** *see* **переламывать.**

перем. *abbr.* (**переменный**) alternating, variable.

перемагни/тить, —чивать *v.* reverse magnetism; **—чение, —чивание** *n.* magnetic reversal, alternating magnetization.

перематыв/ание *n.* rewinding; reeling; **—ать** *v.* rewind; wind; reel.

перемеж/аемость *f.* intermittence; **—аться** *v.* intermit; alternate; **—ающийся** *a.* intermittent, alternate; intermediate; interbedded; **—ающееся течение** intermittent flow.

перемен/а *f.* change, variation; alternation; interval; move, shift; **п. движения, п. направления, п. хода** reversal; **поддающийся —е** alterable; **—ить** *see* **переменять.**

переменная *f.* (math.) variable; **п. действия** action variable; **п. составляющая** variable component; alternating (-current) component.

переменно *adv.* alternately; **п.-возвратное движение** reciprocating motion; **—сть** *f.* variability.

переменн/ый *a.* variable, varying; interchangeable, alternative; alternate; (elec.) alternating; **п. ветер** variable wind; **п. индекс** running index; **п. ток** (elec.) alternating current; variable current; **—ая величина** *see* **переменная; —ая звезда** variable star; **—ая нагрузка** variable (changing, alternating, live) load; **—ая туманность** variable nebula; **—ое поле** variable (or alternating) field.

переменчив/ость *see* **переменность; —ый** *a.* changeable, variable, inconstant.

переменять, —ся *v.* vary, change, transform; shift; exchange, interchange; **п. направление** reverse.

переместит/ельность *f.* commutativity; **—ельный закон** commutative law; **—ь** *see* **перемещать.**

перемеш/анность *f.* mixing; **—анный** *a.* mixed, stirred; confused; **—ать, —ивать** *v.* mix, stir, agitate; intermingle, intermix; confuse; **—ивание** *n.* mixing, stirring, agitation; intermixing; confusion; **турбулентное —ивание** turbulent mixing.

перемещаем/ость *f.* movability; transportability; **—ый** *a.* mobile; transportable.

перемещ/ать *v.* transpose, commute, transfer, transport, move, shift, displace; **п. вперед** advance; **—аться** *v.* move, shift, commute; migrate, travel; **—ающее возмущение** traveling disturbance; **—ающийся** *a.* moving, mobile, shifting, traveling.

перемещен/ие *n.* transfer, transposition; transit; shift; movement, motion, travel, migration, drift, translation; displacement, dislocation; (math.) permutation; **п. наносов** transportation of sediment; **п. полюсов** polar wandering; **п. центра давления** center-of-pressure travel (or displacement); **—ный** *a.* commuted, permuted, interchanged; transferred, shifted, displaced.

перемнож/ать, —ить *v.* multiply; **—ение** *n.* multiplication.

перемолоть *v.* regrind.

перемотка *f.* rewinding.

перемы/вать, —ть *v.* rewash.

перемычка *f.* connector, connecting neck, bridge, crosspiece; (elec.) cross-connecting jumper; bulkhead; cofferdam.

пере/нагревание *n.* superheating; **—наладка** *f.* readjustment; **—наложенный** *a.* superposed; **—напряжение** *n.* overvoltage; (elec.) surge; overstress; stress concentration; set.

перенасыщ/ать *v.* supersaturate; **—ение** *n.* supersaturation; **—енный** *a.* supersaturated.

перенес/ение *n.* transference; **—ти** *see* **переносить.**

перенимать *v.* imitate; take over.

перенормир/овка *f.*, **—овочный** *a.* re

normalization; **—уемый** *a.* renormalizable.

перенос *m.* transfer, transport, translation; migration, drift, shifting, displacement; (math.) transposition, carry; **п. вихря скорости** vorticity transfer; **п. воздушной массы** airmass transport; **п. ионов** ion migration; **п. массы** mass transfer (or transport); **п. осей** translation of axes; **п. радиации** radiation transfer; **п. тепла** heat transfer; heat transport; **коэффициент —а** transfer coefficient; **ток —а** connection current; **уравнение —а** transfer equation; transport equation; **число —а** (math.) carry quantity; electrolysis (or transference) number.

перенос/имый *a.* transferable; carried; endurable; **п. по воздуху** airborne; **—итель** *m.* carrier; transporter, transmitter; **—ить** *v.* transfer, carry, transmit, transport, shift; (math.) transpose; endure; postpone; **—ка** *see* **перенесение.**

переносн/ый *a.* transferable, portable, movable; translational; applicable; figurative; **п. источник** portable source; **п. контейнер** transfer container; **—ая скорость** (mech.) velocity of following; **—ое движение** migratory motion.

переносчик *m.* carrier; **п. заряда** charge carrier; **п. тока** current carrier.

перенумер/ация *f.* numbering; renumbering, relabeling; **—овать** *v.* number, index, label; renumber.

перенять *see* **перенимать.**

переоблучение *n.* (radiation) overexposure, overdosage.

переоборудов/ание *n.* reequipment, retooling; reconstruction; **—ать** *v.* reequip, retool; reconstruct.

переопредел/енность *f.* overdetermination; **—енный** *a.* overdetermined; **—ить, —ять** *v.* overspecify, overdetermine; redefine.

переопрокидывание спина spin flip.

переориент/ация *f.* reorientation; reversal, flipping; **п. спина** spin flip; **—ирование** *n.* reorientation; reversal, flipping.

переотклонение *n.* overswing, overshoot.

переотожженный *a.* overannealed.

переохлажден/ие *n.* supercooling; **—ный** *a.* supercooled.

переоцен/ивать, —ить *v.* overestimate; revalue; **—ка** *f.* overestimation; revaluation.

перепад *m.* drop, differential; (hyd.) overfall; **п. давления** pressure drop (or differential); **п. температуры** temperature drop.

перепа/ивать, —ять *v.* resolder; **—йка** *f.* resoldering.

перепечат/ать, —ывать *v.* reprint; **—ка** *f.* reprint, reprinting.

перепис/ать, —ывать *v.* copy; rewrite; transcribe; list; **—ка** *f.* copying; typing, transcription; correspondence; **—ываться** *v.* correspond; **—чик** *m.* copyist; typist; **—ь** *f.* inventory; census.

переплав/ить, —лять *v.* remelt, melt; smelt; float; **—ка** *f.*, **—ление** *n.* remelting, melting; smelting; **—ленный** *a.* remelted, melted; smelted.

переплата *f.* overpayment.

переплет *m.* (book) binding; interlacing; **—ать** *v.* bind (a book); interweave; **—аться** *v.* interweave, entangle; **—ающийся** *a.* interwoven, entangled; **—ение** *n.* interlacement, interweaving, interlocking; entanglement; link, linkage; **—ная** *f.* bindery.

переползание *n.* creeping (over); (sol.) climb (of dislocations).

переполн/ение *n.* overfilling; **—енный** *a.* overfull, overcrowded, overflowing; **—ить, —иться, —ять, —яться** *v.* overflow.

переполюсование *n.* polarity reversal.

перепонка *f.* membrane, diaphragm; **барабанная п.** eardrum.

перепра/ва *f.* crossing; **—лять, —ить** *v.* convey; ferry; revise, correct.

перепроизводство *n.* overproduction.

перепуск *m.* bypass; **—ать** *v.* let pass.

перепускн/ой *a.* bypass; passage; **п. канал** bypass; **п. клапан** bypass (valve); **—ая труба** bypass (connecting, overflow) pipe.

перепустить *see* **перепускать.**

перепут/ать, —ывать *v.* entangle; confuse; **—ывание** *n.* intermingling, interchanging; confusion.

перерабатыв/аемый *a.* processable; reprocessable; **—ать** *v.* process, treat; reprocess; revise; **—ать на** convert to.

переработ. *abbr.* (**переработанный**) revised.

переработ/анный *a.* processed, treated; reprocessed; revised; **—ать** *see* **перерабатывать; —ка** *f.* processing, treatment; reprocessing; revision.

перерасположение *n.* rearrangement.

перераспредел/ение *n.* redistribution; **—ить, —ять** *v.* redistribute.

перерасход *m.* overexpenditure.

перерасчет *m.* recomputation.

перерегулирование *n.* overcontrol, overregulation.

перерез/ать, —ывать *v.* cut off (or across); intersect, intercept.

переро/дить, —ждать *v.* regenerate; **—диться, —ждаться** *v.* regenerate; degenerate; **—ждение** *n.* regeneration; degeneration.

перерыв *m.* interruption, break, discontinuity; gap, interval; **с —ами** intermittent, interrupted, discontinuous.

пересек/ать, —аться *v.* intersect, intercept, cross, cut; **—ающая линия** secant; **—ающийся** *a.* intersecting.

пересечен/ие *n.* intersection; **место —ения, точка —ения** point of intersection; **—ный** *a.* intercepted, crossed; **—ная местность** broken ground, rugged terrain; **—ная спираль** barred spiral (galaxy).

пересечь *see* **пересекать.**

пересжатие *n.* supercompression.

перескак/ать, —ивать *v.* jump over, skip; **—ивание** *n.* jumping over, skipping; **—ивание искр** sparkover.

перескок *m.* skip, jump; (chem.) migration.

переслаив/ание *n.* (geo.) interstratification, interbedding; **—ать, —аться** *v.* interstratify; **—ающийся** *a.* interstratified, interbedded.

переслать *see* **пересылать.**

пересло/ить *see* **переслаивать; —йка** *f.* stratification.

пересматривать *v.* look over, review; r examine, reconsider; revise.

пересмотр *m.* inspection; review; rev sion; reconsideration; **—енный** inspected; reviewed; revised; **—е** *see* **пересматривать.**

пересн/имать, —ять *v.* (phot.) cop rephotograph.

пересоедин/ить, —ять *v.* change co nections, reconnect.

пересох/нуть *see* **пересыхать; —ший** dried-out.

переставать *v.* stop, discontinue.

перестав/ить, —лять *v.* permute, co mute, interchange; transpose, r arrange, adjust; **—ной** *a.* adjustabl reversible.

перестаиваться *v.* stand too long.

перестан/авливать *see* **переставит —овка** *f.* permutation, commut tion, interchange; transposition, r arrangement.

перестановочн/ость *f.* commutivit permutability, interchangeabilit exchangeability; **—ый** *a.* exchang commutation, permutation; adju able; reversible; **—ый эффект** e change effect; **—ое соотношен** commutation relation.

перестать *see* **переставать.**

перестояться *see* **перестаиваться.**

перестраив/аемый магнетрон tunal magnetron; **—ать** *v.* rebuild, reco struct; reorganize; tune, retune.

перестро/ение *n.* reorganization; **—е ный** *a.* reorganized; rebuilt; retune **—ить** *see* **перестраивать; —йка** *f.* arrangement, reorganization, chang over; reconstruction; replottin tuning, retuning.

переступ/ать, —ить *v.* step over, ov step.

пересуш/ивать, —ить *v.* overdry.

пересчет *m.* scaling, scale; conversio recalculation; **п. на два** scale-of-tw **коэффициент —а** scaling fact **таблица (для) —а** conversion tab **—ка** *f.* scaler.

пересчет/ный *a.* scaling; conversion; **блок** scaling circuit, scaler; **п. коэ фициент** conversion ratio; scali factor; **—ная схема** scaler, scali circuit; **—ная схема с самописц**

scaler-printer; **—ное устройство, —чик** *m.* scaler.

ересчит/анный *a.* converted; recounted; **—ать, —ывать** *v.* recalculate; recount; scale; convert; **—ывание** *n.* conversion; recounting.

ересылать *v.* send forward; transport, convey; remit.

ересып/ание *n.* interspersion; overfilling; **—ать** *v.* intersperse; pour over; overfill.

ересыхать *v.* overdry.

ересыщ/ать *v.* supersaturate; **—ение** *n.* supersaturation; **—енный** *a.* supersaturated.

еретапливать *v.* remelt.

еретасов/ать, —ывать *v.* shuffle, reshuffle.

еретек/ание *n.* flow, overflowing; (meteor.) overrunning; **—ать** *v.* overflow.

еретереть *see* **перетирать.**

еретечь *see* **перетекать.**

еретир/ание *n.* wearing, grinding; **—ать** *v.* wear, grind.

ереток *m.* return flow.

ереточка *f.* regrinding, resharpening, sharpening.

ретрансформация *f.* retransformation.

ретя/гивать, —нуть *v.* outweigh, overbalance; draw (tight); restretch; **—жка** *f.* drawing tight, constriction; overtightening; **—нутый** *a.* constricted, tightened; **—нутая петля гистерезиса** constricted hysteresis loop.

реуплотненный *a.* overdense.

реуспокоение *n.* overdamping.

реустр/аивать *v.* rebuild; reorganize; modify; **—ойство** *n.* rebuilding, reconstruction; reorganization.

реуступ/ать, —ить *v.* cede.

реутом/ить, —лять *v.* overwork; **—ление** *n.* overwork, overstrain; **—ленный** *a.* overworked, overstrained.

реучет *see* **учет.**

рефокусировка *f.* overfocusing.

реформулировать *v.* reformulate.

рехват *m.* interception; **—ать, —ить** *v.* intercept; **—чик** *m.* interceptor.

перехватыв/ание *see* **перехват; —ать** *see* **перехватать.**

переход *m.* transition; (semicond.) junction; transformation, conversion; migration, passage; switching; jump; overtravel, overshoot; **п. без излучения** nonradiative transition; **квантовый п.** quantum transition (or jump); **п. первого рода** first-order transition; **п. электрона** electron transfer; electron transition; **коэффициент —а** conversion (or scale) factor; joining factor; **при —е от** in progressing (or passing) from; **точка —а** transition point; **набор —ов** (spect.) transition array.

переход/ить *v.* convert to, change, become, develop into; proceed, pass (over), cross; **—ник** *m.* adapter, reducer.

переходн/ый *a.* transition, transitional, transitory, transient, passing, intermediate, connecting, adapter, crossover; circulatory; reversible; **п. коэффициент** *see under* **переход; п. металл** transition metal; **п. множитель** conversion factor; **п. мультипольный момент** transition multipole moment; **п. оттенок** transition color; **п. режим** transient conditions; **п. слой** transition layer; (semicond.) transition region; **п. элемент** transition element; **п. эффект** transition effect; transient effect; **п. эффект плотности** (cosmic-ray) transition effect; **—ая волна** intermediate wave; **—ая втулка, —ая муфта** adapter, coupling, reducer; **—ая группа** transition group; **—ая кривая** transition curve; **—ая стадия** intermediate (or transition) stage; **—ая труба** reducing pipe; **—ая характеристика** transient response; transfer characteristic; **—ое отравление** (reactor) transient poison; **—ое равновесие** transient equilibrium; **—ое сопротивление** intermediate resistance; **—ое течение** transition flow.

переходящий *a.* transitory, transient; changing (into), passing over; erratic.

перечень *m.* list, catalog; inventory; compendium; enumeration.

перечерк/ивать, —нуть *v.* strike out, cancel.
перечесть *see* **пересчитать.**
перечисл/ение *n.* enumeration; **—енный** *a.* enumerated; **—имый** *a.* countable, enumerable; **—ить, —ять** *v.* enumerate, list.
перечистить *see* **перечищать.**
перечит/ать, —ывать *v.* reread.
перечищать *v.* clean up; reclean.
перешеек *m.* isthmus; neck.
перешиб *m.* fracture; **—ать, —ить** *v.* fracture, break.
периастр, —он *m.* periastron.
перигей *m.* perigee; **—ный** *a.* perigean.
перигелий *m.* perihelion.
периклаз *m.* periclase.
периклин *m.* pericline.
перила *pl.* handrail, rail.
перимагматический *a.* perimagmatic.
периметр *m.* perimeter.
период *m.* period; cycle; (geo.) age, stage; **п. жизни** life cycle; **п. полувыведения** (bio.) half-life; **п. полуобмена** half-time of exchange; **п. полупревращения, п. полураспада** half-life; **п. решетки** lattice constant; **п. сдваивания** doubling time; **п. спонтанного деления** spontaneous fission, half-life; **—ика** *f.* periodicals.
периодическ/ий *a.* periodic; periodical; recurrent; **п. закон** periodic law; **—ая дробь** recurring (repeating, circulating) decimal; **—ая перегонка** batch distillation; **—ая система** periodic system; **—ая таблица** periodic table.
период/ичность *f.* periodicity, spacing; **п. загрузки урана** uranium feed ratio; **п. импульсов** pulse repetition period; **п. решетки** lattice spacing; **длина —ичности** (periodic) spacing; **50 —ный ток** 50-cycle current; **—ограмма** *f.* periodogram.
перископ *m.* periscope, altiscope; **—ический** *a.* periscopic.
перисто/видный, —образный *a.* cirriform; **—кучевые облака** cirrocumulus; **—слоистые облака** cirrostratus; **—слоистые туманообразные облака** cirrostratus nebulosus.
перист/ый *a.* feather, feathery; featherlike; **—ые грозовые облака** cirrus nothus, thunderstorm cirrus; **—ые облака** cirrus; **—ые плотные облака** cirrus spissatus, cirrus (densus, nothus).
перитект/ика *f.*, **—ический** *a.* peritectic; **—оид** *m.* peritectoid.
перифер/ийный, —ический *a.* peripheral; **—ия** *f.* periphery.
перицикл/ический *a.* pericyclic; **—ическое соединение** pericyclo compound; **—оида** *f.* pericycloid.
перка *f.* bit, drill.
Перкина явление Perkin phenomenon.
перкол/ировать *v.* percolate; **—ирующий** *a.* percolating; **—ятор** *m.* percolator; **—яционный** *a.*, **—яция** *f.* percolation.
перкусс/ионный *a.*, **—ия** *f.* percussion.
перл *m.* pearl, bead.
перламутр *m.* mother-of-pearl, nacre; **—овая накипь** pearl sinter; **—овое облако** nacreous (or mother-of-pearl) cloud.
Перла-Рида кривая Pearl-Reed (or logistic) curve.
перлинь *m.* hawser.
перлит *m.* (met.) pearlite; (petr.) perlite.
пермаллой *m.* Permalloy (nickel-iron alloy).
перманганат *m.* permanganate.
перманентн/ость *f.* permanence; **—ый** *a.* permanent, lasting.
перманит *m.* Permanite (nickel-iron alloy).
пермендюр *m.* Permendur (iron-cobalt alloy).
перменорм *m.* Permenorm (iron-nickel alloy).
пермет *m.* Permet (copper-cobalt-nickel alloy).
перминвар *m.* Perminvar (nickel-iron-cobalt alloy).
пермиссивный *a.* permissive.
пермский *a.* Permian.
пермут/ация *f.*, **—ирование** *n.* permutation.
пермутит *m.* permutite.
пермь *f.* Permian period.
Перно печь Pernot furnace.
Перо лампа Pérot lamp.
перо *n.* pen, stylus; feather; **—видный** featherlike.
перовскит *m.* perovskite.

пероксид *m.* peroxide.
перпендикуляр *m.*, **—ный** *a.* perpendicular; **—но** *adv.* perpendicularly, at right angles, transversely; **—ность** *f.* perpendicularity.
Перрена уравнение Perrin equation.
Персеиды Perseids (meteors).
Персей Perseus (Per) (constellation).
пер/сек *abbr.* (**периоды в секунду**) cycles per second (cps).
персистентный *a.* persistent.
персона *f.* person; **—л** *m.* personnel, staff; **—льный** *a.* personal.
перспекс *m.* Perspex.
перспектив/а *f.* perspective, view, prospect, outlook; **—ный** *a.* promising, prospective; perspective, oblique; **—ный план** long-term plan.
перспектограф *m.* perspectograph.
перст *m.* finger; **—овидный** *a.* digital.
пертинакс *m.* Pertinax.
пертио— *prefix* perthio—.
пертит *m.* perthite.
пертурбац/ионный *a.*, **—ия** *f.* perturbation, disturbance.
перфо/карта, —карточка *f.* punched (or punch) card; **—лента** *f.* punched (or punch) tape.
перфора/тор *m.* perforator, punch; drill, drilling machine; **—ционная карта** *see* **перфокарта**; **—ция** *see* **перфорирование.**
перфорир/ование *n.* perforation, punching; drilling, boring; **—ованный** *a.* perforated, punched; drilled, bored; **—овать** *v.* perforate, punch; drill, bore; **—ующий** *a.* perforating; **—ующая коррозия** pitting.
Перхэпсатрон *m.* Perhapsatron (thermonuclear device).
перцентиль *m.* percentile.
перцепция *f.* perception.
перцилит *m.* percylite.
перчат/ка *f.*, **—очный** *a.* glove.
перья *pl. of* **перо.**
пес *m.* dog.
песко/дувка *f.*, **—дувный** *a.* sandblast; **—ловка** *f.* sand trap; **—струй** *m.*, **—струйный** *a.* sandblast.
пес/ок *m.* sand; **—очный** *a.* sand, sandy; **—очный фильтр** sand filter.
пестик *m.* pestle.
пестрый *a.* variegated, mottled.
песчаник *m.*, **—овый** *a.* sandstone.
песчан/истый *a.* sandy, arenaceous; **—ый** *see* **песочный**; **—ая буря** sandstorm.
песчинка *f.* sand grain.
Петавий Petavius (lunar crater).
петарда *f.* detonating cartridge.
петель/ка *f.* small loop, eyelet, mesh; **—ный** *a.* loop; **—чатый** *a.* netted, mesh; **—чатая структура** mesh (net, lattice) structure.
Петерсена катушка Petersen coil.
петле/вание *n.* looping; **—видный, —образный** *a.* loop, loop-shaped; **—вой** *a.* loop; hinge; **—вая антенна** folded-dipole antenna; **—вая обмотка** lap (or parallel) winding.
петлистый *a.* loop, looped.
петля *f.* loop; hinge; **п. гистерезиса** hysteresis loop; **п. связи** coupling (or pickup) loop; **п. упругого гистерезиса** stress-strain loop; **п. циркуляции** circulation loop; **на —х** hinged.
Петри чашка Petri dish.
петро— *prefix* petro—.
петроген/езис *m.* petrogenesis; **—етический** *a.* petrogenetic; **—ия** *f.* petrogeny.
петрограф *m.* petrographer; **—ический** *a.* petrographic; **—ия** *f.* petrography.
петрология *f.* petrology.
Петцваля условие Petzval condition.
петцит *m.* petzite.
петь *v.* sing.
пехит *m.* poechite.
печ. *abbr.* (**печатный**) printed; (**печать**) press; printing.
печат/ание *n.*, **—ающий** *a.* printing; **—анный** *a.* printed; **—ать** *v.* print; **—ник** *m.* printer.
печатн/ый *a.* printing; printed, published; stamped, sealed; **п. станок** printing press; **—ая машина** printing machine; **—ая схема** (elec.) printed circuit.
печат/ь *f.* printing; print, type; press; seal, stamp; **накладывать п.** stamp; seal; **в —и** in press; **выйти из —и** come off the press, appear; **посылать в п.** send to press.
печ/ка *see* **печь**; **—ной** *a.* oven, furnace;

—ной газ furnace gas; **—ная труба** chimney, flue.

Печь Formax (For) (constellation).

печь *f.* furnace, oven, kiln; **п. сопротивления** resistance oven (or furnace).

пещер/а *f.* cave, cavern; **—истый** *a.* cavernous; **—ный** *a.* cave.

пз *abbr.* (**пьеза**) pressure unit (10^4 dynes per cm^2).

пи (math.) pi (π); **п.-мезоатом** *m.* pimesic atom; **п.-мезон** *m.* pion; **п.-фотомезон** *m.* photopion.

Пиацци Piazzi (lunar crater).

пигмент *m.* pigment.

пиезо— *see* **пьезо—**.

пижонит *m.* pigeonite.

пизанит *m.* pisanite.

пизолит *m.* pisolite.

пик *m.* peak; spike; crest.

Пикар Picard (lunar crater).

Пикара метод последовательных приближений Picard method.

пике *n.* (aero.) dive.

пикет *m.* (geo.) station; **—ажная книжка** (geo.) field book.

пикир/ование *n.* (aero.) diving, dive; **—овать** *v.* dive; **—ующий** *a.* diving.

пиккерингит *m.* pickeringite.

пиккеринговая серия Pickering series.

Пикколомини Piccolomini (lunar crater).

пикнит *m.* pycnite.

пикно— *prefix* pycno—.

пикнометр *m.* pycnometer.

Пико Pico (lunar crater).

пикоампер *m.* micromicroampere.

пиковершинность *f.* peakedness.

пиков/ый *a.* peak; **—ая нагрузка** peak load; **—ая полоска** peaker (or peaking) strip.

пико/грамм *m.* picogram, micromicrogram; **—кулон** *m.* picocoulomb, micromicrocoulomb.

пикообразный айсберг pinnacled iceberg.

пикотит *m.* picotite.

пикофарада *f.* picofarad, micromicrofarad.

пикро— *prefix* picro—.

пикролит *m.* picrolite.

пил/а *f.* saw; **—ение** *n.* sawing; filing; **—ильный** *a.* sawing, saw; filing; **—ить** *v.* saw; file.

пилон *m.* pylon, tower.

пилообразный *a.* sawtoothed, serrate, notched; **п. импульс** sawtooth pulse.

пилот *m.*, **—ировать** *v.* pilot; **—аж** *m.* pilotage; **—ажный** *a.* piloting, flight.

пильбарит *m.* pilbarite.

пильзенит *m.* pilsenite.

пиль/ный *a.* sawing, saw; file; **—чатый** *a.* serrate, notched.

П-импульс *m.* rectangular pulse.

пинакоид *m.* pinacoid; **—альный** *a.* pinacoidal, pinacoid.

пинахром *m.* pinachrome.

пингвит *m.* pinguite.

пинта *f.* pint.

пинцет *m.* pincers.

пинч-эффект *m.* pinch effect, rheostriction.

пион *see* **пи-мезон.**

пионер *m.* pioneer.

Пионер Pioneer (rocket).

пипет/ка *f.* pipet; **—очное устройство** pipetting apparatus.

Пиппарда уравнение Pippard equation.

пир— *prefix* pyr—, pyro—.

пиральспит *m.* pyralspite.

пирамида *f.* pyramid; **—льный** *a.* pyramidal, tapered; **—льный куб** tetrahexahedron.

Пирани манометр Pirani gauge.

пирано/граф *m.* pyranograph; **—метр** *m.* pyranometer.

пираргиллит *m.* pyrargillite.

пираргирит *m.* pyrargyrite.

пиргелиометр *m.* pyrheliometer.

пиргео/граф *m.* pyrgeograph; **—метр** *m.* pyrgeometer.

пиргом *m.* pyrgom, fassaite.

пирекс *m.* Pyrex.

пиридин *m.* pyridine.

пиринеит *m.* pyreneite.

пирит *m.* pyrite, pyrites; **—изация** *f.* pyritization; **—изировать** *v.* pyritize; **—ный, —овый** *a.* pyritic; **—оид** *m.* pyritoid, pyritohedron.

пиритоэдр *m.* pyritohedron; **—ический** *a.* pyritohedral.

пиро— *prefix* pyro—.

пирог *m.* cake.

пирогаллол *m.* pyrogallol.

пироген/етический, —ный, —овый *a.* pyrogenic, pyrogenous, igneous; **—ная реакция** pyrogenic reaction.

пироксен *m.* pyroxene.
пироксмангит *m.* pyroxmangite.
пиро/лиз *m.* pyrolysis; **—литический** *a.* pyrolytic; **—логия** *f.* pyrology.
пиромагн/етизм *m.*, **—итный** *a.* pyromagnetic; **—етик** *m.* pyromagnetic substance.
пиро/металлургия *f.* pyrometallurgy; **—метаморфизм** *m.* pyrometamorphism.
пирометр *m.* pyrometer; **—ический** *a.* pyrometric, **—ия** *f.* pyrometry.
пироп *m.* pyrope.
пиро/скоп *m.* pyroscope; **—стат** *m.* pyrostat; **—сфера** *f.* (geo.) pyrosphere, centrosphere.
пиротехни/ка *f.* pyrotechnics; **—ческий** *a.* pyrotechnic.
пиро/трон *m.* pyrotron; **—урановая кислота** pyrouranic acid; **—филлит** *m.* pyrophillite; **—фор** *m.* pyrophore; **—форный** *a.* pyrophoric; **—фосфат** *m.* pyrophosphate; **—химия** *f.* pyrochemistry; **—хлор** *m.* pyrochlore.
пироэлектр/ик *m.*, **—ический** *a.* pyroelectric; **—ичество** *n.* pyroelectricity.
пиррарсенит *m.* pyrrharsenite.
пиррит *m.* pyrrhite.
пирросидерит *m.* pyrrhosiderite.
пирро/тин, —тит *m.* pyrrhotite, pyrrhotine.
пирс *m.* pier.
пирсеит *m.* pearceite.
Пирсона критерий согласованности Pearson chi-square compatibility test.
писат/ель *m.* writer, author; **—ь** *v.* write.
писк *m.* squeak; **—ливый** *a.* squeaky, squeaking.
пистацит *m.* pistacite.
пистолет *m.*, **—ный** *a.* pistol.
пистомезит *m.* pistomesite.
пистон *m.* percussion cap; (mus.) piston; **—фон** *m.* pistonphone.
Писциды Piscids (meteors).
письменн/о *adv.* in writing; **—ый** *a.* writing, written; (petr.) graphic; **—ая руда** graphic ore, sylvanite.
письмо *n.* letter; script.
питаемый *a.* fed.
питан/ие *n.* (elec.) power supply; feed, feeding, supply; **п. накала** filament power supply; **блок —ия** power pack; **линия —ия** feed line.
Питат Pitatus (lunar crater).
питатель *m.* feeder; **—но-водяная система** feedwater system.
питательн/ый *a.* feed, feeding, supply; **п. кран** feed cock; **п. насос** feed pump; **п. провод, —ая линия** (elec.) feeder; **—ая точка** (elec.) driving point; **—ая труба** feed or supply pipe; **—ое вещество** nutrient, food.
питать *v.* feed, deliver, supply.
питающ/ий *a.* feeding, feed, **п. диполь** emitting dipole; **п. коллектор** supply header; **п. механизм** feed mechanism, feeder; **п. провод** (elec.) power lead; **—ая вода** feed water.
Пито трубка Pitot tube.
питометр *m.* pitometer.
питтасфальт *m.* pittasphalt.
питтинит *m.* pittinite.
питтицит *m.* pitticite.
пить *v.* drink; **—евая вода** drinking water.
Пифагор Pythagoras (lunar crater).
Пифагора (пифагорова) теорема Pythagoras theorem.
Пифей Pytheas (lunar crater).
пицеин *m.* Picein.
пицит *m.* picite.
Пише испаритель Piché evaporimeter.
пишущ/ий *a.* writing; **—ая машинка** typewriter; **—ее перо** recording pen.
пищик *m.* buzzer.
ПК *abbr.* (**Полярная комиссия Академии наук СССР**) Polar Commission of the Academy of Sciences, USSR.
пл. *abbr.* (**плавление**) melting, smelting; (**площадь**) area.
плав/ание *n.* swimming, floating; navigation; voyage; **—ательный** *see* **плавающий**; **—ать** *v.* swim, float; navigate.
плавающ/ий *a.* swimming, floating; **п. реактор** swimming pool reactor; **—ая запятая** floating (decimal) point; **—ая льдина** ice floe.
плавень *m.* flux, fusing agent.
плавик *m.*, **—овый** *a.* fluoric; **—овый шпат** fluorspar, fluorite.
плавильник *see* **плавильный тигель.**
плавильн/ый *a.* melting; smelting; **п. тигель** melting crucible; **—ая печь**

melting (or smelting) furnace; **—я** *f.* foundry, smelter.

плав/ить *v.* melt, fuse; smelt; **—ка** *f.* melting, smelting, fusion; melt.

плавк/ий *a.* fusible, smeltable; **п. предохранитель, п. штепсель, —ая вставка** (elec.) fuse; **—ая проволока** (elec.) fuse wire; **—ость** *f.* fusibility.

плавлен/ие *n.* melting, smelting, liquation, fusing, fusion; **температура —ия, точка —ия** melting point; **теплота —ия** heat of fusion; **—ный** *a.* fused, melted, smelted; **—ный кварц** fused quartz.

плавно/регулируемый *a.* continuously adjustable; **—сть** *f.* smoothness, evenness; facility.

плавн/ый *a.* smooth, even; **п. ход** smooth running; **—ая кривая** smooth curve, flat curve; **—ая регулировка** fine (slide, stepless) control.

плавочный *see* **плавильный.**

плавуч/есть *f.* buoyancy; **—ий** *a.* floating.

плаги/ат *m.* plagiarism; **—ировать** *v.* plagiarize.

плагиоклазы *pl.* plagioclase.

плазм/а *f.* plasma; **магнитно удерживаемая п.** magnetically confined plasma; **—енный** *a.* plasma; **—енный шнур** plasma filament; **—енная волна** plasma wave; **—оид** *m.* plasmoid; **—он** *m.* plasmon.

плакиров/ание *n.*, **—ка** *f.* cladding, plating; **—анный** *a.* plated, clad; **—ать** *v.* plate, clad.

плакодин *m.* placodine.

пламенн/ый *a.* flame; **п. двигатель** flame-type engine; **—ая дуговая угольная лампа** flame arc lamp.

плам/естойкий *a.* flameproof; **—я** *n.* flame, fire, blaze; **выбрасывание —ени** flareback.

план *m.* plan, scheme, project; map; design; layout; device; surface; **задний п.** background; **передний п.** foreground; **п. реактора** reactor design; **составлять п.** plan, design, project; **на первом —е** first and foremost.

Плана Plana (lunar crater).

планальный *a.* planar.

планер *m.* (aero.) glider; **—ный полет** (aero.) gliding.

планета *f.* planet; **—рий** *m.* planetarium.

планетарный *a.* planet, planetary; **п. электрон** planetary electron; **—ая передача** planetary gear; **—ая циркуляция** planetary circulation.

планет/езимальный *a.* planetesimal; **—ный** *see* **планетарный**; **—оид** *m.* planetoid.

планиметр *m.* planimeter; **—ирование** *n.* planimetry; **—ировать** *v.* measure with a planimeter; **—ирующий индикатор** integrating indicator; **—ический** *a.* planimetric; **—ия** *f.* plane geometry; planimetry.

планиров/ание *n.* planning, designing; programming; systematization; leveling, smoothing; (aero.) gliding; **—ать** *v.* plan, design; systematize; level, smooth; glide; **—ка** *f.* planning; design.

планисфера *f.* planisphere.

планка *f.* strip, slat, lath; cleat.

Планка квантовая теория Planck quantum theory; **П. постоянная** P. constant; **планковский** *a.* Planckian.

планктон *m.* (bio.) plankton; **—ный** *a.* planktonic.

планов/ик *m.* planner; **—ость** *f.* development according to plan, planned character; **—ый** *a.* planned, systematic; **—ая аэрофотосъемка** vertical aerial photography.

планомерн/ость *f.* regularity, systematic character; **—ый** *see* **плановый.**

Планте аккумулятор Planté battery.

планшайба *f.* face chuck, face plate.

планшеит *m.* plancheite.

планшет *m.* (surv.) plane table, plotting board; **—ная съемка** plane-table survey.

пласт *m.* layer, sheet; stratum, bed, seam, rockshelf; blanket; **п.-проводник** (geo.) rider.

пластик *m.*, **—а** *f.* plastic; **—атор** *m* plasticator; **—ация** *f.* plastication.

пластилин *m.* plasticine.

пластин/а, —ка *f.* plate; platelet, lamina, lamella, slab, wafer; (phonograph) record; **п. в полволну** half wave plate; **п. в четверть волны**

quarter-wave plate; —**образный** *a.* platelike, lamellar.

ластинчат/ость *f.* lamination; —**ый** *a.* lamellar, laminar, laminated, foliated; flaked; plate, platy, sheet, sheetlike; —**ый домен** laminar domain; —**ый конденсатор** plate condenser; —**ый магнит** laminated magnet; —**ый сердечник** laminated core.

ластифи/катор *m.* plasticizer; —**цированный** *a.* plasticized.

ластич/еский, —**ный** *a.* plastic; **п. сцинтиллятор** plastic scintillator; —**еская деформация** plastic deformation; plastic flow; —**еское последействие** relaxation; —**ность** *f.* plasticity, pliability; ductility.

ластмасс/а *f.*, —**овый** *a.* plastic.

ласто/вой, —**вый** *a.* stratified, sheeted, bedded, layer; —**вая скорость** (seis.) layer velocity; —**мер** *m.* plastomere; —**метр** *m.* plastometer.

ластообразн/ый *a.* sheet, sheetlike; —**ое месторождение** (geo.) blanket formation (or deposit).

ласты *pl. of* **пласт.**

лат/а *f.* salary, wages; fee; —**еж** *m.* payment.

латина *f.* platinum (Pt).

латиниров/ание *n.*, —**ка** *f.* platinization, platinum plating; —**анный** *a.* platinized, platinum-plated; —**анный асбест** platinum asbestos; —**ать** *v.* platinize.

латинистый *a.* platinous, platinum; **п. иридий** platiniridium.

латинит *m.* platynite.

латино/вый *a.* platinic, platinum; —**вая чернь** platinum black; —**синеродистый** *a.* platinocyanide.

латить *v.* pay; —**ся** *see* **поплатиться.**

латкообразная дисторсия (opt.) pocket-handkerchief distortion.

лато *n.* plateau; **п. по напряжению** (counter) plateau.

лато опыт Plateau experiment.

латон Plato (lunar crater).

латформ/а *f.*, —**енный** *a.* platform; flatcar.

лачек Placzek.

лашмя *adv.* flatwise, flat.

лезанский ярус Plaisancian stage.

плезиоморфизм *m.* plesiomorphism.

Плейона Pleione.

плейстоцен *m.*, —**овая эпоха,** —**овый** *a.* Pleistocene.

Плейфер Playfair (lunar crater).

плейштейнит *m.* pleysteinite.

плексиглас *m.* Plexiglas.

плена *f.* (met.) blister; platelet.

пленарный *a.* plenary.

пленение *n.* capture.

пленка *f.* film; tape.

пленочн/ый *a.* film, pellicular, tape; **п. дозиметр** film dosimeter (or badge), dosifilm; **п. конденсатор** film capacitor; —**ая дозиметрия** film dosimetry; —**ая запись** film (or tape) recording; —**ое кипение** film boiling; —**ое охлаждение** film cooling.

пленчатый *a.* filmy.

плеоморф/изм *m.* pleomorphism; —**ный** *a.* pleomorphic.

плеонасит *m.* pleonasite.

плеохрои/зм *m.* pleochroism; —**чный** *a.* pleochroic; —**чное кольцо,** —**чная оболочка** pleochroic halo.

плеск *m.* splash; —**ание** *n.* splashing; —**ать** *v.* splash.

плеснуть *see* **плескать.**

плести *v.* braid, weave.

плетен/ие *n.* network, netting; braiding, weaving; —**ый** *a.* woven.

плечевой сустав shoulder joint.

плечо *n.* arm, leg, branch; shoulder; **п. задающее** master arm (of manipulator); **п. исполнительное** slave arm (of manipulator); **п. креста** arm of cross; **п. моста** bridge arm; **п. пары сил** arm of couple; **п. рычага** lever arm.

плеяда *f.* pleiad; **п. изотопов** isotope group.

Плеяды Pleiades.

пликативн/ый *a.* plicate; —**ая дислокация** (geo.) folding.

Плиний Plinius (lunar crater).

плио/динатрон *m.* pliodynatron; —**трон** *m.* pliotron; —**фильм** *m.* pliofilm; —**форм** *m.* plioform.

плиоцен *m.*, —**овая эпоха,** —**овый** *a.* Pliocene.

плит/а *f.* plate, slab; —**ка** *f.* slab, block; **измерительная** —**ка,** —**ка-калибр** gauge block; —**но-контрфорсная**

плотина flat-slab buttress dam; **—ный** *see* **плиточный**; **—ообразный** *a.* platelike.

плит/очный *a.* plate, slab, laminated; **(бесконечный) п. реактор** (infinite) slab reactor; **—чатый** *a.* (geo.) platy.

пловец *m.* swimmer; floater.

плавуч/есть *f.* buoyancy; **—ий** *a.* floating, buoyant; **—ий затвор** floating gate.

плод *m.* fruit; **—ить** *v.* produce; **—иться** *v.* multiply, breed; **—овая мушка** fruit fly, drosophila.

плодород/ие *n.*, **—ность** *f.* fertility, productivity; **—ный** *a.* fertile, productive.

плодотворный *a.* fruitful.

пло/ение *n.* folding; **—еный** *a.* folded; **—ить** *v.* fold.

плойчат/ость *f.* (geo.) plication; folding, contortion; **—ый** *a.* plicated.

пломба *f.* stamp, seal.

плоск/ий *a.* flat, plane, two-dimensional; **п. источник** plane source; **п. конденсатор** plane-parallel capacitor; **п. пленочный дозиметр** film badge; **п. реактор** slab reactor; **п. теплообменник** flat-tube heat exchanger; **—ая волна** plane wave; **—ая граница раздела** plane interface; **—ая деформация** plane strain; **—ая задача** two-dimensional problem; **—ая ионизационная камера** parallel-plate (plane-parallel, shallow, flat) ionization chamber; **—ая молния** sheet lightning; **—ая поверхность** plane surface, plane; **—ая поляризация** plane polarization; **—ая система координат** two-dimensional coordinate system; **—ая характеристика** flat response; **коэффициент —ой земли** plane earth factor; **—ое поле** plane field; **—ое течение** plane (or two-dimensional) flow; **—ие кучевые облака** cumulus humilis (clouds).

плоско— *prefix* plane.

плоско/вогнутый *a.* planoconcave; **—выпуклый** *a.* planoconvex.

плоскогор/ье *n.* plateau, tableland; **ледник —ий** plateau glacier.

плоскокомпаундированный *a.* (elec.) flat-compounded, level-compounded.

плоско/параллельный *a.* plane-parallel; **п. счетчик** parallel-plate counter; **—поляризованная волна** plane-polarized wave.

плоскостн/ой, —ый *a.* planar, two-dimensional; **п. диод** junction diode; **п. транзистор** junction transistor; **—ость** *f.* planeness, smoothness, levelness.

плоскост/ь *f.* plane; surface, level, tier; flatness; face; **п. базиса** basal plane; **п. зеркального отражения** reflection plane; **п. колебания** plane of vibration; **п. кристалла** crystal plane (or face); **п. легкого скольжения** plane of easy slip; **п. меридиана** meridian plane; **оптическая п.** optical flat; **п. отражения** reflecting plane; **п. падения** incident plane; **п. плавания** plane of buoyancy; **п. поляризации** plane of polarization; **п. сдвига, п. скалывания, п. среза** shear plane; **п. сечения** plane section, sectional plane; **п. симметрии** plane of symmetry, reflection plane; **п. скольжения, п. скользящего отражения** slip (or glide) plane; **п. спайности** cleavage surface (or plane); **п. сравнения** datum plane; **геометрия на —и** plane geometry.

плот *m.* raft, float.

плотина *f.* dam, dike; weir.

плотн. *abbr.* **(плотность)** density.

плотник *m.* carpenter.

плотно *adv.* tightly, densely, closely, compactly; **—зернистый** *a.* close-grained; **—лежащий** *a.* dense, close; **—мер, —стемер** *m.* densimeter, areometer; **—стный элемент** (elec.) gravity cell.

плотность *f.* density; closeness, tightness; compactness, massiveness, solidity; frequency; rate; **вакуумная п.** vacuum tightness; **п. вероятности** probability density; **п. вуали** (photo.) fog density; **п. замедления** slowing-down density; **п. зерен** grain density; **п. излучения** radiation density; **п. паров** vapor density; **поверхностная п.** surface density; **п. потока** flux density; **п. потока нейтронов** neutron flux density; **п. потока энергии** energy current density; **п. разрыво**

gap density (or count); **п. распределения** probability density function; **п. тепловыделения** volumetric heat-release rate; **п. тока** current density; **п. электронов** electron density; **п. ядерных уровней** nuclear level density.

плотноупакованный *a.* close-packed, tightly packed.

плотн/ый *a.* dense, compact, close, tight; solid; (min.) massive; **п. в себе** (math.) dense in itself; **—ая пригонка** tight fit; **—ая упаковка** close (or tight) packing; **—ое вещество** solid matter; **—ое множество** dense set; **—ое строение** close texture.

плох/о *adv.* poorly, badly; **п. обтекаемое тело** bluff body; **—ой** *a.* poor, bad; **—ая геометрия** poor geometry; **—ая сходимость** poor convergence.

площ. *abbr.* (**площадь**) area.

площад/ка *f.* small area; ground; landing field; platform; **—ный** *a.* areal.

площад/ь *f.* area; cross section (of antenna or target); surface, space; **п. поглощения** (antenna) absorption cross section; **п. поперечного сечения** cross-sectional area; **п. проекции** projected area; **п. рассеяния** (antenna) scattering cross section; **единица —и** unit of area.

плунжер *m.*, **—ный** *a.* plunger, ram, piston.

Плутон Pluto.

плутон/изм *m.* (geo.) plutonism; **—ий** *m.* plutonium (Pu); **—ил** *m.* plutonyl; **—ический** *a.* plutonic, intrusive.

плывун *m.* quicksand, running sand; quick ground.

плывуч/есть *f.* deliquescence; **—ий** *a.* deliquescent, flowing; (geo.) quick-running.

плыть *see* **плавать.**

плюви/альный *a.* pluvial, rain; **—ограф** *m.* pluviograph.

плювиометр *m.* pluviometer; **—ический** *a.* pluviometric; **—ический коэффициент** pluviometric (or hyetal) coefficient; **—ическое отношение** pluviometric quotient.

плюкеровы координаты прямой Plücker coordinates (or abridged notation).

плюмбониобит *m.* plumboniobite.

плюмозит *m.* plumosite.

плюри— *prefix* pluri—, multi—.

плюс *m.*, **—овый** *a.* plus, even; **п.-активное ядро** positron emitter.

плющ/ение *n.* laminating, flattening; spreading; **—енный** *a.* laminated, flattened; **—ильный** *a.* laminating, flattening; **—ильный станок** rolling mill; **—ить** *v.* flatten, laminate, spread.

ПМ *abbr.* (**пневматический молот**) pneumatic hammer.

ПММ *abbr.* (**Прикладная математика и механика**) Applied Mathematics and Mechanics (journal).

пн. *abbr.* (**понедельник**) Monday.

п.н. *abbr.* (**порядковый номер**) serial (ordinal, index) number.

ПН *abbr. see* **помнач.**

пневматик *m.* pneumatic tire; **—а** *f.* pneumatics.

пневматический *a.* pneumatic; **п. выключатель** pressure (-operated) switch; **п. датчик** pneumatic transmitter; **п. затвор** pressure lock; **п. молот** pneumatic hammer.

пневматоли/з *m.* pneumatolysis; **—товый** *a.* pneumatolytic.

пневмо/костюм *m.* pressurized suit; **—почта** *f.* tube conveyer, shuttle, pneumatic rabbit; **—шлем** *m.* pressurized helmet.

ПНР *abbr. see* **Польская Народная Республика.**

по *prep. dat.* along; on, by, at, over, through, in, to, of; according to, conforming to; at the rate of; **по ветру** downwind; **по временам** at times, sometimes; **по желанию** at will, as desired; **по капле** dropwise; **по линии** along the line; **по масштабу** to scale; **по меньшей мере** at least; **по обыкновению** as usual; **по порядку** in sequence; **по причине** because of, by reason of; **судя по** judging from; **по существу** essentially; **по этому образцу** after this model; *prep. acc.* as far as, up to, to; **с . . . по** from . . . to; *prep. with prepositional case* on, after.

по— *prefix* (*with verbs*) action weak or

short or of unknown duration; (*with adjectives and adverbs*) somewhat more; as possible; each, —ly (daily, hourly, etc.).

побег *m.* flight.

победа *f.* victory, triumph.

победит *m.* Pobedit [tungsten-cobalt-carbon (-titanium) alloy].

побед/итель *m.* victor; **—ить** *see* **побеждать**; **—ный** *a.* victorious, triumphant.

побежалость *f.* iridescent tarnish; oxide tint.

побеждать *v.* conquer, overcome.

побережье *n.* shore, coast, littoral.

поблизости *adv.* nearby.

побольше *a.* (just) a little larger, (just) a little more.

поборник *m.* advocate, supporter.

побороть *v.* overcome.

побочн/ый *a.* secondary, side, by-, subsidiary, subordinate, accessory; indirect; extraneous; spurious; **п. продукт** by-product; **п. процесс, —ая реакция** side reaction, secondary reaction; **п. счет** spurious count; **—ая валентность** secondary (auxiliary, supplementary) valence; **—ая ось** (cryst.) secondary axis; **—ая серия** (spect.) subordinate series; **—ое квантовое число** orbital quantum number; **—ое солнце** parhelion; **—ое течение** secondary (or subsidiary) flow.

П-образный импульс square (or rectangular) pulse.

побудитель *m.* stimulator, stimulus; **—ный** *a.* stimulating, inciting; **—ная причина** incentive.

побудить *see* **побуждать.**

побужд/аемый *a.* stimulated, impelled; **—ать** *v.* stimulate, impel; **—ающий** *a.* stimulating, impelling; **—ение** *n.* stimulation, prompting; motive, incentive.

поваленный *a.* thrown-down; upset, overturned.

поваренная соль sodium chloride.

поведение *n.* behavior.

повеллит *m.* powellite.

поверг/ать, —нуть *v.* throw down, plunge, precipitate.

повер/енный *a.* checked; **—ить** *see* **верить, поверять.**

поверка *f.* check, checking, verification; proof; control.

повернут/ый *a.* turned; **—ь** *see* **повертывать.**

поверочн/ый *a.* checking, check, verifying; **п. анализ** check analysis; **—ая точка** control point; **—ое испытание** examination; **—ое свидетельство** calibration certificate.

повертыв/ание *n.* turning; **—ать, —аться** *v.* turn (around).

поверх *prep. gen.* over, above.

поверх. *abbr.* (**поверхностный**) surface.

поверхностно *adv.* superficially, on the surface; **п.-активный** surface-active; **—сть** *f.* superficiality.

поверхностн/ый *a.* surface; superficial; **п. заряд** surface charge; **п. интеграл** surface integral; **п. ослабитель** (phot.) subtractive reducer; **п. разряд** surface discharge, creeping discharge, flashover; **п. эффект** surface effect; (elec.) skin effect; **—ая волна** (rad.) ground wave; **—ая ионизация** surface ionization; **—ое натяжение** surface tension; **—ое состояние** surface state; **—ое трение** surface (or skin) friction; **—ые колебания** surface vibrations, surface waves.

поверхность *f.* surface; area; plane, face; **п. восходящего скольжения** upslide (or upglide) surface, anafront; **п. вращения** surface of revolution; **п. излучения** radiating surface; **п. кристаллизации** crystallization surface; **п. напряжений** stress surface; **п. нисходящего скольжения** downslide surface (katafront); **п. одинаковой фазы** equiphase surface; **п. переноса** surface of translation; **п. поглощения** (antenna) absorption cross section; **п. приведения** reference (or datum) surface; **п. равного потенциала** equipotential surface; **п. раздела** interface, surface of separation, boundary surface; **п. разрыва** discontinuity surface; **п. скола** cleavage plane; **п. теплопередачи** heat-transfer area; **п. теплосъема** cooling surface; **п. тока** stream su[rface]

face; **п. трения** rubbing surface; **п. фронта** frontal surface.

поверять *v.* verify, check; confide; entrust.

повесить *v.* suspend.

повести *v.* lead, conduct.

повестка *f.* notice, notification.

повидимому *adv.* apparently, evidently.

повин/ность *f.* duty, obligation; **—оваться** *v.* obey, comply with; **—овение** *n.* obedience, compliance.

повис/ать, —нуть *v.* hang, be suspended; **—лый** *a.* hanging.

повлечь *v.* imply, entail, involve.

повлиять *v.* influence.

повод *m.* occasion, reason, cause; **давать п.** cause, occasion, give rise to; **по —у** in connection with, apropos of.

повозка *f.* vehicle, cart.

поворачив/ание *n.* turning; **—ать** *v.* turn, swing, swivel; divert; reverse; **—аться** *v.* turn, swing, swivel; **—ающийся** *a.* swinging, swivel; rotating; reversible; **—ающая призма** right angle prism.

поворот *m.* turn, turning; bend, deflection; rotation; precession; change; reversal; **п. ветра** wind rotation (or shift); **п. н-ого порядка** n-fold rotation; **п. перигелия (орбиты)** precession of the perihelion; **п. спина** spin flip (or reversal); **угол —а** angle of turn (rotation, deflection); **—ить** *see* **повертывать, поворачивать.**

поворотлив/ость *f.* maneuverability; **—ый** *a.* maneuverable.

поворотн/ый *a.* turning, rotating, rotational, rotatable, rotary, revolving; swivel, tilting, pivoted; reversible; hinged; **—ая изомерия** rotational isomerism; **—ая станина** turntable mounting (or frame); rotatable pedestal.

повредить *see* **повреждать.**

поврежд/ать *v.* damage; impair; **—ение** *n.* damage, impairment; defect; **—енный** *a.* damaged; defective.

повременн/о *adv.* periodically; **—ый** *a.*, **—ое издание** periodical.

повседневный *a.* daily, everyday.

повсеместно *adv.* universally, generally.

повсюду *adv.* everywhere, throughout.

повторение *n.* repetition, recurrence, iteration; **п. импульсов** pulse repetition.

повторит/ель *m.* repeater; follower; **импульсный п.** transponder; **катодный п.** cathode follower; **—ельный** *a.* reiterative, repeating; **—ь** *see* **повторять.**

повторно *adv.* repeatedly; once more; re—; **п. возвращающийся** recurrent; **п. растворять** redissolve.

повторн/ый *a.* repeated, repetitive, iterated, re—; multiple, duplicate; **п. логарифм** iterated logarithm; **п. цикл** recycle; **—ая активация, —ое активирование** reactivation; **—ая вероятность делений** iterated fission expectation; **—ая локализация** relocalization, retrapping; **—ая новая (звезда)** repeating nova; **—ая ошибка** repetitive error; **—ое использование (горючего)** recycling (of fuel); **—ое наблюдение** repeat measurement; **—ое нагревание** reheating; **—ое облучение** reirradiation; **—ое появление** recurrence; **—ое ядро** (math.) iterated kernel.

повтор/яемость *f.* recurrence period (or interval); frequency; repetition, duplication; **—ять** *v.* repeat, reiterate; **—яться** *v.* recur; be repeated; **—яющийся** *a.* recurrent, iterated.

повысит/ельный *a.* increasing, boosting; step-up; **п. бустер** positive booster; **—ь** *see* **повышать.**

повыш/ать *v.* raise, increase, heighten, enhance; advance, step up; **—аться** *v.* rise, increase; **—ающий трансформатор** step-up transformer; **—ение** *n.* rise, increase, enhancement, elevation; stepping up; **—енный** *a.* raised, increased, elevated, stepped-up; enhanced, advanced; **—енная температура** elevated temperature; fever.

повяз/ать, —ывать *v.* tie, bind.

погас/ание *n.* extinction; going out; **—ать** *v.* go out, die out, become dim; **—ить** *see* **погашать**; **—нуть** *v.* go out; **—ший** *a.* gone-out, died-out.

погашать *v.* extinguish, cancel; quench.

погашен/ие *n.* extinction; cancellation; **п. интенсивности колебаний** cancellation of intensities; **коэффициент**

—ия extinction coefficient; damping coefficient; **—ный** *a.* extinguished, out; quenched; cancelled.

Поггендорфа весы Poggendorf balance; **компенсационный метод П. Р.** compensation method.

поглотитель *m.* absorber, filter; absorbent; **—ный** *a.* absorbing, absorption, absorbent; **—ная способность** *see* **поглощающая способность.**

поглотить *see* **поглощать.**

поглощаем/ость *f.* absorbability; absorptivity; **—ый** *a.* absorbable.

поглощат/ельный *see* **поглощающий**; **—ь** *v.* absorb, consume.

поглощающ/ий *a.* absorbing, absorbent; **п. элемент** (elec.) dissipative element; **—ая насадка** dissipative element, power termination; absorption cell; **—ая способность** absorptivity, absorptive power, absorptance; **—ая ячейка** absorption cell.

поглощен/ие *n.* absorption; **п. нейтронов** neutron absorption (or capture); **п. нейтронов без деления** nonfission neutron absorption; **коэффициент —ия** absorption coefficient (or factor), absorptivity; **первая основная полоса —ия** first fundamental absorption band; **—ный** *a.* absorbed.

погну/вшийся *a.* bent; **—ть** *v.* bend, curve.

поговорить *v.* discuss.

погода *f.* weather.

погодн/о *adv.* annually, per year; **—ый** *a.* annual.

погодостойкий *a.* weatherproof.

поголовн/о *adv.* without exception, all; **—ый** *a.* general.

погон *m.* distillate.

погонный *a.* linear; running.

погоня *f.* pursuit.

пограничн/ый *a.* boundary, bordering; **п. слой** boundary (or surface) layer; **—ая кривая жидкости** liquidus curve; **—ая линия** boundary line; **—ая область** border zone; **—ые лучи** grenz rays.

погрешност/ь *f.* error, mistake; **абсолютная п. отсчета** accuracy of reading; **величина —и, значение —и** magnitude of error.

погруб/елый *a.* roughened, coarse; **—еть** *v.* roughen.

погруж/аемый *a.* submersible; immersed; **п. счетчик** dipping counter; **—ать** *v.* immerse, sink, submerge, plunge; insert; imbed; **—ающаяся орбита** penetrating orbit.

погружен/ие *n.* immersion, subsidence, sinking, plunging; insertion; imbedding; **п. в атмосферу** immersion in the atmosphere; **—ный** *a.* plunged, immersed, submerged, sunk; inserted; imbedded; **—ный реактор** swimming-pool reactor.

погружной *a.* immersible, immersion, submersible; **п. нагреватель** immersion heater.

погруз/ившийся *a.* sunken, buried; **—ить** *see* **погружать.**

погубить *v.* ruin, destroy.

под *m.* hearth; bottom.

под *prep. acc. and instr.* under; by; for; near; toward; to; from; **п. вопросом** open to question, not certain; **п. рукой** at hand, close by; **п. 40° северной широты** at latitude 40° north.

под— *prefix* (*with verbs*) upward; under; approach; addition; (*with nouns*) sub—, under; near.

подават/ель *m.* conveyor; **—ь** *v.* give, present; supply, feed.

подав/итель *m.* suppressor; **—ить, —лять** *v.* repress, inhibit, suppress, depress; overwhelm; **—ление** *n.* repression, inhibition; suppression, depression; **—ление пар** pair suppression; **—ленный** *a.* suppressed, repressed; inhibited; **—ляющее большинство** overwhelming majority.

подавно *adv.* all the more.

подалгебра *f.* subalgebra.

податлив/ость *f.* pliability, pliancy; compliance; **акустическая п.** acoustic compliance; **—ый** *a.* pliable, pliant; compliant.

подать *see* **подавать.**

подач/а *f.* giving, presenting; supply, feed, feeding, delivery, conveyance, admission, input; **механизм —и** feed mechanism; **объем —и** delivery volume.

подающ/ий *a.* feeding, feed, conveying, supply, delivery; **п. механизм** feed mechanism; **п. червяк** head screw; **—ая лента** feed belt; **—ая труба** supply (delivery, feed) pipe.

подбав/ить, —лять *v.* add; **—ка** *f.* adding, addition.

подбарьерная частица subbarrier particle (with energy below potential barrier).

подбив/ать *v.* line, pad; incite; drive under; **—ка** *f.* lining, padding; driving under.

подбир/ание *n.* selection; matching; **—ать** *v.* select; match; assort.

подбить *see* **подбивать.**

подбой *m.* lining.

подбор *m.* selection, choice; sorting, matching, fitting; set; **п. кривой** curve fitting; **метод —а** trial-and-error method; **—ом** by trial and error; **подборка** *f.* set; selection.

подбр/асывать, —осить *v.* toss.

по два *adv.* in pairs, in twos.

подведен/ие *n.* supply; **—ный** *a.* led up to, conducted, supplied.

подведомственный *a.* dependent upon, within the jurisdiction of.

подверг/ать, —нуть *v.* subject, submit, expose to; **п. испытанию** test; **п. облучению** expose to radiation; **—аться, —нуться** *v.* be subjected to, undergo; be exposed to.

подвержен/ие *n.* subjection; **п. изгибу** bending load; **—ность** *f.* liability, susceptibility; **—ный** *a.* subjected to, exposed; subject.

подвер/нуть, —теть *see* **подвертывать.**

подвертыв/ание *n.* screwing, tightening; **—ать** *v.* screw, tighten; **—аться** *v.* turn up.

подвес *m.* suspension, suspension device; **—ить** *see* **подвешивать**; **—ка** *f.* suspension, hanging; hanger, bracket; **—ной, —ный** *a.* suspension, suspended, hanging; overhead.

подвести *see* **подводить.**

подветренн/ый *a.* lee, leeward; **п. прилив** lee tide; **—ая волна** lee wave.

подвеш/енный *see* **подвесной**; **—ивание** *n.* suspension, hanging; **—ивать** *v.* suspend, hang, hang up.

подвиг *m.* exploit, feat, heroic deed.

подвигать *v.* advance, push, promote; **—ся** *v.* advance, progress.

подвижка *f.* movement, shift.

подвижн/ой *a.* mobile, moving; portable; traveling, migratory, sliding; **п. контакт** sliding contact; **п. масштаб, —ая шкала** sliding scale; **п. реактор** mobile reactor; **п. циклон** migratory cyclone (or low); **—ая установка** mobile unit; **—ая шкала времени** (elec.) triggered time base; **—ое равновесие** transient equilibrium, dynamic equilibrium.

подвижн/ость *f.* mobility; portability; **п. ионов** ion mobility; **—ый** *see* **подвижной.**

подвинтить *see* **подвинчивать.**

подвинуть *see* **подвигать.**

подвинчивать *v.* screw up, tighten.

подвод *m.* supply, delivery, feed, inlet, admission; **—имый** *a.* fed, supplied; **—имая мощность** (power) input; **—ить** *v.* lead up to; feed, supply; place under; **—я итоги** summing up; **—ка** *f.* leading in; delivery, supply; supply lead, feed.

подводн/ый *a.* underwater, submarine, submerged; **п. взрыв** underwater explosion; **—ая лодка** submarine; **—ое течение** undercurrent.

подводящ/ий *a.* admission, inlet, conveying, feed, supply, delivery; **п. провод** lead.

подвоз *m.* supply; transport, transportation; **—ить** *v.* transport.

подвспышка *f.* (astr.) subflare.

подгон/ка *f.*, **—очный** *a.* fitting, adjusting; **п. кривой** fitting of curve; **—ять** *v.* adapt, match, adjust, fit.

подготовитель *m.* preparator; **—ный** *a.* preparatory.

подготов/ить, —лять *v.* prepare; train; **—ка** *f.*, **—ление** *n.* preparation; training; **—ленность** *f.* preparedness; **—ленный** *a.* prepared.

подгруппа *f.* subgroup.

поддавать *v.* add; **—ся** *v.* yield.

поддать *see* **поддавать.**

поддающийся *a.* amenable to, yielding to; **п. анализу** analyzable; **п. расчету** calculable; **п. регулированию** adjustable, controllable.

поддвиг *m.* (geo.) underthrust.

поддел/ать, —ывать *v.* falsify; adulterate; **—ка** *f.* imitation; adulteration;

—**ьный** *a.* false, spurious; artificial, imitation; adulterated.

поддерж/ание *n.*, —**ка** *f.* support, prop, rest; sustaining, maintenance; backing, sponsorship; —**ать,** —**ивать** *v.* support, bear, sustain; maintain; advocate; back (up); —**иваемый** *a.* supported; sustained, maintained; —**иваемая реакция** sustained reaction; —**ивающий** *a.* supporting, maintaining; —**ивающая сила** lift, buoyancy.

поддиапазон *m.* subrange, subband.

поддон, —**ок** *m.* tray, pan.

подействовать *see* **действовать.**

поделить *see* **делить.**

подел/ка *f.* article; —**очные камни** ornamental colored stones.

поденный *a.* by the day, daily.

подержать *v.* keep, hold (for some time).

подернуться *v.* be covered with.

подетальный *a.* (in) detail, (in) parts.

поджать *see* **поджимать.**

поджечь *see* **поджигать.**

поджиг *m.*, —**ание** *n.* ignition, firing; —**атель** *m.* igniter; —**ать** *v.* ignite, fire; set fire to; —**ающий электрод** keep-alive electrode.

поджимать *v.* press down; tighten.

подзаголовок *m.* subtitle.

подзаря/д *m.* booster charge; —**дить,** —**жать** *v.* charge (further), recharge; —**дка** *f.* additional charge; recharging.

подзвуковой *a.* subsonic, subaudio.

подземный *a.* underground, subterranean, subsurface; **п. удар** earth shock.

подзол *m.* podzol; —**истый** *a.* podzolic.

подзорная труба telescope, field glass; viewing scope.

подинтегральная функция integrand.

подинтервал *m.* subinterval.

подкалывать *v.* split, cleave.

подкапывать *see* **подкопать.**

подкасательная *f.* subtangent.

подка/тать, —**тить,** —**тывать** *v.* roll up; roll under; —**чивающий насос** booster pump.

подкисл/ение *n.* acidification; —**енный** *a.* acidified; —**ять** *v.* acidify; —**яющий** *a.* acidifying.

подклад/ка *f.* backing, lining; cushion; block; —**очный** *a.* lining; —**ывать** *v.* put under, back, line.

подкласс *m.* subclass; subset.

покле/ивание *n.*, —**йка** *f.* pasting, gluing; —**ивать,** —**ить** *v.* paste, glue.

подклинивать *v.* wedge up, shim.

подключ/ать, —**ить** *v.* connect; —**ение** *n.* connection.

подковообразный *a.* horseshoe (-form, -shaped); **п. магнит** horseshoe magnet.

подкожная игла hypodermic needle.

подколоть *see* **подкалывать.**

под/комиссия *f.*, —**комитет** *m.* subcommittee.

подкоп *m.*, —**ный** *a.* undermining; —**ать** *v.* undermine.

подкоренн/ая (величина), —**ое выражение,** —**ое число** radicand.

подкормка *f.* feeding.

подкос *m.* strut, brace.

подкра/сить, —**шивать** *v.* tint, color, retouch; —**шенный** *a.* colored.

подкреп/ить, —**лять** *v.* strengthen, reinforce; substantiate, confirm; —**ление** *n.* support, reinforcement; substantiation, confirmation; —**ленный** *a.* reinforced; confirmed; —**ленная струна** braced string; —**ляющий** *a.* strengthening; supporting; confirming.

подкритич/еский *a.* subcritical; —**ность** *f.* subcriticality.

подкрученный *a.* twisted.

подкрылок *m.* wing flap.

подла/дить, —**живать** *v.* fit, suit, adapt.

подламывать, —**ся** *v.* break, crack, split.

подле *prep. gen.* near, beside, next to.

подледниковый *a.* subglacial.

подлеж/ать *v.* be subject to; **п. решению** require solution; —**ащий** *a.* subject, liable; applicable, relevant; —**ащий определению** to be determined.

подлинн/ик *m.* original; —**ость** *f.* authenticity, originality; —**ый** *a.* authentic, original; real, genuine, true, actual.

подлож/ить *see* **подкладывать;** —**ка** *f.* backing.

подложный *a.* false, spurious.

подлом/ать, —**ить** *see* **подламывать.**

подлунный *a.* sublunar.

подмагничив/ание *n.* (superposed) magnetization; **—ать** *v.* magnetize, bias; **—ающий** *a.* magnetizing.

подмаз/ать, —ывать *v.* grease, oil; **—ка** *f.* greasing, oiling.

подматрица *f.* submatrix.

подмачивать *v.* wet, moisten, dampen.

подмедненный *a.* copper-plated.

подмен *m.*, **—а** *f.* substitution; **—енный, —ный** *a.* substituted, substitute; **—ивать, —ить, —ять** *v.* substitute, exchange, replace.

подмесь *f.* adulteration, admixture.

подме/тить, —чать *v.* observe, notice.

подмеш/анный *a.* mixed, impure; **—ать, —ивать** *v.* mix in, add.

подмножество *n.* subset.

подмодулятор *m.* (elec.) driver.

подмор/аживать, —озить *v.* freeze; **—оженный** *a.* frozen.

подмост/и, —ки *pl.* scaffold.

подмоч/енный *a.* slightly wet, moistened, damp; **—ить** *see* **подмачивать.**

подмыв *m.*, **—ание** *n.* washing; washing away; **—ать** *v.* wash; wash away, undermine.

подмыт/ый *a.* washed; washed away, undermined; **—ь** *see* **подмывать.**

подначальный *a.* subordinate.

поднесущая *f.* (rad.) subcarrier.

подним/ание *n.* raising, lifting; **—ать** *v.* raise, lift; **—аться** *v.* rise, ascend; **—ающий** *a.* raising, lifting; **—ающийся** *a.* rising, ascending.

поднов/ить, —лять *v.* renovate, renew; **—ление** *n.* renovation; **—ленный** *a.* renovated.

поднормаль *f.* subnormal.

поднутр/ение *n.* undercutting, undercut; **—енный** *a.*, **—ять** *v.* undercut.

поднят/ие *n.* rise, raising, ascent, lift, elevation; (geo.) uplift, upheaval; **—ый** *a.* raised; **—ь** *see* **поднимать.**

подоб/ать *v.* suit; **—ающий** *a.* suitable, proper; **—ающим образом** properly; **—ие** *n.* similarity, similitude.

подобн/о *adv.*, **—ым образом** similarly; **п. тому как** in the same way as; **—ый** *a.* similar, like; such; *suffix* —like, —oid, similar to, resembling; **—ое увеличение** (math.) isogonal (or conformal) magnification.

подоболочка *f.* subshell.

подобр/анный *a.* selected; matched; **—ать** *see* **подбирать.**

подовой *a.* hearth; bottom.

подогн/анная кривая fitted curve; **—ать** *see* **подгонять.**

подогрев *m.*, **—ание** *n.* warming up, heating; preheating.

подогреватель *m.* heater; preheater; **—ный** *a.* heating; preheating; **—ный катод** indirectly heated cathode, heater cathode; **—ный фон** heater-cathode hum; **—ная лампа** heater (-type) tube; **—ная печь** preheating furnace.

подогре/вать, —ть *v.* warm up, heat up; preheat; **—тый** *a.* warmed-up, heated; preheated.

пододви/гать, —нуть *v.* push (or move) up.

подозре/вать *v.* suspect; **—ние** *n.* suspicion.

подозрительн/о *adv.* suspiciously, with suspicion; it is suspicious; **—ость** *f.* suspiciousness; **—ый** *a.* suspicious.

подойти *see* **подходить.**

подонки *pl.* sediment, residue, dregs.

подоплека *f.* underlying situation, real state of affairs.

подопытн/ый *a.* experimental, under test; **—ое животное** experimental (or test) animal.

подорвать *see* **подрывать.**

подостлать *see* **подстилать.**

подотдел *m.* subdivision, section.

подошв/а *f.*, **—енный** *a.* bottom; foot, base; **п. волны** wave trough.

подпа/ивать, —ять *v.* solder up.

подпер/еть *see* **подпирать; —тый** *a.* supported.

подпил/ивать, —ить *v.* saw; file; **—ок** *m.* file.

подпир/ание *n.* supporting, propping; **—ать** *v.* prop up, support; **—ающий** *a.* supporting.

подпис/авшийся *a.* signatory; **—ание, —ывание** *n.* signing; **—анный** *a.* signed, authorized; **—ать, —ывать, —аться, —ываться** *v.* sign; subscribe; **—ка** *f.* subscription; signed statement; **—ной** *a.* signed; subscribed; **—чик** *m.* subscriber; **—ь** *f.* signature; underline (caption).

подпитка *f.* maintenance of water level; additional feeding, makeup.

подпиточн/ый *see* **питательный; п. насос** makeup pump; **—ая вода** makeup water.

под/пласток *m.* substratum; **—поверхностный** *a.* subsurface; **—поле** *n.* subfield.

подпор *m.* (hyd.) backwater.

подпор/а, —ка *f.* support, brace, strut; stand; bracket; **—ная стена** bulkhead.

подпоследовательность *f.* subsequence.

подпочв/а *f.* subsoil, substratum; **—енный** *a.* subsoil, subsurface; **—енная вода** ground water.

подправ/ить, —лять *v.* correct, rectify; retouch.

подпредельная масса subcritical mass.

подпространство *n.* subspace.

подпрыг/ивание *n.* jumping, springing; **—ивать, —нуть** *v.* jump up, bounce, spring.

подпус/кать, —тить *v.* admit; allow to approach.

подпятник *m.* step bearing, thrust bearing (or plate); **кольцевой п.** collar (step) bearing.

подравн/ивать, —ять *v.* level, even, trim.

подраж/ание *n.* imitation; **—атель** *m.* imitator; **—ательный** *a.* imitative; **—ать** *v.* imitate.

подраздел/ение *n.* subdivision; classification; **—енный** *a.* subdivided, divided; **—ить, —ять** *v.* subdivide, divide, partition.

подразумев/ается *v.* it is understood; **—ать** *v.* imply, mean.

подрегулиров/ание *n.*, **—ка** *f.* slight adjustment, readjustment; **—ать** *v.* adjust slightly, readjust.

под ред. *abbr.* (**под редакцией**) edited by.

подрез/ание, —ывание *n.*, **—ка** *f.* cutting, trimming; undercutting; **—анный** *a.* cut, trimmed; undercut; **—ать, —ывать** *v.* cut, trim; undercut; **—ной** *a.* cutting, trimming; undercutting.

подрессор/енный *a.* spring-mounted, cushioned; **—ивание** *n.* cushioning; **—ивать** *v.* mount on springs.

подрешетка *f.* sublattice.

подрисов/ать, —ывать *v.* touch up, retouch.

подробн/о *adv.* in detail, thoroughly, minutely; **—ость** *f.* detail; **вдаваться в —ости** particularize; **—ый** *a.* detailed, thorough, minute.

подровнять *see* **подравнивать.**

подручный *m.* apprentice, helper; *a.* at hand; improvised.

подрыв *m.* injury, detriment; blasting; **—ать** *v.* undermine; blast; **—ной** *a.* blasting; **—ной заряд** blasting charge.

подрыть *see* **подрывать.**

подряд *adv.* successively, in succession.

подря/д *m.*, **—жать** *v.* contract.

подсасыв/ание *n.* indraft, inflow; **—ающая сила** suction force.

подсборка *f.* subassembly.

подсвет *m.* illumination; **—ка** *f.* short exposure; preliminary irradiation (or illumination); (elec.) brightening, intensification; **импульс —ки** intensifier pulse.

подсвечив/ание *see* **подсветка; —ающий электрод** intensifier electrode.

под/синхронный *a.* hyposynchronous; **—система** *f.* subsystem.

подсказ/ать, —ывать *v.* prompt, suggest.

подскакив/ание *n.* jumping (up); **—ать** *v.* jump (up).

подскочить *see* **подскакивать.**

подсл/аивание *n.* subcoating; **—ой** *m.* sublayer.

подсобный *a.* secondary, subsidiary, accessory, auxiliary.

подсолевой *a.* (geo.) subsalt.

подсолнечный *a.* subsolar, sunlit.

подсос *m.* suction; indraft, inflow.

подсостояние *n.* substate.

подсохнуть *see* **подсыхать.**

подстав/ить, —лять *v.* substitute, replace; insert; place under; **—ка** *f.* support; stand, base, rest; **—ленный** *a.* substituted, replaced; inserted; placed under; **—ляемый** *a.* substituted; **—ляемое (выражение)** *n.* substituend; **—ной** *a.* false; **—очный** *a.* supporting.

подстанов/ить, —лять *v.* substitute; interchange; **—ка** *f.* substitution; permutation; interchange; **линейная**

—ка linear substitution; **группа —ок** (math.) permutation group; —**ление** *n.* substitution; interchange.

одстанция *f.* substation.

одстилаемый *a.* underlain.

одстилать *v.* underlie.

одстилающ/ий *a.* underlying; **п. слой, —ая порода** (geo.) base, bottom.

одстраивать *v.* fine-adjust (or tune).

одстроечный конденсатор trimmer (capacitor), padder.

одстройка *f.* fine adjustment (or tuning); frequency trim.

одстрочн/ый *a.* interlinear; **п. индекс** subscript; —**ое примечание** footnote.

одступ *m.* approach; access.

одсч/ет *m.* computation, calculation; count; **п. крови** blood count; —**итанный** *a.* computed, calculated; counted; —**итать, —итывать** *v.* compute, calculate; count.

одсыпать *v.* add; pour (in addition).

одсых/ание *n.* drying; —**ать** *v.* dry.

одтаивать *v.* begin to thaw (or melt).

одталкив/ать *v.* push; —**ающий** *a.* pushing, actuating.

одтачив/ание *n.* sharpening; undermining; —**ать** *v.* sharpen; undermine.

одтаять *see* **подтаивать.**

одтвержд/ать, подтвердить *v.* confirm, corroborate, verify; —**ающий** *a.* confirmatory; —**ение** *n.* confirmation, corroboration; verification; —**енный** *a.* confirmed, corroborated.

одтекать *v.* flow under; leak.

одтепловой нейтрон cold neutron.

одтерм *m.* subterm, sublevel.

одтечь *see* **подтекать.**

одтип *m.* subtype.

одтолкнуть *see* **подталкивать.**

одтональный *a.* subsonic.

одтопление *n.* water-table elevation.

одточ/енный *a.* sharpened; undercut; —**ить** *see* **подтачивать;** —**ка** *f.* sharpening.

одтропический *a.* subtropical.

одтягив/ание *n.* pulling; approach; —**ать** *v.* pull; tighten; move closer.

одтянуть *see* **подтягивать.**

одуровень *m.* sublevel.

одуч/ивать, —ить *v.* teach.

одуш/ка *f.*, cushion, pillow, pad; —**кообразная дисторсия** (opt.) pincushion distortion.

подфронтальное облако subfrontal cloud.

подфункция *f.* minorant (function).

подхват *m.* pickup; —**ить, ывать** *v.* catch, pick up.

подход *m.* approach, treatment; manner, procedure; —**ить** *v.* approach; suit, fit; (math.) be subsumed; —**ный** *a.* approach; —**ящий** *a.* suitable, fitting, appropriate, proper; approaching; —**ящая дробь** convergent (of a continued fraction).

подцве/тить, —чивать *v.* dye, color.

подцеп/ить, —лять *v.* hook, hook up.

подчас *adv.* sometimes, occasionally.

подчерк/ивание *n.* underlining; emphasis, stress; —**ивать, —нуть** *v.* underline; stress, emphasize.

подчин/ение *n.* subordination, submission, subjection; —**енность** *f.* subordination; —**енный** *a.* subordinate, inferior; —**ить, —ять** *v.* subordinate, subdue, subject; —**иться, —яться** *v.* be subordinated; submit, conform, obey, satisfy.

подчи/стить, —щать *v.* clean; erase.

подшивка *f.* lining; filing, file (of papers).

подшипник *m.*, —**овый** *a.* bearing; **п. на камнях** jeweled bearing; **опорный п.** journal bearing; **роликовый п.** roller bearing; **упорный п.** thrust bearing; **шариковый п.** ball bearing.

подшлифовать *v.* grind, polish.

подщелачив/ание *n.* alkalization; —**ать** *v.* alkalize.

подъем *m.* rise, advance, progress; raising, lift; ascent, climb, upclimbing; upgrade; —**ник** *m.* hoist, elevator; —**ный** *a.* lifting, raising; buoyant; —**ная сила** supporting power, carrying capacity, lifting power, lift; buoyancy.

подъярус *m.* (geo.) substage.

подымать *see* **поднимать.**

подыск/ание *n.* finding; —**ать** *v.* seek out, find; —**ивать** *v.* search for; find.

подытож/енный *a.* summed up; summarized; —**ивание** *n.* summation, addition; —**ивать, —ить** *v.* sum up, total.

подэра *f.* pedal (curve).

поездка *f.* trip, journey.

пожалов/ание *n.* granting, conferring, presenting; award; **—ать** *v.* grant, confer, present.

пожалуй *adv.* perhaps; likely; **—ста** *adv.* please, kindly.

пожар *m.* fire; **—ный** *a.* fire.

пожать *see* **пожимать.**

пожелать *v.* wish.

пожимать *v.* press, squeeze.

позаботиться *see* **заботиться.**

позади *adv.* behind, back; *prep. gen.* behind.

позапрошлый *a.* before the last; **п. год** the year before last.

позвол/ение *n.* permission; **—енный** *a.* permitted, allowed; **—ительный** *a.* permissible; **—ить, —ять** *v.* permit; enable; **—яет думать** it suggests; **—яющий** *a.* permitting; enabling.

поздн/ее *comp. of* **поздно,** later; **—ейший** *a.* last, latest; recent; **—ий** *a.* late, retarded; subsequent; **—ее сгорание** retarded combustion; afterburning; **—о** *adv.* late.

поздрав/ительный *a.* congratulatory; **—ить, —лять** *v.* congratulate; **—ление** *n.* congratulation.

поземный туман ground fog.

поземок *m.* drifting snow (storm).

позже *see* **позднее.**

позитив *m.*, **—ный** *a.* positive.

позитрон *m.*, **—ный** *a.* positron; **п.-активный** positron-emitting; **—ий** *m.* positronium.

позиционер *m.* positioner.

позиц/ионный *a.*, **—ия** *f.* position; attitude; **п. переключатель** stepping switch; **п. угол** position angle; **—ионное значение** (math.) place (or local) value.

познав/аемость *f.* cognizability; **—аемый** *a.* cognizable, knowable; **—ание** *n.* cognizance, knowledge; **—ать** *v.* cognize, learn to apprehend.

позн/ание *n.* knowledge, cognition; **—ать** *see* **познавать.**

позоло/та *f.* gilding, gold plating; **—тить** *v.* gild; **—ченный** *a.* gilded, gold-plated.

позонный *a.* zone, zonal.

позывн/ой *a.* (rad.) call; **п. сигнал** call signal; **—ые** *pl.* call letters.

поимен/но *adv.* by name; **—ный** *a.* nominal; **—овать** *v.* name, mention, designate.

поимка *f.* capture.

по-иному *adv.* differently.

поиск *m.* search; scanning; **—и** *pl.*, **—овый** *a.* search, prospecting; research; **—и урановых месторождений** prospecting for uranium deposits; **—ать** *v.* seek, search for.

поистине *adv.* indeed, in truth.

пойма *f.* floodplain.

поймать *v.* capture, entrap.

Пойнтинга вектор Poynting vector; **теорема П.** P. theorem.

пойти *see* **идти, ходить.**

пока *conj.* while, so long as, until; for the present, as yet; **п. еще** at present; **п. не** until; **п. что** for the time being.

показ *m.* demonstration, exhibition.

показание *n.* indication; reading, response (of an instrument).

показанный *a.* shown; demonstrated.

показатель *m.* index, exponent; indicator, pointer; characteristic, sign, property; **п. адиабаты** adiabatic exponent; **п. добротности, п. качества** figure of merit; **п. поглощения** absorption coefficient; **п. политропы** polytropic exponent (or index); **п. преломления** index of refraction; **п. степени** exponent; **п. (степени) корня** index of radical; **п. цвета** (astr.) color index; **это —но** it is significant.

показательн/ый *a.* exponential, power, indicative, significant; representative, model, demonstration; **п. закон** exponential law; **—ая кривая** exponential curve; **—ая функция** exponential (or power) function.

показ/ать *see* **показывать**; **—ной** *a.* display.

показыв/ание *n.* showing, exhibiting; **—ать** *v.* show, exhibit, display; denote, indicate, register; **—аться** *v.* seem, appear.

покаскадный *a.* in stages.

покат/ить *v.* roll, set rolling; **—о** *adv.* slopingly; **—ость** *f.* slope, declivity, inclination, grade; **—ый** *a.* sloping, slanting, inclined.

покач/ать *v.* swing, rock; **—ивание** *n.*

swinging, rocking; **—ивать, —нуть** *v.* shake, unsettle.

поки/дать, —нуть *v.* leave, abandon; **—нутый** *a.* abandoned.

поковка *f.* forging.

покоиться *v.* be at rest; lie.

пок/ой *m.* rest, quiescence; **масса —оя** rest mass; **точка —оя** point of rest, stationary point; **трения —оя** static friction; **угол —оя** angle of repose; **энергия —оя** potential energy.

покойн/о *adv.* quietly; **—ый** *a.* quiet, quiescent, resting; deceased; **—ое положение** rest position.

поколебаться *v.* swing, fluctuate, oscillate; hesitate.

поколение *n.* generation.

покор/ение *n.* subjugation; **—ить** *see* **покорять.**

покороб/ившийся, —ленный *a.* warped, buckled; **—ить** *v.* warp, bend.

покорять *v.* subdue, subjugate; **—ся** *v.* submit, yield.

поко/сившийся *a.* lopsided; **—сить** *v.* slope, slant; **—шенный** *a.* slanted, sloping.

покоящ/ийся *a.* stationary, at rest, quiescent; **—аяся масса** rest mass.

покрас/ить *v.* paint, color; **—ка** *f.* painting, coloring.

покрасн/евший *a.* reddened; **—ение** *n.* reddening; **—еть** *v.* redden.

покривленный *a.* curved, bent.

покров *m.* cover; mantle, sheath; coating, coat, (geo.) blanket, sheet; **облачный п.** cloud cover; **—ный** *a.* cover, covering; **—ный эффект** (astr.) blanketing effect; **—ная залежь** (geo.) blanket deposit; **—ное стекло, —ное стеклышко** cover glass.

покрыв/ание *n.* covering, coating; **—ать** *v.* cover; cap; sheathe, envelop, mantle; overlay, coat, plate; span, bridge; **—ать диапазон** span a range.

покрывающ/ий *a.* covering; **п. слой** superstratum; coating, coat; **—ая порода** (geo.) cap rock.

покрытие *n.* covering; coverage, coating; layer, film, deposit; cladding, jacketing; capping; (astr.) obscuration, occultation; **п. бридера** (reactor) breeder blanket.

покрыт/ый *a.* covered, coated, clad; insulated; **п. железом** ironclad; **п. медью** copper-plated; **п. облаками** overcast; **п. оболочкой** sheathed; **—ь** *see* **покрывать.**

покрыш/ка *f.*, **—ечный** *a.* covering, cover, lid, cap; mantle, jacketing, case; tire casing.

покуп/ать *v.* purchase; **—ка** *f.* purchasing; purchase.

пол *m.* floor; sex.

пол— *see* **полу—.**

полаг/ать *v.* assume, suppose; **положим** let us assume; **—аться на** rely upon.

поладить *v.* come to an understanding, agree.

пол/века *m.* half a century; **—года** *m.* half a year.

полдень *m.* noon; **истинный п.** apparent noon.

пол/е *n.* field; **п. аксиальной симметрии** axially symmetrical (or cylindrical) field; **п. ветра** wind field; **вихревое п.** vorticity field; **п. зрения** field of view, visual field; **п. зрения антенны** antenna coverage; **п. напряжений** stress field; **п. тяготения** gravitational field; **п. тяжести** gravitational field; **п. удаления ионов** ion-clearing field; **п. центральных сил** central-force field; **п. центробежных сил** centrifugal field; **п. ядра** nuclear field; **теория —я** field theory.

полев/ой *a.* field; **п. квант** field quantum; **п. шпат** feldspar; **—ая масса** electromagnetic mass; **—ая теория** field theory; **—ая частица** field particle.

полезность *f.* usefulness.

полезн/ый *a.* useful, helpful; effective; **п. напор** net (pressure) head; **п. пучок** useful beam; **—ая лошадиная сила** effective (actual, working) horsepower; **—ая мощность** effective (useful, net) power (or output); **—ая нагрузка** net load, payload; **—ая отдача тепла** thermal efficiency; **—ая работа** useful work; **—ое действие** efficiency, useful effect; **коэффициент —ого действия** efficiency.

полеми/зировать *v.* dispute, argue; **—ка** *f.* controversy, dispute.

полет *m.* flight; **—еть** *v.* fly off, take flight, take off.

полз/ание *n.* creeping; **—ать, —ти** *v.* creep.

ползун *m.* slide block, slider, slide, guide shoe; **—ок** *m.* (elec.) sliding contact, slider.

ползуч/есть *f.* creep, creeping, creepage; **—ий** *a.* creeping; **—ая деформация** creep.

ползушка *see* **ползун.**

ползущий *see* **ползучий.**

поли— *prefix* poly—, multi—, many, multiple.

Полиа распределение Pólya distribution.

полиада *f.* (spect.) polyad.

полиатомный *a.* polyatomic.

Полибий Polybius (lunar crater).

полибутадиен *m.* polybutadiene.

полив *see* **поливка.**

полива *f.* glaze.

поливариантный *a.* polyvariant.

поливать *v.* water, irrigate; wet.

поливиниловый *a.* polyvinyl.

полив/ка *f.*, **—очный** *a.* watering, irrigation; wetting.

полигамма-функция polygamma function.

полигирный *a.* cubic, isometric.

полигон *m.* polygon; proving ground, firing range.

полиграф/ический *a.* polygraphic; **—ия** *f.* polygraphy.

полидимит *m.* polydymite.

полидисперсн/ость *f.* polydispersity; **—ый** *a.* polydisperse; **—ая сетка** polydisperse network.

поли/ен *m.* polyene; **—зональная оболочка** polyzonal can; **—кислота** *f.* polyacid; **—конденсация** *f.* condensation polymerization; **—краз** *m.* polycrase; **—кремневая кислота** polysilicic acid.

поликристалл *m.* polycrystal; **—ический** *a.* polycrystalline.

поликсен *m.* polyxene.

полимер *m.*, **—ное соединение** polymer; **—изатор** *m.* polymerizer; **—изация** *f.* polymerization; **—изованный** *a.* polymerized; **—изовать, —изоваться** *v.* polymerize; **—ия** *f.* polymerism; **—ный** *a.* polymeric.

полиметр *m.* polymeter.

полимодальное распределение polymodal distribution.

полимолекулярный *a.* polymolecular, multimolecular.

полиморф *m.* polymorph; **—изм** *m.* polymorphism; **—ический, —ный** *a.* polymorphous, polymorphic.

полином *m.*, **—иальный** *a.* polynomial, multinomial.

полипептид *m.* polypeptide.

полипрен *m.* polyprene.

полиров/альный *a.*, **—ание** *n.*, **—очный** *a.* polishing, buffing; **—анный** *a.* polished; **—ать** *v.* polish, buff; **—ка** *f.* polishing, buffing.

полирующий *a.* polishing.

поли/силоксан *m.* polysilicone; **—синтетический** *a.* polysynthetic.

полиспаст *m.* pulley block, block and tackle.

полистирол *m.* polystyrene.

политен *m.* polythene.

политетрафторэтилен *m.* Teflon.

политехни/ка *f.* technology, polytechnology; **—кум** *m.* polytechnic (school); **—ческий** *a.* polytechnic.

полит/ика *f.* politics; policy; **—ический** *a.* political.

политоп *m.* polytope.

политроп/а *f.* polytrope; polytropic curve; **—ический, —ный** *a.* polytropic.

полихроизм *m.* polychroism, pleochroism.

полихром *m.* polychrome, esculin; **—атический** *a.* polychromatic, polychromic; **—ия** *f.* polychromy.

полициклическ/ий *a.* polycyclic, polynucleated.

полиэдр *m.* polyhedron; **—ический** *a.* polyhedral.

полиэлектролит *m.* polyelectrolyte.

полиэнергетический пучок polyenergetic (or polychromatic) beam.

полиэтилен *m.* polyethylene.

полка *f.* rack, shelf.

Поллукс Pollux.

поллуцит *m.* pollucite.

полн/ейший *a.* fullest, utmost; **—о** *adv* fully, completely.

полно— *prefix* full, fully, holo—.

полновесность *f.* full weight; soundness.

полногранн/ик *m.* holohedron; **—ый** *a.* holohedral.

полнокристаллический *a.* holocrystalline.

полнолуние *n.* full moon.

полномасштабный *a.* full-scale.

полномочие *n.* authorization, authority; competence.

полноосный *a.* holoaxial.

полноразмерный *a.* full-scale.

полностью *adv.* completely, totally, fully; **п. ионизованный** fully ionized.

полнот/а *f.* completeness; fullness; **аксиома —ы** axiom of completeness.

полноценный *a.* full-valued; fully adequate; valid.

полночь *f.* midnight.

полн. собр. соч. *abbr.* (**полное собрание сочинений**) complete collected works.

полн. собр. тр. *abbr.* (**полное собрание трудов**) complete works.

полн/ый *a.* total, complete, full, whole, overall; **п. гамильтониан** complete (or general) Hamiltonian; **п. дифференциал** total (exact, perfect) differential; **п. излучатель** complete radiator, blackbody; **п. момент вращения** total angular momentum; **п. напор** total head; **п. размах** peak-to-peak amplitude; **п. цикл** complete cycle; **п. эллиптический интеграл** complete elliptic integral; **—ая вариация** total variation; **—ая кривизна** total (or Gaussian) curvature; **—ая нагрузка** full load; **—ая обработка** full (or detailed) treatment; **—ая производная** total derivative; **—ая система функций** complete system of functions; **—ая удельная ионизация** total specific ionization; **—ая фаза затмения** totality (of an eclipse).

полн/ый *cont.*, **—ое (внутреннее) отражение** total (internal) reflection; **—ое давление** total pressure; (hyd.) dynamic (or ram) pressure; **—ое дневное освещение** broad daylight; **—ое замирание** (rad.) complete fade-out; **—ое затмение** total eclipse; **—ое изменение** total variation; **—ое квадратное уравнение** general form of (or affected) quadratic equation; **—ое квантовое число** inner quantum number; **—ое короткое замыкание** (elec.) dead short; **—ое отношение масс** overall mass ratio; **—ое сечение** total cross section; **—ое солнечное затмение** total solar eclipse; **—ое сопротивление** impedance; **—ое упорядочение** complete (or perfect) ordering; **—ое усиление** (elec.) overall gain; **в —ой мере** fully, completely.

пол-оборота *m.* half turn.

половин/а *f.* half; **п. отлива** half-ebb; **п. прилива** half-flood; **в —у** half as much; **на —у меньше** half as large.

половин/ка *f.*, **—ный** *a.* half; **—ный угол при вершине** vertex half-angle; **—чатый** *a.* halved; undecided.

половодье *n.* high water.

половой *a.* floor; sex.

полог/ий *a.* mildly sloping; **п. откос** flat slope; **п. уклон** mild slope, flat gradient; **п. ход спектра** flat spectrum; **—ая залежь** (geo.) flat; **—ая кривая** flat curve.

полого/падающий *a.* flat-dipping; **—сть** *f.* slope, declivity.

поло/дия, —ида *f.* polhode; **—идальный** *a.* poloidal.

положен/ие *n.* position, location, situation; statement, proposition, thesis, theorem; state, condition; regulation, statute; **п. вещей** state of affairs; **п. равновесия** equilibrium configuration; **геометрия —ия** topology, analysis situs; **правило ложного —ия** rule of false position, regula falsi; **—ный** *a.* placed; fixed; prescribed.

положительно *adv.* positively; decidedly; **п. определенный** (math.) positive definite; **—сть** *f.* positiveness.

положительн/ый *a.* positive, plus; affirmative; favorable; **п. знак** plus, positive sign; **п. мениск** positive meniscus, concavo-convex lens; **п. столб** positive column; **—ая линза** converging lens; **—ая проводимость** *p*-type conductivity; **—ая четность** even parity; **—ое качество** positiveness; **—ые лучи** positive rays.

положить *see* **класть.**

полом/ать *v.* break (down); **—ка** *f.* breakdown; breakage.

полон/иевый *a.* polonium; **—ий** *m.* polonium (Po).

поло/са *f.* band; strip, stripe, bar; streak; zone, belt; page; sheet; **п. деформации** deformation band; **п. заграждения фильтра** filter attenuation (or stop) band; **п. затмения** eclipse path; **п. интерференции** interference fringe; **п. испускания** emission band; **п. падения дождя (или осадков)** trail of precipitation, Fallstreifen, virga; **п. поглощения** absorption band; **п. пропускания** pass (or transmission) band; **п. скольжения** slip band; **п. собственного поглощения** fundamental absorption band; **п. спектра** spectral band; **система —с** (spect.) band system; (rad. astr.) strip system.

полосат/ый *a.* banded, striped, striated, streaky; **п. спектр** band spectrum; **—ое сложение** (geo.) banded structure.

полоска *f.* band, strip, streak, stripe.

полоск/ание *n.* rinse, rinsing; **—атель-ный** *a.* rinsing; **—ать** *v.* rinse.

полоснозаграждающий фильтр band-elimination filter.

полос/ный, —овой *a.* band; strip, bar; **п. усилитель** band-pass amplifier; **п. фильтр** band-pass filter.

полост/ной *a.* cavity; **—ь** *f.* hollow, cavity, void, gap; (math.) sheet; **эффект —ей** *see* **каналовый эффект.**

полосчат/ость *f.* banding, striation; **—ый** *a.* banded, banding, striped, striated; lamellar, laminated.

полотенце *n.* towel.

полотн/ище *n.* width, breadth; strip; **—о** *n.* linen; roadbed; curtain antenna array.

полпути *m.*, **на п.** halfway.

полтора one and one half, sesqui—; **—ста** one hundred and fifty.

полу— *prefix* semi—, demi—, hemi—, half—.

полуавтомат *m.* semiautomatic device or machine; **—ический** *a.* semiautomatic.

полубесконечн/ый *a.* semi-infinite; **—ая линия** (infinite) half-line.

полуволн/а *f.*, **—овой** *a.* half-wave.

полугидрат *m.* hemihydrate.

полугод/ие *n.* half year; **—ичный —овой** *a.* semiannual.

полугранн/ик *m.* hemihedron; **—ый** *a.* hemihedral.

полугруппа *f.* semigroup.

полуда *f.* tinning.

полуденн/ый *a.* noon, meridian, meridional; **—ая линия** meridian line **—ые часы** midday, about noon.

полу/диагональный *a.* semidiagonal **—диаметр** *m.* semidiameter, radius.

полудистанционн/ый *a.* semiremote **—ое управление** semiremote control.

полуженный *a.* tin-plated.

полу/жесткий *a.* semirigid; **—жидкий** *a.* semiliquid, semifluid; **—зазор** *m.* half-gap.

полузакрепленная дислокация sessil dislocation.

полу/интервал *m.* half-open interval **—количественный** *a.* semiquantitative; **—коллоид** *m.* semicolloid **—комплект** *m.* subassembly; **—коронирующий разряд** semicorona discharge; **—кристаллический** *a.* semicrystalline, hemicrystalline, hypocrystalline.

полукруг *m.* semicircle; half-disk; **—лый** *a.* semicircular.

полу/кубическая парабола semicubical parabola; **—логарифмический** *a.* semilogarithmic; **—лунный** *a.* crescent-shaped.

полуметалл *m.* semimetal; **—ический** *a.* submetallic.

полу/механизированный *a.* semimechanized; **—микроскопический масштаб** semimicro scale; **—непрерывный** *a.* semicontinuous.

полуночный *a.* midnight.

полу/оборот *m.* half turn; **—обработанный** *a.* semiprocessed; **—обратный** *a.* semi-inverse; **—окатанность** *f.* subangularity; **—окружность** *f.* semicircumference, semicircle; **—опал** *m.* semiopal, common opal; **—определенный** *a.* semidefinite.

полуостров *m.* peninsula.

полуось *f.* semiaxis; differential axle; **большая п.** semimajor axis.

полу/отделанный *a.* semifinished; **—открытый** *a.* half-open; **—параболический** *a.* semiparabolic.

полупериод *m.* half-period, half-cycle; **п. распада** half-life; **п. реакции обмена** half-time of exchange.

полу/плоскость *f.* half-plane; **—поглощающий слой** half-thickness; **—полоса** *f.* (opt.) half-fringe; **—полярный** *a.* semipolar; **—правильный** *a.* semiregular.

полупревращени/е *n.* half-reaction; **период —я** half-life.

полупризма *f.* hemiprism; **—тический** *a.* hemiprismatic.

полупровод/ник *m.* semiconductor; **—никовый** *a.* semiconductor, semiconducting; **—никовый триод** transistor; **—ящий** *a.* semiconducting.

полу/продукт *m.* intermediate product; **—прозрачный, —просвечивающий** *a.* semitransparent, translucent; **—проницаемый** *a.* semiporous, semipermeable; **—пространство** *n.* half-space; **—профиль** *m.* half-section; **—прямая** *f.* half-line; ray.

полу/размах *m.* amplitude; semirange; **—разность** *f.* half-difference; **—распад** *m.* half-decay, half-disintegration; **период —распада** half-life; **—сегмент** *m.* (math.) half-open interval.

полусернистая медь cuprous sulfide.

полу/смола *f.* resinoid; **—спекшийся** *a.* semisintered; **—стеклянный** *a.* subvitreous; **—сумма** *f.* half-sum, average; **—суточный** *a.* semidiurnal; **—сухой** *a.* semiarid.

полусфер/а *f.* hemisphere; **—ический** *a.* hemispherical.

полусходиться *v.* semiconverge.

полу/твердый *a.* semisolid; medium-hard; **—телескопическое изображение** semitelescopic imaging; **—тело** *n.* half-body.

полутен/евой прибор half-shade device; **—ь** *f.* penumbra.

полутолщина *f.* half-thickness.

полутон *m.*, **—овый** *a.* halftone, semitone.

полутора—, полуторно— *prefix* sesqui—.

полуторн/ый *a.* one and one-half; sesqui—; **—ая окись урана** uranium sesquioxide.

полуточный *a.* semiexact.

полу/тропический *a.* semitropical; **—турбулентный** *a.* semiturbulent; **—тяжелый** *a.* semiheavy.

полууgловат/ость *f.* (geo.) subangularity; **—ый** *a.* subangular.

полуугол *m.* half-angle.

полу/упорядоченный *a.* partially ordered; **—устойчивый** *a.* metastable.

полу/фабрикат *m.* semifinished product; intermediate product; **—финитный** *a.* semifinite.

полуцел/ый *a.* half-integral; **—ое число** half-integer.

полуценный *a.* half-value.

полуцилиндр *m.* semicylinder; **—ический** *a.* semicylindrical.

получаемый *a.* resulting, resultant, produced.

получасовой *a.* half-hourly.

получат/ель *m.* recipient; **—ь** *v.* prepare, produce; derive, extract; receive, obtain; **—ь обратно** recover; **—ься в результате** result, ensue.

получен/ие *n.* production, preparation; derivation, extraction; result, outcome; receipt; **обратное п.** recovery; **—ный** *a.* produced, prepared, product; derived, resulting; received, obtained; **—ное ядро** product nucleus.

получ/ившийся *a.* resulting; **—ить** *see* **получать.**

полушар/ие *n.* hemisphere; **—овой** *a.* hemispheric.

полу/ширина *f.* halfwidth, halfbreadth; **—элемент** *m.* half-cell; **—эллиптический** *a.* semielliptical; **—эмпирический** *a.* semiempirical.

пол/ый *a.* hollow, tubular; **п. шар** spherical shell; **—ая вода** high water; **—ая ионизационная камера** cavity ionization chamber.

полынья *f.* polynya, ice clearing (or window).

полыхать *v.* blaze.

польз/а *f.* use, good; favor, benefit, advantage; **в —у** in favor of; **—ование** *n.* use; **—оваться** *v.* make use of, employ, profit by; **—уемся случаем** we take this opportunity.

Польмана свисток Pohlman whistle.

польск. *abbr.* (**польский**) Polish.

Польская Народная Республика Polish People's Republic.

Польша Poland.

полюс *m.* pole; terminal; **п. возбуждения** (mag.) field pole; **дополнительный п.** (elec.) commutating pole, interpole; **п. мира** celestial pole; **п. холода** (meteor.) cold pole; **переключатель —ов** pole changer (or reverser).

полюсн/ый *a.* polar, pole; **п. башмак, п. наконечник** pole piece (tip, shoe); **п. выступ** pole horn; **п. магнит** field magnet; **—ая обмотка** pole-face (or field) winding; **—ая ось** polar axis; **—ая система** (elec.) field magnet; **—ая фигура** (cryst.) pole figure.

полюсоопределитель *m.* polarity indicator.

поляра *f.* polar (line, curve); **ударная п.** shock polar (curve).

поляризатор *m.* polarizer.

поляризационн/ый *a.* polarization, polarizing; **п. микроскоп** polarizing microscope; **—ая катастрофа** polarizability (or polarization) catastrophe; **—ая призма** polarizing prism, polarizer.

поляриз/ация *f.*, **—ование** *n.* polarization; **—ируемый** *a.* polarizable.

поляризов/анный *a.* polarized; **п. влево (по кругу)** left-handed (or counterclockwise) polarized; **п. вправо (по кругу)** right-handed (or clockwise) polarized; **п. по кругу** circularly polarized; **—ать** *v.* polarize.

поляриз/уемость *f.* polarizability; **п. диэлектрика** electric susceptibility; **—уемый, —ующийся** *see* **поляризируемый**; **—ующий** *a.* polarizing.

поляриметр *m.* polarimeter; **—ия** *f.* polarimetry.

полярископ *m.* polariscope; **—ия** *f.* polariscopy.

поляристробометр *m.* polaristrobometer.

Полярная звезда Polaris, North Star.

полярн/ость *f.* polarity; **—ый** *a.* polar; arctic; **—ый пояс** frigid zone; **—ая диаграмма** polar diagram, Argand diagram; directional diagram; **—ая крона** (astr.) polar crown; **—ая ось** *see* **полюсная ось**; **—ая связь** polar bond; **—ая система координат** polar coordinate system; **—ое вещество** polar substance; **—ое расстояние** polar distance, codeclination; **—ое сияние** aurora polaris, aurora.

поляро/грамма *f.* polarogram; **—граф** *m.* polarograph; **—графия** *f.* polarography; **—ид** *m.* polaroid; **—н** *m.* polaron.

пом. *abbr.* (**помощник**) aid, assistant.

помаз/ать, —ывать *v.* grease, oil.

помеднен/ие *n.* copper plating; **—ный** *a.* copper-plated.

поменять *see* **менять**; **—ся** *v.* exchange; **—ся местами** exchange places.

Померанчука эффект Pomeranchuk effect.

померк/лый *a.* dimmed; **—нуть** *see* **меркнуть.**

поместительн/ость *f.* spaciousness; **—ый** *a.* capacious, spacious.

поместить *see* **помещать.**

местн/ый *a.* (math.) place, positional; **—ое значение** place value.

помесячный *a.* monthly.

помет/ить *see* **помечать**; **—ка** *f.* mark; note.

помех/а *f.* obstacle, interference, disturbance, difficulty; **—и** *pl.* (elec.) interference, noise; **атмосферные —и** atmospherics, static; **—и от зажигания** ignition noise; **—и от солнечного излучения** solar noise.

помехо/ограничитель *m.* noise limiter; **—устойчивый** *a.* interference-free, antijamming, noiseproof.

помеч/ать *v.* mark; date; **—енный** *a.* marked.

помеш/ать *v.* mix, stir, agitate; **—ивание** *n.* mixing, stirring, agitation.

помещать *v.* place, locate, seat; (math.) imbed; **—ся** *v.* be placed in, fit.

помещение *n.* room, place; putting, setting.

помзав. *abbr.* (**помощник заведующего**) assistant chief, assistant manager.

помимо *prep. gen.* apart from, besides, in addition to; unknown to; **п. того** moreover, besides.

поминутно *adv.* every minute.
помириться с *v.* be reconciled to.
помнач. *abbr.* (**помощник начальника**) assistant chief.
помнить *v.* remember, bear in mind.
помнож/ать, —**ить** *v.* multiply.
помогать *v.* help, assist, aid.
по-моему *adv.* in my opinion.
помост *m.* stage; gantry.
помочь *see* **помогать.**
помощ/ник *m.* aid, assistant; —**ь** *f.* help, assistance, aid; —**ью, при —и, с —ью** with the help of, by means of; **оказать —ь** help; **первая —ь** first aid.
помпа *f.* pump.
помпаж *m.* surging.
помутить *v.* make turbid; —**ся** *v.* become turbid (cloudy, dim); blur.
помутнение *n.* turbidity, cloudiness; dimness; fogging; **п. воздуха** atmospheric turbidity; **испытание на п.** cloud test.
понадобиться *v.* be necessary.
по-настоящему *adv.* properly.
пондеромоторная сила ponderomotive force.
поневоле *adv.* against one's will; necessarily.
понедельн/ик *m.* Monday; —**о** *adv.*, —**ый** *a.* weekly, per week.
понемногу *adv.* gradually.
понижать *v.* decrease, reduce, lower; degrade, depress; (elec.) step down; —**ся** *v.* fall, drop, diminish, decrease.
понижающий *a.* reducing; (elec.) step-down; —**ся** *a.* falling, dropping downward.
понижен/ие *n.* reduction, lowering, drop, decrease, fall, subsiding; settling; depression; (elec.) stepping down; **п. горизонта** dip of the horizon; **п. температуры с высотой** lapse rate; —**ный** *a.* reduced, lowered, depressed.
понизитель *m.* reducer; —**ный** *a.* reducing; (elec.) step-down; —**ный бустер** negative booster.
понизить *see* **понижать.**
поним/ание *n.* understanding, comprehension; conception; sense; —**ать** *v.* understand, comprehend, realize.
по-новому *adv.* in a new way.
понор *m.* (geo.) sinkhole.
Понс-Виннекиды Pons-Winnecke meteors.
понселет *m.* poncelet, Poncelet wheel.
понтия *f.* punty, pontil.
Понтан Pontanus (lunar crater).
понтон *m.*, —**ный** *a.* pontoon.
понудительн/ый *a.* compelling, coercive, impellent; —**ая сила** (mag.) coercive force.
пону/дить, —**ждать** *v.* compel, force, drive, impel; —**ждение** *n.* compulsion, coercion.
понят/ие *n.* conception, concept, idea; —**ливость** *f.* understanding, comprehension; —**но** *adv.* clearly, plainly; naturally, of course; —**ность** *f.* clearness, intelligibility; —**ный** *a.* clear, intelligible; natural; —**ый** *a.* understood; —**ь** *see* **понимать.**
поодаль *adv.* at some distance.
поочередн/о *adv.* alternately, successively, by turns; —**ый** *a.* alternate, successive.
поощр/ение *n.* encouragement; —**ительный** *a.* encouraging, stimulating; —**ить,** —**ять** *v.* encourage, stimulate; advance.
попадан/ие *n.* hit, incidence, entrance into; **п. в цель** hitting the target, hit; **точка —ия** point of impact.
попадать *v.* hit, reach, enter; fall; **как попало** anyhow, haphazardly; **куда попало** at random, anywhere; —**ся** *v.* fall into; encounter.
попарно *adv.* in pairs, pairwise, mutually, coupled; **п. непересекающиеся подмножества** disjoint subsets; **п. простой** relatively prime; **связывать п.** couple.
попасть *see* **попадать.**
поперек *adv., prep. gen.* across.
попеременн/о *adv.* alternately.
попереч/ина *f.* crossbeam, crossbar, crosspiece, crossarm; —**ник** *m.* diameter, thickness; —**ность** *f.* transverse character; **условие —ности** transversality condition.
поперечн/ый *a.* transverse; lateral; cross, diametrical; **п. импульс** transverse impulse; **п. разрез,** —**ое сечение** cross section; **п. сдвиг** shear; —**ая**

балка crossbeam; —**ая волна** transverse wave; —**ая деформация** lateral deformation (or strain); —**ая магнитострикция** transverse magnetostriction; —**ая нагрузка** transverse load; —**ая ось** (elec.) quadrature axis; —**ая связь** cross link; —**ая сила** transverse (or shearing) force; —**ое колебание** transverse vibration; —**ое поле** transverse field; —**ое расширение** lateral expansion; —**ое скольжение** (cryst.) cross slip; —**ое смещение** lateral displacement; —**ое сужение** transverse (or lateral) contraction; —**ое сшивание** cross linkage; —**ое увеличение** lateral magnification; **в —ом направлении** across.

попечение *n.* care.

поплав/ковый *a.* floating, float; **п. клапан** float (or ball) valve; —**ок** *m.* float; (aero.) pontoon.

поплатиться *v.* pay (with, for).

пополам *adv.* in half, by halves; **делить п.** halve, bisect.

поползушка *f.* slide.

пополн/ение *n.* supplement; addition; completion; enrichment; replenishment; refilling; **п. горючим** refueling; —**ить,** —**ять** *v.* supplement; complete; fill up; refill, replenish; enrich; enlarge.

пополу/дни *adv.* in the afternoon (P.M.); —**ночи** *adv.* after midnight (A.M.).

попр. *abbr.* (**поправленный**) corrected.

поправ/имый *a.* correctable, repairable; —**ить** *v.* correct; rectify; repair.

поправ/ка *f.* correction, rectification; repair, readjustment; **п. на** correction for; **п. на концевой эффект** end correction; —**ление** *n.* correction; —**лять** *see* **поправить.**

поправочный *a.* correction; **п. коэффициент, п. множитель** correction factor.

по-прежнему *adv.* as formerly; as usual.

поприще *n.* field, profession.

попробовать *see* **пробовать.**

попросту *adv.* simply, merely.

популяр/изация *f.* popularization; —**изировать** *v.* popularize; —**ный** *a.* popular.

попутн/о *adv.* in passing, incidentally; —**ый** *a.* incidental, passing; —**ый поток** wake (current); —**ая струя** wake, back eddy.

попыт/аться *see* **пытаться**; —**ка** *f.* trial, attempt; **метод —ок** trial-and-error method.

попятный *a.* retrograde.

пóра *f.* pore.

пор/á *f.* time, season; it is time to; **давно п.** it is high time; —**ой** occasionally; **до сих пор** thus far, up to the present; **до тех пор, пока (не)** until; as long as; **на первых —ах** at first; **с тех пор** since then; **с этих пор** henceforth, from now on; since that time.

пораж/ать *v.* strike; affect; —**ающее действие** damaging (or casualty) effect.

поражен/ие *n.* striking; injury; disease; **п. от излучения** radiation injury; —**ный** *a.* struck; affected; surprised.

пораз— *double prefix for verbs, see under* **раз—, рас—.**

поразительный *a.* remarkable, striking, astonishing.

поразить *see* **поражать.**

пораньше *adv.* as early as possible.

порас— *see* **пораз—.**

порв/анный *a.* torn, broken; —**ать** *v.* tear, break.

порез *m.*, —**ать** *v.* cut.

порист/ость *f.* porosity; —**ый** *a.* porous, spongy; pore; —**ое охлаждение** transpiration cooling; —**ое пространство** pore space.

пориц/ание *n.* blame, censure; —**ать** *v.* blame, censure.

поровну *adv.* equally, in equal parts.

пор/ый *a.* pore; —**ая вода** interstitial water.

порог *m.* threshold; cutoff; (cryst.) jog (in dislocation); **п. деления** fission threshold; **топочный п.** baffle; **п. фотоэффекта** photoelectric threshold; **п. частоты** threshold frequency; **п. чувствительности** threshold of sensitivity (or response); —**и реки** rapids.

порогов/ый *a.* threshold; cutoff; **п. вход** cutoff input; **п. детектор** threshold detector; —**ая доза** threshold dose; —**ая реакция** threshold reaction.

порода *f.* rock; kind, type; race, species; **горная п.** rock.

поро/дить, —ждать *v.* produce, generate; **оператор —ждения** creation operator; **—жденный** *a.* produced, generated, induced.

порожний *a.* empty; unloaded.

порознь *adv.* separately, independently, apart.

порок *m.* flaw, defect, imperfection, fault.

порох *m.*, **—овой** *a.* powder, gunpowder; **—овидный** *a.* powdery, powdered.

пороч/ить *v.* blame, censure; **—ный** *a.* defective, faulty; **—ный круг** vicious circle.

пороша *f.* sprinkle of snow.

порош/ечный *a.* powder, powdered; **—инка** *f.* grain of powder.

порошко/ватый, —видный, —образный *a.* powdery, powdered; **—вый** *a.* powder; **—вая металлургия** powder metallurgy; **—вая рентгенограмма** powder x-ray pattern; **—вая фигура** powder pattern (or figure); **—грамма** *f.* powder pattern.

порошок *m.* powder.

порпецит *m.* porpezite.

Порро призма Porro prism.

порт *m.* port, harbor.

портативн/ость *f.* portability; **—ый** *a.* portable.

портить *v.* damage, spoil; **—ся** *v.* be damaged, get out of order; deteriorate.

портовый *a.* port, harbor.

портфель *m.* portfolio, briefcase.

поруч/ать *v.* assign, commission, entrust; **—ение** *n.* commission; mission.

поручень *m.* handrail.

поручит/ель *m.* guarantor; **—ельство** *n.* guarantee; **—ь** *see* **поручать.**

порфир *m.* porphyry.

порц/ионный *a.*, **—ия** *f.* portion, batch.

порч/а *f.* damage; defect, flaw; **—енный** *a.* damaged, defective.

поршень *m.* piston, plunger; **п. волновода** waveguide plunger.

поршнев/ой, —ый *a.* piston; **п. двигатель** piston (or reciprocating) engine; **—ая камера Вильсона** volume-defined cloud chamber.

порыв (ветра) *m.* gust, rush; **—истость** *f.* gustiness; **—истый** *a.* gusty, rushing; jerky.

порядков/ый *a.* serial, ordinal, index; **п. номер, —ое число** serial (ordinal, index) number; **п. номер элемента** atomic number; **—ая корреляция** (stat.) rank correlation; **—ая погрешность** index error; **—ое числительное** ordinal (number).

поряд/ок *m.* order; order of magnitude; sequence; series; procedure, agenda; **п. величины** order of magnitude; **п. возрастания** ascending order; **п. мультипольности** multipole order, multipolarity; **на п.** by one order of magnitude, tenfold; **п. отражения** order of reflection; **п. приближения** order of approximation; **приводить в п.** put in order, arrange, adjust; **п. связности** (math.) connectivity number; **по —ку** in order, in succession.

порядочный *a.* considerable, sizable.

посадить *see* **сажать.**

посад/ка *f.* fit, fitting, setting; (aero.) landing; **п. напряжения** voltage dip; **ячейка —ки** checker opening; **—ный, —очный** *a.* (aero.) landing; **—очная площадка** landing field (or strip).

посветлеть *v.* grow light.

посвящ/ать, посвятить *v.* devote; dedicate; **—ение** *n.* devotion; dedication; **—енный** *a.* devoted; dedicated; in commemoration of.

посел/ить, —ять *v.* settle, establish.

посеребр/енный *a.* silver-plated, silvered; **—ить** *v.* silver plate, silver.

посе/тить, —щать *v.* visit; attend.

посещаемость *f.* attendance.

Посидоний Posidonius (lunar crater).

посильный *a.* feasible, within one's power.

посинеть *see* **синеть.**

поскользнуться *v.* slip.

поскольку *adv.* as far as; as long as, provided that; as, since; **п. постольку** so far as, to the extent that; **п. речь идет об этом** in this connection.

послабление *n.* slackening.

послан/ие *n.* sending; message; **—ник** *m.* ambassador; **—ный** *a.* sent; transmitted.

послать *see* **посылать.**

после *prep. gen.* after, following; *adv.*

later, subsequently; **п. того, как** after.

после— *prefix* re—; post—, after.

послевоенный *a.* postwar.

последействие *n.* aftereffect; **упругое п.** elastic lag; spring-back.

последки *pl.* remainder, residue.

последн/ий *a.* last; latter; outermost; latest; recent; **в —ее время** for some time past, lately; **до —его времени** until (very) recently; **за —ие годы** in recent years, recently.

последователь *m.* follower, successor.

последовательно *adv.* successively, serially; tandem; (elec.) in series; **п. параллельный** (elec.) series-parallel; **п. соединенный** series-connected.

последовательност/ь *f.* succession, sequence, order; consistency; **п. во времени** time sequence; **п. операций** operational procedure; **в —и** consequently.

последовательн/ый *a.* successive, consecutive, sequential; gradual, step-by-step; consistent, systematic; (elec.) series; serial; **п. порядок** consecutive order, sequence, succession; **п. распад** series decay; **—ая обмотка** (elec.) series winding; **—ая цепь** series circuit; **—ое разложение** progressive (sequential, straight-line) scanning; **—ое соединение** series connection; **метод —ых приближений** method of successive approximations; trial and error.

последствие *n.* consequence, result, aftereffect; (time) lag.

последующ/ий *a.* following, next, subsequent; posterior; **п. толчок** aftershock; **п. член** (math.) consequent; **—ая обработка** aftertreatment; **—ая форма** sequential form; **—ее сгорание** afterburning; **—ее ускорение** afteracceleration, postacceleration; **—ие волны** (seis.) subsequent waves.

послеимпульс *m.* afterpulse.

после/ледниковый *a.* postglacial; **—свечение** *n.* afterglow, persistence; **—теплота** *f.* afterheat; **—третичный** *a.* post-Tertiary.

послеускор/ение *n.* postdeflection acceleration; **—яющий электрод** intensifier electrode, postdeflection accelerating electrode; **—яющее поле** post-acceleration field.

послефокусировка *f.* secondary focusing.

послефронтальный туман postfrontal fog.

пословный *a.* word for word; literal.

послойный *a.* laminar, layered.

послушный *a.* obedient, manageable.

посменно *adv.* by turns, alternately.

посмертный *a.* posthumous.

пособие *n.* help, assistance, grant; textbook.

посол *m.* ambassador.

посотенно *adv.* by hundreds.

посп/евать, —еть *v.* arrive in time; **п. за** keep up with.

поспешн/о *adv.* hastily, hurriedly; promptly; **—ость** *f.* haste, speed; **—ый** *a.* hasty, hurried; prompt.

посреди *adv. and prep.* in the middle, among; **—не** *adv. and prep.* in the middle, halfway.

посредни/к *m.* intermediary, mediator; arbitrator; **—ческий** *a.* intermediary; **—чество** *n.* mediation.

посредственн/о *adv.* fairly well; **—ый** *a.* mediocre; fair, satisfactory (school grade).

посредств/о *n.* means; **через п., при —е** by, through, thanks to; **—ом** by means of; **—ом этого** thereby.

посредствующий *a.* intermediate.

Поссио уравнение Possio equation.

пост. *abbr.* (**постоянный**) constant.

пост *m.* post, station; **вакуумный п., откачный п.** vacuum station.

поставить *v.* put, place, set; set up; *see also* **поставлять, ставить; п. в соответствие** to establish correspondence; **п. опыты** run tests.

постав/ка *f.* delivery, supplying; **—ки** *pl.* supplies; **—ленный** *a.* placed, set; **—лять** *v.* supply, furnish, deliver; **—щик** *m.* supplier.

постановить *see* **постановлять.**

постановка *f.* erection, raising; arrangement; organization; **п. задачи** statement (or formulation) of a problem.

постановл/ение *n.* decision, resolution, decree; **—ять** *v.* decide, resolve, establish; decree.

постатейно *adv.* by paragraph; clause by clause.

постел/ить *see* **постилать;** **—ь** *f.*, **—ьный** *a.* bed.

постепенн/о *adv.* gradually, by degrees, by stages; **—ость** *f.* gradualness; course; **—ый** *a.* gradual, progressive, step-by-step.

пости/гать, —гнуть *v.* understand, comprehend; **—жение** *n.* understanding, comprehension; **—жимый** *a.* understandable, comprehensible, conceivable.

постил/ать *v.* spread, lay; **—ка** *f.* spreading, laying.

постичь *see* **постигать.**

постлать *see* **постилать.**

постольку поскольку so far as, to the extent that.

посторонн/ий *a.* extraneous, foreign, contaminant; **—яя примесь, —ее включение** impurity, foreign substance, contaminant.

постоянная *f.* constant; **п. времени** time constant; **п. затухания** attenuation (damping, decay) constant; **п. передачи** transfer constant; **п. пространственного заряда** (elec.) perveance; **п. радиоактивного распада** radioactive (decay) constant, disintegration constant; **п. решетки** lattice constant; **п. связи** coupling constant; **п. составляющая** constant component; direct-current component; mean value (of periodic quantity); **п. тонкой структуры** fine structure constant; **п. экранирования** screening constant.

постоянно *adv.* constantly, continually, consistently; **п. закрепленный** rigidly bound.

постоянн/ый *a.* constant, steady, stable, permanent, fixed; persistent, perennial, continuous; **п. во времени** time-independent; **п. источник** steady source; **п. магнит** permanent magnet; **п. момент** permanent moment; **п. пучок** steady beam; **п. сомножитель** constant factor; scale factor; **п. ток** direct current; **—ая величина** constant; **—ая конфигурация** permanent configuration; **—ая орбита** stable orbit; **—ая точка** fixed point; **—ое напряжение** direct-current voltage; **—ое поле** static (or constant) field; **—ое смещение** fixed bias; **—ое сопротивление** fixed resistance (or resistor); **—ое удаление** permanent removal (or disposal).

постоянств/о *n.* constancy, permanence, steadiness; continuance, uniformity; **п. отношений** constant proportions; **закон —а состава** law of definite proportions.

постплиоценовая эпоха post-Pliocene epoch.

пострад/авший *a.* having suffered; having undergone; *m.* victim; **—ать** *v.* suffer; undergo.

постраничный *a.* per page, paginal.

построен/ие *n.* structure, construction; plotting, plot (of a curve); **по —ию** by construction; by definition; **—ный** *a.* constructed, built; plotted.

постро/ечный *a.* building; **—ить** *v.* build, construct; plot (curve); **—йка** *f.* building, structure, construction.

построчный *a.* row.

постул/ат *m.*, **—ировать** *v.* postulate; **—ативный** *a.* postulational.

поступательн/ый *a.* translational; progressive, forward, advancing; **—ая волна** progressive wave; **—ая скорость** forward speed; **—ое движение** translational motion; progressive (or forward) movement.

поступать *v.* act; treat; proceed; enter, be admitted; **п. в редакцию** be received (by the editors).

поступающ/ий *a.* entering, incoming; **—ая вода** inflow.

поступить *see* **поступать.**

поступление *n.* entrance, entering, entry; **п. воды** water inflow; **п. воздуха** air intake; **п. импульсов** pulse arrival; **п. сигналов** signal arrival.

поступок *m.* action, act.

постучать *v.* knock.

посуда *f.* vessels, glassware.

посуточн/о *adv.*, **—ый** *a.* per day (24 hours).

посыл/ать *v.* send; mail; transmit; **—ка** *f.* sending; message; parcel; premise; **большая —ка** major premise; **меньшая —ка** minor premise; **—ка ускорителя** accelerator pulse.

посып/ание *n.*, **—ка** *f.* strewing, powdering; **—анный** *a.* sprinkled, powdered; **—ать** *v.* strew, sprinkle, powder; pour.

посяг/ание *n.*, **—ательство** *n.* encroachment, infringement; **—ать, —нуть** *v.* encroach, infringe; **—ающий** *a.* encroaching, infringing.

потайной *a.* sunk, countersunk, flush.

потамология *f.* potamology.

поташ *m.* potash.

потемневший *a.* grown dark, dim.

потемн/ение *n.* darkening, blackening; **п. к краю** (astr.) limb darkening; **п. пленки** film blackening; **коэффициент —ения** opacity; **—еть** *v.* darken.

потенц. *abbr.* (**потенциальный**) potential.

потенциал *m.* potential; **п. возбуждения** excitation potential; **п. восстановления и окисления** redox potential; **п. действия** action potential; **п. зажигания** firing potential; **п. ионизации** ionization potential; **п. повторного зажигания разряда** restriking voltage; **п. появления** appearance potential; **п. пробоя** breakdown potential; **п. регулятор** voltage regulator; **п. скорости** velocity potential; **п. текучести** flow potential; **падение —а** potential drop; **разность —ов** potential difference; **—оскоп** *m.* charge-storage (or memory) tube; **—ьность** *f.* potentiality.

потенциальн/ый *a.* potential; **п. барьер** potential barrier; **п. вихрь** potential vorticity; **п. напор** potential head; **п. поток** potential (or irrotational) flow; **—ая энергия** potential energy; **—ая яма** potential well; **—ое вырывание** field (-induced) emission; **—ое движение** irrotational motion; **—ое поле** potential field; **—ое течение** potential (or irrotational) flow.

потенциометр *m.* potentiometer; **автоматический п.** self-balancing potentiometer; **—ический** *a.* potentiometric; **—ический самописец** recording potentiometer.

потенц/ирование *n.* (math.) involution, raising (or converting) to a power; **—ия** *f.* potential, potentiality.

потери *see under* **потеря.**

потерп/евший *a.* having suffered; having undergone; *m.* victim; **—еть** *v.* undergo, suffer.

потертый *a.* worn.

потер/я *f.* loss, waste; **п. напора** lost head; **п. от завихрения** eddy loss; **—и** *pl.* losses, loss; **—и в диэлектрике** dielectric loss; **—и в стали** core (or iron) loss; **—и на излучение** radiative loss; **—и энергии** energy loss; **коэффициент —ь** loss factor; **метод отдельных —ь** loss-summation method.

потер/явший *a.* having lost; **—янный** *a.* lost; **—ять** *v.* lose.

потеть *v.* sweat.

поток *m.* flow, flux; stream, current; **высокоинтенсивный п.** high flux; **п. излучения** radiation flux; **п. импульса** momentum flow; **п. индукции** magnetic flux, normal magnetic induction; **п. количества движения** momentum flux; **п. лучистой энергии** light flux, flow of radiant energy; **магнитный п.** magnetic flux; **п. массы** mass flux; **п. метеоров** meteor stream (or shower); **п. мощности** power flux; **п. нейтронов** neutron flux; **п. несжимаемой жидкости** incompressible flow; **обратный п.** reflux; **п. радиации** radiation flux; **п. рассеяния** (mag.) leakage (or stray) flux; **п. тепла** heat flux; **п. частиц** particle flux; **п. электрического смещения** electric flux (or displacement); **п. электронов** electron stream (flow, flux); **п. энергии** energy flux **линия —а** streamline.

потокосцепление *n.* flux (or magnetic linkage.

потол/ок *m.*, **—очный** *a.* ceiling, top **—очный прожектор** (meteor.) ceiling projector (or light).

потом *adv.* then, next, subsequently afterwards.

потом/ок *m.* descendant; **—ство** *n* posterity.

потому *adv.* therefore, consequently; **п. что** because.

потоп *m.* flood, inundation; **—ить** **—лять** *v.* sink, immerse; **—ление** *n* sinking, immersion; —**ленный** *a.* submerged, immersed.

точечный *a.* pointwise.

точить *v.* sharpen.

точн/ый *a.* flow; continuous; **п. счетчик** flow counter; —**ая ионизационная камера** flow-type ionization chamber; —**ая линия** assembly line; (**массовое**) —**ое производство** assembly-line production.

требит/ель *m.* consumer, user; —**ь** *see* **потреблять.**

требл/ение *n.* consumption, use; (elec.) drain; requirement; **п. энергии** power (or energy) consumption; —**яемый** *a.* consumable; —**ять** *v.* consume, use.

требн/ость *f.* necessity, need, requirement, demand; —**ый** *a.* necessary, required; —**ая мощность** power requirement.

треб/овать *v.* demand, request, require; —**уется** it will be necessary.

трескив/ание *n.*, —**ающий** *a.* crackling; —**ать** *v.* crackle.

тряс/ающий *a.* shaking, shattering; stupendous, tremendous; —**ение** *n.* shock.

отсдамский главный каталог (astr.) Potsdam Generalkatalog.

тускн/евший, —**елый** *a.* tarnished, dull; dim; —**ение** *n.* tarnishing; fogging, dimming, clouding; —**еть** *v.* tarnish; fog, cloud.

тух/ание *n.* decay, extinction; —**ать,** —**нуть** *v.* be extinguished; —**ший** *a.* extinguished.

тушить *v.* extinguish.

отье электродвижущая сила Potier electromotive force.

тягивание *n.* pulling, pull.

учительный *a.* instructive.

ОХ *abbr.* (**Промышленность органической химии**) Organic Chemical Industry (journal).

хвал/а *f.* praise, commendation; —**ить** *v.* praise.

ход *m.* expedition; trip; (mil.) campaign.

ходить *v.* resemble.

хож/е *adv.* like; —**ий** *a.* like, resembling.

похолодание *n.* temperature drop, cooling.

почасно *adv.* hourly.

почв/а *f.*, —**енный** *a.* soil, ground; —**енная вода** ground water; —**овед** *m.* soil scientist; —**оведение** *n.* soil science.

почему *adv.* why; **вот п.** that is why.

почерн/евший, —**елый** *a.* blackened, darkened; —**ение** *n.* blackening; **большое** —**ение** heavy blackening; **оптическая плотность** —**ения** optical (or photographic) density.

почесть *f.* honor; respect.

почет *m.* honor, respect, esteem; —**ный** *a.* honorable; honorary.

почечный *a.* kidney.

почин *m.* initiative; innovation.

почин/ить *v.*, —**ка** *f.* repair.

почитать *v.* honor, respect.

почк/а *f.* kidney; bud; nodule; —**овидный** *a.* nodular.

почленно *adv.* termwise, term by term.

почта *f.* mail; post office; **пневматическая п.** *see* **пневмопочта.**

почтен/ие *n.* respect, esteem; —**ный** *a.* honorable, dignified.

почти *adv.* almost, nearly; **п. до** short of; **п. не** scarcely; **п. что** nearly; **п. бридерный реактор** near-breeder; **п. круговая орбита** near-circular orbit; **п.-мгновенный** *a.* near-prompt; **п. монохроматический** near-monochromatic; **п. монохроматическое излучение** near-monochromatic radiation; **п. нормальный** subnormal; **п. периодический** almost periodic; **п. постоянная орбита** near-permanent orbit; **п.-равнина** *f.* peneplain.

почтительный *a.* respectful.

почтовый *a.* mail, postal.

пошепниит *m.* posepnyite.

пошлина *f.* duty, customs, tax.

поэтому *adv. and conj.* therefore, consequently.

поющ/ий *a.* singing; —**ее пламя** singing flame.

появ/иться, —**ляться** *v.* appear, be published; emerge; originate; —**ление** *n.* appearance; occurrence; manifestation; emergence; —**ление кометы** apparition of a comet; —**ляю-**

щийся *a.* appearing, emerging, forthcoming.

пояс *m.* belt, girdle; zone, region; collar, hoop; loop.

поясн/ение *n.* explanation, elucidation; **—ительный** *a.* explanatory; **—ить** *see* **пояснять.**

поясн/ой *a.* belt; zone, zonal; **—ое время** zone time, standard time.

поясн/ять *v.* explain, expound, illustrate, exemplify; **—яющий** *a.* explanatory, illustrative, clarifying.

поясок *m.* band; shoulder.

пп. *abbr.* (**параграфы**) paragraphs; (**пункты**) sections, items.

п/п *abbr.* (**по порядку**) in sequence (*in tables best rendered in translation as* No.).

ППК *abbr.* (**противоперегрузочный костюм**) antiblackout (or anti-G) suit.

ППУ *abbr.* (**противоперегрузочное устройство**) antiblackout (or anti-G) equipment.

пр. *abbr.* (**правый**) right, right-hand; clockwise; (**проспект**) avenue; (**прочий**) other(s), remaining.

прав. *abbr.* (**правый**) right, right-hand, clockwise.

правд/а *f.* truth; to be sure, it is true (that); **—ивый** *a.* truthful, honest.

правдоподоб/ие *n.* probability, plausibility; **—ный** *a.* probable, plausible.

правее *comp. of* **правый** (more) to the right (of).

прави́ло *n.* straightedge; guide rod.

пра́вил/о *n.* rule; principle; *see also* **закон; —а** *pl.* rules, regulations; **п. запрета** selection rule; **п. интервалов** interval rule; **п. левой руки** left-hand rule; **п. ложного положения** (math.) regula falsi (rule of false position); **п. отбора** selection rule; **п. постоянства Г-суммы** Pauli *g*-sum rule; **п. правой руки** right-hand rule; **п. прямолинейного диаметра** law of rectilinear diameters; **п. смещения** displacement law; **п. трех пальцев** Fleming's rule; **п. фаз** phase rule; **как п.** as a rule, as usual.

правильно *adv.* accurately, correctly; uniformly, regularly; **—сть** *f.* accuracy, correctness; regularity.

правильн/ый *a.* accurate, correct, proper; true; regular; **п. делитель** aliquot part; **п. закон дублетов** true doublet law; **п. квадрат** perfect square; **п. многоугольник** regular polygon; **—ая дробь** proper fraction; **—ая игральная кость** true (or perfect) die; **—ая система** regular (or cubic) system; **—ое отражение** regular reflection.

правительств/енный *a.*, **—о** *n.* government.

прав/ить *v.* govern, rule, manage, direct; steer; correct; straighten; **п. корректуру** proofread; **—ка** *f.* correcting; straightening.

правление *n.* government; direction, administration, management; board (of directors).

право— *prefix* right-.

прав/о *n.* right; law; *adv.* really, truly; **международное п.** international law; **на равных —ах** of equal validity; on the same footing; **предъявлять —** lay claim to.

право/бережный *a.* right-bank; **—винтовый** *a.* right-handed; **—вой** *a.* legal, lawful; rightful.

правовращающ/ий *a.* right-handed, dextrorotatory, clockwise; **п. кристалл** right-handed crystal; **—аяся поляризация** right-hand polarization.

правоинвариантный *a.* right-invariant.

правомерн/ость *f.* legitimacy, admissibility; **—ый** *a.* legitimate, admissible, rightful.

правомоч/ие *n.* competence; **—ный** *a.* competent.

правонарушение *n.* infringement of the law.

правописание *n.* orthography.

правополяризованный *a.*, **п. по круг** clockwise-polarized.

право/судие *n.* justice; **—та** *f.* rightness, correctness; integrity.

прав/ый *a.* right, right-handed, right-hand, dextrorotatory, clockwise, dextro—; **п. борт** starboard; **п. кристалл** right-handed crystal; **—ая граница** upper boundary (or end); **—ая кривая** (math.) right-handed curve, dextrorse curve, dextrorsum

—**ая круговая поляризация** right-handed circular polarization; —**ая система координат** right-handed coordinate system; —**ая часть уравнения** right-hand side (or right member) of an equation; —**ое вращение** dextrorotation, clockwise rotation; veering (of wind); **быть —ым** be right.

авящий *a.* governing, ruling, managing.

аздный *a.* idle; useless, unnecessary.

азем *m.* prase.

азеодим, —ий *m.*, **—иевый** *a.* praseodymium (Pr).

азеолит *m.* praseolite.

актик *m.* practical worker; —**а** *f.* practice; **на —е** in practice; —**овать** *v.* practice, engage in; —**ум** *m.* practical work.

актич/ески *adv.* practically, in practice; —**еский, —ный** *a.* practical; effective; efficient; —**ность** *f.* practicalness, practicality; efficiency.

андтля критерий (число) Prandtl number.

аута гипотеза Prout hypothesis.

ащ/а *f.*, —**евой** *a.* sling; —**евой психрометр** sling psychrometer.

В *abbr.* (**прямые равных высот**) lines of equal altitudes.

-во *abbr.* (**правительство**) government.

е— *prefix* very, most; *prefix with verbs* over, across; anew, re—; sur—.

ебы/вание *n.* stay, period; —**вать, —ть** *v.* stay, reside; continue, remain.

евалировать *v.* prevail, predominate.

евзой/денный *a.* surpassed; —**ти** *see* **превосходить.**

ево правило Prévost law.

евозмо/гать, —чь *v.* overcome.

евосход/ить, —ствовать *v.* exceed, surpass; —**но** *adv.* excellently, superiorly; —**ный** *a.* excellent; —**ство** *n.* excellence, superiority; —**ящий** *a.* superior, surpassing, exceeding; —**ящий ряд** majorizing series.

еврат/имый *see* **превращаемый**; —**ить** *see* **превращать.**

евратн/о *adv.* wrongly; **п. истолковать** misinterpret, misunderstand; —**ый** *a.* wrong; changeable.

превращ/аемость *f.* convertibility, transmutability; —**аемый** *a.* convertible, transformable; —**ать** *v.* convert, transform, change; —**аться** *v.* be converted, change, turn, become, pass into.

превращен/ие *n.* conversion, transformation, transition, change, transmutation; **п. атомного ядра** nuclear transformation; **п. элементов** transmutation of elements; **точка —ия** transition point, critical point; —**ный** *a.* converted, transformed, changed; —**ный в порошок** powdered, pulverized.

превысить *see* **превышать.**

превыш/ать *v.* exceed, surpass; —**ение** *n.* excess, exceeding; —**ение (числа) нейтронов** neutron excess.

прегра/да *f.* obstacle, obstruction, barrier; —**дить, —ждать** *v.* obstruct, block, impede, bar; —**ждение** *n.* obstruction, blocking.

пред— *prefix* pre—, fore—, before.

пред *see* **перед.**

пред. *abbr.* (**предисловие**) preface, foreword, introduction; (**председатель**) chairman; (**предыдущий**) preceding, previous, foregoing.

предавать *v.* commit (to), give up.

преданный *a.* devoted, loyal.

предаццит *m.* predazzite.

предвакуум *abbr.* (**предварительный вакуум**) forevacuum, initial vacuum.

предварение *n.* advance, lead; (astr.) precession; forestalling.

предварительно *adv.* beforehand, in advance; pre—; **п. напряженный** prestressed; **п. обрабатывать** pretreat; **п. сжатый** precompressed.

предварительн/ый *a.* preliminary, provisional, prior, pre—, fore—; **п. вакуум** forevacuum, initial vacuum; **п. толчок землетрясения** foreshock; **п. усилитель** preamplifier; —**ая реакция** prereaction; —**ая сборка** preliminary assembly; subassembly; —**ая щель** foreslit; —**ое горение** precombustion; —**ое нагревание** preheating; —**ое напряжение** prestressing; —**ое усиление** preamplification.

предвар/ить, —ять *v.* warn; anticipate, forestall.

предвестить *v.* foreshadow, foretell, betoken.

предвестник *m.* forerunner; sign, indication; **п. землетрясения** foreshock; **п. погоды** weather sign.

предвещать *see* **предвестить.**

предвзят/ый *a.* preconceived; —**ое мнение** preconception, bias.

предвид/ение *n.* foresight; insight; —**еть** *v.* foresee; —**еться** *v.* be foreseen, be expected.

предводительство *n.* leadership.

предвосхи/тить, —щать *v.* anticipate; —**щение** *n.* anticipation.

предвычисл/ение *n.* precomputation; —**ить** *v.* precalculate.

предгорье *n.* foothills.

преддверье *n.* threshold.

преддетонация *f.* predetonation.

предел *m.* limit; boundary, bound, end; threshold; capacity, extent; —**ы** *pl.* limits, range, scope; **п. видимости** limit of visibility; **п. выносливости** endurance (or fatigue) limit; **п. на усталость при кручении** torsional endurance limit; **п. погрешности** limit (or margin) of error; **п. ползучести** creep strength (or limit); **п. прочности** tensile strength, breaking point; **п. прочности на растяжение (разрыв)** tensile strength; **п. прочности на сжатие** compression strength; **п. прочности на срез** shear strength; **п. текучести** yield stress; **п. упругости** elastic limit; **в —ах 30°** through an angle of 30°; **в —ах ошибок эксперимента** within (the limits of) experimental error; **за —ами** outside the scope; **за —ы** outside of, beyond.

предельно *adv.* extremely; ultimately; maximally; in the limit; **п. допустимая доза** maximum permissible dose; **п. низкая температура** extremely low temperature; **п. постоянный** constant in the limit.

предельн/ый *a.* limiting, limit, boundary, asymptotic; maximum; extreme, outer; utmost; critical; (chem.) saturated; **п. вакуум** ultimate vacuum; **п. калибр** limit gauge; **п. переход** limiting process; passage to the limit; **п. пробег** ultimate range; **п. радиус** maximum (terminal, ultimate) radius; **п. случай** extreme (or limiting) case; **п. угол** critical angle; —**ая величина** limit, limiting value, threshold (value); —**ая кривая** limiting curve, limit curve; —**ая линия** limiting (or boundary) line, border; (spect.) ultimate line; —**ая масса** critical mass; —**ая нагрузка** limit (or limiting) load; —**ая плоскость** end plane, base; —**ая поверхность** boundary surface, surface of contact; —**ая погрешность** maximum error, limit of error; —**ая скорость** maximum velocity; critical velocity; terminal velocity; —**ая теорема** limit theorem; —**ая точка** limit point, end point, accumulation point (of a set); —**ая формула** asymptotic formula; —**ая функция** limit function; —**ая частота** cutoff frequency.

предельн/ый *cont.*, —**ое значение** limiting value; —**ое напряжение** breaking point; pressure limit; —**ое поведение** asymptotic behavior; —**ое положение** end position; —**ое равенство** boundary condition; —**ое разрывающее усилие** ultimate stress; —**ое соединение** saturated compound; —**ое соотношение** asymptotic relation; —**ое сопротивление излому, —ое сопротивление разрыву** breaking point; —**ое состояние** limiting state; —**ые размеры** limiting dimensions; critical size.

предзажигание *n.* prefiring.

предиктор *m.* predictor.

преинтегральный *a.* pre-integral.

предисловие *n.* preface, foreword.

предиссоциация *f.* predissociation.

предкамер/а *f.* precombustion chamber; —**ное горение** precombustion.

предлагать *v.* offer, propose, propound, suggest; **п. вниманию** call attention to.

предлог *m.* pretext; (gram.) preposition; **под —ом** under the pretext of.

предложение *n.* statement, propositio

proposal, suggestion, offer; (gram.) sentence, clause; supply; **вспомогательное п.** lemma; **делать п.** propose; **спрос и п.** supply and demand.

предложить *see* **предлагать.**

предмет *m.* subject, topic; object; article.

предметн/ый *a.* object; **п. столик** (microscope) stage; **п. указатель** subject index; **п. урок** object lesson; **—ое стекло** (microscope) slide.

предметодержатель *m.* (microscope) stage, stand; slide, mount.

предназнач/ать, —ить *v.* intend for; **—ение** *n.* destination.

преднамерен/ие *n.*, **—ность** *f.* forethought; **—но** *adv.* intentionally; **—ный** *a.* premeditated, intentional; **—ная выборка** purposive sampling.

предначерт/ание *n.* outline, plan, design; **—ать, —ывать** *v.* outline beforehand.

предок *m.* ancestor, progenitor.

предоминирующий *a.* predominant.

предопредел/ение *n.* predetermination, predesignation; **—ить, —ять** *v.* predetermine, predesignate.

предостав/ить, —лять *v.* leave; grant, allow; **—ление** *n.* assigning, granting; **—ленный самому себе** left to himself (itself).

предостере/гать, —чь *v.* warn, caution; **—гающий** *a.* warning, cautioning; **—жение** *n.* warning, caution.

предосторожност/ь *f.* precaution; **мера —и** precautionary measure, precaution.

предотвра/тить, —щать *v.* prevent, preclude, avert, obviate; **—щаемый** *a.* preventable; **—щение** *n.* prevention, precluding, averting.

предохранен/ие *n.* protection; preservation; **—ный** *a.* protected; preserved.

предохранитель *m.* safety device (or (lock); guard, protector; (elec.) cutout, fuse; **п. от перенапряжений** surge arrester; **плавкий п.** fuse.

предохранительн/ый *a.* safety, protective, guard; preventive; preservative; **п. клапан** safety (relief, dump) valve; **п. стержень** safety rod; **—ые меры** precautionary measures.

предохран/ить, —ять *v.* protect, guard; preserve; **—яющий** *see* **предохранительный.**

предпис/ание *n.* order, instruction, direction; **—анный** *a.* specified; **—ать, —ывать** *v.* order; instruct, direct; assign; prescribe.

предполаг/аемый *a.* assumed, supposed, presumable, likely; proposed; **—ать** *v.* assume, conjecture, suppose; presuppose, postulate; propose; **предположим, что** let us assume that; **—аться** *v.* be supposed, be assumed; **—ая** assuming.

предполож/ение *n.* assumption, supposition; **—енный** *a.* supposed, assumed; proposed; **—ительно** *adv.* supposedly, presumably, hypothetically; tentatively; **—ительный** *a.* hypothetical, conjectural; presumable; **—ить** *see* **предполагать.**

предполярный *a.* subarctic.

предпоследний *a.* penultimate.

предпос/ылать, —лать *v.* premise; preface.

предпосылка *f.* prerequisite; premise.

предпоч/есть, —итать *v.* prefer; **—тение** *n.* preference.

предпочтительн/о *adv.* preferably; **—ость** *f.* preferableness; **—ый** *a.* preferable; preferred; **—ая ориентация** preferred orientation; **—ые числа** preferred numbers.

предприн/имать, —ять *v.* undertake.

предприятие *n.* undertaking, enterprise.

предпробивной *a.* prebreakdown, predischarge; **п. ток** prebreakdown current.

предразрушение *n.* preexisting imperfection.

предразрядный *a.* predischarge.

предраспол/агать, —ожить *v.* predispose; **—ожение** *n.* predisposition.

предрассудок *m.* prejudice.

предреш/ать, —ить *v.* predetermine, decide beforehand; foreclose.

председатель *m.* chairman, president; speaker; **—ствовать** *v.* preside.

предсказ/ание *n.* forecast, prediction; **п. погоды** weather forecast; **—ать, —ывать** *v.* predict.

представим/ость *f.* representability; **—ый** *a.* representable.

представитель *m.* representative; **—ный** *a.* representative; impressive; **—ство** *n.* representation.

представ/ить *see* **представлять**; **—ление** *n.* concept, idea; presentation; representation; **—ление группы** group representation; **—ленный** *a.* presented, introduced; represented, shown.

представлять *v.* present, offer, submit; represent, describe; **п. интерес** be of interest (or importance); **п. себе** imagine; **п. собой** be, represent; **—ся** *v.* be presented; occur; seem.

предстать *v.* appear.

предсто/ять *v.* be imminent; have to; **—ящий** *a.* forthcoming.

предубежд/ать, предубедить *v.* prejudice; **—ение** *n.* prejudice; **—енный** *a.* prejudiced, biased.

предуведом/ить, —лять *v.* notify in advance; **—ление** *n.* notification, forewarning.

предугад/ать, —ывать *v.* foresee.

предумышленный *see* **преднамеренный.**

предупредительный *a.* preventive, precautionary; warning; **п. знак** warning sign.

предупредить *see* **предупреждать.**

предупрежд/аемый *a.* preventable; **—ать** *v.* prevent; avert; notify beforehand, warn, caution; **—ающий** *a.* preventing; warning; **—ение** *n.* prevention; warning; notification; **—енный** *a.* prevented; warned; notified.

предусил/ение *n.* preamplification; **—итель** *m.* preamplifier.

предускорение *n.* preacceleration.

предусматривать *see* **предусмотреть.**

предусмотр/енный *a.* provided for, specified; **—еть** *v.* provide for, specify, stipulate; foresee; **—ительность** *f.* foresight; **—ительный** *a.* foreseeing, prudent.

предустановленный *a.* predetermined, preestablished.

предфронтальный туман prefrontal fog.

предхолодильник *m.* precooler.

предшеств/енник *m.* precursor, predecessor; **—ие** *n.* precedence; **—овать** *v.* precede; **—ующий** *a.* preceding, antecedent, prior, previous.

предъяв/ить, —лять *v.* show, present; **—лять требования** make demands impose requirements.

предыдущий *a.* preceding, previous foregoing.

предыонизация *f.* preionization.

предыстория *f.* previous history; pre history.

предэкспоненциальный *a.* preexponential; **п. множитель** preexponential factor.

преем/ник *m.* successor; **—ственность** *f* succession; **—ственный** *a.* successive.

прежде *adv.* before, previously, formerly; *prep. gen.* before; **п. всего** first of all, in the first place, to begin with **п. чем** before, prior to.

преждевременн/ый *a.* premature, untimely; **—ая детонация** predetonation; **—ое зажигание** preignition.

прежн/ий *a.* previous, former; **по —ему** as previously.

през. *abbr.* (**президент**) president.

презервация *f.* preservation.

президент *m.* president.

преим. *abbr. see* **преимущественно.**

преимуществ/енно *adv.*, **по —у** principally, mainly, largely; **—енный** *a* preferred, preferential, predominant primary; **—енная ориентация** preferred orientation; **—енное поглощение** preferential absorption; **—** *n.* advantage; preference; preeminence.

преисполн/енный *a.* full; **—ить, —ять** *v* fill.

прекрасн/о *adv.* excellently; **—ый** *a.* excellent, fine; beautiful.

прекра/тить, —щать *v.* discontinue stop, cut off, finish, end, suspend shut down; **—титься, —щаться** *v* end, cease, stop; **—щение** *n.* discontinuation, cessation, stoppage **—щенный** *a.* discontinued, stopped cut off; shut down.

прелом/имый *see* **преломляемый; —ить** *see* **преломлять.**

преломлен/ие *n.* refraction; **двойное п** double refraction, birefringence; **коэффициент —ия, показатель —ия** refractive index; **—ный** *a.* refracted

преломл/яемость *f.* refractivity, refrangibility; **—яемый** *a.* refractable refrangible; —ять *v.* refract; —ять-ся *v.* be refracted.

преломляющ/ий *a.* refracting, refractive; **п. угол** refracting angle; **—ая способность** refractivity; **—ее поле** refractive field.

премиров/ание *n.* awarding a prize; **—анный** *a.* prize; rewarded; **—ать** *v.* award a prize.

премия *f.* prize; bonus; premium.

пренебрег/аемый *a.* negligible; **—ать** *v.* neglect, disregard, omit; **—ая** disregarding; barring.

пренебреж/ение *n.* neglect, disregard; **—имо** *adv.* negligibly; **—имо малый** negligible; **—имый** *see* **пренебрегаемый**; **—ительный** *a.* neglectful.

пренебречь *see* **пренебрегать.**

пренит *m.* prehnite.

преоблад/ание *n.* predominance, dominance, preponderance, prevalence; **—ать** *v.* predominate, dominate, prevail; **—ающий** *a.* predominant, dominant, prevailing, preponderant; **—ающий ветер** prevailing wind.

преобразован/ие *n.* transformation, conversion; reorganization; (math.) transform; **п. прикосновения** contact transformation; **коэффициент —ия** conversion factor.

преобразов/атель *m.* transformer, converter; transducer; **идеальный п.** ideal transducer (or transformer); **п. изображений** image converter; **импульсный п.** pulse converter; **п. с кварцевым стабилизатором** crystal converter; **п. частоты** frequency converter (or changer); **—анный** *a.* converting, transforming, transformation; **—ная лампа** transducer tube.

преобразов/ать, —ывать *v.* convert, transform, change; reorganize, reform; **—ываться подобно** undergo a similarity transformation.

преобразующий *a.* transforming, converting, transducing.

преодол/евание, —ение *n.* overcoming, surmounting; **—евать, —еть** *v.* overcome, surmount; **—имый** *a.* surmountable.

препарат *m.* specimen, sample; preparation; **—ор** *m.* laboratory assistant, demonstrator.

препариров/ание *n.* preparation; **—ать** *v.* prepare.

препод/авание *n.* instruction, teaching, lecturing; **—аватель** *m.* teacher, instructor, lecturer; **—авать, —ать** *v.* teach, instruct, lecture.

преподн/есение *n.* presentation; **—ести, —осить** *v.* present, bring.

препрово/дительный *see* **сопроводительный**; **—дить, —ждать** *v.* forward, send.

препятств/ие *n.* obstacle, obstruction, barrier, check; **—ование** *n.* prevention; inhibition, obstruction, hindering; interruption; **—овать** *v.* prevent; inhibit, obstruct, hinder, impede; oppose.

прерв/анный *a.* discontinuous, interrupted; **—ать** *see* **прерывать.**

прерогатива *f.* prerogative.

прерыв/аемый пучок chopped beam; **—ание** *n.* interruption, break; **—ание луча** beam chopping.

прерыват/ель *m.* interrupter, chopper, interceptor; breaker, cutout; **п. импульсов** pulse chopper; **п. света** light chopper; **—ь** *v.* interrupt; discontinue; (elec.) break contact.

прерывающий *a.* interrupting; breaking; **п. диск** chopper disk; **—ся** *a.* intermittent, discontinuous.

прерывист/ость *f.* discontinuity, intermittence, brokenness; **—ый** *a.* discontinuous, broken, interrupted, intermittent; **—ый генератор** (elec.) squegging oscillator; **—ая генерация** (elec.) squegging.

прерыв/ность *see* **прерывистость**; **—ный, —чатый** *see* **прерывистый.**

пресе/кать, —чь *v.* suppress; interrupt; **—чение** *n.* interruption.

преселекция *f.* preselection.

преследовать *v.* pursue.

пресн/ая вода fresh water; **—оводный** *a.* fresh-water.

пресс *m.* press.

пресса *f.* press (newspapers).

прессов/альный *a.* press, pressing; **—ание** *n.*, **—ка** *f.* pressing, compression; molding; bonding; **—анный** *a.* pressed, compressed, compacted; **—ать** *v.* press, compress, extrude.

пресс/уемый *a.* pressed, extruded; extrudable; **—ующий** *a.* pressing, press; **—форма** *f.* die, die-casting mold; **—шпан** *m.* pressboard.

Престона правило Preston rule.

преступ/ать, —ить *v.* violate.

претвор/ить, —ять *v.* change, convert; carry out; **п. в жизнь** realize, put into practice.

претен/довать *v.* pretend, claim; **—зия** *f.* claim.

претерп/евать, —еть *v.* undergo.

преувелич/ение *n.* exaggeration; **—енный** *a.* exaggerated, excessive; too large; **—ивать, —ить** *v.* exaggerate.

преуменьш/ать, —ить *v.* minimize, underestimate.

преуспевающий *a.* successful.

преференциальный *a.* preferential.

преход/ить *v.* pass; **—ящий** *a.* transient, passing.

прецедент *m.* precedent.

прецесс/ировать *v.* precess; **—ирующий** *a.* precessing, precessional; **—ия** *f.* precession.

прецизионн/ость *f.* precision, accuracy; **—ый** *a.* precision.

преципитат *m.* precipitate.

при— *prefix with verbs* arrival, approach; attaching, addition.

при *prep.* in, at, by, near; in the presence of; at the time of; about; with; attached, affiliated with; **п. анализе** on analysis; **п. всем том** moreover; nevertheless; **п. входе** at the entrance; **п. нагревании** upon heating; while heating, while being heated; **п. условии** under the condition that; **п. этом** (*often untranslated, with following verb rendered as present participle*) during which, at the same time.

приб. *abbr.* (**приблизительно**) approximately.

прибав/ить, —лять *v.* add, increase, augment; **п. на** allow for; **—иться, —ляться** *v.* increase; be added; **—ка** *f.*, **—ление** *n.* increase, addition, supplement; **—ленный** *a.* added; **—очный** *a.* additional.

прибег/ать, —нуть *v.* have recourse to, resort to; **не —ая к** without recourse to.

приб/ивать, —ить *v.* nail.

прибл. *abbr.* (**приблизительно**) approximately.

приближ/ать *v.* approximate, approach; **—аться** *v.* approximate, approach, converge; **—ающийся** *a.* approaching, forthcoming.

приближен/ие *n.* approximation; approach; **п. (ближайших) соседей** nearest neighbor approximation; **—ность** *f.* degree of approximation; nearness, proximity.

приближен/ный *a.* approximate; rough, proximate; **п. анализ** (chem.) proximate analysis; **п. метод** approximation method; **—ая оценка** rough estimate.

приблизительн/о *adv.* approximately; **—ость** *f.* approximateness; **—ый** *a.* approximate, rough.

приблизить *see* **приближать.**

прибой *m.* surf.

прибол/тить, —чивать *v.* bolt on; **—ченный** *a.* bolted (on).

прибор *m.* instrument, device, apparatus; **—ы контроля и управления реактором** reactor instrumentation **—ный** *a.* instrument; instrumental **—ная доска** instrument panel.

приборостр. *abbr. see* **приборостроение**

приборостроение *n.* instrument manufacture.

прибрежный *a.* littoral, coastal; riparian.

прибыв/ание *n.* increase, rise; **—ать** *v.* increase, rise; arrive.

прибыль *f.* gain, benefit; increase, rise.

прибыт/ие *n.* arrival; **—ь** *see* **прибывать.**

привар/енный *a.* welded; **—ивать —ить** *v.* weld on; **—ка** *f.* welding **—ной** *a.* welded; welding.

приведение *n.* bringing; adduction (math.) reduction; **п. в движени[е]** starting, actuating; **п. в порядо[к]** putting in order, arranging.

приведенн/ый *a.* reduced; cited; presented, shown; brought; **—ая вероятность перехода** reduced transition probability; **—ая единиц[а]** normalized unit; **—ая масса** reduce[d] mass; **—ое время** reduced time (of beta decay).

ривезти *see* **привозить.**

ривerженн/ость *f.* adherence; **—ый** *a.* attached.

ривер/нуть, —теть, —тывать *v.* screw on; **—тный** *a.* screwed-on.

ривес *m.* increase in weight; **—ить** *see* **привешивать; —ка** *f.*, **—ок** *m.* pendant.

ривести *see* **приводить.**

ривешивать *v.* hang, suspend; add (weight).

ривив/ание *n.*, **—ка** *f.* inoculation, seeding; **—ать** *v.* inoculate.

ривилег/ированный *a.* privileged; **—ия** *f.* privilege.

ривин/тить, —чивать *v.* screw on; **—ченный** *a.* screwed-on; **—чивание** *n.* screwing on.

ривит/ой, —ый *a.* graft; **—ь** *see* **прививать.**

ривле/кать, —чь *v.* attract, draw, pull; **—чение** *n.* attraction, drawing; inclusion.

ривн/ести, —осить *v.* introduce; add; **—ос** *m.* introduction, addition.

ривод *m.* drive (mechanism); actuator; servo; (elec.) homing; **—имый** *a.* driven; cited; (math.) reducible.

риводить *v.* bring, lead; drive; reduce; adduce; cite; **п. в движение** set in motion, actuate, drive; **п. в исполнение** accomplish; **п. в равновесие** equilibrate, balance; **п. к общему знаменателю** reduce to a common denominator; **—ся** *v.* be brought.

риводн/ой *a.* driving, drive; **п. винт** drive screw; **п. механизм** actuator; **п. механизм стержней** rod drive; **—ая радиостанция** homing radio station.

риводный *a.* adjacent to water.

ривоз *m.* bringing, supply; import, importation; **—ить** *v.* bring, convey; import; **—ной** *a.* imported.

ривы/кание *n.* becoming accustomed; **—кать, —кнуть** *v.* become accustomed to; **—чка** *f.* habit, custom, behavior; **—чность** *f.* familiarity, habit; **—чный** *a.* usual.

ривяз/анный *a.* attached; **—ать, —ывать** *v.* attach, bind, fasten; **—ка** *f.* joining, binding; tying in.

пригибать *v.* bend down.

пригла/дить, —живать *v.* smooth.

пригла/сить, —шать *v.* invite, ask; **—шение** *n.* invitation.

приглуш/ать, —ить *v.* damp down; muffle.

пригн/анность *f.* matching, fitting together; **—анный** *a.* matched, fitted, adjusted; **плотно —анный** tightly fitting; **—ать** *see* **пригонять.**

пригнуть *see* **пригибать.**

пригод/иться *v.* be suitable (or useful); **—ность** *f.* usefulness, appropriateness; (math.) validity; **—ный** *a.* useful, suitable, applicable, adequate, valid.

Пригожина теорема Prigogine theorem.

пригон/ка *f.* fitting, jointing; adjustment; **п. вновь** readjustment; **плотная п.** tight fit; **п. частей** assembling; **—очный** *a.* adjusting; **—ять** *v.* fit, joint; adjust; **—ять гнездо клапана** reseat a valve.

пригор/ание *n.* scorching, burning; **—ать, —еть** *v.* scorch, burn; **—елый** *a.* scorched, burnt.

пригород *m.* suburb; **—ный** *a.* suburban; local.

пригорок *m.* hillock.

пригоршня *f.* handful.

приготов/ительный *a.* preparatory; **—ить, —лять** *v.* prepare, produce; **—ление** *n.* preparation, production; **—ленный** *a.* prepared, produced.

приграничный *a.* at the limit.

придавать *v.* give, add, impart; attribute; **п. значение** attach importance.

придав/ить, —ливать *v.* press, squeeze; **—ленный** *a.* pressed, squeezed.

придан/ие *n.* giving, conferring, imparting; **п. обтекаемой формы** streamlining; **—ный** *a.* given, added, imparted.

прида/ток *m.* attachment, accessory, addition, supplement; **—точный** *a.* additional, accessory; **—ть** *see* **придавать; —ча** *f.* addition; **в —чv** in addition.

придви/гать, —нуть *v.* move near; **—гаться, —нуться** *v.* approach.

придел/ать, —ывать *v.* attach; adapt, fit.
придерж/анный *a.* held, clamped; **—ать, —ивать** *v.* hold (back); **—аться, —иваться** *v.* hold to, adhere to; confine oneself to.
прид/ираться, —раться *v.* find fault (with).
придти *see* **приходить.**
придум/ать, —ывать *v.* devise, develop, invent.
приез/д *m.* arrival; **—жать** *v.* arrive.
прием *m.* method, process, procedure; device; reception; admission; **в несколько —ов** in stages; **—истость** *f.* pickup (of motor); **—ка** *f.* reception, acceptance; **—лемость** *f.* acceptability; **—лемый** *a.* acceptable, admissible, tenable.
приемник *m.* receiver, catcher; collector, receptacle, container, vessel, acceptor; **п. ионов** ion collector; **п.-передатчик** *see* **приемопередатчик.**
приемн/ый *a.* receiving; **п. зонд** pickup probe; **—ая лампа** receiving tube; **—ая площадь** sensitive area; **—ое отверстие** intake, inlet; **—ое пространство** (elec.) catcher space; **—ое устройство** intake.
приемопередатчик *m.* transponder.
приемочный *a.* reception, acceptance; *see also* **приемный.**
приемщик *m.* receiver; inspector.
приехать *see* **приезжать.**
прижать *see* **прижимать.**
прижим/ание *n.* pressing; tightening, clamping; **—ать** *v.* press; tighten, clamp; **—ающий** *a.* pressing; tightening, clamping; **—ной** *a.* pressing, tightening, clamp; **—ной контакт** clamped contact, rubbing contact.
приз *m.* prize.
призвание *n.* vocation.
призем/ление *n.* (aero.) landing; **—литься, —ляться** *v.* land.
приземн/ой, —ый *a.* surface, (near the) ground; **п. слой** surface (or atmospheric) boundary layer, surface (or ground) layer; **—ая дымка** ground mist; **—ая инверсия** surface (or ground) inversion.
призма *f.* prism; **опорная п.** *see* **призматическая опора; п. полного (внутреннего) отражения** total reflecting prism; **п. прямого зрения** direct-vision prism.
призматин *m.* prismatine.
призматическ/ий *a.* prismatic; **п. бинокль** prism binocular; **—ая опора** knife edge, knife-edge bearing, blade bearing.
призм/атоид, —оид *m.* prismatoid; **—енный** *see* **призматический; —ообразный** *a.* prismoid, prismoidal; **—очка** *f.* small prism.
признавать *v.* acknowledge, recognize, admit.
признак *m.* sign, indication, mark, criterion; feature, characteristic; **п. делимости** criterion of divisibility; **п. сходимости** convergence test; **служить —ом** indicate, denote.
призн/ание *n.* acknowledgment, recognition; **—анный** *a.* acknowledged; **—ательный** *a.* appreciative, grateful; **—ать** *see* **признавать; надо —аться, что** it must be admitted that.
призыв *m.* call, appeal; **—ать** *v.* call.
прииск/ание *n.* finding; **—ать** *v.* find; **—ивать** *v.* seek.
прийти *see* **приходить.**
приказ *m.*, **—ание** *n.* order; **—ать, —ывать** *v.* order.
прикасат/ельный гониометр contact goniometer; **—ься** *v.* make contact, be tangent, touch, abut, graze.
прики/дка *f.* (rough) estimate; **—дочное вычисление** rough calculation; **—дывать, —нуть** *v.* estimate; throw in, add.
прикл. *abbr. see* **прикладной.**
прикладн/ой *a.* applied; **п. гониометр** *see* **прикасательный гониометр; —ая задача** application; **—ая ядерная физика** applied nuclear physics.
прикладыв/ание *n.* application; **—ать** *v.* apply; add, annex, affix, join; enclose; **—ать к** apply to.
прикле/енность *f.* sticking, adherence; **—енный** *a.* glued; **—ивание** *n.*, **—йка** *f.* gluing, sticking; **—ивать, —ить** *v.* glue, attach; **—иваться, —иться** *v.* be glued to; adhere.
приклеп/ать, —ывать *v.* rivet.

приключ/ать, —аться, —ить *v.* connect; **—ение** *n.* (elec.) connection; adventure.

приконтактный слой contact layer.

прикосновен/ие *n.* contact, tangency; **точка —ия** point of contact; **—ность** *f.* contiguity, proximity; **—ный** *a.* adjacent, adjoining; involved.

прикоснуться *see* **прикасаться.**

прикра/сить, —шивать *v.* embellish.

прикреп/итель *m.* fastener; **—ить, —лять** *v.* attach, fasten, fix, secure; **—ление** *n.* fastening, attachment; **—ленный** *a.* fastened, attached.

прикру/тить, —чивать *v.* bind, fasten.

прикры/вать, —ть *v.*, **—тие** *n.* cover, screen; **—тый** *a.* covered.

прилагать *see* **прикладывать.**

прила/дить, —живать *v.* adapt, adjust, fit; **—дка** *f.*, **—живание** *n.* fitting, adjustment.

прилег/ать *v.* adjoin, be adjacent to, border; **плотно п. к** fit; **—ающий** *a.* adjacent, contiguous, adjoining.

прилежаева реакция Prilezhaev (Prileschaiev) reaction.

прилежание *n.* diligence; studiousness.

прилежащий *a.* adjacent, adjoining, contiguous; **п. катет** adjacent side; **п. угол** adjacent angle.

прилежный *a.* diligent.

прилеп/ить, —лять *v.* glue, attach to.

прилет *m.* arrival (by flight); **—ать, —еть** *v.* arrive (by flight).

прилечь *see* **прилегать.**

прилив *m.* influx, flow; high tide; boss, lug; **—ать** *v.* flow to; add (liquid); **—ающий** *a.* inflowing, affluent.

приливн/ый *a.* tide, tidal; **п. вал** (tidal) bore; **—ая волна** tide (or tidal) wave; **—ое течение** tidal flow (or current), floodstream, floodcurrent.

приливо/мер *m.* tide gauge; **—образующая сила** tide-generating (tide-raising, tide-producing) force.

прилипан/ие *n.* adhesion, sticking, attachment; capture; **коэффициент —ий** sticking probability.

прилип/ать, —нуть *v.* adhere; **—ший** *a.* adhesive, adherent; trapped.

прилит/ый *a.* added (liquid); **—ь** *see* **приливать.**

приличный *a.* proper.

приложен/ие *n.* application; appendix, supplement; **точка —ия** point of application; **—ный** *a.* applied; **—ное напряжение** applied (or impressed) voltage.

приложить *see* **прикладывать.**

прим *m.* prime.

прим. *abbr.* (**примечание**) note.

прима *f.* (mus.) tonic.

примачивать *v.* moisten, wet.

примен/ение *n.* application, use; **—енный** *a.* applied, utilized; **—имость, —яемость** *f.* applicability; **—имый** *a.* applicable, appropriate; available; **—ительно к** in conformity with; as applied to; **—ительный** *a.* applicable; suitable; **—ить, —ять** *v.* apply, employ, put into practice; **—иться, —яться** *v.* be applied; conform to; **—яемый, —яющийся** *a.* applicable.

пример *m.* example, model, instance; **приводить в п.** cite as an example, illustrate with; **на —е** as illustrated by, using as an example; **по —у** after the example of, like.

примерз/ание *n.* freezing on; **—ать, —нуть** *v.* freeze on (or to); **—лый** *a.* frozen to.

примерн/о *adv.* approximately, roughly; excellently; as an example; **—ый** *a.* approximate; exemplary; typical, model.

примесн/ый *a.* foreign, admixed, impurity, extrinsic; **п. полупроводник** extrinsic semiconductor; **п. центр** impurity center; **—ая проводимость** impurity (or extrinsic) conductivity.

примесь *f.* impurity, admixture, addition, contaminant; **акцепторная п.** acceptor impurity; **п. газов** gaseous contamination; **побочная п., посторонняя п., случайная п.** impurity, foreign matter; **п. типа внедрения** interstitial impurity; **п. типа замещения** substitutional impurity.

примет/а *f.* sign, indication, mark, characteristic; **—ы** *pl.* description, distinctive marks.

примечан/ие *n.* note, annotation, comment, remark; footnote; **п. при**

корректуре note added in proof; **снабжать —иями** annotate.

примечательн/ость *f.* noteworthiness; **—ый** *a.* noteworthy.

примеш/ать, —ивать *v.* admix, add; **—ивание** *n.* admixture; impurity.

примир/ительный *a.* conciliatory; **—ить, —ять** *v.* reconcile; **—иться, —яться** *v.* reconcile oneself to.

примитивн/ый *a.* primitive; **п. период** primitive period; **—ая трансляция** primitive translation; **—ая ячейка** primitive cell.

примкнуть *see* **примыкать.**

примор/ский *a.* maritime; **—ье** *n.* seashore.

примочить *see* **примачивать.**

прим. пер. *abbr.* (**примечание переводчика**) translator's remark, translator's note.

прим. ред. *abbr.* [**примечание редакции (редактора)**] editor's note.

примык/ать *v.* adjoin, border (upon), touch; **—ающий** *a.* adjoining, abutting, adjacent; affiliated.

принадлеж/ать *v.* belong, pertain to, appertain; **—ность** *f.* membership; **—ности** *pl.* accessories; outfit, equipment.

принести *see* **приносить.**

принимать *v.* take, receive, accept, admit; assume; **п. во внимание** take into account (or consideration), bear in mind; **п. за** mistake for; **п. на себя** assume; **—ся** *v.* be received; begin, set about.

принор/авливать, —овить *v.* adapt, adjust.

приносить *v.* bring.

принудительн/о *adv.* compulsory; **—ый** *a.* compulsory, forced, coercive; **—ая циркуляция** forced circulation; **—ое воздушное охлаждение** forced-air cooling.

принудить *see* **принуждать.**

принужд/ать *v.* force, constrain; **—ение** *n.* forcing, constraint; **—енный** *a.* forced, constrained, compelled.

принцип *m.* principle; **п. взаимности** principle of reciprocity; **п. детального равновесия** principle of detailed balancing; **п. исключения** exclusion principle; **п. наименьшего действия** principle of least action; **п. наименьшего принуждения** Gauss principle of least constraint; **п. неопределенности** uncertainty principle; **п. прямейшего пути** principle of least curvature (of Hertz); **п. смещения равновесий** Le Chatelier principle; **п. соответствия** correspondence principle; **в —е** in principle; theoretically.

принципиальн/о *adv.* in principle, theoretically; fundamentally, essentially; **—ый** *a.* (of) principle, based on principle; fundamental, basic; theoretical; **—ая возможность** possibility in principle; **—ая схема** schematic diagram; basic circuit (scheme, configuration).

принцметалл *m.* Prince's metal.

принят/ие *n.* taking, acceptance, admission, assumption; **—о** *adv.* customarily, commonly; **—ый** *a.* assumed, accepted, taken; **—ь** *see* **принимать.**

приобре/сти, —тать *v.* acquire, get, obtain; **—тение** *n.* acquisition, gaining obtaining.

приобщ/ать, —ить *v.* unite, join.

приорит *m.* priorite.

приоритет *m.* priority.

приостан/авливать, —овить *v.* stop suspend; **—овка** *f.* stopping, stop suspension; **—овленный** *a.* stopped suspended.

приотвор/ить, —ять *v.* open slightly.

припаив/ание *n.* soldering; **—ать** *v* solder.

припай *m.* shore ice, ice ledge.

припайка *see* **припаивание.**

припал/енный *a.* burnt; **—ить** *v.* burn scorch.

припасы *pl.* supplies.

припа/янный *a.* soldered; **—ять** *se* **припаивать.**

припекание *n.* sintering, baking; coalescence.

припис/ать, —ывать *v.* ascribe, attribute, assign; **—ка** *f.* postscript; **—ывание** *n.* assignment, attribution ascribing.

приплю/снуть, —щивать *v.* flatten.

приповерхностный слой surface layer.

приподн/имать, —ять *v.* raise slightly **—ятие** *n.*, **—ятость** *f.* elevation

—**ятый** *a.* elevated; (geo.) raised, upheaved; —**ятый туман** lifted fog.

припой *m.* solder; **крепкий п.** brazing solder.

приполярный *a.* circumpolar.

припом/инание *n.* remembering, recollection; —**инать,** —**нить** *v.* remember, recollect, recall.

припороговый *a.* near-threshold.

припудривать *v.* dust, powder.

припуск *m.* allowance, margin; **п. на** allowance for; **оставлять п.** allow for.

припус/кать, —**тить** *v.* couple, pair; add; admit.

приравнив/ание *n.* equating; —**ать** *v.* equate; equalize.

прира/стать, —**сти** *v.* adhere; increase; —**стить,** —**щать** *v.* make adhere, attach; increase; —**щение** *n.* increment, increase; **отношение** —**щения** difference quotient.

приречный *a.* riparian.

прировнять *see* **приравнивать.**

природ/а *f.* nature; character; **по** —**е** by nature, inherently; —**ный** *a.* natural; inherent, intrinsic; native.

природовед *m.* naturalist; —**ение** *n.* natural history.

прирожденный *a.* innate.

прирост *m.* growth, increase; —**ок** *m.* excrescence, growth.

присад/ка *f.* addition, supplement, admixture, additive; —**очный** *a.* additional; —**очный элемент** (elec.) addition agent.

присажив/ание *n.* addition; —**ать** *v.* add.

присасыв/ание *n.* suction; —**ать** *v.* suck, draw in; —**аться** *v.* stick, adhere; —**ающий** *a.* sucking.

присв/аивать, —**оить** *v.* appropriate, assume; confer, award; —**оение** *n.* appropriation; awarding, conferring.

прислон/енный *a.* leaning; —**ить,** —**ять** *v.* lean against.

прислу/га *f.* servant; crew, attendants; —**живать** *v.* serve, attend.

присматривать *v.* look for; **п. за** attend; supervise; —**ся** *v.* examine, scrutinize.

присмотр *m.* care, attendance; supervision, superintendence; —**еть** *v.* find.

присоединен/ие *n.* connection, connecting, joining; addition, combination; (math.) adjunction; **п. фтористого водорода** hydrofluorination; **коэффициент** —**ия** attachment coefficient; **реакция** —**ия** addition (or combination) reaction.

присоединенн/ый *a.* additional, added, joined, attached; (math.) associated, adjoint; connected, combined; **п. полином Лежандра** associated Legendre polynomial; **п. скачок** attached shock; —**ая масса** (hyd.) apparent (additional) mass; (astr.) virtual mass; —**ая матрица** adjoint matrix; —**ая форма** (math.) concomitant.

присоедин/ительный зажим binding post; —**ить,** —**ять** *v.* join, add, attach; combine; connect; associate, adjoin; —**яющийся** *a.* additive; joining, adjoining.

приспос/абливать, —**обить** *see* **приспособлять.**

приспособл/ение *n.* adaptation, accommodation; device, appliance, apparatus; equipment; **п. поля** adaptation (or adjustment) of a field; —**енный** *a.* fitted, adapted; —**яемость** *f.* adaptability; —**яемый** *a.* adjustable, adaptable; —**ять** *v.* adapt, fit, adjust, accommodate.

пристав/ание *n.* adhesion; —**ать** *v.* adhere.

пристав/ить, —**лять** *v.* set, put, lean; appoint; —**ка** *f.* attachment; (gram.) prefix; —**ной** *a.* added, attached; —**ная лестница** ladder; —**ший** *a.* adherent.

пристальн/ый *a.* intent, fixed; —**ое внимание** close attention.

прист/ать *see* **приставать**; —**ающий** *a.* adhering, adhesive.

пристеночный слой boundary layer.

пристраивать *v.* build on.

пристрастный *a.* biased, prejudiced.

пристрелка *f.* ranging.

пристро/енный *a.* added on, built on; —**йка** *f.* annex, extension, outbuilding.

приступ *m.* access; beginning; —**ать,** —**ить** *v.* approach; begin, enter upon; proceed.

прису/дить, —ждать *v.* award, confer; **—ждение** *n.* awarding, conferment.

присутств/ие *n.* presence; **—овать** *v.* be present, attend, assist; **—ующий** *a.* present, attending, assisting.

присущ/ий *a.* inherent, characteristic; **—ность** *f.* inherence.

присч/ет *m.* addition; **—итать, —итывать** *v.* add on.

присылать *v.* send.

присып/ать *v.* add; powder, sprinkle; **—ка** *f.* sprinkling, powdering; powder.

притворить *see* **притворять.**

притворный *a.* simulated.

притворять *v.* shut, close.

притворяться *v.* pretend, simulate.

притек/ать *v.* flow to; **—ающий** *a.* inflowing, incoming.

притереть *see* **притирать.**

притерт/ый *a.* ground; ground-in; **—ая пробка** ground glass stopper; **—ое стекло** ground glass.

притир *m.* lap; **—ание** *n.* grinding, lapping; **—ать** *v.* grind, lap; rub; **—ка** *f.* grinding, lapping, abrading, attrition.

приткнуть *see* **притыкать.**

приток *m.* tributary; influx, inflow, afflux; intake, indraft; **п. к оси** (or **к линии**) confluence; **уравнение —а тепла** heat flux equation.

притом *adv.* besides, moreover, furthermore.

притти *see* **приходить.**

притуп/ить, —лять *v.* blunt, dull, deaden; truncate; **—ление** *n.* blunting, dulling; truncation; **—ленный** *a.* blunted, dulled; truncated.

притык *m.* joint; abutment; **—ать** *v.* stick, fasten to.

притяг/ательный *a.* attractive; **—ивать** *v.* attract.

притяжен/ие *n.* attraction; **сила —ия** attraction, attractive force, pull; gravity.

притяз/ание *n.* claim; **—ательный** *a.* exacting; **—ать** *v.* lay claim to.

притянут/ый *a.* pulled, attracted; **—ь** *see* **притягивать.**

приумнож/ать, —ить *v.* increase, augment, multiply; **—ение** *n.* augmentation, multiplication.

приуроч/ивать, —ить *v.* time, coordinate, adapt.

приуч/ать, —ить *v.* accustom, train.

прифугов/ка *f.* joint, jointing; **—ывать** *v.* joint.

прихват/ить, —ывать *v.* fasten; **—ка** *f.* clamp.

приход *m.* coming, arrival, advent; **—ить** *v.* come, arrive; **—иться** *v.* be obliged to; fit; occur; **—ящий** *a.* arriving, incoming; **—ящийся** *a.* necessary; fitting; (math.) per, taken over.

прихотливость *f.* capriciousness.

прицеит *m.* priceite.

прицел *m.* aim, sight; **—ивание** *n.* aiming, sighting.

прицельн/ый *a.* aiming, sighting; sight; target; **п. параметр, —ое расстояние** impact parameter.

прицеп *m.* trailer; **—ить, —лять** *v.* hook, hitch, connect; couple; **—ка** *f.* hooking, hitching; **—ление** *n.* hooking, hitching, connecting; coupling; **—ленный** *a.* hooked, connected; coupled; attached.

причал *m.* hawser; mooring; **—ивание** *n.* mooring; **—ивать, —ить** *v.* moor.

причастн/ость *f.* participation; **—ый** *a.* participating in, involved.

причем *conj.* during which (*usually untranslated*; *see* **при этом**); **п. известно, что** it being known that.

причин/а *f.* cause, reason; **п. ошибки** source of error; **по —е** because of, on account of; **служить —ой** cause, be the cause of.

причин/ение *n.* causing; **—енный** *a.* caused; **—ить, —ять** *v.* cause, occasion; **—ность** *f.* causality; **—ный** *a.* causal, causative; **—ная связь** causal relationship.

пришабр/ивать, —ить *v.* scrape, scour.

пришлифованный *a.* ground, ground down (or in).

пришлось *see* **приходиться.**

прищем/ить, —лять *v.* pinch.

приэлектродный *a.* adjacent to an electrode.

про *prep. acc.* of, about; for.

про— *prefix* (*with verbs*) over, across; through, thoroughly; past.

проб/а *f.* trial, test; sample, specimen; **п. на** test for; **п. руды, рудная п.** assay; **брать —у, взять —у** sample; **взятие —ы, отбор —ы** sampling; **золото 96-й —ы** pure gold; **серебро высокой —ы** sterling silver.

пробег *m.* range, (mean free) path; run; **п. рассеяния** scattering mean free path; **длина —а** mean free path.

пробе/гать, —жать *v.* run through (or past); look through (book).

пробел *m.* gap, blank; omission; vacancy, spacing, interval; flaw, deficiency.

пробив/ание *n.* piercing, punching, puncture, rupture, breakdown; **—атель** *m.* puncher; **—ать** *v.* pierce, punch, puncture, perforate; breach; **—ать дорогу** open a way; **—аться** *v.* rupture, break down; **—ающий** *a.* piercing, punching, puncturing; **—ка** *f.* punching.

пробивн/ой *a.* piercing, punching, puncturing; penetrative; (elec.) breakdown, disruptive; **п. разряд** disruptive discharge; **—ая прочность** disruptive strength; **—ая разность потенциалов** breakdown potential (difference); **—ое напряжение** breakdown (disruptive, puncture) voltage.

пробирка *f.* test tube.

пробирный *a.* test, testing; assay, assaying; **п. камень** touchstone; **п. металл** test metal.

пробит/ый *a.* perforated, punctured; **—ь** *see* **пробивать.**

пробка *f.* stopper, plug, cork; tap; plug (or internal) gauge; bottleneck; fuse; **газовая п.** vapor lock; **магнитная п.** magnetic mirror.

пробковый *a.* cork, stopper, plug; **п. уголь** burnt cork.

проблема *f.* problem; **п. многих тел** many-body problem. **—тический, —тичный** *a.* problematic.

проблес/к *m.* gleam, flash, ray; **—ковый** *a.* flashing, intermittent; **—нуть** *v.* gleam, flash.

пробник *m.* sample, tester; probe; **п. со счетчиком** probe counter.

пробн/ый *a.* test; trial, sampling; **п. газ** probe gas; **п. импульс** test pulse; **п. камень** *see* **пробирный камень; п. рисунок** test figure; **п. экземпляр** specimen; **—ая катушка** search coil, test coil; **—ая полоса** test strip; **—ая функция** trial function; **—ая частица** test particle; **—ое бурение** test hole; **—ое значение** trial value; **—ое предложение** tentative proposal.

пробов/ание *n.* testing; attempting; **—ать** *v.* test, sample; essay, attempt.

пробо/дение *n.* puncture, perforation; **—ина** *f.* hole, gap.

пробой *m.* puncture, rupture, breakdown; clamp; **внутренний п.** intrinsic (dielectric) breakdown; **—ник** *m.* punch; **—ное напряжение** breakdown voltage.

пробо/отбиратель, —отборник *m.* sampler.

пробочн/ик *m.* corkscrew; **—ный предохранитель** screwplug fuse.

пробрасывание *n.* propulsion.

пробуксовка *f.* slipping, skidding.

пробурав/ить, —ливать *v.* bore, perforate, drill; **—ливание** *n.* boring, perforation, drilling.

пробыть *v.* remain.

провал *m.* gap; dip; collapse, failure; (geo.) sink; **п. волны** wave trough; **п. в чувствительности** dead spot; **—иваться, —иться** *v.* collapse, break down, fail.

проваривание *n.* boiling.

проведен/ие *n.* leading, conducting; passing; drawing; **порядок —ия** procedure; **—ный** *a.* conducted; drawn, traced; performed.

провер/енный *a.* checked, inspected; **—ить** *see* **проверять; —ка** *f.* verification, checking, check, control, examination, inspection; test.

провернуть *see* **провертеть.**

провероч/ный *a.* verifying, checking, control, test; **—ная точка** control point.

проверт/еть, —ывать *v.* bore, perforate, pierce.

провер/яемый *a.* under examination; **—ять** *v.* verify, check; calibrate; examine, test, inspect; **—яющий** *m.* inspector, checker.

провес *m.* slack, sag, dip, deflection; **стрела —а** deflection, sag.

провесить *see* **провешивать.**

провести *see* **проводить.**

проветр/иваемый *a.* ventilated; **—ивание** *n.* ventilation, aeration; **—ивать, —ить** *v.* ventilate, aerate.
провешивать *v.* make vertical.
провиниться *v.* be guilty (of), be at fault.
провис *see* **провес**; **—ать** *v.* sag, dip; **—ший** *a.* sagged, slack.
провод *m.* wire, conductor; lead; duct; **монтировать —а** wire; **прокладка —ов** wiring.
проводимостный *a.* conduction, conductivity; **п. ток** conduction current.
проводимость *f.* conduction, conductivity; admittance, conductance, susceptance; **активная п., ваттная п.** conductance; **волновая п.** wave conductance, characteristic (or natural) admittance; **емкостная п.** capacity susceptance; **индуктивная п.** inductive susceptance; **комплексная п., полная (динамическая амплитудная) п.** complex admittance; **магнитная п.** permeance; **реактивная п.** susceptance; **удельная п.** specific conductance, conductivity; **п. утечки** leakage conductance.
провод/ить *v.* lead, conduct; carry out (on, through); install, construct; draw; pass (time); **—ка** *f.* wiring, installation; conduit; **—ник** *m.*, **—никовый** *a.* conductor; **—ный** *a.* conducting wire; **—ящий** *a.* conducting, conductive.
провоз *m.* conveying, transport; **—ить** *v.* convey, transport.
проволок/а *f.* wire; **—ообразный** *a.* wire-shaped, filiform.
проволочка *f.* short (or fine) wire; delay.
проволочн/ый *a.* wire; **—ая печь** resistance furnace; **—ая разделительная колонна** hot-wire separating column; **—ая сетка, —ая ткань, —ое сито** wire gauze (screen, mesh); **—ая спираль** coil; **—ое сопротивление** wire-wound resistance (or resistor).
проворачивать *v.* crank.
провор/ный *a.* quick, prompt, alert, dexterous; **—ство** *n.* quickness, promptness, dexterity.
провоцировать *v.* provoke.
провощенный *a.* waxed.
прогад/ать, —ывать *v.* miscalculate.
прогалина *f.* (astr.) lane.
прогар *m.* burnout.
прогиб *m.* sag, (bending) deflection, buckling, bowing; depression; **п. центра пролета** central deflection.
прогиб/ание *n.* downwarping; sagging; **—ать** *v.* deflect; **—аться** *v.* deflect, sag, collapse; **—омер** *m.* deflectometer.
прогляд/еть, —ывать *v.* overlook, miss; look through.
прогнать *see* **прогонять.**
прогноз *m.*, **ставить п.** forecast; **п. погоды** weather forecast (or forecasting); **—ирование** *n.* prediction, forecasting; **—ировать** *v.* predict, forecast.
прогностический *a.* prognostic.
прогнуться *see* **прогибаться.**
прогон *m.* run; girder; **—ка** *f.* screw die; **—ять** *v.* drive away, drive off; dismiss.
прогор/ание *n.* burning through; burnout; **—ать, —еть** *v.* burn through.
проградуиров/анный *a.* calibrated, graduated; **—ать** *v.* calibrate, graduate.
программ/а *f.* routine, schedule; program; **учебная п.** curriculum, syllabus; **—ирование** *n.* programming.
прогрев *m.* (initial) heating or tempering; warmup; **—ание** *n.* heating, warming up; **—ать** *v.* warm up, heat, temper.
прогресс *m.* progress, development; **—ивно** *adv.* progressively, gradually; **—ивный, —ирующий** *a.* progressive, progressing, gradual; **—ировать** *v.* progress; **—ия** *f.* progression, series.
прогреть *see* **прогревать.**
прогрохоченный *a.* screened.
продав/ить, —ливать *v.* press down; press through, punch; **—ливание** *n.* punching; extrusion.
продви/гать, —нуть *v.* advance, promote; propel; **—гаться, —нуться** *v.* advance, progress; **—жение** *n.* advancement, advance, progress; propulsion; **—жение материала** flow of material.
продевать *v.* pass through, put through, run through.

продел/ать, —ывать *v.* do, perform, make, accomplish.

продерж/ать, —ивать *v.* keep, hold, detain.

продеть *see* **продевать.**

продиктовать *v.* dictate, impose.

продиффундировавшее вещество diffusate.

продл/евать, —ить *v.* prolong, lengthen, extend; **—ение** *n.* prolongation, extension; **—иться** *v.* be prolonged.

продолговат/ость *f.* oblong form; **—ый** *a.* oblong, elongated.

продолжать *v.* continue, proceed; prolong, extend, lengthen; **—ся** *v.* continue, be prolonged, be extended.

продолжен/ие *n.* continuation; prolongation, extension; duration; **аналитическое п.** analytic continuation; **в п.** during, in the course of, throughout; **—ный** *a.* continued, extended, lengthened, prolonged.

продолжительность *f.* duration, period, time, continuance; endurance; **п. горения** burning time; **п. жизни** lifetime, survival time, life span; **п. затухания** decay time; **п. полета спутника** satellite lifetime; **п. работы, полезная п. службы** (useful) life; **п. существования** lifetime; **п. флуоресценции** fluorescent lifetime.

продолжительн/ый *a.* continuous, prolonged, long-term; **на —ое время** for a long time; **—ое облучение** protracted irradiation.

продолжить *see* **продолжать.**

продольно *adv.* longitudinally, lengthwise.

продольн/ый *a.* longitudinal, lengthwise; drawn out; **п. изгиб** buckling; **п. момент** (aero.) pitching moment; **п. напор** longitudinal thrust; **п. разрез, —ое сечение** axial (or longitudinal) section; **—ая волна** longitudinal (or dilatational) wave; **—ая ось** longitudinal (long, direct) axis; **—ое изменение** linear deformation; **—ое натяжение** tensile stress; **—ое развитие атмосферных ливней** longitudinal development of air showers; **—ое увеличение** longitudinal magnification; **—ое удлинение** longitudinal extension; **в —ом направлении** lengthwise; **—ые колебания** longitudinal vibrations (or oscillations).

продор/аживать *v.* groove; **—оженный** *a.* grooved, channeled.

продув/ание *n.*, **—ка** *f.* blowing through (off, out); scavenging, purging; **—ательный, —ной** *see* **продувочный**; **—ать** *v.* blow through (off, out); scavenge, purge.

продувочный *a.* blow through, blow off; **п. клапан** blow-through valve, drain valve; **п. кран** drain cock; **п. насос** scavenging pump.

продукт *m.* product; **п. активации** activate; **п. деления** fission product; **п. диффузии** diffusate; **конечный п.** end product; **побочный п.** by-product; **п. распада** decay (or disintegration) product.

продуктивн/о *adv.* productively, efficiently; **—ость** *f.* productivity, efficiency; **—ый** *a.* productive, producing, efficient.

продукция *f.* production, output.

продум/ать, —ывать *v.* think over, reason out.

продут/ый *a.* blown, blown through (or out); **—ь** *see* **продувать.**

продуцирующий *a.* producing, productive.

продыряв/ить, —ливать *v.* pierce, punch, perforate; **—ленный** *a.* pierced, perforated.

проед/ать *v.* corrode; **—енный** *a.* corroded.

проез/д *m.* passage; **—жать** *v.* pass, travel.

проект *m.* project, plan, scheme, design; draft; **состовлять п.** plan, devise; **—ант** *see* **проектировщик.**

проектив *m.* projector lens; **—ность** *f.* projectivity; **группа —ности** projective group.

проективн/ый *a.* projective, projection; **п. оператор** projection operator; **—ое сокращение** foreshortening.

проектиров/ание *n.*, **—ка** *f.* projection, design, planning; **п. решетки** lattice design; **—ать** *v.* project, design, plan, devise, engineer; **—щик** *m.* projector, planner, designer.

проектн/ый *a.* project, design, plan; **—ая величина** rating; **—ая мощ-**

ность rated capacity; —**ая схема** layout; —**ые данные** design features, data, specifications.

проектор *m.* projector; **электронный п.** field-emission microscope.

проекционн/ый *a.* projection; **п. аппарат, п. фонарь, —ое соединение** projector; **п. оператор** *see* **проективный оператор.**

проекция *f.* projection; component; **вертикальная п.** front view, elevation, vertical projection; **горизонтальная п.** top view, ground plan; **п. на ось z** *z* component; **п. угла** projected angle.

проем *m.* aperture, opening.

проесть *see* **проедать.**

проехать *see* **проезжать.**

проецирующий *a.* projecting, projection.

прожектор *m.*, —**ный** *a.* searchlight; projector; gun; **п. ближнего действия** floodlight; **облачный п.** ceiling projector (or light); **электронный п.** electron gun.

прожигание *n.* arc-over; burning through.

прожилок *m.* vein, veinlet; streak, apophysis.

прозопит *m.* prosopite.

прозрачн/ость *f.* transparency, transmittance, transmissivity; **п. для тепловых лучей** diathermancy; **коэффициент —ости** transmission coefficient; —**ый** *a.* transparent, clear.

проигр/ать, —ывать *v.* lose; play back; —**ывание** *n.* playback; —**ыватель** *m.* (sound) reproducer; record player; —**ыш** *m.* loss.

произведен/ие *n.* production, work; composition; (math.) product; **внешнее п.** vector product; **внутреннее п.** scalar (dot, inner) product; **п. инерции** product of inertia; **избранные —ия** selected works; —**ный** *a.* produced.

произвести *see* **производить.**

произ-во *abbr.* (**производство**) production, manufacture.

производимый *a.* producible.

производитель *m.* producer; manufacturer; **п. работ** works superintendent.

производительн/ость *f.* productivity, output, rate, delivery; capacity, efficiency, performance; rating; —**ый** *a.* productive, efficient.

производить *v.* produce, make, manufacture; generate; effect, perform, do; promote; **п. опыты** experiment.

производн/ая *f.* (math.) derivative; **индивидуальная п.** individual (particle, material, substantial) derivative; **косая п.** directional derivative; **п. по направлению** directional derivative; **п. по нормали** normal derivative; —**ое** *n.* (chem.) derivative; —**ый** *a.* derivative, derived.

производственн/ый *a.* industrial, manufacturing, production; **п. контроль** plant supervision; **п. реактор** production reactor; —**ая мощность** productive capacity; —**ая практика** practical training; —**ая установка** production plant.

производство *n.* production, output; preparation, manufacture, generation; factory; derivation; effecting.

производящ/ий *a.* producing, generating; productive; **п. оператор** (math.) generator; —**ая (линия)** (math.) generatrix; —**ая функция** generating function; —**ийся** *a.* being produced, in process, in progress.

произвол *m.*, —**ьность** *f.* arbitrariness; —**ьно** *adv.* arbitrarily, at will, at random; —**ьный** *a.* arbitrary, random; —**ьная единица** arbitrary unit.

произн/ести, —осить *v.* pronounce, utter; —**ошение** *n.* pronunciation, utterance.

произойти *see* **происходить.**

произраст/ание *n.* growth; —**ать, —и** *v.* grow.

проиллюстрировать *v.* illustrate.

проиндицировать *v.* index.

происте/кать, —чь *v.* result; —**кающий** *a.* resulting, resultant.

происходить *v.* result, originate, be derived; occur, take place.

происхождение *n.* origin; derivation; **п. видов** (bio.) origin of species; **п. ядер** nucleogenesis.

происшествие *n.* incident, event; accident.

пройти *see* **проходить.**

Прока уравнение Proca equation.

прокаленный *a.* fired, annealed, tempered; calcinated.

прокалиброванный *a.* calibrated.

прокал/ивание *n.* roasting; annealing, tempering; calcination; **—ивать, —ить** *v.* calcine, bake, fire; anneal, temper; **—ка** *f.* firing, annealing, tempering.

прокалывать *v.* puncture, pierce, perforate, punch.

прокатанный *a.* rolled, flattened; **п. лист** rolled sheet.

прокат/ать, —ить *see* **прокатывать**; **—ка** *see* **прокатывание.**

прокатн/ый *a.* rolling; rolled; hired; **п. валок** roller; **п. стан** rolling mill.

прокат/ывание *n.* rolling, flattening; **—ывать** *v.* roll, flatten.

прокачивать *v.* pump through.

проквантовать *v.* quantize.

Прокл Proclus (lunar crater).

прокладка *f.* gasket, washer, packing, padding, lining; insert, spacer, shim; laying, construction; **изоляционная п.** insulation spacer; **п. курса** course plotting.

проклад/ной *a.* packing, stuffing, lining; gasket; **—очный** *a.* packing; **—очное кольцо** packing ring; **—ывать** *v.* lay, construct; interlay.

прокле/ивание *n.*, **—йка** *f.* pasting, gluing, sizing; **—ивать, —ить** *v.* paste, glue, size.

прокованный *a.* forged, hammered.

прокол *m.* puncture; **—оть** *see* **прокалывать.**

прокоп *m.* cutoff.

Проксима Центавра Proxima Centauri.

проксимальный *a.* proximal.

прол. *abbr.* (**пролив**) strait, sound, channel, narrows.

пролагать *see* **прокладывать.**

проламывать *v.* break, fracture; break through.

пролектит *m.* prolectite.

пролет *m.* flight, transit; span, arch; **—ать, —еть** *v.* pass (or fly) through, traverse.

пролетн/ый *see* **пролет**; **—ая база** path length; **—ая трубка** drift tube; **—ое время** time of flight, transit time; **—ое пространство** drift space.

пролив *m.* strait, sound, channel, narrows.

проли/вать, —ть *v.* spill; **—вающий свет** illuminating; **—тие** *n.* spilling; **—тый** *a.* spilled.

прологарифмировать *v.* take the logarithm of.

пролож/енный *a.* laid, constructed; interlaid; **—енные эмульсии** sandwiched emulsions; **—ить** *see* **прокладывать.**

пролом *m.* breach, gap, break; **—анный** *a.* breached, broken; **—ать, —ить** *see* **проламывать.**

пролонг/ация *f.* prolongation; **—ировать** *v.* prolong.

пром. *abbr.* (**промышленность**) industry; (**промышленный**) industrial.

промазать *v.* coat, oil.

промасл/енный *a.* oiled, greased; **—ивать, —ить** *v.* oil, grease.

промах *m.* miss; blunder; **—иваться, —нуться** *v.* miss.

промачив/ать *v.* wet thoroughly, soak; **—ающий** *a.* soaking, steeping.

промедление *n.* delay.

промеж. *abbr.* (**промежуточный**) intermediate.

промежуток *m.* interval, space, vacancy; distance, gap; clearance; **п. времени** period, interval; **искровый п.** spark gap; **п. между импульсами** pulse separation; **п. решетки** lattice spacing; **п. сходимости** convergence interval.

промежуточн/ый *a.* intermediate, intermediary, intervening, interstitial; **п. контур** intermediate circuit; **п. электрод** dynode; **—ая связь** intermediate coupling; **—ая частота** intermediate frequency; **—ое пространство** interspace; **—ое ядро** intermediate nucleus, compound nucleus.

промер *m.* measurement; error in measurement.

промерз/ание *n.* freezing; **линия —ания** frost line; **—ать, —нуть** *v.* freeze through; **—лый** *a.* frozen.

промер/ивать, —ить, —ять *v.* measure, survey; **—ный** *a.* measuring, surveying.

прометий *m.* promethium (Pm).

промешивать *v.* mix thoroughly.

промкомбинат *abbr.* (**промышленный комбинат**) industrial kombinat.

промок/ательная бумага blotting paper; **—ать, —нуть** *v.* be permeated, be wetted; blot; **—ший** *a.* wet, soaked, permeated.

промотор *m.* promoter.

промочить *see* **промачивать.**

Промстройиздат *abbr.* (**Издательство строительной промышленности**) Building Industry Press.

пром-сть *abbr.* (**промышленность**) industry.

промыв/ание *n.* washing, flushing; **п. газа** gas scrubbing; **—атель** *m.* washer; **—ательный** *a.* washing; **—ать** *v.* wash, bathe, flush; **—ающий воздух** flushing air; **—ка** *f.* washing, flushing, bathing; **—ной, —очный** *a.* washing, flushing, rinsing; **—ная колонка** scrubbing column.

промыс/ел *m.* trade, business, occupation; **—ловый** *a.* occupational.

промыт/ый *a.* washed, flushed; **—ь** *see* **промывать.**

промышленн/ик *m.* manufacturer; **—ость** *f.* industry.

промышленн/ый *a.* industrial, commercial; **—ая руда** pay (or minable) ore; **—ое месторождение** minable deposit; **в —ом масштабе** on a large scale; **—ые технические условия** production specifications.

Пром. энергет. *abbr.* (**Промышленная энергетика**) Industrial Power (journal).

пронести *see* **проносить.**

пронзительный *a.* piercing, sharp, shrill.

Прони нажим (тормоз) Prony brake.

прониз/ать, —ывать *v.* pierce, perforate, penetrate.

проник/ание, —новение *n.* penetration, permeation; **—ать** *v.* penetrate, permeate; percolate, pass through; **—ающий** *a.* penetrating, thorough; **—ающая компонента** penetrating component; **—ающее излучение** penetrating radiation.

проникнут/ый *a.* penetrated, permeated; **—ь** *see* **проникать.**

проницаем/ость *f.* penetrability, penetration factor, penetrance; permeability; transmission; **п. барьера** barrier penetration (or factor); **диэлектрическая п.** permittivity, dielectric constant; **магнитная п.** magnetic permeability; **п. на кривой коммутирования** (mag.) normal permeability; **п. на частном цикле** (mag.) incremental permeability; **п. по индуктивности** (mag.) inner (or intrinsic) permeability; **п. (сетки)** (elec.) penetration factor, penetrance; **—ый** *a.* penetrable, permeable.

прониц/ание *n.* permeation; **—ательность** *f.* insight; understanding; penetrability; **—ательный** *a.* penetrating; perspicacious.

пронормировать *v.* normalize.

проносить *v.* carry (by, past, through); **—ся** *v.* rush (by, past, through).

прообраз *m.* prototype, standard; sign; preimage, inverse image; original.

пропавший *a.* missing, lost.

пропаганда *f.* propaganda.

пропадать *v.* disappear, be missing; be wasted.

пропан *m.* propane; **—овый** *a.* propane, propanoic.

пропар/ивание *n.*, **—ка** *f.* steaming; **—ивать** *v.* steam.

пропасть *v. see* **пропадать**; *f.* precipice, abyss.

пропеллер *m.*, **—ный** *a.* propeller.

прописать, —ывать *v.* register, record; prescribe; **—ная буква** capital letter.

пропитанн/ость *f.* impregnation; **—ый** *a.* impregnated, permeated, saturated.

пропит/ать, —ывать *v.* impregnate, saturate, soak; **—ка** *f.*, **—ывание** *n.* impregnation, saturation, soaking; **—очный, —ывающий** *a.* impregnating.

проплав/ить, —лять *v.* fuse, melt; **—ленный** *a.* fused, melted.

пропласток *m.* (geo.) intercalation.

проплы/вать, —ть *v.* float (or drift) past (or through).

проповедывать *v.* advocate.

прополаскивать *v.* rinse.

пропорциональн/о *adv.* proportionally; **среднее —ое** mean proportion.

пропорциональност/ь *f.* proportionality, proportion; **прямая п.** direct ratio; **коэффициент —и** proportionality factor.

пропорциональный *a.* proportional, proportionate; **обратно п.** reciprocal; **п. счетчик** proportional counter.

пропорция *f.* proportion, ratio; **п. флегмы** reflux ratio.

пропуск *m.* admission, passing, passage; omission, lapse; blank, gap; **п. зажигания** misfire; **—аемость** *f.* transmissivity; **—ание** *n.* transmission, passage; (elec.) gating; **коэффициент —ания** transmission coefficient; **схема —ания** (elec.) gate; **—ать** *v.* pass, transmit; omit, miss; admit; (elec.) gate.

пропускающ/ий *a.* passing, transmitting; omitting; admitting; (elec.) gating, gate; **п. импульс** gate pulse; **п. свет** translucent; **п. эшелон** transmission echelon; **—ая лампа** gate tube; **—ая решетка** transmission grating; **—ая схема** gating circuit, gate.

пропускн/ой *a.* permeable; passing, carrying; **п. ток** forward current; **—ая способность** throughput; carrying (or transmitting) capacity; permeability; **—ое направление** direction of easy flow.

пропустить *see* **пропускать.**

прораб *m.* foreman, construction superintendent.

прораб/атывать, —отать *v.* work through; **—отка** *f.* working out, development; study.

прораст/ание *n.* intergrowth, penetration; **двойник —ания** penetration twin; **—ать, —и** *v.* intergrow.

прорвать *see* **прорывать.**

прореагировать *v.* react.

прорез *m.* slit, groove; notch, cut, channel; aperture; **меридианный п.** (astr.) meridian slit; **—анный** *a.* slotted, slit; notched, cut; **—ать** *see* **прорезывать.**

прорезин/енный *a.* rubberized; **—ивание** *n.*, **—ка** *f.* rubberizing; **—ивать, —ить** *v.* rubberize.

прорез/ывать *v.* cut through, slit, perforate, notch; **—ь** *see* **прорез.**

прореферированный *a.* reviewed, abstracted.

прореха *f.* slit, tear; gap.

проржав/евший *a.* rusted through; **—еть** *v.* rust through.

прорис *m.* tracing; **—овать, —овывать** *v.* trace.

проросший *a.* intergrown, interpenetrating.

пророческий *a.* prophetic.

прорыв *m.* breach, break, gap; outburst; **полный п.** breakdown; **—ать** *v.* break through; **—аться** *v.* burst open, break (through).

просал/ивание *n.* greasing; **—ивать, —ить** *v.* grease.

просасыв/ание *n.* suction; **—ать** *v.* draw through.

просачив/ание *n.* soaking; penetration; infiltration, percolation; seepage, leakage; **—аться** *v.* infiltrate, filter, percolate; seep, leak; **—ающийся** *a.* percolating; leaking.

просверл/енный *a.* drilled, perforated; **—ивание** *n.* drilling, boring, perforation; **—ивать, —ить** *v.* drill, bore, perforate.

просвет *m.* clearance, gap, opening; transillumination; **на п.** by transillumination; **п. следа** track gap.

просветитель *m.* enlightener, teacher; **—ный** *a.* enlightening, instructive.

просветить *see* **просвечивать; просвещать.**

просветл/ение *n.* illumination, lightening, clearing up, brightening; enlightenment; **п. поля** field brightening; **—енная линза** coated lens; **—еть** *v.* clear up; **—ить, —ять** *v.* clear.

просвечив/аемость *f.* translucence; **—ание** *n.* translucence, transillumination, transmission; radioscopy, x-raying; **—ать** *v.* be translucent; x-ray; **—ающий** *a.* translucent; **—ающий электронный микроскоп** transmission electron microscope; **—ающие облака** translucidus.

просвещ/ать *v.* enlighten, teach, educate; **—ение** *n.* instruction, education; enlightenment; **—енный** *a.* educated, intellectual, informed.

просе/ивание *n.*, **—ивающий** *a.* screening, sifting; **—ивать, —ять** *v.* screen, sift; **—янный** *a.* screened, sifted.

просить *v.* ask, request.

проскакивать *v.* jump, slip past (or through).

проскальзыв/ание *n.* slippage, slipping past (or through); **—ать** *v.* slip.

проскользнуть *see* **проскальзывать.**

проскочить *see* **проскакивать.**

прославленный *a.* famous, celebrated.

прослаивать *v.* sandwich; interlay, interstratify.

проследить *see* **прослеживать.**

прослежив/ание *n.* tracing, tracking; **—ать** *v.* trace, track.

просло/ек *m.* layer, seam, streak; **—енный** *a.* interstratified, interbedded; **—ить** *see* **прослаивать.**

прослой *m.*, **—ка** *f.* layer; filler; lamella; seam, streak; interstratification, interlayer.

просмаливать *v.* tar.

просматривать *v.* look through, scan; overlook, miss.

просмол/ение *n.* tarring; **—енный** *a.* tarred; **—ить** *see* **просмаливать.**

просмотр *m.* survey, review; scanning; oversight; **п. вдоль следа** scanning along a track; **п. по площади** area scanning; **—енный** *a.* reviewed; revised; scanned; examined; **—енное и исправленное издание** revised edition; **—еть** *see* **просматривать.**

просовывать *v.* force through.

прососать *see* **просасывать.**

просохший *a.* dried.

просочиться *see* **просачиваться.**

проспект *m.* prospect; prospectus; avenue.

просроч/енный *a.* overdue; **—ивать, —ить** *v.* be overdue; hold over, delay; **—ка** *f.* delay; expiration.

простаивать *v.* stand; stand idle.

простенок *m.* partition.

простереть *see* **простирать.**

простир/ание *n.* stretch, extension; (geo.) strike, course, trend; **п. пластов** direction of strata; **—ать** *v.* stretch, extend; **—аться** *v.* stretch, reach, extend; (geo.) trend.

просто *adv.* simply, plainly; merely; **п. противоречивый** flatly contradictory.

простой *m.* standstill, lost time.

прост/ой *a.* simple; plain, ordinary; single; **взаимно п.** relatively prime; **п. корень** simple root; **п. множитель** prime factor; **п. полюс** simple pole; **п. слой** (math.) single layer; **п. уровень** single level; **п. эфир** ether; **—ая балка** beam supported at both ends; **—ая дробь** common (or simple) fraction; **—ое вещество** element; **—ое поле** (math.) prime field; **—ое число** (math.) prime number; **—ым глазом** with the naked eye.

простор *m.* spaciousness, scope; **—ный** *a.* spacious, capacious; **—ная упаковка** loose packing.

простота *f.* simplicity.

простоять *see* **простаивать.**

пространн/о *adv.* extensively; in detail; **—ость** *f.* extensiveness; **—ый** *a.* extensive, vast; lengthy.

пространственно/-временное отражение space-time reversal; **п.-подобный** spacelike.

пространственн/ый *a.* space, spatial, steric, three-dimensional; solid; **п. заряд** space charge; **п. изомер** stereoisomer; **п. множитель** space factor; **п. поток** three-dimensional flow; **п. угол** solid angle; **—ая волна** sky wave; **—ая группа** space group; **—ая диагональ** body diagonal; **—ая задача** three-dimensional problem; **—ая изомерия** stereoisomerism; **—ая ориентировка** dimensional orientation; **—ая переменная** space variable; **—ая производная** space derivative; **—ая решетка** space lattice; **—ая химия** stereochemistry; **—ое затруднение, —ое препятствие** steric hindrance; **—ое квантование** space quantization; **—ое производное** gradient; **—ое распределение** spatial distribution; (cosmic rays) lateral (or radial) distribution; **—ые координаты** space coordinates.

пространство *n.* space; expanse, region; room; gap; area, volume; chamber, compartment; **вредное п.** waste (idle, dead) space; **п.-время** space-time; **п**

горения combustion chamber (or area); **п. изотопического спина** isotopic spin space; **п. импульсов** momentum space; **п. отсчета** frame of reference; **пустое п.** void; vacuum; **п. событий** space-time; **п. состояний** state space; **п. функций** function space.

прострел *m.*, **—ивание** *n.* shooting through; **—ивать, —ить** *v.* shoot through.

проступ/ать, —ить *v.* show through, protrude; pass through.

проступок *m.* fault, offense.

просуммировать *v.* sum.

просунуть *see* **просовывать.**

просуш/енный *a.* dried; **—ивание** *n.*, **—ка** *f.* drying, dehumidifying; **—ивать** *v.* dry, dehumidify.

просуществовать *v.* exist.

просч/ет *m.* checking; miscalculation; counting error (or loss); **—итать, —итывать** *v.* check; count; **—итаться, —итываться** *v.* miscount; miscalculate.

просыпать *v.* spill.

просыхать *v.* dry (up).

просьб/а *f.* request; **обращаться с —ой** make a request.

прот. *abbr.* (**протокол**) minutes, proceedings, official record.

протактинид *m.* protactinide.

протактиний *m.* protactinium (Pa).

проталина *f.* thawed patch of earth.

проталкив/ание *n.* forcing through; **—ать** *v.* press (or force) through.

протапливать *v.* heat.

протарировать *v.* calibrate.

прота/скивать, —щить *v.* pull through.

протачивать *v.* sharpen; turn on lathe.

протежировать *v.* protect, favor.

протеин *m.*, **—овый** *a.* protein.

протек/ание *n.* flow, flowing; passage; course; **—ать** *v.* flow past, run through; leak; elapse; proceed; occur; **—ать нормально** take a normal course; **—ающий** *a.* flowing, streaming.

протектор *m.*, **—ный** *a.* protector.

протерозой *m.*, **—ская эра** Proterozoic era.

протечка *f.* (small) flow.

против *prep. gen.* opposite; against; counter; contrary to; as compared to; **за и п.** pro and con; **п. часовой стрелки** counterclockwise.

противень *m.* pan.

противиться *v.* oppose, resist, object to.

противн/ик *m.* adversary, opponent; **—о** *adv.* contrary to, against; **—ый** *a.* opposed, contrary, adverse; alien; **—ый ветер** head wind; **в —ом случае** otherwise; **доказательства от —ого, способ от —ого** indirect proof.

противо— *prefix* counter—, anti—, back—; *suffix* —proof.

противо/атомная защита atomic defense; **—вес** *m.* counterweight, counterbalance, counterpoise; **—взрывной экран** blast shield; **—включение** *n.* (elec.) opposition, balancing; **—давление** *n.* counterpressure, back pressure.

противодейств/ие *n.* reaction, counteraction; opposition, bucking; **оказывать п.** counteract; **—овать** *v.* react against, counteract; buck, resist, oppose; **—ующий** *a.* counteracting; opposing.

противо/динатронная сетка suppressor grid; **—излучение неба** sky counterradiation (or back radiation); **—ион** *m.* counter ion; gegenion; **—колебательный контур** antihunting circuit; **—лежащий угол** opposite (or alternate) angle; **—луна** *f.* antiselene; **—натяжение** *n.* backpull; **—окислитель** *m.* antioxidant; **—осколочный** *a.* fragmentproof; **—перегрузочный костюм** antiblackout (or anti-G) suit.

противополагать *see* **противопоставить.**

противополож/ение *n.* contrast, contradistinction; **—ить** *see* **противопоставить**; **—но** *adv.* contrarily, in contrast to, oppositely; **—ное** *n.* the contrary, the reverse; **—ность** *f.* opposition, contrast; **в —ность** on the contrary, in contrast; **прямая —ность** the exact opposite; **—ный** *a.* contrary, opposite, opposed; reverse, inverse; counter—; **—ная фаза** opposite phase, antiphase.

противопомеховый *a.* antinoise; **п. фильтр** noise (or interference) filter.

противопостав/ить, —лять *v.* oppose; contrast; compare; **—ление** *n.* opposition; contrasting; comparing.

противорадиация *f.* counterradiation, back radiation.

противореч/иво *adv.* in contradiction; **—ивость** *f.* inconsistency, discrepancy, contradiction; **—ивый** *a.* contradictory, inconsistent; **—ие** *n.* contradiction, discrepancy, inconsistency, variance; **—ить** *v.* contradict, be at variance with.

противо/сияние *n.* counterglow, gegenschein; **—совпадение** *n.* anticoincidence; **—солнечный** *a.* antisolar.

противосолнце *n.* anthelion; **ложное п., побочное п.** paranthelion.

противостаритель *m.* antiager.

противосто/яние *n.* resistance; (astr.) opposition; **—ять** *v.* resist, withstand, face; **—ящий** *a.* opposed, resisting; opposite.

противосумер/ечный *a.* anticrepuscular; **—ечная дуга** antitwilight (or anticrepuscular) arc; **—ки** *pl.* antitwilight, anticrepuscular rays.

противо/течение *n.* counterflow; **—ток** *m.*, **—точный** *a.* countercurrent, counterflow; reflux; **—точная колонка** countercurrent column.

противофаз/а *f.* opposite phase, antiphase; **в —е** out of phase, antiphased, in opposition; **—ный** *a.* antiphase, antiphased.

противофоновый *a.* antibackground.

противо/-эдс, —электродвижущая сила back (or counter) emf.

протий *m.* protium.

протис/кать, —кивать, —нуть *v.* press, force through.

прото— *prefix* proto—.

протоактиний *m.* protoactinium (Pa).

протозвезда *f.* protostar.

проток *m.* canal, channel.

протокол *m.* minutes, proceedings, official record; **—ировать** *v.* record.

протолитионит *m.* protolithionite.

протолитическая реакция protolytic reaction.

протолк/ать, —нуть *see* **проталкивать.**

протон *m.*, **—ный** *a.* proton; **п. отдачи** recoil proton; **—ный синхротрон** proton synchrotron; **—ный цикл** proton-proton chain.

протоплазма *f.* protoplasma.

протопланета *f.* protoplanet.

прототип *m.* prototype.

проточить *see* **протачивать.**

проточн/ость *f.* flowage; **—ый** *a.* flowing, running, circulating; **—ый воздушный счетчик** air-flow counter; **—ый газовый счетчик** gas-flow counter; **—ый калориметр** continuous-flow calorimeter; **—ый счетчик** flow counter.

протрав/а *f.* mordant; stain; **—ка** *f.* etching; pickling; **—ленный** *a.* etched; pickled; **—ливать** *v.* etch; pickle.

протрузия *f.* protrusion.

протуберанц *m.* protuberance, prominence; **возвратный п.** (astr.) surge prominence.

протягив/ание *n.* drawing; broaching; **—ать** *v.* draw out, stretch, extend; broach; prolong; **—аться** *v.* extend.

протяжен/ие *n.* extent, length, dimension; spread, expansion, extension, elongation; range; **п. времени** duration; **на —ии** over a period of; throughout.

протяженн/ость *f.* dimension, extension, extent, length; **—ый** *a.* extended; **—ый источник** extended (or distributed) source; **—ая оболочка** extended envelope; **—ая частица** extended particle; **—ое ядро** finite (or extended) nucleus.

протяж/ка *f.* drawing; broach; **—ной** *a.* drawing, pulling; broaching; **—ная обмотка** pull-through winding; **—ность** *f.* lengthiness, slowness; **—ный** *a.* lengthy, slow.

протянут/ый *a.* stretched, extended; prolonged; **—ь** *see* **протягивать.**

Проута гипотеза Prout hypothesis.

проф. *abbr.* (**профессиональный**) professional; (**профессор**) professor; (**профсоюзный**) trade union.

профессионал *m.* professional; **—ьный** *a.* professional, vocational, trade, occupational; **—ьное облучение** occupational exposure.

професс/ия *f.* profession, occupation; **—ор** *m.* professor; **—орско-преподавательский состав** faculty; **—орство** *n.* professorship; **—ура** *f.* professorate; professorship.

профилакт/ика *f.* prevention, preventive inspection (or maintenance); **—ический** *a.* prophylactic, preventive.

профилиров/ание *n.* profiling, shaping, designing; **—анный** *a.* profiled, shaped; **—ать** *v.* profile, cut a profile, shape.

профилограф *m.* profilograph.

профиль *m.* profile, outline, shape; section, cross section, side view; **поперечный п.** transverse section; **продольный п.** longitudinal section; **сложный п.** irregular outline; compound section; **—ный** *a.* profile, section; -shaped; **—ное сопротивление** profile drag.

профильтров/анный *a.* filtered (through); **—ать, —ывать** *v.* filter (through.)

профсоюз *abbr.* (**профессиональный союз**) trade union.

прохлорит *m.* prochlorite.

проход *m.* passage; duct, canal; pass; opening; **за один п.** in one operation.

проходим/ость *f.* permeability, penetrability; passability; **—ый** *a.* permeable, passable; traversed.

проходить *v.* pass; traverse; penetrate; elapse, terminate; take place; overlook; study; **п. мимо** pass by, bypass; **п. сквозь, п. через** penetrate, pass through.

проходка *f.* cutting (through).

проходн/ой *a.* going through, straight-through, transfer; **п. изолятор, —ая втулка** bushing; **п. конденсатор** duct capacitor; **—ая емкость** (elec.) transfer capacitance; **—ая проводимость** (elec.) transfer admittance; **конденсатор —ого типа** feed-through capacitor.

проходящ/ий *a.* passing, going through; transient, transmitted; progressive; **п. свет** transmitted light; **—ая волна** forward wave.

прохож/дение *n.* passage, passing; crossing, transit, transmission; **п. частиц через вещество** penetration of particles through matter; **п. через меридиан** (astr.) meridian passage, transit; **п. через перигелий** perihelion passage; **п. через центральный меридиан** central meridian passage; **коэффициент —дения** transmission coefficient; penetration factor; **—ий** *a.* passing.

процвет/ание *n.* prosperity; **—ающий** *a.* prosperous.

процедить *see* **процеживать.**

процедура *f.* procedure.

процеж/енный *a.* filtered, strained; **—ивание** *n.* filtration, straining; **—ивать** *v.* filter, strain.

процент *m.* percent, percentage; **—ы** *pl.*, **число —ов** percent; percentage, interest; **в весовых —ах** percent by weight; **—ность** *f.* percentage; degree; **—ный** *a.* percent, percentage; rate; **—ное содержание** percentage.

процесс *m.* process, procedure.

Процион Procyon.

прочерк/ивать, —нуть *v.* draw a line through.

прочесть *see* **прочитать.**

проч/ий *a.* other, remaining; **и —ее** and so forth, et cetera; **между —им** incidentally, in passing; **при —их равных условиях** other conditions being equal.

прочист/ить *see* **прочищать**; **—ка** *f.* cleansing.

прочит/ать, —ывать *v.* read through, peruse.

прочищать *v.* cleanse thoroughly.

прочно *adv.* firmly, stably, securely; **—стный показатель** tensile strength.

прочност/ь *f.* stability, firmness, solidity; durability, strength, toughness, endurance, resistance, permanence; **п. на изгиб** bending strength; **п. на излом** breaking strength; **п. на износ** resistance to wear; **п. на кручение** torsional strength; **п. на отрыв** cleavage strength; **п. на пробой** disruptive strength; **п. на разрыв** tensile (or breaking) strength; tear resistance; **п. на растяжение** tensile strength; **п. на сдвиг** shearing strength; **п. на сжатие** compressive strength; **п. на скалывание, п. на срез** shearing strength; **п. на удар**

resistance to impact; **запас —и** safety factor.

прочн/ый *a.* durable, solid; rigid; tough, strong, firm; stable; lasting, permanent; **—ое основание** stable foundation.

прочтение *n.* reading, perusal.

прошедш/ее *n.* the past; **—ий** *a.* previous; past; passing.

прошение *n.* application; petition.

прошеств/ие: по —ии after the lapse (of), on expiration (of).

прошив/ать *v.* pierce; broach; sew; **—ка** *f.* piercing; broaching; broach, reamer; **—ной, —очный** *a.* piercing; broaching.

прошить *see* **прошивать.**

прошлифовывать *v.* hone; polish.

прошлогодний *a.* last year's.

прошл/ое *n.* the past; **—ый** *a.* past, former; last.

прощальный *a.* farewell, parting.

прощать *v.* pardon.

проще *comp. of* **просто, простой,** simpler, easier.

проявит/ель *m.* (phot.) developer; **—ь** *see* **проявлять.**

проявл/ение *n.* manifestation, effect, display; (phot.) development; **—енный** *a.* manifested, shown; developed; **—яемость** *f.* developability; **—ять** *v.* manifest, display, show, exhibit, reveal; develop; **—яться** *v.* develop, appear.

проясн/ение *n.* clearing; **—еть, —ивать** *v.* clear up, brighten; **—ить, —ять** *v.* clear, clarify; **—яться** *v.* clear up.

пруд *m.* pond; **—ить** *v.* dam.

пружин/а *f.* spring; **п.-волосок** hairspring; **главная п.** mainspring; **—ить** *v.* spring, be elastic; **—ка** *f.* small spring; hairspring; (elec.) cat whisker; **—ность** *f.* springiness, elasticity.

пружинн/ый *a.* spring, spring-loaded; **п. зажим** (elec.) alligator clip; **—ая упорка** stop spring; **—ое кольцо** snap ring.

пружинодержатель *m.* spring holder.

прусская синь Prussian blue.

прустит *m.* proustite.

прут *m.* rod, bar; **—ковый** *a.* rod, rod-shaped; **—ковое железо** rod iron, wire rod; **—ок** *m.* bar, rod; rung.

прыг/ание *n.* jumping; **—ать** *v.* jump.

прыгающ/ий *a.* jumping; **—ая катушка** flip coil; **—ая пленка** jumping film.

прыгнуть *see* **прыгать.**

прыжок *m.* jump.

прыс/калка *f.* sprayer; **—кать, —нуть** *v.* spray, sprinkle.

прям/ая *f.* straight line; **п. равновесия** equilibrium line; **п. совместимости** line of compatibility; **—изна** *f.* straightness; **—ить** *v.* straighten.

прямо *adv.* straight, directly.

прямо— *prefix* straight, rect—, recti—.

прямо/волновый конденсатор square-law capacitor; **—действующий** *a.* direct-acting, direct; **—емкостный конденсатор** straight-line capacitor.

прямой *a.* straight, direct, straightway, straightforward; right; upright, erect; forward; **п. конус** right circular cone; **п. накал** direct heating; **п. отрезок** linear segment; **п. отсчет** direct reading; **п. пробег** linear range; **п. скачок уплотнения** normal shock; **п. ток** (elec.) forward current; **п. убыток** sheer waste; sure loss; **п. угол** right angle; **п. удар** head-on collision; **п. ход** direct run; forward stroke; **п. цилиндр** right cylinder; **п. цилиндрический реактор** right circular cylindrical reactor.

прям/ой *cont.*, **—ая волна** direct wave; **—ая линия** straight line; **—ая призма** right prism; **—ая реакция** direct (forward, straight, simple) reaction; **—ая решетка** (cryst.) lattice; **—ая связь** direct coupling; **—ая сумма матриц** direct sum of matrices; **—ое восхождение** (astr.) right ascension; **—ое действие** direct action (or effect); **—ое изображение** erect image; **—ое направление** forward direction; **—ое напряжение** forward voltage; **—ое облучение** direct exposure; **—ое произведение** direct product; **—ое смещение** forward bias; **—ое соответствие** direct correspondence; **—ое усиление** straight amplification; **—ым путем** directly; **—ые скобки** square brackets.

прямолинейно/-поляризованный *a.* plane-polarized; **—сть** *f.* rectilinearity.

прямолинейн/ый *a.* rectilinear, straight, straight-line, linear; **п. пробег** straight-line flight; **—ая тригонометрия** plane trigonometry; **—ое движение** rectilinear (or linear) motion; **—ое распространение** rectilinear propagation.

прямонакальный *a.* directly heated, filamentary; **п. катод** filamentary cathode.

прямо/сторонний *a.* straight-sided; **—струйный** *a.* direct-spray, direct-jet; **—та** *f.* straightforwardness, rectitude.

прямоточн/ый *a.* uniflow, straight-through, once-through, single-flow, single-pass; concurrent; ramjet; **п. (воздушно-реактивный) двигатель** ramjet (engine); **п. (паровой) котел** single-pass boiler; **—ая активная зона** straight-through (or one-pass) core (of reactor); **—ая ракета** ram rocket; **—ое охлаждение** direct-flow (once-through, uniflow) cooling.

прямоугольник *m.* rectangle; **п. текучести** yield rectangle.

прямоугольн/ый *a.* rectangular, right-angled, square; **п. импульс** square (or rectangular) pulse; **п. параллелепипед** rectangular parallelepiped; **п. сигнал** square-wave signal; **п. треугольник** right triangle; **—ая волна** square (or rectangular) wave; **—ая яма** square well.

прямочастотный *a.* straight-line frequency.

пс *abbr.* (**парсек**) parsec (pc).

ПС [*in steel mark* (**полуспокойная**)] semikilled steel.

псевд. *abbr.* (**псевдоним**) pseudonym.

псевдо— *prefix* pseudo—, pseud—; false.

псевдоадиабат/а *f.* pseudoadiabat; **—ический** *a.* pseudoadiabatic.

псевдовектор *m.*, **—ный** *a.* pseudovector.

псевдо/гравитационная сила pseudogravitational force; **—евклидов** *a.* pseudo-Euclidean; **—изомерия** *f.* pseudoisomerism; **—инвариант** *m.* pseudoinvariant; **—квадрупольный** *a.* pseudoquadrupole; **—кислота** *f.* pseudo acid; **—кливаж** *m.* false cleavage.

псевдокристалл *m.* pseudocrystal; **—ический** *a.* pseudocrystalline.

псевдокубический *a.* pseudoisometric.

псевдоморф *m.* pseudomorph; **—ия** *f.* pseudomorphy; **—ный** *a.* pseudomorphic, pseudomorphous; **—оза** *f.* pseudomorphosis.

псевдоним *m.* pseudonym.

псевдоожижен/ие *n.* quasi-liquefaction, fluidization; **—ный** *a.* quasi-liquid, fluidized.

псевдооснование *n.* pseudo base.

псевдопотенциал *m.* pseudopotential; **—ьная функция** pseudopotential function.

псевдо/раствор *m.* pseudo solution; **—симметрия** *f.* pseudosymmetry.

псевдоскаляр *m.*, **—ный** *a.* pseudoscalar; **—ная связь** pseudoscalar coupling.

псевдо/соединение *n.* pseudo compound; **—фит** *m.* pseudophite; **—циклоида** *f.* pseudocycloid; **—эргодическая гипотеза** quasi-ergodic hypothesis.

пситтацинит *m.* psittacinite.

психрометр *m.* psychrometer; **пращевой п.** sling psychrometer.

психрометрическ/ий *a.* psychrometric; **—ая разность** wet-bulb depression; **—ая температура** wet-bulb temperature.

пт. *abbr.* (**пятница**) Friday.

птица *f.* bird.

Птолемей Ptolemaeus (lunar crater).

Птолемея система Ptolemaic system.

ПТС *abbr.* (**проволочный тензометр сопротивления**) wire tensiometer.

ПТЭ *abbr.* (**Приборы и техника эксперимента**) Instruments and Experimental Techniques (journal).

пуаз *m.* poise.

Пуазейля закон Poiseuille equation; **формула П.** P. formula.

Пуанкаре возвратная теорема Poincaré theorem of return.

Пуансо движение Poinsot motion.

пуансон *m.* punch, die.

Пуассон Poisson (lunar crater).

Пуассона коэффициент, скобка П. Poisson bracket.

публик/а *f.* public; **—ация** *f.* publication; **—овать** *v.* publish; announce.
публичный *a.* public.
пуг/ать, —нуть *v.* frighten.
пугов/ица *f.*, **—ичный** *a.* button, stud; **—ка** *f.* knob, stud.
пудлингов/ание *n.* (met.) puddling; **—ать** *v.* puddle; **—ый** *a.* puddling, puddle.
пудра *f.* powder.
пузыр/ек *m.* bubble; vial, phial; **—ение** *n.* bubbling; **—истость** *see* **пузырчатость**; **—истый** *see* **пузырчатый**; **—иться** *v.* bubble.
пузырчат/ость *f.* vesiculation; (met.) blistered condition; **—ый** *a.* bubbly; vesicular; blistered; **—ое кипение** nucleate boiling; **—ые поры** vesicular cavities.
пузырь *m.* bubble, blister, blowhole; **газовый п.** gas cavity; **—ковый** *a.* bubble; **—ковая камера** bubble chamber.
Пуйе принцип Pouillet principle.
пулемет *m.*, **—ный** *a.* machine gun.
Пулковская обсерватория Pulkovo observatory.
пульвериз/атор *m.* pulverizer; atomizer, sprayer; **—ационный** *a.* pulverization, pulverizing; atomizing, spraying; **—ация** *f.*, **—ирование** *n.* pulverization; atomization, spraying; **—ированный, —ованный** *a.* pulverized; atomized, sprayed; **—ировать, —овать** *v.* pulverize; atomize, spray.
пульпа *f.* pulp.
пульс *m.* pulse; **п.-реле** pulse relay, relay interrupter.
пульс/атор *m.* pulser; pulsator; **—ация** *f.* pulsation; ripple, flutter; surge; **коэффициент —ации** ripple ratio; **—ирование** *n.* pulsation; **—ировать** *v.* pulsate.
пульсирующ/ий *a.* pulsed, pulsating; **п. источник** pulsed source; **п. реактивный двигатель** pulse-jet engine; **—ее магнитное поле** pulsed magnetic field.
пульсометр *m.* pulsometer.
пульт *m.* desk; panel; **п. управления** control desk (console, panel).
Пульфриха рефрактометр Pulfrich refractometer.
пуля *f.* bullet, projectile.
пумпеллиит *m.* pumpellyite.
пункт *m.* point; station, post; paragraph, section, item; **конечный п.** end point, terminal point.
пунктир *m.* dashed (or broken) line; dotted line; **точечный п.** dotted line.
пунктирн/ый *a.* dotted; dotting; **—ая кривая** dashed (or dotted) curve; **—ая линия** *see* **пунктир.**
пунктиров/ать *v.* dot; stipple; **—ка** *f.* dotting; stippling.
пунктуальн/ость *f.* punctuality, exactness; **—ый** *a.* punctual, precise.
пунсон *see* **пуансон.**
пунширов/ание *n.* punching; **—ать** *v.* punch, stamp.
Пупина катушка Pupin (or loading) coil.
пупиниз/ация *f.* coil (or lumped) loading; **шаг —ации** coil spacing; **—ированный** *a.* coil-loaded.
пупиновская катушка *see* **Пупина катушка.**
Пурбах Purbach (lunar crater).
пурга *f.* purga, blizzard.
Пуркинье явление (эффект) Purkinje effect.
пурпур *m.*, **—ный, —овый** *a.* purple.
пуск *m.* starting, start-up, triggering; admission; **п. в ход** start up, set in motion; **п. ракеты** rocket launching (or firing); **—ание** *n.* starting; **—атель** *m.* starter.
пускать *v.* set in motion, start up; let, allow, permit; admit; **п. в ход** set in motion.
пусков/ой *a.* start-up; (reactor) starting, launching, triggering, actuating; **п. анод** starting anode; **п. выброс** trigger pip; **п. двигатель** starting motor; **п. импульс** triggering pulse; **п. период** start-up time; **п. промежуток** starter gap; **п. селекторный импульс** trigger gate; **п. стол** launching platform; **—ая башня** launching tower; **—ая площадка** launching platform (or site); **—ая ракета** booster rocket; **—ая схема** trigger circuit; **—ая установка** launcher, launching ramp (or installation); **—ая характеристика** (elec.) control characteristic; **—ое действие** trigger

action, triggering; —**ое напряжение** starting (or trigger) voltage; —**ые приборы** start-up instrumentation.

устеть *v.* (become) empty.

устить *see* **пускать.**

уст/ой *a.* empty, void; hollow; blank, bare; (min.) barren; futile; **п. узел** (cryst.) vacancy; —**ота** *f.* vacuum, void; hollow, cavity, free space; blankness; **в —оте** in a vacuum.

устотел/ость *f.* hollowness; —**ый** *a.* hollow.

устотн/ость *f.* vacuum; hollowness; **коэффициент —ости** (reactor) void factor; —**ый** *a.* vacuum, void; hollow; —**ая лампа** vacuum lamp.

устыня *f.* desert.

усть *particle with verbs* let; *conj.* although.

устяк *m.* trifle; —**овый** *a.* trifling.

ут/аница *f.* confusion, tangle; —**анный** *a.* confused; confusing; —**ать** *v.* confuse, tangle.

утев/одный *a.* guiding; —**ой** *a.* traveling, track; road.

утем *prep. gen.* by, by means of.

утемер *m.* odometer; pedometer.

утешеств/енник *m.* traveler; —**ие** *n.* travel, journey; —**овать** *v.* travel.

ут/ь *m.* path, track, trajectory, route, course; way, means; journey; **п. метеора** meteor trail; **п. перемешивания** mixing length; **на ложном —и** on the wrong track; **на пол —и** halfway.

уфалит *m.* pufahlite.

ух *m.* down; nap.

ухерит *m.* pucherite.

учение *n.* swelling, heaving.

учина *f.* chasm, abyss.

учить *v.* swell, raise, inflate, distend; —**ся** *v.* swell, rise, heave.

учко/вание *n.* bunching; —**ванный** *a.* bunched; —**ватель** *m.* buncher; —**видный** *a.* bunched, clustered.

учность *f.* antinode, loop, crest.

учок *m.* beam; bunch, bundle; pencil; wisp; **п. лучей** pencil of rays; **п. молекул** molecular beam; **п. плоскостей** sheaf (or bunch) of planes; **п. прямых** pencil of lines.

ушечн/ый *a.* gun, cannon; —**ая бронза** gun metal.

пушинка *f.* flake.

пушка *f.* gun, cannon; **электронная п.** electron gun.

пушкинит *m.* puschkinite.

пушпул *m.*, —**ьный** *a.* push-pull.

пф *abbr.* [**пикофарада** (**микромикрофарада**)] picofarad, micromicrofarad.

Пфаффова форма Pfaffian form.

Пфеффера закон Pfeffer law.

Пфунда серия Pfund series.

п. ч. *abbr.* (**потому что**) because.

ПЧ *abbr.* (**промежуточная частота**) intermediate frequency.

Пшорр Pschorr; **синтез по —у** P. synthesis.

пыл *m.* flame, blaze, heat; —**ание** *n.* flaming, blazing; —**ать** *v.* flame, blaze; —**ающий** *a.* flaming, blazing.

пыле/видный, —образный *a.* pulverized, powdered; —**защищенный** *a.* dustproof; —**мер** *m.* dust counter; —**непроницаемый** *a.* dustproof; —**улавливание** *n.* dust collection (or precipitation); —**уловитель** *m.* dust collector (extractor, catcher, settler, separator).

пыл/инка *f.* dust particle, grain (in interstellar space); —**ь** *f.* dust, grains (in interstellar space); —**ьник** *m.* dust coat; —**ьный** *a.* dusty, dust, dust-laden.

пытаться *v.* attempt, try, endeavor.

пытлив/ость *f.* searchingness, keenness; —**ый** *a.* searching, keen.

пьедестал *m.* pedestal.

пьеза *f.* pressure unit (10^4 dynes per cm^2).

пьезо— *prefix* piezo—, piezoelectric; pressure.

пьезо/генератор *m.* piezo oscillator; —**громкоговоритель** *m.* crystal loudspeaker.

пьезодатчик *m.* piezoelectric transducer (gauge, pickup), piezoprobe, pressure-sensitive detector; **п.-излучатель** piezoelectric transmitter.

пьезо/диффузия *f.* pressure diffusion; —**ид** *m.* piezoid.

пьезокварц *m.*, —**евый** *a.* (piezoelectric) quartz crystal; —**евый преобразователь** quartz crystal transducer; —**евые часы** quartz crystal clock.

пьезокристалл *m.* piezocrystal; —**изация** *f.* piezocrystallization.

пьезомагн/етизм *m.* piezomagnetism, magnetostriction; —**итный** *a.* piezomagnetic.

пьезометр *m.* piezometer; —**ический** *a.* piezometric; —**ический напор** pressure (or piezometric) head, hydrostatic pressure; —**ическая высота** piezometric (or hydraulic pressure) head; —**ия** *f.* piezometry.

пьезо/микрофон *m.* crystal microphone; —**модуль** *m.* piezoelectric modulus; —**оптический** *a.* piezo-optic; —**пластинка** *f.* piezoelectric crystal plate; —**приемник** *m.* piezoelectric receiver (pickup, transducer); —**резонатор** *m.* piezoelectric resonator; —**тропия** *f.* piezotropy; —**химия** *f.* piezochemistry.

пьезоэлектр/ик *m.* piezoelectric crystal; —**ический** *a.* piezoelectric; **обратный —ический эффект** converse piezoelectric effect.

пьезоэлемент *m.* piezoelectric element; pressure-sensitive element.

пьемонтит *m.* piedmontite.

пьерпонтит *m.* pierrepontite.

Пэджа явление Page effect.

пята *f.* heel, foot, sole; abutment; pivot, pivot journal.

пятер/ичный, —ной *a.* fivefold, quinary, quintuple, five-part; —**ка** *f.*, —**о** five.

пяти— *prefix* penta—.

пятиатомный *a.* pentatomic.

пятивалентн/ость *f.* pentavalence; —**ый** *a.* pentavalent.

пятигранн/ик *m.* pentahedron; —**ый** *a.* pentahedral.

пяти/десятилетие *n.* semicentennial; —**десятый** *a.* fiftieth; —**дневка** *f.* five-day period.

пяти/зарядный ион quintuply charged ion; —**значный** *a.* five-digit, five place; —**кратный** *a.* fivefold, quintuple; —**кратное замещение** penta substitution.

пятилет/ие *n.* five-year period (or fifth anniversary); —**ка** *f.* Five-Year Plan; —**ний** *a.* five-year, five-year old.

пяти/мерный *a.* five-dimensional; —**месячный** *a.* five-month; —**окись** *f* pentoxide; —**основный** *a.* pentabasic; —**ричный** *a.* quinary; —**сотлетний** *a.* quincentenary.

пятисторонн/ий *a.* pentahedral; —**ик** *m.* pentahedron.

пятитысячный *a.* five-thousandth.

пятиугольн/ик *m.* pentagon; —**ый** *a* pentagonal.

пяти/фтористый *a.* pentafluoride (of) —**хлористый** *a.* pentachloride (of) —**хлористый уран** uranium pentachloride; —**членный** *a.* five-membered; —**электродная лампа** pentode.

пятка *f.* heel.

пятнадцат/ый *a.* fifteenth; —**ь** fifteen.

пятнист/ость *f.* spottiness, mottling patchwork; —**ый** *a.* spotty, spotted mottled, blotchy, patchy.

пятница *f.* Friday.

пятно *n.* spot, blotch, patch; **ионное п** ion burn; **солнечное п.** sunspot **максимум —образовательной деятельности** sunspot maximum.

пятов/ой, —ый *a.* heel; pivot; abutment; **п. камень** abutment stone; **п шарнир** pivot hinge (or joint).

пяточный *a.* heel.

пят/ый *a.* fifth; —**ая часть** one fifth.

пять five; —**десят** fifty; —**сот** five hundred.

Р

р *abbr.* (**рентген**) roentgen.

р. *abbr.* (**район**) district, raion; (**река**) river; (**родился**) born; (**рубль**) ruble.

Р [*in steel mark* (**бор**)] boron.

Р. *abbr.* (**республика**) republic.

Р$_1$ *abbr.* (**русская литература дореволюционного периода**) Russian literature of the prerevolutionary period (in library cataloguing); **Р**$_2$ (**русская литература советского периода**) Russian literature of the Soviet period (in library cataloguing).

Раабе признак сходимости Raabe test for convergence.

рабдофанит *m.* rhabdophanite.

рабитит *m.* rabbittite.

ıбот/а *f.* work, energy; paper, article; experiment; operation, performance; task, job; **р. адгезии** energy of adhesion; **р. выхода** work function; **р. диссоциации** dissociation energy; **р. ионизации** ionization potential; **р. испарения** heat of evaporation; **р. на валу** shaft work; **р. намагничивания** energy of magnetization; **р. перехода** transition energy; **быть в —е** operate, work, be in operation; **режим —ы** operating conditions; procedure; **условия —ы** working conditions; **ход —ы** operation.

бот/ать *v.* work; (mach.) run, operate, function; **—ающий** *a.* running, operating, functioning; working, at work; **—ающая модель** working model; **—ник** *m.* worker.

ботоспособн/ость *f.* capacity for work, efficiency; **—ый** *a.* possessing great capacity for work, efficient.

бочий *m.* worker, operator; *a.* working, work; running, functioning, operating, operative, operational; process; effective, active; **р. газ** process gas; driver gas; **р. интервал** operating range; **р. канал** (reactor) fuel tube (or channel); **р. кулачок** actuating cam; **р. объем** active (or sensitive) volume; effective volume; **р. пар** live steam; **р. период** operating cycle; **р. потолок** operational ceiling; **р. предел** effective range; **р. процесс** operation, procedure; **р. режим** operating conditions; **р. ход** power (driving, working) stroke.

боч/ий *cont.*, **—ая жидкость** pressure fluid; working fluid; **—ая мощность** operating power; **—ая нагрузка** working (or useful) load; **—ая площадка** effective area, area of operation; **—ая площадь** effective area; **—ая поверхность** effective area; **—ая сила** manpower, labor; **—ая точка** operating point; **—ая характеристика** performance (characteristics); performance curve; **—ее время** running time (of machine); **—ее давление** working (or effective) pressure; **—ее колесо** driving wheel, rotor; **—ее напряжение** operating voltage; **—ее сопротивление** working strength; **—ее состояние** operating condition, working order; **—ее тело** working medium.

равен (short form of **равный**) equal, is equal to.

равенство *n.* equality, equivalence, parity; equation; constancy.

равн/ение *n.* leveling, equalization, alignment; **—ина** *f.* plain; **—инный** *a.* level, flat; plain.

равно *adv.* equally, alike; is equal to; **р. как и** as well as; **р. по модулю единице** unimodular (number).

равно—*prefix* equi—, iso—, equally, uniformly.

равно/бедренный *a.* isosceles; **—бочный** *a.* equilateral; isosceles; **—великий** *a.* equal, equivalent, equally large; **—вероятный** *a.* equally probable.

равновес/ие *n.* equilibrium, balance; **р. двух фаз** biphase equilibrium; **константа —ия** equilibrium constant; **отношение —ия** equilibrium ratio; **состояние —ия** state of equilibrium, equiponderant state.

равновесн/ый *a.* equilibrium; equiponderant, balanced; stable; **—ая влага** equilibrium water; **—ая концентрация** equilibrium concentration; **—ая реакция** balanced reaction; **—ая частица** resonant (or equilibrium particle); **—ое значение** equilibrium value; **—ое излучение** radiation equilibrium; **—ое отношение** stability relation.

равновозможный *a.* equally likely, equally possible.

равновременн/ость *f.* isochronism, tantochronism; **—ый** *a.* isochronous, simultaneous.

равнодействующ/ее *n.* resultant; **—ий** *a.* resultant, equal, equivalent; **—ая сила** resultant, equivalent force.

равноделение энергии equipartition of energy.

равноденств/енный *a.* equinox, equinoctial, equidiurnal; **р. шторм** equinoctial gale; **—ие** *n.*, **точка —ия** equinox; **весеннее —ие** vernal equinox.

равнозернист/ость *f.* even-grained texture; **—ый** *a.* equigranular, even-grained.

равнознач/ность *f.* equivalence; **—ный** *a.* equivalent; **—ащий** *a.* equivalent, synonymous.

равномерно *adv.* uniformly, evenly; **р. распределенная нагрузка** evenly distributed load; **—сть** *f.* uniformity, evenness.

равномерн/ый *a.* uniform, steady, smooth, even; proportional, equal; isometric; **р. поток** steady (or uniform) flow; **—ая шкала** evenly divided scale; **—ое движение** uniform motion (or flow); **—ое распределение** homogeneous distribution, equipartition; **—ое смешивание** homogeneous mixing.

равномощн/ость *f.* (math.) equivalence (of sets); **—ый** *a.* (math.) equivalent (set); of equal strength.

равно/непрерывный *a.* equicontinuous; **—осный** *a.* equiaxial; **—остаточный** *a.* congruent (number); **—отстоящий** *a.* equally spaced, equidistant.

равноплощадн/ый *a.* equiareal; **—ая проекция** equal-area projection.

равно/потенциальный *a.* equipotential; **—правный** *a.* equally justified; possessing equal rights; **—приливный** *a.* cotidal; **—пропорциональный** *a.* (math.) homothetic.

равнораспределен/ие *n.*, **—ность** *f.* equipartition, equidistribution.

равносигнальная зона equisignal zone.

равносил/ие *n.* equivalence; **—ьный** *a.* equivalent, of equal strength.

равностепенн/о непрерывный equicontinuous; **—ый** *a.* of equal degree.

равно/сторонний *a.* equilateral; **—стоящий** *a.* equidistant; **—сть** *f.* equality; **—та** *f.* evenness; **—температурный** *a.* isothermal; **—точный** *a.* equal point-for-point; equally accurate.

равноугольн/ик *m.* isogon; **—ый** *a.* equiangular, isogonal.

равно/удаленный *a.* equidistant; **—фазная зона** equiphase zone.

равноускоренный *a.* uniformly accelerated.

равноценн/ость *f.* equivalence; **—ый** *a.* equivalent; of equal value; **—ый по точности** equally accurate.

равночастотный *a.* equal-frequency.

равночисленн/ость *f.* equality in number; **—ый** *a.* of equal number, numerically equivalent.

равноэнергетический *a.* equal-energy, isoenergetic.

равн/ый *a.* equal, alike, similar, congruent; **—ым образом** equally.

равнять *v.* equalize; equate; even, level; compare; **—ся** *v.* be equalized; be equal (or equivalent) to.

рагит *m.* rhagite.

рад *abbr.* (**радиан**) radian; **рад.** (**радио**) radio.

рад *m.* rad (unit of absorbed radiation energy); *a.* glad.

радар *m.*, **—ный** *a.* radar.

ради *prep. gen.* for the sake of, for.

радиально/волокнистый, **—столбчатый** *a.* radial-columnar, divergent-columnar; **—лучистая структура** divergent structure.

радиальн/ый *a.* radial; **р. поток** radia[l] flux; **р. узел** radial node; **—ая производная** radial derivative.

радиан *m.*, **—ный** *a.* radian; **—на[я] мера** circular measure.

радиант *m.* (astr.) radiant.

радиатор *m.* radiator; cooler, coole[r] block.

радиационно-химический *a.* radiochem[-]ical.

радиационн/ый *a.* radiation, radiative[;] **р. захват** radiative capture; **р[.] катод** radiation cathode; **р. перехо[д]** radiative transition; **р. пиромет[р]** radiation pyrometer; **р. поток** radia[-]tion flux; **р. пояс земли** Van Alle[n] radiation belt; **р. распад** radiativ[e] decay; **р. термометр** solar thermom[-]eter; **р. туман** radiation fog; **—а[я] длина** radiation length; **—ая по[-]правка** radiative correction; **—а[я] разведка** radiation reconnaissanc[e;] **—ая рекомбинация** radiative re[-]combination; **—ая температура** ra[-]diation temperature; **—ая устойчи[-]вость** radiation resistance; **—ое за[-]тухание**, **—ое трение** radiatio[n] damping; **—ое повреждение** radi[a-]tion damage; **—ое равновесие** radia[-]tion equilibrium.

радиация *f.* radiation.

диево-бериллиевый источник radium-beryllium source.

диевый *a.* radium; **р. свинец** radium lead.

дий *m.* radium (Ra); **—содержащий** *a.* radium-bearing.

дикал *m.* radical; **знак —а** radical sign.

дикальн/ость *f.* radicalness; efficiency, completeness; **—ый** *a.* radical; efficient, complete; **—ое количество** radical.

дио *n.* radio, radio set.

дио— *prefix* radio—.

диоавто/граф, —снимок *m.* radioautograph, autoradiograph; **—графический** *a.* radioautographic, autoradiographic; **—графия** *f.* radioautograph, autoradiograph.

диоактив/ационный анализ radioactivation analysis; **—ность** *f.* radioactivity.

диоактивн/ый *a.* radioactive; **р. захват** radiative capture; **р. индикатор** radioactive tracer; **р. коллоид** radiocolloid; **р. распад** radioactive decay (or disintegration); **р. ряд** radioactive series (chain, family), decay chain; **р. элемент** radioactive element, radioelement; **—ое заражение** radioactive contamination; **—ое ядро** radioactive nucleus, radionuclide; **—ые осадки** radioactive fallout; **—ые отходы** radioactive waste.

диоактиний *m.* radioactinium (RaAc).

диоальтиметр *m.* radio altimeter.

диоаппарат *m.* radio (receiving) set; **—ура** *f.* radio (or electronic) equipment.

диоастроном *m.* radio astronomer; **—ия** *f.* radio astronomy.

дио-бериллиевый источник нейтронов radium-beryllium neutron source.

диобиолог/ический *a.* radiobiological; **—ия** *f.* radiobiology, radiation biology.

диобуря *f.* (rad.) noise storm.

диовещ/ание *n.*, **—ательный** *a.* broadcast, broadcasting.

диовзрыватель *m.* proximity fuse.

дио/вождение *n.* radio aids to navigation; **—волна** *f.* radio wave; **—восход** *m.* radio rising (of satellite); **—высота** *f.* radio altitude; **—высотомер** *m.* radio altimeter; **—вышка** *f.* radio tower.

радио/геничный, —генный *a.* radiogenic; **—геодезия** *f.* radiogeodesy; **—горизонт** *m.* radio horizon; **—грамма** *f.* roentgenogram.

радиограф *m.* radiograph; **—ировать** *v.* radiograph; **—ический** *a.* radiographic; **—ическое изображение** radiograph; **—ия** *f.* radiography.

радио/данные *pl.* radio data; **—дефектоскопия** *f.* radiographic flaw detection, radiography; **—диагностика** *f.* x-ray diagnostics; **—диапазон** *m.* radio-frequency (or microwave) region.

радио/заход *m.* radio setting (of satellite); **—звезда** *f.* radio star.

радиозонд *m.* radiosonde; **—ирование** *n.* radiosonde observation.

радио/излучение *n.* radio-frequency radiation; radio emission; **—изотоп** *m.* radioisotope; **—индикатор** *m.* radioactive tracer; **—индуцированный** *a.* radiation-induced; **—иод** *m.* radioactive iodine.

радио/коллоид *m.* radiocolloid; **—компас** *m.* radio compass; **—лампа** *f.* electron tube; **—лечение** *n.* radiotherapy; **—лиз** *m.* radiolysis; **—литический** *a.* radiolytic.

радиолог *m.* radiologist; **—ический** *a.* radiological; **—ия** *f.* radiology.

радиолокатор *m.* radar (equipment).

радиолокац/ия *f.*, **—ионный** *a.* radar; **—ионная индикация** radar display (indication, presentation); **—ионная чаша** radar dish (or antenna); **—ионное обнаружение бурь** radar storm detection.

радио/луч *m.* radio beam; **—любитель** *m.* radio amateur; **—люминесценция** *f.* radioluminescence.

радио/мачта *f.* radio mast; **—маяк** *m.* radio beacon.

радиометалл *m.* radiometal (alloy of Permalloy type); **—ография** *f.* radiometallography; **—ургический** *a.* radiometallurgical.

радиометео/донесение *n.*, **—сводка** *f.* (meteor.) synoptic radio report; **—рограф** *m.* radiometeorograph.

радиометр *m.* radiometer; radiation meter; **—ический** *a.* radiometric.

радио/навигация *f.* radio navigation; **—непроницаемый** *a.* radiopaque; **—нуклид** *m.* radionuclide.

радиопеленг *m.* radio bearing (or direction finding); **—атор** *m.* radiogoniometer (or direction finder); **—ация** *f.* radio direction finding.

радио/передатчик *m.* radio transmitter; **—передача** *f.* radio transmission (or broadcasting); **—прием** *m.* radio reception; **—приемник** *m.* radio receiver; **—прогноз** *m.* radio forecast; **—проницаемый** *a.* radiotransparent; **—пятно** *n.* radio spot.

радио/разведка *f.* radioprospecting; **—свет звезд** radio starlight; **—свечение** *n.* radioluminescence; **—свинец** *m.* radiolead; **—связь** *f.* radio communication; **—сеть** *f.* radio network; antenna system.

радиоскоп *m.* radioscope; **—ический** *a.* radioscopic; **—ия** *f.* radioscopy.

радиоспектрометр *m.* microwave spectrometer.

радиоспектроскоп *m.* microwave spectroscope; **—ия** *f.* microwave spectroscopy.

радио/станция *f.* radio station; **—схема** *f.* electronic circuit.

радиотелеграф/ировать *v.* send a radiotelegram; **—ист** *m.* radio operator; **—ия** *f.* radiotelegraphy.

радиотелеметр/ический *a.* radiotelemetric; **—ия** *f.* radiotelemetry.

радиотелемеханический автомат radio robot.

радио/телефон *m.* radiophone; **—теллур** *m.* radiotellurium; **—тень** *f.* radio shadow; **—терапевтический** *a.* radiotherapeutic; **—терапия** *f.* radiotherapy; **—термия** *f.* radiothermy; **—термолюминесценция** *f.* radiothermoluminescence.

Радиотех. *abbr.* (**Радиотехника**) Radio Engineering (journal).

радиотехн/ика *f.* radio engineering; **—ический** *a.* radio engineering; electronic.

радио/торий *m.* radiothorium (RdTh); **—туманность** *f.* radio nebula.

радиоуглерод *m.* radiocarbon; **—ный метод датирования** radiocarbon dating.

радио/узел *m.* radio center; radio receiver and feeder set of loudspeakers; **—установка** *f.* radio set; radio installation; **—устойчивость** *f.* radioresistance.

радио/физика *f.* radiophysics; **—фикация** *f.* radio installation (esp. of wire-broadcast network); **—фон** *m.* radiophone; **—фотолюминесценция** *f.* radiophotoluminescence.

радиохим/ик *m.* radiochemist; **—ический** *a.* radiochemical; **—ия** *f.* radiochemistry.

радио/хроматография *f.* radiochromatography; **—центр** *m.* broadcasting center; **—цепь** *f.* radio circuit.

радиочастот/а *f.* radio frequency; **—ный спектр** radio-frequency spectrum.

радиочувствительн/ость *f.* radiosensitivity; **—ый** *a.* radiation-sensitive; radiosensitive.

радио-шар-зонд *m.* radiosonde.

радио/шум *m.* radio noise; **—экранировка** *f.* radio shielding.

радиоэлектро/кардиограф *m.* radioelectrocardiograph; **—миограф** *m.* radioelectromyograph; **—энцефалограф** *m.* radioelectroencephalograph.

радио/элемент *m.* radioelement; **—эхо** *n.* radio echo.

радист *m.* radio operator.

радиус *m.* radius; range; **р. апсиды** apsidal radius; **р.-вектор** radius vector, position vector, separation vector; **р. действия** radius (or range) of action, reach, coverage; **р. действия ядерных сил** range of nuclear forces; **р. изгиба** bending radius; **р. инерции** radius of gyration (or inertia); **р. кривизны** radius of curvature; **р. кручения** radius of torsion; **р. окружности вращения** radius of gyration; **р. поражения** effective casualty radius; **р. ядра** nuclear radius; **большим —ом действия** long-range.

радон *m.* radon (Rn).

Радона преобразование Radon transform.

рад/сек *abbr.* (**радианов в секунду**) radians per second.

радуга *f.* rainbow; **белая р.** fogbow; **вторичная р.** secondary rainbow; **первичная р.** primary rainbow.

радужн/ость *f.* iridescence; **—ый** *a.* rainbow; iridescent, opalescent; **—ая оболочка** iris (of eye).

раз— *prefix* un—, dis—; mis—; away, off, apart; out of.

раз *conj.* since.

раз *adv.* once, one time; **р. навсегда** once and for all; **единственный р.** the only time; **еще р.** once more, again; **как р.** just, exactly; **много р.** often, repeatedly; **на этот р.** for the present, this time; **не р.** more than once; **—ом** at once, at one time, simultaneously; **в два —а меньше** one half (as much).

разбав/итель *m.* diluent; **—ить, —лять** *v.* dilute; thin, rarefy; **—ление** *n.* dilution; rarefaction; **—ленный** *a.* dilute, diluted; **—ляющий** *a.* diluent.

разбаланс *m.*, **—ировка** *f.* unbalance; **—ированный** *a.* unbalanced.

разбалтывать *v.* agitate, shake, stir.

разбе/г *m.* starting (or take-off) run; racing (of engine); **—гание** *n.* (astr.) recession; dispersal, scattering; **—гаться, —жаться** *v.* start running, warm up; gather momentum; disperse.

разбив/ать *v.* break, fracture; decompose, divide, split; lay out, mark off, space; **—ка** *f.* partition, division, splitting, layout; dismantling; **в —ку** haphazardly, at random; **—ной** *a.* separable; **—очный** *a.* marking; spacing; **—чивый** *a.* brittle, frangible.

разбиение *n.* partition, separation, division, subdivision.

разбир/аемый *a.* under discussion, in question; being dismantled; **—ание, —ательство** *n.* examination, discussion.

разбирать *v.* disassemble, dismount, strip; discuss, analyze; sort, choose; decipher; **р. на примере** apply to a specific case (or to an example); **—ся** *v.* investigate; understand.

разбит/ие *n.* partition, division; breaking; **—ость** *f.* breakdown; **—ый** *a.* broken; **—ь** *see* **разбивать.**

разболт/анный *a.* stirred, shaken up, loose; **—ать** *see* **разбалтывать.**

разболчивать *v.* unbolt.

разбор *m.* choice, selection; analysis, examination, review, criticism; **без —а** without distinction.

разбор/ка *f.* disassembly, dismantling; separation, sorting; **—ный** *a.* collapsible, dismountable, separable, sectional; portable.

разборчив/о *adv.* clearly, plainly; **—ость** *f.* intelligibility; readability; **—ый** *a.* clear, legible; discriminating.

разбрасыв/ание *n.* scattering, dispersion; **—ать** *v.* scatter, disperse; **—ающий** *a.* scattering, dispersing.

разброс *m.* spread, scatter, scattering, straggling; dispersal, dispersion, (stat.) variance; **р. по углам** angle straggling; angular spread; **р. пробегов** range straggling.

разбросанн/ость *f.* dispersion, disconnectedness, incoherence; **—ый** *a.* dispersed, disconnected, incoherent; scattered, straggling.

разброс/ать *see* **разбрасывать; —ный параметр** straggling parameter.

разбрызг/анный *a.* sprayed, sputtered; **—ивание** *n.* spraying, sputtering; **—иватель** *m.* sprayer; atomizer, pulverizer; **—ивать** *v.* spray; atomize; sputter; **—ивающий** *a.* spraying; atomizing; sputtering.

разбух/ание *n.* inflation, distension; **—ать, —нуть** *v.* expand, inflate, distend.

развал *m.* disintegration, decay, collapse, breakup, breakdown; **—енный** *a.* collapsed, broken-down; **—ивать, —ить** *v.* undo, unmake; **—иваться, —иться** *v.* fall, collapse.

развальцов/анный *a.* laminated; expanded; **—ка** *f.* lamination; expansion; **—ывать** *v.* laminate; expand.

разве *adv.* perhaps; unless; really?.

развев/ание *n.* blowing, scattering; (geo.) deflation; **—ать** *v.* blow, scatter.

развед/анный *a.* explored, investigated, proved, tested; **—ать** *see* **разведывать.**

разведен/ие *n.* dilution, thinning; **—ный** *a.* diluted, dilute; thin.

развeдк/а *f.* prospecting, reconnaissance, exploration; **производить —у** reconnoiter, prospect.
разведочн/ый *a.* exploring, prospecting; **—ая выработка, —ая работа** prospecting; **—ая геофизика** exploration geophysics; **—ая скважина** test well; test hole.
разведчик *m.* prospector.
разведыв/ание *n.*, **—ательный** *a.* searching, exploring; prospecting; **—ать** *v.* investigate, explore; prospect.
развезти *see* **развозить.**
развернут/ый *a.* developed, unfolded, comprehensive; (math.) expanded; **—ая форма** expanded form; **—ь** *see* **развертывать.**
разверст/ать, —ывать *v.* apportion, allot; **—ка** *f.* apportionment, allotment.
разверт/ка *f.* development, unfolding; (elec.) scan, scanning, sweep; time base (or scale); (math.) involute; **р. по частоте** frequency sweep; **ось —ки** timing axis; **—очный генератор** sweep oscillator.
развертыв/ание *n.* unrolling, unfolding; (math.) development; evolution, (elec.) scanning, sweep; roaming; **—атель** *m.* scanner; **—ать** *v.* open, unroll, expand, unfold; (math.) develop; unwind; (elec.) scan; **—аться** *v.* expand, develop.
развертывающ/ий двигатель sweep motor; **—ая кривая** involute; **—аяся поверхность** developable surface; **—ее устройство** scanning device.
развес/ить *see* **развешивать**; **—очный** *a.* weighing.
развести *see* **разводить.**
разветвиться *see* **разветвляться.**
разветвлен/ие *n.* branching, ramification, bifurcation; branch, fork; **точка —ия** branch point; **—ность** *f.* branching; **—ный** *a.* branched, branching, forked, divided; **—ная цепная реакция** branching chain reaction; **—ная цепь** divided circuit.
разветвл/ять *v.* branch, branch out, ramify; **—яться** *v.* branch, branch out, fork; **—яющий, —яющийся** *a.* branching.
развешивать *v.* suspend, hang up.

развеять *see* **развевать.**
развив/аемый *a.* developed, generated; **—ание** *n.* development, generation; **—ать** *v.* develop, generate, evolve; unwind; **—аться** *v.* develop, grow.
развил/ина *f.* fork; bifurcation; **—истый** *a.* forked; **—ка** *f.* fork; **в —к** Y-shaped.
развин/тить, —чивать *v.* unscrew; **—ченный** *a.* unscrewed.
развит/ие *n.* development, growth; evolution; **—ой, —ый** *a.*, **—ая поверхность** developed (or extended) surface; **—ь** *see* **развивать.**
развод/ить *v.* dilute, thin; separate; **—ка** *f.* separation; **—ной** *a.* separating.
развозбуждение *n.* de-excitation.
развоз/ить *v.* convey, transport; **—ка** *f.* conveyance, transport.
разволокнение *n.* separation of fibers.
разворачив/ание *n.* unrolling; turning; **—ать** *v.* unroll; **—аться** *v.* turn around.
разворот *m.* turn; development.
развяз/ать, —ывать *v.* untie, loosen; **—ка** *f.* (elec.) decoupling; **—ывание** *n.* uncoupling, decoupling, unfastening; **—ывающий** *a.* uncoupling, decoupling.
разгад/ать, —ывать *v.* solve; guess.
разгар *m.* climax, height; (heat) erosion.
разгиб/ание *n.* unbending, straightening; **—ать** *v.* unbend, straighten; **—ающий** *a.* straightening.
разгла/дить, —живать *v.* smooth (out).
разгла/сить, —шать *v.* divulge, publish.
разгляд/еть, —ывать *v.* examine, consider; discern.
разгов/аривать *v.* talk, speak; **—ор** *m.* talk, conversation.
разгон *m.* acceleration; (reactor) excursion; dispersal; (naut.) fetch; **р. двигателя** acceleration, pickup (of engine); **р. реактора** reactor runaway (or power excursion); **—ка** *f.* distillation; **—ный** *a.* accelerating; dispersal; **—ять** *v.* accelerate; (reactor) run away; distill; disperse.
разгораживать *v.* separate, partition.
разгор/ание *n.* build-up, flare-up, rise; **кривая —ания** rise curve; **—аться, —еться** *v.* flare up.

азгородить *see* **разгораживать.**

азгранич/ение *n.* rebounding; delimitation, demarcation; discrimination; **черта —ения, —ивающая линия** boundary line; **—енный** *a.* delimited, bound; **—ивать, —ить** *v.* delimit, differentiate.

азграф/ить, —лять *v.* rule; **—ление** *n.* ruling.

азгром *m.* destruction; **—ить** *v.* destroy, ruin.

азгруж/атель *m.* discharger; **—ать** *v.* discharge, unload; **—ающий** *a.* discharging, unloading; relieving; **—енный** *a.* discharged, unloaded; relieved.

азгруз/ить *see* **разгружать; —ка** *f.* discharge, discharging, unloading; weight distribution; relief; **—ка давления** pressure relief; **—очный** *a.* discharging, discharge, unloading, dumping; **—очный клапан** dump valve.

азгруппиров/ание *n.*, **—ка** *f.* debunching.

азд. *abbr.* (**раздел**) division, partition; section.

аздав/ание *n.* distribution, dispensing; **—ать** *v.* distribute, dispense; **—аться** *v.* be distributed; expand; resound.

аздав/ить, —ливать *v.* crush; **—ливание** *n.* crushing; **—ливающее усилие** crushing stress.

аздат/очный *a.* distributing; **—ь** *see* **раздавать.**

аздача *f.* distribution, allotment; spread, expansion.

аздваивать, —ся *v.* bifurcate, split.

аздвиг *m.*, **—ание** *n.* separation; extension; **—ать** *v.* separate; extend; **—аться** *v.* separate, slide apart.

аздвиж/ение *n.*, **—ка** *f.* spacing, separation; **—ной** *a.* extensible, telescopic; collapsible; sliding; **—ной калибр** sliding calipers (or gauge).

аздвинут/ый *a.* separated; extended; **—ь** *see* **раздвигать.**

аздвоен/ие *n.* bifurcation, splitting; **—ный** *a.* forked, bifurcate, split; double.

аздев/ание *n.* undressing, stripping; **—ать** *v.* undress, strip.

раздел *m.* division, partition; divide; section; **линия —а** dividing (or boundary) line; **поверхность —а** interface; **—ать** *see* **разделывать.**

разделен/ие *n.* separation, division, disjunction, partition; distribution; classing, indexing; splitting; fractionation, fission; **диффузное р.** separation by diffusion; **р. изотопов** isotope separation; **р. переменных** separation of variables; **коэффициент —ия** separation factor, fractionation factor; **линия —ия** dividing (or boundary) line; **точка —ия** separation point; **—ный** *a.* divided, split, separated; classed, graded; **—ный источник** split source.

разделившийся *a.* split, fissioned, divided, separated.

разделим/ость *f.* divisibility, separability; **—ый** *a.* divisible, separable.

разделитель *m.* separator, separating agent; divider, divisor; **—ный** *a.* separating; fractionating; spacing; **—ный трансформатор** (elec.) isolation transformer; **—ный элемент** separative element; **—ная колонна** separating (or fractionating) column; **—ная способность** separative power.

разделить *see* **разделять.**

разделывать *v.* finish.

раздельн/ый *a.* separate, distinct; **р. подшипник** split bearing; **—ое картирование** close mapping.

раздел/ять *v.* divide, separate; share; **—яться** *v.* divide, split, fission; **—яющий** *a.* dividing, separating; **—яющийся** *a.* separable.

раздет/ый *a.* undressed, stripped; **—ь** *see* **раздевать.**

раздирание *n.* stripping, shredding.

раздрабливающий *see* **раздробляющий.**

раздраж/ать, —ить *v.* irritate, annoy; (bio.) stimulate; **—ение** *n.* irritation, annoyance; (bio.) stimulation; **—имость** *f.* irritability; (bio.) stimulability; **—итель** *m.* irritant; (bio.) stimulus.

раздроб/ить, —лять *v.* break up; shatter; crush; (math.) reduce; **—ление** *n.* breaking up; **—ленный** *a.* broken, shattered, crushed; **—ляю-**

щий *a.* crushing, grinding; **—ляющее усилие** crushing stress.

раздув *m.* bulge; **—альный** *a.* inflating; **—альный мех** bellows; **—ание** *n.* blowing; inflation; **—ать** *v.* inflate; fan, blow.

раздут/ость *f.* inflation; dilation; **—ый** *a.* inflated; bulging; **—ь** *see* **раздувать.**

разжать *see* **разжимать.**

разжиж/аемость *f.* liquescence; **—аемый** *a.* liquescent; **—ать** *v.* dilute; liquefy, fluidize; rarefy; **—ающий** *a.* diluting; rarefying; liquefying; **—ающее вещество, —итель** *m.* diluent; **—ение** *n.* dilution; thinning, rarefaction; liquefying; **—енность** *f.* fluidity; **—енный** *a.* diluted, dilute; thin, rarefied; liquefied.

разжим/ание *n.* opening, releasing; **—ать** *v.* open, release, unfasten, unclamp.

разительный *a.* marked, striking, impressive.

разлаг/аемый *a.* decomposable; analyzable; **—ать** *v.* separate, decompose, dissociate; scan; (math.) factor, expand; **—ать в ряд** expand in a series; **—ать на множители** factor; **—аться** *v.* decompose, disintegrate, separate; dissolve.

разла/д *m.* disorder; discord; **—диться, —живаться** *v.* go wrong, fail; **—женность** *f.* maladjustment; **—живать** *v.* derange.

разламывать *v.* break (down).

разлет *m.* separation, dispersion, scattering, divergence; **р. осколков** separation of fragments; **—аться, —еться** *v.* fly apart, scatter; disperse, disintegrate.

разлив *m.* overflow, inundation, flood; **—ание** *n.* pouring out; filling; diffusion; **—ать** *v.* pour (out); diffuse; **—аться** *v.* overflow; **—ающийся** *a.* overflowing; flowing; **—ка** *f.* casting; pouring; bottling, filling; **—очный** *a.* pouring.

разлин/евание *n.*, **—овка** *f.* ruling; **—евать, —овать, —овывать** *v.* rule (lines).

разлит/ие *n.* pouring; overflow; **—ый** *a.* poured; cast; **—ь** *see* **разливать.**

различ/ать, —ить *v.* discern, distinguish, discriminate; **—аться** *v.* differ, be distinguished; **—ение** *n.* distinction, discrimination; **—енный** *a.* distinct, distinguished, different; **—ие** *n.* distinction, difference; diversity; discrepancy; **—имость** *f.* discernibility, distinguishability; **—имый** *a.* distinguishable; **—ительно** *adv.* in contradistinction to; **—ительный** *a.* distinctive.

различн/о *adv.* differently; **—ость** *f.* difference; **—ый** *a.* different, distinct, diverse; various; **—ый по существу** essentially different.

разложение *n.* resolution; disintegration; reduction; sweep, scanning; (math.) expansion, decomposition, development; dissociation; dispersion (of light); **р. бинома** binomial expansion; **р. в ряд** series expansion; **р. в ряд Тэйлора** Taylor expansion; **р. в ряд Фурье** harmonic (or Fourier) expansion; **р. единицы** resolution of unity; **р. на множители** factoring; **р. сил** resolution of forces.

разлож/енный *a.* decomposed; expanded; **—ившийся** *a.* putrefied; **—имый** *a.* decomposable, dissociable; separable; **—имый на множители** factorable; **—ить** *see* **разлагать, раскладывать.**

разлом *m.* break, fracture; rupture; abruption; **—ать, —ить** *see* **разламывать.**

разлуч/ать, —ить *v.* separate; **—ение** *n.* separation.

размагни/тить, —чивать *v.* demagnetize; **—чение, —чивание** *n.* demagnetization; degaussing; **—чивания коэффициент** demagnetizing factor; **—чивания кривая** demagnetization curve.

размагничивающ/ий *a.* demagnetizing, degaussing; **р. фактор** demagnetization (or demagnetizing) factor; **—ее поле** degaussing field.

размаз/анный *a.* smeared (out), blurred; **—ать, —ывать** *v.* smear (out), spread, blur; **—ка** *f.* smearing (out); **—ывание** *n.* smearing, spreading, blurring; diffusion.

размалыв/ание *n.* grinding, milling; **—ать** *v.* grind, crush, mill.

разматыв/ание *n.* unwinding, unreeling; **—ать, —аться** *v.* unwind, unreel, uncoil, unroll.

размах *m.* swing, throw, sweep, spread, span; range; (double or peak-to-peak) amplitude; **р. крыла** wing span; **р. крыла относительный** (aero.) aspect ratio; **критерий —а** (stat.) range test; **по —у** spanwise; **—ивание** *n.* swinging; **—ивать, —нуть** *v.* swing.

размачив/ание *n.* soaking, wetting; **—ать** *v.* soak, wet.

размежев/ание *n.* demarcation, delimitation; **—ать, —ывать** *v.* mark limits, bound.

размельч/ать, —ить *v.* crush, grind, pulverize; **—ение** *n.* crushing, grinding, powdering, pulverization; breakdown; **—енный** *a.* crushed, pulverized.

размен *m.*, **—ный** *a.* exchange, change.

размер *m.* size, dimension, diameter, gauge, caliber; rate; extent, amount; **р. зерен** grain size.

размер/ение, —ивание *n.* measuring, measurement; **—ивать, —ить, —ять** *v.* measure (off); **—ность** *f.* dimension, dimensionality; **уравнение —ности** dimensional equation; **—ный анализ** dimensional analysis; **—ный эффект** size effect.

разместить *see* **размещать.**

размет/ить *see* **размечать**; **—ка** *f.* marking (out); **—очный** *a.* marking, layout; **—чик** *m.* marker.

размеч/ать *v.* mark (off), lay out; graduate (scale, vessel); **—енный** *a.* marked, graduated.

размеш/анный *a.* stirred, mixed; **—ать, —ивать** *v.* stir, mix; **—ивание** *n.* stirring, mixing, agitation; **—ивающий** *a.* stirring, mixing, agitating.

размещ/ать *v.* dispose, distribute, place; **—ение** *n.* arrangement, disposition, order, position, spacing; partition; **—ение из *n* элементов по *m*** number of permutations of *n* things taken *m* at a time; **—енный** *a.* distributed, allocated; arranged, positioned.

размножать, —ся *v.* multiply, breed.

размножающ/ий ядерный реактор breeder reactor; **—ая сборка** (reactor) blanket assembly; **—ая узловая сборка** (reactor) blanket subassembly.

размнож/ение *n.* multiplication, breeding; **р. на быстрых нейтронах** fast multiplication effect; **р. на мгновенных нейтронах** prompt multiplication; **р. нейтронов** neutron multiplication; **коэффициент —ения** multiplication constant (or factor); **—итель** *m.* breeder; **—ить, —иться** *see* **размножать.**

размол *m.* grinding, pulverization; **—отый** *a.* crushed, ground, pulverized; **—оть** *see* **размалывать.**

размот/ать *see* **разматывать**; **—ка** *see* **разматывание.**

размыв *see* **размывание.**

размыв/ание *n.* washing out, erosion; **р. антициклона** (meteor.) anticyclosis; **р. облаков** dissolution of clouds; **р. фронта** (meteor.) frontolysis; **р. циклона** (meteor.) cyclolysis; **—ать** *v.* wash out, blur; erode.

размык/ание *n.* (elec.) breaking, opening, disconnection; **—ать** *v.* open, unlock; break, disconnect; release, trip; **—ающий** *a.* releasing; breaking, disconnecting; **—ающий механизм** tripping mechanism.

размыслить *see* **размышлять.**

размыт/ие *n.* spread, spreading, blurring, diffusion; washing out; **р. линий** line broadening (or diffusion); **—ость** *f.* smearing, spread; breadth; imprecision; **—ый** *a.* smeared, diffuse, diffused; washed out, fuzzy; eroded; **—ый максимум** broad peak; **—ый фронт** diffuse front.

размышл/ение *n.* reflection, speculation; **—ять** *v.* reflect, consider, speculate.

размягч/ать, —ить *v.* soften; **—ающий** *a.*, **—ение** *n.* softening; **температура —ения, точка —ения** softening point (or temperature); **—итель** *m.* softener.

разнашивание *n.* wearing (away).

разнесен/ие *n.* spacing; **—ный** *a.* spaced; **—ная дипольная решетка** spaced-dipole array.

разнести *see* **разносить.**

разнимать *v.* part, separate; dismantle, dismount.

разн/иться *v.* differ; **—ица** *f.* difference, disparity; **—о** *adv.* differently, diversely, variously.

разно— *prefix* different, hetero—.

разновероятный *a.* unequally probable.

разновес *m.* small weights.

разновидн/ость *f.* variety, species, variant; **атомная р.** atomic species; **—ый** *a.* various, diverse.

разновременн/ость *f.* time difference, noncoincidence; (elec.) diversity; **коэффициент —ости** (elec.) diversity factor; **—ый** *a.* at different times; nonsimultaneous; noncontemporary.

разноглас/ие *n.* disagreement, discrepancy; **—ный** *a.* conflicting, disagreeing.

разное *n.* variety, miscellany.

разнозначащий *a.* of different meaning.

разноименн/ый *a.* unlike, opposite; of opposite sign (or charge); **—ые ионы** oppositely charged ions; **—ые полюсы** unlike poles.

разно/калиберный *a.* different-caliber, different-sized; **—мыслие** *n.* difference of opinion, disagreement.

разнообраз/ие *n.* variety, diversity, range, multiplicity, manifold; **—ить** *v.* vary, diversify; **—ный** *a.* various, diverse, diversified, manifold.

разнополярный *a.* heteropolar.

разноречив/ость *f.* contradiction, inconsistency, discrepancy; **—ый** *a.* contradictory, inconsistent, erratic.

разнородн/ость *f.* heterogeneity, diversity; **—ый** *a.* heterogeneous, mixed, diversified, unlike, manifold.

разнос *m.*, dispersion; separation, spacing; (mach.) racing; **—ить** *v.* carry, convey, deliver; disperse, scatter; **—иться** *v.* spread; resound.

разностенность *f.* variable wall thickness.

разностн/ый *a.* difference; different; (elec.) differential; **р. метод** difference method; **р. оператор** difference operator; **р. тон** difference tone; **—ая частота** difference frequency; **—ое исчисление** calculus of finite difference; **—ое отношение** (math.) difference quotient; **—ое сочетание** subtractive combination; **—ое уравнение** difference equation.

разносторонн/ий *a.* many-sided, manifold; resourceful; scalene; **—ость** *f.* resourcefulness; multiplicity.

разность *f.* variety, diversity; difference; (math.) remainder; **р. потенциалов** potential difference; **р. фаз** phase difference; **р. хода** path difference.

разнотипн/ость *f.* diversity; **—ый** *a.* of different types (or kinds).

разно/цветный *a.* multicolored, polychromatic; **—центренность** *f.* eccentricity; **—чтение** *n.* variant reading.

разный *a.* different, unlike, diverse, various.

разнять *see* **разнимать.**

разоблачение *n.* disclosure, exposure.

разобр/анный *a.* dismounted, dismantled; analyzed; sorted; **—ать** *see* **разбирать.**

разобщ/ать *v.* separate, uncouple, disengage, release; **—ающий** *a.* dissociative, disconnecting, disengaging, releasing; **—ение** *n.* separation, disconnecting, uncoupling, release; interruption; disjunction; **—енность** *f* disconnection; **—енный** *a.* disconnected, disengaged, released; separate, discrete.

разобщитель *m.* disconnector; **—ный** *a* disconnecting, releasing.

разобщить *see* **разобщать.**

разовый *a.* single.

разогн/ание *n.* dispersion, scattering **—анный** *a.* dispersed, scattered **—ать** *see* **разгонять.**

разогнуть *see* **разгибать.**

разогрев *m.* warming up, warmup, heating up, runup; **—ание** *n.* warming up; **—ать** *v.* warm up.

разогрет/ый *a.* warmed up, heated; **—ь** *see* **разогревать.**

разойтись *see* **расходиться.**

разомкнут/ый *a.* open, clear; (elec.) disconnected, broken, interrupted; **—ая цепь** open circuit; **—ь** *see* **размыкать**

разорванн/о-дождевые облака fractonimbus; **р.-кучевые облака** fractocumulus; **р.-слоистые облака** fractostratus; **—ый** *a.* broken; (geo.

faulted; —**ая облачность** broken clouds (or cloud cover); —**ые облака** ragged clouds, fractus.

разорвать *see* **разрывать.**

разорен/ие *n.* ruin, destruction; —**ный** *a.* ruined, destroyed.

разориентировка *f.* disorientation, misorientation.

разорит *m.* rasorite.

разорит/ельный *a.* destructive; —**ь** *see* **разорять.**

разоруж/ать *v.* disarm; dismantle; —**ение** *n.* disarmament; dismantling.

разорять *v.* ruin, destroy.

разослать *see* **рассылать.**

разостлать *see* **расстилать.**

разотравление *n.* poison removal.

разочаров/ание *n.*, —**анность** *f.* disappointment; —**анный** *a.* disappointed, disillusioned; —**ать,** —**ывать** *v.* disappoint.

разраб/атывание *n.*, —**отка** *f.* development; exploitation; working out; —**атывать,** —**отать** *v.* develop; work out, devise, elaborate; exploit, treat, process; —**отанный** *a.* developed, worked-out, exploited; treated, processed.

разравнивать *v.* level.

разра/жать, —**зить** *v.* break, shatter, destroy; —**жаться,** —**зиться** *v.* burst, explode.

разраст/ание *n.* expansion, growth; —**аться,** —**ись** *v.* expand, grow.

разрегулированность *f.* misadjustment, misalignment.

разре/дить, —**жать** *v.* rarefy; evacuate.

разрежен/ие *n.* vacuum, evacuation; (meteor.) underpressure; (seis.) dilatation; —**ность** *f.* rarefaction; thinness, rarity; **фактор** —**ности** (astr.) dilution factor; —**ный** *a.* evacuated; rarefied, rare, tenuous; —**ный лед** open pack (ice); —**ное пространство** evacuated space, vacuum.

разреживать *see* **разредить.**

разрез *m.* cut, slit, incision; profile, log, section, cross section, plan; layer; (math.) branch cut; **в р.** contrary; **горизонтальный р.** plan; **продольный р.** longitudinal section; **вид в** —**е** sectional view, cut-away view; —**анный** *a.* cut, slit; —**ать** *see* **разрезывать.**

разрезн/ой *a.* cut, split; slitted, slotted; sectional, detached, gapped; **р. анод** split anode; **р. магнетрон** slot (or split-anode) magnetron; —**ое ребро** slotted rib.

разрезыв/ание *n.* cutting, slitting; —**ать** *v.* cut, slit, slice.

разрешаемый отрезок (opt.) least resolved distance.

разрешать *v.* allow; solve; resolve; disentangle (knot).

разрешающ/ий *a.* (math.) solving, resolving; **р. процесс** (stat.) decision process; —**ая способность** resolving power, resolution; discrimination; —**ая способность по энергии** energy resolution; —**ее время** resolving time; —**ее уравнение** (math.) resolvent; —**ее ядро** (math.) solving kernel, resolvent.

разрешение *n.* permission, permit, allowing, authorization, license; solution; resolution.

разрешенн/ый *a.* allowed, permitted, authorized; solved; resolved; **р. переход** allowed transition; **р. по форме** shape-allowed (beta rays); **р. по четности** parity-favored; —**ая зона** allowed band.

разрешим/ость *f.* solvability; —**ый** *a.* solvable; decidable.

разрешит/ельный *a.* resolving; permitting; —**ь** *see* **разрешать.**

разровнять *see* **разравнивать.**

разрозн/енно *adv.* singly, separately; —**енный** *a.* disconnected, separate; —**ивать,** —**ить** *v.* disconnect, separate.

разруб/ание *n.* chopping, cleaving, slashing, cutting; —**ать,** —**ить** *v.* chop, cleave, slash, cut.

разруш/ать *v.* demolish, destroy; crush, break down; corrode, attack; —**аться** *v.* collapse; fail, disintegrate; —**ающий** *a.* destructive, devastating, disruptive; —**ающая нагрузка** breaking load; —**ающее напряжение** breaking point.

разрушен/ие *n.* destruction, dissolution; fracture, breaking, rupture, failure; disintegration, decay; imperfection, damage, disruption, distortion; **пластическое р.** plastic yielding; **хрупкое р.** brittle fracture (or failure); **предел —ия** breaking point; **—ность** *f.* disintegration; **—ный** *a.* destroyed, ruined, disintegrated; damaged.

разруш/ившийся *a.* crumbled, loosened; **—ительный** *a.* destructive; **—ить** *see* **разрушать.**

разрыв *m.* rupture, fracture, dislocation; gap, discontinuity; break, breaking; crack, interruption; burst, explosion; (geo.) fault; **испытание на р.** tensile (strength) test; **р. кольца** (chem.) ring (or cyclic) cleavage; **р. непрерывности** discontinuity; **прочность на р., сопротивление —у** tensile strength; **р. пузырька** bubble collapse; **р. связей** bond breaking; **сильный р.** (math.) nonremovable discontinuity, second-order discontinuity; **слабый р.** (math.) removable discontinuity, first-order discontinuity; **р. следа** track gap; **р. тропаузы** tropause discontinuity (or fracture); **р. энергии** energy discontinuity; **р. ядра на осколки** fragmentation of nucleus; **зажигание —ом** make-and-break ignition; **линия —а** line of discontinuity; **число —ов** gap count (in particle track).

разрыв/ание *n.* disruption, rupture, breaking, tearing; **—атель** *m.* breaker; **—ать** *v.* decouple, break, disrupt; tear; **—аться** *v.* break; explode, burst; **—ающий** *a.* tearing, rupturing; disrupting; splitting, cleaving; **—ающая нагрузка** breaking load; **—ающее усилие** tensile force, tensile strength.

разрывн/ой *a.* breaking, bursting, explosive; disruptive; **—ая машина** tensile testing machine; **—ая мощность** (elec.) breaking capacity; **—ая прочность** tensile (or breaking) strength; **—ая сила** explosive force; **—ое усилие** breaking load, rupture stress; **—ость** *f.* discontinuity.

разрывн/ый *a.* discontinuous, disconnected; **—ая задача** discontinuity problem.

разрывомер *m.* gap meter.

разрыхл/ение *n.* loosening, disintegration; **—ить, —ять** *v.* break up, loosen; **—иться, —яться** *v.* separate, disintegrate; **—яющая орбита** antibonding orbital.

разряд *m.* discharge; class, order, category, rank; digit; digital order (place, column); **темный р., тихий р.** silent discharge; **первого —а** first class; **характеристика —а** flashover characteristic.

разрядит/ель *m.* discharger; **—ь** *see* **разряжать.**

разряд/ка *f.* discharging, discharge, unloading; de-excitation; **—ник** *m.* discharger; spark gap, arc gap; lightning arrester.

разрядн/ый *a.* discharging, discharge; **р. промежуток** discharge gap; **р. счетчик** Geiger counter; **—ая трубка** discharge tube; **—ое напряжение** disruptive voltage; **—ое расстояние** arcing distance.

разряж/ать *v.* unload, discharge; **—ающийся** *a.* discharging; **—ение** *n* discharging, discharge, unloading.

разуб/едить, —еждать *v.* dissuade.

разубожив/ание *n.* (min.) impoverishment, depletion, exhaustion; **—ать** *v.* (min.) impoverish, deplete, exhaust.

разузна/вание *n.* inquiry, investigation; **—вать, —ть** *v.* inquire, investigate.

разукрупн/ение *n.* subdivision; **—ить, —ять** *v.* subdivide.

разум *m.* reason, intelligence; **—ение** *n* understanding; **—еть** *v.* understand, comprehend; **(само собой) —ется** it is obvious, of course, naturally.

разумн/ость *f.* reasonableness, soundness; **—ый** *a.* reasonable, intelligent, judicious.

разупорядоч/ение *n.* disorder; **—енный** *a.* disordered; **—ивать** *v.* disorder, randomize.

разупрочнение *n.* weakening, softening, resoftening.

разуч/ивать, —ить *v.* learn, study; practice; **—иваться, —иться** *v.* forget, unlearn.

разъед/аемость *f.* corrosibility; **—а**

мый *a.* corrosible; —**ание,** —**ение** *n.* corrosion; (geo.) erosion; —**ать** *v.* corrode; erode; —**ающий** *a.* corrosive; —**енный** *a.* corroded; eroded.

разъединен/ие *n.* disjunction, dissociation, separation; disconnection, release, interruption; —**ный** *a.* disconnected, disengaged; separate, discrete.

разъедин/итель *m.* disconnecting switch; —**ить,** —**ять** *v.* separate, detach, disengage; disconnect; —**яющий** *a.* dissociative, separating; disconnecting, cutoff; releasing, disengaging.

разъем *m.* joint; —**ный** *a.* divided, split, detached; separable, demountable, dismountable; disengaging, release; —**ный подшипник** split bearing; —**ная установка** demountable installation.

разъесть *see* **разъедать.**

разъясн/ение *n.* explanation, interpretation; —**ительный** *a.* explanatory; —**ить,** —**ять** *v.* explain, elucidate.

разыгрывать *v.* play, perform; draw (in lottery); —**ся** *v.* develop.

разыск/ание, —**ивание** *n.* research, investigation; finding; —**ать** *v.* find, discover; —**аться** *v.* be found, be discovered; —**ивать** *v.* search, look for; investigate.

Райля радиотелескоп Ryle radio telescope.

раймондит *m.* raimondite.

район *m.,* —**ный** *a.* district, raion, section (of city).

Райская Птица Apus (Aps) (constellation).

рак *m.* cancer, carcinoma.

Рак Cancer (Cnc) (constellation).

Рака коэффициент Racah coefficient.

ракет/а *f.* rocket; **высокая р.** high-altitude rocket; **р.-носитель** rocket-carrier; **р.-спутник** rocket satellite, satellite vehicle; —**ница** *f.* rocket launcher.

ракетн/ый *a.* rocket; **р. двигатель** rocket engine; —**ая камера** rocket compartment; —**ая навигация** rocket navigation; —**ая техника** rocket engineering, rocketry; —**ое дело** rocketry; —**ое оборудование** rocket equipment (or instrumentation).

ракето/план *m.* rocket aircraft; —**строение** *n.* rocket design (or engineering).

раковидный *see* **раковый.**

ракови/на *f.* (met.) gas cavity, pit; shell; sink, basin; —**нный** *a.* shell; sink, basin; —**нообразный** *a.* shell-like, conchoidal; —**стый** *a.* shell, shell-like, conchoidal; (met.) blistered; —**стый излом** conchoidal fracture.

раковый *a.* cancerous.

ракурс *m.* foreshortening; aspect; —**ная чувствительность** aspect sensitivity.

рама *f.* frame.

Рамана спектр, раман-спектр Raman spectrum (or spectra).

Рам-Джангл Rum Jungle.

рамдорит *m.* ramdohrite.

рамзаит *m.* ramsayite.

Рамзауэра эффект Ramsauer effect; **Р.-Таунсенда эффект** R.-Townsend effect.

Рамзая-Юнга закон (правило) Ramsay-Young rule.

рамк/а *f.* (picture) frame; loop (antenna); pickup loop; —**и** *pl.* limits, bounds, scope.

рамочн/ый *a.* picture frame; **р. прибор с постоянным магнитом** permanent-magnet moving-coil instrument; —**ая антенна** frame (loop, closed) antenna.

Рамсден Ramsden (lunar crater).

РАН *abbr.* **(Российская Академия Наук)** Russian Academy of Sciences.

ранг *m.* rank.

рандит *m.* randite.

ранее *see* **раньше.**

ранжированный *a.* arrayed, ordered; ranked.

Ранкина/-Гюгонио соотношения Rankine-Hugoniot relations; **Р. цикл** R. cycle.

ран/ний *a.* early; previous; —**о** *adv.* early; soon; —**ьше** *comp. of* **рано,** earlier, sooner; previously, formerly.

рансьеит *m.* ranciéite.

рапорт *m.* report, account; —**овать** *v.* report.

рас— *see* **раз—.**

расевинит *m.* racewinite.

раскаленн/ость *f.* incandescence, glow, heat; **—ый** *a.* incandescent, glowing; **—ый добела** incandescent, white-hot; **—ый докрасна** red-hot; **—ая нить** filament.

раскал/ивать, —ить *v.* heat, incandesce; **—иваться, —иться** *v.* heat up, begin to glow.

раскалываем/ость *f.* cleavability; cleavage; **—ый** *a.* cleavable.

раскалыв/ание *n.* splitting, cracking, fracturing; (nucl.) spallation; **—ать, —аться** *v.* split, crack, cleave.

раскалывающийся *a.* cleavable; cleaving, splitting; **р. пластами** fissile.

раскалять *see* **раскаливать.**

раскат/ать, —ывать *v.* roll out, flatten; unroll; **—ка** *f.*, **—ывание** *n.* rolling, flattening; unrolling.

раскат грома peal of thunder.

раскач/ать, —ивать, —иваться *v.* swing; **—ивание** *n.* swinging, swaying.

раскачк/а *f.* (elec.) driving; (buildup of) oscillation; **р. контура** building up (characteristic) of circuit; **время —и** buildup time.

раскид/ать, —ывать *see* **разбрасывать**; **—ной** *a.* unfolding, folding, collapsible; **—ывание** *n.* spreading, scattering; unfolding.

раскинут/ый *a.* extended, spread; **—ь** *v.* extend, spread.

раскисл/ение *n.* deoxidation, reduction; **—енный** *a.* deoxidized, reduced; **—итель** *m.*, **—ительное вещество, —яющее средство** deoxidizing agent, deoxidizer, reducing agent, reducer; **—ительный, —яющий** *a.* deoxidizing, reducing; **—ить, —ять** *v.* deoxidize, reduce.

расклад/ка *f.* distribution, allotment; **—очный** *a.* distributing; **—ывать** *v.* spread, distribute; (math.) decompose.

расклассифицировать *v.* classify.

расклеп/ать, —ывать *v.* unrivet, unclench.

расклинивающее давление, р. действие disjoining pressure; wedge effect.

раскол *m.* split, fracture, crack; **—отый** *a.* split, cleaved.

раскомпенс/ация *f.* decompensation; **—ированный** *a.* decompensated, unbalanced.

раскос *m.* angle brace, diagonal, strut; **—ная система** latticework; **—ость** *f.* slant.

раскрас/ить *see* **раскрашивать**; **—ка** *f.* coloration, tinting.

раскраш/енный *a.* painted, colored; **—ивание** *n.* painting, coloring; **—ивать** *v.* paint, color.

раскрош/енный *a.* crumbled; **—ить, —иться** *v.* crumble, disintegrate.

раскру/тить, —чивать *v.* unwind; **—титься, —чиваться** *v.* untwist, uncoil.

раскрыв *m.* aperture; **р. антенны** antenna aperture (or flare); **угол —а** angular aperture; **—ать** *v.* uncover, open, reveal; (math.) expand; **—ать скобки** remove brackets; **—ающийся** *a.* opening.

раскрыт/ие *n.* opening; (math.) expansion; **—ый** *a.* open; disclosed; explicit; **—ь** *see* **раскрывать.**

распад *m.*, **—ение** *n.* decay, disintegration, decomposition, dissociation; destruction; **р. ядра** nuclear disintegration; **коэффициент —а** disintegration constant; **продукты —а** decomposition products; **теплота —а** heat of dissociation; **—аться** *v.* decay, disintegrate, decompose, break up; collapse; **—ающийся** *a.* disintegrating, decomposing.

распаив/ание *n.* unsoldering; **—ать** *v.* unsolder.

распасться *see* **распадаться.**

распаять *see* **распаивать.**

распис/ание *n.* schedule; **—ать, —ывать** *v.* describe, depict; **—аться** *v.* sign.

расплав *m.* melt; fusion; **—ить** *see* **расплавливать**; **—ка** *f.*, **—ление** *n.* melting, fusion; smelting.

расплавленн/ый *a.* molten, melted, fused; smelted; **р. металл** molten metal, smelt; **—ая масса** melt.

расплавл/ивание *see* **расплавка**; **—ивать, —ять** *v.* melt, fuse, liquefy; smelt.

распланиров/ать, —ывать *v.* lay out, mark out; **—ка** *f.* layout.

распласт/ать, —ывать *v.* spread; split.
расплата *f.* payment.
расплеск/ать, —ивать *v.* spill.
распле/сти, —тать *v.* untwist, **—тание** *n.* untwisting.
расплыв/ание *n.* spreading; leakage; **—аться** *v.* spread, blur; leak; **—чатость** *f.* diffuseness, indistinctness; **—чатый** *a.* diffuse, indistinct, blurred, vague.
расплюснуть *see* **расплющивать.**
расплющ/енный *a.* flattened; **—ивание** *n.* flattening; **—ивать, —ить** *v.* flatten.
распозн/аваемый сигнал distinguishable signal; **—авание, —ание** *n.* discernment, discrimination, recognition, identification; **—авать, —ать** *v.* recognize, discern, distinguish; **—анный** *a.* identified, recognized; **—ающий** *a.* discriminative.
располаг/аемый *a.* available; **—ать** *v.* arrange, order, dispose; have available; intend.
расползание *n.* spreading apart.
расположен/ие *n.* arrangement, disposition; situation, location; distribution, spacing, siting; order, ordering, sequence; alignment; inclination, tendency; **р. уступами** staggering; **—ный** *a.* positioned, arranged, ordered, disposed, spaced; situated, located; disposed, inclined (to).
расположить *see* **располагать.**
распор/ка *f.* spacer, stay rod, strut, brace, tie rod; **—ный** *a.* thrust, brace, distance; **—ный болт** distance (or stay) bolt.
распоряд/иться *see* **распоряжаться**; **—ок** *m.* order, arrangement; routine.
распоряж/аться *v.* order; dispose of; **—ение** *n.* disposition, disposal; arrangement, order; **в —ении** at the disposal of, available.
расправ/ить, —лять *v.* straighten.
распределен/ие *n.* distribution; **р. плотности** density distribution; **р. по скоростям** velocity distribution; **р. по углам** angular distribution; **р. по энергии** energy distribution; **р. совокупности** array; **р. температуры с высотой** temperature-height graph; **р. тепловыделения** heat-source distribution; **коэффициент —ия** distribution coefficient (or ratio); **функция —ия** distribution function (or law), partition function.
распределенн/ый *a.* distributed, interspaced; **—ая постоянная** distributed constant.
распределитель *m.* distributor; **—ность** *f.* distributivity.
распределительн/ый *a.* distributing, distributive; **р. закон** distributive law; **р. пункт** distributing center; **р. щит, —ая доска** switchboard; **—ая коробка** distributing box, panel box; **—ая сеть** distributing network; **—ая хроматография** partition chromatography.
распредел/ить, —ять *v.* distribute, assign; disperse; **—яющий** *a.* distributing.
распрост/ереть, —ереться, —ирать, —ираться *v.* stretch, extend, spread.
распространен/ие *n.* propagation; extension; extent; spreading, dispersal; diffusion, circulation; **р. волн** wave propagation; **коэффициент —ия** propagation constant; **функция —ия** propagation function, propagator; **—ность** *f.* abundance; prevalence, dissemination; **—ность изотопов** isotopic abundance; **—ный** *a.* extended; propagated; abundant; widespread, common, general, standard; **широко —ный** widespread, popularized.
распростран/ить, —иться, —ять, —яться *v.* extend; spread, propagate, diffuse; popularize.
распрыск/ать, —ивать *v.* spray.
распрям/ить, —иться, —лять, —ляться *v.* straighten; **—ление** *n.* straightening.
распус/кание *n.* melting; opening; **—кать, —тить** *v.* melt, dissolve; disperse, diffuse.
распут/ать, —ывать *v.* untangle.
распух/ание *n.* swelling; **—ать** *v.* swell.
распылен/ие *n.* sputtering, atomization, spraying; pulverization; erosion; **р. геттера** getter flash; **р. катода** cathode sputtering; **коэффициент —ия** sputtering ratio; **—ный** *a.* sputtered, atomized,

sprayed; pulverized, powdered; deflocculated; **тонко —ный** finely divided.

распыл/ивание *see* **распыление**; **—итель** *m.* atomizer, sprayer; pulverizer; **—ить, —ять** *v.* sputter, spray, atomize; pulverize; **—иться, —яться** *v.* disperse, scatter; be pulverized; **—яющий** *a.* spray, spraying; pulverizing.

рассасыв/ание *n.* resorption, dissipation; **—ать** *v.* resorb, dissipate.

рассверливание *n.* boring, drilling.

рассвет *m.*, **—ать** *v.* dawn.

рассеив/ание *n.* dispersal, dispersion, scattering, dissipation, diffusion; **р. тумана** fog dissipation; **—атель** *m.* scatterer, diffuser; **—ать, —аться** *v.* scatter, dissipate, disperse, diffuse; emit; diverge.

рассеивающ/ий *a.* dispersion, diffusion, diffusing; **р. фотометр** dispersion photometer; **—ая линза** diverging lens; **—ая способность** scattering power; dispersive power; **—ая среда** dispersive medium; **—ее вещество** scatterer.

рассек/ание *n.* cleaving, cutting; **—ать** *v.* cleave, cut.

рассекреченный *a.* declassified, no longer secret.

Рассела эффект Russell effect.

расселина *f.* split, rift, crack.

рассеченный *a.* split; **р. поток** split flow.

рассеч/ка *f.* (min.) crosscut; **в —ку** (elec.) in series; **—ь** *see* **рассекать.**

рассеян/ие *n.* scattering, dissipation, dispersion, diffusion, leakage; **р. вперед** forward scattering; **р. мощности** power attenuation (or dissipation); **р. на аноде** plate (or anode) dissipation; **р. на малые углы** small-angle scattering; **р. на связанных атомах** bound scattering; **р. облаков** cloud dispersal; **р. тепла** heat dissipation; **р. энергии** energy (or power) dissipation; **коэффициент —ия** scattering factor; dispersion coefficient; **коэффициент магнитного —ия** (magnetic) leakage factor; **поле —ия** stray field; fringing field.

рассеянн/ый *a.* scattered, diffused, stray, dispersed, dissipated; sparse; **р. свет** diffuse (or scattered) light; **р. электрон** stray electron; **р. элемент** trace element; **—ая величина** erratic value; **—ая волна** scattered wave; **—ая граница** diffuse boundary; **—ая мощность** dissipated power; **—ая радиация** diffuse radiation; **—ое излучение** scattered (or stray) radiation; **—ое освещение** diffused illumination; **—ое отражение** diffuse (or scattered) reflection; **—ое поле** stray field, fringing field; **—ое пропускание** diffuse transmission; **—ое скопление** (astr.) open cluster.

рассеять *see* **рассеивать.**

рассказ/ать, —ывать *v.* tell, narrate.

расслаив/ание *see* **расслоение**; **—ать, —аться** *v.* stratify, laminate; demix.

расспанц/евание *n.*, **—овка** *f.* (geo.) schist formation, shearing; **—ованный** *a.* sheared.

расследов/ание *n.* investigation; **—ать** *v.* investigate.

рассло/ение *n.* stratification, differentiation; foliation; lamination; subdividing; demixing; **—енный** *a.* stratified, laminated; **—ить** *see* **расслаивать**; **—йка** *f.* *see* **расслоение**; **—яемый** *a.* stratifiable.

рассматрив/аемый *a.* under consideration, considered; **—ание** *n.* examination; consideration; **—ать** *v.* examine, observe, study, investigate, analyze; discuss, consider, treat.

рассмотр/ение *n.* examination, inspection, investigation; discussion, consideration, treatment; **представлять на р.** submit for consideration; **—енный** *a.* considered, discussed; examined, investigated; **—еть** *see* **рассматривать**; **—им** let us consider, we shall consider.

рассогласование *n.* mismatch, error.

рассортиров/ать, —ывать *v.* sort out, classify.

расспр/ашивание *n.* questioning, inquiry; **—ашивать, —осить** *v.* question, inquire; **—ос** *m.* question, inquiry.

рассредоточение *n.* dispersal, spread.

рассроч/ивать, —ить *v.* defer.

расстав/ание *n.* separation; **—аться** *v.* separate.

расстав/ить, —лять *v.* place, set, dispose, arrange.

расстан/авливать, —овить *v.* place, arrange; **—овка** *f.* arrangement, order, spacing.

расстаться *see* **расставаться.**

расстеклов/ание, —ывание *n.* devitrification; **—анный** *a.* devitrified; **—ывать** *v.* devitrify.

расстил/ание *n.*, **—ка** *f.* spreading; unfolding; **—ать, —аться** *v.* spread; unfold, extend.

расстоян/ие *n.* distance, space, spacing, interval, separation, range; **р. до объекта** object distance; **р. максимального сближения** distance of closest approach, collision diameter; **р. между уровнями** level spacing; **на равном —ии** equally spaced, equidistant; **управление на —ии** remote control.

расстраив/ание *see* **расстройка**; **—ать** *v.* unbalance, disorganize, disturb, disrupt, disarrange; detune.

расстро/енный *a.* disorganized; detuned; **—енные контуры** (elec.) staggering, staggered tuning; **—ить** *see* **расстраивать**; **—йка** *f.* detuning, frequency difference; maladjustment.

расстройство *n.* disorder, disorganization, disarrangement, derangement, disturbance; **р. хода** breakdown.

рассудительн/ость *f.* common sense, reasonableness; **—ый** *a.* reasonable.

рассуд/ить *see* **рассуждать**; **—ок** *m.* reason; sense; **—очно** *adv.* rationally; **—очность** *f.* rationality; **—очный** *a.* rational.

рассужд/ать *v.* reason, discuss, judge, consider; **—ение** *n.* reasoning, consideration, argument.

рассчит/анный *a.* calculated, computed; designed, intended (for); **—ать, —ывать** *v.* calculate, compute; design, intend (for); count (on).

рассыл/ание *n.*, **—ка** *f.* distribution; **—ать** *v.* distribute.

рассып/ание *n.*, **—ка** *f.* scattering; **р. кристаллов** intumescence of (heated) crystals; **—анный** *a.* scattered; **—ать** *v.* scatter, disperse, diffuse; intersperse; **—аться** *v.* crumble, disintegrate; **—ной** *a.* loose.

рассыпчат/ость *f.* friability; **—ый** *a.* friable, crumbly, powdery.

расталкив/ание *n.* repulsion; **—ать** *v.* push apart; **—ающий** *a.* repulsive, repelling.

растаплив/ание *n.* lighting, kindling, firing; melting, thawing; **—ать** *v.* light, kindle; melt, thaw.

растачивать *v.* bore, chisel out.

растаявший *a.* melted, thawed.

раствор *m.* solution, mixture; opening, span; **р. изотопов** isotopic mixture; **твердый р.** solid solution; **р. угла** opening span (or aperture) of angle; **угол —а** aperture angle.

растворен/ие *n.* solution, dissolution; diffusion; **упругость —ия** solution pressure; **—ный** *a.* dissolved; **—ное вещество** solute.

растворим/ое *n.* solute; **—ость** *f.* solubility; **—ый** *a.* soluble; **—ый в воде** water-soluble; **легко —ый** readily soluble.

раствор/итель *m.* solvent, dissolver; **р. экстракции** extractant; **—ить, —ять** *v.* dissolve; **—иться, —яться** *v.* dissolve, be dissolved; **—ный** *a.* solution, solution-type; **—яемый** *see* **растворимый.**

растворяющ/ий *a.* dissolving, solvent; **—ая способность** solvent action; **—ее вещество, —ее средство** solvent; **—ийся** *a.* soluble.

растек/ание *n.* spreading (out), flowing; **—аться** *v.* spread, flow.

растение *n.* plant.

растер/еть *see* **растирать**; **—тый** *a.* ground, powdered.

растеч/ка *see* **растекание**; **—ься** *see* **растекаться.**

расти *v.* grow, increase, enhance.

растир/аемый *a.* pulverizable, friable; **—ание** *n.* pulverization, grinding, trituration; **—ательный** a. pulverizing, grinding; **—ать** *v.* pulverize, grind, triturate, crush.

растис/кивать, —нуть *v.* push apart.

растительн/ость *f.* vegetation; **—ый** *a.* plant, vegetable.

растолков/ать, —ывать *v.* interpret, explain; **—ывание** *n.* interpretation, explanation.

растолочь *v.* grind, pulverize, crush.

растоп/ить, —лять *see* **растапливать; —ка** *f.* kindling, firing; melting; **—ление** *see* **растапливание; —ленный** *a.* kindled, fired; melted, molten.

растор/гать, —гнуть *v.* nullify, cancel, void; **—жение** *n.* cancellation, dissolution.

расточ/ать *v.* dissipate, waste; **—ительный** *a.* wasteful, extravagant; **—ить** *v.* dissipate, waste; sharpen; wash out, erode.

расточка *f.* hollow.

растр *m.* raster; grating; (opt.) screen.

растрата *f.* spending, waste.

растреск/аться, —иваться *v.* crack, split; **—ивание** *n.* splitting, cracking; (nucl.) spallation; **—ивание ядра** spallation; **—ивающий** *a.* cracking, splitting; friable.

растреснуться *see* **растрескаться.**

растров/ый *a.* raster; (opt.) screen, screened; **р. микроскоп** scanning microscope.

раструб *m.* funnel, bell mouth.

растущий *a.* growing, rising, increasing.

растягив/ание *n.* distension, stretching, elongation, spreading; **—атель** *m.* stretcher; **—ать, —аться** *v.* stretch, extend, lengthen, expand, spread.

растягивающ/ий *a.* stretching; **—ая нагрузка** tension; **—ая сила, —ее напряжение, —ее усилие** tensile stress, tension, pull.

растяжен/ие *n.* extension; stretching, dilatation; tension, pull; **р. времени** (rel.) time dilatation; **прочность на р., сопротивление —ию** tensile strength; **коэффициент —ия** (math.) modulus of expansion; **кривая —ия** stress-strain curve; **сила —ия** tensile force, tension.

растяж/имость *f.* extensibility, expansibility, tensility; ductility; **—имый** *a.* extensible, tensile, expansible; ductile; **—ка** *f.* stretching, extension; brace; tension wire; **—ной** *a.* stretching, extension.

растянут/ость *f.* lengthiness; **—ый** *a.* extended, expanded, stretched (out), elongated; prolate; **—ь** *see* **растягивать.**

расфасовка *f.* packing, packaging.

расфокусиров/ание *n.* defocusing; debunching; **—анный** *a.* defocused, out of focus; **—ка** *f.* defocusing; debunching.

расформиров/ание *n.* dissolution, disbanding; **—ать, —ывать** *v.* dissolve, break up, disband.

расформовка *f.* unforming.

расфракционированный *a.* fractionated.

расхищ/ать *v.*, **—ение** *n.* waste; plunder.

расход *m.* expense, expenditure; consumption; (hyd.) discharge, flow rate; span (of vise); **р. горючего** fuel consumption, burn-up; **р. источника** source strength; **коэффициент —а** coefficient of discharge.

расход/имость *f.* divergence, dispersion; **—иться** *v.* diverge, disperse, separate; disagree, differ; dissolve; radiate; be spent; go out of print.

расход/ный *a.* expense, expenditure; **—ование** *n.* expenditure; consumption; **—овать** *v.* spend; consume.

расходомер *m.* flow meter.

расходящ/ийся *a.* divergent, diverging; flared; **р. ряд** divergent series; **—аяся волна** outgoing wave, diverging wave.

расхождение *n.* divergence; disagreement; discrepancy, disparity, deviation; dispersion; separation.

расхолаживание *n.* cooling; **р. реактора** reactor cooling.

расцен/ивание *n.* evaluation, estimation, appraisal; **—ивать, —ить** *v.* evaluate, estimate, appraise; **—ка** *f.* evaluation, estimation.

расцеп *m.* tripping device, uncoupling, decoupling; **—ить, —лять** *v.* uncouple, disconnect, release, disengage, throw out of gear, trip; **—ка** *f.* release; **—ление** *n.* uncoupling, disconnecting, release; **—ленный** *a.* disconnected, disengaged; **—ляющий** *a.* disconnecting, disengaging, releasing; **—ляющий механизм** releasing (or trip) mechanism; **—ной** *a.* detachable.

расчал/ивать, —ить *v.* brace; **—ка** *f.* brace, bracing wire.

расчер/тить, —чивать *v.* trace.

расчет *m.* calculation, computation, estimate; design; account; crew, squad; **р. мощности** capacity rating; **не принимаемый в р.** negligible; **принять в р.** take into consideration, take into account, allow for; **р. цепи** circuit design.

расчетн/ый *a.* calculating, calculated, design, rated, reference; **—ая линия** reference line; **—ая мощность** design (or rated) capacity (output, power); **—ая формула** design equation, standard working formula; **—ое моделирующее устройство** analog computer.

расчетчик *m.* computer; estimator; designer.

расчисл/ение *n.* calculation, computation; **—ить, —ять** *v.* calculate, compute.

расчист/ить *see* **расчищать**; **—ка** *f.* clearing.

расчит/ать, —ывать *v.* calculate, compute.

расчищ/ать *v.* clear; **—енный** *a.* cleared, freed.

расчлен/ение *n.* separation, disjunction, partition; disintegration; **—енный** *a.* separated, disjoint; **—итель изображения** image slicer; **—ить, —ять** *v.* separate, break down.

расшат/анность *f.* looseness, instability; **—анный** *a.* loose, unstable; **—ывание** *n.* loosening.

расширен/ие *n.* expansion, dilation; widening, broadening; spread, enlargement, extension; **коэффициент —ия** expansion coefficient; **коэффициент объемного —ия** dilation; **степень —ия** expansion ratio.

расширенн/ый *a.* expanded, widened, dilated, enlarged, extended; comprehensive; **р. ливень** extensive shower; **—ая матрица** augmented matrix; **—ое воспроизводство** (nucl.) breeding.

расширитель *m.* expander, widener, extender; **—ный** *a.* expanding, widening, expansion; **—ный бачок** expansion tank; **—ный болт** expansion bolt; **—ная камера** expansion chamber; **—ная орбита** expansion orbit.

расшир/ить, —иться, —ять, —яться *v.* expand, dilate, widen, broaden, enlarge; **—яемость** *f.* expansibility, extensibility, dilatability; **—яемый** *a.* expansible, extensible, dilatable; **—яющий** *a.* expanding, dilating; **—яющийся** *a.* expansible, extensible, dilatable; expanding.

расшифров/анный *a.* deciphered; **—анная линия** identified line; **—ать, —ывать** *v.* decipher, interpret; **—ка** *f.* interpretation, deciphering; (phot.) reading.

расщел/иваться, —иться *v.* crack, split; **—ина** *f.* crack, split, crevice, crevasse, interstice.

расщеп/ившийся *a.* split, fissioned; **—ить** *see* **расщеплять.**

расщеплен/ие *n.* splitting, division, disintegration, breakup, scission, cleavage; (nuc.) spallation; resolution; **р. кольца** *see* **разрыв кольца; спектроскопическое р.** spectroscopic splitting; **—ный** *a.* split, cleaved.

расщепл/яемость *f.* cleavability, fissility; **—яемый** *a.* fissile, cleavable; **—ять, —яться** *v.* split, cleave; **—ять на тонкие слои** foliate; **—яющийся** *a.* fissile, decomposing, cleavable, splitting.

ратит *m.* rathite.

ратифи/кация *f.* ratification; **—цировать** *v.* ratify.

ратовкит *m.* ratofkite.

Раттена светофильтр Wratten filter.

раувит *m.* rauvite.

Рауля закон Raoult law.

Рауса метод Routh procedure; **Р. правило** R. rule.

раусиан *m.* Routhian.

рафин/ация *see* **рафинирование**; **—ер** *m.* refiner.

рафиниров/ание *n.*, **—ка** *f.* refining; **—анный** *a.* refined; **—ать** *v.* refine; **—очный** *a.* refining.

рац. *abbr.* (**рационализаторский**) efficiency.

рацем/ат *m.* racemate; **—ический** *a.* racemic.

рационализ/атор *m.* innovator; **—аторское предложение** efficiency suggestion, innovation; **—ация** *f.* efficiency; rationalization; **—ировать** *v.* rationalize; innovate.

рациональн/ость *f.* rationality, reasonableness; efficiency; **—ый** *a.* rational, reasonable; efficient; **—ая формула** rational formula; **—ое число** rational number.

рация *f.* (portable) radio set (or station).

Рашига кольцо Raschig ring.

рашпиль *m.* rasp.

РБЭ *abbr.* (**радиобиологический эквивалент**) *see* **БЭР**

РВ *abbr.* (**радиовысота**) radio altitude.

рван/ина *f.* fissure; **—ый** *a.* ragged, broken.

РВМ *abbr.* (**радиосигнал времени Москвы**) Moscow-time radio signal.

рвущее усилие breaking stress.

РД *abbr.* (**ракетный двигатель**) rocket engine.

рде/лый *a.* red; **—ние** *n.* redness, glow; **—ть, —ться** *v.* redden, glow; **—ющий** *a.* glowing.

Ре *abbr.* (**число Рейнольдса**) Reynolds number.

реабсорбция *f.* reabsorption.

реагент *m.* reagent, reactant; **р. активного воздействия на облака** (meteor.) seeding agent.

реагир/ование *n.* reacting, reaction; **—ованный** *a.* reacted; **—овать** *v.* react; respond; **—ующий** *a.* reacting, reactive; responsive to; **не —ующий** nonreacting, nonreactive.

реактанс *m.* reactance.

реактив *m.* reagent; **—ность** *f.* reactivity; reactance; **коэффициент паровой —ности** (reactor) void coefficient.

реактивн/ый *a.* reactive, reaction; jet, rocket; reactance; reagent; **р. волномер** reactive wavemeter; **р. двигатель** jet engine; **р. конус** exhaust cone, reaction nozzle; **р. поток** jet stream; **р. самолет** jet-propelled aircraft; **р. снаряд** rocket missile; **р. ток** reactive current; **—ая бумага** indicator paper; **—ая катушка** reactance (or choke) coil; **—ая проводимость** susceptance; **—ая сила** reaction (force); **—ая склянка** reagent bottle; **—ая составляющая** reactive component; **—ая струя** jet stream, rocket exhaust; **—ая техника** jet engineering; **—ая турбина** reaction turbine; **—ая тяга** jet thrust (or propulsion); **—ое давление** reaction pressure; **—ое движение** jet (reaction, rocket) propulsion; **—ое действие** reaction; **—ое сопло** jet (or exhaust) nozzle; **—ое сопротивление** reactance; **—ое средство** reagent.

реактиметр *m.* reactimeter, reactivity meter.

реактор *m.* reactor; **р. без отражателя** bare reactor; **р.-бридер** breeder reactor; **р. двойного назначения** dual-purpose reactor; **р. для двигателей** propulsion reactor; **р. для производства технологического тепла** process-heat reactor; **мнимый р.** virtual (or image) reactor; **р. на быстрых нейтронах** fast reactor; **р. на надтепловых нейтронах** intermediate reactor; **р. на резонансных нейтронах** resonance reactor; **р. на тепловых нейтронах** thermal reactor; **р. нулевой мощности** zero-power reactor; **р.-парокотел** boiling-water reactor; **р.-размножитель** breeder reactor; **р. РФТ** (**реактор для физических и технических исследований**) Soviet reactor for physical and technological research; **р. с замедлителем** moderated reactor; **р. с разжиженным горючим** fluidized reactor; **р. с расширенным воспроизводством ядерного горючего** breeder reactor; **р. с тяжелой водой** heavy-water reactor; **р. с циркулирующим горючим** circulating-fuel reactor; **р. с шламообразным горючим** slurry reactor.

реактор/ный *see* **реактор**; **—остроение** *n.* reactor construction (or engineering).

реакционноспособный *a.* reactive; **р. материал** reactive material.

реакционн/ый *a.* reaction; **—ая колонка** processing column.

реакц/ия *f.* reaction; response; **р. дополнительная** side reaction; **р. обмена** exchange reaction; **р. связей** constraint; **конец —ии** end point; **константа скорости —ии** (chem.) reaction rate constant; **продукты —ии** reaction products; **скорость —ии** reaction rate.

реализ/ация *f.* realization, execution, application; **—ировать, —овать** *v.* realize; **—уемый** *a.* realizable.

реалист *m.* realist; **—ический** *a.* realistic.

реальн/ость *f.* reality; **—ый** *a.* real, actual, practicable; substantial, concrete, realistic; existing, realizable, natural.

ребатрон *m.* Rebatron (relativistic electron-bunching accelerator).

реберный *a.* rib, fin; edge.

реблингит *m.* roeblingite.

ребристо-призматический *a.* angular-prismatic.

ребрист/ый *a.* ribbed, fin-type, finned; edged; **р. нагреватель** radiator; **р. охладитель** fin cooler; **—ая трубка** finned tube.

ребр/о *n.* rib, fin; edge; riffle; **—а** *pl.* ribbing; **р. возврата** edge of regression, cuspidal edge; **р. куба** cube edge (or axis); **р. схода** trailing (or rear) edge; **—ом** edgewise.

ревербер *m.* reverberator; **—ационная камера** reverberation chamber; **—ация** *f.* reverberation; **—ировать** *v.* reverberate; **—ометр** *m.* reverberometer.

реверс *m.* reversing gear; reverser; (reactor) rundown; **—ивность** *f.* reversibility; **—ивный** *a.* reversing, reversible, duodirectional; reverse.

реверсиров/ание *n.* reversing, reversal; **—анный** *a.* reversed; **—ать** *v.* reverse.

реверс/ируемость *f.* reversibility; **—ируемый** *a.* reversible; **—ирующий** *a.* reversing; **—ия** *f.* reversion; **—овать** *see* **реверсировать**; **—ор** *m.* reverser.

ревивификация *f.* reactivation.

ревиз/ионный *a.* revisory; **—ия** *f.* revision, examination, inspection; **—овать** *v.* examine, inspect.

револьвер *m.* turret; **—ный** *a.* revolving; turret; **—ная головка** turret head.

революц/ионизировать *v.* revolutionize; **—ионный** *a.* revolutionary; **—ия** *f.* revolution.

ревун *m.* (elec.) howler.

регенерат *m.* regenerate, reclaim, reclaimed rubber.

регенеративн/ый *a.* regenerative, regeneration; **р. каскад** stripping cascade; **р. реактор** regenerative reactor; **—ая печь** regenerative furnace; **—ая схема** regenerative (or feedback) circuit.

регенератор *m.* regenerator.

регенер/ация *f.*, **—ирование** *n.* regeneration, recovery, reprocessing, recuperation, reclaiming; reactivation, rejuvenation; **р. импульсов** pulse regeneration; **р. отходов** waste recovery; **р. урана** recovery of uranium; **р. ядерного горючего** nuclear fuel regeneration.

регенериров/анный *a.* regenerated, recovered, restored; reclaimed; **—анное горючее** regenerated fuel; **—ать** *v.* regenerate, recover, recuperate, reclaim; reactivate.

региональный *a.* regional, district.

регистр *m.* register, list; **—атор** *m.* register, recorder, detector, meter, monitor; **—атор прозрачности** transmissometer, transmittance meter; **—атор пульса** sphygmograph; **—атура** *f.* registry.

регистрац/ионный *a.* registration; **р. прибор** recording device, recorder; **—ионная камера** recording camera; **—ия** *f.* registration, recording, detection; **—ия на расстоянии** telerecording; **карта —ии** recording chart.

регистриров/ание *see* **регистрация**; **—ать** *v.* record, register.

регистрирующ/ий *a.* registering, recording; **р. прибор** recorder; **р. термометр** thermograph; **—ая схема** recording circuit.

регистрограмма *f.* trace.

регламент *m.* regulation, rule.

регресс *m.* regress, regression, retrogression; **—ивный** *a.* regressive, retrograde; **—ировать** *v.* regress, retrogress, turn back; **—ия** *f.* regression; **линия —ии** regression line.

Регул Regulus.

регулиров/ание *n.* regulation, control, governing; setting, adjustment, tuning; **р. по производной** derivative (or rate) control; **р. усиления** gain control; **р. частоты** frequency control; **—анный** *a.* regulated, adjusted; **—ать** *v.* regulate, control; set, adjust.

регулиров/ка *see* **регулирование**; **р. усиления** gain control; **р. фаз** phasing; **—очный** *a.* regulating, adjusting; *see also* **регулирующий**; **—очный стержень** control rod.

регулируем/ость *f.* controllability; **—ый** *a.* adjustable, variable; controlled; **—ый процесс** controlled process; **—ая связь** variable coupling; **—ая ядерная реакция** controlled nuclear reaction; **—ое сопло** variable-area nozzle.

регулирующий *a.* regulating, regulator, controlling, control, adjusting; **р. клапан** control valve; **р. стержень** control rod; **—ся** *a.* adjustable; controlled.

регуляриз/ация *f.* regularization; **—ируемый** *a.* regularizable; **—ирующий, —ующий** *a.* regularizing.

регулярн/о *adv.* regularly; **—ость** *f.* regularity; **—ый** *a.* regular, ordinary, normal; orderly.

регулятор *m.*, **—ный** *a.* regulator, control, controller; governor; **р. громкости** volume control.

ред. *abbr.* (**редактор**) editor; (**редакция**) editorial staff (or office); editing.

редактировать *v.* edit, revise.

редактор *m.* editor; **главный р.** editor-in-chief.

редакц/ионный *a.* editorial; **—ионная коллегия** editorial board; **—ия** *f.* editorial staff (or office); editing; rewording.

Редже полюс Regge pole.

редк/ий *a.* infrequent, rare, scarce, widely spaced; **р. лед** open pack (ice); **—ие земли** rare earths, rare-earth elements; **—о** *adv.* rarely, seldom.

редкоземельный металл rare-earth metal; **р. элемент** rare-earth element.

редколлегия *abbr.* (**редакционная коллегия**) editorial board.

редкость *f.* rarity, infrequency.

редмет *abbr.* (**редкие металлы**) rare metals; (**редкая металлургия**) metallurgy of rare metals.

редокс-потенциал redox potential.

редрутит *m.* redruthite.

Редстоун Redstone (rocket).

редуктор *m.* reducer; reductor; reducing gear (train).

редукц/ионный *a.*, **—ия** *f.* reduction, reducing; **р. клапан** reducing (or relief) valve.

редуцир/ование *n.* reduction; **—ованный** *a.* reduced; **—овать** *v.* reduce; **—ующий** *a.* reducing; **—ующая способность** reducing power.

реестр *m.* register, list; record.

реечный *a.* rack.

режектор *m.* rejector.

режим *m.* regime, conditions; cycle; mode; process, system, method; rate; **р. работы** procedure; operating conditions; performance, duty (of machine or apparatus); **тяжелый р.** heavy duty

режущий *a.* cutting.

рез/ак *m.* cutter, chopper; cutting torch; **—альная машина** cutting machine.

Резаля теорема Résal theorem.

рез/ание *n.* cutting; **—ать** *v.* cut, slit; **—ачок** *m.* tool bit.

резерв, —аж *m.* reserve; **—ирование** *n.* reservation; emergency arrangement; **—ный** *a.* reserve, spare, emergency, stand-by; **—ная мощность** stand-by power.

резервуар *m.*, **—ный** *a.* reservoir, receptacle, tank, vessel; **р. термометра** thermometer bulb.

резерфорд *m.* rutherford (unit); **—ит** *m.* rutherfordite; **—овская формула рассеяния** Rutherford scattering law.

резец *m.* cutting tool; blade, chisel.

Резец Caelum (Cae) (constellation).

резильянс *m.* resilience.

резин/а *f.* (vulcanized) rubber; **искусственная р.** synthetic rubber; **—овый** *a.* rubber; **—овый клей** rubber cement.

резистентный *see* **резистивный.**

резистивн/о-емкостная связь resistance-capacitance coupling; **—ый** *a.* resistance; **—ый гиратор** resistance gyrator; **—ый усилитель** resistance-coupled amplifier; **—ый фотоэлемент** photoconductive cell.

резистор *m.* (elec.) resistance, resistor.

резк/ий *a.* abrupt, sudden; steep; sharp, critical; pronounced; **р. резонанс** sharp resonance; **—ая граница** sharp cutoff; **—ая зависимость** critical dependence; **—ая закалка** rapid quenching; **—ая серия** sharp series; **—ое течение** (elast.) abrupt (or sharp) yielding.

резко *adv.* sharply, abruptly; extremely, strongly; **р. выраженный** pronounced, sharply defined; **—сть** *f.* sharpness, abruptness; definition; **глубина —сти** (opt.) depth of field.

резнатрон *m.* resnatron.

резной *a.* cut.

резольвент/а *f.*, **—ное ядро** resolvent; resolvent (or solving) kernel.

резолюция *f.* resolution, decision.

резонанс *m.* resonance; **р. с испусканием гамма-лучей** gamma-ray resonance; **р. токов** (elec.) parallel resonance, antiresonance.

резонансн/ый *a.* resonance, resonant; **р. интеграл** resonance integral; **р. контур** resonant (or tuned) circuit; tank circuit; **р. уровень** resonance level; **—ое излучение** resonance radiation; **—ое испускание** resonance radiation; **—ое рассеивание** resonance scattering.

резонатор *m.* resonator; cavity resonator; (resonant) cavity; **входной р.** input resonator; **выходной р.** output resonator; **р. проходного типа** reentrant resonator.

резонир/овать *v.* resonate; **—ующий** *a.* resonant, resonating.

резонный *a.* rational, reasonable, sensible.

резорбция *f.* resorption.

результат *m.* result, consequence, effect; **в —е** as a result, in consequence; **иметь —ом** result in, give rise to; **—ы** *pl.* results, data, findings; **—ный** *a.* resulting, resultant.

результирующий *a.* resulting, resultant, net.

рез/цовый *a.* tool, cutter; **—чик** *m.* cutter, engraver.

резьб/а *f.* screw thread; **нарезать —у** thread; **—овой** *a.* thread, threaded; **—омер** *m.* screw pitch gauge.

резюм/е *n.* résumé, summary, recapitulation; **—ировать** *v.* summarize.

рейб/ал, —ол, —ор *m.* reamer.

рейд *m.* roadstead.

рейерит *m.* reyerite.

рейка *f.* rod, staff; rack; **мерная р.** surveying rod.

Рейнгольд Reingold (lunar crater).

Рейнер Reiner (lunar crater).

рейнит *m.* reinite.

Рейнольдса критерий Reynolds criterion (or number); **Р. число** R. number.

рейс *m.* passage, trip, run.

рейсмус *m.* marking tool; shifting gauge.

Рейсса теория Reuss theory.

рейссит *m.* reissite.

рейстрек *m.* racetrack.

рейсфедер *m.* drawing pen.

рейсшина *f.* T square.

Рейта Rheita (lunar crater).

рейтер *m.* rider.

рейхардтит *m.* reichardtite.

река *f.* river.

рекалесценция *f.* recalescence.

рекапитуляция *f.* recapitulation.

рекарбюризатор *m.* recarburizer.

реквиз/ировать *v.*, **—иционный** *a.*, **—иция** *f.* requisition.

реклама *f.* advertisement; advertising, publicity.

рекогносциров/ка *f.* preliminary survey, reconnaissance; **—очный** *a.* preliminary, exploratory, reconnaissance.

рекомбин/атор *m.* recombiner; **—ационный** *a.*, **—ация** *f.* recombination; **—ация дырка-электрон** hole-electron recombination; **—ация тройным столкновением** three-body recombination; **—ировать** *v.* recombine.

рекоменд/ательный *a.* recommendation, recommending; **—ация** *f.* recommendation; **—ованный** *a.* recommended, preferred; **—овать** *v.* recommend; **—уется** it is recommended that, it is advisable to.

реконстру/ировать *v.* reconstruct, remodel; **—ктивный** *a.* reconstructive; **—кция** *f.* reconstruction, rearrangement.

реконцентрация *f.* reconcentration.

рекорд *m.* record; **—ер** *m.* recorder,

counter; **—ный** *a.* record, record-breaking.

рекристаллизация *f.* recrystallization.

ректифи/кат *m.* distillate; **—катор** *m.*, **—кационный прибор** rectifier; **—кационный** *a.* rectification; fractionating; **—кационная колонна** fractionating column; **—кация** *f.*, **—цирование** *n.* rectification; **—цированный** *a.* rectified; **—цировать** *v.* rectify.

рекупер/ативный *a.* recuperative, regenerative; **—атор** *m.* recuperator, regenerator; **—ация** *f.* recuperation, regeneration; **—ированный** *a.* recuperated, regenerated; recovered; **—ировать** *v.* recuperate, regenerate; recover.

рекуррентн/ый *a.* recurrent; **—ая формула, —ое соотношение** recurrence (or recursion) formula.

рекурсивный *a.* recursive, recursion.

релаксатор *m.* relaxation oscillator.

релаксационн/ый *a.* relaxation; **—ая кривая свечения** luminescence relaxation curve; **—ая теория** relaxation theory.

релакс/ация *f.* relaxation; **—ировать** *v.* relax.

реле *n.* relay; **р. времени** timing relay; **р.-повторитель** repeating relay.

релеевское рассеяние Rayleigh scattering.

релейн/ый *a.* relay; **—ое регулирование** discontinuous (or on-off) control.

релейно-контактная схема relay-contact network.

Релея дифракционный предел разрешения Rayleigh limit of resolution; **закон Р.** R. law; **Р. рефрактометр** R. refractometer; **формула Р. для рассеяния света** R. scattering law; **Р.-Джинса формула** R.-Jeans law (formula, equation).

реликт *m.* relict.

рельеф *m.* relief, contour, contour map, topography; **—но** *adv.* in relief; **—ность** *f.* relief, prominence; **—ный** *a.* relief, embossed, raised, prominent; **—ная карта** relief map; **—ная линия скольжения** contour slip line, slip step.

рельс *m.*, **—овый** *a.* rail, track.

релятив/изм *m.*, **—ность** *f.* relativity; **—истский** *a.* relativistic; **—истское уравнение массы** relativistic mass equation.

ремаллой *m.* Remalloy (iron-molybdenum-cobalt alloy).

реманентн/ость *f.* remanence, retentivity; **—ый** *a.* remanent.

ремен/ный *a.* belt; **р. привод, —ная передача** belt drive; **—ь** *m.* belt, strap.

Ремер Römer (Roemer).

Ремер Roemer (lunar crater).

ремерит *m.* römerite.

ремесленн/ик *m.* workman; **—ичество** *n.* workmanship; **—ый** *a.* trade, industrial; **—ое училище** trade school.

ремесло *n.* trade, craft.

ремонт *m.* repair; upkeep, maintenance; **мелкий р.** minor repair; **текущий р.** ordinary (or current) maintenance; **в —е, при —е** under repair; **—ирование** *n.* repairing, repair, overhauling; **—ировать** *v.* repair, overhaul; **—ный** *a.* repair.

рему *n.* (aero.) bump.

рен/иевый *a.* rhenium; **—ий** *m.* rhenium (Re).

ренит *m.* rhönite.

Ренкина *see* **Ранкина.**

ренормализационный *a.* renormalization.

ренселерит *m.* rensselaerite.

рентабельн/о *adv.* profitably; it is economical, it is profitable; **—ость** *f.* profitableness; **—ый** *a.* profitable, commercial.

рентген *m.* roentgen (unit); **р.-эквивалент** roentgen equivalent.

Рентгена лучи x rays, Röntgen (Roentgen) rays.

рентген/изация *f.* x-irradiation, x-raying; **—изировать** *v.* x-ray; (med.) treat with x rays; **—метр** *m.* roentgen meter, roentgenometer, r-meter

рентгено— *prefix* Roentgen, x-ray.

рентгеновск/ий *a.* Roentgen, x-ray; **р. анализ** x-ray analysis; **р. аппарат, р. прибор** x-ray unit (or machine); **р. вакуум** x-ray vacuum; **р. гониометр** x-ray goniometer; **р. рефлекс** x-ray reflection; **р. снимок** *see* **рентгенограмма; р. спектрометр** x-ray spec trometer; **р. эмиссионный спектр** x-ray emission spectrum; **—ая трубка** x-ray tube; **—ая установка** x-ray unit; **—ая флуоресценция** x-ray fluorescence; **—ое К-излучение** K x rays; **—ие лучи** x rays, Roentgen rays; **—ие лучи флуоресценции** fluorescent x rays; **подвергать действию —их лучей** x ray.

рентгеновый *see* **рентгеновский.**

рентгенограмма *f.* x-ray photograph (or pattern), radiograph, roentgenogram; **р. вращения** rotating-crystal x-ray photograph; **р. колебаний** oscillating-crystal x-ray photograph.

рентгенограф/ирование *n.* roentgenography, radiography; **—ический** *a.* x-ray, radiographic; **—ия** *f.* roentgenography, radiography; **—ия металлов** x-ray metallography, radiometallography.

рентгено/дефектоскопия *f.* x-ray flaw detection; **—кристаллография** *f.* x-ray crystallography.

рентгенолог *m.* roentgenologist, radiologist; **—ический** *a.* roentgenologic, x-ray; **—ический анализ** x-ray analysis; **—ия** *f.* roentgenology.

рентгено/люминесценция *f.* roentgenoluminescence; **—метр** *see* **рентгенметр**; **—прозрачный, —проницаемый** *a.* radiolucent, radiotransparent.

рентгенопросвечив/ание *n.* fluoroscopy, roentgenoscopy, radioscopy; **—ающий** *see* **рентгенопрозрачный.**

рентгеноскоп/ический *a.* roentgenoscopic, fluoroscopic; **—ия** *f.* roentgenoscopy, fluoroscopy.

рентгено/снимок *see* **рентгенограмма**; **—спектральный анализ** x-ray spectral analysis; **—структурный анализ** x-ray structural analysis; **—терапия** *f.* roentgenotherapy, x-ray therapy; **—техник** *m.* x-ray technician, radiographer; **—чувствительный** *a.* radiosensitive.

реньо калориметр Regnault calorimeter.

рео/ид *m.* rheoid; **—логия** *f.* rheology; **—метр** *m.* rheometer, flow meter.

реомюр Réaumur (lunar crater).

реомюра термометр Réaumur thermometer; **шкала Р.** R. scale.

реономный *a.* rheonomic.

реопирометр *m.* resistance pyrometer.

реорганиз/ация *f.* reorganization; **—овать** *v.* reorganize.

реоскоп *m.* rheoscope.

реостат *m.* rheostat; **р. возбуждения** field rheostat; **—ный** *a.* rheostat, rheostatic.

реотан *m.* rheotan (copper alloy).

рео/том *m.* (elec.) rheotome; **—хорд** *m.* slide wire.

репер *m.*, **—ный** *a.* datum, datum point, reference mark, bench mark; frame of reference;(math.) *n*-hedral; **сопровождающий р.** (math.) moving *n*-hedral; **—ный знак** bench mark; **—ная линия, —ная точка** reference (datum, fixed) line.

репитер *m.* repeater.

реплика *f.* replica.

репорт/аж *m.* reporting; **—ер** *m.* reporter.

репперит *m.* roepperite.

репрезентативный *a.* representative.

репресс/ивный *a.* repressive; **—ия** *f.* repression.

репродук/тор *m.* reproducer; loudspeaker; **—ционный** *a.* reproduction, reproducing; **—ция** *f.* reproduction.

репроекция *f.* reprojection.

Репсольд Repsold (lunar crater).

репульсионный *a.* repulsion.

репутация *f.* reputation.

ресеквентный *a.* resequent.

ресивер *m.* receiver.

республика *f.* republic; **—нский** *a.* republican.

Ресселя-Герцшпрунга диаграмма Russell-Hertzsprung diagram; **Р.-Саундерса связь** R.-Saunders coupling.

рессор/а *f.*, **—ный** *a.* spring.

ресурс *m.* resource.

ретзерфордин *m.* rutherfordine.

ретикулярная плотность reticular density.

ретина *f.* retina.

ретинасфальт *m.* retinasphalt.

ретицит *m.* rhetizite.

реторт/а *f.*, **—ный** *a.* retort; (met.) converter.

ретрансляция *f.* radio relaying.

ретроактивн/ость *f.* retroaction; **—ый** *a.* retroactive.

ретрогрессивный *a.* retrogressive.
ретроспек/тивный *a.* retrospective; **—ция** *f.* retrospection.
реттизит *m.* röttisite.
ретуширов/ание *n.* (phot.) retouching; **—ать** *v.* retouch.
ретциан *m.* retzian.
реф. *abbr. see* **реферат.**
реферат *m.* review; abstract, summary; **—ивный журнал** journal of abstracts; referativnyĭ zhurnal.
рефер/ент *m.* reviewer; abstractor; **—енц-линия** *f.* reference line; **—енция** *f.* reference; **—ировать** *v.* review; abstract.
Реф. жур. *abbr.* (**Реферативный журнал**) Abstract Journal.
рефикит *m.* refikite.
рефлекс *m.*, **—ный** *a.* reflex; (cryst.) reflection; **р.-камера** reflex camera; **—ия** *f.* reflection.
рефлект/ивный *a.* reflective; **—ирующий** *a.* reflecting; **—ометр** *m.* reflectometer; **—ор** *m.* reflector; (antenna) dish; **—орный** *a.* reflector; reflex; **—орное зеркало** reflecting mirror.
рефлюкс *m.* reflux.
рефокусировка *f.* refocusing.
реформ/а *f.* reform, amendment; **—ировать** *v.* reform, amend; **—ирующий** *a.* reformative, reforming.
рефракс *m.* refrax.
рефракт/ометр *m.* refractometer; **—ометрический** *a.* refractometric; **—ор** *m.* refractor; **—орный** *a.* refractor; refracting; **—орный телескоп** refracting telescope.
рефракц/ия *f.*, **—ионный** *a.* refraction.
рефрижер/атор *m.* refrigerator; condenser; **—ация** *f.* refrigeration.
Рефсдаля аэрограмма Refsdal aerogram.
рец. *abbr.* (**рецензент**) reviewer, critic; (**рецензия**) review, critique.
рецбаниит *m.* rezbanyite.
реценз/ент *m.* reviewer, critic; **—ировать** *v.* review, criticize; **—ия** *f.* review, critique.
рецепт *m.* formula, rule; prescription; **—ура** *f.* prescribing; formula.
рецепция *f.* reception.
рецессивный признак recessive character.
рециркул/ированное горючее recycled fuel; **—ировать** *v.* recirculate, recycle; **—яционный насос** recirculating pump; **—яция** *f.* recirculation, recycling.
речев/ой *a.* speech, vocal; **—ая частота** voice frequency.
речной *a.* river.
реч/ь *f.* speech, address; **р. идет о** the topic of discussion is, the question is; **органы —и** vocal organs.
решать *v.* solve; decide, determine, conclude; **—ся** *v.* decide, determine, resolve.
решающий *a.* deciding, determinant; conclusive; decision, resolving; **р. фактор** controlling factor; **р. элемент** decision element; **—ее устройство** resolver.
решен/ие *n.* solution; resolution, decision, determination; judgment; derivation; **р. подбором** trial-and-error solution; **—ный** *a.* determined; solved.
решетина *f.* lath.
решетк/а *f.* (cryst.; nucl.) lattice; (antenna) array; grill, grid; network; **р.-замедлитель** moderator lattice; **р. из урана и замедлителя** uranium-moderator lattice; **р. с плотной упаковкой** close-packed lattice; **коэффициент —и, множитель —и** array factor; **постоянная —и** lattice constant; **—ообразный** *a.* latticelike, lattice.
решето *n.* screen, sieve; **—чный** *a.* screen; network; **—чная релаксация спина** spin-lattice relaxation.
решетчат/ый *a.* lattice; grating, grid, grill; meshed, screen; **р. реактор** lattice reactor; **—ая линза** lattice lens; **—ое распределение** lattice distribution; **—ое строение** lattice structure.
решимость *f.* determination; solvability.
решительн/о *adv.* absolutely; resolutely, determinedly; **—ость** *f.* resolution, determination, decisiveness; **—ый** *a.* determined, decisive, resolved; deciding, crucial.
решить *see* **решать.**
реэкстра/гировать *v.* reextract; **—кция** *f.* reextraction.

ржав/еть *v.* rust; **—ление** *n.* rusting; **—ленный, —ый** *a.* rusted; **—чина** *f.* rust.

Р.З.Э. *abbr.* (**редкоземельные элементы**) rare-earth elements.

риаколит *m.* rhyacolite.

РИАН *abbr.* (**Радиевый институт Академии наук**) Radium Institute of the Academy of Sciences.

рибекит *m.* riebeckite.

риверсайдит *m.* riversideite.

ригель *m.* crossbar.

Ригель Rigel.

Риги-Гальвакса эффект Righi-Hallwachs effect; **Р.-Ледюка эффект** R.-Leduc effect.

ридберг *m.* rydberg.

Ридберга постоянная Rydberg constant.

ризерит *m.* risörite.

рикардит *m.* rickardite.

Рике диаграмма Rieke diagram.

Риккати уравнение Riccati equation.

риколит *m.* ricolite.

рикошет *m.*, **—ировать** *v.* ricochet, rebound; **—ный** *a.* rebounding; **—ом** on the rebound.

Римана лист поверхности sheet of Riemann surface.

риманнит *m.* riemannite.

риман/ова геометрия Riemannian geometry; **—ово пространство** Riemannian space.

римпилит *m.* rimpylite.

римская цифра Roman numeral.

рис. *abbr.* (**рисунок**) figure, diagram.

рисберма *f.* (hydraulic engineering) apron.

РИСИ *abbr.* (**Ростовский-на-Дону инженерно-строительный институт**) Rostov-on-Don Engineering and Construction Institute.

риск *m.* risk.

риска *f.* reference (graduation, calibration) line; fiducial line.

риск/нуть, —овать *v.* risk, hazard, venture; **—ованность** *f.* riskiness; **—ованный** *a.* risky, speculative.

РИСО *abbr.* [**Редакторско-издательский совет (Академии наук СССР)**] Editorial and Publishing Council (of the Academy of Sciences, USSR).

рисов/альный *a.* drawing; **—ание** *n.* drawing, designing; **—ать** *v.* draw, design.

Рисса-Фишера теорема Riesz-Fisher theorem.

рисский век Rissian stage.

рисунок *m.* figure, diagram; drawing; pattern.

ритм *m.*, **—ика** *f.* rhythm; **—ический, —ичный** *a.* rhythmic.

ритрон *m.* retron (type of gamma spectrometer).

Риттер Ritter (lunar crater).

Ритца баллистическая гипотеза Ritz ballistic hypothesis; **Р. комбинационный принцип** R. combination principle; **Р. уравнение** R. formula; **Р.-Пашена серия** Paschen series.

риф *m.* reef, ledge.

рифл/евать, —ить *v.* groove, corrugate; **—ение** *n.* groove, grooving, striation; corrugation; **—енный** *a.* grooved, fluted, corrugated, ribbed, riffled; **—я** *f.* riffle, groove, flute.

рифовый *a.* reef.

рифтовать *v.* groove, flute, corrugate.

рихтерит *m.* richterite.

рихтов/альный, —очный *a.* straightening; **—ать** *v.* straighten, level; **—ка** *f.* straightening.

Ричардсона закон Richardson law; **Р. (-Дэшмана) формула** R.-Dushman equation.

Риччи Ricci (lunar crater).

Риччиоли Riccioli (lunar crater).

ришеллит *m.* richellite.

РК *abbr.* (**радиоактивный каротаж**) radioactive logging, radiologging.

рлк *abbr.* (**радиолокация**) radar.

РНР *abbr. see* **Румынская Народная Республика.**

Роберваля весы Roberval balance.

робинзонов чашечный анемометр Robinson cup anemometer.

Робича актинограф Robitzsch actinograph.

робот *m.* robot, automatic device.

Робэна задача Robin problem.

ров *m.* ditch, trench.

ровит *see* **раувит.**

ровн/о *adv.* equally; exactly; regularly, evenly, smoothly; **—ость** *f.* equality; uniformity; evenness, flatness; **—ый**

a. equal; uniform, steady; even, flat, plane; —**ять** *v.* even, align.
рог *m.* horn; —**овидный** *a.* horn-shaped.
роговик *m.* hornstone, chert.
рогов/ица *f.*, —**ая оболочка** cornea; —**ой** *a.* horn, horny.
Роговского пояс Rogowski loop.
рогообразный *see* **роговидный.**
род. *abbr.* [**родился (с датой)**] born (with date).
род *m.* kind, type, sort; family, generation; species; genus; gender; **р. действия** method of operation; type of action; **в некотором —е** in some way.
родан *m.* thiocyanogen; —**истоводородная кислота** thiocyanic (or sulfocyanic) acid.
роджерсит *m.* rogersite.
род/иевый, —**истый** *a.* rhodium; —**ий** *m.* rhodium (Rh).
родит *m.* rhodite.
родит/ель *m.* parent, father; —**ели** *pl.* parents; —**ельский** *a.* parental, paternal; —**ь** *see* **рождать.**
родицит *m.* rhodizite.
род/ной *a.* native; own; —**овой** *a.* generic.
родолит *m.* rhodolite.
родометр *m.* rodometer.
родоначальник *m.* ancestor, precursor; parent.
родонит *m.* rhodonite.
родоскоп *m.* rodoscope.
родо/тилит *m.* rhodotilite; —**филлит** *m.* rhodophyllite; —**хрозит** *m.* rhodochrosite; —**хром** *m.* rhodochrome.
Родрига формула Rodrigues formula.
родств/енный *a.* related, cognate, allied, kindred; parent; —**енные функции** contiguous (hypergeometric) functions; —**о** *n.* relationship; affinity, alliance.
родусит *m.* rhodusite.
рожд/аемость *f.* birth rate; breeding; —**ать** *v.* bear, produce; —**ающийся** *a.* nascent.
рожден/ие *n.* production, creation; birth; **оператор —ия** creation operator; —**ный** *a.* born; originated, produced.
рожок *m.* burner, jet; horn, siren.
роза *f.* rose; **плювиометрическая р.** precipitation rose.
розазит *m.* rosasite.
Розе сплав Rose metal (bismuth-lead-tin alloy).
розелит *m.* roselite.
розенбушит *m.* rosenbuschite.
розетка *f.* rose, rosette; (elec.) socket.
розит *m.* rosite.
розицкит *m.* rosickyite.
розн/ый *a.* unmatched, odd; —**ь** *f.* difference, diversity.
розов/атый *a.* pinkish; —**ый** *a.* rose-colored, pink; —**ый кварц** rose quartz.
розолит *m.* rosolite.
розыгрыш *m.* (lottery) drawing; draw game.
розыск *m.* research, inquiry.
розьерезит *m.* rosieresite.
рой *m.* swarm, cluster.
рокот/ание *n.* rumble; —**ать** *v.* roar, rumble.
ролик *m.* roller; —**овый** *a.* roller, roll; —**овый подшипник,** —**оподшипник** *m.* roller bearing.
Ролля теорема Rolle theorem.
роль *f.* role, part; **играть р.** act as, serve as, play a part.
роль/ный *a.* rolled; —**танг** *m.* roll table, roll tram.
романешит *m.* romanechite.
романский *a.* Roman.
ромб *m.* rhomb, rhombus, rhombohedron, diamond; —**ический** *a.* rhombic, orthorhombic, diamond-shaped; —**ическая симметрия** rhombic (or orthorhombic) symmetry.
ромбо— *prefix* rhombo—.
ромбо/видный *a.* rhombiform; diamond-shaped; —**гемиморфный** *a.* rhombohemimorphous; —**двупирамидальный** *a.* rhombobipyramidal.
ромбоид *m.* rhomboid; —**альный** *a.* rhomboid, rhomboidal.
ромбоклаз, —**ит** *m.* rhomboclase, rhomboclasite.
ромбообразный *see* **ромбовидный.**
ромбоэдр *m.* rhombohedron; —**ический** *a.* rhombohedral.
рометалл *m.* Rhometal (iron-nickel-chromium-silicon alloy).
ронять *v.* drop, let fall.

роракский ярус Rauracian stage.
РОРИ *abbr.* (**Российское общество радиоинженеров**) Russian Society of Radio Engineers.
рос/а *f.* dew; **точка —ы** dew point; **—истость** *f.* dewiness.
роскоэлит *m.* roscoelite.
росомер *m.* drosometer.
роспуск *m.* dismissal; dissolution.
росс. *abbr.* (**российский**) Russian.
Росс Ross (lunar crater).
Россби волны Rossby waves.
россбиграмма *f.* Rossby diagram.
Росселанда теорема Rosseland theorem; **росселандово среднее** R. mean (coefficient).
Российская Советская Федеративная Социалистическая Республика Russian Soviet Federated Socialist Republic.
российский *see* **русский.**
Россия Russia.
россып/ное золото (min.) placer (or alluvial) gold; **—ь** *f.* alluvial deposit.
рост *m.* growth, increase, development, advance; height.
ростверк *m.* grillage.
росторнит *m.* rosthornite.
росянка *f.* (astr.) dew cap.
ротаметр *m.* rotameter.
ротат/ивный *a.* rotary, rotating; **—ор** *m.* rotator.
ротационн/ый *a.* rotation, rotational, rotary; **р. спектр** rotational spectrum; **р. уровень** rotational level; **—ая полоса** rotational band; **—ая энергия** rotational energy; **—ое квантовое число** rotational quantum number; **—ое состояние** rotational state.
ротация *f.* rotation.
ротгоффит *m.* rothoffite.
ротограф *m.* (phot.) rotograph; **—ия** *f.* (phot.) rotography.
ротон *m.*, **—ный** *a.* roton.
ротор *m.*, **—ный** *a.* rotor, rotary; (math.) curl; **р. скорости** vorticity; **—ный вольтметр** rotary voltmeter.
ротоскоп *m.* rotoscope.
Роуз Rose.
Роуланда круг Rowland circle; **Р. решетка** R. grating.
роуландит *m.* rowlandite.
Роша плотность Roche density.
рошерит *m.* roscherite.
Рошона призма Rochon prism.
р.п. *abbr.* (**русский патент**) Russian patent.
рр. *abbr.* (**реки**) rivers.
РСФСР *abbr. see* **Российская Советская Федеративная Социалистическая Республика.**
РТО *abbr.* (**Русское техническое общество**) Russian Technical Society.
рт. ст. *abbr.* (**ртутный столб**) mercury column; **мм рт. ст.** mm Hg.
ртутисто— *prefix* mercuro—, mercurous.
ртут/истый *a.* mercurous, mercury; **—ник** *m.* mercury-arc rectifier.
ртутно— *prefix* mercuri—, mercuric.
ртутн/ый *a.* mercury, mercuric; mercurial; **р. вентиль, р. выпрямитель, р. газотрон** mercury-arc rectifier; **р. катод** mercury-pool cathode; **р. манометр** mercury gauge; **р. столб** mercury column; **—ая лампа** mercury-vapor lamp (or tube).
ртуть *f.* mercury (Hg); **хлорная р.** mercuric chloride.
РУ *abbr.* (**рентгеновская установка**) x-ray unit.
руб. *abbr.* (**рубль**) ruble.
рубанок *m.* plane (tool).
рубашка *f.* jacket, housing, sleeve; lateral area (of cone).
рубеж *m.* border, boundary, limit; **за —ом** abroad; **—ная черта** boundary line.
рубид/иевый *a.* rubidium; **—ий** *m.* rubidium (Rb).
рубильн/ик *m.* knife switch; **—ый** *a.* chopping.
рубин *m.*, **—ный, —овый** *a.* ruby; **—овая обманка** ruby blende.
рубить *v.* chop, cut.
рубицелл *m.* rubicelle.
рубленый *a.* chopped, cut.
рубль *m.* ruble.
рубр. *abbr. see* **рубрика.**
рубрика *f.* heading; column.
руда *f.* ore; **р. теркифэт** turkey-fat ore.
рудимент *m.* rudiment; **—арный** *a.* rudimentary, vestigial.

рудн/ик *m.* mine, pit; —**ичный** *a.* mine, mining, miner's; —**ичный газ** fire-damp, mine methane.

рудн/ый *a.* mining; ore; metalliferous; —**ое месторождение** ore deposit.

рудо— *prefix* ore.

рудо/искатель *m.* prospector; —**проявление** *n.* ore manifestation; —**содержащий** *a.* ore-bearing.

ружье *n.* gun, rifle.

рук/а *f.* hand; arm; **от —и** manually, by hand.

рукав *m.* sleeve; hose; bag, sock; branch; estuary; —**ный** *a.* sleeve; hose; —**ный фильтр** bag filter; —**ное соединение** sleeve (coupling); hose coupling.

руководитель *m.* leader, supervisor, instructor; —**ство** *n.* direction, leadership; —**ствовать** *v.* lead, guide.

руковод/ить *v.* direct, lead, guide, instruct; —**ство** *n.* guidance, leadership; direction, supervision; handbook, manual; —**ствовать** *see* **руководить**; —**ствоваться** *v.* follow; —**ящий** *a.* leading, guiding; —**ящие органы** authorities.

рукопис/ь *f.*, —**ный** *a.* manuscript.

рукоятка *f.* handle, grip; lever, crank.

рулев/ой *a.* steering, rudder; **р. механизм** steering gear; —**ое колесо** steering wheel; —**ое управление** steering system (or gear); control system.

рулет/ка *f.*, —**очный** *a.* tape measure; reel.

рулеуправление *see* **рулевое управление.**

рулон *m.* roll, reel.

руль *m.* steering wheel, rudder.

рум. *abbr.* (**румынский**) Romanian (Rumanian).

румб *m.* bearing, point of compass.

румбатрон *m.* rhumbatron.

Румкорфа катушка, румкорфовая катушка Ruhmkorff coil.

Румфорда фотометр Rumford photometer.

Румын/ия Romania; —**ская Народная Республика** Romanian People's Republic.

румэнит *m.* rumanite.

румянцовит *m.* romanzovite.

Рунге правило Runge rule; **Р.-Кутта метод** R.-Kutta method.

рупельский ярус Rupelian stage.

рупор *m.* horn; mouthpiece; —**ный** *a.* horn (-type); mouthpiece.

рус. *abbr.* (**русский**) Russian.

русло *n.* channel, river bed.

рус. пер. *abbr.* (**русский перевод**) Russian translation.

русский *a.* Russian.

Руссо диаграмма Rousseau diagram.

рутен/иевый *a.* ruthenium, ruthenic; —**ий** *m.* ruthenium (Ru); —**истый** *a.* ruthenium, ruthenous.

рутил *m.* rutile; —**овый кристалл** rutile crystal.

рутин/а *f.*, —**ный** *a.* routine.

рухляк *m.* marl.

рухнуть *see* **рушиться.**

ручат/ельство *n.* guaranty; —**ься** *v.* guarantee, warrant.

руч/еек *m.* brook; —**ей** *m.* brook, stream; groove; —**ьи разряда** (elec.) streamers.

ручк/а *f.* handle; knob; shaft; (aero.) stick; —**и управления** control knobs.

ручн/ой *a.* manual, hand; **р. анемометр** pocket anemometer; —**ое манипулирование** manual manipulation; —**ое управление** manual control.

руш/ение *n.*, —**иться** *v.* collapse.

РФТ реактор *abbr. see* **реактор РФТ.**

РФХО *abbr.* (**Русское физико-химическое общество**) Russian Physico-Chemical Society.

рыб/а *f.*, —**ий** *a.* fish; —**ообразный** *a.* fish-shaped.

Рыбы Pisces (Psc) (constellation).

рывок *m.* jerk, kick.

рыжеватый *a.* reddish, rust-colored.

рысий *a.* lynx.

рыск/ание *n.* (radar) hunting; (aero.) yaw, wobble; —**ать** *v.* yaw; search.

рысь *f.* lynx.

Рысь Lynx (Lyn) (constellation).

рытвина *f.* rut, groove.

рыть *v.* dig; mine; —**е** *n.* digging.

рыхл/еть *v.* become friable; —**ость** *f.* friability; —**ый** *a.* friable, loose.

рычаг *m.* lever, arm; **плечо —а** lever arm.

рычаж/ный *a.* lever; —**ные весы** beam balance; —**ок** *m.* small lever, blade.

Рэлея *see* **Релея.**
рэт *m.*, **—ический ярус** Rhaetian stage.
ряб/ить *v.* ripple; **—ой** *a.* pitted; spotted; **—ь** *f.* ripple, ripples.
ряд *m.* series, row, train, array, a number of; succession, sequence, order; set, bank; rank, category; **р. лантанидов** lanthanide series; **р. напряжений** electromotive series; **р. нептуния** neptunium family; **р. радия** radium family; **р. счетчиков** counter tray; **р. урана** uranium family; **р. элементов** series (or family) of elements; **помещать в р., ставить в р.** range, put in a row, align; **на —у с** on a line with; **ставить на —у с** class with; **—ами** *adv.* in rows, in banks, in batteries.
рядов/ой *a.* ordinary, common, unsorted; consecutive, serial; **—ое железо** commercial iron.
рядом *adv.* beside, next to, near; side by side, in a row; **р. друг с другом** adjacent.
ряж *m.*, **—евый** *a.* crib, cribwork; **—евая плотина** crib dam.

С

с *prep. instr.* with; *prep. gen.* from; since; on; *prep. acc.* about (size of).
с *abbr.* **(секунда)** second; **с. (северный)** north, northern; **(село)** village; **(сила)** power; **(страница)** page.
с— *prefix with verbs* completion of action.
С [*in steel mark* **(кремний)**] silicon (Si).
С. *abbr.* **(север)** north.
СА *abbr.* **(стандартная атмосфера)** standard atmosphere.
Сабатье явление Sabattier effect.
сабин *m.* (acous.) sabin.
Сабин Sabine (lunar crater).
Сабина *see* **Сэбина.**
сабля *f.* sword, saber.
саботаж *m.*, **—ировать** *v.* sabotage.
Савара пластинка Savart plate; **С. полярископ** S. polariscope.
сагитта *f.* sagitta; **—льный** *a.* sagittal.
САГУ *abbr.* **(Среднеазиатский государственный университет)** Central Asia State University.
садить *see* **сажать.**
садиться *v.* sit; shrink; settle.
садка *f.* thickening; shrinkage; melt.
Садовского эффект Sadovskii effect.
сажа *f.* carbon black; soot; **ламповая с.** lamp black.
сажать *v.* set, place, put.
сажевый *a.* carbon black; soot.
сажень *f.* fathom.
саж/истый, —ный *a.* soot, sooty.
Саккура-Тетроде (Тетрода) постоянная Sackur-Tetrode constant; **формула С.-Т.** S.-T. equation.
Сакле Saclay; **саклеевский реактор** S. reactor.
Сакробоско Sacrobosco (lunar crater).
Саксмита весы Sucksmith balance.
салазки *pl.* sled, runners, slide, rails; (sliding) carriage.
салеит *m.* saleite.
салицилат *m.* salicylate.
сало *n.* grease; ice slush (fat, scum).
сальник *m.*, **—овый** *a.* (packing) gland; stuffing box.
сам *pron.* self, himself, itself; **с. по себе** alone, by itself; **—а** *f.* herself, itself; **—и** *pl.* themselves, yourselves; **—о** *n.* itself; **—о собой** automatically; **—о собой разумеется** it is understood, of course, it is self-evident.
САМ *abbr.* **(Завод счетно-аналитических машин)** Computing and Analytical Machine Plant.
самар/иевый *a.* samarium, samaric; **—ий** *m.* samarium (Sm); **—истый** *a.* samarium, samarous.
самарскит *m.* samarskite.
самересит *m.* samiresite.
само *see* **сам.**
само— *prefix* self—, auto—, automatic, spontaneous.
самобалансирующийся *a.* self-balancing.
самоблокирующий, —ся *a.* self-locking, interlocking.
самобытн/ость *f.* originality; **—ый** *a.* original, distinctive.
самовозбужд/ающийся *a.* self-excited;

—ение *n.* self-excitation, autoexcitation, self-triggering.

само/возврат *m.* self-restoration, self-reset; **—возгорание** *see* **—воспламенение**; **—воздействие** *n.* self-stress; **—возникающий** *a.* spontaneous.

самовольн/о *adv.* arbitrarily, unwarranted; **—ый** *a.* unwarranted.

самовоспламен/ение *n.* autoignition, self-ignition; spontaneous combustion; self-combustion; **—яемость** *f.* spontaneous combustibility; **—яемый, —яющийся** *a.* spontaneously inflammable; self-igniting; **—яющееся топливо** hypergolic propellant.

самовосстан/авливающийся *a.* self-regenerating, self-restoring, self-healing; **с. конденсатор** self-healing capacitor; **—овление** *n.* self-recovery.

самовыпрямляющийся *a.* self-rectifying.

самогасящий, —ся *a.* self-quenched, self-quenching; **с. счетчик** self-quenched counter.

самодвиж/ная лестница escalator; **—ущийся** *a.* automatic, self-propelled.

самодейств/ие *n.* self-action, self-force, self-stress; **—ующий** *a.* automatic, self-propelled.

само/диффузия *f.* self-diffusion; **—довлеющий** *a.* independent, self-sufficient; **—дуальный тензор** self-dual tensor.

самозажиг/ание *n.* self-ignition; **—ающийся** *a.* self-igniting.

самозакал/ивающийся *a.*, **—ка** *f.* self-hardening.

само/закрывающийся *a.* automatic closing, self-locking; **—заливающийся** *a.* self-priming.

само/замыкающийся, —запирающийся, —запорный *see* **самозакрывающийся**; **—запирание** *n.* automatic closing, automatic locking; **—запускающийся** *a.* self-starting, self-triggering.

самозащи/та *f.* self-shielding; self-defense, self-protection; **—щенный** *a.* self-protecting, self-shielded.

самозеркальный *a.* self-mirrored.

самоиндукц/ионный *a.* self-inductive; **—ия** *f.* self-induction; **коэффициент —ии** self-inductance.

самоинтерференция *f.* self-interference.

самоионизация *f.* self-ionization, autoionization.

самоиспарение *n.* spontaneous evaporation.

самокал *m.*, **—ка** *f.* air-hardened steel.

само/калибрующийся *a.* self-calibrating; **—касаться** *v.* (math.) be self-tangent; **—компенсированный** *a.* self-compensated.

самолет *m.* airplane, aircraft; **с. с ядерным двигателем** nuclear-powered plane; **—ный** *a.* airplane, aircraft; airborne; **—ная разведка** airborne prospecting (or reconnaissance); **—овождение** *n.* aeronavigation, avigation.

самоликвид/атор *m.* safety exploder ditching device; **—ация** *f.* self-destruction.

самонав/едение *n.* homing, homing guidance; **—одящийся снаряд** self-guided (or homing) missile.

самонакаливающийся катод ionic-heated cathode.

самонасыщающийся *a.* self-saturating.

само/ненарушимость *f.* stability; **—непересекающийся** *a.* non-self-intersecting.

самообразование *n.* self-education, self instruction.

самообращен/ие *n.* self-reversal; **—ная линия** self-reversed line.

само/ограничивающаяся реакция self limiting reaction; **—окисление** *n* autoxidation; **—опирающийся** *a* unsupported, independent; **—определение** *n.* self-determination **—ориентирующийся** *a.* self-orientating.

самоостан/авливающийся *a.* self-stopping; **—овка** *f.* automatic stop (or check).

само/отключение *n.* automatic opening **—отталкивание** *n.* self-repulsion.

самоохлажд/ающийся *a.*, **—ение** *n* self-cooling.

самоочевидный *a.* self-evident.

амоочищ/ающийся *a.* self-cleaning, self-purifying; **—ение** *n.* self-purification.

амо/пад *m.* free fall; **—передвигающийся** *a.* self-moving, automatic; **—пересечение** *n.* self-intersection, crunode.

амописец *m.* recorder, (automatic) recording instrument; **с. влажности** recording hygrometer, hygrograph.

амопишущий *a.* recording, self-registering; **с. барометр** barograph; **с. дождеметр** hyetograph; **с. манометр** monograph; **с. прибор** recorder, recording instrument; **с. тахометр** tachygraph.

амо/плавкий *a.* self-fluxing; **—поглощение** *n.* self-absorption.

амопод/аватель *m.*, **—ающий механизм** automatic feeder; **—ающий** *a.* self-feeding.

амоподдерживающ/ийся *a.* self-sustaining, self-maintaining; unsupported; **—аяся реакция** self-sustaining reaction.

амоприваривание *n.* self-welding.

амоприкосновен/ие *n.* self-tangency; **точка —ия** point of osculation, double cusp, tacnode.

амопроизвольн/о *adv.* spontaneously; **—ость** *f.* spontaneity; **—ый** *a.* spontaneous; **—ый распад** spontaneous decay (or disintegration); **—ая намагниченность** spontaneous magnetization; **—ое деление** spontaneous fission.

мопуск *m.* self-starting; self-starter; **—ающийся** *a.* self-starting.

мо/развивающийся *a.* self-developing; self-propagating; **—разгружающийся** *a.* self-discharging; **—разложение, —разрушение** *n.* spontaneous decomposition; **—размагничивающая сила** self-demagnetizing force; **—размножающийся** *a.* self-multiplying; **—разогрев** *m.*, **—разогревание** *n.* self-heating.

моразря/д *m.*, **—жение** *n.* self-discharge; **—жающийся** *a.* self-discharging.

мораспад *m.* spontaneous decay (or disintegration).

самораспространяющий, —ся *a.* self-propagating.

само/рассеяние *n.* self-scattering; **—расходящаяся цепная реакция** self-propagating chain reaction.

саморасцепл/ение *n.* self-detachment, automatic uncoupling; **—яющийся** *a.* self-detaching.

само/реагирующий двигатель spontaneous ignition engine; **—регистрирующий** *see* **самопишущий.**

саморегулир/ование *n.*, **—овка** *f.* automatic regulation; **—овать** *v.* regulate (or adjust) itself; **—ующийся** *a.* self-regulating, self-adjusting, self-aligning; **—ующийся реактор** self-regulating reactor.

самород/ный *a.* natural; native; **—ок** *m.* native metal, native ore; nugget.

само/светящийся *a.* self-luminous; **—сгорание** *see* **самовоспламенение.**

само/сжатие *n.* self-constriction, pinch, self-compression; **—сжатый** *a.* self-constricted, pinched; **—сжимающийся** *a.* self-constricted.

самосинхрониз/ация *f.* self-synchronization; **—ирующий** *a.* self-synchronizing.

самосмаз/ка *f.*, **—очный, —ывающий, —ывающийся** *a.* self-lubricating; **—ывание** *n.* self-lubrication, automatic lubrication.

само/смещение *n.* self-bias; **—совпадение** *n.* self-coincidence.

самосогласованн/ость *f.* self-consistency; **—ый** *a.* self-consistent; **—ое поле** self-consistent field.

самосопряженн/ость *f.* self-adjointness, hermiticity; **—ый** *a.* self-conjugate; self-adjoint, Hermitian; **—ый оператор** self-adjoint operator; **—ый треугольник** self-conjugate triangle; **—ое уравнение** self-adjoint equation.

самостолкновение *n.* self-collision.

самостоятельн/о *adv.* independently; **—ость** *f.* independence; **—ый** *a.* independent; **—ый разряд** self-maintained discharge; **—ый термический дуговой заряд** thermionic arc.

самостягив/ание *n.* self-constriction, pinch; **—ающаяся плазма** self-pinched plasma.

самосчитывающий *a.* self-reading.

самотек *m.* gravity flow; **—ом** by gravity; haphazardly.

самотечн/ый *a.* self-flowing; automatic; **—ая циркуляция** gravity circulation; **—ое орошение** wild flooding.

самотормо/жение *n.* retardation; automatic breaking, self-stopping; **—зиться** *v.* stop automatically; **—зящий, —зящийся** *a.* self-breaking, self-stopping.

само/точка *f.* automatic lathe; **—уверенный** *a.* self-confident.

самоуплотн/ение *n.*, **—яющийся** *a.* self-packing, self-sealing.

самоуправл/ение *n.* self-government, autonomy; **—яющийся** *a.* self-governing.

самоуравновешивающийся *a.* self-balancing.

самоустанавлив/ание *n.* self-adjustment, automatic adjustment; **—ающийся** *a.* self-adjusting, automatically adjusting, self-aligning; floating.

само/устойчивость *f.* autostability; **—учитель** *m.* self-instruction manual.

самофазиров/ание *n.*, **—ка** *f.* autophasing.

самофлюсующийся *a.* self-fluxing.

самоход *m.* power feed; self-action; **—ный** *a.* automotive, self-propelled, self-acting; power-operated; **—ная подача** power feed.

самоцель *f.* end in itself.

самоцентр/ирующийся *a.* self-centering, self-aligning; **—овка** *f.* self-centering, self-alignment.

само/шлакующийся *a.* self-fluxing; **—экранирование** *n.* self-protection, self-shielding.

самум *m.* (meteor.) simoom.

сам/ый *a.* same, the very, self; most; **с. верхний** uppermost; **с —ого начала** from the beginning; **тем —ым** thereby.

санатрон *m.* sanatron.

санафант *m.* sanaphant.

сангвинит *m.* sanguinite.

сандвич *m.*, **—евый** *a.* sandwich.

сани *pl.* sledge, sleigh, sled.

санитар/ия *f.* sanitation; **—ный** *a.* sanitary; **—ная физика** health physics.

санкционир/ованный *a.* sanctioned, approved; **—ать** *v.* sanction, approve assent to.

Сантбек Santbech (lunar crater).

санти— *prefix* centi—.

санти/бар *m.* centibar; **—бел** *m.* centibel; **—грамм** *m.* centigram; **—литр** *m.* centiliter.

сантиметр *m.* centimeter; **—овые волны** (centimeter) microwaves.

сантипуаз *m.* centipoise (cp).

Саньяка опыт Sagnac experiment.

сапфир *m.*, **—овый** *a.* sapphire; **—ин** *m* sapphirine.

сард, —ер *m.* sard.

Сарджента кривая Sargent curve.

сардоникс *m.* sardonyx.

сарколит *m.* sarcolite.

саркома *f.* sarcoma.

саркопсид *m.* sarcopside.

сармат *m.*, **—ский ярус** Sarmatian stage

сарос *m.* saros.

Сарруса (Саррюса) правило Sarrus rule

сателлит *m.* satellite, planet pinion planet wheel; **—овый** *a.* satellite subordinate.

сатура/тор *m.* saturater; **—ционный** *a* **—ция** *f.* saturation.

Сатурн Saturn.

Саха уравнение Saha equation.

сахар *m.*, **—ный** *a.* sugar; **—иметр** *m* saccharimeter; **—иметрия** *f.* saccharimetry; **—истость** *f.*, **—истый** *a* saccharine; saccharoidal; **—ные леденцы** sucrose crystals; **—оза** *f* saccharose, sucrose.

сб *abbr.* **(стильб)** stilb; **сб. (сборник)** collection.

сбав/ить, —лять *v.* reduce, lower; deduct, subtract; **—ка** *f.* reduction lowering; deduction.

сбалансиров/анный *a.* balanced; **—ать** *v.* balance.

сбалтывать *v.* stir, mix, shake.

сбе/гание *n.* running off; **—гать, —жать** *v.* run off, flow off; run down.

сбегающий край, с. скат trailing edge.

сбере/гать, —чь *v.* save; stock; keep preserve; **—жение** *n.* economy, saving.

бивать *v.* knock off; throw down; put together.

бивчивый *a.* confused, inconsistent.

битый *a.* out of position, out of alignment, biased; put together.

бли/жать, —зить *v.* bring together, bind, connect; compare; **—жаться** *v.* approach, converge; **—жение** *n.* approach, convergence; connecting, binding; **—женный** *a.* contiguous, adjacent, close-lying.

блокированный *a.* interlinked, interlocked.

боку *adv.* on the side, from the side; **вид с.** side view.

бол/тить, —чивать *v.* bolt, fasten; **—ченный** *a.* bolted-together, fastened; **—чивание** *n.* bolting together, fastening.

бор *m.* assemblage, gathering, collection.

борка *f.* assembly, erection, installation, fitting, joining; **предварительная с., узловая с.** preliminary assembly, subassembly.

борник *m.* collection, compilation; collector, receiver, catcher, tank, header, manifold; **с. памяти** memorial volume; **с. статей** collected papers; symposium.

борн/ый *a.* composite, aggregate, built-up, assembled, sectional; collecting; **с. бак** collecting tank; **—ая группа** assembly; **—ая карта** composite map; **—ая шина** (elec.) collecting main; busbar.

борочн/ая *f.*, **—ый цех** assembly shop, assembly plant; **—ый** *a.* assembly, erecting; **—ый конвейер** assembly belt; **—ая метка** matchmark.

борщик *m.* assembler, fitter, mounter; collector.

расыв/аемый *a.* expendable, jettisonable; **—ание** *n.* dropping, dumping, discarding; (geo.) faulting; **—ание давления** depressurizing; **—ать** *v.* cut off, drop, discard, dump; **—ающий** *a.* dumping; **—ающая трещина** (geo.) fault fissure.

рос *m.* discharge; break; (geo.) fault; (cryst.) kink; **линия —а** fault trace.

росить *see* **сбрасывать.**

сбросов/ый *a.* (geo.) fault; **—ая гора** block mountain; **—ая группа дислокаций** (cryst.) piled-up dislocation group; **—ая деятельность** faulting; **—ая линия** fault trace; **—ое строение** faulted structure, block faulting; **—ые воды** waste liquid, effluent.

сброшенный *a.* discarded, dumped; (geo.) faulted.

сбывать *v.* dispose of; **—ся** *v.* come true, be realized.

сбытие *n.* diminution.

св *abbr.* [**свеча (международная)**] international candle; (**среднее время**) mean time; **св.** (**сверху**) from the top (of page); (**свыше**) above, greater than.

с.-в. *abbr.* (**северо-восточный**) northeast, northeastern.

С.-В. *abbr.* (**северо-восток**) northeast.

свайка *f.* pole.

свайнобойный *a.* pile-driving.

сваленный *a.* dumped, unloaded.

свалив/ание *n.* dumping; **—ать** *v.* dump, unload; accumulate, heap up; **—аться** *v.* fall.

свал/ить *see* **сваливать**; **—ка** *f.* dump, dumping ground; **—очный** *a.* dumping, unloading.

сваренный *a.* welded; cooked.

сварив/аемость *f.* weldability; **—аемый, —ающийся** *a.* weldable; **—ать, сварить** *v.* weld.

сварка *f.* weld, welding; **с. в стык** butt welding, butt weld.

сварн/ой, —ый *a.* welded.

сварочн/ый *a.* weld, welding; **с. металл** weld metal; **—ое железо** weld iron, wrought iron.

Свартхольма-Зигбана магнитный спектрограф Svartholm-Siegbahn magnetic spectrograph.

свая *f.* pile.

Сведберга опыт Svedberg experiment.

сведен/ие *n.* knowledge, information; reduction; **с. в таблицу** tabulation; **—ия** *pl.* information, data; **доводить до —ия** notify; **принять к —ию** take into consideration; **сообщать —ия** inform.

сведенный *a.* reduced; **с. к нулю** nullified.

сведущ/ий *a.* expert, skilled; —**ее лицо** expert.
свеже— *prefix* freshly, recently.
свеже/перегнанный *a.* freshly distilled; —**сть** *f.* freshness.
свежий *a.* fresh, recent; **с. ветер** fresh breeze (Beaufort number 5); **с. нейтронный поток** virgin neutron flux; **с. пар** live steam.
свезти *see* **свозить.**
свер/ение *n.*, —**ка** *f.* comparison, verification, collation; —**ить** *see* **сверять.**
сверк/ание *n.* sparkle, glitter, flash; —**ать,** —**нуть** *v.* flash, sparkle, glitter, glare, scintillate; —**ающий** *a.* sparkling, glittering, flashing, bright.
сверление *n.* boring, drilling.
сверлильн/ый *a.* boring, drilling; **с. станок,** —**ая машина** drill, drill press; —**ая стружка** borings.
сверл/ить *v.* bore, drill, perforate; —**о** *n.* (boring) bit, drill, borer.
сверн/увшийся *a.* coagulated; coiled; —**утость** *f.* convolution.
свернут/ый *a.* convolute, coiled, rolled; stripped; coagulated; **с. катод** wrapped cathode; **с. тензор** contracted tensor; —**ь** *see* **свертывать;** —**ься в петлю** kink.
сверстанный лист imposed page.
свертеть *see* **свертывать.**
свертка *f.* convolution, folding; (math.) faltung; contraction; **с. тензора** tensor contraction.
свертн/ый *a.* screwed-on; —**ая гайка,** —**ая муфта** screw cap.
свертываем/ость *f.* coagulability; (math.) contractibility; —**ый** *a.* coagulable; contracted.
свертыван/ие *n.* coagulation; (math.) convolution, folding, contraction (of tensor); coiling, rolling; curtailment; **интеграл —ия** convolution (integral).
свертывать, —**ся** *v.* coagulate; (math.) contract, fold; roll (up), coil, curl, wrap, turn; curtail.
сверх *prep. gen.* above, over, beyond; besides, in addition to; **с. ожидания** beyond expectation; **с. того** moreover, furthermore.
сверх— *prefix* super—, hyper—, ultra—, extra—, over—; excess.
сверх/адиабатический *a.* superadiabatic; —**большая энергия** ultrahigh energy.
сверхбыстрый *a.* ultrafast, ultrahigh speed; **с. прерыватель** superchopper.
сверхвозбуждение *n.* superexcitation.
сверхвысок/ий *a.* ultrahigh; superhigh; —**ая температура** ultrahigh temperature; —**ая частота** superhigh frequency; —**ая энергия** ultrahigh energy; —**ое давление** ultrahigh pressure; —**ое напряжение** ultrahigh voltage; —**очастотный** *a.* superhigh-frequency.
сверх/генерация *f.* supergeneration; —**геострофический ветер** supergeostrophic wind; —**гигант** *m.* supergiant; —**градиентный ветер** supergradient wind; —**группа** *f.* supergroup.
сверх/давление *n.* overpressure; excessive pressure; —**дальний полет** extra-long-range flight.
сверхжестк/ий *a.* ultrahard; —**ие лучи** ultrahard rays.
сверх/закалка *f.* (met.) superhardening; —**затухание** *n.* overdamping.
сверхзвуков/ой *a.* supersonic; ultrasonic; **с. поток** supersonic flow; —**ая скорость** supersonic velocity; —**ая техника** supersonics; —**ая частота** ultrasonic frequency.
сверхзвуко/запись *f.* ultrasonography; —**скопия** *f.* ultrasonoscopy.
сверх/корона *f.* supercorona; —**критический** *a.* supercritical; —**легкий** *a.* superlight; —**линейный** *a.* ultralinear; —**миниатюрный** *a.* subminiature.
сверхмощн/ый *a.* superpower, high power; **с. реактор** superpower reactor; —**ая лампа** superpower tube; —**ое ракетное топливо** superpowered rocket fuel.
сверхмультиплет *m.* hypermultiplet.
сверхнизкая температура extremely low temperature; **с. частота** ultralow frequency.
сверхникель *m.* supernickel (copper nickel alloy).
Сверхновая (звезда) Supernova.
сверх/обменный *a.* superexchange; —**оболочечный** *a.* outside of close

shell; —**определенный** *a.* overdetermined; overdefined; —**отжиг** *m.* overannealing; —**переходная постоянная времени** subtransient time constant; —**плотный** *a.* overdense; —**преломление** *n.* superrefraction.

верхпровод/имость *f.* superconductivity; —**ник** *m.* superconductor; —**ящий** *a.* superconducting.

верх/размерный *a.* oversize; —**расчетное напряжение** overrating voltage; —**регенеративный** *a.* superregenerative; —**рефракция** *f.* superrefraction; —**световой** *a.* faster-than-light; —**сжатие** *n.* overcompression.

верхразрешенный *a.* superallowed; **с. переход** superallowed transition.

верхскоростн/ой *a.* ultrafast, ultrahigh-speed, hypersonic; —**ая центрифуга** ultracentrifuge.

верх/сопряжение *n.* hyperconjugation; —**старение** *n.* overaging; —**стационарный** *a.* superstationary; —**стехиометрический** *a.* stoichiometrically in excess; —**счетный** *a.* odd.

верхструктур/а *f.* superstructure; (cryst.) superlattice; —**ная линия** superstructure line.

верхтвердый *a.* superhard, extra-hard.

верхтеку/честь *f.* superfluidity; —**щий** *a.* superfluid.

верх/ток *m.* overcurrent, excess current; —**тонкий** *a.* hyperfine; —**точный** *a.* ultra-accurate; —**тяжелый** *a.* superheavy.

верху *adv.* from above; on top; **вид с.** top view; **с. вниз** downward.

верхупруг/ий *a.* hyperelastic; —**ое столкновение** superelastic collision.

верхусиление *n.* overamplification.

верхустойчив/ость *f.* overstability; —**ый** *a.* overstable.

верх/человеческий *a.* superhuman; —**чистый** *a.* ultrapure; —**чувствительный** *a.* supersensitive; —**фокусное расстояние** hyperfocal distance; —**фоторегистрация** *f.* moving-image (or streak) camera photography.

ерять *v.* compare, collate.

ес *m.* overhang, projection; —**ить** *see* **свешивать.**

ести *see* **сводить.**

свет *m.* light; world; —**а** *pl.* lights, highlights; **рассеянный с.** diffuse light; **в —е** in the light (of); in view of; **в —у** clear, in the clear, inside; **высота в —у** inside height, clearance; **диаметр в —у** inside diameter; **расстояние в —у** clear spacing, clear distance; **сила —а** candlepower; **ширина в —у** clearance.

светать *v.* dawn, grow light.

светил/о *n.* star, luminary, light; —**а** *pl.* heavenly bodies.

светильн/ик *m.* illuminating lamp, lighting fixture; —**ый** *a.* illuminating.

светимость *f.* luminous (or radiant) emittance; (astr.) luminosity.

светить *v.* shine, give light; —**ся** *v.* shine, gleam.

светлеть *v.* lighten, brighten; clear up.

светло *adv.* light, bright, clear; it is light; —**адаптированный** *a.* light-adapted; —**вина** *f.* bright spot; —**окрашенный** *a.* light-colored, light.

светлопольн/ый *a.* bright-field; —**ое изображение** bright-field image.

светлость *f.* clearness, lucidity; lightness, brightness.

светл/ый *a.* light, bright, luminous; clear, lucid; **с. столб** light pillar; —**ая точка** open circle; —**ое сияние** aureole.

светность *see* **светимость.**

свето— *prefix* light, photo—; *see also* **фото—.**

световод *see* **светопровод.**

светов/ой *a.* light, luminous; **с. вектор** electric vector (of electromagnetic wave); **с. выход** luminescence yield (or efficiency); **с. год** light year; **с. заряд** flare, flashpowder charge; **с. затвор** light valve; **с. импульс** light pulse; **с. квант** light quantum; **с. конус** beam of searchlight (or lamp); (rel.) light cone; **с. луч** light ray (or beam) **с. маяк** light beacon; **с. носитель тока** photocurrent carrier; **с. поток** luminous flux; **с. спектр** light spectrum; **с. эталон** standard light source; **с. эфир** luminiferous ether.

светов/ой *cont.*, —**ая волна** light wave; —**ая вспышка** light flash, scintillation; —**ая дуга** luminous arc; —**ая единица** light unit; —**ая копия** *see*

светокопия; **—ая лунная постоянная** light constant of the moon; **—ая мощность** luminosity; **—ая отдача** luminous efficiency; **—ая плотность** luminous density; **—ая сумма** light sum; **—ая телефония** phototelephony; **—ая частица** light particle, photon; **—ая энергия** luminous energy; **—ое давление** light pressure; **—ое пятно** light spot; **—ое старение** light aging; **—ое явление** luminous phenomenon; optical phenomenon.

свето/делительное зеркало color-selective mirror; **—делящий** *a.* light-dividing; **—излучение** *n.* light emission; **—испускающий** *a.* light-emitting, luminous.

светокоп/ировальный *a.* blueprint, blueprinting; **—ия** *f.* print.

светомаскировка *f.* blackout.

светомер *m.* photometer; **—ный** *a.* photometric; **—ный шар** integrating (or sphere) photometer.

свето/метрия *f.* photometry; **—модулятор** *m.* light modulator; **—непроницаемый** *a.* lightproof, light-tight, opaque; **—носный** *a.* luminiferous.

светоотдач/а *f.* luminous efficiency; luminescence efficiency (or yield); **коэффициент —и** luminescence efficiency (or yield).

свето/отрицательный *a.* light-negative; **—писное копирование** blueprinting; photostating; **—погодостойкость** *f.* light and weather resistance.

светопоглощ/аемость *f.* luminous absorptivity; **—ение** *n.* luminous absorption.

свето/положительный *a.* light-positive; **—провод** *m.* light conductor (pipe, guide); **—прозрачный** *a.* transparent.

светопроницаем/ость *f.* translucence; **—ый** *a.* translucent.

светопрочный *a.* photostable.

светорассе/ивающий *a.* light-diffusing; **—яние** *n.* diffusion of light.

светосигнализация *f.* light signaling.

светосил/а *f.* (phot.) aperture ratio, relative aperture; transmission, luminosity (of spectrometer, etc.); **—ьный** *a.* high-transmission; fast (lens).

свето/собирающий *a.* light-collecting; **—состав** *m.* luminous compound, phosphor.

светостойк/ий *a.* lightproof, photostable, fast (dye); **—ость** *f.* light resistance.

светосумма *f.* light sum.

светотеневое изображение black-and-white picture.

светотехн/ика *f.* lighting (or illumination) engineering; **—ический** *a.* illumination, photometric.

свето/устойчивость *f.* fastness to light; **—фильтр** *m.* light (or color) filter; **—фор** *m.* signal light.

светочувствительн/ость *f.* light sensitivity, photosensitivity; **—ый** *a.* light-sensitive, photosensitive; **—ый элемент** photocell, phototube; **—ая поверхность** photosurface; **—ая проводимость** photoconductivity; **—ое сопротивление** photoresistance.

светоэлектрический *a.* photoelectric.

светящ/ийся *a.* luminous; luminescent, fluorescent, phosphorescent; **с. разряд** glow discharge; **с. электрон** radiating electron; **—аяся краска** luminous paint; **—иеся облака** noctilucent clouds.

свеч/а *f.* candle; **зажигательная с., запальная с.** spark plug; **международная с.** international candle; **нормальная с., стандартная с.** standard candle; **сила света в —ах, число —ей** candlepower.

свечение *n.* luminescence, fluorescence, phosphorescence; radiation, emission; luminosity, glow; **с. Альп** alpenglow; **белое с.** white heat; **вторичное с.** secondary emission; **красное с.** red heat; **с. накаленного тела** incandescence; **с. ночного неба** night airglow; **с. от трения** triboluminescence.

свечн/ой *a.* candle; **—ость** *f.* candlepower.

свешив/ать *v.* lower; **—аться** *v.* overhang; **—ающийся** *a.* overhanging.

свив/ание *n.*, **—ка** *f.* coiling, twisting; **—ать** *v.* coil, twist, wind.

свидание *n.* meeting.

свидетель *m.* observer, witness.

свидетельств/о *n.* evidence; document, certificate, record; **поверочное с.** calibration certificate; **—овать** *v.* attest; indicate; **—ующий** *a.* indicating, indicative.

свиль *f.* stria, cord (in glass, etc.); **—ный** *a.* schlieren.

свинец *m.* lead (Pb).

свинтить *see* **свинчивать.**

свинц/евание *n.* lead plating, lead lining; **—овистый** *a.* lead, plumbous.

свинцово-оловянный сплав lead-tin alloy; **с.-сульфидный фотоэлемент** lead sulfide photocell.

свинцов/ый *a.* lead, plumbic; **с. аккумулятор** (elec.) lead accumulator, battery; **с. блеск** galena; **с. пепел, —ая изгарина** lead dross; **с. эквивалент** lead equivalent; **—ая почка** bindheimite; **—ое стекло** lead glass.

свинч/енный *a.* screwed (together); **—ивание** *n.* screwing; **—ивать** *v.* screw (together).

свис/ать, —нуть *v.* hang loose; **—лый** *a.* hanging, sagging.

свист *m.* whistle, hiss; (rad.) howl; **—ать, —еть, —нуть** *v.* whistle; **—ок** *m.* whistle.

свистящий *a.* whistling; **с. метеор** whistling meteor; **с. шум** hissing noise.

свита *f.* suite, series.

свит/ый *a.* coiled, convoluted; **—ь** *see* **свивать.**

свищ *m.* flaw; (met.) airhole, honeycomb.

свобода *f.* freedom, liberty.

свободно *adv.* freely, easily; **с. опертый** simply supported; **с. стоящий** self-supported.

свободн/ый *a.* free, vacant, unoccupied; clear; available; **с. от** free from; devoid of; **с. от носителя** carrier-free; **с. от пыли** dust-free; **с. поток** free (or unrestricted) flow, free stream; **с. пробег** (mean) free path; **с. радикал** free radical; **с. ток** (elec.) transient current; **с. электрон** free electron; **—ая атмосфера** free atmosphere (or air); **—ая оболочка** vacant shell; **—ая сетка** (elec.) floating grid; **—ая энергия** free energy; **—ое место** vacancy; **—ое пространство** free space; **—ое течение** free (or unrestricted) flow; **—ые колебания** free (or natural) oscillations, normal mode.

свод *m.* arch, vault, dome; (geo.) anticline; summary, digest.

сводим/ость *f.* reducibility; **—ый** *a.* reducible.

сводить *v.* lead; trace back; bring together; (math.) reduce; **с. в таблицу** tabulate; **с. к нулю** nullify, reduce to zero; **—ся** *v.* amount to; reduce to; **—ся на нет** disappear, lose strength, come to naught (nothing), taper off, converge at infinity.

сводка *f.* summary, résumé; **с. погоды** weather forecast (or report).

сводн/ый *a.* compound, composite, combined, cumulative, summarizing; **—ая таблица** summary table; **—ые годографы** combined travel–time curves.

сводчатый *a.* arched, vaulted.

свое *see* **свой.**

своевременн/о *adv.* at the proper time, opportunely; **—ость** *f.* opportuneness; **—ый** *a.* opportune, timely, well-timed.

своеобраз/ие *n.*, **—ность** *f.* peculiarity, originality, uniqueness, unusualness; **—ный** *a.* peculiar, unusual, distinctive, different, unique, original.

своз/ить *v.* bring (together); carry, transport; **—ка** *f.* conveyance, transport, removal.

свой *a. and possessive pron.* my, his, her, its, our, your, their; one's own; domestic, home.

свойственн/ость *f.* peculiarity, singularity; **—ый** *a.* peculiar, distinctive, characteristic; natural, inherent, intrinsic.

свойств/о *n.* property, characteristic, feature, aspect; nature, character; **физические —а** physical properties.

свор/ачивание *n.* turning; **—ачивать, —отить** *v.* displace, dislodge, remove; turn.

СВЧ *abbr.* (**сверхвысокая частота**) superhigh frequency.

свык/аться, —нуться *v.* become accustomed.

свыше *prep. gen.* above, beyond, greater than.

связан/ие *see* **связывание**; **—но-свободный переход** bound-free transition.

связанн/ый *a.* bound, bonded, combined; connected, coupled, linked, allied; associated; due to; related, coherent; **с. атом** bound atom; **с. вектор** localized (or field) vector; **с. вихрь** bound (or attached) vortex; **с. водородной связью** hydrogen-bonded; **с. заряд** bound charge; **не с.** free; **химически с.** chemically combined, bonded, bound; **с. электрон** bound electron; **с. эффект** coupled effect; **—ая активность** related activity; **—ая вода** bound water; **—ая волна** associated wave; **—ая пара** coupled pair; **—ое состояние** bound state; **—ые звезды** close-pair stars; **—ые контуры** coupled circuits; **—ые поля** coupled fields; **—ые системы** coupled systems; **—ые уравнения** coupled equations; **—ые частицы** associated particles; bound particles.

связать *see* **связывать.**

связи *see under* **связь.**

связк/а bunch, bundle, bond; binding, strap; **с. магнетрона** magnetron strap; **с. плоскостей** sheaf (or bundle) of planes; **голосовые —и** vocal cords.

связной *a.* communication.

связн/ость *f.* connectedness, connectivity, coherence, cohesion; **—ый** *a.* connected, cohesive, coherent; compendent.

связочный *a.* bundle, bunch; strapped.

связующ/ий *a.* binding, cementing, connecting, connective, conjunctive, coupling, bonding; **с. агент** (chem.) complexing agent; **—ая способность** binding power, cementing power; **—ее вещество, —ее средство** binder, adhesive, glue, cement; agglutinant.

связыв/ание *n.* capture, binding, combining, linking, coupling; **с. магнетрона** magnetron strapping; **—ать** *v.* bind, combine; link, associate, couple, connect; cement, bond; **—ать попарно** couple; **—аться** *v.* be bound, combine; communicate with.

связывающий *see* **связующий**; **с. член** coupling term; **с. электрон** bondin electron.

связ/ь *f.* bond, tie, connection, couplin link, linkage, joining, bonding, bin ing; relation, association; liaiso coherence, continuity; communica tion; binder; tie piece, stay, brac constraint; **атомная с.** atomic bon **двойная с.** (chem.) double bond; **с затяжка** bracing; **идеальная** smooth contact; **катодная с.** cat ode coupling; **с. окном, с. отве стием** iris coupling; **слишком сил ная с.** overcoupling; **константа —** coupling constant; **коэффициент —** (elec.) coupling coefficient (or factor coupling constant; **момент —и** (stat covariance; **регулируемый орга —и** variocoupler; **служба —и** com munication service; **энергия —** binding energy; **в —и с** in conne tion with; in view of; **в этой —и** this connection; accordingly.

сг *abbr.* (**сантиграмм**) centigram; **с.** (**сего года**) this year, current year.

сгиб *m.* bend, flexure, fold; **—аемость** pliability, flexibility; **—аемый** pliable, flexible, collapsible; **—ание** flexure, bending, deflection; **—атель ный** *a.* bending; **—ать, —аться** bend, flex, fold; deflect.

сгибающ/ий *a.* bending, flexing; **—ийс** *see* **сгибаемый.**

сгла/дить, —живать *v.* smooth (ou over); fit; flatten, level; plan **—живание** *n.* smoothing (out planing; leveling; **—живатель** *n* smoother; **—живаться** *v.* we smooth.

сглаживающий *a.* smoothing; **с. дро сель** smoothing choke; **с. филь** ripple filter.

сговариваться *v.* agree upon, arran for.

сгон *m.* driving together; surge; **—ять** join, fit.

сгораем/ость *f.* combustibility, inflan mability; **—ый** *a.* combustible, i flammable.

сгоран/ие *n.* combustion; **с. горюче** fuel burnup; **двигатель внутренне —ия** internal-combustion engin **камера —ия** combustion chambe коэффициент —ия burnup factor; продукты —ия combustion products.

сгор/ать, —еть *v.* burn, burn up, burn out; —ающий *a.* burning, combustible; —евший *a.* burnt.

сгруппиров/ание, —ывание *n.* grouping, bunching; —анный *a.* grouped, bunched; —анные данные (stat.) classified data; —ать, —ывать *v.* group.

СГС система *abbr.* (система сантиметр-грамм-секунда) cgs system.

СГСЕ система *abbr.* cgse system, cgs electrostatic system (esu).

СГСМ система *abbr.* cgsm system, cgs electromagnetic system (emu).

сгустившийся *a.* thickened, coagulated.

сгуститель *m.* thickener, coagulant, condenser; —ный *a.* thickening, coagulating; —ное средство coagulant.

сгуст/ить *see* сгущать; —кообразующее устройство buncher; —ок *m.* cluster, bunch, blob, clot; —ок электронов electron bunch.

сгущаем/ость *f.* condensability, compressibility; —ый *a.* condensable; compressible.

сгущ/ать *v.* thicken, condense; compress; coagulate, clot, curdle; bunch; crowd; —ающий *a.* condensing, concentrating; coagulating; bunching; crowding; —ающее вещество coagulant.

сгущен/ие *n.* condensation; crowding, bunching; clotting, coagulation, thickening; с. состояний crowding of levels; —ный *a.* condensed; bunched; coagulated, clotted.

сдавать *v.* give up, yield.

сдавл/енный *a.* pressed, squeezed, compressed; —ивание *n.* pressing, compression; pinching; —ивать *v.* press, squeeze, compress; pinch; —ивающий *a.* compressive.

сдать *see* сдавать.

сдваив/ание *n.* doubling, duplication; —ать *v.* double, duplicate; combine in pairs.

сдвиг *m.* shift, displacement; drift; shear, shearing; slip; (geo.) fault, heave; lag; improvement, progress; с. ветра wind shear; с. нуля zero drift; с. уровня level shift; с. фаз phase shift (or difference); коэффициент —а coefficient of shear; напряжение —а shear stress; плоскость —а shear plane; площадь —а shear area; сопротивление —у shear strength; угол —а angle of displacement; угол —а фаз phase angle.

сдвиг/ание *n.* displacement, shifting; —ать *v.* displace, shift, slide, remove; shear; draw together; —аться *v.* shift, shear, move; —ающий *a.* shifting, shearing; —ающая сила shear (or shearing) force (or stress); shear.

сдвигов/ый *a.* shift, shear, displacing; —ая волна shear wave; —ая вязкость shear viscosity; —ая деформация shear; —ая неустойчивость shearing instability; —ое превращение displacement transformation; модуль —ой упругости shear modulus.

сдвигообразование *n.* generation of dislocations.

сдвиж/ение *n.* displacement, shifting, shearing; bringing together; —ной *a.* movable.

сдвинут/ый *a.* shifted, displaced, moved; disaligned; staggered, offset; с. по фазе out of phase, dephased; —ое совпадение delayed coincidence; —ые настроенные контуры stagger-tuned circuits; —ь *see* сдвигать.

сдвоение *n.* doubling, duplication; twinning.

сдвоенн/ый *a.* double, dual, duplex; twin, twinned; binary, paired, tandem, matched; с. электрон paired electron; —ая ионизационная камера double (or back-to-back) ionization chamber; —ая лампа dual tube.

сдвоить *see* сдваивать.

сдвойникованный *a.* twinned; с. кристалл twinned crystal.

сдел/анный *a.* made, manufactured; done; —ать *v.* make, manufacture; do, accomplish; —ать вывод draw a conclusion; —аться *v.* become.

сделка *f.* agreement; transaction.

сдерж/ать, —ивать *v.* check, restrain; contain; —ивание *n.* check, restraint; —ивать газ contain a gas; —ивающий *a.* restrictive.

сдир/ание *n.* stripping, peeling; **—ать, —аться** *v.* strip, peel off.
сду/вать, —ть *v.* blow away, blow off.
себестоимость *f.* cost.
себоллит *m.* cebollite.
себя *pron., gen of* **сам,** oneself, myself, himself, herself, itself, ourselves, yourselves, themselves.
сев. *abbr.* (**северный**) north, northern.
север *m.* north; **—нее** *adv.* to the north (of).
Северная Корона Corona Borealis (CrB) (constellation).
северн/ый *a.* north, northern, northerly; **с. полярный круг** Arctic Circle; **—ая полярность** north-seeking polarity; **—ая широта** north latitude; **—ое (полярное) сияние** aurora borealis.
северо/-восток *m.* northeast; **с.-восточный** *a.* northeastern, northeasterly; **с.-запад** *m.* northwest; **с.-западный** *a.* northwestern, northwesterly; **с.-магнитный** *a.* north-magnetic.
Северо-Осетинская АССР North Ossetian ASSR.
северо-экваторное течение north equatorial current.
сегмент *m.* segment, section; **—ация** *f.* segmentation; **—ный, —ообразный** *a.* segmental, segmentary.
Сегнер Segner (lunar crater).
сегнерово колесо Segner wheel.
сегнетоактивный *see* **сегнетоэлектрический.**
сегнетова соль Rochelle salt, Seignette salt.
сегнетокерамика *f.* ferroelectric ceramic.
сегнетоэлектр/ик *m.* ferroelectric (crystal); **—ический** *a.* ferroelectric; **—ичество** *n.* ferroelectricity.
сего *see* **сей.**
сегодня *adv.* today; **—шний** *a.* today's.
Сегре Segrè.
сегрега/т *m.* segregate; **—ционный** *a.* segregation, segregated; **—ция** *f.* segregation.
седиментац/ионный *a.,* **—ия** *f.* sedimentation.
седиментометр/ический *a.* sedimentometric; **—ия** *f.* sedimentometry.
седло *n.* saddle; valve seat; (meteor.) col; (geo.) anticline; **—видный, —образный** *a.* saddle-shaped, saddle, saddle-point; **—видная точка** saddle point; **—вина** *f.* saddle, valley, trough; (meteor.) col; (geo.) anticline.
седьмой *a.* seventh.
Сезерланда уравнение Sutherland equation.
сезон *m.* season; **—ный** *a.* seasonal; **—ное неравенство** annual inequality.
сей *pron. m.* this; **сии** *pl.* these; **до сих пор** up to now.
Сейболта вискозиметр Saybolt viscosimeter.
сейсм *m.* seism.
сейсмич. *abbr. see* **сейсмический.**
сейсмическ/ий *a.* seismic; **—ое пересечение** seismic traverse.
сейсмограмма *f.* seismogram.
сейсмограф *m.* seismograph; **с.-термофон** *m.* hot-wire (resistance) seismometer; **—ия** *f.* seismography.
сейсмо/конвертор *m.* seismoconverter; **—логия** *f.* seismology; **—метр** *m.* seismometer; **—метрия** *f.* seismometry; **—приемник** *m.* seismic detector; **—разведка** *f.* seismological prospecting; **—скоп** *m.* seismoscope; **—стойкий** *a.* earthquakeproof; **—электрический эффект** seismoelectric effect.
сейчас *adv.* now, immediately; just now.
сейш *m.,* **—а** *f.* seiche.
сек. *abbr.* (**секретный**) secret, confidential; (**секунда**) second.
секанс *m.* secant.
Секки диск Secchi disk; **классификация С.** S. classification.
секр. *abbr.* (**секретарь**) secretary.
секретар/ский *a.* secretarial; **—ь** *m.* secretary.
секретн/ость *f.* secrecy; **установление степени —ости** classification; **—ый** *a.* secret, confidential, classified; **—ая работа** classified work.
сексагональный *a.* hexagonal.
Сексмита весы Sucksmith balance.
Секстан Sextans (Sex) (constellation).
секстан, —т *m.* sextant.
секстет *m.,* **—ный** *a.* sextet.
секстиль *m.* sextile.
секстильон *m.* sextillion.
сектор *m.* sector; segment; group

—**иальная скорость** *see* **секторная скорость**; —**иальная функция** sectorial harmonic.

екторн/ый *a.* sector, sectoral, sectorial; **с. рупор** sectoral horn; **с. спектрометр** sector spectrometer; —**ая волна** sectoral wave; —**ая скорость** areal velocity; —**ое магнитное поле** magnetic sector field; —**ое поле** sector field.

екторообразный луч sector-shaped beam.

екулярное уравнение secular equation.

екунд/а *f.* second; —**ный** *a.* second, per second; —**омер** *m.* stopwatch, timer.

екущ/ая *f.*, —**ая линия** secant; transversal; —**ий** *a.* cutting, intersecting, secant.

екционирова/ние *n.* partitioning; —**анный** *a.* sectioned, subdivided, sectional; —**анная катушка** sectional (or tapped) coil; —**ать** *v.* sectionalize; subdivide, partition.

екц/ионно-кольцевой резонатор annular-sector resonator; —**ионный** *a.* section, sectional, divided; —**ия** *f.* section, unit; (elec.) loop.

еладонит *m.* celadonite.

елевк Seleucus (lunar crater).

елективн/ость *f.* selectivity, discrimination; —**ый** *a.* selective, discriminatory; —**ый фотоэффект** selective photoeffect; —**ое отражение** selective reflection; —**ое травление** (cryst.) etch-pit technique.

електиров/ание *n.* selection; (elec.) gating, strobing; —**ать** *v.* select; (elec.) gate, strobe.

електор *m.* selector; **с. амплитуды импульсов** pulse-height selector; **с. быстроты нейтронов** neutron-velocity selector; **временной с.** (elec.) time gate; **с. нейтронов** neutron-velocity selector, neutron chopper; **с. по времени пролета** time-of-flight (velocity) selector; **с. скоростей** velocity selector.

електорн/ый *a.* selector; (elec.) gate, strobe; **с. импульс** gate (or strobe) pulse; —**ая щель** selector slit.

елек/трон *m.* selectron; —**ция** *f.* selection.

елен *m.* selenium (Se); —**ид** *m.* selenide; —**истый** *a.* selenious, selenium; selenide (of); —**истый теллур** selentellurium.

селено— *prefix* seleno—, selenium.

селеновый *a.* selenium, selenic; seleniferous; **с. (твердый) выпрямитель** selenium rectifier; **с. фотоэлемент** selenium photocell; **с. элемент** selenium cell.

селено/графия *f.* selenography; —**центрический** *a.* selenocentric.

селитра *f.* saltpeter, niter.

Сельмейера формула Sellmeier equation.

сельсин *m.*, —**ный** *a.* selsyn, synchro; **бесконтактный с.** mag slip; **с.-датчик** transmitting selsyn; **с.-приемник** synchro repeater; —**ный двигатель** selsyn motor.

сельск/ий *a.* rural; —**ое хозяйство** agriculture, farming; —**охозяйственный** *a.* agricultural, farm.

сем *see* **сей**; **при сем** herewith, enclosed.

семафор *m.* semaphore; —**ный** *a.* semaphore, semaphoric, signal-arm.

семей/ный *a.* domestic; family; —**ство** *n.* family, series; —**ство урана** uranium family (or series).

семер/ка, —о seven.

семестр *m.* semester; —**овый** *a.* semiannual.

семи— *prefix* semi—; hepta—, septi—, seven.

семиатомный *a.* heptatomic.

семивалентн/ость *f.* heptavalence, septivalence; —**ый** *a.* heptavalent, septivalent.

семиводный гидрат heptahydrate.

семигранн/ик *m.* heptahedron; —**ый** *a.* heptahedral.

семи/десятый *a.* seventieth; —**значный логарифм** seven-place logarithm.

семи/инвариант *m.* semi-invariant; —**коллоид** *m.* semicolloid; —**кратный** *a.* sevenfold, septuple; —**летальный** *a.* semilethal.

семилет/ка *f.*, —**ний план** Seven-Year Plan; —**ний** *a.* seven-year, septennial.

семиполярная связь semipolar bond.

семи/ричный *a.* septenary; —**сотый** *a.* seven-hundredth; —**сторонний** *a.* heptalateral.

семиугольн/ик *m.* heptagon; **—ый** *a.* heptagonal.
семи/циклический *a.* heptacyclic; **—членный** *a.* seven-membered, heptacyclic.
семнадцат/ый *a.* seventeenth; **—ь** seventeen.
семсейит *m.* semseyite.
семь seven; **—десят** seventy; **—сот** seven hundred.
семья *f.* family.
семя *n.* seed.
Сен-Венана условия St. Venant conditions.
сендаст *m.* Sendust (iron-silicon-aluminum alloy).
сеноман *m.*, **—ский ярус** Senoman stage.
сенперм *m.* Senperm (iron-nickel-silicon alloy).
сенсибилиз/атор *m.* sensitizer; **—ация** *f.* sensitization, sensitizing; **—ированный, —ованный** *a.* sensitized.
сенситограмма *f.* sensitogram, sensitometric strip.
сенситометр *m.* sensitometer; **—ический** *a.* sensitometric; **—ия** *f.* sensitometry.
сент *m.* (acous.) cent.
сент. *abbr.* (**сентябрь**) September.
Сентри Sentry (satellite).
сентябрь *m.* September.
сепарабельн/ость *f.* separability; **—ый** *a.* separable.
сепарат/ный *a.* separate, independent; separative; **—ная способность** separative power; **—ор** *m.* separator; **—риса** *f.* separatrix, limiting curve.
сепарац/ионный *a.* separative; **—ионная способность** *see* **сепаратная способность**; **—ия** *f.* separation.
септариевый *a.* (geo.) septarian.
септима *f.* (mus.) seventh.
Септр Sceptre (thermonuclear device).
сер— *see also* **цер—**.
сер. *abbr.* (**серия**) series.
сера *f.* sulfur (S).
Сербера сила, серберовская сила Serber force.
серводвигатель *m.* servomotor.
серво/манипулятор *m.* servomanipulator; **—механизм** *m.* servomechanism; **—мотор** *m.* servomotor; **—передача управляющих стержней** servo and control mechanism; **—привод** *m.* servodrive.
сервоуправл/ение *n.* servocontrol; **—яемый** *a.* servocontrolled.
сервоусилитель *m.* servoamplifier.
Сер. геоф. *abbr.* (**Серия геофизическая**) Geophysical Series.
сердечник *m.*, **—овый** *a.* core; arbor; **выдвижной с.** plunger.
сердце *n.* heart; **—видный** *a.* heart-shaped; **—вина** *f.* core, center, heart, interior.
серебрение *n.* silver plating.
серебристо— *prefix* silver, argento—.
серебрист/ый *a.* silvery; silver, argentous; **—ая сталь** *see* **серебрянка**; **—ые облака** noctilucent clouds.
серебрить *v.* silver plate.
серебро *n.* silver (Ag); **азотнокислое с.** silver nitrate; **бромистое с.** silver bromide; **—носный** *a.* argentiferous.
серебрян/ка *f.* silver steel; **—одисковый актинометр** silver-disk actinometer; **—ый** *a.* silver.
середина *f.* middle; mean; **с. полной фазы затмения** midtotality (of eclipse).
серединн/ый *a.* central, middle, center mean; **—ая ось** central axis; **—ое питание** center feed.
сережка *f.* shackle.
Серенсена шкала pH Sørensen pH scale
сериальн/ый *a.* serial, series; **—ая формула** series formula.
сериес/машина *f.* series generator **—ный** *a.* series; **—ный двигатель** series motor.
серийн/ый *a.* series, serial; commercial (-type); **с. распад** series decay; **—ое производство** mass (or quantity) production.
серицит *m.* sericite.
серия *f.* series, train, succession, order **с. волн** wave train; **с. измерений** run (of measurements).
сернистокислый натрий sodium sulfite.
сернист/ый *a.* sulfur, sulfurous; sulfide (of); **с. водород** hydrogen sulfide; **с. натрий** sodium sulfide; **с. углерод** carbon bisulfide; **с. цинк** zinc sulfide **—ая кислота** sulfurous acid; **соли —ой кислоты** sulfite.

серноватистокислый натрий sodium thiosulfate.

сернокислый *a.* sulfuric acid, sulfate (of); **с. иод-хинин** quinine-iodine sulfate (polaroid); **с. уранил** uranyl sulfate.

сверносеребряный фотоэлемент silver sulfide cell.

серн/ый *a.* sulfur, sulfuric; **с. колчедан** pyrite; **—ая кислота** sulfuric acid.

серо— *prefix* sulfur; gray.

серо/водород *m.* hydrogen sulfide; **—содержащий** *a.* sulfur-containing.

серость *f.* grayness.

сероуглерод *m.* carbon bisulfide.

серп *m.* crescent; sickle.

серпентин/изация *f.* (min.) serpentinization; **—изированный** *a.* serpentinous; **—овый** *a.* serpentine.

Серпинск/ий Sierpinski; **—ого ковер** S. carpet.

серпо/видный, —образный *a.* crescent shaped, crescent.

сертификат *m.* certificate.

сер/ый *a.* gray; **с. клин** gray wedge; **с. след** gray track (or prong); **—ое олово** gray tin; **—ое тело** gray body.

серьга *f.* link, shackle.

серьезн/ость *f.* seriousness, gravity; **—ый** *a.* serious, grave; **—ые основания** strong arguments (for).

сескви— *prefix* sesqui—.

сессия *f.* session.

сесть *see* **садиться.**

сетевой *a.* network, power-line; mesh.

Сетка Reticulum (Ret) (constellation).

сетк/а *f.* grid; mesh, net, network, screen, gauze; reticle; lattice; graticule; **географическая с.** graticule; **с. дислокаций** dislocation network; **защитная с.** (elec.) suppressor grid; guard net; **с. координат** coordinate grid (network, system); **проволочная с.** wire gauze; **с. резонатора** cavity grid; **с. течения** (hyd.) flow net; **экранирующая с.** (elec.) screen grid; **метод —и (метод сеток)** net-point method; **—ообразный** *a.* net-shaped, reticular, reticulate; gridlike.

сеточн/ый *a.* grid; net; **с. агрегат, с. комплект** grid assembly; **с. детектор** grid detector; **с. потенциал** (math.) net-point potential; (elec.) grid potential; **с. электрод** grid electrode; **—ая батарея** C battery; **—ая краевая задача** net boundary problem; **—ая утечка** grid leak; **—ая ячейка** wire mesh; **—ое напряжение** grid voltage; **—ое смещение** grid bias; **—ое сопротивление** grid resistor (or leak).

сетчатка *f.* retina.

сетчат/ый *a.* mesh, network, reticulate, reticular; cellular; latticed; **с. барабан** revolving screen; **с. узор** reticulation; **с. шов** mesh weld; **с. экран** wire screen; **—ая модель** lattice model; **—ая оболочка** *see* **сетчатка;** **—ая плоскость** lattice plane; **—ая структура, —ое строение** reticular (or lattice) structure; **—ая тарелка** sieve plate.

сеть *f.* net, network, mesh; (elec.) line, supply system; **сопряженная с.** (math.) conjugate net.

сечение *n.* cross section, section, profile; cut, intersection, division; gauge, size; **с. весовое потоком** flux-weighted cross section; **с. деления тепловыми нейтронами** thermal-neutron fission cross section; **с. захвата нейтронов** neutron-capture cross section; **коническое с.** conic section; **с. переноса** transport cross section; **поперечное с.** cross section; **с. торможения** stopping cross section.

сжат/ие *n.* compression, constriction, contraction, shrinking; flattening; confinement, pinching; pinch effect; **с. Земли** flattening of the earth; **с. тока** current constriction; **камера —ия** compression chamber; **коэффициент —ия** contraction coefficient; **модуль всестороннего —ия** compression (or bulk) modulus; **сопротивление —ию** compressive strength; **степень —ия** compression ratio.

сжат/о *adv.* concisely; **—ость** *f.* conciseness, compactness; compression; **большая степень —ости** high compression ratio.

сжат/ый *a.* condensed, compressed, cramped; contracted; compact, concise; oblate; constricted, pinched; **с. газ** pinched gas; **с. собственным**

магнитным полем self-pinched (plasma); **с. эллипсоид** oblate ellipsoid; **—ая дислокация** contracted dislocation; **—ая плазма** pinched plasma; **—ая шкала** compressed scale; **—ое сечение** contracted section; **метод —ых отображений** method of contractive mappings.

сжечь *see* **сжигать.**

сжиг/ание *n.* combustion, burning, incineration, consumption; **камера —ания** combustion chamber; **—ать** *v.* burn (up), consume; **—ать дотла** ash, incinerate.

сжиж/ать *v.* liquefy; liquate out; **—ение** *n.* liquefaction; liquation; **—енный** *a.* liquefied; liquated.

сжим *m.* grip, clamp.

сжимаем/ость *f.* compressibility, condensability; contractibility; constrictibility; **коэффициент —ости** compressibility (factor); **—ый** *a.* compressible, condensable; contractible; **—ая жидкость** compressible fluid; **—ое течение** compressible flow.

сжим/ание *n.* compression, condensation; contraction, constriction, shrinkage; *see also* **сжатие**; **—ать** *v.* contract, constrict; squeeze, press, pinch; **—аться** *v.* condense; contract, shrink.

сжимающ/ий *a.* compressing, compressive, condensing; **с. ход** compression stroke; **—ая нагрузка** compression load; **—ее давление, —ее напряжение** compression (compressional, compressive) stress; **—ее усилие** compressive force; **—ийся** *a.* contractile.

сжимки *pl.* clamp.

с.-з. *abbr.* **(северо-западный)** northwestern.

С.-З. *abbr.* **(северо-запад)** northwest.

сзади *adv.* behind, from behind, at the rear of.

сзывать *see* **созывать.**

сиал/ический *a.* sialic; **—ь** *m.* (geo.) sial.

Сиаччи функция Siacci function.

сиб *abbr.* **(сибирский)** Siberian (used as a prefix).

сибирский *a.* Siberian.

Сиборг Seaborg.

сиботаксис *m.* cybotaxis.

сигарообразный *a.* cigar-shaped.

сигма *f.* sigma; **с.-связь** sigma bond; **с.-функция** sigma function.

сигмо/идальный, —образный *a.* sigmoid.

сигнал *m.* signal, alarm; **с. бедствия** distress signal, SOS; **с.-генератор** signal generator.

сигнализ/ация *f.*, **—ирование** *n.* signaling; **—ировать** *v.* signal; **—ирующий** *a.* signaling.

сигнальн/ый *a.* signal, signaling, alarm; **—ая лампа** pilot lamp, signal lamp; **—ая цепь** alarm circuit.

сигнум *m.* signum.

сидерак *m.* maghenite.

сидерит *m.* siderite.

сидерический *a.* sidereal.

сидеро/лит *m.* siderolite; **—плезит** *m.* sideroplesite; **—скоп** *m.* sideroscope; **—стат** *m.* siderostat; **—сфера** *f.* (geo.) barysphere, centrosphere; **—тил** *m.* siderotil; **—филлит** *m.* siderophyllite; **—шизолит** *m.* sideroschisolite.

сидеть *v.* sit, be seated.

сидя/чий *a.* sitting; sessile; **—ая дислокация** sessile dislocation; **—щий** *a.* sitting; **—щий в** set in.

сиенит *m.* syenite.

сизиг/ий *m.*, **—ия** *f.* syzygy; **—ийный, —иский** *a.* syzygial, spring; **—ийный прилив** spring tide.

сиккатив *m.* siccative, desiccant.

сиклерит *m.* sicklerite.

сикромо *m.* Sicromo (silicon-chromium-molybdenum steel).

Сикса термометр Six thermometer.

сил/а *f.* force, strength, power; intensity; **с. влечения** tractive force, traction; **живая с.** kinetic energy; **с. звука** sound intensity; **с. излучения** radiant intensity; **с. инерции** inertia force; **с. кручения** torsional force; **с. линии** line strength; **лошадиная с.** horse power; **с. натяжения** stretching (or straining) force, tensile stress; **с. осцилятора** oscillator strength; **с. отдачи** recoil force; **с. отталкивания** repulsive force; **с. поперечного сопротивления** cross-wind force; **с. поступательного движения** propelling power; **с. притяжения** attractive force; **с. притяжения близкого дей**

ствия short-range attractive force; **с. противодействия** counteracting force.

сил/а *cont.*, **с. равнодействующая, с. результирующая** resultant force; **реактивная с.** reaction; **с. света** luminous intensity, candlepower; **с. сцепления** cohesive (or adhesive) force; **с. тока** current strength; **с. трения** frictional force; **с. тяги** tractive force, traction; **с. тяготения** (force of) gravitational attraction; **с. тяжести** (force of) gravity; **с. уровня** level intensity; **с.-час** horsepower-hour; **вектор —ы** line of force; **в —у** in virtue of, on account of; according to; **единица —ы** unit of force; **оставаться в —е** remain valid, hold good.

силал *m.* Silal (a high-silicon cast iron).

силан *m.* silane.

Силард Szilard.

силезит *m.* silesite.

силекс *m.* silex.

силектрон *m.* Silectron (iron-silicon alloy).

силикагель *m.* silica gel.

силикат *m.*, **—ный, —овый** *a.* silicate; silica; **—изация** *f.* silication, silification.

силико— *prefix* silico—, silicon.

силиколь *m.* Silicol.

силикон *m.*, **—овое масло** silicone.

силитовый элемент Silit (silicon carbide heating element).

силлиманит *m.*, **—овый** *a.* sillimanite.

Силов Sylow.

силов/ой *a.* power, force; **с. бридер** power breeder; **с. винт** (mech.) wrench; **с. интервал** power range; **с. коэффициент** power coefficient; **с. провод** power line; **с. реактор** power reactor; **с. трансформатор** power transformer; **с. центр** center of force; **с. цикл** power cycle.

силов/ой *cont.*, **—ая линия** line of force, field line; **—ая нагрузка** force (or power) loading; **—ая постоянная** force constant; **—ая связь** strong coupling; **—ая система** power system; **—ая станция** power station (or plant); **—ая трубка** tube of force, field tube; **—ая установка** power unit (or plant); means of propulsion; **—ая функция** force function; strength function; **—ая цепная реакция** power chain reaction; **—ая цепь** power circuit; **—ое питание** power supply; **—ое поле** force field.

силовская группа Sylow group.

силоксан *m.* siloxane.

силомер *m.* dynamometer.

силумин *m.* Silumin (silicon-aluminum alloy).

силунд *m.* silundum.

силур *m.*, **—ийский период** Silurian period.

силуэт *m.* silhouette.

сильванит *m.* sylvanite.

сильватрон *m.* sylvatron.

Сильвестра теорема Sylvester theorem.

сильвин *m.*, **—овый** *a.* sylvite.

сильманал *m.* Silmanal (silver-manganese-aluminum alloy).

сильно *adv.* highly, strongly, powerfully; **с. возбужденный уровень** highly excited level; **с. обогащенное горючее** highly enriched fuel; **с. сингулярный** highly singular.

сильно/действующий *a.* drastic, violent; **—деформированный** *a.* strongly deformed; **—запрещенный** *a.* highly forbidden; **—изменчивый** *a.* highly variable; **—ионизированный** *a.* highly ionized; **—ионизирующий** *a.* heavily ionizing; **—кислый** *a.* highly acid; **—магнитный** *a.* highly magnetic; **—проникающий** *a.* highly penetrating; **—связанный** *a.* strongly coupled, tightly bound.

сильноточн/ый *a.* power; high-current; heavy-current; **—ая промышленность** power industry; **—ая техника** power engineering.

сильнофокусирующий *a.* strong-focusing.

сильн/ый *a.* powerful, strong, violent, intense, sharp, severe; **с. ветер** moderate gale (Beaufort number 7); **с. дождь** heavy rain; **с. мороз** severe frost; **с. разрыв** (math.) second-order discontinuity; **с. снег** heavy snow; **с. туман** dense fog; **с. шторм** whole gale (Beaufort number 10); **—ая гроза** severe thunderstorm; **—ая деформация** severe strain; **—ая особая точка** essential singular point;

—ая связь strong coupling; tight (or strong) binding (or bond); (elec.) tight (or close) coupling; **—ая топология** strong topology; **—ая фокусировка** alternating-gradient focusing, strong focusing; **—ое взаимодействие** strong interaction; **—ое волнение** high sea (Douglas number 6); **—ое натяжение** high tension; **—ое облучение** acute irradiation (or exposure).

Сильсби гипотеза Silsbee hypothesis; **С. правило** S. rule.

сильфон *m.*, **—ное соединение** sylphon bellows.

сильхром *m.* Silchrome (chromium-silicon steel).

сим *abbr.* (**сименс**) Siemens unit (mho).

СИМ *abbr.* (**Сибирский научно-исследовательский институт металлов**) Siberian Scientific Research Institute of Metals.

симанит *m.* seamanite.

симатический *a.* simatic.

симбатность *f.* similarity of slope.

символ *m.* symbol; **—изировать** *v.* symbolize, represent; **—ический** *a.* symbolic.

сименс, Сименса единица Siemens unit (mho); **С.-мартеновский процесс** S.-Martin (or open-hearth) process.

симилор *m.* Similor, Mannheim gold (variety of brass).

симметр/изация *f.*, **—ирование** *n.* symmetrization, balancing; **—ирующий** *a.* symmetrizing, balancing; **—ирующее преобразование** symmetrization.

симметрич/еский, —ный *a.* balanced, symmetric, symmetrical; **—ное деление** symmetrical fission; **—ность** *see* **симметрия.**

симметрия *f.* symmetry; **с. по вращению, с. по отношению вращения** rotation symmetry; **с. по временному отражению, с. по отношению времени** time-reflection symmetry; **с. по отношению отражения, с. по отражению** reflection symmetry; **с. по отношению смещения, с. по смещению** translation symmetry.

симониит *m.* simonyite.

симпатический *a.* sympathetic.

Симпелий Simpelius (lunar crater).

симплезит *m.* symplesite.

симплекс *m.*, **—ный** *a.* simplex.

симплектический *a.* symplectic, simplicial.

Симпсона правило Simpson rule.

симптом *m.* symptom; **—атический** *a.* symptomatic.

симпьезометр *m.* sympiesometer.

симул/ировать *v.* simulate; **—яция** *f.* simulation.

синадельфит *m.* synadelphite.

сингенит *m.* syngenite.

синглет *m.*, **—ный** *a.* singlet.

сингония *f.* (cryst.) system.

сингулет *see* **синглет.**

сингулярн/ость *f.* singularity; **—ный** *a.* singular.

синдиотактический *a.* sindiotactic.

синдром *m.* syndrome.

синева *f.* (dark) blue; **—тый** *a.* bluish.

синекалильный *a.* at blue heat.

синеломк/ий *a.* (met.) blue brittle, blue short; **—ость** *f.* blue brittleness.

синерезис *m.* syneresis.

синерод *m.* cyanogen.

син/еть *v.* turn blue; **—ий** *a.* (dark) blue; **—ее свечение** blue glow.

синильная кислота hydrocyanic (or prussic) acid.

синимакс *m.* Sinimax (iron-nickel-silicon alloy).

синклиналь *f.*, **—ный** *a.* synclinal.

синклинорий *m.* synclinorium, synclinore.

синкозит *m.* sincosite.

синодический *a.* synodic; **с. оборот** synodic rotation.

синоним *m.* synonym; **—ический** *a.* synonymous.

синопсис *m.* synopsis.

синопти/к *m.* weather forecaster; **—ка** *f.* synoptic meteorology (or forecasting); synoptic chart; **—ческий** *a.* synoptic; **—ческая карта** synoptic chart, weather map.

синтагматит *m.* syntagmatite.

синтез *m.* synthesis; fusion; **с. ядер** nuclear fusion; **—ированный** *a.* synthesized; **—ировать** *v.* synthesize; **—ируемый** *a.* synthesizable; synthesized; **—ное вещество** fusionable material.

синтермалический *a.* synthermal.

синтеров/ание *n.*, **—очный** *a.* sintering; **—анный** *a.* sintered.

синтетически *adv.* synthetically; **—й** *a.* synthetic.

Синт. кауч. *abbr.* (**Синтетический каучук**) Synthetic Rubber (journal).

синтониз/ация *f.* syntonization, tuning; **—ированный** *a.* syntonized, tuned; **—ировать** *v.* syntonize, tune.

синтонический *a.* syntonic.

синус *m.*, **—ный** *a.* sine; **с.-косинусный генератор** sine-cosine generator; **с.-счетчик** sine meter; **с. угла потерь** power factor (of a dielectric); **условие —ов** (Abbé) sine condition.

синусоида *f.* sinusoid, sine curve; **—льный** *a.* sinusoidal; **—льная волна** sine wave.

синфаз/ирование *n.* cophasing; **—ный** *a.* cophased, cophasal, in-phase; **—ная антенна** broadside array.

синхизит *m.* synchisite.

синхро *n.* synchro; synchro—; **—генератор** *m.* synchro generator.

синхрониз/атор *m.* synchronizer; **—ация** *f.*, **—ирование** *n.* synchronization, synchronizing; **—ированный** *a.* synchronized, synchronous; **—ирующий** *a.* synchronizing; **—ирующий смеситель** (elec.) lock-in mixer.

синхронизм *m.* synchronism; **входить в с.** synchronize, pull in step; (elec.) lock in; **приводить в с.** synchronize.

синхрон/ический, —ичный, —ный *a.* synchronous; **—но** *adv.* in step; **—ность** *f.* synchronism, simultaneity, coincidence.

синхро/носкоп, —скоп *m.* synchroscope.

синхротрон *m.* synchrotron; **с. с жесткой (или сильной) фокусировкой** strong-focusing synchrotron.

синхро/фазотрон *m.* synchrophasotron, proton synchrotron; **—циклотрон** *m.* synchrocyclotron.

синь *f.* blue; **—ка** *f.* blueprint.

синьоритет *m.* seniority.

синэргический *a.* synergic.

сипилит *m.* sipylite.

сирена *f.* siren.

Сиренсена *see* **Серенсена.**

Сириус Sirius.

сирлезит *m.* searlesite.

система *f.* system, arrangement; **с. клеток** grid system; **с. координат** coordinate system; **с. многих частиц** many-particle system; **с. отсчета** frame of reference, reference system; **с. покоя** (rel.) rest frame; reference system; **с. скольжения** (cryst.) slip system; **с. сопряженных связей** conjugated system of bonds; **с. счетчиков** counter array; **с. трех тел** three-body system; **с. уравнений** system (or set) of equations; simultaneous equations; **с. центра инерции, с. центра масс** center-of-mass system, center-of-gravity system.

системат/изация *f.* systematization; classification; **—изировать** *v.* systematize; classify, arrange; **—ика** *f.* systematics, systematization; classification; **—ически** *adv.* systematically; consistently; **—ический** *a.* systematic, methodical; **—ическая ошибка** systematic error.

ситалл *m.* pyroceramic, glassceramic.

сито *n.* sieve, screen; **—видный** *see* **ситообразный.**

сито/вой, —чный, —вый *a.* sieve, screen; **с. анализ** sieve (screen, mesh, size) analysis; **с. состав** size grading; **—образный** *a.* screenlike, screen.

ситуац/ионный *a.*, **—ия** *f.* situation.

ситчатый *see* **ситовый.**

сифон *m.* siphon; **сливать —ом** siphon (off).

сифонн/ый *a.* siphon, siphonal; **с. барометр** siphon barometer; **с. водосброс** (hyd.) siphon spilling; **с. трубопровод, —ая трубка** siphon, siphon tube, siphon tubing.

сих *see under* **сей.**

сихнодимит *m.* sychnodymite.

сия/ние *n.* glow, luminescence; aurora; aureole, halo; **с. Альп** alpenglow; **—ть** *v.* shine, radiate.

сияющ/ий *a.* shining, radiant; **с. спектр** auroral spectra; **—ая зона** auroral zone.

СК *abbr.* (**синтетический каучук**) synthetic rubber.

скажем let us say.

сказ/анный *a.* said, asserted; **—ать** *v.* say, assert; tell; **так —ать** so to speak; **—аться, —ываться** *v.* affect; appear (in), be expressed (in).

скак/ание *n.* jumping; **—ать** *v.* jump.

скала *f.* scale; rock, cliff.

скалар *m.*, **—ный** *a.* scalar; **—ное произведение** scalar (inner, dot) product.

скаленоэдр *m.* scalenohedron; **—ический** *a.* scalenohedral.

скалистый *a.* rocky, craggy.

скалк/а *f.*, **—овый** *a.* roller; valve stem, plunger pin.

скалообразующий *a.* (geo.) petrogenic.

скалыв/ание *n.* splitting, cleaving; shear, shearing; spallation; **структура —ания** (geo.) shear structure; **—ать** *v.* cleave, split (off), chop off, shear.

скалывающ/ий *a.* shearing; cleavage; **—ее напряжение** cleavage stress; **—ее усилие** shearing force (or stress).

скальный *a.* rock.

скальчатый *a.*, **с. поршень** plunger; **с. насос** plunger pump.

скам/ейка, —ья *f.* bench.

сканд/иевый *a.* scandium; **—ий** *m.* scandium (Sc).

скан/дирование, —ирование *n.* scan, scanning; **—ировать** *v.* scan.

скапливать, —ся *v.* collect, accumulate, store.

скаполит *m.* scapolite.

скат *m.* slope, incline, pitch; ramp; **—ать** *see* **скатывать**; **—ить** *v.* roll down.

скатыв/ание *n.* rolling, sliding; **—ать, —аться** *v.* roll down, slide.

скафандр *m.* pressurized (space, diving) suit.

скач/енный *a.* run-off; **—ивание** *n.* running (or drawing) off; **—ивать** *v.* run (draw, drain) off.

скачкообразн/ость *f.* unevenness; jerkiness; **—ый** *a.* uneven, jerky, intermittent, stepwise, discontinuous, staggered; abrupt; sudden; **—ая функция** jump (or step) function.

скач/ок *m.* jump, discontinuity, step, abrupt (sudden, rapid) change; **с. ветра** wind shift; **с. давления** compression shock, pressure jump; **с. деформации** abrupt deformation; **с. мощности** power flash-up; **с. разряжения** expansion shock; **с. уплотнения** shock wave, compression shock; **с. фазы** phase discontinuity; **слой —ка** layer of discontinuity; **линия —ков** step-function curve; **функция —ков** step function; **—ком** abruptly, discontinuously, precipitously; **—ками** in stages (or steps), irregularly; **—ущий фильм** jumping film.

скашив/ание *n.* sloping, beveling; **—ать** *v.* slope, bevel.

скважин/а *f.* hole, bore; aperture, slit, interstice, pore; (oil) well; **буровая с.** borehole; **со —ами** porous; **—ный снаряд** borehole probe (sonde, sensing unit).

скваж/истость, —ность *f.* porosity; spacing; (elec.) off-duty factor (reciprocal of duty factor); **—истый** *a.* porous.

скверн/о *adv.* badly, poorly; **—ый** *a.* bad, poor.

сквозить *v.* pass through, appear through, be seen through.

сквозн/ой *a.* through, straight-through; open; continuous; **с. переход** direct transition; **—ая трещина** through crack.

сквозь *adv.* through.

скелет *m.* skeleton, frame; **—ная схема** block diagram.

скепти/к *m.* sceptic; **—ческий** *a.* sceptical.

скетч *m.* sketch.

скиаметр *m.* sciameter.

скиатрон *m.* skiatron, dark-trace tube.

скид/ка *f.* allowance, reduction, deduction; discount; **—ывать** *v.* allow, deduct; throw off.

скинут/ый *a.* deducted; thrown off; **—ь** *see* **скидывать.**

скин-эффект *m.* skin effect.

склад *m.* warehouse, storehouse, storeroom; storage, stock; character; constitution; **с. ума** mentality.

складк/а *f.* crease, wrinkle, fold; (geo.) fold; (math.) convolution; **с. местности** geological feature; **—ообразование** *n.* folding, fold formation.

складной *a.* folding, collapsible; portable.

склад/очный, —ской *a.* warehouse, storehouse; storage; **—ской бак**

storage tank; —**ские помещения** storage facilities.

складчат/ость *f.* (geo.) folding; —**ый** *a.* folded; (met.) wrinkled.

складыв/ание *n.* putting together; folding; storing; —**ать,** —**аться** *v.* add, compute, sum up, combine; comprise; put together; fold; accumulate, pile, store.

склеенн/ость *f.* adhesion; —**ый** *a.* glued, cemented, pasted; joined.

склеив/ание *n.* gluing, cementing, pasting; —**ать** *v.* glue, cement, conglutinate; splice, join; —**ающее вещество** adhesive.

скле/ить *see* **склеивать**; —**йка** *f.* patch, splice; cementing, pasting, gluing (together).

склеп/анный, —**ный** *a.* riveted (together); —**ка** *f.*, —**ывание** *n.* riveting; —**ывать** *v.* rivet (together), clench; —**ывающий** *a.* riveting.

склеретинит *m.* scleretinite.

склероклаз *m.* scleroclase.

склерометр *m.* sclerometer.

склерометрическ/ий *a.* sclerometric; —**ая твердость** scratch hardness; —**ое испытание (царапанием)** scratch (or scratch-hardness) test.

склерон *m.* Scleron (aluminum-base alloy).

склерономный *a.* scleronomous.

склероскоп *m.*, —**ический** *a.* scleroscope.

склодовскит *m.* sklodowskite.

склон *m.* slope, side, descent, decline, dip; —**ение** *n.* (mag.) declination, variation; (astr.) declination; (math.) inclination; —**ение копмаса** compass bearing; **круг** —**ения** (astr.) hour circle; —**енный** *a.* inclined, sloped; —**ить** *see* **склонять.**

склонн/ость *f.* inclination, tendency; **иметь с.** tend, be inclined to; —**ый** *a.* inclined, disposed.

склонять *v.* incline, bend, persuade; —**ся** *v.* incline, bend; yield; tend (to).

склянка *f.* vial, bottle, flask; ice crust.

с.к.о. *abbr.* (**среднее квадратическое отклонение**) root-mean-square (rms) deviation.

скоб/а *f.* bracket; cramp (iron), clamp, cleat, shackle; hook; fastening, catch, claw, detainer; buckle; staple; **железная с.** cramp iron; **калиберная с.** external gauge; **скрепить** —**ой** cramp, clamp.

скобель *m.* scraper.

скобк/а *see* **скоба;** —**и** *pl.* parentheses, brackets; **взять в** —**и** parenthesize, enclose in parentheses; **вынести за** —**и** factor out.

скобл/ение *n.* scraping; —**ильный инструмент** scraper; —**ить** *v.* scrape, smooth, plane.

скобяные изделия, с. товары hardware.

сков/анный *a.* forged, welded; constrained, bound; —**ать** *see* **сковывать.**

сковиллит *m.* scovillite.

сковка *f.* forging, welding.

сковород/ень, —**ник** *m.* dovetail.

сковыв/ание *n.* welding, forging; —**ать** *v.* weld, forge.

скогбелит *m.* skogbölite.

скол *see* **скалывание.**

сколачивать *v.* put together; knock off.

сколецит *m.* scolecite.

сколлимированный *a.* collimated.

сколовая зона shear zone.

сколок *m.* spallation fragment.

сколотить *see* **сколачивать.**

сколот/ый *a.* sheared, cleaved; —**ь** *see* **скалывать.**

сколь *see* **сколько.**

скольжен/ие *n.* slip, slipping, glide, slide; glancing, skidding; **восходящее с.** upside motion, upgliding; **с. дислокации** glide of dislocation; **нисходящее с.** downside motion, downgliding; subsidence; **критическое напряжение** —**ия** critical shearing stress (or slip); **линия** —**ия** glide (slip, shear) line; **плоскость** —**ия** glide (or slip) plane; **система** —**ия** glide system.

скольз/ить, —**нуть** *v.* slip, slide, skid; glide; —**кий** *a.* slippery; —**кость** *f.* slipperiness, lubricity.

скользящ/ий *a.* slipping, slip, sliding, gliding; glancing, grazing; skidding; **с. камень** slide block; **с. контакт** sliding contact; **с. удар** glancing collision; —**ая волна** glancing wave; —**ая дислокация** glissile dislocation; —**ее столкновение** grazing collision; —**ие разряды** (elec.) creepage.

сколько *adv.* how much, how many(?); **с. раз** how frequently(?); **с. угодно** as much as desired, at pleasure; arbitrary; unlimited.
скомбинированный *a.* combined, combination.
скомк/анный *a.* crumpled, bunched; **—ать** *v.* wrinkle, bunch.
скомпенсированный *a.* compensated, balanced.
скомпилированный *a.* compiled.
скомплектованный *a.* assembled.
сконденсированный *a.* condensed.
сконструиров/анный *a.* constructed, designed; **—ать** *v.* construct, design, engineer.
сконцентрированный *a.* concentrated.
скоп/ившийся *a.* accumulated, piled-up; (geo.) segregated; **—ить** *see* **скапливать.**
скопл/ение *n.* accumulation, cluster, crowd, swarm, aggregate; agglomeration, agglomerate, blob; (astr.) cluster; (geo.) segregation; **с. дислокаций** dislocation pile-up; **с льда** ice accretion; **—енный** *a.* accumulated, collected; **—яемый** *a.* cumulative; **—ять** *see* **скапливать.**
скопометр *m.* scopometer; **—ия** *f.* scopometry.
скорее *comp. of* **скоро,** sooner, more quickly; rather, preferably; **с. всего** much rather; most likely; **как можно с.** as soon as possible.
скорлуп/а *f.* shell, hull; **—ный** *a.* shell.
скорлупо/ватый *a.* shell; **—ватая структура** (geo.) conchoidal structure; **—образный** *a.* conchoidal, shell-shaped.
скоро *adv.* rapidly, promptly.
скородействующий *a.* high-speed, quick-acting, fast; **с. прерыватель** fast chopper.
скородит *m.* scorodite.
скороподъемность *f.* (aero.) climbing rate.
скоро/постижный *a.* sudden, unexpected; **—преходящий** *a.* transitory, short-lived.
скоростник *m.* high-speed machine.
скоростн/ой *a.* velocity; high-speed; **с. микрофон** velocity microphone; **с. напор** velocity (kinetic-energy, dynamic) head; **с. осциллограф** high-speed oscillograph; **с. узел** velocity node; **с. эффект** ram effect; **—ая модуляция** velocity modulation; **—ая фотокамера** high-speed camera.
скорост/ь *f.* velocity, speed, rate; **с. беспорядочного движения** random velocity; **с. восстановления, с. выздоровления** recovery rate; **с. деления** fission rate; **с. деформации** rate of straining; **с. наростания** growth (or rise) rate; response (of instrument); **с. отрыва** escape velocity; **с. повторения импульсов** pulse repetition rate; **с. ползучести** creep rate; **с. распада** disintegration (or decay) rate; **с. реакции** reaction rate; **с. счета** counting rate; **с. теплового движения** thermal speed; **коэффициент —и** speed ratio; (hyd.) coefficient of velocity; **набирание —и** acceleration, speeding up; **снижение —и, уменьшение —и** deceleration; **указатель —и** speedometer.
скоротечн/ость *f.* transiency, short duration; **—ый** *a.* transient, short-lived, brief.
Скорпион Scorpius (Sco) (constellation).
Скорпиона-Центавра поток Scorpio-Centaurus stream.
скорректиров/анный *a.* corrected; **—ать** *v.* correct.
скор/ый *a.* rapid, fast, speedy; **—ая помощь** first aid; **в —ом будущем** in the near future; **в —ом времени** in a short time, soon.
скос *m.* bevel, chamfer, slope, taper; **с. потока** downwash; **—ить** *see* **скашивать.**
скотография *f.* scotography.
скоутит *m.* scawtite.
скошенн/ость *f.* skewness; **—ый** *a.* chamfered, beveled, tapered.
скрадывать *v.* conceal.
скрап *m.* scrap, scrap iron.
скрасть *see* **скрадывать.**
скрепа *f.* tie, clamp.
скрепер *m.,* **—ный** *a.* scraper.
скреп/ить *v.* fasten, fix, secure; bolt, clamp; cement; brace, strengthen; authenticate; **—ка** *f.* fastener, clamp; clip.

скрепл/ение *n.* fastening, clamping; brace, bond; strengthening, reinforcement; **—енный** *a.* fastened, clamped; cemented; reinforced; **—ять** *see* **скрепить; —яющий** *a.* fastening, clamping; cementing; strengthening, reinforcing.

скрести *v.* scrape.

скрестить *v.* cross.

скрещен/ие *n.* crossing, crossover; junction; **—ный** *a.* crossed; (elec.) lattice-type; **—ный четырехполюсник** lattice network; **—ное звено** (elec.) lattice section.

скрещив/ание *see* **скрещение; —ать, —аться** *v.* cross; **—ающиеся прямые** skew lines.

скрив/ить, —лять *v.* bend, twist, curve; **—ленный** *a.* twisted, crooked; warped.

скрип *m.*, **—еть, —нуть** *v.* creak, squeak; **—ение** *n.*, **—учий** *a.* creaking, squeaking.

скромн/ый *a.* modest; **—ая оценка** conservative estimate.

скруббер *m.*, **—ный** *a.* scrubber.

скругл/ение *n.* rounding (off), roundness, curvature; **—ять** *v.* round (off).

скрупулезный *a.* scrupulous, meticulous.

скру/тить *see* **скручивать; —тка** *f.* twist; **—ченный** *a.* twisted, contorted.

скручив/ание *n.* torsion, twisting; **момент —ания** torque; **угол —ания** torsion angle; **—ать** *v.* twist; roll up; **—ающий** *a.* torsion, twisting; **—ающее усилие** torque, twisting force.

скрыв/ание *n.* concealment; **—ать** *v.* conceal; **—аться** *v.* hide, vanish, disappear; **—ающийся** *a.* hiding, disappearing.

скрытие *see* **скрывание.**

скрытн/о *adv.* secretly; *prefix see* **скрыто—; —ый** *a.* secretive.

скрыто— *prefix* crypto—.

скрыто/зернистый *a.* (geo.) cryptoclastic; **—кристаллический** *a.* cryptocrystalline, microcrystalline.

скрыт/ый *a.* hidden, concealed, secret; latent; **с. период** latent period; **—ая теплота испарения** latent heat of vaporization; **—ая теплота плавления** latent heat of fusion; **—ое изображение** latent image; **—ое состояние** latency.

скрыть *see* **скрывать.**

скудн/ость *f.* meagerness, sparseness; **—ый** *a.* scanty, sparse, meager; small, short.

Скульптор Sculptor (Scl) (constellation).

скупит *see* **шепит.**

скученн/ость *f.* congestion, density, crowdedness; conciseness; **—ый** *a.* crowded, dense, compressed.

скучив/ание *n.* crowding; **—ать** *v.* crowd together, pile.

скучный *a.* tedious, laborious.

сл *abbr.* (**сантилитр**) centiliter; **сл.** (**следующий**) following, next.

слабеть *v.* diminish, slacken.

слабо *adv.* weakly, slightly, mildly; loosely; **с. зависящий от** slowly varying function of.

слабо/возбужденный *a.* feebly excited; **—запрещенный** *a.* unfavored; **—затухающий** *a.* slowly decaying; **—ионизированный** *a.* lightly (or weakly) ionized; **—кислотный** *a.* slightly (or weakly) acid, subacid; **—кислый** *a.* weakly acid; **—летучий** *a.* nonvolatile; **—натянутый** *a.* slack, loose; **—неоднородный** *a.* slightly inhomogeneous; **—облученный** *a.* lightly irradiated; **—основный** *a.* weakly basic; **—поглощающий материал** low-capture material; **—радиоактивный** *a.* slightly radioactive; **—связанный** *a.* weakly coupled, loosely bound; **—сильный** *a.* weak.

слабость *f.* weakness, disadvantage.

слабофокусирующий *a.* weak-focusing.

слаб/ый *a.* weak, feeble, slight, faint, light; soft, mild; low, poor; loose, lax, slack; thin (negative); **с. ветер** gentle breeze (Beaufort number 3); **с. дождь** light rain; **с. поток** low flow (or flux); **с. разрыв** removable (or first-order) discontinuity; **с. раствор** dilute solution; **с. ток** weak (low, light) current; **с. туман** light fog; **—ая видимость** poor visibility; **—ая звезда** faint star; **—ая компонента** soft component (of radiation); **—ая связь** weak bond; weak (or loose) coupling; **—ое волнение, —ое море** slight sea (Douglas number 2);

—**ое затухание** underdamping; —**ое излучение** low-level radiation; —**ое натяжение** low tension.

слав/а *f.* fame, repute; —**ный** *a.* famous, renowned; pleasant.

слаг *m.* slug.

слаг/аемое *n.* component, term, addend, summand; —**ать** *v.* add; comprise; put together, join; —**аться** *v.* be added, be combined; be composed of; —**ающая** *f.* component; —**ающий** *a.* component, constituent; cumulative.

сладить *see* **слаживать.**

сладкий *a.* sweet.

слаж/енный *a.* well-organized, coordinated; —**ивание** *n.* arrangement, agreement; —**ивать** *v.* arrange, agree; piece, join.

сламывать *v.* break.

сланец *m.* schist; shale; slate.

сланцеват/ость *f.* schistosity; fissility, (cleavage) foliation; —**ый** *a.* schistose, schistous; fissile; shaly, slaty.

сланцев/ый a. schist, schistose, schistous; shale; slate, slaty; foliated; **с. пласт** schist; —**ое масло** shale oil.

слать *v.* send.

слева *adv.* from the left; to the left; on the left; **с. направо** from left to right.

слегка *adv.* slightly, somewhat, superficially; **с. облученный** lightly irradiated.

след. *abbr.* (**следовательно**) consequently, therefore; (**следующий**) following, next.

след *m.* track, trace, wake, trail; (math.) Spur; sign, mark, marking; —**ы** *pl.* traces, trace amount; **с. звезды** star trail; **с. ионизирующей частицы** ionization path (or track); **с. развертки** sweep trace; **с. частицы отдачи** recoil track.

следить *v.* follow, keep track of, observe; track; watch, attend.

след. обр. *abbr.* (**следующим образом**) as follows.

следован/ие *n.* sequence, succession, following; movement; investigation; **с. примеру** imitation; **период —ия** repetition interval.

следовательно *adv.* therefore, consequently, hence.

след/овать *v.* follow, succeed, result; —**ует** one should, one must; —**ует заметить** it should be noted; **как —ует** properly; as follows; **как и —овало ожидать** as was to be expected.

следом *adv.*, **с. за** immediately after.

следствие *n.* consequence, effect; inference; (math.) corollary; inquiry, investigation; **причина и с.** cause and effect.

следующ/ий *a.* following, next, subsequent, succeeding; **с. ближайший сосед** next-nearest (or second) neighbor; —**им образом** as follows, in the following manner.

следящ/ий *a.* (elec.) follow (-up), slave; **с. мотор** slave motor; **с. развертыватель** follow scanner; **с. робот** slave robot.

слеж/ение *n.* following, tracking, tracing; —**ечное наведение** track homing.

слеживание *n.* deterioration; caking.

слезка *f.* insulating bead.

Слейтера функция Slater function.

слеп/имость *f.* glare; —**ить** *v.* dazzle, blind; paste together.

слепл/ивать, —**ять** *v.* glue together, paste to.

слеп/о *adv.* blindly; —**ой** *a.* blind; —**ое отверстие** blind opening; —**ое пятно** blind spot.

слепок *m.* mold, cast; copy, counterpart.

слесар/ня *f.* metal workshop; locksmith's shop; —**ь** *m.* metal worker; locksmith.

слет *m.* flight; assembly, gathering; —**ать,** —**еть** *v.* fly off, fly down.

слив *m.* overflow, discharge; sink, drain; —**ание** *n.*, —**ка** *f.* draining off, decantation; pouring together; —**ать** *v.* pour off, decant, run off; pour together; —**аться** *v.* run (or flow) together, interflow; merge, fuse, combine, blend; —**ающийся** *a.* flowing-together, interfluent, confluent, blending, fusing.

сливн/ой *a.* overflow, drainage; pouring; mixed; **с. вентиль** drain valve; —**ая камера** overflow chamber; —**ая труба** overflow pipe; —**ые воды** effluent.

слип *m.* slipstream.

слип/ание *n.* adhesion, sticking; agglomeration, flocculation; **—аться** *v.* adhere, stick together; **—шийся** *a.* adhering.

слитн/ость *f.* fusion, coalescence; **—ый** *a.* fused, coalescent, united.

слиток *m.* (met.) ingot, pig, bar.

слит/ый *a.* poured off, decanted; **—ь** *see* **сливать.**

слич/ать *v.* compare; collate; **—ение** *n.* comparison; collation; **—итель** *m.* collator; **—ительный** *a.* comparative.

слишком *adv.* too, too much, too many; over—; **с. замедленный** overmoderated; **с. много** too many, too much.

слияние *n.* fusion, blending, merging, amalgamation, coalescence; confluence; **с. линий** (spect.) confluence of lines; **с. особенностей** (math.) confluence of singularities.

словар/ь *m.*, **—ный** *a.* dictionary.

словно *adv.* as, as if, as though, like.

слово *n.* word; speech, address; **с. в с.** word for word, verbatim; **одним —м** in short.

слог *m.* syllable.

слоеват/ость *f.* schistosity; lamination, sheeting; **—ый** *a.* schistous; slaty; foliated, flaky.

слоевой *a.* layer, bed.

слоен/ие *n.* foliation; **—ый** *a.* foliated, sandwiched; **—ый детектор** sandwich detector; **—ый источник** sandwiched source.

слоеобразный *a.* stratiform.

сложен/ие *n.* addition, summation; combination; structure; **с. волн** wave interference; **с. сил** composition of forces; **правило —ия** summation (sum, combination) rule.

сложенный *a.* added; folded; built; **с. подогреватель** folded heater; **с. фильтр** composite filter.

слож/ить *see* **складывать, слагать**; **заранее —ившееся мнение** foregone conclusion.

сложно *adv.* in a complicated manner.

сложност/ь *f.* complexity, intricacy, complication; **в общей —и** on the whole, in sum.

сложн/ый *a.* complex, complicated; composite, compound, combined; multiple; intricate, involved; irregular; **с. катод** composite cathode; **с. комплекс** complex aggregate; **с. люминофор** multiple (or composite) phosphor; **с. микроскоп** compound microscope; **с. переход** combined (or double) transition; **с. поглотитель** composite absorber; **с. проводник** composite conductor; **с. распад** complex decay; **с. резонатор** compound resonator; **с. спектр** complex spectrum; **с. ток** combination current; **с. цикл** compound cycle; **с. эфир** ester.

сложн/ый *cont.*, **—ая антенна** antenna array; **—ая высотная фронтальная зона** compound upper front zone; **—ая кривая распада** composite decay curve; **—ая молекула** complex molecule; **—ая радуга** supernumerary rainbow; **—ая ракета** composite (or stage) rocket; **—ая решетка** (reactor) composite lattice; **—ая руда** complex ore; **—ая структура** fine structure; **—ая тропопауза** multiple tropopause; **—ая функция** composite function; **—ая частота** combination frequency; **—ое напряжение** combined stress, complex stress; **—ое отношение** cross (or anharmonic) ratio; **—ое событие** compound event; **—ое управление** multiple control; **—ое ядро** complex nucleus; **—ые проценты** compound interest.

слоисто/-дождевые облака nimbostratus; **с.-кучевые облака** stratocumulus; **с.-кучевые растекающиеся вечерние облака** stratocumulus vesperalis; **с.-кучевые растекающиеся дневные облака** stratocumulus diurnalis; **с.-спиральный рост** (cryst.) spiral growth.

слоистост/ь *f.* lamination, foliation, schistosity; stratification; **коэффициент —и** lamination factor.

слоист/ый *a.* laminated, lamellar, layered, foliated, flaky; stratified, sheetlike; (min.) schistose, schistous; (geo.) bedded; **с. излом** cleavage; **с. поток, —ое течение** laminar flow; **с. разряд** striated discharge; **с. транзистор** junction transistor; **—ая решетка** layer lattice; **—ая структура** laminar structure; **—ое строение ядра** shell model of the nucleus; **—ые облака** stratus, stratiformis.

слоиться *v.* flake, scale.

сло/й *m.* layer, stratum; bed; sheath; lamella, flake, lamina, sheet; striation; ply, thickness; coat, coating; foil; **с. адвекции** advection layer; **вихревой с.** vortex sheet; **с. генерации** generating layer; **с. кипения** boiling bed; **с. половинного ослабления, с. половинного поглощения** half-thickness, half-value layer; **с. скачка солености** halocline; **с. температурного скачка** thermocline; **тонкий с.** thin layer, film; **с. эмульсий** pellicle, emulsion sheet; **метод —ев** (meteor.) slice method; **—ями** in layers.

слом *m.* breaking, wrecking, scrapping, demolition; **—анный** *a.* broken, truncated; **—ать, —ить** *see* **сламывать**; **—аться** *v.* break; get out of order.

служащий *a.* serving; *m.* employee.

служб/а *f.* service, attendance; office; duty, job, work; **с. здравоохранения** Public Health Service; **с. погоды** weather bureau; **с. солнца** solar survey; **время —ы, продолжительность —ы, срок —ы** service, useful (or working) life, lifetime.

служебн/ый *a.* service; official; auxiliary; **с. персонал** office personnel (or staff); **—ые инструкции** operating procedures (or directions); **—ые обязанности** official duties.

служ/ение *n.* service; **—итель** *m.* servant, attendant; **—ить** *v.* serve.

слух *m.* hearing; rumor, report, news; **на с.** orally.

слухов/ой *a.* acoustic, auditory, aural; **с. аппарат, с. протез** hearing aid; **с. нерв** auditory nerve; **—ая трубка** (tel.) receiver; **—ое восприятие** aural perception; **—ое ощущение** auditory sensation.

случ/ай *m.* case, event, occurrence, instance, occasion; chance, opportunity; level; **на всякий с.** in any case; **несчастный с.** accident; **в —ае** in case of, in the event of; **в лучшем —ае** at best; **во всяком —ае** in any event; **в противном —ае** otherwise; **в этом —ае** in this instance; **ни в коем —ае** in no case; **по —аю** on account of.

случайно *adv.* by chance, accidentally, casually; **—сть** *f.* randomness, chance; accident, emergency.

случайн/ый *a.* chance, random, stochastic; accidental, fortuitous; stray, scattered; occasional, incidental; **с. вектор** random vector; **с. пробег** random flight; **с. процесс** random (or stochastic) process; **с. разброс** straggling; **с. разброс (длины) пробега** range straggling; **—ая ошибка** random error;**—ая переменная** chance (random, stochastic) variable; **—ая флюктуация** random fluctuation; **—ая функция** random (or stochastic) function; **—ое блуждание** random walk, random flight; random movement; **—ое вырождение** accidental degeneracy; **—ое поле** stray field; **—ое рассеяние** random scattering; **—ое совпадение** random (or accidental) coincidence; **—ое срабатывание** random operation; **—ое угловое рассеяние** angle straggling; **—ые испытания** random trials, trial and error.

случ/аться, —иться *v.* occur, come about.

слуш/ание *n.* hearing, listening; **—атель** *m.* listener, hearer; **—атели** *pl.* audience; **—ать** *v.* listen; **—аться** *v.* heed, obey.

слыхать *see* **слышать.**

слыш/ать *v.* hear; **—аться** *v.* be heard; **—имость** *f.* audibility; **—имый** *a.* audible; **—имая генерация** (elec.) howl; **—ный** *a.* audible, heard.

слэг *m.* slug (unit of mass).

Слэтер *see* **Слейтер.**

слюд/а *f.* mica; **листовая с.** sheet (or shell) mica; **с. со стеклянным наполнением** glass-bonded mica; **—истый, —яной** *a.* mica, micaceous.

слякоть *f.* mire, slush.

см *abbr.* **(сантиметр)** centimeter (cm); **см. (смотри)** see.

смаз/анный *a.* lubricated, greased; smeared, blurred; **—ать** *see* **смазывать**; **—ка** *f.* grease, lubricant; lubrication.

смазочн/ый *a.* lubricating, lubrication, grease; **с. материал, —ое вещество, —ое средство** lubricant; **—ое масло** lubricating oil.

смазчик *m.* lubricator.

смазыв/ание *n.* lubrication, greasing, oiling; **—ать** *v.* lubricate, grease, oil; smear.

сматыв/ание *n.* winding, reeling; unreeling; **—ать** *v.* wind, reel; unreel, unroll, uncoil.

смах/ивать, —нуть *v.* brush aside.

смачив/аемость *f.* wettability; **—аемый** *a.* wettable; being wetted; **—ание** *n.* wetting, moistening; **—ать** *v.* wet, moisten; **—ающий** *a.* wetting; **—ающее вещество** wetting agent.

СМВ *abbr.* (**сантиметровые волны**) centimeter waves.

смежность *f.* contiguity, adjacency.

смежн/ый *a.* adjacent, contiguous, proximate, neighboring, adjoining; **с. угол** contact angle; adjacent angle; **—ое нахождение** juxtaposition; **—ые двойники** contact twins; **—ые области науки** related sciences.

смект/ит *m.* smectite; **—ический** *a.* smectic, metamorphic.

смел/ость *f.* boldness, courage; **—ый** *a.* daring, bold, courageous.

смен/а *f.* change, shift, exchange, succession, interchange, replacement, relief; **с. волны** (seis.) wave exchange; **с. прилива** turning of tide; **на —у ему** in his (or its) place; **—ить** *see* **сменять.**

сменн/ый *a.* changeable, interchangeable, exchangeable, renewable; removable, detachable; spare; plug-in (type); **—ая секция** plug-in unit.

сменяем/ость *f.* interchangeability; removability; **—ый** *a.* interchangeable; removable.

сменять *v.* change, interchange, exchange, replace, remove, renew; relieve; **—ся** *v.* alternate, shift.

смерз/ание *n.* freezing (together); regelation; **—лый** *a.* frozen, congealed.

смер/ивать, —ить *v.* measure.

смертельн/ость *f.* lethality; **—ый** *a.* mortal, lethal.

смертн/ость *f.* mortality, death rate; **—ый** *a.* mortal.

смертоносн/ость *f.* deadliness; **—ый** *a.* deadly, lethal, fatal.

смерть *f.* death.

смерч *m.* waterspout; tornado, dust (or sand) whirl.

смесим/ость *f.* miscibility; **—ый** *a.* miscible.

смеситель *m.* mixer; mixing tank; **с.-отстойник** mixer-settler; **—ный** *a.* mixing; **—ный каскад** mixer stage; **—ная лампа** mixer tube.

смести *see* **сметать.**

сместит/ель линий line shifter; **—ь** *see* **смещать.**

смесь *f.* mixture, blend; **с. изотопов** isotopic mixture.

смета *f.* estimate, appraisal; budget.

сметать *v.* sweep away.

сметный *a.* estimated, planned.

сметь *v.* venture, dare.

смешанн/ый *a.* mixed, miscellaneous; composite, compound, combined, combination, blended; confused; hybrid; (elec.) compound-wound; **с. ливень** mixed shower; **с. момент** (stat.) product moment; **с. момент инерции** product of inertia; **с. переход** mixed transition; **с. полимер** interpolymer, copolymer; **с. прилив** mixed tide; **—ая нагрузка** combined load; **—ая полоса** (spect.) hybrid band; **—ая электромагнитная волна** hybrid electromagnetic wave; **—ое произведение, —ое тройное произведение** (math.) scalar triple product; **—ое соединение** (elec.) series-parallel connection; **—ое число** mixed number.

смеш/ать *see* **смешивать**; **—ение** *n.* mixture, mixing, combination, blending; confusion; **критическая температура —ения** critical solution temperature.

смешив/аемость *f.* miscibility; **взаимная с.** intermiscibility; **—аемый** *a.* miscible; **—ание** *n.* mixing, blending; **—ать** *v.* mix, blend, combine; confuse; **—аться** *v.* intermix, intermingle, interblend; **—ающий** *a.* mixing; **—ающийся** *a.* miscible.

смещ/ать *v.* displace, remove, shift; **—аться** *v.* (geo.) heave; **—ающее напряжение** voltage bias.

смещен/ие *n.* shift, displacement, jog, removal; translation, migration; (elec.) bias; (geo.) dislocation, slip, heave; parallax; **с. линии** line shift; **с. нуля** zero drift; **с. фаз** phase shift; **с. частоты** frequency drift; **закон —ия, правило —ия** displacement law; **напряжение —ия** grid bias; **ток —ия** (elec.) displacement current; **эффект —ия** (cryst.) discomposition (or Wigner) effect; **ядро —ия** (math.) displacement kernel.

смещенн/ый *a.* shifted, displaced, offset; biased; **с. атом** displaced atom; **с. волновод** offset waveguide; **с. луч** shifted (displaced, offset) beam; **с. по фазе** dephased; **—ая оценка** biased estimate.

смеяться *v.* laugh (at), ridicule.

Смита доклад Smyth Report.

смит/ит *m.* smithite; **—сонит** *m.* smithsonite.

смоделировать *see* **моделировать.**

смола *f.* resin; rosin, gum; tar, pitch; **искусственная с.** synthetic resin.

смол/евой *a.* resin; tar; **—ение** *n.* resinification; tarring; **—истый** *a.* resinous, resin; tarry; **—ить** *v.* resin; tar, pitch.

смолка *see* **урановая смолка.**

смолк/ать, —нуть *v.* become silent.

смолоносный *a.* resiniferous.

смолян/ой *a.* resin, resinous; tar, tarry, pitch; **—ая колонна** (ion-exchange) resin column; **—ая обманка, —ая урановая руда** pitchblende.

смонтированный *a.* mounted, assembled, erected.

смораживаться *v.* congeal, freeze.

сморозь *f.* ice breccia (or mosaic).

сморщ/енный *a.* wrinkled; **—ивание** *n.* wrinkling; **—ивать, —ить, —иваться, —иться** *v.* wrinkle.

смотать *see* **сматывать.**

смотр *m.* inspection; **произвести с.** examine, inspect; **—еть** *v.* examine, look (at), regard; **—еть за** supervise; **не —я на** in spite of, notwithstanding; **—я по** according to, depending on.

смотров/ой *a.* inspection, observation, viewing; **—ое окно, —ое отверстие** observation (inspection, viewing) window (port, hole).

смоч/енный *a.* wetted, moistened, soaked; **—ить** *see* **смачивать.**

смочь *v.* be able, prove able.

смутн/ость *f.* dimness; confusion; **—ый** *a.* dim, indistinct, vague.

смыв/аемая мишень wipe-off target; **—ание** *n.* washing off (or away); erosion; **—ать** *v.* wash off (or away); erode.

смык/ание *n.* joining, linking; closing; **—ать** *v.* link; close; **—аться** *v.* join, connect with, interlock; close in, close up; **—ающийся пузырек** collapsing bubble.

смысл *m.* sense, meaning; judgment; **здравый с.** common sense; **в переносном —е** figuratively; **нет —а** there is no point (or sense); **по —у** according to.

смыт/ый *a.* washed (away); eroded; **—ь** *see* **смывать.**

смычка *f.* union, coupling, linking.

смыч/ок *m.*, **—ковый** *a.* (mus.) bow.

смягч/ать *v.* soften; moderate, ease; damp; **—ающий** *a.* softening; **—ение** *n.* softening; moderation, damping; **—енный** *a.* softened; moderated, weakened.

смягчитель *m.* softener; plasticizer; **—ный** *a.* softening; plasticizing.

смягчить *see* **смягчать.**

смят/ие *n.* crumpling; **—ый** *a.* crumpled; **—ь** *v.* crumple.

сн *abbr.* **(стен)** sthene; **сн. (снизу)** from the bottom (of page).

снабж/ать, снабдить *v.* supply, provide, furnish; **—ающий** *a.* supply, delivery; **—ение** *n.* provision, supply, furnishing; equipment, outfit; **—енный** *a.* provided, supplied; fitted, equipped.

Снайдера электропечь Snyder furnace.

снаружи *adv.* (on the) outside; from the outside.

снаряд *m.* missile, projectile, shell; implements, apparatus, gear; **с.-ракета, ракетный с.** rocket, rocket missile; **с. с ядерным взрывчатым веществом** nuclear shell; **—ить** *see* **снаряжать.**

снаряж/ать *v.* equip, outfit; **—ение** *n.* equipment, outfit; implements; **—енный** *a.* equipped.

снасть *f.* equipment, gear.

сначала *adv.* first, at first; from the beginning; **начать с.** start all over again.

снашив/ание *n.* wear, abrasion; **—ать** *v.* wear out, abrade.

снег *m.*, **—овой** *a.* snow; **—овая граница, —овая линия** snow line.

снегомер *m.* snow gauge; **—ная линейка, —ная рейка** snow stake (or scale).

снегопад *m.* snowfall.

снеж/инка *f.* snowflake; **—ить** *v.* snow.

снежн/ый *a.* snow; **с. нанос** snowdrift; **—ая буря** snowstorm, blizzard; **—ая крупа** soft hail, graupel, snow pellets; **—ая пыль** powder snow; **—ые зерна** snow grains, granular snow; **—ые хлопья** snowflakes.

Снеллий Snellius (lunar crater).

Снелля закон Snell law.

снес/ение *n.* removal; **—ти** *see* **сносить.**

сниж/ать *v.* lower, lessen, reduce; **—аться** *v.* descend; sink, drop; **—ение** *n.* reduction, decrease, lowering; degradation; descent; **—ение давления** decompression.

снизить *see* **снижать.**

снизу *adv.* underneath, below; from below; from the bottom; **вид с.** bottom view.

сним/ание *n.* taking off, removing; **—атель** *m.* pickup.

сним/ать *v.* remove, strip; photograph, copy; map, plot; **с. нагрузку** unload; **с. план** survey, map out; **с. показания** read (an instrument); **—аться с места** start; **—ающееся покрытие** strippable coating, stripcoat.

снимок *m.* photograph; copy.

СН и П *abbr.* (**строительные нормы и правила**) construction specifications and regulations.

снова *adv.* again, anew, re—.

сноп *m.* sheaf; cone, shaft; **—овидный** *a.* sheaflike.

снос *m.* drift, deflection; demolition; washing away; **с. ветром** wind drift (or deflection); **угол —а** drift angle; **—ить** *v.* demolish; take, carry away; **—иться** *v.* communicate.

сноска *f.* reference, footnote.

сношен/ие *n.* relation, connection, communication, dealings; **прервать —ия** sever relations.

снуперскоп *m.* snooperscope.

снят/ие *n.* removal; **с. возбуждения** de-excitation; **с. напряжений** relaxation of stress; **—ый** *a.* removed, stripped; **—ая эмульсия** stripped emulsion; **—ь** *see* **снимать.**

со *see* **с.**

соавторы *pl.* coauthors, collaborators.

соба/ка *f.* dog; **—чий** *a.* dog, canine; **—чий клык** dogtooth spar.

собачка *f.* catch, detent, stop, latch, pawl, dog; trigger.

собир/ание *n.* collection, assembling; **с. в группах** grouping, bunching; **с. запасов** stockpiling; **—атель** *m.* collector.

собирательн/ый *a.* collecting, collective; **с. сосуд** collecting vessel, receiver; **—ая линза, —ое стекло** condensing lens, condenser, converging lens; **—ая полоса, —ая шина** (elec.) busbar; **—ое кольцо** (elec.) collector ring, slip ring.

собир/ать *v.* collect, accumulate, assemble; equip; install, mount, fit up; connect, hook up; **—аться** *v.* gather, collect, agglomerate, congregate; intend, plan to, prepare to; **—ающий** *a.* collecting.

соб. корр. редакции *abbr.* (**собственный корреспондент редакции**) special correspondent, reporter.

соблю/дать, —сти *v.* fulfill, satisfy, observe; **—дение** *n.* observance, maintenance, fulfillment; **—денный** *a.* observed, fulfilled, maintained.

собран/ие *n.* collection, accumulation; assembly, meeting; **—ный** *a.* collected; gathered, assembled; arranged; built-up; mounted; **в —ном виде** assembled.

собрать *see* **собирать.**

собр. соч. *abbr.* (**собрание сочинений**) collected works.

собств. *abbr.* (**собственный**) proper, eigen—.

собственно *adv.* properly, strictly, truly; **с. говоря** strictly speaking.

собственност/ь *f.* property; **право —и** proprietary rights.

собственн/ый *a.* intrinsic, own, proper, natural, characteristic, inherent, eigen—, self—, internal; **с. вектор** eigenvector; **с. импеданс** self-impedance; **с. магнетизм** intrinsic magnetism; **с. магнитный момент** intrinsic magnetic moment; **с. момент** intrinsic moment, spin; **с. фон** intrinsic background; **—ая анизотропия** intrinsic anisotropy; **—ая длина** proper length; **—ая длина волны** natural wavelength; **—ая емкость** self-capacitance; **—ая функция** eigenfunction; **—ая частота** natural frequency, normal mode; **—ая энергия** proper (or characteristic) energy, self-energy.

собственн/ый *cont.*, **—ое вращение** spin; **—ое время** proper time; intrinsic time; **—ое движение** proper motion; **—ое значение** eigenvalue, proper (or characteristic) value; **—ое излучение** self-radiation; **—ое поглощение** fundamental absorption (band); **—ое поле** proper field, self-field; **—ое сопротивление** internal resistance; **—ое состояние** eigenstate; **—ое трение** internal friction; **—ое управление** internal (or inherent) control; **—ое число** eigenvalue; **—ые колебания** natural oscillations (or vibrations); normal mode.

событие *n.* event, occurrence.

сов. *abbr.* (**совет**) council; soviet; **сов—** (**советский**) Soviet (used as a prefix).

соверш/ать *v.* accomplish, effect, perform, achieve; commit; **—аться** *v.* be accomplished; **—ение** *n.* accomplishment, completion, performance, achievement, fulfillment.

совершенно *adv.* quite, entirely, thoroughly, totally, perfectly, absolutely.

совершенн/ый *a.* perfect, ideal, complete; perfected, refined; **с. газ** ideal (or perfect gas); **с. диэлектрик** ideal (or perfect) dielectric; **с. излучатель** complete (perfect, ideal) radiator, blackbody; **с. кристалл** perfect crystal; **с. проводник** perfect conductor; **—ая жидкость** ideal (or perfect) liquid; **—ая спайность** perfect cleavage; **—ое число** perfect number.

совершенство *n.* perfection, ideality; **—вание** *n.* perfecting, improvement, development; **—вать** *v.* perfect, improve, develop, refine; complete; **—ваться** *v.* perfect oneself (in), improve, progress.

совершить *see* **совершать.**

совесть *f.* conscience.

совет *m.* council; soviet; advice, counsel; **—ник** *m.* adviser, counselor; **—овать** *v.* advise, counsel; **—оваться** *v.* consult, discuss.

советский *a.* Soviet; **С. Союз** Soviet Union.

советчик *see* **советник.**

совещ/ание *n.* conference, meeting; consultation, discussion; communication; **—ательный** *a.* consultative, deliberative, advisory; **—аться** *v.* deliberate, confer.

совмест/имость *f.* compatibility; **—имый** *a.* compatible; **—ить** *see* **совмещать.**

совместно *adv.* jointly, together; concurrently; **работающий с.** collaborating, cooperating; **—сть** *f.* compatibility, consistency, concertedness.

совместн/ый *a.* joint, combined, associated, common, cooperative, concurrent, concerted, compatible, consistent, congruent; co—; **с. объем** covolume; **—ая полимеризация** copolymerization; **с. растворитель** cosolvent; **—ая кристаллизация** cocrystallization; **—ая работа** collaboration, cooperation; **—ое действие** joint action, cooperation; **—ое осаждение** coprecipitation; **—ое решение** common solution; **—ые уравнения** consistent (compatible, simultaneous) equations.

совмещ/ать *v.* combine; (math.) superpose; **—аться** *v.* coincide, be congruent; **—ающийся** *a.* superposable; coinciding.

совмещен/ие *n.* congruence; matching, agreement; combination; **—ный** *a.* combined, joint, integrated; superposed; matched.

совокупн/ость *f.* combination, assembly, totality, aggregate; (math.) set, aggregate, ensemble, Menge; **критическая с.** (reactor) critical assembly;

нормальная с. (stat.) normal universe; **в —ости** in the aggregate, altogether; **—ый** *a.* joint, collective, aggregate, combined; cumulative.

совпадать *v.* coincide, match, conform, agree; **с. во времени** synchronize; **с. по фазе** be in phase; **с. частично** overlap.

совпадающ/ий *a.* coincident, concurrent, corresponding; **с. осями** coaxial; **с. по фазе** cophasal; **—ие корни** (math.) multiple (or repeated) roots.

совпаден/ие *n.* coincidence, agreement, concurrence, conformity, concordance, correspondence, matching; accordance; superposition, congruence; **с. импульсов** pulse coincidence; **с. осей** alignment; **схема —ий** coincidence scheme (or circuit).

совпасть *see* **совпадать.**

совр. *abbr.* (**современный**) contemporary.

современн/ик *m.* contemporary; **—ость** *f.* contemporaneousness, modernity; **—ый** *a.* contemporary, recent, contemporaneous, modern, up-to-date, present-day, current; **—ое поле Земли** present terrestrial field.

совсем *adv.* altogether, absolutely, quite, completely, entirely; **с. не** nothing, not at all; **не с.** not exactly.

соглас/ие *n.* consent; conformity, fit; assent; accord, agreement; congruence; **в —ии** in accordance with; **критерий —ия** (stat.) test of goodness of fit; **—ительный** *a.* conciliatory; **—иться** *see* **соглашаться.**

согласн/о *prep. dat.* according to; *adv.* in accordance, in harmony; **с. определению** by definition; **с. предположению** by hypothesis; **—ость** *f.* consistency; harmony; concordance; **—ый** *a.* agreeing, conforming, concordant, harmonious; matched; consonant, consonantal; **—ые звуки** consonants.

согласован/ие *n.* agreement, concordance; congruence, conformity, harmony, coordination; matching; **с. импедансов** impedance matching; **—ность** *f.* coordination, consistency, compatibility; match, adjustment; agreement, harmony; **—ный** *a.* consistent, adjusted, matched, coordinated; approved; **—ное сопротивление** matched impedance; **—ные поля** adjusted fields.

соглас/овательный, —ующий *a.* matching; **—овать, —овывать** *v.* coordinate, harmonize, match, reconcile; adjust, fit; accommodate, comply; **—оваться, —овываться** *v.* conform with, agree; **—ующийся** *a.* compatible; consistent, congruent.

соглаш/ать *v.* reconcile; **—аться** *v.* consent, agree, comply with; coincide; **—ение** *n.* agreement.

согнать *see* **сгонять.**

согнут/ый *a.* bent, curved; **—ь** *v.* bend, curve.

согрев/ание *n.* warming, heating; **—атель** *m.* heater; **—ательный** *a.* heating; **—ать** *v.* warm, heat; **—аться** *v.* be heated, get warm.

согрет/ый *a.* warmed, heated; **—ь** *see* **согревать.**

сода *f.* soda, sodium carbonate.

Содди-Фаянса закон смещения group (Soddy-Fajans) displacement law.

соддит *m.* soddyite.

содейств/ие *n.* assistance, cooperation; **—овать** *v.* assist, cooperate; contribute, further, expedite, promote.

Содерберга электрод Söderberg electrode.

содержание *n.* contents, content, capacity, volume, area; maintenance; salary; (logic) intension; **краткое с.** summary, abstract; **кубическое с.** volume; **процентное с.** percentage; **с. урана** uranium content; **с большим —м, с высоким —м** rich in, high in; **с низким —м** low in, low-grade, poor in.

содержать *v.* contain, hold, comprise; support, maintain; **с. в себе** include, contain.

содержащий *a.* containing; **с. металл** metalliferous; **не с.** free (of); **не с. урана** uranium-free; **с. четырехвалентный уран** uranous; **с. шестивалентный уран** uranic.

содержим/ое *n.* contents; **—ость** *f.* capacity, volume.

содовый *a.* soda.

содоклад *m.* joint report; —**чик** *m.* co-speaker, coauthor (of report).

содр/анный *a.* stripped; —**ать** *see* **сдирать.**

соединен/ие *n.* (chem.) compound; combination; connection, joining, junction; coupling; union, joint, bond, link; splice; fastening, binding; (astr.) conjunction; **с. включения** (chem.) clathrate compound; **вступать в с., входить в с.** enter into combination; **в —ии с** in connection with; **место —ия, точка —ия** joint; junction; **объем —ия** combining volume; **схема —ий** (elec.) circuit diagram; **теплота —ия** heat of formation.

Соединенные Штаты Америки United States of America.

соединенный *a.* combined, united, connected, coupled, joined, joint.

соединитель *m.* connector, bond, coupler, coupling; —**ный** *a.* connecting, coupling, binding, combining; connective, conjunctive; —**ный вес** combining weight; —**ный объем** combining volume.

соедин/ить, —ять, —иться, —яться *v.* connect, join, unite, link, couple, bridge; combine; bond; engage, mesh.

сожал/ение *n.*, —**еть** *v.* regret; **к —ению** unfortunately.

сожжен/ие *n.* burning, combustion; **анализ —ием** combustion analysis; —**ный** *a.* burnt.

созвать *see* **созывать.**

созвездие *n.* constellation.

созвучие *n.* consonance, harmony, accord.

созд/авание *n.* creation, founding, establishment; —**авать, —ать** *v.* create, construct, found, establish; originate, produce; —**авшееся положение** present situation; —**ание** *n.* creation; —**атель** *m.* creator, founder, originator.

созид/ание *see* **создание;** —**атель** *see* **создатель;** —**ательный** *a.* constructive; creative; —**ать** *see* **создать.**

созн/авать, —ать *v.* realize; acknowledge; —**ание** *n.* consciousness; acknowledgment; —**ательно** *adv.* consciously, knowingly; —**ательность** *f.* consciousness, awareness; —**ательный** *a.* conscious, intentional; conscientious.

созрев/ание *n.* ripening; —**ать** *v.* ripen, mature.

созывать *v.* summon, convene.

соиздатель *m.* copublisher.

соизмерим/ость *f.* commensurability; —**ый** *a.* commensurable, commensurate.

соиск/ание *n.* competition; —**атель** *m.* competitor.

сойти *see* **сходить.**

соколебательные приливы cooscillating tides.

Соколовского овал Sokolovskii oval.

сократим/ость *f.* reducibility; —**ый** *a.* reducible, contractile.

сократит/ельный *a.* contracting; —**ь** *see* **сокращать.**

сокращ/аемость *f.* contractibility, contractility; —**аемый** *a.* contractible, contractile; —**ать** *v.* shorten, abbreviate, abridge; reduce, cancel; contract, constrict; —**аться** *v.* shorten, contract, shrink; cancel out, reduce; —**ающий** *a.* abbreviating; contracting; reducing.

сокращен/ие *n.* abbreviation, abridgment; cancellation; reduction, decrease; contraction, constriction; shrinkage; shortcut; —**но** *adv.* briefly, concisely; —**ность** *f.* brevity; —**ный** *a.* abbreviated, abridged; brief, concise; reduced; canceled; contracted; —**ное умножение** abridged multiplication.

сокристаллизация *f.* cocrystallization.

сокровище *n.* treasure.

сокруш/ать, —ить *v.* break, shatter, ruin; —**ение** *n.* destruction; —**ительный** *a.* destructive, shattering.

сокслет *m.* Soxhlet apparatus.

сол/ат *m.* solate; —**ация** *f.* solation.

соле/вой *a.* salt; —**дробилка** *f.* salt crusher.

Солейля компенсатор Soleil plate.

солемер *m.* salinometer.

соленоид *m.*, —**ный** *a.* solenoid; —**альный** *a.* solenoidal.

солен/осный *a.* saliferous; —**ость** *f.* salinity; —**ый** *a.* salt, saline.

олеобраз/ование *n.* salt formation, salification; **—ователь** *m.* salt-former; **—ующий** *a.* salt-forming; **—ующая способность** salting strength.

оле/подобный *a.* saltlike, saline; **—содержание** *n.* salinity; **—содержащий** *a.* saliferous.

олидар/изироваться *v.* identify oneself with; **—но** *adv.* jointly; **—ность** *f.* solidarity.

олидн/ость *f.* solidity, firmness, reliability, soundness; **—ый** *a.* solid, firm, reliable, sound, sturdy, substantial.

олидус *m.* solidus (curve).

олить *v.* salt, brine, pickle, cure.

олифлюкция *f.* (geo.) solifluction.

олнечн/ый *a.* solar, sun; **с. взрыв** solar outburst; **с. гид** (astr.) sun-follower; **с. крест** (meteor.) sun cross; **с. свет** sunlight; **с. спектр** solar spectrum; **—ая вспышка** solar flare; **—ая постоянная** solar constant; **—ая реакция** solar-type reaction; **—ая система** solar system; **—ая составляющая прилива** solar tidal component; **—ая энергия** solar energy (or power); **—ое время** (apparent) solar time, apparent time; **—ое затмение** solar eclipse; **—ое пятно** sunspot; **—ые сутки** (apparent) solar day, apparent day; **—ые часы** sundial.

олнце *n.* sun; **ложное с.** parhelion; **—стояние** *n.* solstice.

оль *f.* salt; **с. закиси металла** —ous salt; **кислая с.** acid salt; **с. окиси металла** —ic salt; **основная с.** basic salt, subsalt.

ольват *m.*, **—ный** *a.* solvate; **—ационный** *a.*, **—ация** *f.* solvation; **—ированный** *a.* solvated; **—ная оболочка** solvation sheath.

ольвация *see* **сольватация.**

ольвент *m.* solvent.

ольвея способ Solvay process.

ольвол/из *m.* solvolysis; **—итический** *a.* solvolytic.

ольфатара *f.* (geo.) solfatara.

олюбилизация *f.* solubilization.

олян/ой *a.* salt, saline; **—ая кислота** hydrochloric acid.

олянокислый *a.* hydrochloric (acid); chloride (of metals); hydrochloride (of organic base).

соляр/изация *f.* solarization; **—иметр** *m.* solarimeter; **—ный** *a.* solar; **—овое масло** solar oil.

соматический *a.* somatic.

сомкнут/ый *a.* locked, closed; joined; **—ь** *see* **смыкать.**

сомне/ваться *v.* doubt, question; **—ние** *n.* doubt; **без —ния** undoubtedly.

сомнеров круг Sumner circle.

сомнительн/о *adv.* doubtfully; it is doubtful; **—ость** *f.* doubtfulness, uncertainty; **—ый** *a.* doubtful, questionable, problematical, equivocal.

сомножитель *m.* factor, multiplier, cofactor.

сон *m.* sleep; (acous.) sone.

сонар *m.* sonar.

Сонина полином Sonin (Sonine) polynomial.

соно/граф *m.* sonograph; **—метр** *m.* sonometer, monochord.

соображ/ать *v.* consider; reason out; contrive; comprehend; **—ение** *n.* consideration, reason; deliberation; comprehension; **—ения размерности** dimensional considerations.

сообразительн/ость *f.* alertness, quick thinking; **—ый** *a.* alert.

сообразить *see* **соображать.**

сообразн/о *adv.* in conformity with, according to; **—ость** *f.* suitability, compatibility, conformity, compliance, congruence; **—ый** *a.* suitable, compatible, conformable, congruent.

сообразов/ать, —ывать *v.* adapt, adjust, conform; **—аться, —ываться** *v.* fit, conform, comply.

сообщ. *abbr.* (**сообщение**) communication, information, report.

сообща *adv.* together, jointly; **действие с.** joint action.

сообщ/ать *v.* communicate, inform, report, notify; impart, transmit; **—аться** *v.* be in communication with; **—ающийся** *a.* communicating.

сообщен/ие *n.* communication, information, report; **пути —ия** means of communication; **—ный** *a.* communicated; imparted, given.

сообщество *n.* society, association.

сообщить *see* **сообщать.**

сообщн/ик *m.* participant; **—ичество** *n.* participation.

соору/дить, —жать *v.* build, construct, install; **—жение** *n.* building, construction, installation; edifice, structure, facility.

соосажд/ать *v.* coprecipitate; **—ение** *n.* coprecipitation.

соосн/ость *f.* (axial) alignment; **—ый** *a.* coaxial, uniaxial.

соотв. *abbr.* (**соответственно**) respectively; (**соответствующий**) corresponding.

соответственн/о *adv.* accordingly, according to, correspondingly, consequently; respectively; **—ость** *f.* conformity, correspondence, accordance; **—ый** *a.* expedient; suitable, pertinent; corresponding, conforming, congruent, homologous; **—ые углы** corresponding angles; **закон —ых состояний** law of corresponding states.

соответств/ие *n.* conformity, agreement, correspondence, congruence; homology; expediency; fitness; **взаимное с.** congruence; **в —ии** in conformity with, in accordance with; consistent with; **в —ии с этим** accordingly; **принцип —ия** correspondence principle.

соответствовать *v.* correspond, match, conform, parallel; represent; agree with, satisfy; **с. магнитному полю** track the magnetic field; **точно с.** fit.

соответствующ/ий *a.* corresponding, respective; appropriate, proper, pertinent; conformable, concomitant, homologous; characteristic; **—ие системы** matching systems.

соотнесенный *a.* related, correlated.

соотносительн/ость *f.* correlation; **—ый** *a.* correlative.

соотношение *n.* correlation, relation, relationship, homology; proportion, ratio; **с. баланса** balance equation; **с. ветвей (распада)** branching ratio; **с. коммутативности** commutation rule (or relation); **с. между массой и светимостью** mass-luminosity law; **с. между массой и энергией** mass-energy relation; **с. пробег-энергия** range-energy relation; **с. составных частей смеси** ratio of mixture; **установить правильное с.** bring into correlation, coordinate.

сопельный *a.* nozzle, jet.

Сопера сила Soper force.

соперни/к *m.* rival, competitor; **не имеющий —ка** unrivaled; **—чать** *v.* rival, compete; **—чество** *n.* rivalry, competition.

сопка *f.* small volcano, mound.

сплавленный *a.* fused.

сопло *n.*, **—вой** *a.* nozzle, jet, effusor.

сополимер *m.* copolymer; **—изация** *f.* copolymerization; **—ный** *a.* copolymerized.

сопостав/ить, —лять *v.* compare, contrast; associate, juxtapose; **—ление** *n.* comparison, contrast; association, juxtaposition; **в —лении с** in comparison with; **—ленный** *a.* compared, contrasted; associated.

сопредельный *a.* contiguous, adjoining, adjacent.

соприкас/ание *see* **соприкосновение**; **—аться** *v.* come into contact with border, be adjacent to, abut; (math.) osculate; **—аться с** have bearing on engage, mesh; **—ающий, —ающийся** *a.* touching, contiguous, adjoining, abutting; (math.) osculating **—ающийся круг** osculating circle.

соприкосновен/ие *n.* contact; contiguity; (math.) osculation; touching **место —ия, точка —ия** point of contact (tangency, osculation); **поверхность —ия** contact surface; **—ность** *f.* contiguity; **—ный** *a.* contiguous.

сопрово/дительный *a.* accompanying **—дить, —ждать** *v.* accompany track, follow.

сопровожд/ающий *a.* accompanying tracking, following, associated; **с трехгранник** (math.) moving trihedral; **—ающая радиолокация** radar tracker; **—ение** *n.* accompaniment, tracking, following; **—енный** *a.* accompanied.

сопротивлен/ие *n.* resistance, strength opposition, drag; (elec.) resistor **активное с.** (elec.) effective resistance; **волновое с.** wave impedance **временное с.** ultimate stress (or strength); **с. давления** (aero.) pressure drag; **действующее с.** effective resistance; **емкостное с.** capacitive reactance; **с. изгибу** bending (o transverse) strength; **с. излучения** (elec.) radiation resistance; **с. износу** resistance to wear; **индуктивное с.** inductive reactance; **комплексное с.** (elec.) (vector) impedance; **с. контакта** contact resistance; **с. коррозии** corrosion resistance; **с. кручению** torsional strength (or rigidity); **магнитное с.** reluctance; **оказать с.** resist; **с. отрыву** rupture strength; **полное с.** impedance; **с. продольному изгибу** buckling resistance; **профильное с.** (hyd.) profile drag.

сопротивлен/ие *cont.*, **с. разрушению** breaking strength; **с. разрыву** tensile (breaking, rupture) strength; **с. растяжению** tensile strength; **с. реактивное** (elec.) reactance; **с. связи** (elec.) coupling (or reflected) impedance; **с. сжатию** compressive (or compression) strength; **с. скручиванию** torsional strength; **с. срезу** shearing strength; **с. трению** frictional resistance, friction drag; **с. удару** impact strength (or resistance), shock resistance; **удельное с.** specific resistance, resistivity; **с. усталости** fatigue strength (or limit), endurance; **коэффициент —ия** drag coefficient; **линия наименьшего —ия** line of least resistance; **сила —ия** resisting force; **сила —ия воздуха** air resistance, drag; **магазин —ий** (elec.) resistance box.

сопротивл/енность *f.* resistance rating; **—яемость** *f.* capacity to resist, strength; resistivity; **—яться** *v.* resist, oppose; **—яющийся** *a.* resisting, resistant.

сопряг/ать *v.* couple, join; **—ающий конденсатор** padding capacitor.

сопряжен/ие *n.*, **—ность** *f.* coupling, union; contingency; conjunction, conjugation, adjunction; (elec.) padding; **зарядовое с.** charge conjugation; **с. связей** conjugation of bonds; **энергия —ия** conjugation energy.

сопряженн/ый *a.* conjugate, conjugated, combined, linked, coupled; ganged; correlated, coordinated, interlinked, associated; (math.) adjoint, conjugate; **с. импульс** conjugate momentum; **комплексно с.** complex conjugate; **с. корень** conjugate root; **с. оператор** adjoint operator; **—ая двойная связь** conjugated double bond; **—ая функция** adjoint function; **—ое излучение** associated emission; **—ое краевое условие** adjoint boundary condition; **—ое сопротивление** conjugate impedance; **—ое уравнение** adjoint equation; **—ые ветви** conjugate branches; **—ые лучи** conjugate rays; **—ые переменные** conjugate variables; **—ые слои** conjugate layers; **—ые точки** conjugate points; **—ые углы** conjugate angles; **—ые фокусы** conjugate foci.

сопрячь *see* **сопрягать.**

сопутств/ование *n.* accompaniment; **—овать** *v.* accompany; **—ующий** *a.* accompanying, attendant, concomitant, satellite; **—ующее пространство отсчета** comoving (or attached) reference frame.

сор *m.* rubbish, waste.

соразмер/ение *n.* matching, corresponding; **—ить, —ять** *v.* match, proportion; **—но** *adv.* in proportion to; **—ность** *f.* proportionality, commensurability; **—ный** *a.* proportionate, commensurate; adequate; balanced.

сорб/ент *m.*, **—ирующее вещество** sorbent; **—ирование** *see* **сорбция;** **—ированное вещество** sorbate.

сорбц/ионный *a.*, **—ия** *f.* sorption; **с. слой** adsorbed layer.

сорв/анный *a.* torn off; stripped; **—ать** *v.* tear off; strip.

Соре пластинка Soret zone plate; **эффект С.** S. effect.

соревн/ование *n.* competition; **—овать, —оваться** *v.* compete; **—ующийся** *a.* competing.

сорок forty.

сорокавосьмигранн/ик *m.* hexoctahedron; **—ый** *a.* hexoctahedral.

сорок/алетний *a.* forty-year; **—овой** *a.* fortieth.

сорт *m.* sort, kind, variety, type; quality, grade.

сортамент *m.* assortment, set; grades; gauge (of wire).

сортиров/анный *a.* sorted, classified, sized, screened; **—ать** *v.* sort, assort, classify, grade, screen, size; **—ка** *f.*

sorting, assortment, classification, grading, separation, sizing; screener, sorter; —**очный** *a.* sorting, separating, screening.

сортир/овщик *m.* sorter, grader; —**ующий** *a.* sorting, classifying, grading, screening.

сортный *a.* high-quality.

сортов/ой *a.* sort, variety; section, section-shaped; high-quality; **с. номер** brand number; —**ое железо** profiled (section-shaped) iron.

сортутить *see* **сортучивать.**

сортуч/ение, —**ивание** *n.* amalgamation; —**енный** *a.* amalgamated; —**ивать,** —**ить** *v.* amalgamate; —**ка** *f.* amalgam.

сос/ание *n.* suction; —**ать** *v.* suck.

сосед *m.* neighbor; —**ний** *a.* neighboring, nearby, adjacent; —**ство** *n.* neighborhood, vicinity, proximity.

соскабливать *v.* scrape off.

соскальзывать *v.* slide down, slip; launch.

соскоблить *see* **соскабливать.**

соскользн/увший *a.* slipped; —**уть** *see* **соскальзывать.**

соскре/бать, —**сти** *v.* scrape off.

сослаться *see* **ссылаться.**

сосредоточен/ие *n.*, —**ность** *f.* concentration; —**но** *adv.* intently; —**ный** *a.* concentrated, focused; lumped; —**ный параметр** lumped parameter.

сосредоточ/ивать, —**иваться,** —**ить,** —**иться** *v.* concentrate, center, focus.

Соссюр Saussure (lunar crater).

соссюрит *m.* saussurite.

состав *m.* composition, constitution; abundance; compound; structure; staff, personnel; **с. в космосе** cosmic abundance; **войти в с.** become part (or member) of; **гранулометрический с., ситовой с.** size grading; **закон постоянства** —**а** law of definite proportions.

состав/итель *m.* author, compiler; —**ить,** —**лять** *v.* form, comprise, constitute; put together, compile, construct; formulate, set up; —**ление** *n.* composition, construction, formulation; compilation; structure, constitution; —**ленный** *a.* composed.

составляющ/ая *f.*, —**ая часть,** —**ий элемент** component, ingredient, constituent; —**ий** *a.* component, constituent; —**ая сила** component force, force component.

составн/ой *a.* compound, composite; combined; sectional, jointed; component; aggregative; link; telescopic; **с. газ** composite gas; **с. люминофор** composite phosphor; **с. профиль** divided profile; **с. тон** combination tone; —**ая антенна** composite antenna; —**ая деталь** unit; —**ая дислокация** compound dislocation; —**ая кривая** compound curve; —**ая линза** compound lens; —**ая ракета** stage (composite, combination) rocket; —**ая часть** component, constituent, ingredient; —**ое число** composite number; —**ое ядро** compound nucleus.

состар/ивание *n.* aging; —**ить** *v.* age.

состоян/ие *n.* state, condition, status, position, stage; **с. по изотопическому спину** isotopic spin state; **с. равновесия** balanced state; **диаграмма** —**ия** phase (or constitution) diagram; **уравнение** —**ия** equation of state; **быть в** —**ии** be in a position, be able.

состоятельн/ость *f.* justifiability; competence; strength (of argument); —**ый** *a.* justified, well-grounded.

состоять *v.* consist of, comprise; —**ся** *v.* consist; occur.

состр/игать, —**ичь** *v.* shear (off).

состяз/ание *n.* competition; —**ательный** *a.* controversial; —**аться** *v.* compete.

сосуд *m.* vessel, container, receptacle; **с. высокого давления** pressure vessel; —**истый** *a.* vascular.

сосулька *f.* icicle.

сосуществ/ование *n.* coexistence; —**овать** *v.* coexist; —**ующий** *a.* coexistent.

сосчит/анный *a.* counted; —**ать,** —**ывать** *v.* count, calculate.

сотая *f.* one hundredth.

сотвор/ение *n.* creation; making; —**ить,** —**ять** *v.* create, make.

сот/енный *a.* centesimal, hundredth; —**ня** *f.* one hundred; —**ни** *pl.* hundreds.

ото/вый *a.* honeycomb; **—вая катушка** honeycomb coil; **—образный** *a.* honeycombed.

отр. *abbr.* (**сотрудники**) colleagues, collaborators, staff.

отрудни/к *m.* collaborator, contributor; worker; **—ки** *pl.* colleagues, collaborators, staff; **—чать** *v.* collaborate, contribute, cooperate; **—чество** *n.* collaboration, cooperation.

отряс/ательный *a.* shaking, shocking; **—ать, —ти** *v.* shake; **—ающийся** *a.* shaking; **—ение** *n.* shaking, percussion, vibration, tremor; impact; shock, concussion.

от/ый *a.* hundredth, centesimal; **—ая** *a.* hundredth.

оударение *see* **столкновение.**

оучаст/вовать *v.* participate, cooperate, collaborate; **—ие** *n.* participation, cooperation, collaboration; **—ник** *m.* participant; **—ный** *a.* participating.

офокусный *a.* confocal.

охнуть *v.* dry.

охранен/ие *n.* conservation, preservation, maintenance; **с. импульса** conservation of momentum; **с. углов** isogonality; **с. четности** conservation of parity; **с. энергии** conservation of energy; **закон —ия вещества, закон —ия массы** law of conservation of matter.

охранит/ельный *a.* preservative; **—ь** *see* **сохранять.**

охранн/о *adv.* safely, securely; **—ость** *f.* safety; preservation; **—ый** *a.* safe, secure; conserved.

охранять *v.* conserve, preserve; maintain, keep; **с. силу** remain valid; **—ся** *v.* last; remain.

оч. *abbr.* (**сочинения**) works.

очет/ание *n.* combination, union, association, set; conjunction, coupling; **с. из *k* элементов по *l*** combination of *k* elements *l* at a time; **в —ании с** in conjunction with, coupled (or combined) with.

очетательн/ость *f.* associativity; **—ый** *a.* associative; combined; **—ый закон** associative law.

очетать *v.* combine, associate; match; connect, join.

сочин/ение *n.* composition, writing, work; **полное собрание —ений** complete works; **—ять** *v.* compose.

сочиться *v.* trickle, ooze.

сочлен *m.* fellow member.

сочлен/ение *n.* junction, joint, coupling, connection, articulation; **—енный** *a.* articulated, coupled, linked; keyed; **—ить, —ять** *v.* join, link.

сочувств/ие *n.* sympathy; **—овать** *v.* sympathize.

сошлифов/ка *f.* grinding off, abrasion; **—ываемость** *f.* abradibility; **—ывать** *v.* grind off, abrade, mill off.

союз *m.* union, alliance.

Союз Советских Социалистических Республик Union of Soviet Socialist Republics.

союзн/ик *m.* ally, associate; **—ый** *a.* union; allied, adjoined; **—ое уравнение** associated equation.

спад *m.*, **—ание** *n.* decrease, falling off, decline, coastdown, decay, drop, diminution, abatement; **—ание интенсивности** decay of intensity; **—ать** *v.* decrease, fall (off), decline, decay, drop, diminish, abate; **—ающая волна** decaying wave; **—ающая кривая** decay curve, decrement curve.

спазматический *a.* spasmodic.

спаив/ание *n.* soldering; **—ать** *v.* solder (together), unite.

спай *m.* (soldered) joint; junction (of thermocouple); seal; **с. металла со стеклом** glass-to-metal seal.

спайка *f.* soldering; solder; (soldered) joint, connection; junction; union, cohesion.

спайн/ость *f.* cleavage; cleavability; **—ости** *pl.* cleavage cracks; **—ый** *a.* cleavage.

спалзывать *v.* creep off, creep down, slip, slide.

спар/енный *a.* coupled, paired; duplex, twin, dual; **—ивание** *n.* coupling, pairing, matching; **—ивать, —ить** *v.* pair, couple, match; **—иваться** *v.* pair; **—ивающий** *a.* coupling, pairing, matching.

спарывать *v.* rip off.

спас/аемый *a.* recoverable; **—ание, —ение** *n.* rescue, salvage; **—атель-**

ный *a.* rescue; safety; —**ать** *v.* save, rescue; —**ать дело** save (or correct) the situation.

спасибо thank you, thanks.

спасти *see* **спасать.**

спасть *see* **спадать.**

спа/янность *f.* unity, cohesion; —**янный** *a.* soldered; —**ять** *see* **спаивать.**

СПБ, СПб *abbr.* (**Санкт-Петербург**) St. Petersburg.

спейсистор *m.* spacistor.

спек *m.* sinter; —**аемость** *f.* tendency to cake; —**ание** *n.* caking; sintering, baking, agglomeration; burning; —**аться** *v.* cake, sinter; bake; —**ающийся** *a.* caking, sintering.

спектр *m.* spectrum, range, distribution; **с. аннигиляционного излучения** annihilation spectrum; **с. бета-излучения** beta-ray spectrum; **с. вспышки** flash spectrum; **с. второго запрещения** second forbidden spectrum; **с. гамма-лучей** gamma-ray spectrum; **с. деления** fission spectrum; **с. допплеровских частот** Doppler spectrum; **с. замедления** slowing-down spectrum; **с. искры** spark spectrum; **с. испускания, излучения** emission spectrum; **с. нейтронов** neutron spectrum; **нормальный с.** normal spectrum; **с. первого запрещения** first forbidden spectrum; **с. плотности мощности** power density spectrum; **с. поглощения** absorption spectrum; **с. радиочастот** radio spectrum; **с.-светимость диаграмма** spectrum-luminosity diagram; **с. сравнения** comparison spectrum; **с. энергии** energy spectrum; **с. ядер отдачи** recoil spectrum.

спектрально/-аналитическая рентгеновская трубка x-ray spectrometer tube; —**сть** *f.* spectral character; **с.-чистый** *a.* spectroscopically pure.

спектральн/ый *a.* spectral, spectrum; **с. анализ** spectrum (spectral, spectroscopic) analysis; **с. параллакс** spectroscopic parallax; —**ая линия** spectral line; —**ая плотность излучения** spectral density; —**ая серия** spectral series; —**ая характеристика** spectral characteristic (response, selectivity); color-response curve; —**ая ширина щели спектрометра** spectrometer band width; —**ое разложение** spectral decomposition; —**ое распределение** spectral distribution (sensitivity) response.

спектро/болограф *m.* spectrobolograph —**болометр** *m.* spectrobolometer; —**гелиограф** *m.* spectroheliograph —**гелиоскоп** *m.* spectrohelioscope —**грамма** *f.* spectrogram.

спектрограф *m.* spectrograph; **с. постоянного угла** constant-deviation spectrograph.

спектро/дензограф *see* **спектрофотометр;** —**зональный** *a.* spectrozonal —**интерферограмма** *f.* spectral interference pattern; —**компаратор** *m* spectrocomparator.

спектрометр *m.* spectrometer; **с. по времени пролета** time-of-flight spectrometer; **с. с двойной фокусировкой** double-focusing spectrometer; **с. с фокусировкой на 180°** 180° spectrometer; —**ический** *a.* spectrometric —**ия** *f.* spectrometry.

спектро/радиометр *m.* spectroradiometer; —**сенситометр** *m.* spectrosensitometer.

спектроскоп *m.* spectroscope; —**ист** *m* spectroscopist; —**ически чистый** spectroscopically pure; —**ический** *a* spectroscopic; —**ия** *f.* spectroscopy.

спектрофон *m.* spectrophone.

спектрофотометр *m.* spectrophotometer —**ический** *a.* spectrophotometric.

спектрофотоэлектрический *a.* spectrophotoelectric.

спектрохимический анализ spectrochemical analysis.

спекулировать *v.* speculate.

спекулум *m.* speculum.

спекуля/тивный *a.* speculative; —**ция** *f* speculation, venture.

спекшийся *a.* caked, sintered, baked.

спелый *a.* ripe; refined, finished.

спенсерит *m.* spencerite.

сперва *adv.* initially, at first, first.

спереди *adv. and prep.* in front (of); **вид с.** front view, face.

сперматогенез *m.* spermatogenesis.

сперрилит *m.* sperrylite.

сперрит *m.* spurrite.

спеть *v.* ripen, mature.

спец. *abbr.* (**специальный**) special.

спец *see* **специалист.**

специаит *m.* speziaite.

специал/изация *f.* specialization; **—изироваться** *v.* specialize; **—ист** *m.* specialist, authority; **—ьно** *adv.* specially; **—ьность** *f.* specialty, profession; **—ьный** *a.* special, specific; **—ьная теория относительности** special theory of relativity.

специфи/ка *f.* specific properties, characteristics; **—кация** *f.* specification; **давать —кацию** specify; **—ческий** *a.* specific, unique.

спечь *v.* bake.

спеш/ить *v.* hurry, rush; **—ка, —ность** *f.* hurry, urgency; **—но** *adv.* hastily, hurriedly; urgently; it is urgent; **—ный** *a.* hasty; urgent.

спз *abbr. see* **спуаз.**

спидометр *m.* speedometer.

Спика Spica.

спикула *f.* spicule.

спин *m.* spin; **с.-орбитальная связь** spin-orbit coupling; **с.-решеточная релаксация** spin-lattice relaxation; **с. ядра** nuclear spin.

спина *f.* back.

спинвалентность *f.* spin valency.

спинель *see* **шпинель.**

спин/ка *f.* back, back edge; **—ной** *a.* back; spinal.

спинов/ый *a.* spin; **с. магнитный момент** spin magnetic moment; **с. момент** spin angular momentum; **—ая волна** spin wave; **—ая восприимчивость** spin susceptibility; **—ая детонация** spinning detonation; **—ая температура** spin temperature; **—ая функция** spin wave function; **—ое эхо** spin echo.

спинор *m.*, **—ный** *a.* spinor; **с. первого ранга** spinor of first rank; **—ное поле** spinor field.

спинтарископ *m.* spinthariscope, scintilloscope.

спирал/еобразный *a.* spiral; **—изация** *f.* spiraling, coiling.

спираль *f.* spiral, helix, winding; **—ка** *f.* helix; **—но-лучевая лампа** spiral-beam tube; **—ность** *f.* helicity; **—ный** *a.* spiral, helical; **—ный рукав, —ная ветвь** (astr.) spiral arm; **—ная линия** spiral line, helix; **—ная рессора** coil spring; **—ная туманность** spiral nebula; **—ное поле** helical field.

Спирмена коэффициент Spearman coefficient.

спиро— *prefix* spiro—.

спиро/трон *m.* spirotron; **—циклан** *m.* spirocyclane.

спирт *m.* alcohol; **безводный с.** absolute alcohol; **древесный с.** wood alcohol, methyl alcohol; **этиловый с.** ethyl alcohol; **—ной, —ный** *see* **спиртовой.**

спиртов/ка *f.* alcohol lamp; **—ой, —ый** *a.* alcohol, alcoholic, spirit.

спиртомер *m.* alcoholimeter.

спис/ать *see* **списывать**; **—ок** *m.* copy; list, register.

списыв/ание *n.* copying, transcription; **—ать** *v.* copy, transcribe; **—аться с** correspond with.

спица *f.* spoke.

спичка *f.* match.

сплав *m.* alloy; melt; **с. замещения** substitutional alloy; **—ить** *see* **сплавливать**; **—ка** *see* **сплавление.**

сплавл/ение, —ивание *n.* alloying; melting, fusion, melting together; **с. контактов** (elec.) sticking of contacts; **—енный** *a.* (met.) alloyed; fused, molten; **—енный переход** alloy (or alloyed) junction; **—енный транзистор** alloyed-junction transistor; **—ивать, —ять** *v.* alloy; melt, fuse (together); **—яемый** *a.* alloyable.

сплавн/ой *a.* alloy, alloyed, alloy-type; fused; buoyant; **—ая сила** buoyancy.

сплачивать, —ся *v.* unite, join, consolidate.

сплесн/ение, —ивание *n.* splice, splicing; **—ивать, —ить** *v.* splice, join.

сплe/сти, —тать *v.* interweave; **—тение** *n.* entanglement, complication; interlacing.

сплотить *see* **сплачивать.**

сплочен/ие, *n.*, **—ность** *f.* solidarity, cohesion, unity; joining; **—ный** *a.* (packed) solid; **—ный лед** packed ice.

сплошн/ой *a.* continuous; solid, dense, compact, bulk; complete; **с. про-**

водник solid conductor; **с. спектр** continuous spectrum, continuum; **—ая кривая** continuous (full, solid, unbroken) curve; **—ая молния** sheet lightning; **—ая нагрузка** continuous load; **—ая облачность** solid cloud cover, overcast; **—ая среда** continuous medium.

сплошность *f.* continuity; compactness; completeness.

сплошь *adv.* continuously; completely.

сплы/вать, —ть *v.* overflow; **—ваться, —ться** *v.* blend, merge.

сплюснут/ость *see* **сплющенность**; **—ый** *see* **сплющенный**; **—ь** *see* **сплющивать.**

сплющ/енность *f.* flatness; oblateness; **—енный** *a.* flattened; oblate; **—ивание** *n.* flattening; squashing; **—ивать, —ить** *v.* flatten.

сподиозит *m.* spodiosite.

сподиофиллит *m.* spodiophyllite.

спокойн/ый *a.* quiet, calm, quiescent, resting; mild, gentle; smooth; **с. воздух** still air; **с. ход** smooth running; **—ое море** smooth sea; **—ое солнце** quiet sun.

спокойствие *n.* stability, calm.

сполз/ание *n.* slipping, creep; **с. нуля** zero creep; **с. частоты** frequency drift; **—ать, —ти** *see* **спалзывать.**

сполна *adv.* completely.

спонтанн/ый *a.* spontaneous; **с. распад** spontaneous decay (or disintegration); **—ое деление** spontaneous fission.

спор *m.* debate, controversy, dispute.

спорадический *a.* sporadic.

спор/ить *v.* debate, dispute, argue; **—ный** *a.* debatable, questionable, controversial; disputed.

способ *m.* method, process, procedure, means, way, mode; **с. наименьших квадратов** method of least squares; **с. перехода** transition mode; **с. подстановки** substitution method; **таким —ом** in this way.

способн/ость *f.* power, ability, capacity; competence, aptitude, talent; **с. замедления** slowing-down (or moderating) power; **излучательная с.** emissivity; **с. к намагничиванию** magnetizability; **с. преломления** refractive power; **с. торможения** stopping power; **—ый** *a.* capable, able; **—ый к исправлению** improvable.

способствов/ание *n.* assistance, contribution; **—ать** *v.* assist; promote, further, contribute; favor, facilitate.

справа *adv.* to the right; from the right side; **с. налево** from right to left.

справедлив/ость *f.* correctness; justice; **отдать ему с.** do him justice; **по —ости** in all fairness; **—ый** *a.* correct, true, valid; just.

справ/иться, —ляться *v.* consult, inquire; manage, cope with, handle; **—ка** *f.* information, reference; certificate.

справочн/ик, *m.*, **—ая книга** reference book, handbook; **—ый** *a.* reference information, inquiry.

спрашивать *v.* ask, inquire.

спрессов/анный *a.* pressed; compressed; **—ать, —ывать** *v.* press.

спринклер *m.* sprinkler.

спринц/евать *v.* squirt, inject, syringe; **—овка** *f.* syringe; syringing, injecting.

спровоцировать *v.* provoke, incite.

спроектиров/анный *a.* projected, designed, planned; **—ать** *see* **проектировать.**

спрос *m.* demand; **—ить** *see* **спрашивать.**

спрыг *m.*, **—ивать, —нуть** *v.* jump (or spring) off.

спрыс/кать, —кивать, —нуть *v.* spray, sprinkle, moisten; **—кивание** *n.* spraying, sprinkling; **—нутый** *a.* sprayed, sprinkled.

спрягать *v.* conjugate.

спрям/итель *m.* squarer; **—ление** *n.* rectification; squaring; **—ленный** *a.* rectified, linearized; **—ляемость** *f.* rectifiability; **—ляемый** *a.* rectifiable; **—ляющая плоскость** rectifying plane.

спуаз *abbr.* **(сантипуаз)** centipoise (cp).

спуск *m.* descent, slope, incline; lowering, landing; discharge, outlet, escapement; draining, emptying; trigger, release; launching; **с. (воды) самотеком** gravity drainage; **метод —а** (math.) method of descent; **—ать** *v.* lower; discharge, drain empty, deflate; release; **—аться** *v.* descend; **—аться отлого** slope; **—ающийся** *a.* sloping; descending.

пускн/ой *a.* lowering; drain, discharge, outlet; release; **с. механизм** trigger mechanism; **—ая труба** drain pipe.

пусков/ой *see* **спускной**; **—ая кнопка** release button; **—ая схема** trigger circuit.

пустя *prep. acc.* after, later; **немного с.** shortly after.

пут/анный *a.* tangled; **—ать** *see* **спутывать.**

путн/ик *m.* sputnik, satellite; companion; **—ая струя** (hyd.) wake.

путыв/ание *n.* entanglement; **—ать** *v.* entangle.

пущенный *a.* lowered; drained; deflated.

пя/чка *f.* sleep, somnolence; **—щий** *a.* sleeping, dormant; **—щий волчок** sleeping top.

р. *abbr.* (**сравни**) compare; (**среда**) Wednesday; (**средний**) middle, mean, average, medium, central.

рабатыв/аемость *f.* wearing capacity; **—ание** *n.* operation, action; response, actuation; firing, triggering; wear; **—ание аварийной защиты** safety action, scram; **—ать** *v.* operate; trigger, fire; wear; **неправильное —ание** malfunction.

работ/авшийся *a.* worn; **—анный** *a.* worn out; made; **—ать** *v.* make, fabricate; **—аться** *v.* wear out.

равнен/ие *n.* comparison; equating; congruence (in number theory); **делать с.** compare, contrast; **по —ию с** in comparison with.

равни *imp. of* **сравнивать,** *v.* compare.

равнив/ание *n.* comparing; leveling; **—ать** *v.* compare; equate; level, equalize; **—аться** *v.* equal, be equal.

равним/ость *f.* comparability; congruence; **—ый** *a.* comparable; congruent; **—ые числа** congruent numbers.

равнительн/о *adv.* comparatively, relatively; **—ый** *a.* comparative, relative, respective.

равнить *see* **равнять, сравнивать.**

р.-аз. *abbr.* (**среднеазиатский**) Central Asiatic, Central Asia.

разу *adv.* at once.

сраст/ание *n.* intergrowth, coalescence, concretion; accretion; **двойниковое с.** twinning; **двойник —ания** (cryst.) contact twin; **плоскость —ания** (cryst.) composition plane; **—аться, —ись** *v.* grow together, intergrow, coalesce; **—ить** *see* **сращивать.**

сращ/ение *see* **срастание**; **—енный переход** (semicond.) grown junction; **—ивание** *n.* joining, splicing; **—ивать** *v.* join, splice; **—иваться** *see* **срастаться.**

среда *f.* medium, atmosphere, surroundings, environment; ambient; Wednesday; **охлаждающая с.** coolant.

среди *prep. gen.* among; in the middle (of).

среди— *prefix* inter—.

средина *see* **середина.**

срединн/ый *a.* middle, median, mean; **—ая несущая** (elec.) carrier frequency; **—ая плоскость** middle plane; **—ая поверхность** middle surface.

средн. гринвич. *abbr.* (**среднее гринвичское время**) Greenwich civil time.

средне— *prefix* mean, medium, middle, central, mid—.

средне/арифметический *a.* arithmetic mean; **—весовой** *a.* weighted-mean; **—взвешенное (значение)** weighted mean (value); **—геометрический** *a.* geometric mean.

средн/ее *n.* mean, average; **с. арифметическое** arithmetical mean; **с. взвешенное** weighted mean; **пропорциональное с.** geometric mean; **теорема о —ем** mean-value theorem.

среднезернистый *a.* medium-granular, medium-grained.

среднеквадратич/еский, —ный *a.* mean-square, root-mean-square (rms); **—ное значение** root-mean-square value; **—ное отклонение** root-mean-square deviation, standard deviation.

средне/кубический *a.* root-mean-cube; **—олигоценовый** *a.* Middle Oligocene; **—солнечный** *a.* mean solar; **—сортный** *a.* medium-grade; **—суточный** *a.* daily mean; **—твердый** *a.* medium-hard.

среднетяжел/ый *a.* medium-weight; —**ое ядро** medium (or intermediate) nucleus.

среднеуглеродистая сталь medium steel.

среднечасовой *a.* hourly mean.

средн/ий *a.* mean, average; middle, center, central; medium; intermediate; neutral, neuter; **с. ион** hybrid (or amphoteric) ion, zwitterion; **с. квадрат** mean square; **с. квадратический, с. квадратный** *see* **среднеквадратический; с. логарифм отношения** logarithmic mean difference; **с. нейтрон** intermediate neutron; **с. по времени** time-averaged; **с. полдень** (astr.) mean noon; **с. пробег (для) поглощения** absorption mean free path; **с. (свободный) пробег** mean range, mean free path; **с. (свободный) пробег рассеяния** scattering mean free path; **с. уровень (поверхности) моря** mean sea level; **с. уровень прилива** half-tide level; **с. член** mean (of a proportion); **с. ярус облаков** middle clouds; **в —ем** on the average; **выше —его** above average.

средн/ий *cont.*, —**яя аномалия** mean anomaly; —**яя величина** mean, average; —**яя видимость** moderate visibility; —**яя длина пути** mean range, mean (free) path; —**яя длина (свободного) пробега** mean free path; —**яя линия** center line; —**яя орбита** mean orbit; —**яя плоскость** median (or central) plane, midplane; —**яя реакция** neutral reaction; —**яя соль** neutral salt; —**яя точка** midpoint, midway point; —**яя траектория** median trajectory; —**яя хорда** mean chord; —**яя хромосфера** mid-chromosphere; —**яя частота** mid-band (or center) frequency; mean frequency; medium frequency; —**яя школа** secondary school.

средн/ий *cont.*, —**ее время** mean (or civil) time; —**ее время жизни** mean lifetime; —**ее гармоническое** harmonic mean; —**ее значение** mean (or expectation) value; —**ее линейное отклонение** (stat.) mean deviation; —**ее пропорциональное** mean proportional; —**ее свободное время реакции** reaction mean free time; —**ее солнечное время** mean solar time; —**ее солнце** mean sun; —**ие (солнечные) сутки** mean (solar) day, civil day; —**ие широты** mid-latitudes.

средняя арифметическая *see* **среднеарифметическое.**

средоточие *n.* focus, concentration point, center.

средство *n.* means, agent; **с. охлаждения** cooling agent.

средь *see* **среди.**

срез *m.* shear, shearing; cut, slice; section; cutoff; **с. X** X-cut; **плоскость —а** shear plane.

срез/ание *n.* cutting, shearing; truncation; —**анный** *a.* cut, sheared; truncated; —**анный импульс** clipped pulse; —**анная кривая** sheared curve; —**ать** *see* **срезывать;** —**ающий** *a.* shearing; —**ающая волна** shear wave.

срезыв/ание *n.* cutting, shearing, clipping; truncation; —**атель** *m.* chopper, clipper; —**атель-ограничитель** clipper-limiter; —**ать** *v.* cut off, shear, clip; truncate; —**ающий** *see* **срезающий;** —**ающая сила,** —**ающее усилие** shearing force (or stress), shear.

срисов/ать, —**ывать** *v.* draw, copy.

сродный *a.* innate; allied, related.

сродство *n.* relationship, affinity; **с. электроном** electron affinity; **химическое с.** chemical affinity.

срок *m.* date, (fixed) time, term, period; **с. службы** *see under* **служба.**

срост *m.* coupling, attachment, adhesion; —**ок** *m.* attachment, adhesion, joint, splice; concretion; intergrowth.

сросшийся монокристалл grown single crystal.

срочн/о *adv.* urgently; —**ость** *f.* urgency; —**ый** *a.* urgent, pressing; periodic, routine; —**ое наблюдение** (meteor.) standard observation.

ср. ск. *abbr.* **(средняя скорость)** mean velocity, average speed.

сруб *m.* framework, crib.

срыв *m.* stripping, separation; cutoff, disruption; collapse; **с. дейтрона** deuteron stripping; **с. потока** burbling, separation of flow; —**ать** *se* сорвать; **—ной флаттер** (aero.) stall flutter.

ряду *adv.* successively.

С *abbr. see* **Советский Союз.**

сабоит *m.* szaboite.

сайбелиит *m.* szaibelyite.

смикит *m.* szmikite.

сомольнокит *m.* szomolnokite.

сохнуться *see* **ссыхаться.**

ССР *abbr. see* **Союз Советских Социалистических Республик.**

ст *abbr.* **(сантистокс)** centistoke.

сыл/аться *v.* refer, cite; **—аясь на** with reference to; **—ка** *f.* reference, citation.

сып/ание *n.*, **—ка** *f.* pouring; **—ать** *v.* pour.

сыхаться *v.* shrink.

т *abbr.* **(стокс)** stoke; **ст. (станция)** station; **(старший)** senior; **(старый)** old; **(статья)** article, paper; clause; **(столетие)** century; **(ступень)** grade.

Т *abbr.* **(стандарт)** standard, norm.

табиливольт *m.* stabilivolt, voltage regulator (tube).

табилиз/атор *m.* stabilizer; regulator; balancer; vane; **с. напряжения** voltage regulator; **с. тока** current regulator; **—ация** *f.* stabilization, regulation; **—ация частоты** frequency stabilization; **—ированный** *see* **стабилизованный; —ированная в пространстве платформа** space (-stabilized) platform; **—ировать** *v.* stabilize, regulate.

табилизованный *a.* stabilized; **с. выпрямитель** regulated rectifier; **с. кварцем** crystal-controlled.

табилитрон *m.* stabilitron tube.

табило/вольт *m.* voltage regulator; **—метр частоты** frequency departure meter.

табильн/ость *f.* stability; **общая с.** over-all stability; **—ый** *a.* stable; **—ая орбита** stable orbit; **—ое состояние** stable state.

тавить *v.* put, place, set; **с. вопрос** raise a question (or problem); **с. опыт** perform an experiment; **с. себе целью** aim at.

тавка *f.* rate; stake, bet.

тавролит *m.* staurolite.

тадиальный *a.* stage, phase.

Стадий Stadius (lunar crater).

стадия *f.* stage, phase.

стаж *m.* experience; training period; **—ер** *m.* trainee.

стаивать *v.* melt, defrost, deice.

стакан, —чик *m.* glass, beaker, container; (pump) bucket; can; socket, thimble, sleeve, cup, shell.

сталагмит *m.* stalagmite; **—овый** *a.* stalagmitic.

сталагмометр *m.* stalagmometer; **—ический** *a.* stalagmometric.

сталактит *m.* stalactite; **—овый** *a.* stalactitic.

стале— *prefix* steel.

сталебетон *m.* steel concrete.

сталелитейный *a.* steel casting; **с. завод** steel mill.

сталеплавильный *a.* steel smelting; **—ая печь** steel furnace.

сталепрокатный *a.* steel rolling; **с. завод, с. стан** steel rolling mill.

сталинит *m.* stalinite (tool steel).

сталистый *a.* steely.

сталкив/ать *v.* push (off); **—аться** *v.* collide; encounter; conflict; **—ающийся** *a.* colliding.

стало *see under* **стать.**

сталь *f.*, **—ной** *a.* steel.

стамуха *f.* stranded (or grounded) ice.

стан *m.* mill; **с.-дуо** two-high mill.

станд *see* **стенд.**

стандарт *m.* standard, norm; (stat.) standard deviation.

Стандартгиз *abbr.* **(Государственное издательство стандартов)** State Standards Press.

стандартиз/ация *f.* standardization; **—ировать, —овать** *v.* standardize; **—ованный** *a.* standardized.

стандартн/ый *a.* standard, normal, conventional; **—ое отклонение** standard deviation.

станина *f.* mounting, pedestal, frame; base, stand, bed (plate).

станиол/ь *m.*, **—евый** *a.* tinfoil.

станкостроительный *a.* machine-tool building.

станн/ат *m.* stannate; **—ит** *m.* stannite.

становить *see* **ставить; —ся** *v.* become, turn, get, grow; get upon, stand on; **—ся известным** become known (or famous).

становление *n.* formation, establishment.

стан/ок *m.*, **—очный** *a.* machine, machine tool, lathe; bench.

Стантона число Stanton number.

станц/ионный *a.*, **—ия** *f.* station; plant.

стапливать *v.* melt, fuse.

старание *n.* endeavor, effort, exertion.

старательн/ость *f.* assiduity, diligence; **—ый** *a.* diligent.

стараться *v.* endeavor, strive, try.

старейший *a.* oldest.

стар/ение *n.* aging; **—еть, —иться** *v.* age, become obsolete; **—инный** *a.* antiquated, ancient; **—ить** *v.* age; **—ость** *f.* old age.

старт *see* **стартование.**

стартер *m.* starter; **автоматический с.** self-starter.

стартов/ание *n.* start, launching; **—ать** *v.* start, launch, take off; **—ый** *a.* starting, launching; **—ый ускоритель** booster; **—ая площадка** *see* **пусковая площадка.**

старческая дальнозоркость presbyopia.

старше *comp. of* **старый,** older.

старш/ий *m.* chief, head; *a.* older, oldest, senior; **с. коэффициент** (math.) leading coefficient; **с. курс** senior (or advanced) course; **с. научный сотрудник** senior scientific associate, senior scientist; **с. член** (math.) leading term; **—инство** *n.* seniority, precedence.

старый *a.* old; **с. стиль** Old Style (Julian calendar).

стасит *m.* stasite, dewindtite.

статейный *a.* article; clause.

статика *f.* statics.

статисти/к *m.* statistician; **—ка** *f.* statistics; **—чески** *adv.* statistically.

статистическ/ий *a.* statistical; **—ая величина** statistic; **—ая ошибка, —ая погрешность** statistical error; **—ая флюктуация** statistical fluctuation; **—ое заключение** statistical inference.

статистичность *f.* statistical character.

статический *a.* static.

статор *m.*, **—ный** *a.* stator.

статоскоп *m.* statoscope; **—ограф** *m.* statoscopograph.

статус-кво status quo.

статут *m.* statute, ordinance.

стать *v.* begin to; become; *see also* **становиться; во что бы ни стало** at any cost; **стало быть** so, thus, therefore; it follows that.

статья *f.* article, paper; clause.

стационарность *f.* stationarity, steadiness.

стационарн/ый *a.* stationary, steady, steady-state; fixed; maintained, time-independent; **с. поток** stationary (or steady) flow; **с. разрядник** fixed discharger; **с. реактор** stationary reactor; **с. режим** steady state, steady-state operation; **с. фон** steady background; **с. фронт** stationary front; **—ое поле** stationary (static, steady) field; **—ое решение** steady-state solution; **—ое состояние** steady state; **—ое уравнение непрерывности** steady-state equation of continuity.

стачивать *v.* grind off.

сташицит *m.* staszicite.

стаять *see* **стаивать.**

ствол *m.* shaft; (gun) barrel, tube; core; **с. атмосферного ливня** air-shower core.

створ *m.* alignment, range.

створка *f.* fold, flap.

створчатый *a.* folding; valved, hinged; **с. клапан** clack valve.

стеаро— *prefix* stearo—.

стеатит *m.* steatite.

Стевин Stevinus (lunar crater).

стеенструпин *m.* steenstrupine.

стек/ание *n.* runoff; **—ать** *v.* flow, run off, drain, discharge; **—аться** *v.* converge; collect, accumulate; **—ающий** *a.* draining, discharging, running out.

стеклить *see* **стекловать.**

стекло— *prefix* glass; *see also* **стеклянный, стекольный.**

стекло *m.* glass; **жидкое с., растворимое с.** water glass; **органическое с.** glasslike transparent plastic (usually acrylic); **покровное с.** cover glass.

стекло/вание *n.* vitrification; **—варение** *n.* glassmaking; **—варный горшок** glass pot; **—ватый** *a.* vitreous, glassy; **—ватая порода** rock glass; **—вать** *v.* vitrify; glaze.

стекловидн/ость *f.* glassiness, vitreosity; **—ый** *a.* glassy, vitreous; **—ое тело** vitreous humor.

стекло/графия *f.* manual duplicating process employing a glass plate; **—делие** *n.* glass manufacture; **—дув** *m.* glass blower; **—дувная трубка** blowpipe; **—керамика** *f.* glazed ceramics.

стеклообразн/ость *f.* glassiness, vitreosity; **—ый** *a.* glassy, vitreous.

стеклоплавильн/ый *a.* glass-melting; **с. горшок** glass pot (or crucible); **—ая печь** glass furnace.

стекло/подобный *see* **стеклообразный**; **—рез** *m.* glass cutter.

стеклянн/ый *a.* glass, vitreous; **с. бой** cullet; **с. манометр** glass-tube manometer; **с. шлиф** ground-glass joint; **—ая вата** glass wool; **—ая палочка** glass rod.

стекольн/ый *see* **стеклянный; с. шлак** glass gall.

стекший *a.* discharged, drained.

стелиться *v.* spread; drift.

стеллаж *m.* rack, shelves.

стеллит *m.*, **—овый** *a.* stellite.

стен *m.* sthene.

стена *f.* wall, side.

стенд *m.* stand; bench; (aero.) test bed (or stand); station; **—овое испытание** bench (static, captive) test.

стениерит *m.* stainierite.

стенка *see* **стена.**

стенметр *m.* sthene-meter, kilojoule.

стенной *a.* wall, wall-type.

стенографический *a.* stenographic; **с. отчет** verbatim report.

стеноп *m.* stenopic camera, camera obscura.

степенн/ой *a.* power; **с. закон** power law; **с. ряд** power series; **с. спектр** power-law spectrum; **—ая функция** power function.

степен/ь *f.* degree, extent, order; step, stage; grade, class; (math.) power; **возводить в третью с.** raise to the third power, cube; **с. запрещенности** degree of forbiddenness; **с. затягивания** (elec.) pulling figure; **с. корня** index of a radical; **с. поляризации** degree of polarization; **с. расширения** expansion ratio; **с. свободы** degree of freedom; **с. сжатия** compression ratio; **с. точки** power of a point; **третья с.** third power, cube; **с. уравнения** degree of an equation; **ученая с.** (university) degree; **в значительной —и** largely, to a considerable degree; **в меньшей —и** to a lesser degree; **в некоторой —и** somewhat; **до некоторой —и** to some extent; **корень третьей —и** cube root; **ни в какой —и** not at all.

стер *m.* stere, kiloliter.

стерад *m.* sterad; **—иан** *m.* steradian.

стерео/акустический *a.* binaural; **—бинокль** *m.* stereoscope; **—грамма** *f.* stereogram.

стереограф/ический *a.* stereographic; **—ическая сетка** stereographic net; **—ия** *f.* stereography.

стереоизображение *n.* stereoscopic image.

стереоизомер *m.* stereoisomer, stereomer; **—ия** *f.* stereoisomerism; **—ный** *a.* stereoisomeric.

стерео/компаратор *m.* stereocomparator; **—лупа** *f.* stereomagnifier.

стереометр *m.* stereometer; **—ический** *a.* stereometric; **—ия** *f.* solid geometry, stereometry.

стерео/микроскоп *m.* stereomicroscope; **—планиграф** *m.* stereoplanigraph.

стереоскоп *m.* stereoscope; **—ический** *a.* stereoscopic; **—ический перископ** binocular periscope.

стерео/снимок *m.* stereoscopic photograph; **—труба** *f.* stereoscopic telescope; **—физика** *f.* stereophysics.

стереофон/ия *f.* stereophonics; **—ный** *a.* stereophonic.

стереохим/ический *a.* stereochemical; **—ия** *f.* stereochemistry.

стереть *see* **стирать.**

стеречь *v.* guard, have charge of.

стержень *m.* bar, rod; core; stem, shaft, pin; spindle, pivot; **с. аварийной защиты** safety rod; **с. грубой регулировки** coarse-control rod, shim rod; **с. клапана** valve stem; **с. струйного течения** jet-stream core; **с. точной регулировки** fine-control rod.

стержнев/ой *see* **стержень; с. магнетрон** interdigital magnetron; **с. магнит** bar magnet; **с. разрядник** rod gap;

с. трансформатор core-type transformer; —**ая обмотка** bar winding; —**ая решетка** rod lattice; —**ая установка** rod assembly.

стержнеобразный *a.* bar, rod-shaped.

стерилиз/атор *m.* sterilizer; —**ация** *f.* sterilization; —**ировать,** —**овать** *v.* sterilize; —**ованный** *a.* sterilized; —**ующая доза** sterilization dose.

стерильн/ость *f.* sterility; —**ый** *a.* sterile.

стерин *m.* sterol.

стерическ/ий *a.* steric, spatial; —**ое затруднение** steric hindrance.

стеркорит *m.* stercorite.

стеррометалл *m.* sterro metal (copper-zinc-iron alloy).

стертый *a.* erased; eroded.

стесненн/ый *a.* constrained; —**ая пластическая деформация** contained plastic deformation; —**ая шкала** compressed scale.

стесн/ительный *a.* restrictive, inconvenient; embarrassing; —**ить,** —**ять** *v.* constrain, hamper, handicap, narrow.

Стефана-Больцмана закон Stefan-Boltzmann law.

стефанит *m.* stephanite.

стехио— *prefix* stoichio—.

стехиометр/ический *a.* stoichiometric; —**ия** *f.* stoichiometry.

стеч/ение *n.* confluence, convergence; concurrence, coincidence; —**ь** *see* **стекать.**

стибиконит *m.* stibiconite.

стигматич/еский *a.* stigmatic, punctual, homocentric; —**еское изображение** punctual image; —**ность** *f.* stigmaticalness, homocentricity.

стилоскоп *m.* steeloscope.

стилотипит *m.* stylotypite.

Стилтьеса интеграл Stieltjes integral.

стиль *m.* style, manner.

стильб *m.* stilb.

стильбен *m.* stilbene; —**овый фосфор** stilbene phosphor.

стильпнохлоран *m.* stilpnochloran.

стимул *m.* stimulus, stimulant; —**ирование** *n.* stimulation; —**ировать** *v.* stimulate; —**ятор** *m.* stimulator.

стипенд/иат *m.* scholarship student, fellow; —**ия** *f.* scholarship.

стир/ание *n.* erasure, rubbing off, obliteration; abrasion; —**ать** *v.* abrade, erode; rub off, erase; —**ающий** *a.* abrading; erasing, obliterating; —**ающий луч** (telev.) play-off beam.

Стирлинга формула Stirling formula.

стирол *m.* styrene.

стирофлекс *m.* Styroflex.

стис/кивать, —**нуть** *v.* squeeze, clutch.

стихать *v.* abate.

стих/ийный *a.* elemental; —**ия** *f.* element.

стихнуть *see* **стихать.**

стихтит *m.* stichtite.

стлб. *abbr.* (**столбец**) column.

сто hundred; —**градусный** *a.* centigrade.

стоимость *f.* value, cost.

стоить *v.* cost; be worth, deserve.

стойка *f.* stand, pedestal, rack; support, prop, brace; (aero.) strut; column, pillar, post.

стойк/ий *a.* resistant, stable, firm, persistent; *suffix* —proof, —resistant; —**ость** *f.* resistance, stability, firmness, persistence, durability.

сток *m.* sink; drain; discharge, drainage runoff, effluence; **с. самотеком** gravity drainage; **коэффициент —а** runoff coefficient.

стокезит *m.* stokesite.

стократный *a.* hundredfold, centuple.

стокс *m.* stoke.

Стокса закон (правило) Stokes law; **теорема С.** S. theorem; **стоксовое возбуждение** S.-line excitation.

стол *m.* table, desk; platform; **расчетный с.** network analyzer

столб *m.* column, pillar, post, pole, shaft; **с. жидкости** column (or head) of liquid; **с. разряда** (elec.) positive column; **солнечный с.** sun pillar.

столбец *m.* column.

столбик *m.* column; prism; **с. ртути** mercury column; —**овая диаграмма** column diagram, bar diagram.

столбов/идный *a.* columnar; —**ой** *a.* column, post; —**ой выключатель** (elec.) pole switch.

столб/цевый *a.* column; —**чатый** *a.* columnar; acicular; —**чатая диаграмма** bar graph.

столет/ие *n.* century; —**ний** *a.* centennial; —**няя годовщина** centennial.

Столетова константа Stoletov constant (ratio of field strength to pressure at maximum current in gases).

столик *m.* stand; stage (of microscope).

столи/ца *f.* capital; **—чный** *a.* metropolitan.

столкн/овение *n.* encounter; collision, impact; **с. второго рода** collision of the second kind; **параметр —овения** impact parameter; **—уть** *see* **сталкивать.**

Столовая Гора Mensa (Men) (constellation).

столов/ая гора, —ое плоскогорье (geo.) mesa; **—ая соль** table salt, sodium chloride.

столочь *v.* grind.

столп *m.* pillar.

столь *adv.* so, such.

столько *adv.* so much, so many; **с. же** as much as, as many as; **еще с. же** as much again, as many again; **не с. . . . сколько** not so much . . . as . . ., . . . rather than . . . .

Стонера теория Stoner theory.

стоп *m.* stop; **с.-стержень** shutdown (or scram) rod.

стоп/а, —ка *f.* pile, stack.

стопить *see* **стапливать.**

стоповая кнопка stop button.

стопор *m.* stop, catch, detainer, lock; plug, stopper; **—ить** *v.* plug, stop; lock.

стопорн/ый *a.* stop, stopper; locking; **с. болт** binding bolt; **с. винт** stop (or set) screw; **с. клапан** stop (or shutoff) valve; **с. кран** stopcock; **с. механизм** locking mechanism; **—ая гайка** lock (or check) nut; **—ое кольцо** check ring; **—ое приспособление, —ое устройство** lock, catch; **—ое реле** locking relay.

Стоппани ареометр Stoppani areometer.

стопроцентный *a.* one hundred percent.

сторож *m.* guard, watchman; **—ить** *v.* watch, guard.

сторожок *m.* catch; escapement.

сторон/а *f.* side; direction; aspect; part; place; **передняя с.** forepart; **—ой** sideways; **в —е** aside; **в —у** to the side, laterally; **во все —ы** in different directions; on all sides; **по обе —ы** on both sides; **с другой —ы** on the other hand; **с его —ы** for his part, from his point of view.

сторонн/ий *a.* outside, external, irrelevant, extraneous; *suffix* —hedral, —lateral; **—ее электрическое поле** electric field produced by nonelectromagnetic (thermal, chemical, contact, or mechanical) processes; **—ик** *m.* adherent, supporter; *suffix* —hedron; **—ичество** *n.* adherence, support.

стохастический *a.* stochastic.

сточить *see* **стачивать.**

сточн/ый *a.* sewer, drain, discharge; **с. трубопровод, —ая труба** sewer pipe, drain; **—ые воды** sewage.

стояк *m.* standpipe, riser; stack; post; grounded (or standard) ice.

стоян/ие *n.* standing; **—ка** *f.* stand, station, anchorage.

стоять *v.* stand; be; stop; **с. за то, чтобы . . .** be for . . .; **с. на повестке дня** be on the agenda.

стояч/ий *a.* standing, stationary; **—ая вода** standing (or stagnant) water; **—ая волна** standing wave; **коэффициент —ей волны** standing-wave ratio; **—ие страты** stationary striations.

стоящий *a.* costing; worthy, worthwhile; **дорого с.** costly, expensive.

стр. *abbr.* (**страница**) page; (**строка**) line.

Страбон Strabon (lunar crater).

страв/ить, —лять *v.* scour, etch, cleanse; **—ление, —ливание** *n.* scouring, etching; **—ленный** *a.* scoured, etched.

страд/ание *n.* suffering; **—ать** *v.* suffer; **—ать недостатком** have a defect.

страна *f.* country, land; **с. света** point of the compass.

страница *f.* page.

странн/о *adv.* strangely, oddly; it is strange; **—ость** *f.* strangeness, oddness, singularity; **—ый** *a.* strange, odd, singular.

странствовать *v.* travel.

страта *f.* stria, striation.

стратегия *f.* strategy.

стратиграф *m.* stratigrapher; **—ический** *a.* stratigraphic; **—ия** *f.* stratigraphy.

стратифи/кация *f.* stratification; —**цированный** *a.* stratified.

страто/пауза *f.* stratopause; —**план** *m.* stratoplane; —**стат** *m.* stratosphere balloon.

стратосфер/а *f.* stratosphere; —**ный** *a.* stratospheric.

страх *m.* fear; risk; responsibility; **на свой с.** at one's own risk; **под —ом** under penalty of.

страхов/ание *n.*, —**ка** *f.* insurance; —**ать** *v.* insure.

страшн/о *adv.* terribly, awfully; it is terrible, it is terrifying; —**ый** *a.* terrible, frightful, fearful, dreadful.

стр-во *abbr.* (**строительство**) construction.

стрейнер *m.* strainer.

Стрела Sagitta (Sge) (constellation).

стрела *f.* arrow, pointer, indicator; crane arm, boom; cantilever; rise, camber; **грузовая с., подъемная с.** derrick; **с. подъема** rise (of arch); **с. прогиба** (bending) deflection, sag, dip; depth of arc (or curvature), sagitta.

Стрелец Sagittarius (Sgr) (constellation).

стрелка *f.* pointer, needle, indicator, hand (of clock), arrow; **с. компаса** compass needle; **с. наклонения** dip needle.

стреловидн/ость *f.* sweepback; **с. крыльев** wing sweepback; —**ый** *a.* arrow-shaped, sagittal; (aero.) sweptback, swept; —**ое крыло** sweptback wing.

стрелочный *a.* pointer-type, arrow, needle, indicator; **с. прибор** pointer-type instrument.

стрель/ба *f.* shooting, firing; —**чатый** *a.* arrow-shaped; pointed.

стрелять *v.* shoot, fire.

стремительн/ость *f.* impetus, swiftness; —**ый** *a.* impetuous, swift.

стрем/иться *v.* rush; aim at, strive for; tend; approach; —**ление** *n.* tendency, trend; aspiration; —**ящийся** *a.* striving for, aspiring; tending; approaching.

стресс *m.* stress.

стрикция *f.* striction.

стример *m.*, —**ный** *a.* streamer.

стрипп/ер *m.* stripper; —**инг** *m.* stripping.

строб *m.* strobe, gate; **с. отметки** strobe (or gate) marker; —**генератор** *m.* gate generator; —**импульс** *m.* gate pulse.

стробир/ование *n.* gating, strobing; —**ованная лампа** gated tube; —**овать** *v.* gate, strobe; —**ующий каскад** gating stage; —**ующий осциллоскоп** sampling oscilloscope.

строболюкс *m.* strobolux.

стробоскоп *m.* stroboscope; —**ический** *a.* stroboscopic; —**ический тахометр** strobotac.

стробbooтрон *m.* strobotron.

строг/ание *n.* planing; —**ать** *v.* plane.

строг/ий *a.* strict, rigorous, strictly valid; —**ое неравенство** absolute inequality.

строго *adv.* strictly; **с. говоря** strictly speaking; **с. запрещенный** highly forbidden; **с. обоснованный** rigorously substantiated, well-founded, well-grounded; —**сть** *f.* strictness, rigor.

строе/вой *a.* building, construction; —**ние** *n.* structure; constitution, composition; building, construction; texture; —**ние ядра** nuclear structure.

строитель *m.* builder; —**ный** *a.* building, construction, structural; —**ный материал** building material; —**ный элемент** structural element (or member); —**ство** *n.* building, construction.

строить *v.* build, construct; **с. планы** plan.

стро/й *m.* order, system, arrangement; **вступать в с.** come into play; **вывести из —я** put out of service; **выйти из —я** get out of order.

стройка *see* **строительство.**

стройн/ость *f.* order, orderliness, orderly system; —**ый** *a.* orderly.

строка *f.* line; **с. матрицы** matrix row.

стронц/ианит *m.* strontianite; —**иевый** *a.* strontium; —**ий** *m.* strontium (Sr).

строфоида *f.* strophoid.

строч/ить *v.* stitch; write; —**ка** *f.* short line (or row); —**ный** *a.* line; —**ная буква** lower case letter; —**ная матрица** row matrix.

строящийся *a.* under-construction.

струбцинка *f.* cramp, cramp frame, screw clamp, vise.
Струве функция Struve functions.
струг *m.* plane.
струе— *prefix* jet.
стружк/а *f.* shaving, chip; —**и** *pl.* shavings, cuttings, chips.
струиться *v.* stream, flow.
струй/ка *f.* jet, stream, stream filament; (astr.) streamer; —**ный** *a.* jet; current, flow; —**ный насос** jet pump; —**ная горелка** jet burner; —**ное течение** jet stream (or flow).
струйчат/ость *f.* waviness; (geo.) striations; —**ый** *a.* jetlike; flowing; striated.
структура *f.* structure, constitution; texture; (math.) lattice; **с. уровней** level structure.
структурированный *a.* (chem.) crosslinked.
структурночувствительный *a.* structure-sensitive.
структурн/ый *a.* structural; **с. ливень** structured shower; **с. фактор** (cryst.) structure factor; —**ая амплитуда** structure amplitude; —**ая коррозия** microcorrosion; —**ая схема** block diagram; —**ая формула** structural formula.
структурообразование *n.* structure formation, structurization, crosslinking.
струн/а *f.* string; slide wire; —**ный** *a.* string, stringed; —**ный гальванометр** string galvanometer; —**ный мост** slide-wire bridge; —**ный потенциометр** slide-wire potentiometer; —**ный электрометр** string electrometer.
Струхаля число Strouhal number.
стру/я *f.* jet; stream, current, flow; (hyd.) nappe; **спутная с.** (hyd.) wake; **действие —и** jet action; —**ящийся** *a.* streaming.
стрюверит *m.* strüverite.
стрях/ивать, —**нуть** *v.* shake off.
с.т.с. *abbr.* (**сверхтонкая структура**) hyperfine structure (hfs).
ст. ст. *abbr.* (**старый стиль**) old style (Julian calendar).
СТУ [*in steel mark* (**специальные технические условия**)] special (technical) specifications.
студ. *abbr.* (**студенческий**) student.
студен/еть *v.* gel; —**истый** *a.* gelatinous.
студен/т *m.*, —**ческий** *a.* student; **с.-дипломник** graduate student; **с. старших курсов** senior (student).
студ/еный *a.* frigid; gelled; —**ень** *m.* gelatin; —**ить** *v.* cool; gel.
студия *f.* studio.
студне/видный, —**образный,** —**подобный** *a.* gelatinous.
стужа *f.* hard frost.
стук *m.* knock, rattle; —**ание** *n.* knocking; —**ать,** —**нуть** *v.* knock, tap, rap.
стул *m.*, —**ьный** *a.* chair; anvil block.
ступ. *abbr.* (**ступень**) step; stage; degree.
ступать *v.* step.
ступенчато *adv.* stepwise; —**образный** *a.* steplike; —**сть** *f.* gradation.
ступенчат/ый *a.* step, stepped, step-by-step, stepwise, gradual, graduated; staggered, multistage; **с. блок** step block; **с. выключатель** step switch; **с. клин** step wedge; **с. лидер** stepped leader; **с. ослабитель** step attenuator; **с. регулятор напряжения** step voltage regulator; —**ая пробка** gun-barrel-type plug; —**ая регулировка** (elec.) step control; —**ая решетка** echelon (grating); —**ая связка** echelon strapping; —**ая функция** step function; —**ое возбуждение атома** step-by-step excitation; —**ое разложение** stepwise decomposition.
ступен/ь *f.* step; stage; degree; —**ька** *f.* step; —**ями** by degrees, step by step.
ступить *see* **ступать.**
ступица *f.* hub, nave.
ступня *f.* foot.
стучать *see* **стукать.**
стушев/аться, —**ываться** *v.* disappear, vanish.
стык *m.* joint, butt; junction; —**овой** *a.* joint, butt.
сты/нуть, —**ть** *v.* cool.
Стьюдента закон распределения (stat.) Student distribution.
Стюарта/-Кирхгофа закон Stewart and Kirchhoff law; **С.-Толмена опыт** Tolman-S. experiment.
стюартит *m.* stewartite.
стягив/ание *n.* contraction, constriction, tightening; **с. ядра** collapse of nucleus; —**ать** *v.* constrict, confine;

tighten, contract; (math.) subtend; **—аться** *v.* contract, shrink; tighten.

стяж/ание *n.* acquisition; **—ать** *v.* obtain.

стяжение *n.* concretion, nodule.

стяж/ка *f.* tie rod, coupler; **—ной** *a.* coupling, tie.

стянут/ый *a.* tightened, constricted; contracted; collapsed; (math.) subtended; coupled; **—ь** *see* **стягивать.**

суб— *prefix* sub—, under.

суб/арктический *a.* subarctic; **—атомный** *a.* subatomic; **—аэральный** *a.* subaerial; **—бореальный климат** subboreal climate.

суббота *f.* Saturday.

субгармони/ка *f.* subharmonic; **—ческий** *a.* subharmonic.

суб/гедральный *a.* subhedral; **—гигант** *m.* subgiant; **—зерно** *n.* subgrain; **—карлик** *m.* subdwarf; **—кристаллическая структура** subcrystalline structure; **—летальная доза** sublethal dose.

сублим/ат *m.* sublimate; **—ационный** *a.*, **—ация** *f.*, **—ирование** *n.* sublimation; **—ированный** *a.* sublimated; **—ировать** *v.* sublime; **—ирующийся** *a.* sublimable.

суб/линейный *a.* sublinear; **—матрица** *f.* submatrix; **—металлический** *a.* submetallic; **—микрон** *m.* submicron; **—микроскопический** *a.* submicroscopic; **—миниатюрный** *a.* subminiature.

субнормаль *f.* (math.) subnormal; **—ный** *a.* subnormal.

суб/область *f.* subdomain; **—ординатный** *a.* subordinate; **—параболический** *a.* subparabolic; **—полярный** *a.* subpolar; **—радиант** *m.* subradiant; **—ракета** *f.* subrocket.

субсид/ировать *v.* subsidize; **—ия** *f.* subsidy.

субстантивный *a.* substantive.

субстанц/иальный *a.* substantial, substantive; **—ия** *f.* substance.

субститут *m.* substitute.

суб/страт *m.* substratum, substrate; **—стратосфера** *f.* substratosphere; **—структура** *f.* substructure.

субтрактивный *a.* subtractive.

субтропи/ки *pl.* subtropics; **—ческий** *a.* subtropical.

субтрузия *f.* subtrusion.

субцентр *m.* subcenter.

субъективн/ость *f.* subjectivity; **—ый** *a.* subjective, personal.

субъядерный *a.* subnuclear.

суглин/истый *a.* loamy; **—ок** *m.* loam.

сугроб *m.* snowdrift.

сугуб/о *adv.* doubly, especially, particularly; **—ый** *a.* double, especial, particular.

суд *m.* court, tribunal; **—ебный** *a.* legal, judicial, forensic; **—ейский** *a.* judicial; **—ить** *v.* judge; **—я по** judging by, to judge from.

суд/но *n.* ship, boat; **—овой** *a.* ship, marine.

судостро/ение *n.* shipbuilding; **—итель** *m.* shipbuilder.

судоход/ный *a.* maritime; navigable; **с. шлюз** navigation lock; **—ная глубина** navigable depth; **—ство** *n.* navigation.

судьба *f.* fate, destiny.

судья *m.* judge, justice.

сужающийся *a.* convergent.

сужден/ие *n.* judgment; opinion, idea; inference; **основа —ия** criterion.

суж/ение *n.* narrowing, contraction, constriction; **с. следа** track thindown; **—енный** *a.* narrowed, contracted, constricted; **—енная шкала** compressed scale; **—ивать, —иваться** *v.* narrow (down), shrink, contract, constrict; taper; **—ивающийся** *a.* contracting; tapered, narrowing.

сузаннит *m.* susannite.

сузить *see* **суживать.**

сукно *n.* cloth; **положить под с.** pigeonhole.

сукновальная глина fuller's earth.

сукцинит *m.* succinite.

сулой *m.* (oceanography) rip.

сульф— *prefix* sulf—, sulfo—.

сульфат *m.* sulfate; **—ный** *a.* sulfate, sulfatic.

сульфид *m.*, **—ный** *a.* sulfide.

сульфир/ование *n.* sulfonation; sulfuration, sulfurization.

сульфо— *prefix* sulfo—.

сульфоновая кислота sulfonic acid.

сума *f.* bag, pouch.

сумансит *m.* soumansite.

сумеречн/ый *a.* twilight, crepuscular; **—ая вспышка** twilight flash; **—ая зона** twilight zone; **—ое зрение** twilight (or scotopic) vision.

сумер/ки *pl.* twilight; **дуга —ек** twilight arch; **явления —ек** twilight phenomena.

суметь *see* **уметь.**

сумка *f.* bag, pack, case.

сумм/а *f.* sum, amount; **с. избытков** accumulated excess; **общая с.** total; **с. осадков** total precipitation; **с. по решетке** lattice sum; **в —е с** added to; **правила сумм** sum rules.

суммарн/ый *a.* total, combined, resultant, integrated, cumulative, composite, sum, over-all; summary; **—ая волна** sum wave; **—ая частота** sum frequency; **—ое излучение** total (or integrated) radiation; **—ое свечение** light sum.

сумматор *m.*, **—ное устройство** summation device; totalizer, summator, adder, accumulator; integrator.

суммиров/ание *n.* summation, addition; **—анный** *a.* summed, integrated; accumulated; summarized; **—ать** *v.* sum (up), integrate; summarize.

суммируем/ость *f.* summability; **—ый** *a.* summable, integrable; **—ый ряд** summable series; **—ая функция** summable function.

суммирующ/ий *a.* summing, integrating; summarizing; **—ая цепь** summing circuit.

суммовой *a.* sum, summation; **с. тон** summation tone.

сумрак *m.* dusk.

супер— *prefix* super—.

супер/аэродинамика *f.* superaerodynamics (free molecular flow theory); **—гармонический** *a.* superharmonic; **—генный** *a.* (geo.) supergene.

супергетеродин *m.*, **—ный приемник** superheterodyne receiver.

супериконоскоп *m.* image iconoscope.

суперкритический *a.* supercritical.

супермаллой *m.* Supermalloy (nickel-iron-molybdenum alloy).

супермендур *m.* Supermendur (iron-cobalt-vanadium alloy).

супермультиплет *m.* supermultiplet.

супернильвар *m.* Supernilvar (iron-nickel-cobalt alloy).

супер/ортикон *m.* image orthicon, superorthicon; **—параболический** *a.* superparabolic.

суперпозиц/ионный *a.* superposition; **—ионное приближение** superposition approximation; **—ия** *f.* superposition, overlying; **принцип —ии** superposition principle.

суперрегенерат/ивный *a.* superregenerative; **—ор** *m.* superregenerative receiver.

супер/структура *f.* superstructure; **—фузивные породы** (geo.) superfusive rocks; **—чаржер** *m.* supercharger; **—эмитрон** *m.* superemitron.

супес/ок *m.*, **—ь** *f.* sandy loam.

суп/орт, —порт *m.* support, rest, carriage.

супраквантование *n.* second quantization.

сурдин/а, —ка *f.* silencer, muffler, mute; **—ирующий** *a.* muting.

сурик *m.*, **—овый** *a.* minium, red lead.

суров/ость *f.* severity; **—ый** *a.* severe.

суррогат *m.* substitute.

сурьм/а *f.* antimony (Sb); **—янистый** *a.* antimonous, antimony, antimonial; antimonide; **—яный** *a.* antimonic, antimony, antimonial.

сусаль *f.* tinsel, leaf; **—ное золото** gold leaf; **—ное серебро** silver leaf.

сусептанс *m.* susceptance.

суспен/дированный *a.* suspended; **—зия** *f.* suspension; **—зоид** *m.* suspensoid.

суссексит *m.* sussexite.

сустав *m.* joint, articulation; hinge; **—ной** *a.* joint, hinge; **—ное сочленение** hinge joint; **—очный, —чатый** *a.* jointed, articulated, hinged.

сутки *pl.* day, 24 hours.

суточн/ый *a.* daily, diurnal, 24-hour, one-day; **с. ход** daily variation; **с. эффект** day-night effect; **—ая аберрация** diurnal aberration; **—ая амплитуда** daily range; **—ая параллель** (astr.) diurnal circle.

сут/ь *f.* essence; **с. дела** essence, main point, crux; **по —и дела** in fact.

суффикс *m.* suffix.

сухо *adv.* dry; —**ватый** *a.* rather dry; —**вей** *m.* sukhovei (dry hot wind).

сухой *a.* dry; **с. выпрямитель** dry-disk rectifier; **с. док** dry dock; **с. термометр** dry-bulb thermometer; **с. элемент** dry cell.

сухо/парник *m.* steam dome; —**сть** *f.* dryness, aridity.

суш/а *f.* dry land; —**е** *comp. of* **сухо, сухой,** drier; —**ение** *n.* drying, desiccation; —**еный** *a.* dried, desiccated; —**илка** *f.*, —**ило** *n.* drier, desiccator, drying chamber.

сушильн/ый *a.* drying; —**ое средство** drying agent, desiccant, siccative.

суш/ить, —**иться** *v.* dry, desiccate; —**ка** *f.* drying, dehumidifying, desiccation; siccative, drier; —**ь** *f.* dryness.

существенно *adv.* essentially, substantially, intrinsically; **с. особая точка** essential singularity; **с. сингулярный** (math.) intrinsically singular; **с., что** it is important (or significant).

существенн/ый *a.* essential, important, significant, intrinsic, material, vital; considerable, substantial; —**ое значение** vital importance; —**ым образом** significantly.

существ/о *n.* nature, essence, point; **не по** —**у** off the point; **по** —**у** essentially, intrinsically; substantially.

существ/ование *n.* existence; **с. в природе** natural occurrence; **теорема** —**ования** existence theorem; —**овать** *v.* be, exist; —**ующий** *a.* existing, existent, current.

сущий *a.* real.

сущност/ь *f.* essence; main point; **по своей** —**и** essentially; **в** —**и говоря** actually.

суэзит *m.* souesite.

СФ *abbr.* (**спектрофотометр**) spectrophotometer.

сфазирование *n.* phasing in.

сфалерит *m.* sphalerite.

сфен *m.* sphene, titanite; —**оид** *m.* (cryst.) sphenoid; —**оидальный** *a.* sphenoidal, sphenoid; —**оманганит** *m.* sphenomanganite.

сфер/а *f.* sphere; —**икализация** *f.* sphericalization; —**ики** *pl.* sferics, spherics.

сферит *m.* sphaerite.

сферическ/ий *a.* spherical; —**ая аберрация** spherical aberration; —**ая гармоника,** —**ая функция** spherical harmonics.

сферичность *f.* sphericity.

сфероид *m.* spheroïd; —**альный** *a.* spheroidal; —**изация** *f.*, —**изирование** *n.* spheroidizing; —**изированный** *a.* spheroidized.

сферо/кобальтит *m.* sphaerocobaltite; —**кристалл** *m.* sphaerocrystal.

сферометр *m.* spherometer; —**ический** *a.* spherometric; —**ия** *f.* spherometry.

сферосидерит *m.* spherosiderite.

сферохроматический *a.* spherochromatic.

сфигмо/граф *m.* sphygmograph; —**манометр** *m.* sphygmomanometer.

сформ/ированный, —**ованный** *a.* formed, molded; defined; —**ировать** *v.* form, mold, shape; define.

сформулировать *v.* formulate, state.

СФТИ *abbr.* (**Сибирский физико-технический институт**) Siberian Physico-Technical Institute.

с.х. *abbr.* (**сельское хозяйство**) agriculture, farming; **с.-х.** (**сельскохозяйственный**) agricultural, farm.

схват *m.* gripping device, tongs; —**ы** *pl.* tongs; —**ить** *see* **схватывать**; —**ка** *f.* interlock.

схватыв/ание *n.* gripping; setting, hardening; —**ать** *v.* grip; catch; set, harden; —**ающий** *a.* gripping; —**ающийся** *a.* (cement) setting, binding.

схема *f.* scheme, schematic drawing, diagram, sketch; (elec.) circuit; flow sheet; **с. антисовпадений** anticoincidence circuit; **с. выдержки** delay circuit; **с. движения** flow diagram, flow sheet; **с. задержки** delay circuit; **с. распада** decay scheme; **с. совпадений** coincidence circuit; **с. соединений** circuit diagram; **с. энергетических уровней** energy-level diagram.

схематиз/ация *f.* schematization; —**ированный** *a.* schematized, schematic; —**ировать** *v.* schematize.

схематика *f.* circuitry, schematics.

схематич/ески *adv.* schematically; —**еский** *a.* schematic, diagrammatic;

—еское изображение diagrammatic representation; **—ность** *f.* sketchiness; **—ный** *a.* sketchy; circuit.

схизма *f.* (acous.) schisma.

схлопывание плазмы plasma collapse.

сход *m.* descent.

сходимость *f.* convergence; **с. в среднем** (math.) convergence in the mean.

сходить *v.* go down, descend; **с. на нет** decrease to zero; **—ся** *v.* converge, join; agree, coincide.

сходный *a.* similar, related; suitable, conformable.

сходство *n.* similarity, resemblance, analogy; coincidence, congruity, compatibility.

сходящ/ийся *a.* convergent, concurrent; **—аяся волна** converging (or ingoing) wave; **—аяся последовательность** convergent sequence.

схождение *n.* meeting, convergence.

схожий *a.* similar.

схоластический *a.* scholastic.

сцена *f.* stage, scene.

сцеп/ить *see* **сцеплять**; **—ка** *f.* coupling, clutch.

сцеплен/ие *n.* coupling, linking, bonding; cohesion, adhesion; meshing, engagement; clutch; **сила —ия** cohesive force, cohesion; **—ный** *a.* coupled, linked; enchained; meshed.

сцепл/яемость *f.* adhesiveness, cohesiveness; **—ять** *v.* couple, link, hook up; clutch, mesh; **—яться** *v.* interlock; link; cohere, adhere; mesh, engage; **—яющий** *a.* coupling, engaging; **—яющийся** *a.* cohesive.

сцеп/ной *a.* coupling; **—щик** *m.* coupler.

сцехениит *m.* széchenyiite.

Сцигети Szigeti.

Сциларда-Чалмерса реакция Szilard-Chalmers reaction.

Сцилла Scylla (thermonuclear device).

сцинтилл/ирующий кристалл scintillation crystal; **—ограф** *m.* scintillograph, automatic scintillation scanner; **—оскоп** *m.* scintilloscope; **—ятор** *m.* scintillator.

сцинтилляц/ионный *a.* scintillation; **с. спектрометр** scintillation spectrometer; **с. счетчик** scintillation counter; **—ия** *f.* scintillation.

с.ц.м. *abbr.* **(система центра масс)** center-of-mass system (c.m.s.).

с.-ч. *abbr.* **(сила-час)** horsepower-hour.

счаст/ливый *a.*, **—ье** *n.* fortune, chance; **к —ью** fortunately.

счер/тить, —чивать *v.* copy, trace, draw.

счесть *see* **считать.**

счет *m.* count, counting; calculation; account; score; register; **за с.** owing to, because of; at the expense of.

счетно *adv.* countably, denumerably; **с. аддитивный** countably (or completely) additive; **с.-аналитическая машина, с.-решающая машина, с.-решающее устройство** computer; **с.-решающее устройство непрерывного действия** analog computer.

счетност/ь *f.* denumerability; counting efficiency; **аксиома —и** axiom of denumerability.

счетн/ый *a.* calculating, counting; countable, denumerable; **с. механизм** computing (or counting) mechanism; **—ая ионизационная камера** pulse ionization chamber; **—ая лампа, —ая трубка** counter tube; **—ая линейка** slide rule; **—ая машина** calculating machine; **—ая схема** counting circuit; **—ая характеристика** counter characteristic curve, counting-rate curve; **—ое множество** denumerable set; **—ое устройство параллельного действия** parallel computer; **—ое устройство последовательного действия** serial computer.

счетовод *m.* accountant; **—ство** *n.* accounting, bookkeeping.

счетчик *m.* counter; meter, register; scaler; calculator; **с. альфа-частиц** alpha counter; **с. времени** time meter (register, totalizer); **с. излучения** radiation counter; **с. импульсов** pulse counter; **с. несовпадений** anticoincidence counter; **с. с параллельными пластинами** parallel-plate counter; **с. с полным телесным углом** 4π counter; **с. с потоком газа** gas-flow counter; **—овый** *a.* counter.

счеты *pl.* abacus.

счислен/ие *n.* numeration; reckoning, calculation; arithmetic; **система**

—ия system of notation, nomenclature; number system, numeration.

считить *see* **счищать.**

считательная машина *see* **счетная машина.**

считать *v.* assume, consider, think, reason; count, compute; —**ся** *v.* take into consideration, take into account; be considered; **не —ся** disregard, ignore.

считающий канал counting channel.

считывание *n.* (elec.) reading, readout.

счищать *v.* clear, clean.

США *abbr.* (**Соединенные Штаты Америки**) United States of America.

сшив/ание *n.*, —**ка** *f.* (math.) joining, matching, connection; (chem.) cross-linking; sewing together; —**ать** *v.* (math.) join, match, connect; (chem.) cross-link; sew together.

сшит/ость *f.* joining; fit; —**ый** *a.* (math.) joined, matched, connected; (chem.) cross-linked; sewn; —**ь** *see* **сшивать.**

съедать *v.* eat away, corrode.

съезд *m.* congress, convention, conference, assembly; —**ить** *v.* go.

съезжать *v.* slide off, come off; —**ся** *v.* convene, meet, assemble.

съем *m.* removal; **с. стали** steel output (or yield).

съемк/а *f.* survey, mapping, plot; photographing; **делать —у** film; **производить —у** survey.

съемн/ик *m.* lifter, stripper; —**ый** *a.* detachable, removable, demountable; strippable.

съем/очный *a.* surveying; —**щик** *m.* camera man; surveyor.

съесть *see* **съедать.**

съехать *see* **съезжать.**

сын *m.* son.

сып/ание *n.* strewing, scattering; —**ать** *v.* strew, scatter.

сыпуч/есть *f.* friability; —**ий** *a.* friable, loose, free-flowing.

сыреть *v.* become moist.

сырец *m.* raw material.

сыроват/ость *f.* slight dampness; —**ый** *a.* dampish, moist.

сыро/й *a.* damp, moist; raw, crude; —**стестойкий** *a.* moistureproof; —**сть** *f.* dampness.

сырцовый *a.* raw, crude.

сырье *n.*, —**вой материал** raw material.

Сэбина формула Sabine formula.

сюда *adv.* here.

сюжет *m.* subject, topic.

Сюренсена *see* **Серенсена.**

сюрприз *m.* surprise.

сюрсассит *m.* sursassite.

Т

т. *abbr.* (**товарищ**) comrade; (**том**) volume; (**тонна**) ton; (**точка**) point, period; (**тысяча**) thousand.

Т [*in steel mark* (**титан**)] titanium (Ti).

та *see* **тот.**

Та АССР *abbr. see* **Татарская АССР.**

табель *f.* table, list, schedule.

табл. *abbr.* (**таблица**) table.

таблет/ирование *n.* preforming; —**ировать** *v.* preform; —**ка** *f.* tablet, disk, pellet; preform; —**очный** *a.* preforming.

таблитчатый *a.* tabular, flat.

табли/ца *f.* table, chart; list, schedule; scale; plate; array; **подвижная счетная т.** sliding scale; **вносить в —цу** tabulate; —**цы логарифмов** tables of logarithms; **составление —ц** tabulation; —**чка** *f.* tablet, tabular crystal; —**чный** *a.* table, tabular.

табло *n.* signal panel.

табулиров/ание *n.* tabulation; —**анный** *a.* tabulated; —**ать** *v.* tabulate.

табурет *m.*, —**ка** *f.* stool.

тавистокит *m.* tavistockite.

тавмавит *m.* tawmawite.

тавот *m.*, —**ный** *a.* (lubricating) grease; —**ница** *f.* grease cup; grease gun.

тавро *n.* mark, brand.

тавров/ый *a.* T-, tee-; —**ая балка** T-beam.

тавто— *see* **тауто—.**

Таджикская ССР, Тадж. ССР Tajik (Tadzhik) SSR.

таз *m.* basin, pan; —**ик** *m.* small basin.

тазиметр *m.* tasimeter.

тазовый *a.* basin, pan.

ТАИ *abbr.* (**Труды Всесоюзного арктического института**) Transactions of the All-Union Arctic Institute (journal).

таинственн/ость *f.* secrecy; **—ый** *a.* secret, mysterious.

таить *v.* conceal.

тайга *f.* taiga.

Тайгета Taygeta.

таймер *m.* timer.

тайна *f.* secret, secrecy.

тайниолит *m.* tainiolite.

тайно— *prefix* crypto—.

тайн/о *adv.* secretly, confidentially; **—ый** *a.* secret, mysterious.

тайрит *m.* tayrite.

тайрод *m.* thyrode.

тайфун *m.* typhoon.

так *adv.* so, thus; **если т.** if so; **т. же, как** as, in the same way, as . . . as; **и т. д.** (**и т. далее**) and so forth; etc.; **т. или иначе** somehow or other; **именно т.** just so; **т. как** because, as, for; **т. называемый** so-called; **т. сказать** so to speak; **т. что** so that; **т. чтобы** so as to, so that.

также *adv.* also, likewise, as well, too; **а т. и** as well as; **он т. поедет** he will also go; **он т. не поедет** he will not go either.

таков *a.* such, like; **—ой** *a.* such; **как —ой** as such.

так/ой *a.* such; so; **т. же** the same; **не т. как** unlike; **—им образом** thus, in this manner; **в —ом случае** in that case.

таконийский *a.* Taconian.

такт *m.* cycle; (mech.) stroke; (mus.) time; tact.

такт/ика *f.* tactics; **—ический** *a.* tactical.

талант *m.* talent; **—ливый** *a.* talented.

таленит *m.* thalenite.

тали *pl. of* **таль.**

талл/иевый *a.* thallium, thallic; **т. фотоэлемент** thallofide cell; **—ий** *m.* thallium (Tl).

талофидный элемент *see under* **таллиевый.**

талреп *m.* turnbuckle.

тал/ый *a.* melted, thawed; **—ая вода** melt water.

тал/ь *f.*, **—и** *pl.* tackle, block and tackle.

Тальбота закон Talbot law.

тальвег *m.* thalweg.

тальк *m.* talc; **—овый** *a.* talc, talcose, talcous.

тальреп *see* **талреп.**

там *adv.* there.

тамбур *m.*, **—ный** *a.* drum, reel.

Тамма-Данкова метод Tamm-Dankcoff method.

тампон *m.* plug, wad.

тангаж *m.* (aero.) pitching.

танген/с *m.* tangent; **т.-буссоль** tangent compass; **т.-гальванометр** tangent galvanometer; **т. угла потерь** loss tangent; **—соида** *f.* tangent curve; **—циальный** *a.* tangent, tangential.

тангиваит *m.* tangiwaite.

тандем *m.*, **—ный** *a.* tandem.

танк *m.* tank.

тантал *m.* tantalum (Ta); **—истый** *a.* tantalous, tantalum; **—овый** *a.* tantalic, tantalum.

тантэвксенит *m.* tanteuxenite.

ТАО *abbr.* (**Ташкентская астрономическая обсерватория**) Tashkent Astronomical Observatory.

тара *f.* packing, package, container.

таран *m.*, **—ить** *v.*, **—ный** *a.* ram.

тарапакаит *m.* tarapacaite.

тарел/ка *f.* plate, disk; **—очный** *a.* plate.

тарельчат/ый *a.* plate, platelike, disk; **т. клапан** disk valve; **—ая муфта** disk (or plate) coupling (or clutch).

тариров/ание *n.*, **—ка** *f.*, **—очный** *a.* calibration; **—ать** *v.* calibrate.

тариф *m.*, **—ный** *a.* tariff.

тарновитцит *m.* tarnowitzite.

тартыши *pl.* (ice) growler.

Тарунций Taruntius (lunar crater).

таситрон *m.* tacitron.

таск/ание *n.* dragging, drawing; **—ать** *v.* drag, draw, pull.

тасовать *v.* shuffle.

тат. *abbr.* (**татарский**) Tatar, Tartar.

Татаринова антенна collinear array.

Татарская АССР Tatar ASSR.

таумасит *m.* thaumasite.

тау-/мезон *m.* tau-meson; **—метр** *m.* tau-meter (for measurement of luminescence lifetime).

Таунсенда коэффициент Townsend coefficient.

таунсендовск/ий разряд Townsend discharge; **—ая лавина** T. avalanche.

Тауриды Taurids (meteors).

тауто— *prefix* tauto—.

таутомер *m.* tautomer; **—ия** *f.* tautomerism; **—ный** *a.* tautomeric.

таутохрон/изм *m.* tautochronism; **—ный** *a.* tautochronous; **—ная кривая** tautochrone.

тахгидрит *m.* tachhydrite.

тахеометр *m.* tacheometer, tachymeter; **—ический** *a.* tacheometric, tachymetric; **—ия** *f.* tacheometry, tachymetry.

тахиафальтит *m.* tachyaphaltite.

тахиметр *see* **тахеометр.**

тахо/генератор *m.* tachometer-generator, tachogenerator; **—грамма** *f.* tachogram; **—граф** *m.* tachograph.

тахометр *m.* tachometer; **—ия** *f.* tachometry.

тачка *f.* wheelbarrow.

тащить *see* **таскать.**

тая/ние *n.* thawing, melting; **температура —ния, точка —ния** melting point; **—ть** *v.* thaw, melt.

тв. *abbr.* (**твердость**) hardness.

ТВ *abbr.* (**телевидение**) television.

ТВА *abbr.* (**Таблицы высот и азимутов Солнца, Луны и планет**) tables of altitudes and azimuths of the sun, moon and the planets.

Твадделя гидрометр Twaddle (Twaddell) hydrometer; **шкала Т.** T. scale.

Тваймана интерферометр Twyman (-Green) interferometer.

ТВД *abbr.* (**турбовинтовой двигатель**) turboprop engine.

тверд/ение *n.* hardening; **т. при старении** age hardening; **—еть** *v.* harden.

твердо *adv.* firmly; thoroughly, well; **—мер** *m.* hardness gauge; durometer.

Твердосплав *abbr.* (**Государственный союзный трест твердых сплавов**) State All-Union Trust of Hard Alloys.

твердост/ь *f.* hardness, solidity, firmness; **т. на вдавливание** indentation hardness; **т. по Бринелю** Brinell (or ball) hardness; **т. по Викерсу** Vickers hardness; **т. по Роквеллу** Rockwell hardness; **т. по Шору** Shore (or scleroscope) hardness; **показатель —и, число —и** hardness number.

твердо/тянутый *a.* (met.) hard-drawn; **—фазный** *a.* solid-phase.

тверд/ый *a.* hard, solid, solid-phase; rigid, firm; stable; **т. выпрямитель** dry-disk rectifier; **т. раствор** solid solution; **т. раствор внедрения** interstitial solid solution; **т. раствор замещения** substitutional solid solution; **—ая поверхность** rigid (boundary) surface; **—ая стена** rigid wall; **—ая фаза** solid phase; **—ое вещество** solid matter; **—ое образование** rigid structure; **—ое состояние** solid state, solidity; **—ое тело** solid, solid body; rigid body.

т-во *abbr.* (**товарищество**) company; association.

твор/ение *n.* creation; **—ец** *m.* creator, maker; author; **—ить** *v.* create, make; do.

творчес/кий *a.* creative; **—тво** *n.* creativity, creative power, work; **научное —тво** scientific work.

ТВЧ *abbr.* (**ток высокой частоты**) high-frequency current.

Твэддела *see* **Твадделя.**

ТВЭЛ *abbr.* (**тепловыделяющий элемент**) fuel element.

ТГУ *abbr.* (**Тбилисский государственный университет**) Tbilisi State University; (**Томский государственный университет**) Tomsk State University.

т. е. *abbr.* (**то есть**) that is, that is to say, i.e.

Тевенина теорема Thévenin theorem.

тезис *m.* thesis.

Тейлор Taylor (lunar crater).

Тейлора ряд Taylor series; **теорема Т.** T. theorem; **Т.-Орована дислокация** T.-Orowan (or edge) dislocation.

тейлорит *m.* taylorite.

текст *m.* text.

текстолит *m.* textolite.

Текст. пром. *abbr.* (**Текстильная промышленность**) Textile Industry (journal).

текстуальный *a.* textual.

текстур/а *f.* texture, (special) orientation; grain; (geo.) structure; **—ованный** *a.* oriented, grain-oriented;

—**ованная сталь** grain-oriented steel.

тектогенез *m.* tectogenesis.

тектони/ка *f.* tectonics; structural geology; —**ческий** *a.* tectonic, structural; —**ческий рельеф** structure contour.

текучест/ь *f.* fluidity, flowability, flow; (met.) yield; fluctuation, instability; **поверхность —и** yield surface; **предел —и** (met.) yield point.

текуч/ий *a.* flowing, fluid; fluidized; fluctuating, unstable; **трудно т.** thick, viscous; —**ая вода** running water.

текущ/ий *a.* flowing, streaming, running; current; **т. индекс** running index; —**ая длина** instantaneous length; —**ие события** current events.

теле— *prefix* tele—, remote.

теле/автоматика *f.* teleautomatics, remote control; —**амперметр** *m.* teleammeter; —**вещание** *n.* television broadcasting; —**видение** *n.*, —**визионный** *a.*, —**визия** *f.* television; —**визор** *m.* television receiver; —**гониометр** *m.* telegoniometer.

телеграмма *f.* telegram.

телеграф *m.* telegraph; —**ирование** *n.*, —**ия** *f.* telegraphy; —**ировать** *v.* telegraph, wire, cable; —**ный** *a.* telegraph, telegraphic.

теледатчик *m.* remote pickup unit (or transducer).

тележ/ка *f.*, —**ный** *a.* carriage, trolley, dolly.

телеизмер/ение *n.*, —**ительный** *a.* telemetering, telemetry.

теле/индикатор *m.* teleindicator; —**кино** *n.* film television, telecinematography; —**ключатель** *m.* remote-control switch; —**контроль** *m.* remote (or supervisory) control.

телеметр *m.* telemeter, distance gauge; —**ический** *a.* telemetering; —**ия** *f.* telemetering, telemetry.

телемехан/ика *f.* telemechanics, remote control; —**ическое устройство** telemechanical system; remote-controlled robot.

теле/мотор *m.* telemotor, remote-controlled motor; —**объектив** *m.* telephoto lens; —**передача** *f.* telecommunication; —**пишущий аппарат** telescriptor; —**повторитель** *m.* distant repeater; —**психрометр** *m.* telepsychrometer.

Телеран Teleran.

теле/регистрация *f.* distant recording; —**самописец** *m.* telerecorder, remote-recording instrument; —**связь** *f.* telecommunication; —**сейсм** *m.* teleseism.

Телескоп Telescopium (Tel) (constellation).

телескоп *m.*, —**ировать** *v.* telescope; **т.-рефлектор** reflecting telescope; **т.-рефрактор** refracting telescope, refractor; —**ический** *a.* telescopic; —**ический прицел** telescopic sight; —**ия** *f.* telescopy; —**остроение** *n.* telescope making.

телесный *a.* solid; material; physical; **т. угол** solid angle.

теле/счет *m.* telecount, telemetering; —**тайп** *m.* teletype; —**терапия** *f.* teletherapy; —**термометр** *m.* telethermometer; —**термоскоп** *m.* telethermoscope.

телеуказ/ание *n.* remote indication; —**атель** *m.* remote indicator.

телеуправл/ение *n.* remote control; —**яемый** *a.* remote-controlled.

телефон *m.*, —**ировать** *v.* telephone; —**ия** *f.* telephony.

телефонн/ый *a.* telephone; **т. коммутатор** telephone switchboard; —**ая станция** telephone exchange.

телефотограф/ический *a.* telephotographic; —**ия** *f.* telephotography; telephotograph.

телефотометр *m.* telephotometer; —**ия** *f.* telephotometry.

Телец Taurus (Tau) (constellation).

теллур *m.* tellurium (Te); **письменный т.** graphic tellurium, sylvanite; —**ид** *m.* telluride; —**истосвинцовый фотоэлемент** lead telluride photocell; —**истый** *a.* tellurous, tellurium, telluriferous; telluride (of); —**ический** *a.* telluric; —**ический ток** telluric (or earth) current.

теллуро— *prefix* telluro—.

теллуровый *a.* telluric, tellurium.

тело *n.* body, solid, substance; (math.) field; (tool) shaft, shank; **т. враще-**

ния solid (or body) of revolution; **т. множеств** (math.) field of sets.

тельфер *m.* telpher, telpher line; **—аж** *m.* telpherage.

тельце *n.* corpuscle.

тем *see under* **тот.**

тем/а *f.* theme, subject, topic; **не на —у** off the subject; **—атика** *f.* subjects; **—атический** *a.* thematic; **—атический план** scientific program.

тембр *m.* timbre.

темн/еть *v.* darken; **—о** *adv.* darkly, obscurely.

темно— *prefix* dark.

темноватый *a.* darkish.

темнов/ой *a.* dark; **т. ток** dark (or background) current; **—ая проводимость** dark conduction (or conductivity); **—ое сопротивление** dark resistance.

темно/красный *a.* dark-red, deep-red; **—окрашенный** *a.* dark-colored.

темнопольн/ый *a.* dark-field; **т. метод** dark-field method; **—ое изображение** dark-field image.

темно/та *f.* darkness; obscurity; **—цветный** *see* **темноокрашенный.**

темн/ый *a.* dark, obscure, dim, indistinct; obscure, vague; deep (color); nonluminous (flame); **т. носитель тока** dark current carrier; **первая катодная —ая область** Aston dark space; **—ая туманность** dark nebula; **—ое пространство** dark space.

темп. *abbr. see* **т-ра.**

темп *m.* rate, pace; tempo, time.

температур/а *f.* temperature; **т. замерзания (или застывания)** freezing point; **т. заторможенного слоя, т. торможения** (hyd.) stagnation temperature; **т. инея** frost point; **т. кипения** boiling point; **т. окружающей среды** ambient temperature; **т. плавления** melting point; **т. смоченного термометра** wet-bulb temperature; **т. упорядочения** order-disorder transition temperature; **—нонезависимый** temperature-independent.

температурн/ый *a.* temperature, heat, thermal; **т. градиент** lapse rate; **т. шов** expansion joint; **—ая лампа** standard temperature-calibrated lamp; **—ое излучение** thermal radiation; **—ое напряжение** thermal (or heat) stress.

температуро— *prefix* thermal, thermometric, temperature, thermo—.

температуропроводность *f.* thermal conductivity; thermal diffusivity.

темперированный *a.* tempered; **—ать** *v.* temper.

темплет *m.* templet.

тендем *m.* tandem.

тенденц/иозность *f.* tendentiousness biased nature; **—иозный** *a.* tendentious, biased; **—ия** *f.* tendency trend; **линия —ии** (stat.) trend line

тендер *m.* turnbuckle; tender.

тенев/ой *a.* shadow; shady; **т. гальванометр** shadow galvanometer; **т. конус** shadow cone, umbra; **т. коэффициент** shadow factor; **т. микроскоп** shadow microscope; **т. фотометр** shadow photometer; **—ая зона** shadow zone; **—ое изображение** shadowgraph; **—ое рассеяние** shadow scattering; **—ое фотографирование** shadow photography.

тензо/графия *f.* strain micrography **—датчик** *m.* sensing element of strain gauge; **—метр** *m.* tensometer, strain gauge.

тензор *m.* tensor; **т. напряжений** stress tensor; **—ный** *a.* tensor.

тенси/метр *m.* tensimeter; **—ометр** *m* tensiometer.

тень *f.* shadow; shade; **(полная) т.** umbra.

теодолит *m.* theodolite, transit compass **перекидной т., универсальный т** transit theodolite; **—ный** *a.* theodolite, theodolitic.

теор. *abbr.* (**теоретический**) theoretical.

Теор. вер. и ее прим. *abbr.* (**Теория вероятностей и ее применение** Theory of Probability and Its Application (journal).

теорем/а *f.* theorem, proposition; **т гипотез** (stat.) Bayes formula (for probabilities of hypotheses); **т. косинусов** law of cosines; **обратная т** converse; **т. о среднем** mean value theorem; **т. синусов** law of sines **—ный** *a.* theorematic, theoremic.

теорет/изировать *v.* theorize; **—ик** *m.* theorist, theoretician.

теоретико/-множественный *a.* set-theoretical; **т.-познавательный** *a.* epistemological.

теоретически *adv.* theoretically; **—й** *a.* theoretical; **на —х основаниях** on theoretical grounds, theoretically.

теор/ия *f.* theory; **т. вероятностей** theory of probability; **т. возмущений** perturbation theory; **т. квантов** quantum theory; **т. относительности** theory of relativity; **т. переносов** transport theory; **т. твердого тела** solid state theory; **т. функций** theory of (real) functions; **85% —ии** 85% of theoretical; **возводить —ию, составлять —ии** theorize.

теперешний *a.* present, contemporary.

теперь *adv.* now, at present; **т., когда** now that.

Теплера метод свилей Töpler schlieren method.

тепл/еть *v.* grow warm; **—иться** *v.* gleam; **—ичный** *a.* hothouse; **—ичный эффект** hothouse effect.

тепло— *prefix* thermo—, thermal, heat, thermally.

тепло *n.* heat, warmth; *see also* **теплота**; *adv.* warm, warmly; **остаточное т.** afterheat; **—ватый** *a.* tepid.

тепло/вод *see* **теплопровод**; **—воз** *m.* Diesel locomotive.

теплов/ой *a.* heat, thermal, thermic, calorific, caloric, thermo—; **т. амперметр** hot-wire ammeter; **т. баланс** heat balance; **т. гистерезис** thermal hysteresis; **т. двигатель** heat engine; **т. контраст** infrared contrast; **т. к.п.д.** thermal efficiency; **т. нейтрон** thermal neutron; **т. осциллограф** hot-wire oscillograph; **т. показатель** (astr.) heat index; **т. поток** heat flux (or flow); **т. реактор** thermal reactor; **т. шум** thermal (or Johnson) noise; **т. эквивалент** thermal (or heat) equivalent; calorific value; **т. электрогенераторный агрегат** thermoelectric generating set; **т. эффект** reaction energy, energy release (Q); heating effect; **т. эффект сгорания** heat of combustion.

теплов/ой *cont.*, **—ая ванна** heat (or constant-temperature) bath; **—ая гроза** heat thunderstorm; **—ая единица** thermal unit; **—ая защита** thermal shield; **—ая инерция** thermal inertia; **—ая колонна** thermal column; **—ая машина** heat engine; **—ая мощность** heat output, thermal capacity; **—ая обработка** heat treatment; **—ая смерть** heat death; **—ая трещина** heat crack; **—ая функция** enthalpy; **—ое действие** thermal (or temperature) effect; **—ое излучение** thermal (or heat) radiation; **—ое использование** thermal utilization; **—ое напряжение** thermal (or heat) stress; **—ое сопротивление** thermal (or heat-transfer) resistance; **—ое старение** heat aging; **—ые флуктуации** thermal agitation.

тепловыдел/ение *n.* heat release; **—яющий** *a.* heat-releasing; **—яющий элемент** fuel element; **—яющая сборка** fuel assembly.

теплоемкость *f.* heat capacity, specific heat; **атомная т.** atomic heat; **удельная т.** specific heat.

теплозащитный *a.* heatproof.

теплоизлуч/ающий *a.* heat-radiating; **—ение** *n.* thermal (or heat) radiation.

теплоизол/ирующий, —яционный *a.* heat-insulating, thermal-insulation; **—ятор** *m.* heat insulator; **—яция** *f.* heat insulation.

Теплоинститут *abbr.* (**Теплотехнический институт им. Дзержинского**) The Dzerzhinskii Heat Engineering Institute.

теплоисточник *m.* heat source.

тепло/напряженность *f.* thermal stress; heat release rate; **—непроницаемый** *a.* heatproof, heat-resistant; **—носитель** *m.* coolant, heat-transfer agent.

теплообмен *m.* heat exchange; **—ник** *m.* heat exchanger; **водо-водяной —ник** water-to-water heat exchanger.

теплооборот *m.* (meteor.) thermal economy.

теплообраз/ователь *m.* heat producer, heat generator; **—ующий** *a.* heat-producing, heat-generating.

теплоотвод *m.* heat transfer; **—ящий контур** heat-transfer loop.

тепло/отдача *f.* heat transfer (or emission); **—передача** *f.* heat transfer; **—передающий** *a.* heat-transfer; exothermal.

теплопоглащ/ательный, —ающий *a.* heat-absorbing; **—ательная способность** heat absorption capacity.

тепло/подвод *m.* heat supply; **—поток** *m.* heat flux (or flow).

теплопровод *m.* steam or hot water pipe; heat conductor; **—ник** *m.* heat conductor; **—ность** *f.* thermal (or heat) conductivity, thermal (or heat) conduction; **коэффициент —ности** thermal conductivity coefficient; **уравнение —ности** heat equation; **—ный, —ящий** *a.* heat-conducting, heat-carrying.

теплопрозрачн/ость *f.* diathermaneity, diathermancy; **—ый** *a.* diathermanous, diathermic.

теплопроизвод/ительность *f.* calorific (or heating) power, heating capacity (or efficiency); **—ящий** *a.* heat-producing, heat-generating.

теплорассеивающий *a.* heat-radiating.

теплород *m.* caloric, thermogen; **—ный** *a.* caloric, calorific, thermal.

тепло/силовая установка thermopower plant; **—смена** *f.* thermal cycling; **—снабжение** *n.* heat supply; **—содержание** *n.* heat content, enthalpy.

теплостойк/ий *a.* heatproof, heat-resistant, thermostable; **—ость** *f.* heat resistance, thermostability.

теплосъем *m.* heat removal (or extraction).

теплот/а *f.* heat; **т. гидрации** hydration energy; **т. образования** heat of formation; **т. парообразования** heat of vaporization; **т. плавления** heat of fusion; **т. распада** heat of dissociation; **единица —ы** thermal unit.

теплотворн/ость *f.*, **—ая способность** heating power (value, capacity), calorific power (or value); **—ый** *a.* calorific; heat-resistant.

теплотехн/ик *m.* heat engineer; **—ика** *f.*, **—ический** *a.* heat engineering.

теплофикац/ионный *a.* central-heating; **т. реактор** heat reactor; **—ия** *f.* central heating.

теплоцентраль *f.* central-heating plant.

Теплоэлектропроект *abbr.* (**Всесоюзный государственный институт по проектированию тепловых электростанций**) All-Union State Institute for the Design and Planning of Thermal Electric Power Plants.

тепло/электроцентраль *f.* heat and power plant; **—энергетика** *f.* thermal-power engineering.

теплый *a.* warm, mild; **т. фронт** warm front.

тера— *prefix* tera—, megamega—.

терап/евтический *a.* therapeutic; **—ия** *f.* therapy, therapeutics.

терб/ий *m.*, **—иевый** *a.* terbium (Tb).

тереть *v.* rub, grind.

терилен *m.* Terylene.

терм *m.* term; therm; **—ализация** *f.* thermalization; **—ализировать** *v.* thermalize.

термаллой *m.* Thermalloy (nickel-copper-iron alloy).

термальный *a.* thermal; *see also* **тепловой, термо—**; **т. источник** hot (or thermal) spring.

термин *m.* term.

термин/альный *a.* terminal; **—атор** *m.* terminator.

терминолог/ический *a.* terminological; **—ия** *f.* terminology, nomenclature.

термион *m.* thermion; **—ный** *a.* thermionic.

термистор *m.*, **—ный** *a.* thermistor; **—ный мост** thermistor bridge.

термит *m.*, **—ный** *a.* thermite.

термическ/ий *a.* thermal, heat; *see also* **тепловой, термо—**; **т. ветер** thermal wind; **т. двигатель** heat engine; **—ая единица** thermal unit; **—ая обработка** heat treatment; **—ое напряжение** thermal stress; **—ое старение** heat aging.

термия *f.* therm.

термо— *prefix* thermo—, therm—, heat, thermally; *see also* **тепло—**.

термо/акцептор *m.* thermal acceptor; **—анемометр** *m.* cooling-power anemometer, hot-wire anemometer; **—барометр** *m.* thermobarometer; **—батарея** *f.* thermopile; therma battery; —**батиграф** *m.* bathythermograph; —**вулканизация** *f.* hot vulcanization; —**высвечивание** *n.* thermoluminescence; —**гальванометр** *m.* thermogalvanometer.

термогигро/граф *m.* thermohygrograph; —**метр** *m.* thermohygrometer.

термо/грамма *f.* thermogram; —**граф** *m.* thermograph; —**датчик** *m.* temperature-sensitive element; —**двигатель** *m.* thermomotor, heat engine; —**деление** *n.* thermal fission.

термодинами/ка *f.* thermodynamics; —**ческий** *a.* thermodynamic.

термодиффуз/ионный *a.*, —**ия** *f.* thermal diffusion.

термодиэлектрический эффект (эффект Коста-Рибейро) Costa-Ribeiro (thermodielectric) effect.

термо/единица *f.* thermal unit; —**изоляция** *f.* thermal insulation; —**изоплета** *f.* thermoisopleth; —**интегратор** *m.* thermointegrator.

термоион *m.* thermion; —**изация** *f.* thermal ionization; —**ная эмиссия** thermionic emission.

термокатод *m.* thermionic cathode; —**ная лампа** hot-cathode tube.

термоклина *f.* thermocline.

термокомпенсация *f.* temperature compensation.

термо/лиз *m.* thermolysis; —**литический** *a.* thermolytic.

термолюминесцен/тный *a.* thermoluminescence, thermoluminescent; —**ция** *f.* thermoluminescence.

термомагнит/изм *m.* thermomagnetism; —**ный** *a.* thermomagnetic.

термометр *m.* thermometer; **смоченный т.** wet-bulb (thermometer); **т. сопротивления** resistance thermometer; **сухой т.** dry-bulb (thermometer); —**ический** *a.* thermometer; thermometric; —**ическая будка,** —**ическая защита** thermometer shelter (or screen); —**ия** *f.* thermometry.

термо/механический *a.* thermomechanical; —**микрофонный сейсмограф** thermophone, hot-wire seismic detector; —**мотор** *see* **термодвигатель;** —**намагниченность** *f.* thermoremanent magnetization; —**напряжение** *n.* thermoelectromotive force; —**нейтральность** *f.* thermoneutrality; —**обработка** *f.* heat treatment.

термоостаточн/ый *a.* thermoremanent; —**ая намагниченность** thermoremanent magnification.

термоотрицательный *a.* thermonegative.

термопар/а *f.*, —**ный** *a.* thermocouple.

термоперм *m.* Thermoperm (iron-nickel alloy).

термопластич/еский, —**ный** *a.* thermoplastic.

термо/полимеризация *f.* thermopolymerization; —**положительный** *a.* thermopositive; —**прен** *m.* thermoprene; —**преобразователь** *m.* thermal converter; —**психрометр** *m.* thermopsychrometer.

терморегул/ировка *f.* thermal regulation; —**ятор** *m.* thermoregulator, thermocontroller, thermostat.

термос *m.* vacuum bottle.

термо/сифон *m.* thermosiphon; —**скоп** *m.* thermoscope; —**слияние** *n.* thermofusion; —**сопротивление** *n.* thermistor; —**спай,** —**сросток** *m.* thermojunction, thermocouple.

термостат *m.* thermostat; —**ирование** *n.* thermostatic control; —**ируемый** *a.* thermostated; —**ируемая ванна** constant-temperature bath; —**ический** *a.* thermostatic; —**ный** *a.* thermostat, thermostatic.

термо/столбик *m.* thermopile; —**сфера** *f.* thermosphere; —**ток** *m.* thermocurrent; —**тропический** *a.* thermotropic; —**упругий,** —**эластичный** *a.* thermoelastic; —**устойчивый** *a.* thermally stable.

термофиз/ика *f.* thermophysics; —**ический** *a.* thermophysical.

термофон *m.* thermophone.

термохим/ический *a.* thermochemical; —**ия** *f.* thermochemistry.

термо/холодильник *m.* thermoelectric refrigerator; —**циклогенез** *m.* thermocyclogenesis.

термо-э.д.с. *abbr.* (**термоэлектродвижущая сила**) thermoelectromotive force.

термоэлектричес/кий *a.* thermoelectric; *see also* **термо—; т. ряд** thermoelectric series; **—тво** *n.* thermoelectricity.

термоэлектродвижущая сила thermoelectromotive force, thermoelectric power.

термоэлектрон *m.* thermoelectron, negative thermion; **—ный** *a.* thermoelectronic, thermionic.

термо/электрохолодильник *m.* thermoelectric refrigerator; **—элемент** *m.* thermocouple; thermoelement; **—ядерный** *a.* thermonuclear.

тернарный *a.* ternary.

тернебомит *m.* törnebohmite.

терпе/ливость *f.* patience; **—ливый** *a.* patient; **—ние** *n.* patience, endurance, perseverance.

терпеновый ряд terpenic series.

терпентин *m.*, **—ный, —овый** *a.* terpentine.

терп/еть *v.* endure, tolerate; undergo; **—имость** *f.* tolerance; **—имый** *a.* tolerant; tolerable.

терраса *f.* terrace; (geo.) bench.

терригенный *a.* terrigenous.

территор/иальный *a.* territorial; **—ия** *f.* territory.

терфенил *m.* terphenyl.

терция *f.* (mus.) third; **большая т.** major third; **малая т.** minor third.

терять *v.* lose; waste.

тесать *v.* cut; square, trim.

Тесла трансформатор Tesla transformer.

теснина *f.* gorge.

тесн/ить *v.* press, squeeze; **—о** *adv.* narrowly, tightly, closely; **—оватый** *a.* rather narrow (or tight); **—освязанный** *a.* closely associated; **—ота** *f.* closeness, narrowness, tightness.

тесн/ый *a.* narrow, tight, close; intimate; **т. дублет** close doublet; **т. край полосы** band head; **—ая решетка** close-packed lattice; **—ая связь** *f.* close (or intimate) relationship; **—ые двойные звезды** close binary stars.

тессеральный *a.* tesseral.

тест *m.* test.

тесто *n.* paste.

тетаграмма *f.* thetagram.

тетартоэдрический *a.* tetartohedral.

тета-функция theta function.

тетра— *prefix* tetra—.

тетраг. *abbr.* (**тетрагональный**) tetragonal.

тетрагексаэдр *m.* tetrahexahedron; **—ический** *a.* tetrahexahedral.

тетрагидро— *prefix* tetrahydro—.

тетрагидрокси— *prefix* tetrahydroxy—.

тетрагир/а *f.* fourfold axis of symmetry; **—ная сингония** (cryst.) tetragonal system.

тетрагон *m.* tetragon, quadrilateral; **—альность** *f.* tetragonality; **—альный** *a.* tetragonal.

тетрада *f.* tetrad.

тетрадимит *m.* tetradymite.

тетразамещенный *a.* tetrasubstituted.

тетрафторид *m.* tetrafluoride.

тетраэдр *m.* tetrahedron; **—ит** *m.* tetrahedrite; **—ический** *a.* tetrahedral.

тетрод *m.* tetrode.

тефиграмма *f.* tephigram.

тефлон *m.*, **—овый** *a.* Teflon; **—овая шайба** Teflon bead.

тефроит *m.* tephroite.

тех. *abbr.* (**техника**) engineering; technique; (**технический**) engineering, technical.

Техиздат *abbr.* (**Техническое издательство**) Technical Literature Press.

техн. *abbr.* (**техник**) technician, mechanic; (**техника**) engineering; technique; (**техникум**) technicum; (**технический**) engineering, technical.

технеций *m.* technietium (Tc).

техни/к *m.* technician, mechanic; **—ка** *f.* technique(s), procedure; technology, engineering; **—кум** *m.* technical school; **—чески чистый** commercially pure.

техническ/ий *a.* technical, industrial, engineering; commercial; **—ая документация** technical documentation, technical report; **—ая калория** large calorie; **—ая химия** industrial chemistry; **—ое железо** technical (or commercial) iron; **—ое обслуживание** maintenance; **—ие средства** technique; **—ие требования** specifications; **—ие условия** (technical) specifications; engineering factors.

технолог *m.* technologist.

технологическ/ий *a.* technological; process; **т. газ** process gas; **т. канал**

process channel (or tube); (reactor) fuel channel; **—ая схема** flowsheet, technological layout; **—ие остатки** process residues.

технология *f.* technology.

технорук *abbr.* (**технический руководитель**) works manager.

техред. *abbr.* (**технический редактор**) technical editor.

тече/безопасный *a.* leakproof; **—искатель** *m.* leak detector.

течен/ие *n.* flow, current, stream, course; trend; **в т.** during; **обратное т.** reflux; **вверх по —ию** upstream; **вниз по —ию** downstream.

течь *v.* flow, stream; leak.

тешемахерит *m.* teschemacherite.

т. заст. *abbr.* [**температура** (*or* **точка**) **застывания**] solidification point.

тигель *m.*, **—ный** *a.* crucible.

тизонит *m.* tysonite.

Тизприбор *abbr.* (**Завод теплоизмерительных приборов**) Heat-Measuring Instrument Plant.

тикональ *m.* Ticonal (iron-cobalt-nickel-titanium alloy).

тиксотропия *f.* thixotropy.

тилазит *m.* tilasite.

Тиле теория парциальных валентностей Thiele theory of partial valencies; **Т. формула** T. formula; **Т.-Иннеса постоянная** T.-Innes constant.

тиллеит *m.* tilleyite.

тиллит *m.* teallite.

тилль *m.* till, glacial drift.

тильда *f.* tilde.

тиманнит *m.* tiemannite.

Тимей Timaeus (lunar crater).

Тимохарис Timocharis.

Тиндаля явление Tyndall effect.

тинолит *m.* thinolite.

тинтометр *m.* tintometer.

тинценит *m.* tinzenite.

тио— *prefix* thio—.

тио/керит *m.* thiokerite; **—мочевина** *f.* thiourea; **—рсаунт** *m.* thiorsauite; **—уреид** *m.* thioureide; **—фен** *m.* thiophene; **—цианид** *m.* thiocyanide.

тип *m.* type, mode, kind; model, class; pattern, make; **т. взаимодействия** interaction mode; **т. волн** wave mode; **т. деления** fission mode; **т. колебаний** oscillation mode; **т. распада, т. спада** decay mode; **—а** such as; -type.

типизация *f.* typing, classification.

типичн/ость *f.* typicalness; **—ый** *a.* typical, representative, characteristic, standard; **—ая модель** representative type.

типов/ый *a.* type; standard, model; **—ое испытание** prototype test.

типограф/ия *f.* printing house; **в —ии** in the press; **—ский** *a.* typographic, printing.

тир. *abbr.* *see* **тираж.**

тираж *m.* circulation (number of copies), printing (of book).

тиратрон *m.*, **—ный** *a.* thyratron.

тире *n.* dash; **т. с точкой** dot-dash line.

тирит *m.* tyrite, fergusonite.

Тирринг Thirring.

тиск/ание *n.* squeezing, pressing; **—ать** *v.* squeeze, press; **—и** *pl.* vise.

тисн/ение *n.* impression, stamping; **—еный** *a.* impressed, stamped; **—уть** *v.* impress, stamp.

тисонит *see* **тизонит.**

тисочн/ый *a.* vise; **—ая губка** jaw.

Тисса Tisza.

Тиссо конденсатор Tissot condenser.

титан *m.* titanium (Ti); **—истый** *a.* titanous, titanium, titaniferous.

титанит *m.* titanite, sphene.

титанклиногумит *m.* titanclinohumite.

титано— *prefix* titano—, titanium.

титанов/ый *a.* titanic, titanium, titaniferous; **т. выпрямитель** titanium-dioxide rectifier; **—ая сталь** titanium steel.

титаноморфит *m.* titanomorphite.

тит. л. *abbr.* (**титульный лист**) title page.

тито́н *m.*, **—ский ярус** Tithonian stage.

титр *m.* titer; **—иметр** *m.* titrimeter; **—иметрический** *a.* titrimetric.

титров/альный *a.* titrating, titration; **—ание** *n.* titration; **обратное —ание** back titration.

титрованн/ый *a.* titrated; **т. раствор** standard solution, titrant; **—ая кислота** standard acid.

титровать *v.* titrate.

титул *m.* title, name; **—ьный лист** title page.

Титьенса функция Tietjens function.

тих/ий *a.* quiet, silent; calm; slow; **Т. океан** Pacific Ocean; **—ое дуновение ветра** light air (Beaufort number 1).

тихит *m.* tychite.

Тихо Tycho (lunar crater).

тихо *adv.* quietly, silently; **—океанский** *a.* Pacific; **—ходный** *a.* low speed, slow.

тица *f.* tiza.

тиш/е *comp. of* **тихий, тихо,** more quietly; **—ина, —ь** *f.* quiet, silence, calm.

т.к. *abbr.* (**так как**) because, as, for.

ТК *abbr.* (**турбокомпрессор**) turbocompressor.

ткане/вый *a.* tissue; **—вая доза** tissue dose; **—эквивалентный** *a.* tissue-equivalent.

ткань *f.* fabric, cloth; tissue; **металлическая т., проволочная т., сетчатая т.** wire gauze.

т. кип. *abbr.* (**температура кипения**) boiling point (b.p.).

ткм *abbr.* (**тоннокилометр**) ton-kilometer.

тле/ние *n.* smoldering; **—ть, —ться** *v.* smolder, glow.

тлеющ/ий *a.* glow, glowing, glow-discharge; **т. разряд** glow-discharge; **т. стабилизатор напряжения** glow-discharge voltage regulator; **лампа —его разряда** glow (or glow-discharge) tube (or lamp); **—ая лампа с сеткой** grid-glow tube; **—ее свечение** glow.

тм *abbr.* (**тоннометр**) ton-meter.

ТМ *abbr.* [**месячная таблица** (**метеорологических наблюдений**)] monthly chart (of meteorological data).

Т-мост *m.* balanced-T network.

ТМХ *abbr.* (**телемеханика**) remote control.

т.н., т. наз. *abbr.* (**так называемый**) so-called.

ТНИГЭИ *abbr.* (**Тбилисский научно-исследовательский гидроэнергетический институт**) Tbilisi Hydropower Scientific Research Institute.

т.о. *abbr.* (**таким образом**) in this manner, thus.

то *see also under* **тот**; **то есть** that is, that is to say, i.e.; **то же** ditto, the same; **то ли ... то ли** whether ... or; **то ... то** sometimes ... sometimes; (**а**) **не то** if not, otherwise; **да и то** even then; **если так, то** if so, then; **не то, что** not that.

т. обр. *abbr. see* **т.о.**

Т-образн/ый *a.* T-, T-shaped, tee-; **Т. след** T-track; **Т. фильтр** T-section filter; **—ая мостовая схема** bridged T-network; **—ое звено** T-section.

тов. *abbr.* (**товарищ**) comrade.

товар *m.* merchandise; commodity, material.

товарищ *m.* comrade, companion, colleague, associate; **—ество** *n.* company, society, association.

товарный *a.* goods, commodity.

тогда *adv.* then, at that time; **т. как** while, whereas; **т.-то** at that time.

того *see under* **тот.**

тоддит *m.* toddite.

то есть that is, that is to say.

тождественн/о *adv.* identically; **—ость** *f.* identity, sameness; uniformity; **—ый** *a.* identical, same; **—ый оператор** identity operator, idemfactor; **—ое неравенство** unconditional (or absolute) inequality; **—ое преобразование** identity transformation.

тождество *see* **тождественность.**

тоже *adv.* also, too, likewise.

ток *m.* current, stream, flow; **т. возбуждения** exciting (field, magnetizing) current; **т. действия** action current; **т. делителя напряжения** bleeder current; **т. зажигания** striking current; **т. накала** filament (or heater) current; **т. начальных скоростей** residual current; **переменный т.** alternating current; **т. повреждения** fault (or failure) current; **т. покоя, т. холостого хода** quiescent (standing, zero-signal) current; **постоянный т.** direct current, continuous current; **т. потерь** loss current; **т. проводимости** conduction current; **т. смещения** displacement current; **функция —а** stream (or flow) function.

токарный станок lathe.

токо— *prefix* (elec.) current.

токо/ведущий, —несущий *a.* current-carrying; —**вращатель** *m.* pole changer.

токов/ый *a.* current; **т. лист** current sheet; —**ая полоса** conduction band; —**ая характеристика** current response characteristic.

токограмма *f.* current record.

токоограничитель *m.* current limiter; —**ный** *a.* current-limiting.

токопрерыватель *m.* circuit breaker, interrupter.

токоприемн/ик *m.* current collector, trolley; —**ый** *a.* current-collecting; —**ый ролик** trolley.

токопровод *m.* conductor; —**ящий** *a.* (current-) conducting.

токо/сниматель *m.* current collector; —**съемное кольцо** slip ring.

токсич/еский *a.* toxic, poisonous; —**ность** *f.* toxicity.

токсофор *m.* toxophore.

тол. *abbr.* (**тринитротолуол**) TNT.

толерантная доза tolerance dose.

толк *m.* meaning, sense.

толк/ание *n.* pushing; —**атель** *m.* pushrod, tappet, lifter, plunger; —**ать** *v.* push, thrust; —**ач** *m.* pusher.

толкающ/ий *a.* pushing, thrusting, propelling; —**ая сила** propelling force.

толкнуть *see* **толкать.**

толков/ание *n.* interpretation, explanation, comment; —**атель** *m.* interpreter; —**ать** *v.* interpret, explain, comment; —**ый** *a.* explanatory; intelligible, clear; sensible, intelligent.

Толмена-Стюарта опыт Tolman-Stewart experiment.

толочь *v.* pound, stamp, crush.

толп/а *f.* crowd; —**иться** *v.* crowd, cluster.

толсто— *prefix* thick.

толстомер *m.* thickness gauge.

толстослойн/ый *a.* thick-layered; —**ая фотоэмульсия** nuclear emulsion.

толсто/стенный *a.* thick-walled; —**та** *f.* thickness.

толстый *a.* thick, heavy-gauge.

толчен/ие *n.* stamping, pounding, crushing; —**ный,** —**ый** *a.* stamped, crushed.

толчкообразный *a.* jerking; (elec.) shock.

толч/ок *m.* shock; thrust, impulse, push; jerk, bump, percussion, impact; impetus; **ионизационный т.** ionization burst; **т. при взлете** take-off boost; —**ками** jerkily, intermittently.

толщ/а *f.* thickness; (geo.) strata; interior; —**ина** *f.* thickness, width, depth, gauge; —**ина полупоглощения** half-thickness; —**иномер** *m.* thickness gauge.

только *adv.* only, merely; **если т.** if only; **и т.** and nothing more; **как т.** as soon as; **лишь т.** no sooner than; **т. лишь** little more than; **т. что** just now, just.

том *m.* volume.

Томаса/-Райха-Куна правило сумм Thomas-Reiche-Kuhn sum rule; **Т.-Ферми модель** T.-Fermi model.

томасирование *n.* (met.) Thomas-Gilchrist process (Thomas process).

том/ительный *a.* wearisome, tedious; —**ить** *v.* exhaust, fatigue; (met.) malleablize; —**ление** *n.* fatigue; (met.) malleablizing.

томография *f.* tomography.

томпак *m.* tombac (copper-zinc alloy).

томсенолит *m.* thomsenolite.

Томсона формула Thomson formula; **Т. явление** T. effect.

томсонит *m.* thomsonite.

томсоновское рассеяние Thomson scattering.

тому *see under* **тот.**

тон *m.* tone, note; **т. биений** beat note; —**альность** *f.* tonality; —**альный** *a.* tone.

тонина *f.* fineness.

тонк/ий *a.* thin, fine; narrow; detailed; subtle; delicate; keen; **т. металлический листочек** metal foil; **т. прибор** delicate instrument; **т. след** thin (or light) track; **т. слой** thin layer, film, foil, leaf; —**ая настройка** fine tuning; —**ая регулировка** fine control (or adjustment); —**ая структура** fine structure.

тонко— *prefix* thin, fine.

тонко/волокнистый *a.* fine-fibered; —**волоченый** *a.* fine-drawn; —**дисперсный** *a.* finely dispersed; —**зернистый** *a.* fine-grained, fine.

тонкоизмельченный *a.* finely pulverized (or divided); **т. порошок** fine powder.

тонколист/ный, —**овой** *a.* thin-leaf, sheet; —**овое железо** sheet iron.

тонко/оттянутый *a.* finely drawn; —**размолотый,** —**распыленный** *see* **тонкоизмельченный;** —**слоистый,** —**слойный** *a.* lamellar, thinly laminated; —**стенный** *a.* thin-walled.

тонкость *f.* thinness, fineness, sharpness; delicacy, subtlety; fine point, minute detail.

тонна *f.* ton; **английская т., длинная т.** long ton; —**ж** *m.* tonnage.

тонометр *m.* tonometer.

тонуть *v.* sink.

тончайший *a.* ultrafine.

тоньше *comp. of* **тонкий, тонко,** thinner, finer.

топаз *m.,* —**овый** *a.* topaz.

топи/льный *a.* heating; —**ть** *v.* heat; fire; melt; —**ться** *v.* burn; melt.

топка *f.* furnace; firebox; heating, firing, stoking; melting; **автоматическая т., механическая т.** automatic stoking; stoker.

топлен/ие *n.* heating; melting; —**ный** *a.* heated; —**ый** *a.* melted.

топливн/ый *a.* fuel; —**ое пространство** firebox, heating chamber, combustion chamber.

топливо *n.* fuel, propellant; **двухкомпонентное т.** bipropellant; **жидкое т.** liquid fuel; **однокомпонентное т.** monopropellant; **подвижное т.** circulating (flowing, mobile) fuel; **ракетное т.** rocket propellant; **твердое т.** solid fuel.

топливо/добывающая промышленность fuel industry; —**загрузочный канал** fuel-charge canal; —**использование** *n.* fuel efficiency; —**провод** *m.* fuel line; —**снабжение** *n.* fuel supply; —**содержащий** *a.* fuel-carrying.

топограф *m.* topographer; —**ический** *a.* topographic; —**ия** *f.* topography.

тополог/изировать *v.* topologize; —**ическая степень** topological degree; —**ия** *f.* topology.

топорный *a.* clumsy, coarse; **т. камень** nephrite.

топохимический *a.* topochemical.

топочн/ый *a.* furnace; **т. ход,** —**ая труба** furnace flue; —**ое пространство** firebox; furnace.

топоцентрический *a.* topocentric.

топь *f.* swamp, marsh, morass, quagmire, bog.

тор *m.* (math.) torus; torr (1 mm Hg pressure).

Тор Thor (rocket).

торбернит *m.* torbernite.

торговать *v.* trade.

торгов/ля *f.* commerce, trade; —**о-промышленный** *a.* commercial and industrial; —**ый** *a.* trade, commercial.

Тореуса фильтр Thoraeus filter.

тор/ец *m.* end, end plane, butt, face; **упорный т.** thrust face; **вид с** —**ца** end view.

торжеств/енность *f.* solemnity; —**енный** *a.* solemn, ceremonial; —**о** *n.* celebration; —**овать** *v.* triumph over celebrate.

торзио *see* **торсио.**

тори/анит *m.* thorianite; —**д** *m.* thoride —**евый** *a.* thorium; —**й** *m.* thorium (Th); —**рованный катод** thoriated cathode; —**т** *m.* thorite.

Торичелли *see* **Торричелли.**

торкрет, —**бетон** *m.* gunite.

торможен/ие *n.* slowing, drag, deceleration, retardation, inhibition, braking, damping; (hyd.) stagnation **коэффициент** —**ия** stopping number **сечение** —**ия** stopping cross section —**ный** *a.* slowed-down, stopped, retarded, inhibited, braked.

тормоз *m.* brake, drag; hindrance; —**ить** *v.* slow down, retard, impede, inhibit damp, brake, stop.

тормозн/ой *a.* brake, braking, retarding stopping; **т. башмак,** —**ая колодка** brake shoe; **т. момент** braking torque; **т. путь** braking (or stopping distance; **т. фотон** bremsstrahlung photon; **т. эквивалент** stopping equivalent; **т. эффект** braking efficiency, retardation efficiency; —**ая способность** stopping power; —**ое излучение** bremsstrahlung; —**ое приспособление** brake, stopping device.

тормозящ/ий *a.* stopping, retarding, inhibiting, braking; **т. агент** (chem. inhibitor; **т. потенциал** retarding (or stopping) potential; **т. электрод** suppressor electrode; —**ее вещество**

stopping material; **—ее поле** retarding field.

орнадо *n.* tornado.

орогуммит *m.* thorogummite.

ороид *m.* toroid; **—альный** *a.* toroidal; **—альная камера** toroidal chamber, "doughnut."

оролит *m.* thoreaulite.

орон *m.* thoron.

ороп/ить, —иться *v.* hasten, hurry; **—ливо** *adv.* hurriedly; **—ливость** *f.* haste, hurry; **—ливый** *a.* hurried.

орос *m.* hummock; **—истый лед** hummocky ice.

оро/тунгстит *m.* thorotungstite; **—уранинит** *m.* thoruraninite.

орпед/а *f.* torpedo; **—ирование нефтяных скважин** shooting of oil wells; **—ированная скважина** shot hole.

орричелли закон истечения жидкости Torricelli law of efflux; **торричеллиева пустота** Torricellian vacuum.

орс *m.* torse, developable surface.

орсио/грамма *f.* torsiogram; **—граф** *m.* torsiograph; **—метр** *m.* torsiometer, torque meter; **—нные весы** torsion balance.

ортвейтит *m.* thortveitite.

ортонский подъярус Tortonian substage.

орф *m.* peat, turf.

орцев/ать *v.* face, pave; **—ой** *see* **торцовый.**

орцов/ый *a.* front, face; end, end-type; **т. счетчик** end-window counter; **т. фотокатод** head-on (or end-window) photocathode; **—ая поверхность** end face; **—ое окно** end window.

орч/ание *n.* protrusion, projection; **—ать** *v.* protrude, project; **—ком** *adv.* on end, upright.

от *pron. m.*, **та** *f.*, **то** *n.* that; **те** *pl.* those; **тот же, один и тот же** the same; **тот и другой** both; **тот или другой** either; **ни тот ни другой** neither; **тот или иной** one or another; **тот, кто** the one who; **именно тот** the one; **тем более** all the more; **тем более, что** especially as; **тем временем** in the meantime; **тем не менее** nevertheless; **тем самым** thereby; **вместе с тем** at the same time; moreover; **с тем, чтобы** in order to; **до того** to such a degree; **до того, пока** so long as; **до того, что** so that; until; **к тому же** moreover; **тому назад** ago; **тому подобное** similar, like; such as.

тотальный *a.* total.

тотчас *adv.* instantly, immediately.

точен/ие *n.* sharpening; turning; **—ый** *a.* sharpened, chiseled; machined.

точечно— *prefix* point, pointwise.

точечносваренный *a.* spot-welded.

точечн/ый *a.* point; **т. заряд** point charge; **т. излучатель, т. источник** point source; **т. пунктир** dotted line; **т. транзистор** point-contact transistor; **т. триод** point-contact triode; **—ая группа** point group; **—ая коррозия** pitting; **—ая лампа** point-source lamp; **—ая масса** mass point; **—ая решетка** point lattice; **—ая сварка** spot welding; **—ая счетная трубка** point counter; **—ая частица** point particle; **—ое преобразование** point transformation.

Точизмеритель *abbr.* (**Завод точных измерительных приборов**) Precision Measuring Instruments Plant.

точи/ло *n.* whetstone, grindstone; **—льный** *a.* grinding, sharpening; **—ть** *v.* sharpen, grind.

точк/а *f.* point; dot, spot; period; sharpening, grinding; **т. ветвления** branch point; **т. возврата** point (or distance) of closest approach; (math.) cusp; **т. вращения** pivot, fulcrum; **т. в —у** exactly; **т. вылета** take-off point; **т. зрения** point of view, standpoint; reason; **т. излома** break, knee, kink, salient point (of curve); **т. наблюдения** observation point; **т.-объект** object point; **т. отрыва** separation (or breakaway) point; **т. перевала** (math.) saddle point; **т. перегиба** inflection point; **т. плавления** melting point; **т. поворота** reversal point, point (or distance) of closest approach; **т. покоя** quiescent point; **т. приведения** reference point; **т. разветвления** branch point; **т. сгущения** (math.) condensation point; **т. с запятой** semicolon; **т. собирания** focal point; **т. срыва потока** separation (or burble) point; **т. усилий** force point.

Точмех *abbr.* (**Государственный трест точной механики**) State Trust of Precision Instruments.

точно *adv.* exactly, precisely, accurately; punctually; as, like, as if; **т. так** exactly so; **т. такой** exactly the same.

точност/ь *f.* exactness, precision, accuracy; punctuality; **в —и** exactly; punctually; **с —ью до** (math.) correct to (or within); except for.

точн/ый *a.* exact, precise, precision, accurate, correct; punctual; **т. дифференциал** exact differential; **т. прибор** precision instrument; **—ая регулировка** fine control; **—ая установка** fine adjustment; **—ые науки** exact sciences.

точприбор *abbr.* (**точный прибор**) precision instrument.

точь-в-точь *adv.* exactly, word for word.

Точэлектроприбор *abbr.* (**Завод точных электрических приборов**) Precision Electrical Instruments Plant.

тошнота *f.* nausea.

тощий *a.* lean, poor (ore, gas); thin.

ТПИ *abbr.* (**Томский политехнический институт**) Tomsk Polytechnic Institute.

т. пл. *abbr.* (**температура плавления**) melting point (m.p.).

тр. *abbr.* (**труды**) transactions, proceedings; works.

т-ра *abbr.* (**температура**) temperature.

трава *f.* grass; **морская т.** seaweed.

траверс *m.* traverse; crossarm; **—а** *f.* crosspiece, crossarm; transverse member; **—а щеткодержателя** (elec.) brush-rocker.

трав/ильный *a.* etching; pickling; **—итель** *m.* etching agent, etchant; **—ить** *v.* etch; pickle; **—леная схема** etching circuit; **—ление** *n.* etching; pickling.

травма *f.* trauma.

травящий *see* **травильный.**

традиц/ионный *a.* traditional; **—ия** *f.* tradition.

траектограф *m.* trajectory tracer.

траектория *f.* trajectory, path, track; **т. волны** wave (or ray) trajectory; **долетная т.** preorbital trajectory; **т. напряжения** stress trajectory; **т. полета** flight path.

т-ра кип. *abbr.* (**температура кипения**) boiling point.

тракт *m.* channel; circuit; transmission line; route; tract, train; **т. обратной связи** feedback loop.

тракт/ат *m.* treatise; **—овать** *v.* treat, discuss; **—овка** *f.* treatment, handling, interpretation.

трактор *m.*, **—ный** *a.* tractor.

трактриса *f.* tractrix.

трамбов/ание *n.* ramming, tamping; **—анный** *a.* rammed, tamped; **—ать** *v.* ram, tamp; **—ка** *f.* rammer, tamper; ramming, tamping; **—очный** *a.* ramming, tamping.

транзистор *m.* transistor.

транзит *m.*, **—ный** *a.* transit; **—ивность** *f.* transitivity; **—ивный** *a.* transitive.

транзитрон *m.* transitron.

транкор *m.* Trancor (iron-silicon alloy).

транс— *prefix* trans—.

транс/авроральный *a.* transauroral; **—атлантический** *a.* transatlantic.

трансверсальн/ость *f.* transversality; **—ый** *a.* transversal.

трансвертер *m.* transverter.

трансвлияние *n.* trans-effect.

трансгрессия *f.* transgression, overlap.

трансдуктор *m.* transducer.

транс/звуковая скорость transonic speed; **—изомер** *m.* trans-isomer; **—калифорниевый** *a.* transcalifornium.

транскристалл/изация *f.* transcrystallization; **—итное разрушение** transcrystalline fracture; **—ический** *a.* transcrystalline.

транскюриевый *a.* transcurium.

транслировать *v.* relay, retransmit, (re)broadcast.

трансляционн/ый *a.* translational, translation; relaying, (re)transmission, (re)broadcasting; **—ая группа** translation group; **—ая решетка** translational (or space) lattice; **—ое движение** translational motion.

трансляция *f.* translation; relaying, retransmitting, (re)broadcasting.

трансми/ссия *f.*, **—ссионный** *a.* transmission, transmitting; **—ттер** *m.* transmitter.

трансокеанский *a.* transoceanic.

транспарант *m.* (phot.) transparency.

транспирация *f.* transpiration.

трансплутониевый *a.* transplutonium.

транспозиция *f.* transposition.

транспондер *m.* transponder.

транспониров/ание *n.*, **—ка** *f.* transposition; **—анный** *a.* transposed; **—анная матрица** transposed matrix, transpose; **—ать** *v.* transpose.

транспорт *m.* transport, transportation; **—абельный** *a.* transportable; **—ер** *m.*, **—ерный** *a.* transporter, conveyer, carrier; **ленточный —ер, —ерная лента** conveyer belt; **—ерный червяк** screw conveyer.

транспортир *m.* protractor.

транспортиров/ание *n.* transportation, conveying; **—анный** *a.* transported, conveyed; **—ать** *v.* transport, convey; **—очный** *a.* transfer.

транспортн/ый *a.* transport, conveying, transfer; **т. (свободный) пробег, —ая длина (пробега)** transport mean free path; **—ое сечение** transport cross section.

трансуран *m.* transuranium; **—ид** *m.* transuranium element; **—овый** *a.* transuranium, transuranic.

трансфинитный *a.* transfinite.

трансформант *m.* transform.

трансформатор *m.*, **—ный** *a.* transformer; converter; **т. вида колебаний** mode changer (transformer, transducer, converter); **повысительный т., повышающий т.** step-up transformer; **понижающий т., понизительный т.** step-down transformer; **т. частоты** frequency changer; **—ный усилитель** transformer-coupled amplifier.

трансформ/ационный *a.*, **—ация** *f.*, **—ирование** *n.* transformation, conversion, change; **коэффициент —ации** transformation (transformer, turns, voltage) ratio; **—ировать** *v.* transform, convert, change; **—ирующий** *a.* transforming.

трансцендентн/ость *f.* transcendence; **—ый** *a.* transcendental.

транс-цепочка *f.* trans-chain.

транш/ея *f.*, **—ейный** *a.* trench.

трапец/евидный *a.* trapeziform; **—еидальный, —иевидный** *a.* trapezoidal; **—ия** *f.* trapezoid; trapezium; **—ия Ориона** Trapezium of Orion; **правило —ий** trapezoidal rule; **—оид** *m.* trapezoid; **—оэдр** *m.* trapezohedron.

т-ра пл. *abbr.* **(температура плавления)** melting point.

трапп *m.* trap, traprock.

трасса *f.* route; direction; sketch, drawing.

трассир/овать *v.* trace; **—овка** *f.* tracing; location; laying out; layout; **—ующий** *a.* tracing.

трат/а *f.* expense, expenditure; consumption; waste; **—ить** *v.* expend, disburse, spend; consume; waste.

Траубе правило Traube rule.

трафарет *m.*, **—ный** *a.* stencil; **—ить** *v.* stencil.

трафоперм *m.* Trafoperm (iron-silicon alloy).

ТРД *abbr.* **(турбореактивный двигатель)** turbojet engine.

требов/ание *n.* requirement, demand; request; claim; **высокие —ания** high requirements; exacting demands; **технические —ания** specifications; **—ательность** *f.* exacting demands; **—ательный** *a.* demanding, exacting; **—ать** *v.* require, demand, need, involve; **что и —алось доказать** quod erat demonstrandum (Q.E.D.).

треб/уемый *a.* required, specified; **—ующий** *a.* requiring, demanding; specifying.

тревога *f.* alarm, alert; anxiety.

тревож/ить *v.* alarm, disturb, worry; **—ный** *a.* alarm; alarming, troubling; anxious; **—ный сигнал** alarm signal.

трегерит *m.* troegerite.

трезвучие *n.* triad.

трезвый *a.* sober, sensible.

трезуб/ец *m.* trident; **—чатый, —ый** *a.* trident, three-pronged.

трек *m.* track.

тремадокский *a.* Tremadoc.

тренажер *m.* training apparatus.

трен/ие *n.* friction, rubbing; **внутреннее т.** internal friction, viscosity; **т. движения** kinetic friction; **т. качания** rolling friction; **т. покоя, т. трогания** static (or starting) friction;

т. скольжения sliding friction; без —ия frictionless.

тренииров/анный *a.* trained; aged; —**ать** *v.* train; age; —**ка** *f.* training; aging, conditioning, preliminary processing.

треног/а *f.* tripod; —**ий** *a.* three-legged.

треножн/ик *m.*, —**ый штатив** tripod; —**ый** *a.* tripod, three-legged.

треншальтер *m.* disconnecting switch.

трепел *m.* tripolite.

трепет/ание *n.* trembling; flickering; —**ать** *v.* tremble; flicker; —**ный** *a.* trembling; flickering.

треск *m.* crackling, crack; —**ание** *n.* cracking, crackling; —**аться** *v.* crack, crackle.

тресн/увший, —**утый** *a.* cracked, burst; —**уть** *v.* crack, burst.

трест *m.* trust.

трет/ий *a.* third; **в** —**ьих** thirdly.

третичный *a.* tertiary; **т. период** Tertiary period; **т. спирт** tertiary alcohol.

треть *f.* one third.

Треугольник Triangulum (Tri) (constellation).

треугольн/ик *m.* triangle; (elec.) delta; **соединение** —**иком** (elec.) mesh connection (of polyphase circuit); —**ый** *a.* triangular, delta.

трех— *prefix* tri—, three, triple.

трехатомный *a.* triatomic.

трехвалентн/ость *f.* trivalence; —**ый** *a.* trivalent.

трехвариантный *a.* trivariant.

трехгранн/ик *m.* trihedron; —**ый** *a.* trihedral; —**ая призма** trigonal (or triangular) prism.

трех/замещенный *a.* trisubstituted; —**значный** *a.* three-figure, three-digit, three-place; three-valued.

трехзуб/чатый, —**ый** *see* **трезубчатый, трезубый.**

трех/каскадный *a.* three-stage; —**квантовая аннигиляция** three-quantum annihilation; —**компонентная теория цветного зрения** three-color theory; —**кратный** *a.* triple, three-fold, three-stage.

трехлет/ие *n.* triennial; —**ний** *a.* triennial, three-year.

трехманит *m.* trechmannite.

трех/мерный *a.* three-dimensional; trivariate; —**месячный** *a.* three-month; —**недельный** *a.* three-week; —**окись** *f.* trioxide, teroxide; —**основный** *a.* tribasic; —**осный** *a.* triaxial; —**полюсный** *a.* tripolar; —**проводный** *a.* three-wire; —**размерный** *a.* three-dimensional; —**связный** *a.* triply connected; —**слойный** *a.* three-layered.

трехсот/летие *n.* tercentenary; —**ый** *a.* three-hundredth.

трех/сторонний *a.* trilateral, three-sided; —**ступенчатый** *a.* three-stage, three-step; —**точечная схема** Hartley oscillator circuit; —**фазный** *a.* three-phase.

трехформенн/ость *f.* trimorphism; —**ый** *a.* trimorphous.

трех/фотонная аннигиляция three-quantum annihilation; —**фтористый бор** boron trifluoride; —**хлористый уран** uranium trichloride.

трехходов/ой *a.* three-way, three-pass; **т. кран** three-way cock; —**ая деталь** T-piece.

трехцвет/ность *f.* trichromatism; (cryst.) trichroism; —**ный** *a.* three-color, tricolor; tricolored; trichromatic, trichroic; —**ная колориметрическая система** three-color photometric system; —**ная трубка** tricolor tube.

трехчлен *m.*, —**ный** *a.* trinomial; three-place, three-membered.

трехъядерный *a.* trinuclear.

трещ/ание *n.* cracking, crackling; —**ать** *v.* crack, crackle, burst, split.

трещин/а *f.*, —**ный** *a.* crack, fissure, fracture, split; —**ная вода** (geo.) interstitial water.

трещиноват/ость *f.* fracturing; fissility; —**ый** *a.* fissured, split, cracked.

трещотка *f.* ratchet.

три— *prefix* tri—, three.

три three; **т. четверти** three quarters.

триада *f.* triad; triplet.

триаконтаэдр *m.* (geom.) triacontahedron; —**ический** *a.* triacontahedral.

триаморфный *a.* (cryst.) triamorphous.

триангул/ировать *v.* triangulate; —**ятор** *m.* triangulator; —**яция** *f.* triangulation.

риас *m.* Triassic period; —**овый** *a.* Triassic.

риб *m.*, —**ка** *f.* pinion.

рибо/люминесценция *f.* triboluminescence; —**метр** *m.* tribometer, friction gauge; —**электричество** *n.* triboelectricity.

ривариантный *see* **трехвариантный.**

ривиальн/ость *f.* triviality; —**ый** *a.* trivial.

риг. *abbr.* (**тригонометрический**) trigonometric.

ригатрон *m.* trigatron.

риггер *m.*, —**ный** *a.* trigger; flip-flop.

ригидрокальцит *m.* trihydrocalcite.

ригир/а *f.* threefold axis of symmetry; —**ный** *a.* trigonal, rhombohedral.

ригон *m.*, —**альный** *a.* trigonal; —**додекаэдр** *m.* trigondodecahedron.

ригонометр/ический *a.* trigonometric; —**ия** *f.* trigonometry; **плоская** —**ия** plane trigonometry.

ридимит *m.* tridymite.

ридцатигранник *m.* triacontahedron.

ридцат/ый *a.* thirtieth; —**ь** thirty.

рижды *adv.* three times, triply.

ризамещенный *see* **трехзамещенный.**

рикл. *abbr. see* **триклинический.**

риклин/ический, —**ный** *a.* triclinic, anorthic.

рилатерация *f.* trilateration.

рилистник *m.* trefoil; —**овидный** *a.* cloverleaf.

риллион trillion.

ример *m.* trimer; —**ный** *a.* trimeric.

риметил *m.* trimethyl.

риметрический *a.* trimetric.

риммер *m.* trimmer.

римолекулярный *a.* trimolecular.

риморф/изм *m.* trimorphism; —**ный** *a.* trimorphous.

ринадцат/ый *a.* thirteenth; —**ь** thirteen.

ринитро— *prefix* trinitro—.

ринитротолуол *m.* trinitrotoluene (TNT).

рином *m.* trinomial.

риод *m.* triode; transistor.

риокси— *prefix* trioxy—.

рипафлавин *m.* trypaflavine.

риплан *m.* triplane.

риплекс *m.* triplex; triplex safety glass; —**ный** *a.* triplex.

триплет *m.*, —**ный** *a.* triplet.

трипугиит *m.* tripuhyite.

Трираздельная туманность Trifid Nebula.

трисекция *f.* trisection.

Триснеккер Triesnecker (lunar crater).

триста three hundred.

тритетраэдр *m.* tristetrahedron.

трити/евый *a.*, —**й** *m.* tritium.

тритон *m.* triton.

тритохорит *m.* tritochorite.

триумф *m.* triumph; —**альный** *a.* triumphal.

трифан *m.* triphane.

трифилин *m.* triphylite.

трихальцит *m.* trichalcite.

трихро/изм *m.* trichroism; —**ичный** *a.* trichroic; —**матичный** *see* **трехцветный.**

трицикл/ен *m.* tricyclene; —**ический** *a.* tricyclic.

триэдр *m.* trihedron, trihedral; **переменный т.** moving trihedral; —**ический** *a.* trihedral.

триэтил *m.* triethyl.

трог *m.* (geo.) trough.

трог/ание *n.* touching; starting; —**ать** *v.* touch; —**аться** *v.* start, move.

троговая долина (geo.) trough valley.

трое three; **на т.** in three parts.

троекратн/о *adv.* three times, triply; —**ый** *a.* threefold, triple.

тро/ить *v.* divide into three; —**ица** *f.* triad, three; —**ичный** *a.* ternary; triadic, tripartite.

тройка *f.* three; triple; triplet, set of three; **т. направлений** directed (or coordinate) trihedral.

тройник *m.*, —**овый** *a.* tee, T-junction (-connection, -joint, -pipe); (cryst.) trilling; triplet; **косой т.** Y-fitting (branch, bend).

тройничн/ость *f.* triplicity; —**ый** *a.* triple; ternary.

тройн/ой *a.* triple, ternary, triplex, threefold, tri—; **т. интеграл** triple integral; **т. сплав** ternary alloy; —**ая ось** threefold axis of symmetry; —**ая связь** triple bond; —**ая соль** triple salt; —**ая точка** triple point; —**ое деление** ternary fission; —**ое правило** (math.) rule of three; —**ое скалярное произведение** triple scalar product; **—ое соударение** triple collision.

тройственн/ость *f.* triplicity; **—ый** *a.* triple.

троллей *m.*, **—ный** *a.* (elec.) trolley; **—ный провод** trolley wire.

тромб *m.* (meteor.) spout, tornado; thrombus; **водяной т.** waterspout; **песчаный т.** sand pillar.

тромбопения *f.* thrombopenia.

тромбоцит *m.* platelet.

тромолит *m.* Tromolit (iron-nickel-cobalt-aluminum-copper alloy).

трон/утый *a.* touched, affected; **—уть** *see* **трогать.**

троостит *see* **тростит.**

тропаеолин *m.* tropaeolin, tropeolin.

тропик *m.* tropic; **—и** *pl.* tropics; **т. Козерога** Tropic of Capricorn; **т. Рака** T. of Cancer.

тропический *a.* tropical; **т. пояс** torrid zone.

трополон *m.* tropolone.

тропопауза *f.* tropopause.

тропосфер/а *f.* troposphere; **—ный** *a.* tropospheric.

трос *m.* cable, rope.

тростит *m.* troostite; **—овый** *a.* troostitic.

тростить *v.* twist.

тротил *m.* trotyl, trinitrotoluene; **—овый эквивалент** TNT equivalent.

Троутона постоянная Trouton constant.

трохоида *f.* trochoid.

трохо/идальный *a.* trochoidal; **т. масс-спектрометр** trochoidal mass analyzer, trochotron; **—идный** *a.* trochoid, trochoidal; **—трон** *m.* trochotron.

трощен/ие *n.* twisting; **—ый** *a.* twisted.

трояк/ий *a.* triple, threefold; **—о** *adv.* in three (different) ways.

труба *f.* pipe, tube, duct, channel; funnel, chimney; **аэродинамическая т.** wind tunnel.

трубк/а *f.* pipe, tube; **т. вектора, т. поля** (mag.) tube of force; **т. потока** (mag.) flux tube; **т. тока** (hyd.) tube of flow, streamtube; **элементарная вихревая т.** vortex tube (or filament); **—овидный, —ообразный** *a.* tubiform, tubular.

трубн/ый *a.* pipe, tube; **—ые принадлежности** pipe fittings.

трубо— *prefix* pipe, tube.

трубопровод *m.* pipeline, piping, tubing conduit; manifold.

трубоч/ка *f.* small tube, small-bore tubing; **катодная т.** cathode sleeve **—ная глина** pipe clay.

трубчатый *a.* tubular; **т. катод** sleeve cathode.

труд *m.* labor, work; **—ы** *pl.* transactions, proceedings; works; **без —а** without difficulty, easily; **с большим —ом** with great difficulty; **—иться** *v.* work, labor.

трудно *adv.* with difficulty; it is difficult *prefix* with difficulty, almost un— (in—, im—).

трудно/ватый *a.* fairly difficult; **—доступный** *a.* almost inaccessible **—плавкий** *a.* refractory, (relatively infusible; **—сть** *f.* difficulty.

трудный *a.* difficult; laborious.

трудо/вой *a.* labor; working; **—емкий** *a.* laborious, time-consuming; **—любивый** *a.* industrious; **—любие** *n.* industriousness, industry; **—способность** *f.* capacity for work.

трудящийся *m.* worker; *a.* working.

труп *m.*, **—ный** *a.* corpse; carcass.

трускоттит *m.* truscottite.

Трутона *see* **Троутона.**

трущийся *a.* friction, frictional, rubbing.

тряс/ение *n.* shaking; **—ка** *f.* shaking jolting, jarring, bumping; **—кий** *a.* jolting; shaky; **—ти** *v.* shake, jolt.

тряхнуть *see* **трясти.**

ТСД *abbr.* (**турбина среднего давления**) medium-pressure turbine.

тсилаизит *m.* tsilaisite.

ТСЭ *abbr.* (**Техническая Советская Энциклопедия**) Technical Soviet Encyclopedia.

тт. *abbr.* (**товарищи**) comrades; (**тома**) volumes.

ТТИ *abbr.* (**Государственное технико-теоретическое издательство**) State Technical-Theoretical Press.

ТУ [*in steel mark* (**технические условия**)] (technical) specifications.

ТУ *abbr.* (**телеуправление**) remote control.

убу/латный *a.* tubulate; **—с** *m.* tube.
уго *adv.* tightly; slowly, with difficulty; **—й** *a.* tight; stiff, unyielding; **—натянутый** *a.* tightly drawn, taut.
угоплавк/ий *a.* high-melting, refractory; **—ое стекло** hard glass; **—ость** *f.* infusibility, refractoriness.
уда *adv.* there; **т. и обратно** back and forth.
уже *comp. of* **туго, тугой,** tighter.
уз *m.* ace.
укан Tucana (Tuc) (constellation).
укстлит *m.* tuxtlite.
ула сплав tula metal (silver-copper-lead alloy).
улий *m.* thulium (Tu or Tm).
улит *m.* thulite.
уман *m.* fog, mist, haze; **—ить** *v.* fog, obscure; **—ность** *f.* fogginess, mistiness, mist, haziness; (astr.) nebula; **—ный** *a.* foggy, misty, hazy; nebulous; (meteor.) nebulosus.
уманомер *m.* fog meter.
умблер *m.* tumbler; (elec.) tumbler switch.
уннель *m.*, **—ный** *a.* tunnel; **—ный переход** tunneling.
упик *m.*, **—овый** *a.* dead-end; deadlock, impasse.
упить *v.* blunt, dull; **—ся** *v.* become blunt (or dull).
уп/ой *a.* blunt, dull, stub; obtuse; **—ая настройка** broad (or flat) tuning.
упо/конечный, —носый *a.* blunt-ended, blunt; **—сть** *f.* bluntness, dullness; **—угольный** *a.* obtuse-angled.
ур. *abbr.* (**турецкий**) Turkish.
уранит *m.* turanite.
урбидиметр *m.* turbidimeter; **—ический** *a.* turbidimetric, nephelometric; **—ия** *f.* turbidimetry.
урбин/а *f.*, **—ный** *a.* turbine.
урбо— *prefix* turbo—, turbine.
урбоагрегат *m.* turbine-driven set, turbogenerator set.
урбо/вентилятор *m.*, **—воздуходувка** *f.* turboblower, turbofan; **—винтовой двигатель** turboprop engine.
урбогенератор *m.* turbogenerator; **—ный агрегат** *see* **турбоагрегат.**
урбодинамо *n.*, **—машина** *f.* turbodynamo.
турбо/компрессор *m.* turbocompressor; **—компрессорный воздушно-реактивный двигатель, —реактивный двигатель** turbojet engine.
турбулентн/ость *f.* turbulence, eddy; **—ый** *a.* turbulent, eddy, eddying; **—ый поток** turbulent flow; **—ая вязкость, —ое трение** eddy viscosity; **—ая диффузия** turbulent (or eddy) diffusion; **—ое движение** eddy.
турбул/изация *f.* turbulence, agitation; **—изованный** *a.* turbulent, agitated; **—ировать** *v.* create turbulence, agitate.
тургит *m.* turgite.
турель *f.* ring mount.
турецкий *a.* Turkish.
Туркменская ССР, Туркм. ССР Turkmen SSR.
турмалин *m.* tourmaline.
турнейский *a.* Tournaisian.
турникет *m.* tourniquet; turnstile; **—ная антенна** turnstile antenna.
туронский *a.* Turonian.
Турция Turkey.
ТУС [*in steel mark* (**технические условия специальные**)] special (technical) specifications.
тускл/о *adv.* dimly, without luster; **т.-серый** *a.* dull-gray; **—оватость** *f.* dimness, dullness; tarnish; **—оватый** *a.* rather dim; **—ый** *a.* dim, lusterless, dull, tarnished; obscure.
тускн/еть, —уть *v.* tarnish; become dim (or dull).
Туссена формула Toussaint formula.
тут *adv.* here; then; **т. же** immediately.
туттонова соль Tutton salt.
туф *m.* tuff; tufa; **вулканический т.** volcanic tuff; **известковый т.** calcareous tufa; **—овый** *a.* tuff, tuffaceous; tufa, tufaceous.
тухолит *m.* thucholite.
туча *f.* (storm) cloud; **грозовая т.** thundercloud.
тушев/ание *n.* shading; **—анный** *a.* shaded; **—ать** *v.* shade.
туш/ение *n.*, **—ительный** *a.* quenching; extinguishing; **—итель** *m.* quencher, quenching agent; extinguisher; **—ить** *v.* quench; extinguish.
ТФАН *abbr.* (**Туркменский филиал**

Академии наук ССР) Turkmen Branch of the Academy of Sciences, USSR.

ТЧ *abbr.* (**техническая часть**) technical section.

тщательн/о *adv.* carefully, thoroughly; **—ость** *f.* care, thoroughness; **—ый** *a.* careful, thorough.

тщетн/о *adv.* vainly, futilely; **—ость** *f.* vainness, futility; **—ый** *a.* futile, vain.

тыл *m.*, **—овой, —ьный** *a.* rear, back; **—ок** *m.* back, back edge.

тыс. *abbr. see* **тысяча.**

тысяч/а thousand; **—и** *pl.* thousands.

тысяче— *prefix* thousand, milli—.

тысячелетие *n.* millennium.

тысячн/ый *a.* thousandth; consisting of (numbering) thousands.

тьма *f.* darkness.

Тьюринга машина Türing machine.

тэббиит *m.* tabbyite.

тэгит *m.* tegit.

Тэйлора *see* **Тейлора.**

тэнит *m.* taenite, toenite.

ТЭС *abbr.* (**тепловая электрическая станция**) thermal electric power plant.

тэта-функция theta function.

ТЭЦ *abbr.* (**теплоэлектроцентраль**) heat and electric power plant.

тюб/ик *m.* tube; **—инг** *m.* tubing, piping.

тюк *m.* bale; package.

Тюри регулятор Thury regulator.

тюрингит *m.* thuringite.

тюрингское стекло Thuringian glass.

тюямунит *m.* tyuyamunite.

тяг/а *f.* draft; (aero.) thrust; propulsion pull, traction; bar, drawbar, rod propensity; **т. воздуха** draft; **т. реактивного двигателя** jet thrust **соединительная т.** tie rod; **линия —и** thrust line; **сила —и** tractive force, thrust.

тягач *m.* tow car; tractor.

тягов/ый *a.* traction, tractive; **—ое усилие** thrust; tractive force, pull.

тягомер *m.* draft gauge.

тягот/ение *n.* gravitation, gravity; attraction, pull; **—еть** *v.* gravitate, be attracted.

тягуч/есть *f.* ductility; malleability; viscosity; **—ий** *a.* ductile; malleable viscous, viscid.

тяжел/еть *v.* become heavy; **—о** *adv.* heavily; with difficulty, difficultly.

тяжеловесн/ость *f.* ponderosity, heaviness; **—ый** *a.* unwieldy, heavy.

тяжел/ый *a.* heavy; difficult; ponderous **т. водород** heavy hydrogen, deuterium; **—ая вода** heavy water; **—ая индустрия** heavy industry; **—ое излучение** heavy ionizing radiation

тяжест/ь *f.* weight, gravity, heaviness burden; **сила —и** gravity; **центр —и** center of gravity; emphasis.

тянут/ый *a.* drawn-out; pulled; **т. переход** (transistor) grown junction; **—ь** *v.* draw; protract; stretch; pull **—ься** *v.* stretch, extend; strive.

тянущ/ий *a.* drawing, pulling; **—ая сила** pull; thrust; **—ее крыло** thrust wing.

У

у *prep. gen.* by, near; at; on; of; in; **у власти** in power, in office; **у него (есть)** he (it) has.

У [*in steel mark* (**углерод**)] carbon (C).

уади *n.* wadi.

УАЗ *abbr.* (**Уральский автомобильный завод**) Ural Automobile Plant; (**Уральский алюминиевый завод**) Ural Aluminum Plant.

УАИЗ *abbr.* (**Украинская ассоциация изобретателей**) Ukrainian Association of Inventors.

Уайт-Сандс White Sands.

УАН *abbr.* (**Украинская Академия наук**) Ukrainian Academy of Sciences.

Уатта регулятор Watt governor.

убав/ить, —лять *v.* diminish, lessen, reduce; **—иться, —ляться** *v.* decrease diminish; **—ка** *f.*, **—ление** *n.* diminishing, decreasing, reducing; **—ленный** *a.* diminished, decreased, reduced.

убегать *v.* run away, escape.

бедительн/ость *f.* persuasiveness, conclusiveness; **—ый** *a.* persuasive, convincing, conclusive.

бедить *see* **убеждать.**

бежать *see* **убегать.**

бежд/ать *v.* convince, persuade; **—аться** *v.* make certain, verify; be convinced (or satisfied); **—ение** *n.*, **—енность** *f.* conviction, persuasion; **—енный** *a.* convinced, certain.

бежище *n.* shelter.

бер/егать, —ечь *v.* protect, guard.

бив/ание *n.* killing; **—ать** *v.* kill.

бир/ать *v.* remove, dispose of; **—ающийся** *a.* retractable.

бит/ый *a.* killed; **—ь** *see* **убивать.**

блюд/ковый, —очный *a.* hybrid; **—ковые породы** hybrid rocks.

богий *a.* lean, poor.

бористый *a.* close; compact.

борка *f.* removal.

бр/анный *a.* removed; **—ать** *see* **убирать.**

быв/ание *n.* decrease; subsidence; **—ать** *v.* decrease; attenuate; subside, ebb; **—ающий** *a.* decreasing, diminishing; **—ающая последовательность** descending (or decreasing) sequence.

быль *f.* decrease, diminution, subsidence; **идти на у.** *see* **убывать.**

быт/ок *m.* loss; **—очный** *a.* unprofitable, disadvantageous; **—ь** *see* **убывать.**

важ/ать *v.*, **—ение** *n.* respect; **—ительный** *a.* valid.

ванит *m.* uvanite.

ведом/ительный *a.* informative; **—ить, —лять** *v.* inform, notify; **—ление** *n.* information, notification.

везти *see* **увозить.**

вековеч/ение, —ивание *n.* perpetuation; **—ивать, —ить** *v.* perpetuate.

величен/ие *n.* magnifying power, magnification; increase, enhancement, growth; enlargement; **—ный** *a.* increased, enlarged, magnified.

величив/ание *see* **увеличение**; **—ать** *v.* magnify; increase, augment, enhance; enlarge, extend; **—аться** *v.* increase, grow, augment; **—ающий** *a.* increasing; magnifying; extending.

величитель *m.* enlarger; augmenter; **—ный** *a.* enlarging, magnifying; **—ное стекло** magnifying glass, magnifier.

увеличить *see* **увеличивать.**

увенч/ать, —ивать *v.* crown; **—аться успехом** succeed.

уверен/ие *n.* assurance; **—но** *adv.* confidently; **—ность** *f.* assurance, confidence, certainty; **степень —ности** (stat.) degree of credence; **можно с —ностью сказать** it is safe to say; **—ный** *a.* sure, confident, certain, convinced.

увер/ить, —ять *v.* assure; persuade, convince.

увесистый *a.* heavy, weighty.

увести *see* **уводить.**

увид/ать, —еть *v.* see, become aware, perceive.

увиолевое стекло uviol glass.

увлажнен/ие *n.* moistening, humidifying; **—ность** *f.* moisture, dampness; **степень —ности** moisture content; **—ный** *a.* moistened, humid.

увлажн/итель *m.* moistener, humidifier; **—ительный, —яющий** *a.* moistening, humidifying; **—ить, —ять** *v.* moisten, humidify.

увлек/ательный *a.* absorbing, interesting; **—ать** *v.* entrain, drag, carry away; absorb, interest; **—ать при осаждении** coprecipitate; **теория —аемого эфира** ether drag hypothesis.

увлеч/ение *n.* entrainment, drag; interest, enthusiasm; **у. фононами** phonon drag; **—енный** *a.* entrained, dragged; enthusiastic; **—ь** *see* **увлекать.**

увод *m.* leading away, withdrawal; **—ить** *v.* lead away, withdraw; discharge, drain off.

увозить *v.* remove, carry away.

уволить *see* **увольнять.**

увольн/ение *n.* dismissal, discharge; **—ять** *v.* dismiss, discharge.

УВЧ *abbr.* (**усилитель высокой частоты**) high-frequency amplifier.

УВЧ— *prefix* (**ультравысокочастотный**) ultra-high-frequency.

увяз/ать, —ывать *v.* tie up; link; coordinate; **—ка** *f.* tying up; linking; coordination; **—очный** *a.* tying.

уг. *abbr.* (**угол**) angle.

угад/ать, —ывать *v.* guess; **—ывание** *n.* guessing.

угар *m.*, **—ный** *a.* waste; carbon monoxide fumes (or poisoning); **—ный газ** carbon monoxide.

угас/ание *n.* fading, extinction; **—ать, —нуть** *v.* fade, become extinct; **—ающий** *a.* fading, dying-down; expiring; **—ший** *a.* extinct.

угле— *prefix* carbon; coal.

углевод *m.* carbohydrate.

углеводород *m.*, **—истый, —ный** *a.* hydrocarbon; **непредельный у.** unsaturated hydrocarbon; **предельный у.** saturated hydrocarbon.

углевыжигательн/ый *a.* charring; **—ая печь** charcoal kiln.

угледержатель *m.* carbon holder.

углекислота *f.* carbonic acid; carbon dioxide; **твердая у.** dry ice.

углекислый *a.* carbonic acid, carbonate (of); **у. газ** carbon dioxide (gas); **у. кальций** calcium carbonate.

углерод *m.* carbon (C); **двуокись —а** carbon dioxide; **окись —а** carbon monoxide; **—истый, —ный** *a.* carbon, carbonic, carbonaceous, carboniferous; carbide (of); **—ный цикл** carbon cycle.

углефикация *f.* carbonification, carbonization.

углистый *a.* carbonaceous.

угловато/зернистый *a.* angular-grained; **—круглый** *a.* round-cornered.

угловат/ость *f.* angularity; **—ый** *a.* angular.

углов/ой *a.* angle, angular; corner; **у. коэффициент** gradient, slope; **у. момент** angular momentum; **у. рычаг** crank lever; **у. эффект** corner effect; **—ая корреляция** angular correlation; **—ая полуширина пучка** half-angle of beam; **—ая связь, —ое скрепление** angle brace; **—ая скорость** angular velocity; **—ая частота (вращения)** angular frequency (or velocity); **—ое квантовое число** orbital quantum number; **—ое расхождение** angular separation (spread, divergence); **—ое увеличение** angular magnification.

угломер *m.*, **—ный** *a.* angle gauge; azimuth scale; goniometer.

углуб/ить *see* **углублять**; **—ка** *se* **углубление.**

углубл/ение *n.* deepening; intensifica tion; hollow, depression, recess, pock et; notch; (geo.) dip; close examina tion (or investigation); **—енный** *a* deepened; depressed; **—ять** *v.* deep en; intensify; depress, sink, recess **—яться** *v.* deepen; dip; examin closely, investigate.

угляк *m.* black diamond.

угнать *see* **угонять.**

угов/аривать *v.* persuade, urge; **—орит** *v.* persuade, induce.

угодно: как у. in any manner; **какой у** any; **сколько у.** as much as desired **что у.** anything at all.

уг/ол *m.* angle; corner; **у. возвышени** angle of elevation; **у. входа** angle c incidence; **у. вылета** angle of emis sion; **у. выноса крыла** (aero.) stag ger; **у. выхода** angle of departure; **у диэлектрических потерь** dielectri loss angle; **у. зазора** clearance (o back) angle; **у. зрения, у. наблюде ния** viewing angle; **у. зрения объ ектива** camera angle; **у. места** angl of elevation; **у. отклонения** angle c deflection (or deviation), scatterin angle.

уг/ол *cont.*, **у. падения** angle of incidence **у. панорамирования** scanning angl (of periscope); **у. погружения** di angle; **у. положения** position angle **предельный у.** critical angle; **у преломления** refraction angle; **у проекции** projected angle; **у. разлет** angle of emergence (scattering, diver gence); **у. раскрытия, у. раствор** angle of opening (or aperture), ape angle; **у. расхождения** angle of di vergence (or spread); **у. скольжени** glancing angle; Bragg angle; **у смещения** angle of displacement (o parallax); **у. сужения** taper angle **под —лом** at an angle, obliquely **под прямым —лом** at right angle (to).

угол/ковая антенна corner (or corner reflector) antenna; **—ок** *m.* corner angle bracket.

уголь *m.* coal; carbon; **активированны у.** activated carbon (or charcoal)

бурый у. lignite, brown coal; **древесный у.** charcoal; **каменный у.** (bituminous) coal.

'гольник *m.* try square; corner iron.

'гольный *a.* angle, angular; corner; *see also* **угловой.**

'гольн/ый *a.* carbon, carbonic, graphite; coal; **у. ангидрид** carbon dioxide; **—ая кислота** carbonic acid.

'гольный Мешок Coal Sack (nebula).

'гон *m.* driving away; **—ная скорость** runaway speed; **—ять** *v.* drive away.

'гро/жать *v.* threaten, impend; **—жающий** *a.* threatening, impending; **—за** *f.* threat, menace.

'д. *abbr.* (**удельный**) specific.

'да-Яги антенна Yagi antenna.

'даваться *v.* succeed.

'дален/ие *n.* removal, withdrawal, elimination; departure; **у. отходов** waste disposal; **скорость —ия** recession velocity; **—ность** *f.* remoteness; **—ный** *a.* removed, eliminated; distant, remote; separated, outlying.

'дал/ить, —ять *v.* remove, eliminate, withdraw; **—иться** *v.* move away, recede, retire, withdraw.

'дар *m.* impact, collision; shock; blow, stroke; **у. второго рода** collision of the second kind, superelastic collision; **у. грома** thunder clap; **испытание на у.** impact test; **косой у.** oblique impact; **у. молнии** lightning stroke; **прямой у.** direct impact; **центральный у.** central impact; **одним —ом** at one stroke; **центр —а** center of percussion.

'дарение *n.* stress, emphasis; **делать у. на** emphasize.

'даренный *a.* struck; stressed.

'дар/ить *see* **ударять**; **—ник** *m.* firing pin, striker; shock worker.

'дарн/ый *a.* shock; impact; percussion, percussive; **у. генератор** impulse-excited oscillator; **у. контур** impulsing circuit; **у. параметр** impact parameter; **у. раствор** (electrodeposition) striking solution; **—ая волна** shock wave; **—ая вязкость** resilience, impact strength (or ductility); **—ая ионизация** impact ionization; **—ая нагрузка** impact load, dynamic pressure; **—ая прочность** impact strength; **—ая сила** impulsive force; **—ая труба** shock tube; **—ая флуоресценция** impact fluorescence; **—ое бурение** percussion drilling; **—ое возбуждение** impact (shock, impulse) excitation; **—ое действие** percussion; **—ое задание** urgent task; **—ое зажигание** knocking combustion; **—ое излучение** impact radiation; **—ое испытание** *see under* **удар**; **—ое напряжение** impact stress; **—ое расширение** collision broadening.

удар/яемый *a.* struck; **—яемая частица** struck (or knocked-on) particle; **—ять** *v.* strike, hit; **—яться** *v.* strike, hit, knock against, collide with, impinge; **—яющая частица** colliding (bombarding, incident) particle.

удаться *see* **удаваться.**

удач/а *f.* success; good fortune; **—но** *adv.* successfully, well; **—ный** *a.* successful; fortunate; felicitous.

уд. в. *abbr.* (**удельный вес**) specific gravity.

удваив/ание *n.* doubling; duplication; splitting; **—ать** *v.* double; duplicate; split.

удво/ение *see* **удваивание**; **формула —ения** duplication formula; **—енный** *a.* doubled; duplicate; **—итель** *m.* doubler; duplicator; **—ить** *see* **удваивать.**

удел *m.* lot, destiny; **—ение** *n.* allotment; **—ить** *see* **уделять.**

удельн/ый *a.* specific, unit; **у. вес** specific gravity; specific weight; proportion, share, relative intensity; **у. заряд** specific charge; charge-mass ratio; **у. объем** specific volume; **у. оросительный расход** hydromodulus; **—ая влажность** specific humidity; **—ая мощность** specific power, power density; **—ая нагрузка** unit load; **—ая поверхность** specific surface; **—ая проводимость** conductivity; **—ая рефракция** specific refraction; **—ая теплоемкость** specific heat; **—ая теплопроводимость** heat (or thermal) conductivity; **—ая эмиссия** emissivity; **—ое магнитное сопротивление** reluctivity; **—ое сопротивление** resistivity, specific resistance; —**ое удлинение** elongation per unit length.

уделять *v.* allot; **у. внимание** give consideration.

удерж/ание *see* **удерживание**; —**ать** *see* **удерживать.**

удержив/аемый объем containment volume; —**ание** *n.* retention; restraint; holding; confinement, containment; —**ать** *v.* keep back, hold, restrain, delay; retain; maintain; contain; —**аться** *v.* refrain; maintain itself; —**ающий** *a.* holding, retaining; —**ающий магнит** holding magnet; —**ающий носитель** hold-back carrier; —**ающая сила** restoring force; —**ающее поле** confining field.

удесятер/енный *a.* tenfold, decuple; —**ить,** —**ять** *v.* increase tenfold.

удивительн/о *adv.* astonishingly, wonderfully; extremely; it is remarkable; **не у., что** it is no wonder that; —**ый** *a.* astonishing, striking, surprising.

удив/ить, —**лять** *v.*, **приводить в** —**ление** astonish, amaze; —**иться,** —**ляться** *v.* be surprised, wonder; —**ление** *n.* surprise, astonishment; —**ленный** *a.* surprised.

удлинен/ие *n.* elongation, extension, stretch, (linear) expansion; **у. крыла** (aero.) wing aspect ratio; —**ный** *a.* prolate; elongated, lengthened, stretched, extended.

удлин/итель *m.* extension; extender, lengthener; (elec.) pad; **у. импульса** pulse stretcher; —**ительный** *a.* extension, lengthening; —**ить,** —**ять** *v.* lengthen, elongate, prolong, extend, expand; —**иться,** —**яться** *v.* lengthen, stretch; —**яемость** *f.* extensibility; —**яющийся** *a.* extensible; lengthening, stretching.

Удмуртская АССР Udmurt ASSR.

удобн/о *adv.* conveniently, easily; it is convenient; —**ый** *a.* convenient; favorable, opportune, appropriate, suitable, advantageous; —**ый случай** favorable occasion, opportunity.

удобоисполним/ость *f.* feasibility, practicability; —**ый** *a.* feasible, practicable.

удобоносим/ость *f.* portability; —**ый** *a.* portable.

удобообтекаемый *a.* streamlined.

удобоперевозим/ость *f.* transportab ity; —**ый** *a.* transportable.

удобопонятн/ость *f.* comprehensibilit intelligibility; —**ый** *a.* comprehe sible, intelligible.

удoборегулируемый *a.* adjustable, ea ily regulated.

удобосмешиваем/ость *f.* miscibilit —**ый** *a.* miscible, mixable.

удобоуправляем/ость *f.* maneuverab ity; —**ый** *a.* maneuverable.

удобочитаемость *f.* legibility.

удобство *n.* convenience, accommod tion; advantage.

удовлетвор/ение *n.*, —**енность** *f.* sati faction; —**енный** *a.* satisfied; — **тельно** *adv.* satisfactorily; —**ител ность** *f.* satisfactoriness; —**ител ный** *a.* satisfactory, adequat —**ить,** —**ять** *v.* satisfy, comp with.

удовольств/ие *n.* pleasure, enjoymen —**оваться** *v.* be satisfied.

удостаивать *v.* honor; confer.

удостовер/ение *n.* certificate; certific tion; —**ить,** —**ять** *v.* testify, attes certify; —**иться,** —**яться** *v.* asce tain.

удостоить *see* **удостаивать.**

удуш/ать, —**ить** *v.* stifle, suffocate; a phyxiate; —**ающий** *a.* suffocatin —**ливый** *a.* oppressive, stifling; su focating.

Удэна ток Oudin current.

уедин/ение *n.* seclusion; —**енный** isolated, single, solitary, seclude —**ить,** —**ять** *v.* isolate, seclude.

уезжать, уехать *v.* depart, leave.

ужас *m.* horror; —**ный** *a.* terrible, ho rible.

ýже *comp. of* **узкий, узко,** narrower.

ужé *adv.* already; as early as; **у. не** n longer; **реагирует у. 0.001%** as litt as 0.001% reacts.

УЗ *abbr.* (**ультразвук**) ultrasound; (**ул тразвуковой**) ultrasonic.

узакон/ение *n.* legalization; —**ить** legalize.

узбекит *m.* uzbekite.

Узбекская ССР, Узб. ССР Uzbek SSR.

Узгиз *abbr.* (**Узбекское государстве**

ное издательство) Uzbek State Press.

ел *m.* node, nodal point, vertex; point, junction (point); unit, subassembly; knot; bundle; joint; **у. давления** pressure node; **у. интерполяции** interpolation point; **у. решетки** lattice point (or site); **у. сетки** mesh point (or node).

к/ий *a.* narrow, tight; **у. импульс** spike (pulse); **у. ливень** (cosm.) narrow shower, jet; **—ое место** bottleneck.

ко *adv.* narrowly, tightly; **—колейный** *a.* narrow-gauge; **—направленная антенна** narrow-beam antenna; **—полосный** *a.* narrow-band.

ЗЛГУ *abbr.* (**Ученые записки Ленинградского государственного университета**) Scientific Annals of the Leningrad State University.

ловатый *a.* nodular.

лов/ой *a.* node, nodal, junction; knot; main; **—ая задача** knotty problem; **—ая линия** nodal line; **—ая плоскость** nodal plane; **—ая сборка** subassembly; **—ая точка** nodal point, node; **—ая функция** station function.

ЗМГУ *abbr.* (**Ученые записки Московского государственного университета**) Scientific Annals of the Moscow State University.

ЗМолГУ *abbr.* (**Ученые записки Молотовского государственного университета**) Scientific Annals of the Molotov State University.

на/вание *n.* recognition; learning; **—вать, —ть** *v.* recognize, identify; learn, find out.

ор *m.* pattern, design.

ость *f.* narrowness, tightness.

илер Wheeler.

иллерит *m.* wheelerite.

ИМ *abbr.* (**Уральский научно-исследовательский институт черных металлов**) Ural Scientific Research Institute of Ferrous Metals.

имшерста *see* **Вимшерста.**

иппл Whipple.

ИПФХ *abbr.* (**Украинский научно-исследовательский институт прикладной физико-химии**) Ukrainian Scientific Research Institute of Applied Physical Chemistry.

УИПЭ *abbr.* (**Украинский научно-исследовательский институт промэнергетики**) Ukrainian Scientific Research Institute of Industrial Power Engineering.

Уитстона мостик Wheatstone bridge.

Уиттекера функция Whittaker function.

уйти *see* **уходить.**

указ *m.* decree.

указан/ие *n.* indication, hint; instruction; **—ный** *a.* indicated, denoted, stated, mentioned.

указатель *m.* indicator; pointer; detector; index, directory; marker, sign; **у. утечки** leak detector.

указательн/ый *a.* indicating; indicatory; **у. палец** index finger; **—ая пластинка** dial; **—ая стрелка** pointer.

указ/ать, —ывать *v.* indicate, denote; point out, show, explain; **—ка** *f.* pointer; marker; **—ывающий** *a.* indicating; directing; **—ывать на** indicate, denote, imply.

укат/ать, —ывать *v.* roll, smooth; **—ить** *v.* roll away; **—ывание** *n.* rolling, smoothing.

УКВ *abbr.* (**ультракороткие волны**) ultrashort waves.

Укерт Ukert (lunar crater).

укипание *n.* evaporation.

уклад/ка *f.* packing; stacking up; laying; installation; **—ывание** *n.* packing; piling, stacking; **—ывать** *v.* pack; pile, stack; set, lay; **—ываться** *v.* be packed; fit into; confine oneself; **дефект (нарушение) —ки** stacking fault.

уклон *m.* slope, incline, gradient; inclination, deviation, digression; **у. гидравлический** hydraulic gradient; **под у.** at a slant, downgrade.

уклон/ение *n.* deviation, deflection, digression, aberration; declination; evasion; **—иться** *see* **уклоняться**; **—омер** *m.* inclinometer; clinometer.

уклончив/ость *f.* evasiveness; **—ый** *a.* evasive.

уклоняться *v.* deviate; evade, avoid.

укомплектован/ие *n.* completing, completion; manning; **—ный** *a.* completed; manned.

укорачив/ание *n.* shortening, contraction, reduction; **—ать** *v.* shorten, contract, reduce.
укорен/ение *n.* implanting, inculcating; **—ившийся** *a.* of long standing; **—ить, —ять** *v.* implant, inculcate.
укор/отить *see* **укорачивать**; **—очение** *see* **укорачивание**; **—оченный** *a.* shortened, contracted; curtate; **—оченная циклоида** curtate cycloid.
укосина *f.* strut, brace; cantilever; (crane) jib, boom.
укр. *abbr.* (**украинский**) Ukrainian.
Украинская ССР Ukrainian SSR.
украсить *see* **украшать.**
украш/ать *v.* adorn, decorate; **—ение** *n.* decoration, ornament; **—енный** *a.* decorated.
укреп/ить, —лять *v.* strengthen; fasten; **—ление** *n.* strengthening; reinforcement; fastening; **—ленный** *a.* strengthened; reinforced; fastened, mounted; **—ляющий** *a.* strengthening; reinforcing.
Укрнииредмет *abbr.* (**Украинский научно-исследовательский институт редких металлов**) Ukrainian Scientific Research Institute of Rare Metals.
укрупн/ение *n.* enlargement, coarsening; consolidation; **—ить, —ять** *v.* enlarge, coarsen; consolidate, combine.
Укр. хим. ж. *abbr.* (**Украинский химический журнал**) Ukrainian Chemical Journal.
укрыв/ание *n.* concealment; **—ать** *v.* conceal, cover; **—истость** *f.* covering power (of paint).
укрыт/ие *n.* cover, covering, shelter; concealment; **зона —ия** shelter area; **—ый** *a.* covered, sheltered; concealed; **—ь** *see* **укрывать.**
уксус *m.* vinegar.
уксуснокислый *a.* acetic acid, acetate (of); **у. уранил** uranyl acetate.
уксусн/ый *a.* acetic; **—ая кислота** acetic acid.
укупор/ивание *n.*, **—ка** *f.* corking, capping, sealing; **—ивать, —ить** *v.* cork, cap, seal.
ул. *abbr.* (**улица**) street.
улавлив/ание *n.* catching, tapping; collecting; **—атель** *see* **уловитель**; **—ать** *v.* catch, capture, trap, collect; recover; detect.
уладить *see* **улаживать.**
улажив/ание *n.* settling, reconciliation; **—ать** *v.* settle, reconcile, arrange.
улегаться *v.* subside.
улексит *m.* ulexite.
улет/ать, —еть *v.* fly away, escape.
улетучив/аемость *f.* volatility; **—аемый** *a.* volatile; **—ание** *n.* volatilization, evaporation; **—аться** *v.* volatilize, evaporate; **—ающийся** *a.* volatilizing; volatile, evaporating.
улетучиться *see* **улетучиваться.**
улечься *see* **улегаться.**
улигит *m.* uhligite.
улика *f.* evidence.
улитк/а *f.* (math.) limaçon; cochlea; **—ообразный** *a.* spiral, helical, conchoidal.
ули/ца *f.*, **—чный** *a.* street.
улов/имый *a.* perceptible; **—итель** *m.* catcher, collector, trap; detector; **—ить** *see* **улавливать.**
уловка *f.* stratagem, device, trick.
уловлен/ие *see* **улавливание**; **—ный** *a.* caught, trapped; detected.
улож/енный *a.* packed; laid; **—ить** *see* **укладывать.**
улучш/ать, —ить *v.* improve, amend, ameliorate, refine; **—аться, —иться** *v.* improve; **—ающийся** *a.* improving, progressing; **—ение** *n.* improvement, amendment, refinement, development; **—енный** *a.* improved.
Ульбрихта шаровой фотометр Ulbricht sphere photometer.
ульрихит *m.* ulrichite.
ультра— *prefix* ultra—, excessively; *see also* **сверх—.**
ультраакуст/ика *f.* ultrasonics; **—ический** *a.* ultrasonic, supersonic, ultraacoustic.
ультрабазит *m.* ultrabasite.
ультравысокая частота ultrahigh frequency.
ультрадин *m.* ultradyne.
ультразвук *m.* ultrasonics, ultrasound, supersound; **—овой** *a.* supersonic (velocity); ultrasonic (frequency); **—овая решетка** ultrasonic grating.
ультраионизационный потенциал ultraionization potential.

ультракороткие волны ultrashort waves.
ультралюминесценция *f.* ultraluminescence.
ультрамалое количество trace quantity.
ультрамикро/весы *pl.* ultramicrobalance; **—метр** *m.* ultramicrometer; **—н** *m.* ultramicron.
ультрамикроскоп *m.* ultramicroscope; **—ический** *a.* ultramicroscopic.
ультрамикротом *m.* ultramicrotome.
ультрамикрохим/ический *a.* ultramicrochemical; **—ия** *f.* ultramicrochemistry.
ультраосновные породы ultrabasic rocks.
ультрарелятивистский *a.* ultrarelativistic, extremely relativistic.
ультра/тауметр *m.* ultra-taumeter; **—тепловой** *a.* epithermal.
ультрафильтр *m.* ultrafilter; **—ация** *f.* ultrafiltration.
ультрафиолет *m.*, **—овый** *a.* ultraviolet.
ультрацентрифуг/а *f.* ultracentrifuge; **—ирование** *n.* ultracentrifuging.
ультрачистый *a.* extremely pure.
ум. *abbr.* (**умер**) deceased.
у.м. *abbr.* (**уровень моря**) sea level.
ум *m.* mind, intellect, understanding.
умаление *n.* disparagement, depreciation.
умалить *see* **умалять.**
умалчив/ание *see* **умолчание**; **—ать** *v.* pass over in silence; hold back.
умалять *v.* disparage, depreciate.
умбра *f.* umber.
уме/лый *a.* skillful, expert; **—ние** *n.* skill, ability.
уменьш/аемое *n.* minuend; **—ать, —ить** *v.* diminish, reduce, decrease; minimize; abate; **—ать вдвое** reduce one-half; **—аться, —иться** *v.* diminish, decrease, drop, fall, decline, abate; **—ение** *n.* decrease, reduction; attenuation; abatement; **—енный** *a.* diminished, decreased, reduced; **—ительный** *a.* diminishing; diminutive.
умерение *n.* moderation, tempering, mitigation.
умеренн/о *adv.* moderately; **—ость** *f.* moderation; **—ый** *a.* moderate, medium, temperate; **—ый ветер** moderate breeze (Beaufort number 4); **—ый пояс** temperate zone.
умереть *see* **умирать.**
умерить *see* **умерять.**
умертвить *see* **умерщвлять.**
умерший *a.* dead, deceased.
умерщвл/ение *n.* killing, destruction; **—ять** *v.* kill, destroy.
умерять *v.* moderate.
уместн/ость *f.* pertinence, propriety, relevancy; **—ый** *a.* pertinent, appropriate, relevant; timely, opportune.
уметь *v.* be able, know how.
УМЗ *abbr.* (**Узбекский металлургический завод**) Uzbek Metallurgical Plant.
умир/ание *n.*, **—ающий** *a.* dying; **—ать** *v.* die.
умир/ить, —отворить, —отворять, —ять *v.* pacify, conciliate.
УМН *abbr.* (**Успехи математических наук**) Progress of Mathematical Sciences (journal).
умно *adv.* cleverly, wisely, sensibly.
умнож/ать, —ить *v.* increase, augment; multiply; **у. на** multiply by; **—аться** *v.* increase; be multiplied; **—ающий** *a.* multiplying, multiplier; **—ающий электрод, —ительный электрод** dynode; **—ение** *n.* increase; multiplication; **коэффициент —ения** multiplication factor; **—енный** *a.* increased; multiplied; **—енный на *n*** *n*-tuple; **—итель** *m.* multiplier.
умный *a.* intelligent, clever, sensible wise.
Умова-Пойнтинга вектор Poynting vector.
умозаключ/ать *v.* conclude, infer; **—ение** *n.* conclusion, inference.
умозр/ение *n.* speculation; **—ительный** *a.* speculative.
умолч/ание *n.* omission; passing over in silence; **—ать** *see* **умалчивать.**
умственный *a.* mental, intellectual.
умформер *m.* dynamotor, motor-generator.
умыв/ание *n.* washing; **—ать** *v.* wash.
умыс/ел *m.* design, intention; **без —ла** unintentionally.
умыть *see* **умывать.**
умышленн/о *adv.* intentionally, deliber-

ately; —**ость** *f*. deliberateness; —**ый** *a*. intentional, deliberate.
унарный *a*. unary, one-component.
унаследовать *v*. inherit.
ундекан *m*. undecane, hendecane.
ундор *m*. undor.
ундулир/овать *v*. (geo.) undulate; —**ующий** *a*. undulating.
унести *see* **уносить.**
Унзольда-Крамерса теория Unsöld-Kramer theory.
УНИАДИ *abbr*. (**Украинский научно-исследовательский аэродинамический институт**) Ukrainian Aerodynamics Scientific Research Institute.
унивариантный *a*. univariant.
универсальн/о *adv*. universally; —**ость** *f*. universality, generality; —**ый** *a*. universal, general-purpose, all-purpose, multipurpose, versatile; —**ый прибор** multimeter; —**ый реактор** multipurpose reactor; —**ый шарнир** universal (or gimbal) joint; —**ая пересчетная схема** multiscaler; —**ая постоянная** universal constant.
университет *m*., —**ский** *a*. university.
уникальный *a*. unique.
унимодулярный *a*. (math.) unimodular.
униполярн/ость *f*. unipolarity; —**ый** *a*. unipolar; homopolar; —**ый генератор** homopolar generator.
унисон *m*. unison.
унитарн/ость *f*. unitarity; —**ый** *a*. unitary.
унификация *f*. unification.
унифилярный *a*. unifilar.
унифицировать *v*. unify.
уничтож/ать, —**ить** *v*. annihilate, destroy, suppress, nullify, cancel; —**аться взаимно** cancel out; **взаимно —ающиеся погрешности** compensating errors; —**ение** *n*. annihilation; cancellation; destruction; —**енный** *a*. annihilated; canceled; destroyed; —**ительный** *a*. destructive.
уния *f*. union.
унос *m*. carrying away; entrainment; removal, disposal; —**ить** *v*. carry away, remove.
ун-т *abbr*. (**университет**) university.
унтертон *m*. (acous.) undertone, difference tone.
унция *f*. ounce.

УНЧ *abbr*. (**усилитель низкой частоты**) low-frequency amplifier (lfa).
УОВТИ *abbr*. [**Уральское отделение Всесоюзного теплотехнического института (им. Ф. Дзержинского)**] F. Dzerzhinskii Ural Branch of the All-Union Heat-Engineering Institute.
Уорда теорема Ward theorem.
упад/ок *m*. decline, decay, decrease; —**очный** *a*. decadent.
упаков/ать, —**ывать** *v*. pack; —**ка** *f*. package, packing; wrapping, wrapper; —**ный множитель** packing fraction; —**очный** *a*., —**ывание** *n*. packing.
упасть *v*. fall; decline.
упирать, упереть *v*. rest, place; —**ся** *v*. rest; thrust; persist in; —**ся в** rest (or abut) against.
упла/та *f*. payment; —**тить,** —**чивать** *v*. pay.
уплотнен/ие *n*. condensation, consolidation, thickening, compaction; crowding; sealing, jointing; packing, seal, gasket; **у. грунта** soil compaction; —**ный** *a*. compressed, consolidated, compacted; packed, tightened, sealed.
уплотнитель *m*., —**ный** *a*. thickening; packing, sealing.
уплотн/ить, —**ять** *v*. condense, thicken; compress; pack, tighten; seal; consolidate.
уплотняющ/ий *a*. thickening; packing, sealing; **у. газ** blanketing gas; —**ее кольцо** packing (or gasket) ring.
уплощен/ие *n*. (math.) flattening; —**ный** *a*. flattened.
уплы/вать, —**ть** *v*. float away; elapse.
уподоб/иться, —**ляться** *v*. become similar to.
уполномоч/ие *n*. authorization; power of attorney; —**енный** *a*. authorized; *m*. authorized agent, representative; —**ивать,** —**ить** *v*. authorize, empower.
упомин/ание *n*. mention, reference, citation; —**ать** *v*. mention, cite, refer to.
упомянут/ый *a*. mentioned, cited; —**ь** *see* **упоминать.**
упор *m*., —**ка** *f*. support, rest; stop,

catch, detent, curb; thrust block; emphasis; **делать у. на** emphasize.

упорно *adv.* stubbornly, tenaciously, persistently; **—сть** *f.* stubbornness, tenacity, persistence.

упорн/ый *a.* stubborn, unyielding, persistent; stop, thrust; *suffix* —proof, —resistant; **у. болт** lock (carrying, fixing) bolt; **у. подшипник** thrust bearing; **—ое давление** thrust.

упорство *see* **упорность**; **—вать** *v.* persist in.

упорядоч/ение, —ивание *n.* order, ordering; regulating; **процесс —ения** (cryst.) order-disorder transformation; **—енность** *f.* (degree of) order, ordering; **—енный** *a.* ordered, orderly; regulated; organized; **—ивать, —ить** *v.* regulate; order; **—ивающийся сплав** ordered alloy.

употребит/ельность *f.* use; frequency; usualness; **—ельный** *a.* common, customary; **—ь** *see* **употреблять.**

употребл/ение *n.* use, employment; **—енный** *a.* used; **—ять** *v.* use, employ.

упр. *abbr.* (**управление**) administration, management; administration office; (**управляющий**) manager, director.

управлен/ие *n.* control; steering; government; administration, management, board, directorate; administration office; **автоматическое у.** automatic control; **главное у.** main administration, board; **у. на расстоянии** remote control; **выключатель —ия** master switch; **коэффициент —ия** (elec.) control ratio; **щит —ия** control board.

управляем/ость *f.* controllability; **—ый** *a.* controllable; controlled, guided; **—ый вручную** hand-operated; **—ый реактор** controlled reactor; **—ый снаряд** guided missile.

управлять *v.* control, manage; operate, drive; govern; direct.

управляющ/ий *a.* control, controlling; master; managing; operating; *m.* manager, director; **у. вал** camshaft; **у. импульс** master (or driving) pulse; **у. стержень** control rod; **у. электрод** control electrode; **—ая сетка** control grid; **—ее поле** guiding field; **—ее сочленение** master joint (of manipulator); **—ее устройство** control (or guidance) system.

упражн/ение *n.* exercise, practice; **—ять** *v.* exercise; **—яться** *v.* exercise, practice.

упраздн/ение *n.* abolition; **—ить, —ять** *v.* abolish.

упрежд/ать, упредить *v.* lead, advance, precede; anticipate, predict; **—ающее зажигание** advanced ignition, preignition; **—ение** *n.* lead, advance; anticipation, prediction.

упростить *see* **упрощать.**

упроч/ение *n.* strengthening; reinforcement; fixing, securing; **—ивать, —ить** *v.* strengthen; fix; reinforce.

упрочн/ение *n.* hardening; strengthening; *see also* **упрочение**; **—ять** *v.* harden; strengthen.

упрощ/ать *v.* simplify; **—ение** *n.* simplification; **—енный** *a.* simplified.

упруг/ий *a.* elastic; resilient; **у. гистерезис намагниченности** hysteresis of strain vs. magnetization; **у. зажим** spring clip; **коэффициент —ой связи** force constant (of oscillator); **—ое столкновение** elastic collision.

упруго— *prefix* elastic, elastically.

упруго/вязкий *a.* viscoelastic; **—оптический** *a.* elasto-optical; **—пластический** *a.* elastico-plastic.

упругост/ь *f.* elasticity; resilience; **у. пара** vapor pressure; **модуль —и** modulus of elasticity; **предел —и** elastic limit.

упрям/ство *n.* persistence, stubbornness; **—ый** *a.* persistent, stubborn.

упу/скать, —стить *v.* let escape; omit, overlook, miss; **у. из виду** lose sight of, overlook; **—щение** *n.* omission, neglect; **—щенный** *a.* omitted, neglected, overlooked.

УПЧ *abbr.* (**усилитель промежуточной частоты**) intermediate frequency amplifier (ifa).

упятер/енный *a.* quintuple, fivefold; **—ить, —ять** *v.* increase fivefold.

ур. *abbr.* (**уральский**) Ural.

уравнение *n.* equation; equating; equalizing; **у.** (**барической**) **тенденции** (meteor.) tendency equation; **у. возраста** age equation; **у. в полных**

дифференциалах exact differential equation; **у. в частных производных** partial differential equation; **у. непрерывности** equation of continuity; **у. переноса** transport equation; **у. перехода** transition (or joining) equation; **у. распространения тепла** heat equation; **у. скорости реакции** rate law of reaction; **у. совместности** equation of compatibility; **у. состояния** equation of state; **у. состояния идеального газа** ideal gas law.

уравнив/ание *n.* equalization, compensation; leveling; **—ать** *v.* equate; equalize, compensate; level.

уравнитель *m.* equalizer, balancer; leveler; **у. постоянного тока** direct-current balancer; **—ный** *a.* equalizing, compensating, balancing; leveling; **—ный резервуар** equalizing reservoir.

уравновесить *see* **уравновешивать.**

уравновешенн/ость *f.* equilibrium, balance, steadiness; **—ый** *a.* equilibrated, compensated, balanced, counterpoised; level, steady; **—ый мост** balanced bridge.

уравновешив/ание *n.* equilibration, balancing, counterpoising, compensation; **—ать** *v.* equilibrate, balance, counterbalance, counteract, equalize, compensate; **—ающий** *a.* equalizing, balancing, compensating.

уравнять *see* **уравнивать.**

ураган *m.*, **—ный** *a.* hurricane.

ураконит *m.* uraconite.

Уралгницветмет *abbr.* (**Уральский государственный научно-исследовательский институт цветных металлов**) Ural State Scientific Research Institute of Nonferrous Metals.

уралортит *m.* uralorthite.

Уралфизхим *abbr.* (**Уральский научно-исследовательский физико-химический институт**) Ural Scientific Research Institute of Physics and Chemistry.

Уралфти *abbr.* (**Уральский физико-технический институт**) Ural Physico-Technical Institute.

уральский *a.* Ural, Uralian.

Уран Uranus.

уран *m.* uranium (U); **у.-графитовый реактор** graphite-moderated uranium reactor; **двуокись —а, закись —а** uranium dioxide, uranous oxide; **окись —а** uranic oxide, uranium trioxide.

уран/ат *m.* uranate, tobernite; **—ид** *m.* uranide.

уранил *m.*, **—овый, —ьный** *a.* uranyl; **уксуснокислый у.** uranyl acetate, uranium acetate; **хлористый у.** uranyl chloride; uranium oxychloride.

уранинит *m.* uraninite, pitchblende.

уранисто— *prefix* uranous, uranoso—.

уранистый *a.* uranium, uranous.

уранит *m.* uranite; **известковый у.** lime uranite, autunite; **—овый** *a.* uranitic.

уранниобит *m.* uranniobite.

урано— *prefix* uranium, uranic.

урановокисл/ый *a.* uranic acid, uranate (of); **у. натрий** sodium uranate; **у. уран** uranous-uranic oxide, uranyl uranate; **—ая соль** uranate.

уранов/ый *a.* uranium; **у. желтый** uranium yellow; **у. покров** uranium blanket; **—ая кислота** uranic acid; **—ая слюдка** torbernite; **—ая смолка, —ая смоляная обманка, —ая смоляная руда** pitchblende; **—ая чернь** sooty uranite.

урано/добывающая промышленность uranium-mining industry; **—графия** *f.* uranography.

урано/лепедит *m.* uranolepidite; **—лит** *m.* uranolyte.

уранометр/ический *a.* uranometric; **—ия** *f.* uranometry.

ураннониобит *m.* uranoniobite.

ураноносный *a.* uranium-bearing.

уранопилит *m.* uranopilite.

урано/-радиевый ряд uranium-radium series; **—содержащий** *a.* uranium-bearing, uraniferous.

урано/спинит *m.* uranospinite; **—сферит** *m.* uranospherite; **—таллит** *m.* uranothallite; **—темнит** *m.* uranotemnite; **—тил** *m.* uranotile; **—фан** *m.* uranophane; **—торианит** *m.* uranothorianite; **—торит** *m.* uranothorite; **—хальцит** *m.* uranochalcite; **—цирцит** *m.* uranocircite; **—шпатит** *m.* uranospathite.

урацил *m.* uracil.

ургит *m.* urgite.
ургон *m.*, **—ский ярус** Urgonian stage.
урегулиров/ание *n.* regulation; settlement; **—ать** *v.* regulate, regularize; settle; adjust.
урез/ать, —ывать *v.* cut down, curtail, reduce, abridge; **—ка** *f.* abridgment, curtailment; **—ывание** *n.* cutting down, curtailment.
уриконский *a.* Uriconian.
урна *f.* urn.
ур-ние *abbr.* (**уравнение**) equation.
уров/ень *m.* level; **у. возбуждения** excited level; **у. моря** sea level; **над —нем моря** above sea level; (**опорная**) **отметка —ня** bench mark.
уровнемер *m.* content (or level) gauge.
урод/ливость *f.* deformity; **—ливый** *a.* abnormal; deformed; **—овать** *v.* disfigure, deform; **—ство** *n.* deformity.
уроженец *m.* native (of).
урок *m.* lesson.
урон *m.* loss; damage; **наносить у.** damage.
уронить *v.* drop.
Урсиды Ursids (meteors).
ус *m.* whisker.
усад/ка *f.*, **—очный** *a.* shrinkage; **давать —ку** shrink; **—очная раковина** shrinkage cavity (or hole); **—очное напряжение** shrinkage stress.
усваив/ание *n.* adoption, assimilation; mastering, understanding; **—ать** *v.* adopt, assimilate; master, understand.
усво/ение *see* **усваивание**; **—ивать, —ить** *see* **усваивать**; **—яемость** *f.* assimilability; comprehensibility.
усекать *v.* cut off, truncate.
усерд/ие *n.* diligence; zeal; **—но** *adv.* diligently; **—ный** *a.* diligent, industrious; zealous.
усечен/ие *n.* cutting off, truncation; termination; **—ный** *a.* cut off, truncated; **—ный конус** frustum of a cone; **—ная пирамида** frustum of a pyramid.
усечь *see* **усекать.**
усеянный *a.* strewn, scattered, dotted.
усик *see* **ус.**
усилен/ие *n.* strengthening, reinforcement; amplification, intensification, gain, enhancement; **у. антенны** antenna (power) gain; **у. антенны по полю** antenna field gain; **газовое у.** gas multiplication; **у. (по) мощности** power amplification; **у. с обратной связью** regenerative amplification; **коэффициент —ия** amplification factor, mu factor, gain; enhancement ratio.
усиленн/о *adv.* intensely, strenuously, strongly; **—ый** *a.* strengthened, reinforced; enhanced, intensified; amplified, magnified; strenuous; **—ый закон больших чисел** strong law of large numbers; **—ый реактор** enriched (or enhanced) reactor.
усиливать *v.* strengthen, reinforce; intensify, enhance; amplify; magnify; **—ся** *v.* become stronger, intensify, increase; make an effort.
усиливающ/ий *a.* strengthening; intensifying; amplifying, magnifying; **у. экран** intensifying screen; **—ая интерференция** constructive interference.
усилие *n.* stress, force; effort, endeavor; *see also* **сила.**
усилитель *m.* amplifier; intensifier; booster; **у. высокой частоты** high-frequency amplifier; **у. импульсов** pulse amplifier; **у. на расстроенных контурах** stagger-tuned amplifier; **у. на сопротивлениях** resistance-coupled amplifier; **—ный** *a.* amplifier, amplifying; intensifying; boosting; **—ная лампа** amplifier tube.
усилить *see* **усиливать.**
ускальзывать *see* **ускользать.**
ускольз/ание *n.* escape; **—ать, —нуть** *v.* escape, evade.
ускорен/ие *n.* acceleration, hastening; **добавочное у., поворотное у. точки** Coriolis acceleration; **у. силы тяжести** acceleration of gravity; **—ный** *a.* accelerated.
ускоритель *m.* accelerator; accelerant; **у. ионов** ion accelerator; **у. с бегущей волной** traveling-wave accelerator; **у. с жесткой фокусировкой** strong-focusing accelerator; **четвертьволновый у.** quarter-wave accelerator; **—ный** *a.* accelerating; accelerative; **—ная трубка** accelerator tube.

ускор/ить, —ять *v.* accelerate; hasten, expedite; **—яющий** *a.* accelerating.
уславливаться *see* **условиться.**
услать *see* **усылать.**
усл. ед. *abbr.* (**условная единица**) arbitrary unit.
услов/ие *n.* condition; restriction, stipulation; convention; **у. для знака** sign convention; **у. коммутации** commutation rule; **—ия опыта** experimental arrangement (or conditions); **под —ием, при —ии, с —ием** on condition that, provided; **ставить —ием** stipulate; **при прочих равных —иях** (all) other things being equal.
услов/иться *v.* agree upon, arrange, stipulate; **—ленный** *a.* agreed-upon, stipulated, fixed.
условно *adv.* conditionally; by a convention; **—сть** *f.* conditionality, relativity; arbitrariness; convention.
условн/ый *a.* conditional; relative; conventional, nominal, arbitrary; **у. знак, —ое обозначение** legend; arbitrary (or conventional) symbol; **у. рефлекс** conditioned reflex; **—ая вероятность** conditional probability; **—ая единица** arbitrary unit.
усложн/ение *n.* complication; **—ить, —ять** *v.* complicate.
услуг/а *f.* service, favor; **оказать —у** render a service.
услышать *v.* hear.
усматривать *v.* perceive, discern.
усмир/ить, —ять *v.* pacify; suppress.
усмотр/ение *n.* discretion, judgment; **—еть** *see* **усматривать.**
усовершенствов/ание *n.* improvement, refinement, advancement, perfection; **—анный** *a.* improved, refined, advanced, perfected; **—ать** *v.* improve, develop, perfect, refine.
усомниться *v.* doubt, have misgivings.
Усп. *abbr.* (**Успехи**) Progress, Advances (in journal titles).
успе/вать, —ть *v.* succeed; progress.
успех *m.* success; progress, advance; **делать —и** succeed; improve, advance, make progress.
успешн/о *adv.* successfully; **—ость** *f.* successfulness, success; **—ый** *a.* successful.
успокаив/ание *n.* (met.) killing (of steel); *see also* **успокоение**; **—ать** *v.* damp (out); quiet; **—аться** *v.* slacken, abate; quiet down; **—ающий** *a.* damping; quieting.
успоко/ение *n.* damping; relaxation; quieting; **—енный** *a.* damped; (met.) killed (steel); quiet; **—ившийся** *a.* quiescent; abated.
успокоитель *m.* damper; **—ный** *a.* damping; quieting.
успокоить *see* **успокаивать.**
Усп. физ. наук *abbr. see* **УФН.**
Усп. хим. *abbr.* (**Успехи химии**) Progress of Chemistry (journal).
усредн/ение *n.* averaging; (chem.) neutralization; (min.) blending; **—енный** *a.* average, averaged; (chem.) neutralized; **—итель** *m.* averager; (chem.) neutralizer; **—ять** *v.* average; (chem.) neutralize.
УССР *abbr. see* **Украинская ССР.**
уст. *abbr.* (**установленный**) established, determined; (**устарелый**) obsolete.
устав *m.* regulations, rules.
уставать *v.* tire.
устав/ить, —лять *v.* arrange, place; **—ка** *f.* placing.
устаивать *see* **устоять.**
устал/ость *f.* fatigue; **у. при ударе** impact fatigue; **предел —ости** fatigue (or endurance) limit; **—остная прочность** fatigue strength; **—ый** *a.* tired, fatigued.
устанавлив/ание *see* **установка, установление**; **—ать** *v.* set, place, mount; establish, determine, ascertain, locate; adjust, set; install, erect; **—ающийся** *a.* being established; transient; adjustable.
установивш/ийся *a.* steady, steady-state, stationary, stable, sustained; settled, stabilized; **у. ход** steady running, smooth operation; **—аяся погода** settled weather; **—аяся ползучесть** steady-state creep; **—ееся движение** steady (-state) motion; **—ееся мнение** prevailing opinion; **—ееся состояние** steady state.
установк/а *f.* setting, placing, arrangement; assembly, mounting, installation; establishment; adjustment; plant; set, equipment, apparatus; facility; aim, purpose; **у. кристалла**

crystal derivation; **у. на место** positioning; **у. на нуль** zero adjustment; **у. на фокус** focusing; **у. приборов** instrumentation; **у. силовая** *see under* **силовая установка**; **иметь —у на** aim at.

установл/ение *n.* establishment; setting; determination; build-up; ascertainment; **—енный** *a.* established, determined, fixed; standard, regulation; mounted, installed; adjusted; **—енный киловатт** installed kilowatt; **—ять** *see* **устанавливать.**

установочн/ый *a.* adjusting; **у. винт** set screw, adjusting screw; **у. механизм** adjusting (or setting) mechanism; **—ое приспособление** adjusting device.

устар. *abbr.* (**устарелый**) obsolete.

устар/елость *f.* obsolescence, obsoleteness; **—евший, —елый** *a.* obsolete, out of date; **—еть** *v.* become obsolete.

устать *see* **уставать.**

устный *a.* oral, verbal; **у. счет** mental arithmetic.

устой *m.* abutment, basis, foundation.

устойчив/о *adv.* stably, steadily, firmly; persistently, consistently; **—ость** *f.* stability; steadiness; resistance; **—ый** *a.* stable; steady; durable, resistant; *suffix* —proof, —resistant; **—ая орбита** stable orbit.

устоять *v.* resist, withstand.

устраивать *v.* arrange; organize; place, establish, install.

устран/ение *n.* removal, elimination; **—имый** *a.* removable; **—ить, —ять** *v.* remove, eliminate, dispose of.

устр-во *abbr.* (**устройство**) device, mechanism.

устрем/ить, —лять *v.* direct, turn; rush; **—ление** *n.* directing, tendency; rush; aspiration.

устроит/ель *m.* organizer; **—ь** *see* **устраивать.**

устройство *n.* device, mechanism, equipment, installation; facility; arrangement, layout, design; system, organization, construction.

уступ *m.* step, offset, recess, shoulder, ledge, projection; (geo.) bench, terrace; **—ами** stepped, staggered, graduated; benched, terraced.

уступ/ать, —ить *v.* yield, concede; be inferior to; **—ка** *f.* concession.

уступчатый *a.* stepped, staggered.

уступчив/ость *f.* compliance; **—ый** *a.* compliant, yielding.

устье *n.* orifice, mouth, outlet, opening; **у. реки** river mouth, estuary.

усугуб/ить, —лять *v.* increase, aggravate, worsen; **—ление** *n.* aggravation.

усылать *v.* send away.

усыпать *v.* strew, scatter.

ута/ивание *n.*, **—йка** *f.* concealment; suppression; **—ивать, —ить** *v.* conceal; suppress.

утвердительн/о *adv.* affirmatively; **—ый** *a.* affirmative, positive.

утвер/дить, —ждать *v.* assert, state, maintain; confirm, corroborate; consolidate, strengthen; approve.

утвержден/ие *n.* assertion, statement; confirmation, corroboration; approval; strengthening, consolidation; **—ный** *a.* asserted; confirmed, corroborated; approved.

утекать *v.* flow away; leak.

утес *m.* rock; **—истый** *a.* rocky; steep, precipitous.

утеч/ка *f.* leakage, leak, escape, loss; **у. нейтронов** neutron leakage (or streaming); **—ь** *see* **утекать.**

утилиз/ация *f.* utilization; **—ировать** *v.* utilize, recover; **—ируемый** *a.* utilizable, available.

утилитарный *a.* utilitarian.

утих/ание *n.* abatement, subsidence, fading; **—ать, —нуть** *v.* abate, subside; **—ший** *a.* abated, moderated.

утол/стить, —щать *v.* thicken; **—щение** *n.* thickening, bulge, node; **—щенный** *a.* thickened.

утом/ительный *a.* tedious, fatiguing; **—ить, —лять** *v.*, **—ление** *n.* fatigue; **—ленный** *a.* fatigued, weary.

утон/ение *n.* thinning, tapering; **—енный** *a.* thinned, tapered; **—ить** *v.* thin, narrow down.

утонуть *see* **утопать.**

утонч/ать, —ить *v.* thin, thin out; narrow down; **—аться, —иться** *v.* become thinner, narrow down, taper;

—**ающийся** *a.* tapering; —**ение** *n.* thinning (down); tapering.

утоп/ать, —**ить,** —**лять** *v.* sink, submerge; —**ление** *n.* sinking; —**ленный** *a.* sunk, countersunk, recessed; submerged; buried.

уточн/ение *n.* making more precise (or accurate); more precise definition; refinement; —**енный** *a.* more accurate, precise, refined; —**ить,** —**ять** *v.* determine (or define) more accurately, refine.

утраивать *v.* triple.

утрамбов/анный *a.* rammed; —**ать,** —**ывать** *v.* ram; —**ка** *f.*, —**ывание** *n.* ramming.

утра/та *f.*, —**чивание** *n.* loss; —**тить,** —**чивать** *v.* lose; —**ченный** *a.* lost.

утриров/ание *n.*, —**ка** *f.* exaggeration; —**ать** *v.* exaggerate.

утр/о *n.* morning; **в 5 часов** —**а** at 5 A.M.

утро/ение *n.* tripling; —**енный** *a.* triple, threefold; —**итель** *m.* tripler; —**ить** *see* **утраивать.**

утром *adv.* A.M.; in the morning.

утру/дить, —**ждать** *v.* inconvenience.

утюг *m.* (flat) iron.

утяжел/ение *n.* loading; weighting; —**енный** *a.* heavy, weighted; —**ить,** —**ять** *v.* load; weight.

УФ *abbr.* (**усилитель фототоков**) photocurrent amplifier; (**ультрафиолетовый**) ultraviolet.

УФАН *abbr.* (**Уральский филиал Академии наук СССР**) Ural Branch of the Academy of Sciences, USSR.

УФН *abbr.* (**Успехи физических наук**) Progress of Physical Science (journal) (Soviet Physics—Uspekhi).

УФТИ *abbr.* (**Украинский научно-исследовательский физико-технический институт**) Ukrainian Scientific Research Institute of Physics and Technology.

ухабистый *a.* bumpy, uneven.

ухват *m.* grip; grab; —**ить,** —**ывать** *v.* grip, grasp.

ухищрение *n.* device, contrivance.

ухо *n.* ear; lug, hanger; **тугой на у.** hard of hearing.

уход *m.* departure; drift; withdrawal; resignation; care, servicing, handling, maintenance; **у. мощности** power drift; **у. частоты** frequency drift; —**ить** *v.* depart, withdraw; elapse; —**ящий** *a.* departing, leaving.

ухудш/ать, —**ить** *v.* worsen, impair; —**аться,** —**иться** *v.* deteriorate; —**ение** *n.* worsening, deterioration.

уцелеть *v.* escape destruction, be left intact.

уцеп/иться, —**ляться** *v.* seize, grasp, cling (to).

уч. *abbr.* (**ученый**) scientist; scientific; learned; (**ученые**) scientists.

участв/овать *v.* participate, collaborate; —**ующий** *a.* participating; *m.* participant.

участ/ие *n.* share, participation, collaboration; interest; **принимать у.** participate, take interest in; **при** —**ии** with the assistance of, with the cooperation of.

участить *see* **учащать.**

участковый *a.* section, sectional; district.

участник *m.* participant, collaborator; member.

участок *m.* part, section; region, interval, segment, range; district; strip, lot, plot.

учащ/ать *v.* increase the frequency of; —**ение** *n.* increase of frequency.

учащий *m.* teacher; —**ся** *m.* student.

уч. г. *abbr.* (**учебный год**) academic year.

Учгиз *abbr.* (**Государственное издательство учебно-педагогической литературы**) State Press of Textbooks and Pedagogical Literature.

учеба *f.* studies, training.

учебн. *abbr.* (**учебник**) textbook, manual; (**учебный**) educational, training.

учебник *m.* textbook, manual.

учебн/ый *a.* educational, training; **у. год** academic year; **у. план** curriculum; —**ое заведение** educational institution, school; —**ые пособия** school equipment.

учен/ие *n.* study, learning; teaching, doctrine, theory; —**ик** *m.*, —**ица** *f.* pupil, student; apprentice; —**ический** *a.* student; —**ичество** *n.* apprenticeship.

учено *adv.* scientifically; —**сть** *f.* erudition.

учен. сек. *abbr.* (**ученый секретарь**) scientific secretary.

учен/ый *a.* scientific, learned, academic, scholarly; *m.* scientist, scholar; **у.-атомник** atomic scientist; **у. секретарь** scientific secretary; **у. совет** academic council; **у. сотрудник** scientific collaborator; **у. специалист** scientific specialist; **у.-ядерник** nuclear scientist; **—ая степень** academic degree; **—ое звание** academic rank; **—ое общество** learned (or scientific) society.

учесть *see* **учитывать.**

учет *m.* computation; taking account of, consideration; registration; discount; **брать на у.** register; **без —а** not allowing for, neglecting; **при —е, с —ом** taking account of, allowing for.

учетвер/ение *n.* quadrupling, quadruplication; **—енный** *a.* quadruplicate, quadruple; **—ить, —ять** *v.* quadruple.

учетный *a.* registration; **у. бланк** registration blank (or form).

Уч. зап. *abbr.* (**Ученые записки**) Scientific Annals (journal).

училище *n.* school, college.

учин/ить, —ять *v.* cause; commit.

учитель *m.*, **—ница** *f.* teacher, instructor; **—ский** *a.* teacher's; **—ство** *n.* teaching duties; teaching staff; **—ствовать** *v.* teach.

учитыв/ание *n.* taking into account; **—ать** *v.* take into account, consider, allow for; **не —ая** disregarding, neglecting.

учить *v.* teach, instruct, train; learn, study; **—ся** *v.* learn, study.

учре/дитель *m.* founder, establisher; **—дить, —ждать** *v.* found, establish, set up, institute; **—ждение** *n.* establishment, institution.

уч. сотр. *abbr.* (**ученый сотрудник**) scientific collaborator.

уч. спец. *abbr.* (**ученый специалист**) scientific specialist.

учтем *future pl. and imperative pl. of* **учитывать,** we shall consider, let us consider.

учтенный *a.* taken into consideration, allowed for; computed, evaluated.

ушестер/енный *a.* sextuple, sixfold; **—ить, —ять** *v.* sextuple, increase sixfold.

ушир/ение *n.* widening, broadening, spread; **—ительный** *a.* widening, broadening; **—ить, —ять** *v.* widen, broaden.

уш/ко *n.* ear; lug, hold, shackle; eye; sleeve piece; **—ной** *a.* ear, aural.

ущелье *n.* gorge, ravine, canyon.

ущем/ить, —лять *v.* pinch; jam; infringe.

ущерб *m.* damage, loss; detriment, disadvantage; **в у.** to the detriment of; **наносить у.** damage, injure, impair; **на —е** on the decline, waning.

уэвеллит *m.* whewellite.

уэлльсит *m.* wellsite.

Уэнлокский ярус Wenlock stage.

уязвим/ость *f.* vulnerability; **—ый** *a.* vulnerable.

уярчение *n.* brightening; **у. к краю** (astr.) limb brightening.

уясн/ение *n.* explanation, clarification; understanding; illustration; **—енный** *a.* explained; illustrated; **—ить, —ять** *v.* explain, clarify; understand; illustrate, exemplify.

Ф

ф *abbr.* (**фарада**) farad; (**ферми**) fermi; (**фот**) phot; **ф.** (**фунт**) pound (lb.).

Ф *abbr.* (**Фаренгейт**) Fahrenheit (°F).

Ф [*in steel mark* (**ванадий**)] vanadium (V).

Фабри и Перо эталон Fabry and Perot etalon.

фабрик/а *f.* factory, plant, mill, works, shop; **—ант** *m.* manufacturer; **—ат** *m.* manufactured product; **—ация** *f.* manufacture, fabrication; **—овать** *v.* manufacture, produce, fabricate.

Фабриций Fabricius (lunar crater).

фабричный *a.* factory, manufacturing.

фаз/а *f.*, **—ис** *m.* phase; stage; **правило фаз** phase rule; **—ирование** *n.* phasing; **—ированный** *a.* phased; **—ировать** *v.* phase; **—ировка** *f.*, **—ирующий** *a.* phasing.

фазитрон *m.* phasitron.
фазный *see* **фазовый.**
фазо— *prefix* phase.
фазо/вибратор *m.* phase-sensitive vibrator; **—вращатель** *m.* phase shifter; phase-shift control; phase inverter.
фазов/ый *a.* phase; **ф. анализ** phase (or phase shift) analysis; **ф. множитель** phase factor; **ф. переход** phase transition; **ф. сдвиг** phase shift; **ф. угол пробега** (elec.) transit phase angle; **—ая модуляция** phase modulation; **—ая пластинка** phase plate; **—ое превращение** phase transition.
фазо/выравниватель *m.* phase equalizer; **—импульсная модуляция** pulse-position modulation; **—компенсатор** *m.* phase compensator.
фазометр *m.*, **—ический** *a.* phase meter.
фазор *m.* phasor.
фазо/расщепитель *m.* phase splitter; **—регулятор** *m.* phase shifter; **—сдвигающий** *a.* phase-shifting.
фазотрон *m.* phasotron, synchrocyclotron, frequency-modulated cyclotron.
фазо/тропия *f.* phasotropy; **—указатель** *m.* phase indicator.
ФАИ *abbr.* (**Международная авиационная федерация**) International Aeronautical Federation (FAI); (**Физико-агрономический институт**) Institute of Agricultural Physics.
файрфильдит *m.* fairfieldite.
фак. *abbr.* (**факультет**) faculty, university department.
факел *m.*, **—ьный** *a.* flare; jet; (astr.) facula; **—ьная площадка** (astr.) facular plage, plage faculaire.
фако/идальный *a.* (petr.) phacoidal; **—лит** *m.* phacolite; **—метр** *m.* phacometer.
факсимил/е *n.*, **—ьный** *a.* facsimile.
факт *m.* fact; case; effect.
фактическ/и *adv.* by facts; in fact, practically, actually; **—ий** *a.* factual; actual; **—ое положение дела** actual state of affairs.
фактор *m.* factor; **—иал** *m.*, **—иальный** *a.* factorial; **ф.-пространство** *n.* factor space, quotient space.
факториз/ация *f.* factorization; **—ировать, —овать** *v.* factor.
факультативный *a.* optional, elective.
факультет *m.* faculty, university department.
Фалес Thales (lunar crater).
фалунит *m.* fahlunite.
фалькенгайнит *m.* falkenhaynite.
Фалькон Falcon (missile).
фальсифи/кация *f.*, **—цирование** *n.* falsification, adulteration; **—цировать** *v.* falsify, adulterate.
фальц *m.* rabbet, groove, furrow; **—евать** *v.* rabbet, groove; fold.
фальшивый *a.* false, spurious.
фаменский ярус Famennian stage.
фамилия *f.* family name, surname.
ФАН *abbr.* (**Филиал Академии наук СССР**) Branch of the Academy of Sciences, USSR.
фанер/а *f.*, **—ный** *a.* veneer, plywood; **клееная ф., многослойная ф.** plywood.
фанеро— *prefix* phanero—.
Фано функция Fano function.
фанта/зия *f.* fantasy, imagination; **—стический, —стичный** *a.* fantastic, fabulous.
фантастрон *m.*, **—ный** *a.*, **—ный генератор** phantastron.
фантом *m.*, **—ный** *a.* phantom.
фарад/а *f.* farad; **—еево темное пространство** Faraday dark space; **—ей** *m.* faraday, Faraday constant.
Фарадея закон Faraday law; **Ф. цилиндр** F. cylinder (or cup); **явление Ф.** F. effect.
фарад/изация *f.* faradization, faradism; **—метр** *m.* faradmeter.
фаратсихит *m.* faratsihite.
фарватер *m.* fairway, channel.
Фаренгейта шкала Fahrenheit scale.
фареэлит *m.* faröelite.
фармако/лит *m.* pharmacolite; **—сидерит** *m.* pharmacosiderite.
Фарри *see* **Ферри.**
фарту/к *m.*, **—чный** *a.* apron.
фарфор *m.*, **—овый** *a.* porcelain; **—овая глина** kaolin.
фас *m.* face, front.
фасад *m.* facade, front; (front) elevation; **боковой ф.** side elevation.
фасет *m.*, **—ка** *f.*, **—очный** *a.* facet.
фаска *f.* face, facet; flat; bevel, chamfer, chamfering.
фасонн/ый *a.* shaped; profiled; figured;

form; irregular; **—ая штамповка** molding.
Фата Моргана fata morgana.
фатерит *m.* vaterite.
Фау-2 V-2 (missile).
Фаулера ряд Fowler series (of helium spectrum lines).
фахверков/ый *a.* frame, framework; **—ое сооружение** framework.
фацелит *m.* facellite.
фацет *see* **фасет.**
фаци/альный *a.* (geo.) facies, facial, environmental; **—я** *f.* (geo.) facies, environment.
фаялит *m.* fayalite.
фаянс *see* **фаянсовый.**
Фаянса-Содди закон смещения Fajans-Soddy-Russell displacement law; **Ф.-С. правило** F.-S. law.
фаянсов/ый *a.*, **—ая посуда** faïence, glazed pottery.
ф. гр. *abbr.* (**федоровская группа**) Fedorov group.
Фебит Thebit (lunar crater).
февр. *abbr.* (**февраль**) February.
Федеративная Народная Республика Югославия Federal People's Republic of Yugoslavia.
Федеративная Республика Германия Federal Republic of Germany.
фединг *m.* fading.
федоровская группа Fedorov group.
Фезера правило Feather rule.
фейервер/к *m.* fireworks; **—очная ракета** flare rocket.
Фейнмана диаграмма Feynman diagram; **фейнмановская теория** F. theory.
фельзит *m.* felsite.
фелькнерит *m.* völknerite.
фельшебаниит *m.* felsöbanyite.
фемагастингсит *m.* femaghastingsite.
фен— *prefix* phen—.
фен *m.* (chem.) benzene, phene; (meteor.) foehn; air blast.
фенакит *m.* phenakite.
фенгит *m.* phengite.
феникохроит *m.* phoenicochroite.
Феникс Phoenix (Phe) (constellation).
фенил *m.* phenyl; **—арсоновая кислота** phenylarsonic acid.
фено— *prefix* pheno—.
феновый *a.* (meteor.) foehn.
фенокристалл *m.* phenocryst; **—ический** *a.* phenocrystalline, phanerocrystalline.
фенокси— *prefix* phenoxy—.
фенол *m.* phenol, carbolic acid.
феполог/ический *a.* phenological; **—ия** *f.* phenology.
фенольный *a.* phenol, phenolic.
феномен *m.* phenomenon; **—альный** *a.* phenomenal; **—ологический** *a.* phenomenological.
фенон *m.* phenone.
Феофил Theophilus (lunar crater).
феральси *m.* Feralsi, Sendust (iron-silicon-aluminum alloy).
фер/берит *m.* ferberite; **—ганит** *m.* ferghanite; **—гюсонит** *m.* fergusonite.
Фери Féry.
ферма *f.* girder, truss; farm.
Ферма принцип Fermat principle.
фермент *m.* ferment, enzyme; **—ная реакция** enzymatic reaction.
ферми *m.* fermi.
Ферми граница Fermi level (or limit); **Ф. граничный импульс** (maximum) F. momentum; **Ф. график** F. plot; **температура Ф.** F. temperature; **уровень Ф.** F. level; **Ф.-Дирака закон распределения** F.-Dirac distribution law; **статистика Ф.-Д.** F.-Dirac statistics; **фермиевский** *a.* Fermi.
фермий *m.* fermium (Fm).
фермион *m.*, **—ный** *a.* fermion.
Фернелий Fernelius (lunar crater).
фернико *m.* Fernico (iron-cobalt-nickel alloy).
феррамик *m.* Ferramic (ferrite).
Ферранти эффект (**явление**) Ferranti effect.
феррат *m.* ferrate.
феррацит *m.* ferrazite.
ферри *m.* (met.) Ferry (nickel-copper alloy).
Ферри теорема Furry theorem.
ферриаллофан *m.* ferriallophane.
ферримагн/етизм *m.* ferrimagnetism; **—итный** *a.* ferrimagnetic.
ферри/молибдит *m.* ferrimolybdite; **—мусковит** *m.* ferrimuscovite; **—симплезит** *m.* ferrisymplesite.
феррит *m.*, **—овый** *a.* ferrite.
ферритунгстит *m.* ferritungstite.

феррихром *m.* Ferrichrome (iron-nickel-cobalt-chromium alloy).
ферро— *prefix* ferro—.
ферро/вольфрам *m.* ferrotungsten; **—динамический прибор** ferrodynamic instrument; **—карт** *m.* Ferrocart; **—кобальт** *m.* ferrocobalt.
феррокскуб *m.* Ferroxcube (ferrite).
ферромагнет/изм *m.* ferromagnetism; **—ик** *m.* ferromagnetic (substance), ferromagnet.
ферромагнит *m.* ferromagnet; **—ный** *a.* ferromagnetic; **—ная область** ferromagnetic domain; **—ное превращение** ferromagnetic transition.
ферро/магнон *m.* ferromagnon, spin wave; **—метр** *m.* ferrometer.
ферросилиц/ий *m.*, **—иевый** *a.* ferrosilicon.
ферро/сплав *m.* ferroalloy; **—статический** *a.* ferrostatic; **—сульфатный дозиметр** ferrous sulfate dosimeter; **—торит** *m.* ferrothorite.
ферручит *m.* ferruccite.
феррьерит *m.* ferrierite.
Фессендена генератор Fessenden oscillator.
Фехнера закон Fechner law.
ФИАН *abbr.* [**Физический институт Академии наук СССР (им. П. Н. Лебедева)**] P. N. Lebedev Institute of Physics of the Academy of Sciences, USSR.
фиаско *n.* fiasco, failure.
фибр/а *f.* fiber; **—овый** *a.* fiber, fibrous.
фиг. *abbr.* (**фигура**) figure, illustration, diagram.
ФИГЕЛ *abbr.* (**физическая и геофизическая лаборатория**) laboratory of physics and geophysics.
фигур/а *f.* figure, illustration, diagram, picture; form, shape; **ф. травления** etch figure; **—ально** *adv.* figuratively; **—альный** *a.* figurative, metaphorical; **—ировать** *v.* figure, occur, appear.
фигурн/ый *a.* figure, figured; **—ые скобки** curly brackets, braces.
фидер *m.*, **—ный** *a.* feeder, main.
фидлерит *m.* fiedlerite.
физ. *abbr.* (**физика**) physics; (**физический**) physical.
физалит *m.* physalite.
физелиит *m.* fizelyite.
Физера *see* **Фезера.**
физик *m.* physicist; **ф.-теоретик** theoretical physicist; **ф.-ультразвуковик** ultrasonic physicist; **—а** *f.* physics; **—а твердого тела** solid state physics.
физико— *prefix* physico—, physical.
физико/металлургический *a.* physicometallurgical; **—химический** *a.* physicochemical.
физиограф/ический *a.* physiographic; **—ия** *f.* physiography.
физиолог *m.* physiologist; **—ический** *a.* physiological; **—ия** *f.* physiology.
физиотерапия *f.* physiotherapy.
физическ/ий *a.* physical; manual; **ф. маятник** physical (or compound) pendulum; **ф. эквивалент рентгена** roentgen equivalent physical (rep); **—ая радиология** radiological physics.
физконстанта *f.* physical constant.
Физ. мет. и металлов. *abbr.* (**Физика металлов и металловедение**) The Physics of Metals and Metallography (journal).
Физо опыт Fizeau experiment.
Физприбор *abbr.* (**Завод физических приборов**) Physical Instruments Plant.
Фика закон Fick law; **фиковская диффузия** Fickian diffusion.
фикс/аж *m.* (photo.) fixer, fixative; **—ажная ванна** fixing bath; **—атив** *m.* fixative, fixing agent; **—атор** *m.* index, index pin; stop, catch, retainer; **—ация** *f.*, **—ирование** *n.* fixation, fixing, immobilization; setting; clamping; registration, recording.
фиксир/ованный *a.* fixed, immobilized; specified; registered, recorded; **—овать** *v.* fix, fixate, immobilize; secure; register, record; **—ующий** *a.* fixing; **—ующий реагент** fixing agent, fixative; **—ующая цепь** (computer) hold circuit.
фиктивн/ость *f.* fictitiousness; **—ый** *a.* fictitious, virtual; **—ый заряд** fictitious (or image) charge.
фил. *abbr.* (**филиал**) branch, affiliate; (**философский**) philosophical.
филадельфит *m.* philadelphite.
филиал *m.* branch, affiliate; subsidiary;

—ьный *a.* branch, affiliated; subsidiary.
филипстадит *m.* philipstadite.
филлер *m.* filler, filling material.
филлип/ит *m.* phillipite; **—сит** *m.* phillipsite.
филло/вит *m.* fillowite; **—ретин** *m.* phylloretine.
фило— *prefix* phylo—.
философ *m.* philosopher; **—ия** *f.* philosophy; **—ский** *a.* philosophical.
фильдистер *m.* fieldistor.
фильера *f.* draw plate; die.
фильм *m.* film.
фильтр *m.* filter; absorber; **ф. верхних частот** high-pass filter; **ф. нижних частот** low-pass filter; **решетчатый ф.** lattice filter; **—ат** *m.* filtrate.
фильтрац/ионный *a.*, **—ия** *f.* filtration; filter discrimination; percolation, seepage; diffusion; **коэффициент —ии** permeability.
фильтровальн/ый *a.* filter, filtering; **—ая сетка** filter gauze.
фильтров/ание *see* **фильтрация**; **—анный** *a.* filtered; **—ать** *v.* filter; **—очный** *see* **фильтровальный.**
фильтр/уемый *a.* filterable; **—ующий** *a.* filtering; *see also* **фильтровальный**; **—ующий слой** filter bed.
ФИМ *abbr.* (**фазово-импульсная модуляция**) pulse position modulation (PPM).
финанс/ирование *n.* financing; **—ировать** *v.* finance; **—овый** *a.* financial; **—ы** *pl.* finances.
финитный *a.* finite.
Финляндия Finland.
финский *a.* Finnish.
фиолетовый *a.* violet.
фиорд *m.* fiord.
фирм/а *f.*, **—енный** *a.* firm, company.
Фирминик Firminicus (lunar crater).
фирн *m.* firn, névé.
фитиль *m.*, **—ный** *a.* wick.
фитинг *m.* fitting.
фитогенический *a.* phytogenic.
фитоколлит *m.* phytocollite.
фихтелит *m.* fichtelite.
Фицджеральда- (Фиц-Джеральда-)Лоренца сокращение Fitzgerald-Lorentz contraction hypothesis.
фише *n.* Fichet generator.
Фишера эффект (mag.) Fisher effect.
фишиум *m.* fissium.
фишка *f.* plug; counter.
ф-ия *abbr.* (**функция**) function.
ф-ла *abbr.* (**формула**) formula, equation.
флажок *m.* flag; dummy target.
флайолотит *m.* flajolotite.
флакон *m.* small bottle, flask.
фланг *m.* flank.
фланец *m.* flange, collar; **глухой ф., затворный ф.** blank flange.
фланжиров/альный, —очный *a.* flange, flanging; **—ать** *v.* flange.
фланц/евать *see* **фланжировать**; **—евый** *a.* flange, flanged; **—ованный** *a.* flanged.
флаттер *m.* flutter.
флегм/а *f.*, **—овый** *a.* reflux; **—овое число** reflux ratio.
флексура *f.* flexure; (geo.) fold.
Флеминга правило (**правило правой руки**) Fleming rule, right-hand rule.
Флемстид Flamsteed (lunar crater).
Флетнера ротор Flettner rotor.
Флетчера-Мунсона кривая Fletcher-Munson contour.
флец *m.*, **—овый** *a.* (geo.) fletz.
фликкер-эффект flicker effect.
флинт, —глас *m.* flint glass.
флиш *m.* flysch.
флогопит *m.* phlogopite.
Флоке теорема Floquet theorem.
флокен *m.* floc, floccule.
флоккул *m.* flocculus; **—ированный** *a.* flocculated, flocculent; **—ировать** *v.* flocculate; **—ьный** *a.* floccular; **—яция** *f.* flocculation.
флот *m.* fleet, navy; **воздушный ф.** air force.
флотац/ионный *a.*, **—ия** *f.* flotation.
флотир/ование *see* **флотация**; **—ованный** *a.* floated (off); **—овать, —оваться** *v.* float (off); **—уемый** *a.* floatable; **—ующийся** *a.* floating; floatable.
флотомашина *f.* flotation machine, flotation cell.
флотский *a.* fleet, naval.
флукту/ация *f.*, **—ационный** *a.* fluctuation; jitter; **—ировать** *v.* fluctuate.
флуор/ан *m.* fluoran; **—ен** *m.* fluorene.
флуоресц/еин *m.* fluorescein; **—ентный, —ирующий** *a.* fluorescent; **—енция**

f., **—ирование** *n.* fluorescence; **—ин** *m.* fluorescin; **—ировать** *v.* fluoresce.

флуор/ид *m.* fluoride; **—иметр** *see* **флуорометр.**

флуорометр *m.* fluorometer; **—ический** *a.* fluorometric; **—ия** *f.* fluorometry.

флуоро/скоп *m.* fluoroscope; **—фор** *m.* fluorophor, fluor; **—фотография** *f.* photofluorography, fluorography; **—хром** *m.* fluorochrome.

флювио— *prefix* fluvio—, river.

флювио/гляциальный *a.* (geo.) fluvioglacial; **—граф** *m.* fluviograph.

флюгер *m.* wind vane, anemoscope.

флюеллит *m.* fluellite.

флюид *m.* fluid; **—альный** *a.* fluid, fluidal.

флюидиз/ация *f.* fluidization; **—ированный** *a.* fluidized.

флюкс *m.* flux; **—ия** *f.* fluxion; **—метр** *m.* fluxmeter; **—ометрическая установка** fluxmeter induction installation.

флюктуация *see* **флуктуация.**

флюоборит *m.* fluoborite.

флюор— *see* **флуор—.**

флюо/рид *m.* fluoride; **—рит** *m.* fluorite; **—сидерит** *m.* fluosiderite; **—силикат** *m.* fluosilicate; **—церит** *m.* fluocerite.

флюс *m.* flux, fusing agent; **—ование** *n.* fluxing; **—ованный** *a.* fluxed.

флюсующий *a.* fluxing; **ф. материал** flux.

флютбет *m.* (hyd.) apron.

флютерит *m.* flutherite, uranothallite.

фляга *f.* flask.

фляттер *m.* flutter.

ФМ *abbr.* (**фазовая модуляция**) phase modulation (FM).

ФМИ *abbr.* (**Физико-математический институт**) Institute of Physics and Mathematics.

ФММ *abbr.* (**Физика металлов и металловедение**) The Physics of Metals and Metallography (journal).

ФМО *abbr.* (**физико-математическое отделение**) department of physics and mathematics.

фн. *abbr.* (**фунт**) pound (lb.).

ФНР *abbr.* (**Федеративная Народная Республика**) Federal People's Republic.

ФНРЮ *abbr.* *see* **Федеративная Народная Республика Югославия.**

фоглианит *m.* voglianite.

фоглит *m.* voglite.

Фогт *m.* Vogt; Voigt.

Фойгта контур Voigt profile.

фокальный *a.* focal; **ф. круг** focal circle, Rowland circle (of concave diffraction grating).

Фоккера-Планка уравнение Fokker-Planck equation.

фоковский метод Fock method.

фокометр *m.* focometer, focimeter.

фокус *m.* focus, focal point; **приводить в ф., собирать в —е, —ировать** *v.* focus; **установка на ф., —ирование** *n.*, **—ировка** *f.*, **—ирующий** *a.* focusing; **—ированный** *a.* focused.

фокусн/ый *a.* focus, focal; **ф. круг** focus circle; **—ое относительное расстояние** *f*-ratio; **—ое пятно** focal point, focus; **—ое расстояние** focal length.

Фолди-Ваутхейсена преобразование Foldy-Wouthuysen transformation.

фолерит *m.* pholerite.

фолиант *m.* folio.

фолидолит *m.* pholidolite.

фольбортит *m.* volborthite.

фольга *f.* foil.

Фомальгаут Fomalhaut.

ФОН *abbr.* (**факультет особого назначения**) special faculty (of a university).

фон *m.* background; noise; (acous.) phon; (polarography) supporting electrolyte.

фонар/ик *m.*, **—ный** *a.*, **—ь** *m.* lamp; **электрический (карманный) ф., электрический (карманный) —ь** flashlight; **передовой —ь** headlight.

фонд *m.* fund, stock; foundation.

фонема *f.* phoneme.

фонетика *f.* phonetics.

фонический *a.* phonic.

фоновый *a.* background.

фонограмма *f.* phonogram.

фонограф *m.* phonograph; **—ический** *a.* phonographic.

фонометр *m.* phonometer; noise meter.

фонон *m.*, **—ный** *a.* phonon.

фоно/скоп *m.* phonoscope; **—фор** *m.* phonophore.

фонтан *m.* fountain; oil gusher.

Фонтана Fontana (lunar crater).

фонтанир/ование *n.* fountain effect;

—**овать** *v.* gush, spout; —**ующий** *a.* gushing, spouting.

Фонтенель Fontenelle (lunar crater).

фор— *prefix* fore.

форбезит *m.* forbesite.

Форбуша спад (cosm.) Forbush decrease.

форвакуум *m.* forevacuum; —**ный насос** fore (backing, roughing, preevacuation) pump.

форез *m.* phoresis.

форкамера *f.* prechamber, forechamber.

Форлендера правило Vorlander rule.

форм/а *f.* form, shape; mode; mold; **ф. колебаний** vibrational mode; **ф. распада** decay mode; **коэффициент —ы** form factor, shape factor; **фактор —ы и размеров** (reactor) size-shape factor, buckling.

формализ/ировать *v.* formalize; —**м** *m.* formalism.

формальн/ость *f.* formality; —**ый** *a.* formal.

форманит *m.* formanite.

формат *m.* format, size.

формация *f.* formation; structure.

формвар *m.* Formvar.

формиат *m.* formate, formiate.

формиров/ание *n.* forming, shaping; **ф. тока** current rise (or growth); —**атель** *m.* shaper; —**ать** *v.* form, shape.

формирующее устройство (pulse) shaper.

формов/альный, —очный *a.* molding, mold, casting; forming; —**ание** *n.*, —**ка** *f.* molding, casting; forming; —**анный** *a.* molded, cast; formed; —**ать** *v.* mold, cast; form.

формоизменен/ие *n.* distortion, deformation; **энергия —ия** strain energy of distortion.

формула *f.* formula, equation.

формулиров/анный *a.* formulated; —**ать** *v.* formulate; —**ка** *f.* formulation, statement.

формуляр *m.* log, logbook; form.

формующийся диэлектрик molded dielectric.

формфактор *m.* form factor, shape factor.

форнасит *m.* fornacite.

форсаж *m.* boost; —**ная камера** (aero.) afterburner, augmentor.

форсиров/ание *n.*, —**ка** *f.* forcing; (over)-acceleration, overloading; —**анный** *a.* forced; (over)accelerated, overloaded; —**ать** *v.* force; (over)accelerate, overspeed, overload.

форстерит *m.* forsterite.

форсунка *f.* sprayer, atomizer, injector; nozzle, jet.

Фортеня барометр Fortin barometer.

фортепьяно *n.* piano.

Фортра Fortrat.

фосгенит *m.* phosgenite.

фоссилиз/ация *f.* fossilization; —**ированный** *a.* fossilized; —**ировать** *v.* fossilize.

фосфат *m.*, —**ный** *a.* phosphate.

фосфо— *prefix* phospho—, phosphorus.

фосфор *m.* phosphorus (P).

фосфóр *m.* phosphor, luminophor.

фосфоресц/енция *f.*, —**ирование** *n.* phosphorescence; —**ировать** *v.* phosphoresce; —**ирующий** *a.* phosphorescent.

фосфоризация *f.* phosphorization.

фосфорист/ый *a.* phosphorus, phosphorous; phosphide; —**ая бронза** phosphor bronze.

фосфорит *m.* phosphorite.

фосфорный *a.* phosphorus, phosphoric.

фосфоро— *prefix* phosphoro—, phosphorus.

фосфороген *m.* phosphorogen.

фосфорорганическое соединение organophosphorus compound.

фосфороскоп *m.* phosphoroscope; —**ический** *a.* phosphoroscopic.

фосфуранилит *m.* phosphuranylite.

фот *m.* phot; **ф.-секунда** phot-second; **ф.-час** phot-hour.

фотен *m.* photene.

фотицит *m.* photicite.

фото— *prefix* photo—, photographic, light.

фото/активация *f.* photostimulation; —**аппарат** *m.* camera; —**бумага** *f.* photographic paper; —**варистор** *m.* photovaristor; —**вклад** *m.* photofraction; —**вольтаический, —гальванический** *a.* photovoltaic; —**гальваномагнитный эффект** photoelectromagnetic effect; —**гелиограф** *m.* photoheliograph.

фотоген *m.*, **—овый** *a.* photogen; **—ерация** *f.* photoproduction.

фотограмма *f.* photogram.

фотограмметр *m.* photogrammeter, phototheodolite; **—ический снимок** map-photograph; **—ия** *f.* photogrammetry.

фотограф *m.* photographer; **—ирование** *n.* photographing; **—ировать** *v.* photograph; **—ически** *adv.* photographically.

фотограф/ический *a.* photographic; **ф. аппарат** camera; **ф. снимок** photograph; **—ия** *f.* photography; photograph.

фото/дейтрон *m.* photodeuteron; **—деление** *n.* photofission; **—десорбция** *f.* photodesorption; **—диод** *m.* photodiode, photovoltaic junction; **—диссоциация** *f.* photodissociation; **—дозиметр** *m.* film badge; **—дырка** *f.* photohole.

фото/запись *f.* photorecording; **—затвор** *m.* camera shutter; **—захват** *m.* photoabsorption; **—звезда** *f.* photostar; **—импульс** *m.* photoimpact; **—имущество** *n.* photographic equipment; **—ионизация** *f.* photoionization; **—источник** *m.* photosource.

фотокамера *see* **фотоаппарат; ф. жесткого типа** box camera, fixed-focus camera.

фотокассета *f.* photoplate holder.

фотокатализ *m.* photocatalysis; **—атор** *m.* photocatalyst.

фото/катод *m.* photocathode; **—колориметрический** *a.* photocolorimetric; **—красная величина** photored magnitude.

фото/лампа *f.* photoflood lamp; **—лента** *f.* photographic film; **—лиз** *m.* photolysis; **—линия** *f.* photoline, photopeak.

фотолит *m.* photolyte; **—ический** *a.* photolytic.

фотолог/ический *a.* photologic; **—ия** *f.* photology, photics.

фотолюминесцен/тная лампа fluorescent lamp; **—ция** *f.* photoluminescence.

фотомагнитный *a.* photomagnetic; **ф. эффект** photoelectromagnetic effect.

фотомезон *m.* photomeson.

фотометр *m.* photometer; **ступенчатый ф.** variable-diaphragm photometer; **—ирование** *n.* photometric measurement (or scanning); **—ировать** *v.* measure (or scan) photometrically; **—ический** *a.* photometric; **—ический шар** (integrating) sphere photometer; **—ическая скамья** photometer bench; **—ическое тело** solid of light distribution; **—ия** *f.* photometry; photometric scanning.

фотомеханический *a.* photomechanical.

фотон *m.* photon.

фотонейтрон *m.*, **—ный** *a.* photoneutron.

фотонный *a.* photon.

фото/объектив *m.* camera objective; **—окисление** *n.* photooxidation; **—отрицательный** *a.* photonegative.

фотоотщепление *n.* photodetachment; **ф. электронов** electron photodetachment.

фото/передатчик *m.* picture transmitter; **—переход** *m.* phototransition; **—периодизм** *m.* photoperiodism; **—пик** *m.* photopeak; **—план** *m.* photomap; **—пластинка** *f.* photographic plate, photoplate; **—пластический** *a.* photoplastic; **—пленка** *f.* photographic film, photofilm; **—поглощение** *n.* photoabsorption; **—полимеризация** *f.* photopolymerization; **—положительный** *a.* photopositive.

фотополяриз/ация *f.* photopolarization; **—уемость** *f.* photopolarizability.

фотопровод/имость *f.* photoconductivity; **—ник** *m.* photoconductor; **—ящий** *a.* photoconductive.

фото/протон *m.* photoproton; **—разведка** *f.* photoreconnaissance; **—разложение** *n.* photodecomposition, photodissociation; **—расщепление** *n.* photodisintegration; **—резистивный** *a.* photoconductive; **—реле** *n.* photorelay.

фоторождение *n.* photoproduction; **ф. мезонов** photomeson production.

фотосек *abbr. see* **фот-с.**

фотосинт/ез *m.* photosynthesis; **—етический** *a.* photosynthetic.

фото/слой *m.* photosensitive (or photoconductive) layer; —**снимок** *see* **фотографический снимок**; —**сопротивление** *n.* photoconductive cell, photoresistor, photoresistance, photovaristor; —**стат** *m.* photostat.

фотосфер/а *f.* photosphere; —**ная сетка** réseau photosphérique.

фото/съемка *f.* photography, photographing; —**телеграфия** *f.* phototelegraphy; —**телефония** *f.* phototelephony; —**ток** *m.* photocurrent; —**транзистор** *m.* phototransistor.

фототроп/изм *m.*, —**ия** *f.* phototropism; —**ический** *a.* phototropic.

фото/увеличитель *m.* photographic enlarger; —**удар** *m.* photoimpact.

фотоумножитель *m.* photomultiplier; —**ная трубка** photomultiplier tube.

фотоупруг/ий *see* **фотоэластический**; —**ость** *see* **фотоэластичность.**

фото/флюорография *f.* photofluorography; —**фон** *m.* photophone; —**форез** *m.* photophoresis.

фотохим/ический *a.* photochemical; —**ия** *f.* photochemistry.

фотохром *m.* photochrome; —**атический** *a.* photochromatic; —**ия** *f.* photochromy.

фото/хронограф *m.* moving-image camera; —**чувствительный** *a.* photosensitive.

фото-э.д.с. *abbr.* (**фотоэлектродвижущая сила**) photoelectromotive force, photovoltage (photo-emf).

фотоэкспонометр *m.* photographic exposure meter.

фотоэластич/еский *a.* photoelastic, piezo-optical; —**ность** *f.* photoelasticity.

фотоэлектричес/кий *a.* photoelectric; —**тво** *n.* photoelectricity.

фотоэлектродвижущая сила photoelectromotive force, photovoltage.

фотоэлектрон *m.* photoelectron; —**ный** *a.* photoelectronic; —**ный умножитель** photomultiplier; —**ная эмиссия** photoelectric emission, photoemissive effect.

фотоэлемент *m.* photocell; photoelectric cell, photovoltaic cell, phototube; **эмиссионный ф.** photoemissive cell, photocell.

фото/эмиссия *f.* photoemission; photoemissivity; —**эмульсия** *f.* photographic emulsion; photoemulsion.

фотоэффект *m.* photoelectric effect; **внешний ф.** photoemissive effect; **внутренний ф.** photoconductive effect; **порог —а** photoelectric threshold.

фото/ядерный *a.* photonuclear; —**ячейка** *f.* photocell.

фот-с *abbr.* (**фот-секунда**) phot-second.

фот-ч *abbr.* (**фот-час**) phot-hour.

фоулерит *m.* fowlerite.

Фохт *see* **Фогт.**

Фоциклид Phocyclides (lunar crater).

фоциметр *m.* focimeter.

фоязит *m.* faujasite.

ф. п. (*abbr.*) (**французский патент**) French patent.

фр. *abbr. see* **франц.**

фрагмент *m.* fragment; —**арный** *a.* fragmentary; —**ация** *f.* fragmentation.

фраза *f.* phrase, sentence.

Фракастор Fracastor (lunar crater).

фрактография *f.* fractography.

фракционир/ование *n.* fractionation; —**ованный** *a.* fractionated; fractional; —**ованная перегонка** fractional distillation; —**овать** *v.* fractionate; grade; —**ующий** *a.* fractionating.

фракционн/о *adv.* fractionally; in steps; —**ый** *a.* fractional; —**ый анализ** fractional analysis; size analysis.

фракция *f.* fraction.

Фрама камертонный частотомер Frahm frequency meter.

Франка-Кондона принцип Franck-Condon principle.

франкеит *m.* franckëite.

франколит *m.* francolite.

франц. *abbr.* (**французский**) French.

франций *m.* francium (Fr).

Франция France.

французский *a.* French.

Фраунгофера дифракция Fraunhofer diffraction; **Ф. линии** F. lines.

фрахт *m.*, —**овый** *a.* freight.

ФРГ *abbr. see* **Федеративная Республика Германия.**

фреатический *a.* phreatic.

Фредгольма уравнение Fredholm equation.

фредрикит *m.* fredricite.

фрез/а *f.*, **—ер** *m.* (milling) cutter, mill; **—ерный** *a.* milling.

фрезеров/ание *n.*, **—ка** *f.* milling, cutting; **—анный** *a.* milled; **—ать** *v.* mill, cut.

фрейалит *m.* freyalite.

фрейеслебенит *m.* freieslebenite.

Фрейндлиха изотерма Freundlich isotherm.

фрейринит *m.* freirinite.

Фрелих Fröhlich.

Френе формула Frenet formula.

Френеля бизеркала Fresnel mirrors; **Ф. зона** F. zone; F. region (of antenna); **Ф. интеграл** F. integral; **Ф. коэффициент увлечения** F. drag coefficient; **Ф. параллелепипед** F. rhomb; **Ф. теория двойного преломления** F. theory of double refraction; **Ф.-Араго законы** F.-Arago laws.

Френкеля дефект Frenkel defect.

френцелит *m.* frenzelite.

фреон *m.* Freon.

фрепонтит *m.* fraipontite.

фригориметр *m.* frigorimeter, coolmeter.

фриделит *m.* friedelite.

Фриделя закон Friedel law.

Фридрихса неравенство Friedrichs inequality.

Фриза *see* **Фриса.**

фризеит *m.* frieseïte.

Фрика печь Frick furnace.

фрикативный *a.* fricative.

фрикцион *m.* friction clutch; **—ный** *a.* friction, frictional.

Фриса правило Fries rule.

фритт/а *f.*, **—овый** *a.* frit.

фритчеит *m.* fritzscheïte.

фришев/альный *a.* refining; **—ание** *n.* refining, fining; **—ать** *v.* refine, fine.

Фробениуса метод Frobenius method.

фронт *m.* front; face, surface; **ф. воздушной массы** weather front; **ф. волны** wave front; **ф. нисходящего скольжения** (meteor.) katafront; **ф. окклюзии** occluded front; **—альный** *a.* frontal, front.

фронтогенез *m.* frontogenesis; **—ный** *a.* frontogenetical.

фронтолиз *m.* frontolysis; **—ный** *a.* frontolytical.

фронтология *f.* frontology, frontal analysis.

Фруда кривая Froude curve; **Ф. числ** F. number.

фрукто— *prefix* fructo—, fruit.

фт. *abbr.* (**фут**) foot (ft).

фтал— *prefix* phthal—.

фтал/ат *m.* phthalate; **—имид** *m.* phthalimide.

фтало— *prefix* phthalo—.

фтор *m.* fluorine (F).

фтор— *prefix* fluor—, fluoro—, fluorine

фтор/борат *m.* fluorborate; **—ид** *m* fluoride.

фториров/ание *n.* fluorination; **—анны** *a.* fluorinated; **—ать** *v.* fluorinate.

фтористоводородная кислота hydrofluoric acid.

фтористый *a.* fluorine; (lower or —ous fluoride; **ф. углерод** fluorocarbon; **ф уран** uranium fluoride; **ф. урани** uranyl fluoride, uranium oxyfluoride

фторный *a.* fluorine; (higher or —ic fluoride.

фторо— *prefix* fluoro—.

фтороводород *m.* hydrogen fluoride hydrofluoric acid.

фтор/окись *f.* oxyfluoride; **—окси апатит** *m.* fluoroxyapatite.

фторопласт *m.* Teflon (or related plastic)

фтороуглерод *m.* fluorocarbon.

фтортарамит *m.* fluotaramite.

ФТТ *abbr.* (**Физика твердого тела** Solid State Physics (journal) (Soviet Physics—Solid State).

ФУ *abbr.* (**фотоувеличитель**) photographic enlarger.

Фубини теорема Fubini theorem.

фуг/асность, —итивность *f.* fugacity.

фугов/ание *n.* jointing; **—ать** *v.* joint mortise, join.

фукеит *m.* fouquéite.

Фуко маятник Foucault pendulum; **ф токи** F. (or eddy) currents.

фукозит *m.* fucosite.

фуксин *m.* fuchsin, magenta.

фуксит *m.* fuchsite.

фуксовый *a.* Fuchsian.

фуллерова земля fuller's earth.

фульвен *m.* fulvene.

фумарат *m.* fumarate.

фунгисид *m.* fungicide.

фундамент *m.* foundation; bed, base; seat, seating; (geo.) basement.

фундаментальн/ость *f.* fundamental

character; solidity; **—ый** *a.* fundamental; solid, substantial; foundation; **—ая серия** fundamental series.

ундаментн/ый *a.* foundation, base; **—ая плита** foundation plate.

ункциограф *m.* function plotter.

ункцион/ал *m.*, **—альный** *a.* functional; **—альность** *f.* functionality; **—ирование** *n.* functioning, operation; **—ировать** *v.* function, operate; **—ирующий** *a.* functioning, functional.

ункция *f.* function; **ф. влияния** influence function, Green's function; **ф действия** action function; **ф. состояния** state function; **ф. точки** position (or local) function.

унт *m.* pound; **ф.-вес** pound-force; **ф.-калория** centigrade heat unit (CHU); **—овый** *a.* pound, one-pound.

урмарьерит *m.* fourmarierite.

Фурнерий Furnerius (lunar crater).

Фурье Fourier (lunar crater).

Фурье интеграл Fourier integral; **Ф.-образ, Ф. отображение, Ф. преобразование** F. transform; **Ф. обращение** F. inversion; **Ф. представитель** F. representation; **Ф. ряд** F. series.

фут *m.* foot.

футеит *m.* footeite.

футеров/анный *a.* lined; **—ать** *v.* line; **—ка** *f.* (brick) lining.

футляр *m.* case; casing, cover, sheath, jacket; container, housing.

футо/вый *a.* foot, one-foot; **—свеча** *f.* foot-candle; **—фунт** *m.* foot-pound.

футшток *m.* tide staff.

фушерит *m.* foucherite.

ФХО *abbr.* (**физико-химическое общество**) Physicochemical Society.

ф-ция *abbr.* (**функция**) function.

ф-ч *abbr. see* **фот-ч.**

ФЭ *abbr.* (**фотоэлемент**) photocell.

ФЭР *abbr.* (**физический эквивалент рентгена**) physical roentgen equivalent (rep).

ФЭУ *abbr.* (**фотоэлектронный умножитель**) photomultiplier (PM).

фюзеляж *m.* fuselage.

фюлеппит *m.* fülöppite.

Фюрстенау интенсиметр Fürstenau dose-rate meter.

X

X [*in steel mark* (**хром**)] chromium (Cr).

X *abbr.* (**единица икс**) X-unit; **X и Д** *abbr. see* **Хертер.**

абазит *m.* chabazite.

Хаббл Hubble.

Хагена-Рубенса формула Hagen-Rubens relation.

ХАИ *abbr.* (**Харьковский авиационный институт**) Kharkov Aviation Institute.

алатн/ость *f.* negligence, carelessness; **—ый** *a.* negligent, careless.

алибит *m.* chalybite.

алко— *see* **халько—.**

алцедон *m.*, **—овый** *a.* chalcedony.

алькантит *m.* chalcanthite.

алько— *prefix* chalco—.

алько/зин, —цит *m.* chalcosine, chalcocite, copper glance; **—лит** *m.* chalcolite, torbernite, copper uranite; **—прит** *m.* chalcopyrite.

Хамелеон Chamaeleon (Cha) (constellation).

Хамеля база Hamel basis.

Хammета *see* **Гammета.**

Хана правило Hahn rule.

Ханкеля *see* **Ганкела.**

ХАО *abbr.* (**Астрономическая обсерватория Харьковского университета**) Kharkov University Astronomical Observatory.

хаос *m.* chaos, confusion.

хаотическ/и *adv.* chaotically, in disorder, at random; **—ий** *a.* chaotic, disordered, random; **—ое движение** random motion.

хаотичн/ость *f.* chaotic state, randomness; **—ый** *see* **хаотический.**

характер *m.* character, nature; **—изовать** *v.* characterize; describe, define; **—изующий** *a.* characteristic.

характериограф *m.* cathode-ray curve tracer.

характеристика *f.* characteristic; characteristic curve, pattern, response (curve); performance; characterization, specification; characteristics, properties, essential features; **х. нагрузки** (elec.) load line; **х. направленности** directional characteristic, directivity pattern; **рабочая х.** performance (curve); **х. спектральной чувствительности** spectral characteristic (response, sensitivity).

характеристическ/ий *a.* characteristic; intrinsic; performance; **х. спектр** characteristic (or line) spectrum; **—ая вязкость** intrinsic viscosity; **—ая диаграмма** performance diagram; **—ая функция** characteristic function, eigenfunction; **—ая энергия** characteristic energy, eigenenergy; **—ое значение, —ое число** (math.) characteristic value (or number), eigenvalue.

характеристичн/ость *f.* characteristic nature; **—ый** *see* **характеристический**; **—ые данные** performance figures.

характерн/о *adv.* characteristically; it is characteristic; **—ый** *a.* characteristic, typical.

Харвелл Harwell.

Харкера разрез Harker section; **Х.-Каспера неравенство** H.-Casper inequality.

Харьков Khar'kov (now usually Kharkov).

Хартлея схема Hartley circuit.

Хартри-Фока метод Hartree-Fock method.

Харуэлл Harwell.

хатский ярус Chattian stage.

Хаукинса элемент Hawkins cell.

хаусдорфовый *a.* Hausdorff.

хвал/а *f.* praise; **—ебный** *a.* laudatory; **—еный** *a.* praised; **—ить** *v.* praise, commend.

хват/ать *v.* seize, catch (hold of), grasp, clutch; suffice; **—ить** *v.* suffice; **—ка** *f.* clutch, grip.

хвост *m.* tail, tailpiece; shank, shaft; **—ы** *pl.* (min.) tailings; **—овик** *m.* stem, shaft; **—овой** *a.* tail; rear, posterior, following; **—овое оперение** (aero.) empennage.

ХГИМИП *abbr.* (**Харьковский государственный институт мер и измерительных приборов**) Kharkov State Institute of Measures and Measuring Instruments.

ХГУ *abbr.* (**Харьковский государственный университет**) Kharkov State University.

Хевеши Hevesy.

Хевисайда единичная функция Heaviside unit function; **слой Х.** H. layer; **теорема разложения Х.** H. expansion theorem; **Х.-Кеннели слой** H.-Kennelly layer; **хевисайдовский** *a.* Heaviside.

хегбомит *m.* högbomite.

хегтвейтит *m.* högtveitite.

Хедграна спектрометр Hedgran spectrometer.

Хейфорда эллипсоид Hayford spheroid.

хелат *m.*, **—ный** *a.* chelate.

Хелли теорема Helly theorem.

Хельбергера печь Helberger furnace (crucible).

хемилюминесценция *f.* chemiluminescence.

хемосорбция *f.* chemisorption.

хемосфера *f.* chemosphere.

Хенки теория Hencky theory.

Хенфорд *see* **Хэнфорд.**

Хеплера вискозиметр Höppler viscosimeter.

Херглотца теорема Herglotz theorem.

Хертер: чувствительность по —у и Дриффильду Hurter and Driffield speed number (H and D).

хиастолит *m.* chiastolite.

хиблит *m.* hyblite.

Хигинботама пересчетная ячейка Higinbotham scaling circuit.

ХиД, Х и Д *abbr. see* **Хертер.**

ХИК *abbr.* (**Химический институт им. Л. Я. Карпова**) L. Ya. Karpov Chemical Institute.

хи-квадрат *m.* chi-square.

Хилерааса потенциал Hylleraas potential.

Хилла определитель (детерминант) Hill determinant.

Хил-Шоу Hele-Shaw.

Хильгера спектрограф Hilger spectrograph.

хим. *abbr.* (**химия**) chemistry; (**химический**) chemical.

ХИМ *abbr.* (**Харьковский научно-исследовательский институт металлов**) Kharkov Scientific Research Institute of Metals.
хим— *prefix* chemical.
химаппарат *m.* chemical apparatus (or equipment).
Химгаз *abbr.* (**Всесоюзный научно-исследовательский институт химической переработки газов**) All-Union Scientific Research Institute of the Chemical Treatment of Gases.
химзавод *m.* chemical plant.
хим. зн. *abbr.* (**химический знак**) chemical symbol.
химик *m.* chemist; **—алии** *pl.* chemicals; **—ат** *m.* chemical.
химико— *prefix* chemico—, chemical.
химико-технологический завод chemical processing plant.
химио/синтез *m.* chemosynthesis; **—терапия** *f.* chemotherapy; **—цептор** *m.* chemoceptor.
химисорбированный *a.* chemisorbed.
химически *adv.* chemically; **х. связанный** chemically combined.
химическ/ий *a.* chemical; **—ая технология** chemical engineering (or technology); **—ие материалы, —ие препараты, —ие продукты** chemicals.
химия *f.* chemistry; **прикладная х.** applied chemistry.
Хим. наука и пром. *abbr.* (**Химическая наука и промышленность**) Chemical Science and Industry (journal).
химостойкость *f.* chemical resistance (or durability).
Хим. пром. *abbr.* (**Химическая промышленность**) Chemical Industry (journal).
хим. сост. *abbr.* (**химический состав**) chemical composition.
Хим. тв. топл. *abbr.* (**Химия твердого топлива**) Chemistry of Solid Fuels (journal).
ХИН *abbr.* (**химический институт**) Chemical Institute.
хин— *prefix* quin—.
хинин *m.* quinine.
хино— *prefix* quino—.
хино/лон *m.* quinolone; **—н** *m.* quinone.
Хинчина теорема Khinchin (Khintchine) theorem.
хиолит *m.* chiolite.
Хиросима Hiroshima.
Хисинг: модуляция по —у Heising modulation.
хитр/ость *f.* ruse; intricacy; cunning; **—ый** *a.* clever, cunning; intricate, involved.
хладагент *m.* coolant, refrigerant.
Хладни фигура Chladni figure.
хладнит *m.* chladnite.
хладноломк/ий *a.* cold-short; **—ость** *f.* cold shortness (or brittleness).
хладностойкий *a.* cold-resistant, antifreezing; **х. состав** antifreeze.
хлест/анье *n.* lashing; gushing; **—ать, —нуть** *v.* lash, flap; gush out.
хлоантит *m.* chloanthite.
хлоп/анье *n.* slamming, knocking; flapping; **—ать** *v.* slam, knock; flap.
Хлопина закон Khlopin law.
хлопинит *m.* khlopinite.
хлопковый *a.* cotton.
хлопнуть *see* **хлопать.**
хлопок *m.* cotton.
хлопчато— *prefix* cotton.
хлопчат/обумажный, —ый *a.* cotton.
хлопь/е *n.*, **—я** *pl.* flocs, coagulates, flakes; **образование —ев** flocculation; **—евидный, —еобразный** *a.* floccular, flocculent, flaky; **—евидные облака** floccus.
хлор *m.* chlorine (Cl).
хлор— *prefix* chlor—, chloro—; chloride.
хлор/аллюминит *m.* chloraluminite; **—аргирит** *m.* chlorargyrite; **—бензол** *m.* chlorobenzene; **—ид** *m.* chloride.
хлорир/ование *n.* chlorination; **—ованный** *a.* chlorinated; **—овать** *v.* chlorinate; **—ующий** *a.* chlorinating.
хлористоводородная кислота hydrochloric acid.
хлористый *a.* chlorine, chlorous; **х. натрий** sodium chloride.
хлорит *m.* chlorite; **—оид** *m.* chloritoid.
хлор/манганокалит *m.* chlormanganokalite; **—манкалит** *m.* chlormankalite.
хлорноватист/окислый *a.* hypochlorous-acid, hypochlorite (of); **—ый** *a.* hypochlorous.
хлорный *a.* chlorine; (higher or —ic) chloride (of).

хлоро— *prefix* chloro—, chlor—; chlorine.

хлорокись *f.* oxychloride.

хлоро/ксифит *m.* chloroxiphite; **—меланит** *m.* chloromelanite.

хлоропал *m.* chloropal.

хлоро/фан *m.* chlorophane; **—феит** *m.* chlorophaeite; **—феницит** *m.* chlorophoenicite.

хлорофилл *m.*, **—овый** *a.* chlorophyll.

хлорошпинель *f.* chlorospinel.

хлорциан *m.* cyanogen chloride.

хлынуть *v.* gush (out), spout.

ХММИ *abbr.* **(Харьковский механико-машиностроительный институт)** Kharkov Mechanics and Machinery Institute.

хмурый *a.* gloomy, overcast.

Ховарда теорема Howard theorem.

хогтонит *m.* haughtonite.

ход *m.* motion, movement; course, variation; dependence; behavior; operation, run; stroke, path, travel; rate; move; passage, port; **х. вверх** upstroke; rise; **х. вниз** downstroke; descent; **временный х.** time dependence; **х. дел** course of events; **х. зависимости** variation; behavior; **задний х.** reverse (or backward) motion; **х. кривой** curve shape; **мертвый х.** backlash; **обратный х.** return stroke, reverse (motion); **полный х.** full speed; **пуск в х.** putting into operation; starting; **пускать в х., пустить в х.** put into operation; start (up); **свободный х.** freewheeling; detached escapement; **холостой х.** idling, idle (or free) running; no-load operation; open circuit; idle stroke; **быть в —у** run, be in operation; **на —у** in motion, in operation.

ходектрон *m.* hodectron.

ходить *v.* go, run, work; pass (of current); **х. за** tend, take care of.

ходневит *m.* chodnewite.

ходов/ой *a.* going, running; track, path; usual; **х. валик** feed shaft; **х. винт** lead screw, guide screw; **х. механизм** running gear, train; **х. ролик** traveler, traveling rollgear; **—ая гайка** sliding nut; **—ая пружина** mainspring; **—ая часть** undercarriage, truck.

ходок *m.* conduit, passage.

ходоуменьшитель *m.* reducing gear; **—ный** *a.* speed-reducing.

ходячий *a.* current; common.

хозяин *m.* master; owner, proprietor; (mineral) host.

хозяйственн/ик *m.* economist; industrial executive; **—о** *adv.* economically; **—ость** *f.* economy; **—ый** *a.* economic; economical; **—ый год** fiscal year.

хозяйство *n.* economy; farm; household; **народное х.** national economy; **сельское х.** farming, agriculture.

Хойля сплав Hoyle metal (lead-tin-antimony alloy).

Хойта гравиметр Hoyt gravimeter.

хокутолит *m.* hokutolite.

холденит *m.* holdenite.

Холла эффект Hall effect; **холловская подвижность** H. mobility.

холм *m.* hill, mound; **—ик** *m.* hillock, mound, hummock; **—истый** *a.* hilly, rolling, undulating.

холмквистит *m.* holmquistite.

холод *m.* cold; **—а** *pl.* cold weather; **на —у** in the cold.

холодильник *m.* refrigerator, cooler; condenser; **обратный х.** reflux condenser.

холодильн/ый *a.* cooling, refrigerating, refrigerant; condensing; **—ая соль** freezing salt; **—ая техника** refrigeration engineering; **—ая установка** refrigerating plant.

холодить *v.* cool, chill, refrigerate.

холодно *adv.* cold, coldly; it is cold; **—катаный** *a.* cold-rolled; **—обработанный** *a.* cold-worked; **—сть** *f.* coldness; **—тянутый** *a.* cold-drawn.

холодн/ый *a.* cold, frigid; **х. агент** refrigerant; **х. пояс** frigid zone; **—ая эмиссия** (elec.) field emission; **—ое вторжение** (meteor.) cold-air outbreak.

холодопроизводительность *f.* refrigerating capacity.

холодостойк/ий *a.* cold-resistant; **—ость** *f.* cold resistance.

холост/ой *a.* idle, loose, free; empty, blank, dummy; open-circuit; **х. импеданс** open-circuit impedance; **х. патрон** blank cartridge; **х. ролик**

idler; **в —ую, на —ом ходу** without load, no-load, idle.
хольтсмарковское уширение Holtsmark broadening.
хомут, —ик *m.* collar, yoke, ring, hoop, shackle; clamp, clip.
хон *m.* hone.
хондра *f.* chondrule.
хондрарсенит *m.* chondrarsenite.
хондрит *m.* chondrite.
хондродит *m.* chondrodite.
хонинг *m.*, **—ование** *n.* honing; **—ировать, —овать** *v.* hone.
хорд/а *f.*, **—овый** *a.* chord.
Хорняка детектор Hornyak button.
хоронить *v.* bury; conceal.
хорош/ий *a.* good; **—о** *adv.* well; highly; **—о растворимый** readily soluble.
хотеть *v.* wish, want, desire.
хот/ь *conj.* at least; although; **—я** *conj.* although; **х. бы** if only; even if.
хр. *abbr.* [**хребет (только при названии)**] mountain ridge (or range) (when modifying a name).
хран/ение *n.* keeping, storage; **—илище** *n.* storehouse, storage vault, reservoir; **—итель** *m.* custodian, keeper, curator; **—ить** *v.* keep, store.
храпов/ик *m.*, **—ой** *a.* ratchet; **—ой механизм** ratchet, ratchet gear; **—ая собачка** pawl; **—ое колесо** ratchet wheel.
хреб/ет *m.* spine; crest, mountain ridge (or range); **—товидный, —тообразный** *a.* ridged.
хризматит *m.* chrismatine.
хризо— *prefix* chryso—.
хризо/берилл *m.* chrysoberyl; **—колла** *f.* chrysocolla; **—лит** *m.* chrysolite; **—праз** *m.* chrysoprase; **—тил** *m.* chrysotile.
христианит *m.* christianite.
Христиансена светофильтр Christiansen filter; **эффект Х.** C. effect.
Христоффеля *see* **Кристоффеля.**
хром *m.* chromium (Cr).
хромансиль *m.* Cromansil (chromium-manganese-silicon steel).
хромат *m.* chromate; **—изм** *m.* chromatism; **—ический, —ичный** *a.* chromatic; **—ичность** *f.* chromaticity.
хромато/грамма *f.* chromatogram; **—графический** *a.* chromatographic; **—графия** *f.* chromatography; **—скоп** *m.* chromatoscope.
хроматрон *m.* chromatron.
хроматроп *m.* chromatrope.
хромать *v.* limp; lag.
хром/бейделлит *m.* chrome-beidellite; **—везувиан** *m.* chromovesuvianite; **—герцинит** *m.* chromohercynite; **—диопсид** *m.* chrome-diopside.
хромель *m.* Chromel (nickel-chromium alloy).
хромиров/ание *n.* chrome plating; **—анный** *a.* chrome-plated; **—ать** *v.* chrome plate.
хромист/ый *a.* chromium, chromous; **—ая сталь** chrome steel.
хромит *m.* chromite; **—ит** *m.* chromitite.
хромо— *prefix* chromo—.
хромо/вольфрамовая сталь chrome-tungsten steel; **—вый** *a.* chromium, chromic, chrome; **—вые квасцы** chrome alum; **—калиевые квасцы** potassium chrome alum.
хромолитограф/ия *f.* chromolithography; chromolithograph; **—ский** *a.* chromolithographic.
хромо/метр *m.* chromometer, colorimeter; **—скоп** *m.* chromoscope.
хромосом/а *f.*, **—ный** *a.* chromosome.
хромосфер/а *f.* chromosphere; **—ный** *a.* chromospheric; **—ная вспышка, —ное извержение** solar (or chromospheric) flare.
хромотипия *f.* chromotype; chromotypography, color printing (or print).
хромотропия *f.* chromotropy.
хромофор *m.* chromophore.
хромофото/графия *f.* chromophotography, color photography (or photograph); **—метр** *m.* chromophotometer (colorimeter).
хромпик *m.* bichromate (specif. potassium bichromate).
хром/шпинель *f.* chrome spinel; **—эпидот** *m.* chromepidote.
хронизатор *m.* timer.
хроник/а *f.* chronicle, news items; **—ер** *m.* reporter.
хронир/ование *n.* timing; **—овать** *v.* time; **—ующий** *a.* timing.
хронический *a.* chronic.
хронограмма *f.* chronogram.

хронограф *m.* chronograph; **—ия** *f.* chronography.

хроноизотерма *f.* chronoisotherm.

хронологиз/ация *f.* time ordering; **—ированный** *a.* time-ordered; **—ированное произведение** time-ordered (chronological) product; **—ирующий** *a.* time-ordering.

хронолог/ический *a.* chronological; **—ия** *f.* chronology.

хронометр *m.*, **—овый** *a.* chronometer, timekeeper; **—аж** *m.*, **—ирование** *n.* timing, timekeeping; time study; **—ировать** *v.* time; **—ический** *a.* chronometric; **—ия** *f.* chronometry; **—овый спуск** clock escapement.

хроноскоп *m.* chronoscope.

хронотрон *m.* chronotron.

хрупкий *a.* brittle; fragile.

хрупколомк/ий *a.* short-brittle; **—ость** *f.* friability, brittleness, fragility.

хрупкостное проницание embrittlement penetration.

хрупкост/ь *f.* brittleness; embrittlement; fragility; **критическая температура —и** (plast.) ductile-to-brittle transition temperature.

хруст *m.* cracking.

хрусталик *m.* crystalline lens (of eye).

хрусталь *m.* crystal; crystal glass; **—ный** *a.* crystal, crystalline.

хруст/ение *see* **хруст**; **—еть, —нуть** *v.* crackle.

ХТИ *abbr.* (**Харьковский технологический институт**) Kharkov Technological Institute.

хуанит *m.* juanite.

хугит *m.* houghite.

худ/о *adv.* badly, ill; **—ой** *a.* bad, inferior; lean; **—ший** *a.* worse; the worst.

хуже *comp. of* **худо,** worse; **тем х.** so much the worse.

хуттонит *m.* huttonite.

ХХТИ *abbr.* (**Харьковский химико-технологический институт**) Kharkov Institute of Chemical Technology.

х. ч. *abbr.* (**химически чистый**) chemically pure.

хьельмит *m.* hielmite.

хьюэттит *m.* hewettite.

Хэббл *see* **Хаббл.**

Хэвенса предел Havens limit.

Хэвисайда *see* **Хевисайда.**

Хэвстед Hafstad.

Хэлла кривая Hull-Davey curve (or chart).

Хэнфорд Hanford.

ХЭТИ *abbr.* (**Харьковский электротехнический институт**) Kharkov Electrical Engineering Institute.

Хэя-Уестергорда пространство напряжений Haigh-Westergaard stress space.

Хюггинса полоса Huggins band.

хюльтеновский потенциал Hulthén potential.

Ц

ц. *abbr.* (**центр**) center; (**центнер**) centner.

Ц [*in steel mark* (**цепь**)] chain.

Ц *abbr.* (**Цельсий**) Celsius, centigrade.

ЦАГИ *abbr.* [**Центральный аэро-гидродинамический институт (им. Н. Е. Жуковского)**] N. E. Zhukovskii Central Aero-Hydrodynamics Institute.

цанг/и *pl.*, **—овый** *a.* tongs, clamp; **—овый патрон** collet.

цапон/лак *m.*, **—овый** *a.* Zapon.

цапф/а *f.*, **—овый** *a.* pin, pivot, journal, trunnion; **шаровая ц.** ball journal; **—овый мост** trunnion bascule bridge.

царап/ание *n.* scratching; **—анный** *a.* scratched; **—ать, —нуть** *v.*, **—ина** *f.* scratch.

царство *n.* kingdom.

ЦБНТИ *abbr.* (**Центральное бюро научно-технической информации**) Central Bureau of Scientific-Technical Information.

ЦБП *abbr.* (**Центральное бюро погоды**) Central Weather Bureau.

ЦБТИ *abbr.* (**Центральное бюро технической информации**) Central Bureau of Technical Information.

цвести *v.* flourish.

цвет *m.* color; **основные —а, первичные —а** primary colors.

Цветметиздат *abbr.* (**Государственное научно-техническое издательство цветной и золото-платиновой промышленности**) Scientific and Technical Press for the Nonferrous, Gold and Platinum Industries.

Цветметмин *abbr.* (**Центральный институт металлургии цветных металлов и прикладной минералогии**) Central Institute of the Metallurgy of Nonferrous Metals and Applied Mineralogy.

цветн/ой *a.* color, colored, chromatic; (met.) nonferrous; **—ая маркировка** color code; **—ое стекло** tinted (or stained) glass; **—ость** *f.* chromaticity; chrominance.

цветоведение *n.* chromatics.

цветов/ой *a.* color, chromatic; **ц. избыток** color excess; **—ая температура** color temperature.

цвето/воспроизводящий *a.* chromatogenic; **—деление** *n.* color separation; **—метр** *m.* colorimeter; **—ощущение** *n.* color sensation; **—рассеяние** *n.* chromatic aberration (or dispersion); **—сдвигающее вещество** scintillation converter, color shifter, wavelength shifter.

цветущий *a.* flourishing.

цвизелит *m.* zwieselite.

ЦГМБ *abbr.* (**Центральное гидрометеорологическое бюро**) Central Hydrometeorological Bureau.

ЦД *abbr.* (**центр давления**) center of pressure.

ЦДТС *abbr.* (**Центральный дом техники связи**) Central House of Communications Engineering.

цебедассит *m.* zebedassite.

цев/ка *f.*, **—очный** *a.* bobbin; pin; **—очное колесо** pin wheel.

Цегимбюро *abbr.* (**Центральное гидрометеорологическое бюро**) Central Hydrometeorological Office.

цед/ильный *a.* filter, filtering, straining; **—ить** *v.* filter, strain.

цежен/ие *n.* filtering, straining; **—ный** *a.* filtered, strained.

цезаролит *m.* cesarolite.

цез/иевый *a.* cesium; **—ий** *m.* cesium (Cs).

цезиобиотит *m.* cesium biotite.

цезированный *a.* cesium-coated.

цейнерит *m.* zeunerite.

цейрингит *m.* zeuringite.

Цейсса линза Zeiss lens.

цейтраферная киносъемка time-lapse photography.

целебн/ость *f.* salubrity; **—ый** *a.* curative, medicinal; salubrious.

целев/ой *a.* purposeful; **—ая установка** aim, object, purpose.

Целена Celaeno.

целесообразн/ость *f.* advisability, expediency, appropriateness, feasibility; **—ый** *a.* advisable, expedient, suitable, practical, feasible.

целестин *m.* celestine, celestite.

целеуказание *n.* target designation.

целеустремленн/ость *f.* purposefulness; **—ый** *a.* purposeful.

целиком *adv.* wholly, entirely, completely; **ц. и полностью** completely.

целительность *see* **целебность.**

целить *v.* aim (at), direct at.

целлофан *m.* cellophane.

целлюлоз/а *f.*, **—ный** *a.* cellulose; **—ность** *f.* cellulosity.

целлюлоид *m.*, **—ный** *a.* celluloid.

цело— *prefix* complete, completely.

целое *n.* (math.) integer; the whole.

целостат *m.* coelostat.

целост/ность *f.* completeness; integrity; entirety; **область —ности** integral domain; **—ный** *a.* complete, undivided; integral; **—ь** *f.* wholeness, continuity; integrity; **в —и** completely, entirely; intact.

целочисленн/ость *f.* integrality; **—ый** *a.* integral.

цел/ый *a.* whole, entire; integral, complete, intact; **ц. спин** integral spin; **ц. тон** whole tone; **—ая функция** integral (or entire) function; **—ое кратное** integral multiple; **—ое число** whole number, integral; **в —ом** as a whole; on the whole; in the large; **правило —ых чисел** whole number rule.

цел/ь *f.* aim, goal, object, purpose; target; objective; **попадать в ц.** hit the mark; **с —ью, в —ях** for the purpose of; purposely; **ставить себе —ью** set a goal (or aim at).

цельзиан *m.* celsian.

цельно *adv.* wholly, entirely, all, in a single piece; **—литой** *a.* unit-cast, one-piece; **—металлический** *a.* all-metal; **—сварной** *a.* all-welded; **—сть** *f.* wholeness, entirety, continuity, integrity; **—тянутый** *a.* solid-drawn, seamless, weldless.

цельный *a.* whole, entire, integral; total; one-piece.

Цельсия шкала Celsius (or centigrade) scale.

цельтий *m.* celtium (Ct) (former name of hafnium).

цемент *m.* cement.

цементационн/ый *a.* cementing; (met.) cementation; **—ая смесь** carbonizer.

цемент/ация *f.*, **—ирование** *n.* cementing; (met.) cementation, carburization, carbonization, case hardening; **поверхностная ц.** case hardening.

цементиров/анный *a.* cemented; (met.) carbonized, carburized, case-hardened; cement (steel); **—ать** *v.* cement; carbonize, carburize, case harden.

цементирующий *a.* cementing.

цементит *m.* cementite.

цементный *a.* cement; **ц. раствор** cement mortar.

Цемплена теорема Cemplen theorem.

цен/а *f.* price, value, cost; **ц. деления** scale value; **—ою** at the cost of.

ценз *m.* qualification; **—овый** *a.* qualificatory, qualifying.

ценз/ор *m.*, **—уровать** *v.* censor; **—ура** *f.* censorship.

ценить *v.* value, estimate, rate; **слишком высоко ц.** overrate.

ценн/ость *f.* value, rate; **функция —ости** (nucl.) importance function; **—ый** *a.* valuable; advantageous.

ценозит *m.* cenosite.

цент *m.* cent.

Центавр Centaurus (Cen) (constellation).

Центавр Centaur (rocket system).

центи— *see* **санти—**.

центи/бар *m.* centibar; **—бел** *m.* centibel; **—пуаз** *m.* centipoise.

центнер *m.* centner (100 kg).

центр *m.* center, central point; nucleus; **ц. водоизмещения** center of buoyancy; **ц. действия** center of action; **ц. захвата** trapping center; **ц. инверсии** center of inversion (or symmetry); **ц. качаний** center of oscillation; **ц. конденсации** condensation center (or nucleus); **ц. люминесценции** luminescence center; **ц. окраски, ц. окрашивания** color center; **ц. подобия** center of similitude; **ц. проявления** developable center; **ц. тяжести** center of gravity (or mass); centroid; emphasis.

централиз/ация *f.* centralization; **—ировать, —овать** *v.* centralize; **—ованный** *a.* centralized.

централласит *m.* centrallassite.

центральн/ый *a.* central, center; **ц. момент** (stat.) central moment; moment about the mean; **—ая предельная теорема** central limit theorem; **—ая сила** central force; **—ая часть потока** core of a flow; **—ое взаимодействие** central-force interaction.

центрир/ование *n.*, **—овка** *f.* centering, alignment; **—ованный** *a.* centered; **—овать** *v.* center; **—ующий** *a.* centering.

центрифуг/а *f.*, **—ировать, —овать** *v.* centrifuge; **—ирование** *n.* centrifuging, centrifugal separation; **—ированный** *a.* centrifuged.

центричный *a.* centric.

центро/барический *a.* centrobaric; **—бежный** *a.* centrifugal; **—бежный момент инерции** product of inertia.

центров/ать *see* **центрировать**; **—ка** *see* **центрирование**; **—ой** *a.* center; **—очный** *a.* centering; center.

центрогранный *a.* face-centered.

центроида *f.* centrode; **неподвижная ц.** space centrode; **подвижная ц.** body centrode.

центроклиналь *f.*, **—ный** *a.* centroclinal.

центро/план *m.* center section; **—симметричный** *a.* centrally symmetrical, centrosymmetrical.

центростремительн/ость *f.* centripetence; **—ый** *a.* centripetal.

центросфера *f.* (geo.) centrosphere, barysphere.

цеолит *m.* zeolite; **—изация** *f.* zeolitization; **—овый** *a.* zeolite, zeolitic; **—ообразный** *a.* zeolitic.

цеофиллит *m.* zeophyllite.

цеп/кий *a.* tenacious; **—кость** *f.* tenacity; **—лять** *v.* hook, catch hold of; **—ляться** *v.* clutch, grasp, cling.

цепн/ой *a.* chain; (math.) catenary; **ц. блок, —ое колесо** sprocket wheel; **ц. привод** chain drive; **ц. фильтр** (elec.) ladder filter; **—ая дробь** continued fraction; **—ая линия** catenary; **—ая молекула** chain molecule; **—ая подвеска** catenary suspension; **—ая реакция** chain reaction; **—ое правило** chain rule.

цепоч/ечный, —ный *a.* chain; **—ка** *f.* (small) chain; array, file, line; (elec.) ladder network.

цеппелин *m.* zeppelin.

цепь *f.* chain; bond; (elec.) circuit; loop; **ц. волн** wave train; **горная ц.** mountain range; **ц. связи** coupling circuit.

цераноограф *m.* ceraunograph; sferics receiver, lightning recorder.

цергадолинит *m.* cergadolinite.

церебральный *a.* cerebral.

церемон/иальный *a.* ceremonial, ceremonious; **—ия** *f.* ceremony.

цересин *m.* ceresin.

цер/иевый *a.* cerium, ceric; **—ий** *m.* cerium (Ce).

церин *m.* cerine.

цернстый *a.* cerium, cerous.

церит *m.* cerite.

церматтит *m.* zermattite.

ЦЕРН *abbr. see* **Европейская организация по ядерным исследованиям.**

цероди— *prefix* cerodi—.

церросил *m.* cerroseal.

церулеит *m.* ceruleite.

церулео/лактит *m.* ceruleolactite; **—фибрит** *m.* ceruleofibrite.

церуссит *m.* cerussite.

Цетиды Cetids (meteors).

цефаровичит *m.* zepharovichite.

цефеида *f.* cepheid.

Цефей Cepheus (Cep) (constellation).

цех *m.*, **—овой** *a.* shop, workshop; department.

цехштейн *m.* Zechstein.

ЦИАМ *abbr.* [**Центральный научно-исследовательский институт авиамоторостроения (им. П. И. Баранова)**] P. I. Baranov Central Scientific Research Institute of Aircraft Engines.

циан— *prefix* cyan—, cyano—.

циан *m.* cyanogen; **—ид** *m.*, **—идный** *a.* cyanide; **—ин** *m.* cyanin; cyanine; **—ирование** *n.* cyanidation.

цианистоводородный *a.* hydrocyanic, hydrocyanide (of).

циано— *prefix* cyano—.

циановый *a.* cyanic.

циано/метр *m.* cyanometer; **—типия** *f.* cyanotype (process); blueprinting.

циано/трихит *m.* cyanotrichite; **—хроит** *m.* cyanochroite.

ЦИАТИМ *abbr.* (**Центральный научно-исследовательский институт авиационных топлив и масел**) Central Scientific Research Institute of Aviation Fuels and Lubricants.

циботактический *a.* cybotactic.

цивилиз/ация *f.* civilization; **—ованный** *a.* civilized; **—овать** *v.* civilize.

цигадит *m.* zygadite.

цигота *f.* zygote.

цикл *m.* cycle; (chem.) ring; **ц. солнечной активности** sunspot cycle; **разрыв —а** (chem.) ring cleavage; **—ида** *f.* cyclide; **—изация** *f.* (chem.) ring formation.

циклическ/ий *a.* cycle, cyclic; circular; recurring; batch; **ц. ускоритель** cyclic (or circular) accelerator; **—ая перегонка** batch distillation; **—ая термообработка** thermal cycling; **—ая частота** angular frequency; cyclic frequency; **—ое соединение** cyclic (or ring) compound.

цикличн/ость *f.* cyclicity, (cyclic) recurrence; **—ый** *a.* cyclic, cycle.

цикло— *prefix* cyclo—.

цикло/вой *see* **цикличный**; **—генез** *m.* cyclogenesis; **—генетический** *a.* cyclogenetic.

цикло/ида *f.* cycloid; **—идальный** *a.* cycloid, cycloidal; **—лиз** *m.* cyclolysis.

циклометр *m.* cyclometer; **—ический** *a.* cyclometric; **—ия** *f.* cyclometry.

циклон *m.* cyclone; **—ичность** *f.* cyclonicity; **—ный** *a.* cyclone, cyclonic; **—ометр** *m.* cyclonometer.

циклопит *m.* cyclopite.

цикло/строфический *a.* cyclostrophic; **—томический** *a.* cyclotomic.

циклотрон *m.*, **—ный** *a.* cyclotron.

ЦИЛ *abbr.* (**Центральная измерительная лаборатория**) Central Measurement Laboratory.

цилиндр *m.* cylinder, roller, tube, drum; **тело —а** cylinder barrel; **—ический** *a.* cylindrical; **—ичность** *f.* cylindricality, cylindricity; **—овый** *a.* cylinder; **—оид** *m.* cylindroid.

ЦИМ *abbr.* (**Центральный институт материалов**) Central Institute of Materials; (**Центральный институт металлов**) Central Institute of Metals.

циматолит *m.* cymatolite.

цимофан *m.* cymophane.

цинк *m.* zinc (Zn); **—алуминит** *m.* zinc-aluminite; **—гаусманнит** *m.* zinc-hausmannite; **—дибраунит** *m.* zinc-dibraunite.

Цинкена-Зоммера условие Zinken-Sommer condition.

цинк/енит *m.* zinckenite; **—ит** *m.* zincite; **—мангано-куммингтонит** *m.* zinc-manganese-cummingtonite.

цинков/альный *a.* galvanizing; **—ание** *n.* zinc coating (or plating), galvanizing; **—анный** *a.* zinc-coated (or -plated), galvanized; **—ать** *v.* zinc coat (or plate), galvanize.

цинково-медный халькантит zinc-copper chalcanthite.

цинков/ый *a.* zinc; **—ая обманка** zinc blende.

цинкограф *m.* zincograph; **—ический** *a.* zincographic; **—ия** *f.* zincography.

цинко/зит *m.* zincosite; **—кальцит** *m.* zincocalcite; **—содержащий** *a.* zinciferous.

Цинн Zinn.

циннвальдит *m.* zinnwaldite.

ЦИНС *abbr.* (**Центральный научно-исследовательский институт сахарной промышленности**) Central Scientific Research Institute of the Sugar Industry.

Циолковского формула Tsiolkovskii formula.

ЦИП *abbr.* (**Центральный институт погоды**) Central Weather Institute.

циппеит *m.* zippeite.

циприн *m.* cyprine.

ципрузит *m.* cyprusite.

ЦИРИР *abbr.* [**Центральный научно-исследовательский институт рентгенологии и радиологии** (**им. В. М. Молотова**)] V. M. Molotov Central Scientific Research Institute of Roentgenology and Radiology.

цирк *m.* (geo.) cirque; lunar crater (of walled-plain type).

циркаллой *m.* zircalloy.

циркелит *m.* zirkelite.

цирклерит *m.* zirklerite.

цирковой *a.* (geo.) cirque.

циркон *m.* zircon; **ц.-фавас** *m.* zircon favas; **—иевый** *a.* zirconium, zirconic; **—ий** *m.* zirconium (Zr).

циркулир/овать *v.* circulate; **—ующий** *a.* circulating, circulation.

Циркуль Circinus (Cir) (constellation).

циркуль *m.* dividers; (pair of) compasses; **делительный ц., измерительный ц., разметочный ц.** dividers.

циркуляр *m.* circular; **—ка** *f.* circular saw; **—ный** *a.* circular; circulatory, circulating; **—ная поляризация** circular polarization.

циркулятор *m.* circulator.

циркуляционный *a.* circulation, circulating; **ц. реактор** circulating reactor.

циркуляция *f.* circulation; circulation integral; **ц. скорости** (hyd.) circulation (integral).

циртолит *m.* cyrtolite.

ЦИС *abbr.* (**Центральный институт связи**) Central Communications Institute.

цис— *prefix* cis—.

цис-изомер *m.* cis-isomer; **ц.-соединение** *n.* cis-compound; **ц.-транс-изомерия** *f.* cis-trans-isomerism.

циссоида *f.* cissoid.

цистеин *m.*, **—овый** *a.* cysteine.

цистерна *f.* cistern, reservoir, tank.

цитата *f.* citation, quotation.

цитиров/ание *n.* citing, quoting; **—ать** *v.* cite, quote; extract.

цито/лиз *m.* cytolysis; **—логия** *f.* cytology; **—плазма** *f.* cytoplasm.

цитраконат *m.* citraconate.

цитрин *m.* citrine.

цитрисикит *m.* zietrisikite.

циферблат *m.*, **—ный** *a.* dial.

цифр/а *f.* figure, number, numeral, digit; tail (of tossed coin); **—ователь** *m.* digitizer.

цифров/ой *a.* numerical, digital, digit; **ц. счетчик** digit counter; **—ая вычислительная машина** digital computer; **—ые данные** figures, numerical data.

Цих Cichus (lunar crater).

цицеро *n.* pica (type).

ЦИЧМ *abbr.* (**Центральный научно-исследовательский институт черной металлургии**) Central Scientific Research Institute of Ferrous Metallurgy.

ЦЛА *abbr.* (**Центральная лаборатория автоматики**) Central Laboratory of Automation.

ЦЛЭМ *abbr.* (**Центральная лаборатория и экспериментальная мастерская электрических и измерительных приборов**) Central Laboratory and Experimental Workshop of Electrical and Measuring Instruments.

ц. м. *abbr.* (**центральный меридиан**) central meridian.

ЦНИГМА *abbr.* (**Центральный научно-исследовательский гидрометеорологический архив**) Central Hydrometeorological Archives.

ЦНИГРИ *abbr.* (**Центральный научно-исследовательский геолого-разведочный институт**) Central Scientific Research Institute of Geological Prospecting.

ЦНИИ *abbr.* (**Центральный научно-исследовательский институт**) Central Scientific Research Institute.

ЦНИИС *abbr.* (**Центральный научно-исследовательский институт связи**) Central Communications Scientific Research Institute.

ЦНИИТ *abbr.* (**Центральный научно-исследовательский институт техники**) Central Scientific Research Institute of Technology.

ЦНИИТМАШ *abbr.* (**Центральный научно-исследовательский институт технологии и машиностроения**) Central Scientific Research Institute of Technology and Mechanical Engineering.

ЦНИИЧМ *abbr.* (**Центральный научно-исследовательский институт черной металлургии**) Central Scientific Research Institute of Ferrous Metallurgy.

ЦНИЛ *abbr.* (**Центральная научно-исследовательская лаборатория**) Central Scientific Research Laboratory.

ЦНИЛхимстрой *abbr.* (**Центральная научно-исследовательская лаборатория стройматериалов химической промышленности**) Central Scientific Research Laboratory of Construction Materials of the Chemical Industry.

ЦНИЛэлектром *abbr.* (**Центральная научно-исследовательская лаборатория электрической обработки материалов**) Central Scientific Research Laboratory for Electrical Treatment of Materials.

ЦНИМАШ *abbr.* (**Центральный научно-исследовательский институт машиностроения**) Central Scientific Research Institute of Mechanical Engineering.

ЦНИЭЛ *abbr.* (**Центральная научно-исследовательская электротехническая лаборатория**) Central Electrical-Engineering Research Laboratory.

ЦНОЛ *abbr.* (**Центральная научно-опытная лаборатория**) Central Scientific Experimental Laboratory.

ЦНТБ *abbr.* (**Центральная научно-техническая библиотека**) Central Library of Science and Technology.

ЦНТЛ *abbr.* (**Центральная научно-техническая лаборатория**) Central Scientific and Technical Laboratory.

цоизит *m.* zoisite.

цоколь *m.*, **—ный** *a.* foundation, base, pedestal; **ц. лампы** lamp (or tube) base.

цоргит *m.* zorgite.

ЦПБ *abbr.* (**Центральная политехническая библиотека**) Central Polytechnic Library.

ЦРЛ *abbr.* (**Центральная радиолаборатория**) Central Radio Laboratory.

ЦС *abbr.* (**центральный совет**) Central Council; Central Soviet.

Ц-система *abbr.* (**система центра масс**) center-of-mass system (c.m. system).

ЦСУ *abbr.* (**Центральное статистическое управление**) Central Statistical Administration.
ЦТ *abbr.* (**центр тяжести**) center of gravity.
ЦТВ *abbr.* (**цветное телевидение**) color television.
ЦУ *abbr.* (**центральное управление**) central administration (of an agency).
цуг *m.* train; **ц. волн** wave train.
ЦУЕГМС *abbr.* (**Центральное управление единой гидрометеорологической службы СССР**) Central Administration of the Unified Hydrometeorological Service of the USSR.
ЦУМВ *abbr.* (**Центральное управление мер и весов**) Central Administration of Weights and Measures.
цунами *f.* tsunami (seismic sea wave).
Цухий Zuchius (lunar crater).

Ч

ч *abbr.* (**час**) hour; **ч.** (**часть**) part, portion; unit; (**число**) number.
чад *m.* fumes, smoke; **—ить** *v.* fume, smoke.
Чайльда закон Child law.
чалка *f.* tie rope.
чальмерзит *m.* chalmersite.
чан *m.* vat, tank.
Чандрасекар Chandrasekhar.
чановый *see* **чан.**
Чаплыгина уравнение Chaplygin equation.
Чапмен *see* **Чепмен.**
час. *abbr.* [**часов** (**при цифре**)] hours (after a number).
час *m.* hour; **—ы** *pl.* clock, watch; meter.
часов/ой *a.* hour, one-hour; clock, watch; **ч. круг** hour circle; **ч. механизм** clockwork; **ч. пояс** time zone; **—ая стрелка** hour hand; **по —ой стрелке** clockwise; **против —ой стрелки** counterclockwise.
части/ца *f.* particle; **—чка** *f.* particulate.
частичн/о *adv.* partially, partly; **—ый** *a.* partial, fractional; particle; **—ый тон** partial tone; **—ая широта уровня** partial level width.
частное *n.* quotient; **неполное ч.** partial quotient.
частност/ь *f.* detail, particular; **в —и** in particular, specifically; **останавливаться на —ях** particularize.
частн/ый *a.* particular, special, individual; partial; private; **ч. дифференциал** partial differential; **ч. интеграл** particular integral (or solution); **ч. случай** particular case; **ч. фронт** (meteor.) secondary front; **—ая производная** partial derivative; **—ая теория относительности** special theory of relativity; **—ое значение** special (or particular) value; **—ое решение** particular solution; **—ым образом** privately, unofficially; **дифференциальное уравнение —ых производных** partial differential equation.
часто *adv.* often, frequently; close, thickly.
частот/а *f.*, **—ный** *a.* frequency; density; closeness; **ч. кадров** frame frequency; **ч. посылок импульсов** pulse repetition rate; **ч. следования** repetition frequency (or rate); **—ная характеристика** frequency response (characteristic); **—но-импульсная модуляция** pulse-frequency modulation.
частотомер *m.* frequency meter.
частый *a.* frequent; dense, thick.
част/ь *f.* part, portion; department, section; unit; **большая ч.** the greater part, most; **третья ч.** a third; **ч. уравнения** side (or member) of an equation; **—ью** partly; **большей —ью** for the most part; **по —и** in connection with; **интегрирование по —ям** (math.) integration by parts; **разобрать на —и** take apart, dismantle.
Часы Horologium (Hor) (constellation).
чатамит *m.* chathamite.
Чаша Crater (Crt) (constellation).
чаша *f.* bowl, cup; pan.
чаше/видный, —образный *a.* cup-shaped.
чашеч/ка *f.* small cup; **—ный** *a.* cup-

shaped, cup; —**ный барометр** cistern barometer.

чашк/а *f.* cup, bowl, dish, pan; pan (of balance); —**ообразный** *a.* cup-shaped.

чаще *comp. of* **часто,** more frequently; **ч. всего** mostly.

чв-ч *abbr.* (**человекочас**) man-hour.

ЧГС *abbr.* (**Черноморская гидрофизическая станция**) Black Sea Hydrophysical Station.

ч. д. а. *abbr.* (**чистый для анализа**) analytically pure.

Чебышева многочлены (полиномы) Chebyshev (Tschebyscheff) polynomials; **Ч. функция** C. function; **чебышевское (наилучшее) приближение** C. approximation.

Чевы теорема Ceva theorem.

чего *gen. of* **что.**

Чедвик Chadwick.

Чезаро Cesàro.

чей *pron. m.,* **чья** *f.,* **чье** *n.,* **чьи** *pl.* whose.

чека *f.* key, wedge, cotter; cotter pin.

чекан *m.* stamp, die; calking iron; —**ить** *v.* stamp; mint; chase, calk; —**ка** *f.* stamping, minting; chasing, calking; calking iron; —**ный** *a.* stamped; coined; chased, calked; —**очный** *a.* stamping; coining; calking.

Челлини гало Cellini halo, heiligenschein.

челнок *m.* shuttle.

человек *m.* man, human being, person; —**о-день** *m.* man-day.

человеч/еский *a.* human; **ч. род** mankind; —**ество** *n.* mankind, humanity; —**ный** *a.* humane.

челюст/ной *a.,* —**ь** *f.* jaw.

чем *instr. of* **что** with what; *conj.* than; **ч. . . . тем . . .** the (more) . . . the (more) . . .

чём *prepositional case of* **что**; **о ч.** about what.

чемавинит *m.* chemawinite.

чемодан *m.* suitcase; carrying case.

чему *dat. of* **что,** to what; **к ч.** to what; what for, why.

Чепмена область Chapman region.

чепуха *f.* nonsense.

черв/еобразный *a.* vermiform, vermicular; —**ь** *m.* worm; —**як** *m.* worm, endless screw.

червячн/ый *a.* worm, screw; **ч. привод** worm gear drive; —**ая передача** worm gear.

черед/ование *n.* alternation, interchange; (order of) sequence; —**овать,** —**оваться** *v.* alternate, interchange; —**ующийся** *a.* alternating, alternate, staggered.

через *prep.* through, via, by; per; in terms of; across, over; in, after; **ч. год** in a year, after a year; **ч. день** in a day; every other day; **ч. один** every other one.

Черенкова (-Вавилова) эффект Cherenkov (Cerenkov) effect.

черенок *m.* shank, handle, grip.

череп *m.* skull, cranium.

черепах/а *f.,* —**овый** *a.* tortoise, tortoise shell.

черепи/ца *f.,* —**чный** *a.* tile.

чересчур *adv.* too, excessively.

чермигит *m.* tschermigite.

черн/ение *n.* blackening; —**еный** *a.* blackened; —**еть** *v.* get black, darken.

чернил/а *pl.* ink; —**ьный** *a.* ink, inky; —**ьные волокна** (astr.) inky filaments.

черн/ить *v.* blacken; —**оватый** *a.* blackish, dark.

чернов/ик *m.* rough copy; —**ой** *a.* rough, preliminary.

чернозем *m.* black earth; chernozem.

чернота *f.* blackness.

черн/ый *a.* black; rough, coarse; (met.) ferrous; **ч. кружок** black (or solid) circle; **ч. термометр** black-bulb thermometer; —**ая температура** black-body temperature; (**абсолютно**) —**ое тело** blackbody; —**ое излучение** blackbody radiation.

чернышевит *m.* tschernichéwite.

чернь *f.* black (pigment); black enamel; niello (on silver); black ore; **медная ч.** black copper, melaconite; **урановая ч.** sooty uraninite.

черпак *m.,* —**овый** *a.* spoon, dipper, ladle; bucket.

черпал/ка *see* **черпак**; —**ьный** *a.* spooning, ladling.

черп/ать, —**нуть** *v.* scoop, ladle; draw

out; derive; —**ачный** *a.* scoop, ladle; bucket; —**ачок** *m.* (small) bucket.

черт. *abbr.* (**чертеж**) drawing, draft, sketch.

черт/а *f.* line; mark, stroke; feature, trait; streak; (math.) bar; vinculum; **отличительная ч.** distinguishing feature, characteristic; **в —е** in the boundaries of; **в общих —ах** in (general) outline; **в основных —ах** basically, mainly.

чертеж *m.* drawing, draft, sketch; —**ная** *f.* drafting room; —**ник** *m.* draftsman.

чертежн/ый *a.* drafting, drawing; —**ая доска** drawing board; —**ая игла** drawing point; —**ая линейка** rule, ruler, straightedge.

черт/илка *f.* marking tool; —**ильный** *see* **чертежный**; —**ить** *v.* draw, draft, sketch.

черточка *f.* short line, dash.

черчен/ие *n.* drawing, sketch; —**ный** *a.* drawn, sketched.

черчит *m.* churchite.

чествовать *v.* honor, celebrate.

честн/ость *f.* honesty, integrity; —**ый** *a.* honest.

честолюб/ивый *a.* ambitious; —**ие** *n.* ambition.

честь *f.* honor; **отдавать ч.** give credit to; salute.

чет *m.* even number.

четверг *m.* Thursday.

четверичный *a.* quaternary.

четвер/ка *f.* four; set of four, quadruplet; (elec.) quad; —**ной** *a.* fourfold, quadruple, quaternary, tetra—.

четверо four; —**який** *a.* fourfold.

четверт/ичный *a.* quaternary; (geo.) Quaternary; —**ной** *a.*, —**ая часть** one fourth, one quarter; —**ый** *a.* fourth.

четверть *f.* one fourth, quarter; —**волновый** *a.* quarter-wave; —**оборотный вентиль** quarter-turn valve.

четки *pl.* beads.

четкий *a.* legible, clear, sharp; definite.

четко/видный, —образный *a.* beaded; —**выраженный** *a.* pronounced, distinct; —**сть** *f.* legibility, clearness, sharpness; definition; accuracy.

четно/-нечетный *a.* even-odd; **ч.-четный** *a.* even-even; —**сть** *f.* parity; evenness; symmetry.

четн/ый *a.* even; of even parity; **ч. эффект** parity effect; —**ое состояние** even parity (state); —**ое число** even number; —**ое ядро** even-mass nucleus.

четочн/ый *a.* beaded; —**ая жила** (min.) wavy vein; —**ая молния** beaded (or pearl) lightning.

четыре four; *prefix see* **четырех—**; —**жды** *adv.* four times; —**ста** four hundred.

четырех— *prefix* tetra—, quadri—, four.

четырех/атомный *a.* tetratomic; —**бромистый** *a.* tetrabromide.

четырехвалентн/ость *f.* tetravalence; —**ый** *a.* tetravalent.

четырех-вектор four-vector.

четырехгранн/ик *m.* tetrahedron; —**ый** *a.* tetrahedral.

четырех/замещенный *a.* tetrasubstituted; —**зарядный** *a.* quadruply charged; —**конечный** *a.* four-point; —**кратный** *a.* fourfold, quadruple; —**лепестковая роза** four-leaved rose; —**мерный** *a.* four-dimensional; —**молекулярный** *a.* tetramolecular; —**окись** *f.* tetroxide; —**основный** *a.* tetrabasic; —**осный** *a.* tetraxial, four-axis.

четырехполюсн/ик *m.* quadripole, four-pole; **ч. типа Г** L network; —**ый** *a.* quadripole, quadripolar, tetrapolar, four-pole, four-polar.

четырех/рядный *a.* four-row; —**сотый** *a.* four-hundredth; —**сплавный** *a.* (met.) quaternary, four-component (alloy).

четырехсторонн/ий *a.*, —**ик** *m.* quadrilateral.

четырех/ступенчатый *a.* four-stage, four-stepped; —**точечный зонд** four-point probe.

четырехугольн/ик *m.* tetragon, quadrangle; —**ый** *a.* tetragonal, quadrangular.

четырех/фазный *a.* four-phase; —**хлористый** *a.* tetrachloride; —**ходовой** *a.* four-way; —**цикловый** *a.* four-cycle; —**членный** *a.* four-membered.

четырнадцат/ый *a.* fourteenth; —**ь** fourteen.

чехол *m.* case, cover; jacket, hood, sheath.

Чехослов/акия Czechoslovakia; **—ацкая Социалистическая Республика** Czechoslovak Socialist Republic.

чечевиц/а *f.* lens; **—еобразный** *a.* lens-shaped, lenticular; **—еобразные облака** lenticular clouds, lenticularis.

Чечено-Ингушская АССР Checheno-Ingush ASSR.

чеш. *abbr. see* **чешский.**

чешский *a.* Czechoslovak, Czech.

чешуй/ка *f.* scale, lamella, plate; **—чатый** *a.* scaly, lamellar, laminated, flaky, platy.

чешуя *f.* scale.

Чикала функция Cicala function.

чили-левеит *m.* Chile-löweïte.

ЧИМ *abbr.* (**частотно-импульсная модуляция**) pulse-frequency modulation (PFM).

чин *m.* rank, grade.

чин/ить *v.* repair; sharpen; cause, do; **ч. препятствия** impede; **—ка** *f.* repair.

чиновн/ик *m.* official; **—ический** *a.* bureaucratic.

численн/о *adv.* numerically; **—ость** *f.* number, quantity, frequency; **—ый** *a.* numerical, numeral.

числитель *m.* numerator; **—ный** *a.* numeral; **имя —ное** numeral.

числиться *v.* be reckoned; **ч. в списке** be on the list.

чис/ло *n.* number, quantity; date; **дружественное ч.** amicable number; **ч. заполнения** occupation number; **общее ч.** total number; **ч. переноса** transport (or transference) number; **закон больших —ел** law of large numbers, law of averages; **первое ч.** the first of the month; **в том —ле** among them; including; **помечать —лом** date; **—лом (в)** in number, numbering; **в первых —ах** early (in the month); **в том —ле** including.

числов/ой *a.* numerical, number; **—ая апертура** numerical aperture.

чист/ить *v.* clean, cleanse, scrub; clear; **—ка** *f.* cleaning, cleansing, scrubbing; clearing; **—о** *adv.* purely; cleanly; neatly; **—о мнимый** pure imaginary.

чистов/ой *a.* clean; finishing; **ч. инструмент** finishing tool; **—ая обработка, —ая отделка** finishing (operation).

чистосердечный *a.* frank, sincere, candid.

чистота *f.* purity; cleanness; clarity.

чист/ый *a.* clean, pure, uncontaminated; neat; clear; blank; net; finished, smooth; **ч. вес** net weight; **ч. полупроводник** intrinsic semiconductor; **ч. тон** pure tone; **химически ч.** chemically pure; **—ая отделка** finishing, finish; **—ое кипение** simmering.

чит/альный *a.* reading; **—атель** *m.* reader; **—ать** *v.* read; deliver (a lecture).

ч. и т. д. *abbr.* (**что и требовалось доказать**) which was to be proved (Q.E.D.).

чище *comp. of* **чисто.**

чл. *abbr.* (**член**) member.

член *m.* member; article; (math.) term; **ч.-корреспондент** associate (or corresponding) member; **—истый** *a.* articulate, jointed; **—ить** *v.* divide into parts, articulate.

членораздельн/ость *f.* articulation; **—ый** *a.* articulate.

членс/кий *a.* member, membership; **—тво** *n.* membership.

чл.-корр. *abbr.* (**член-корреспондент**) associate (or corresponding) member.

ЧМ *abbr.* (**частотная модуляция**) frequency modulation (FM).

Чок-Ривер Chalk River.

Чохральского метод Czochralski method.

чрез *see* **через.**

чрезвычайн/о *adv.* extremely, extraordinarily; **—ость** *f.* extreme, excessiveness; **—ый** *a.* extreme, extraordinary.

чрезмерно *adv.* excessively; **ч. активный** overactive; **ч. большой** exaggerated.

чрезмерн/ый *a.* excessive, over—; **—ая доза** overdose; **—ое группирование** overbunching; **—ое напряжение** overstrain.

ЧСР *abbr. see* **Чехословацкая Социалистическая Республика.**

чт. *abbr.* (**четверг**) Thursday.

чте/ние *n.* reading; lecturing; **—ц** *m.* reader; lecturer.

что *pron.* what, which, that; why; *conj.* that; **ч.-либо, ч.-нибудь** something; anything; **ни за ч.** under no circumstances; **ч.-то** something; somehow; **так, ч.** so that; **для того, что** in order that.

чтоб, —ы *conj.* in order that, in order to, so that; **вместо того, ч.** instead of; **ч. не** lest.

Чувашская АССР Chuvash ASSR.

чувствительн/ость *f.* sensitivity, response, sensitiveness, sensibility, susceptibility, excitability; **ч. по отклонению** deflection sensitivity; **спектральная ч.** spectral response; **—ый** *a.* sensitive, sensible, susceptible, responsive; **—ый элемент** sensitive element, sensing element (or unit), sensor.

чувство *n.* feeling, sense; **обман чувств** illusion; delusion; **органы чувств** sense organs; **—вать** *v.* feel, experience.

чугун *m.*, **—ный** *a.* cast iron; pig iron; **ч. в болванках, ч. в свинках, доменный ч., сырцовый ч., штыковой ч.** pig iron; **зеркальный ч.** specular pig iron, spiegeleisen; **болванка —а** pig.

чугуно/литейная *f.*, **—литейный завод** iron foundry; **—плавильный завод** iron works.

чудес/а *pl. of* **чудо**; **—ный** *a.* wonderful, extraordinary.

чудн/о *adv.* strangely; marvelously; **—ой** *a.* odd, strange; **—ый** *a.* marvelous.

чудо *n.* miracle, marvel.

чуж/даться *v.* avoid; **—дый** *a.* foreign, strange, alien, extraneous; **—еродный** *a.* foreign.

чужой *a.* foreign, strange; another's; *m.* foreigner, stranger.

чулок *m.* stocking.

чур/бан *m.* block; **—ка** *f.* chock, block.

Чу теория Chew theory.

чутк/ий *a.* sensitive; tactful; **—ость** *f.* sensitivity, tact.

чуть *adv.* hardly; slightly; **ч. не** almost, nearly; **ч. только** as soon as; **ч.-ч.** *adv.* very nearly; very slightly.

чутье *n.* scent; feeling.

чушка *f.* pig, ingot.

чье, чьи, чья *see* **чей.**

чэзи *n.* Chazy subdivision.

Ш

ш. *abbr.* (**широкий**) wide, broad; (**широта**) latitude.

Ш [*in steel mark* (**шарикоподшипниковая**)] ball-bearing steel.

шабер *m.* scraper.

шаблон *m.*, **—ный** *a.* pattern, template; stencil; mold; gauge; (elec.) former; **угловой ш.** angle template; **—ная обмотка** (elec.) diamond winding.

шабот *m.* anvil block.

шабр/ение *n.*, **—овка** *f.* scraping; **—ить** *v.* scrape; **—ованный** *a.* scraped.

шаг *m.* step, spacing, interval, pitch, pace; **ш. поступания** translation period (or step); **ш. решетки** lattice spacing; **ш. за —ом** step by step; **—ать** *v.* pace, step; **—овый** *a.* step, step-by-step; pitch; **—омер** *m.* pedometer; pitch gauge.

шадеит *m.* schadeite.

шазеллит *m.* chazellite.

шайба *f.* washer; disk; **ш. термистора** thermistor bead.

шайрерит *m.* schairerite.

шаллерит *m.* schallerite.

Шаля теорема Chasles theorem.

шамозит *m.* chamosite.

шамот *m.*, **—ный, —овый** *a.* chamotte, grog; fireclay.

шанс *m.* chance; **—ы** *pl.* chances, odds.

шанцевый инструмент digging tool.

шанявскит *m.* shanyavskite.

шапбахит *m.* schapbachite.

Шаперона обмотка Chaperon resistor.

шап/ка *f.* cap; **—очка** *f.* (small) cap, bonnet; **—очнообразное облако** cap cloud, cloud cap.

шар *m.* sphere, ball, globe; balloon; **воздушный ш.** balloon; **земной ш.** globe, the earth; **ш.-зонд** sounding balloon; **ш.-пилот** pilot balloon; **ш.-**

эталон calibration ball (of depth finder).
шарик *m.* (small) ball; globule, bead, pellet; bulb (of thermometer); (blood) corpuscle.
шариков/ый *a.* ball; **ш. подшипник, —ая опора** ball bearing; **—ая счетная трубка** point (or Geiger-Klemperer) counter; **—ая трубка** bulb tube.
шарикоподшипник *m.* ball bearing; **упорный ш.** ball thrust bearing.
шарицерит *m.* scharizerite.
Шарлье контрольный прием (stat.) Charlier check.
Шарля закон Charles law.
шармут *m.* Charmouthian stage.
шарнир *m.* hinge, joint, link; **ш. складки** (geo.) trough (or crest) of a fold; **универсальный ш.** universal joint; **на —е, на —ах** hinged.
шарнирно закрепленный, ш. опертый, ш. укрепленный hinged.
шарнирн/ый *a.* hinge, joint, link, swivel; hinged, jointed; **ш. болт** link (or swing) bolt; **ш. клапан** flap valve; **—ое соединение** hinged (turning, socket, swivel, articulated) joint; flexible coupling; link connection.
шаровидн/ость *f.* sphericity; **—ый** *a.* spherical, spheroidal, globular; **—ая молния** *see* **шаровая молния.**
шаров/ой *a.* spherical, globular; sphere, ball; **ш. затвор** ball lock; **ш. клапан** ball valve; **ш. фотометр** sphere (or globe) photometer; **ш. шарнир, —ое соединение, —ое шарнирное соединение, —ое сочленение** ball-and-socket joint; **—ая мельница** ball mill; **—ая молния** ball (or globe) lightning; **—ая функция** spherical harmonic (or function); **—ое скопление** (astr.) globular cluster.
шарообразный *see* **шаровидный.**
шарош/ечный *a.* cutting, milling; **—ка** *f.* cutter, milling cutter; mill.
Шарп Sharp (lunar crater).
Шарпи копер Charpy impact machine.
шарфовидное облако scarf cloud, pileus.
шарьяж *m.* overthrust, overthrust folding, overthrust mass.
шасси *n.* chassis, undercarriage; (aero.) landing gear.
шат/ание *n.* swaying; **—ать** *v.* shake, rock, sway; **—аться** *v.* loosen; shake; **—ающийся** *a.* loose.
шатк/ий *a.* unsteady, wavering; **—ость** *f.* unsteadiness, looseness.
шатнуть *see* **шатать.**
шаттукит *m.* shattuckite.
шатун *m.* connecting rod.
шафарцикит *m.* schafarzikite.
шахмат/ный *a.* checkerboard, staggered; checkered; **в —ном порядке** staggered; **—ы** *pl.* chess.
шахт/а *f.* mine, pit, shaft; **—ер** *m.* miner; **—ный** *a.* mine, mining, pit, shaft; **—ный водосброс** shaft spilling.
шашка *f.* saber; charge (of explosive or fuel).
швартцембергит *m.* schwartzembergite.
Шварца неравенство Schwarz inequality; **принцип отражения Ш.** S. principle of reflection; **преобразование Ш.-Кристоффеля** S.-Christoffel transformation.
Шварцшильда коэффициент Schwarzschild coefficient.
швацит *m.* schwazite.
швед. *abbr. see* **шведский.**
шведский *a.* Swedish.
швейц. *abbr.* (**швейцарский**) Swiss.
Швейцария Switzerland.
швейцарский *a.* Swiss.
швейцерит *m.* schweizerite.
швелевание *n.* low-temperature carbonization.
швеллер *m.*, **—ный** *a.* channel bar (or iron).
Швеция Sweden.
Швингер Schwinger.
швыр/нуть, —ять *v.* throw, **—яние** *n.* throwing.
Шевено Cheveneau.
шевронный *a.* herringbone.
шеелит *m.* scheelite.
шеерерит *m.* scheererite.
Шези формула Chézy formula.
шейка *f.* neck, throat; (mech.) pin, journal; **ш. разделения** scission neck; **ш. рупора** horn throat.
Шейнер Scheiner (lunar crater).
Шейнера формула Scheiner formula.
шейный *see* **шейка.**
шелк *m.* silk.

шелков/идный, —истый *a.* silky; **—ина** *f.* silk thread; **—ичный, —ый** *a.* silk.
шеллак *m.*, **—овый** *a.* shellac.
шелохнуть, —ся *v.* move, stir.
шелу/ха *f.* husk, shell, peel; **—шение** *n.* peeling, shelling; scaling.
шельфовый лед shelf ice.
шеневиксит *m.* chenevixite.
шенит *m.* schoenite.
Шеннон, Шенон Shannon.
Шенфлис Schönflies.
шепинг *m.*, **ш.-машина** *f.* shaper, shaping machine.
шепит *m.* schoepite.
шеп/нуть, —тать *v.* whisper.
шерардиз/ация *f.*, **—ирование** *n.* sherardization, sherardizing.
шеренга *f.* rank.
шererит *see* **шеererит.**
Шеринга мост Schering bridge.
шерл *m.* schorl, black tourmaline; **—омит** *m.* schorlomite.
шерохов/альный *a.*, **—ание** *n.*, **—ка** *f.* roughing; buffing; **—атость** *f.* roughness; **—атый** *a.* rough.
шерст/еподобный, —истый *a.* wooly, wool-like; **—яной** *a.* wool, woolen; **—ь** *f.* wool.
шерт *m.* chert.
шертелит *m.* schertelite.
шершав/еть *v.* roughen; **—ость** *f.* roughness; **—ый** *a.* rough.
шест *m.* pole, post.
шествие *n.* procession.
шестер/енка *f.*, **—енный, —еночный, —енчатый** *a.* pinion, gear.
шестер/ик *m.*, **—ка** *f.* six, sextet; **—ной** *a.* six, sixfold; **—о** six.
шестерня *see* **шестеренка.**
шести— *prefix* hex—, hexa—, six.
шести/атомный *a.* hexatomic; **—валентный** *a.* hexavalent.
шестигранн/ик *m.* hexahedron; **—ый** *a.* hexahedral; **—ая призма** hexagonal prism.
шестидесят/иричный *a.* sexagenary, sexagesimal; **—ый** *a.* sixtieth.
шести/дневный *a.* six-day; **—кратный** *a.* sixfold, sextuple.
шестилет/ие *n.* six-year period; **—ний** *a.* six-year.
шести/окись *f.* hexoxide; **—основный** *a.* hexabasic; **—ричный** *a.* senary; **—сотый** *a.* six-hundredth.
шестисторонн/ий *a.* hexahedral; **—ик** *m.* hexahedron.
шестиугольн/ик *m.* hexagon; **—ый** *a.* hexagonal.
шести/фтористый уран uranium hexafluoride; **—членный** *a.* six-membered.
шестнадцатигранн/ик *m.* dioctahedron; **—ый** *a.* dioctahedral.
шестнадцати/польный момент hexadecapole moment; **—ричный** *a.* sexadecimal.
шестнадцат/ый *a.* sixteenth; **—ь** sixteen.
шестоватый *a.* columnar.
шест/ой *a.* sixth; **одна —ая** one sixth.
шесть six; **—десят** sixty; **—сот** six hundred.
шеф *m.* chief; **—ствовать** *v.* head; look after.
Шеффера кислота Scheffer acid; **Ш. соединение** (*or* **звено**) (logic) S. stroke.
шефферит *m.* schefferite.
шея *f.* neck.
шибер *m.*, **—ный** *a.* gate, slide valve.
шизолит *m.* schizolite.
Шиккард Schickard (lunar crater).
Шиллер Schiller (lunar crater).
шиллер-шпат *m.* schiller spar, bastite.
шило *n.* awl.
ШИМ *abbr.* (**модуляция шириной импульсов**) pulse-width modulation (PWM).
шимм/ирование *n.* shimming; **—ы** *pl.* shims.
шина *f.* tire; strip; (elec.) busbar.
Шинколобве Shinkolobwe.
шинколобвит *m.* shinkolobwite.
шинн/ый *see* **шина**; **—ое железо** band (or hoop) iron.
шип *m.* pin, dowel; tongue, tenon; pivot; calk; **ш. и гнездо** tenon and mortise.
шип/ение *n.* hissing; effervescing; **—еть** *v.* hiss; effervesce.
Шиппингпорт Shippingport.
шипуч/есть *f.* effervescence; **—ий** *a.* effervescent.
шипящ/ий *a.* hissing; sibilant; **—ая дуга** hissing arc.
шир. *abbr.* (**широта**) latitude.

шире *comp. of* **широкий, широко,** broader, wider; more broadly (or widely).
Ширекса-Мени антенна Chireix and Mesny antenna.
шир/ение *n.* broadening, widening; **—ина** *f.* width, breadth; gauge.
ширит/ельный *a.* stretching; **—ь** *v.* stretch, widen, enlarge; **—ься** *v.* widen, spread, expand, enlarge.
ширма *f.* screen, shield, blind; baffle (plate).
ширмерит *m.* schirmerite.
широк/ий *a.* wide, broad, extended; extensive; widespread; **ш. атмосферный ливень** extensive air shower; **ш. источник** extended source; **—ая публика** general public; **—о** *adv.* broadly, widely, extensively.
широко— *prefix* wide, widely.
широковещ/ание *n.*, **—ательный** *a.* broadcast, broadcasting.
широко/горлый *a.* wide-necked; **—диапазонный** *a.* wide-range; **—колейный** *a.* broad- (or wide-) gauge; **—полосный** *a.* wide-band, broad-band; **—угольный** *a.* wide-angle.
широт/а *f.* latitude; breadth, width; extension; (stat.) range; **фотографическая ш.** photographic latitude; **—ный** *a.* latitude, latitudinal; lateral.
ширь *f.* extent; (wide) expanse.
шифер *m.*, **—ный** *a.* slate.
шифр *m.* code, cipher; **—атор** *m.* coder; **—ованный** *a.* coded.
шихта *f.* mixture; charge, batch, stock, burden.
шихтов/ание *n.*, **—ка** *f.* burdening, preparing a charge; **—ать** *v.* burden; **—ый** *a.* burden, charge.
шишечный *a.* (foundry) core; **ш. каркас, ш. шпиндель** core mandrel, core rod; **ш. песок** core sand.
шишк/а *f.* bump, lump; knob; (foundry) core; **—оватый, —овидный** *a.* knobby.
шкала *f.* scale; **ш. времени** time scale; time base; **(круговая) ш.** dial.
шкаф *m.*, **—ной** *a.* cabinet, closet; **вытяжной ш.** fume cabinet; **сушильный ш.** desiccator; **—чик** *m.* small closet, locker.
шквал *m.* squall; **—истый** *a.* squally; **—овый воротник** arcus, roll cloud.
шкворень *m.* pin, bolt, pivot; (automobile) king pin.
шкив *m.* pulley; sheave.
школ/а *f.*, **—ьный** *a.* school; **—ьник** *m.* schoolboy.
шкур/а *f.*, **—ный** *a.* hide, skin; **—ка** *f.* emery cloth, sandpaper; skin; rind; **стеклянная —ка** sandpaper.
шлагбаум *m.* barrier, tollgate, lifting gate; turnpike.
шлак *m.* slag.
шлако/бетон *m.* slag concrete; **—вание** *n.* slag formation; slagging; **—ватый, —видный** *a.* slaggy; **—вать** *v.* (form) slag; **—вик** *m.* slag chamber; **—вый** *a.* slag, slaggy.
шлам *m.*, **—овый** *a.* slime; sludge; slurry; **—овый реактор** slurry reactor.
шламообраз/ное горючее slurry fuel; **—ование** *n.* sludging.
шланг *m.*, **—овый** *a.* hose.
шлейф *m.* trail; (elec.) stub; loop; **ш.-вибратор** folded dipole; **—овый осциллограф** loop oscillograph.
шлем *m.* helmet; **ш. перегонного куба** still head (or dome).
Шлемильха ряд (разложение по бесселевым функциям) Schlömilch expansion.
шлемов/ой, —ый *a.* helmet.
шлеп/ать, —нуть *v.* slap; splash.
шлеппер *m.* dragging device, pull-over.
шликер *m.* dross.
шлир/а *f.*, **—овый** *a.*, **—ы** *pl.* schlieren, streaks, striae.
шлиф *m.*, **—ной** *a.* ground-glass joint; ground end; thin section; **стеклянный ш.** ground-glass joint.
шлифовальн/ик *m.* grinding disk (or machine); **—ый** *a.* grinding, polishing; **—ый круг** grinding wheel (or disk).
шлифов/ание *n.*, **—ка** *f.* grinding, polishing; **—анный** *a.* ground, polished; **—ать** *v.* grind, polish.
шлихтов/ание *n.*, **—ка** *f.* smoothing, finishing; dressing, sizing; **—анный** *a.* finished; sized; **—ать** *v.* smooth, finish; dress, size.
шлиц *m.* slit, slot; **—евать** *v.* slit, slot; **—евой** *a.* slit, slot; **—ованный** *a.* slit, slotted.

шлюз *m.*, **—ный** *a.* sluice, lock; **—ование** *n.* locking; sluicing; **—овая камера** transfer chamber.
шляпка *f.* cap, head (of nail, etc.).
Шмидта линия Schmidt line; **шмидтовская камера** S. camera.
Шмитта спусковая схема Schmitt trigger circuit.
шнеебергит *m.* schneebergite.
шнейдерит *m.* schneiderite.
шнек *m.*, **—овый** *a.* auger; worm, endless screw; screw conveyer.
Шнирельмана константа Shnirel'man constant.
шнур *m.* cord; (elec.) filament; **запальный ш.** fuse.
шнуров/ание *n.*, **—ка** *f.* lacing, tying; **—ать** *v.* lace, tie; **—ой** *see* **шнур.**
Ш-образный *a.* E-shaped.
шов *m.* seam, joint, junction, weld.
Шовене критерий Chauvenet criterion.
шовный *see* **шов.**
шок *m.* shock.
шопот *m.* whisper.
Шора склероскоп Shore scleroscope.
шоран *m.* Shoran.
Шорт Short (lunar crater).
Шортли Shortley.
шоссе *n.*, **—йный** *a.*, **—йная дорога** highway, macadam road.
Шоттки дефект Schottky defect.
шпага *f.* sword.
шпагат *m.* twine, cord.
шпаклев/ание *n.*, **—ка** *f.* filling, puttying; filler, putty.
шпангоут *m.* bulkhead frame, rib (of ship); (aero.) former.
шпат *m.* spar; **полевой ш.** feldspar; **тяжелый ш.** heavy spar, barite.
шпатель *m.* spatula.
шпато/видный, —вый *a.* spar, sparry, spathic; **—вый железняк** spathic iron, siderite.
шпация *f.* (typ.) space.
шпейза *f.* speiss.
шпенек *m.* pin, peg, prong.
Шперера закон Spörer law.
шпигель *m.* spiegel, spiegeleisen.
шпиль *m.* spire; needle, pin, pivot; reel, capstan, windlass.
шпилька *f.* tack, brad, stud; hairpin; pin.
шпингалет *m.* (upright) bolt.
шпиндель *m.*, **—ный** *a.* spindle, arbor shaft.
шпинель *m.* spinel; **ш.-рубин** *m.* ruby spinel.
шпион *m.* spy.
шплинт *m.* splint, split pin, cotter, lock pin.
шпон/ка *f.*, **—очный** *a.* key, spline, cotter; **—очная канавка** keyway.
шпора *f.* spur.
шпреуштейн *m.* spreustein.
шприц *m.* injector; syringe; **ш. для смазки** lubrication gun; **ш.-машина** *f.* extruder; **ш.-процесс** *m.* extrusion process; **—гусс** *m.* die casting; **—евание** *n.* extrusion; **—евать** *v.* extrude; **—ованный** *a.* extruded.
шпрудельштейн *m.* sprudelstein.
шпул/ька, —я *f.* spool, bobbin.
шпунт *m.* groove, slot, rabbet; **ш. и гребень** groove and tongue; **—овое соединение** tongue-and-groove joint.
шпур *m.* blast (or shot) hole; (math.) trace, Spur.
шрауфит *m.* schraufite.
Шредингера волновое уравнение Schrödinger wave equation; **шредингеровское дрожание** S. Zitterbewegung.
шрейберзит *m.* schreibersite.
шрекингерит *m.* schroeckingerite.
Шретер Schröter (lunar crater).
шреттерит *m.* schrötterite.
шрифт *m.* type, print.
шрот-эффект shot (or schrot) effect.
шт. *abbr.* (**штука**) piece.
штаб *m.* (mil.) staff, headquarters.
штабел/евать *v.* pile, stack; **—ь** *m.* pile, stack, dump.
штабик *m.* rod.
штабной *a.* staff.
штамп *m.* stamp, punch, die.
штампов/альный *see* **штамповочный**; **—ание** *n.*, **—ка** *f.* stamping, punching; **—анный** *a.* stamped, punched, drop-forged; **—ать** *v.* stamp, punch, drop forge; **горячая —ка** drop forging; **ковочная —ка** drop forging, swaging; **—ка с вытяжкой** extrusion.
штамповочный *a.* stamping, punching, pressing; **ш. молот** drop hammer.

штампов/ый *a.* stamp, punch; *see also* **штамповочный; —ые краски** printing inks.
штанга *f.* rod, bar; pillar; valve stem; **буровая ш.** drill rod.
штанген высоты *see* **штангенрейсмус.**
штанген/зубомер *m.* gear-tooth gauge; **—рейсмус** *m.* height gauge; **—циркуль** *m.* slide caliper.
штанговый *a.* rod, bar.
Штарка квадратичный эффект quadratic (or secondary) Stark effect; **Ш. эффект (явление), штарк-эффект** S. effect; **штарковское расщепление** S. splitting.
штат *m.* state; staff.
штатив *m.* stand, support; rack; base, foot.
штатный *a.* staff, regular.
штатский *a.* civil, civilian; *m.* civilian.
штауфер *m.* lubricating screw, compression grease cup.
штаффелит *m.* staffelite.
штейн *m.* matte.
штейнгейлит *m.* steinheilite.
Штейнера теорема Steiner theorem.
штейнманнит *m.* steinmannite.
Штейнмеца закон Steinmetz law.
Штеккеля определитель Stäckel determinant.
штельцнерит *m.* stelznerite.
штемпел/евание *n.* stamping; **—евать** *v.*, **—ь** *m.*, **—ьный** *a.* stamp.
штенгель *m.* stem.
штепсель *m.*, **—ная вилка** plug; **—ный** *a.* plug, plug-type.
штермеровский конус Störmer cone.
Штерна-Герлаха опыт Stern-Gerlach experiment.
штернбергит *m.* sternbergite.
Штефлер Stöfler (lunar crater).
штил/евой *a.*, **—ь** *m.* calm; **—евые полосы** doldrums.
штифт *m.* pin; dowel; **—ик** *m.* brad.
штихель *m.* graver, burin.
штихмас *m.* end (or inside) gauge.
шток *m.* rod, shaft; (geo.) stock.
Штока термометр Stock thermometer.
штольня *f.* (min.) adit.
штольпенит *m.* stolpenite.
штольцит *m.* stolzite.
штопор *m.*, **—ный** *a.* corkscrew; (aero.) spin; **правило —а** (elec.) right-hand screw rule; **—ить** *v.* spin.
штора *f.* blind.
шторка *f.* screen.
шторм *m.* (strong) gale (Beaufort number 9); **жестокий ш.** storm (Beaufort number 11); **сильный ш.** whole gale (Beaufort number 10); **—овой** *a.* gale, storm.
штоссель *m.* slide (or push) rod.
штраф *m.* fine, penalty.
штрек *m.* (min.) drift.
штренгит *m.* strengite.
штрипс *m.*, **—овый** *a.* strip.
штрих *m.* dash, line, stroke; prime; feature; **ш.-пунктир** *m.*, **ш.-пунктирная линия** dot-dash line.
штрихов/анный *a.* shaded, hatched; (math.) primed; **—ать** *v.* shade, hatch; (math.) prime; **—ка** *f.* shading, hatching; **—ой** *see* **штрих; —ой пунктир, —ая линия** dashed line.
штромейерит *m.* stromeyerite.
штудировать *v.* study.
штука *f.* piece.
штукатур/ить *v.* plaster, stucco; **—ка** *f.* plaster, plastering, stucco.
штуковать *v.* mend.
штурвал *m.* steering wheel, control wheel.
штурм *m.* assault.
штурман *m.* navigator.
Штурма теорема Sturm theorem; **Ш.-Лиувиля (Лиувилля) уравнение** S.-Liouville equation.
штуцер *m.*, **—ный** *a.* connecting pipe, fitting.
штучный *a.* piece.
штык *m.*, **—овой** *a.* bayonet; (met.) pig.
штыр/евой *a.*, **—ь** *m.* pin, dowel; stub; nail.
Штюве диаграмма, штювеграмма *f.* Stüve diagram.
штютцит *m.* stützite.
Шуберт Schubert (lunar crater).
шуга *f.* sludge, frazil ice.
шультенит *m.* schultenite.
шульценит *m.* schulzenite.
шум *m.* noise; **ш.-фактор, коэффициент —а** noise factor (or figure).
шуманнов/а область Schumann region; **—ские фотопластинки** S. plates.

шум/еть *v.* make noise; **—ность** *f.* noisiness; **—ный** *a.* noisy.

шумовка *f.* skimmer.

шумов/ой *a.* noise; **—ая буря** (radio astr.) noise storm; **—ая температура** noise temperature.

шумо/глушитель, —заглушитель *m.* silencer, muffler; **—защитный** *a.* sound-insulating; **—мер** *m.* noise meter; phonometer; **—пеленгатор** *m.* hydrophone.

шум/ы *pl. of* **шум; ш. теплового возбуждения** thermal (agitation) noise; **—ящий** *a.* noisy.

шунгит *m.* schungite, shungite.

шунт *m.* shunt; bypass.

шунтиров/ание *n.*, **—ка** *f.* shunting; bypassing, bridging; **—ать** *v.* shunt; bypass, bridge.

шунт/ирующий *a.* shunting; bypass; **—ование** *see* **шунтирование; —овать** *see* **шунтировать; —овой** *a.* shunt; shunt-wound; bypass; **—овой двигатель** shunt motor; shunt-wound motor.

Шура лемма Schur lemma.

шуровать *v.* rabble, stir.

шуруп *m.* (wood) screw.

шурф *m.* hole, pit, excavation; **—ование** *n.* pitting, excavation.

шуршание *n.* crackling, rustling.

шутка *f.* joke; trick.

шухардит *m.* schuchardite.

Шэн Shane.

Щ

щавелевый *a.* oxalic.

щебень *m.* rubble; ballast; (geo.) detritus.

щедр/ость, —ота *f.* liberality, generosity; **—ый** *a.* liberal, generous.

щека *f.* cheek, side; jaw.

щеколда *f.* latch, catch, pawl.

щекообразный *a.* jaw-shaped.

щел. *abbr.* (**щелочной**) alkaline.

щелев/ой *a.* slit, slot, slotted; **щ. источник** slit source; **щ. спектр** slit spectrum; **—ая антенна** slot antenna; **—ая коррозия** crevice corrosion.

щел/ина *f.* gap; **—ка** *see* **щель.**

щелк/анье *n.* clicking, snapping; **—ать, —нуть** *v.* click, snap.

щелок *m.* lye.

щелочно— *prefix* alkali.

щелочно/-галоидный *a.* alkali-halide; **щ.-земельный металл** alkali-earth metal.

щелоч/ной *a.* alkali, alkaline; **щ. металл** alkali metal; **—ное разложение** caustic soda decomposition; **—ность** *f.* alkalinity; **—ь** *f.* alkali.

щелчок *m.* click.

щель *f.* slit, slot; crack, fissure; gap.

щенки *pl.* calved ice.

щеп/а *f.* chips, shavings; **—ать, —ить** *v.* chip, splinter; **—ка** *f.* chip, sliver, splinter, shaving.

щетина *f.* bristle.

щет/ка *f.* brush; wiper; **—кодержатель** *m.* brush holder; **—очка** *f.* small brush; **—очный** *a.* brush; **—очный палец** brush spindle (or stud).

щип/ать, —нуть *v.* pluck; **—цы** *pl.* tongs, pincers, pliers, forceps; **—чики** *pl.* tweezers.

Щит Scitum (Sct) (constellation).

щит *m.* panel, board; shield, screen; switchboard; (hyd.) sluice (gate); **щ. управления** control board (or panel); **—овидный** *a.* shield-shaped; thyroid; **—овое отверстие** sluice gate.

щито/к *m.* shield, screen; panel, board; **форменный щ.** name plate; **—образный** *a.* shield-shaped.

щуп *m.* probe; feeler, thickness gauge; sounding borer; test rod, dip rod; **—ать** *v.* probe; feel, touch.

Э

э *abbr.* (**эрг**) erg; (**эрстед**) oersted (oe.)

ЭАО *abbr.* (**экспериментально-аэродинамический отдел**) experimental aerodynamics section.

Эбергарда явление Eberhard effect.

Эберта эффект Ebert effect.

эбигит *m.* ebigite.

эбонит *m.*, **—овый** *a.* ebonite.

эбулиометр *m.* ebulliometer.
эбулиоскоп *m.* ebullioscope; **—ический** *a.* ebullioscopic; **—ия** *f.* ebullioscopy.
эв *abbr.* (**электронвольт**) electron volt.
ЭВ *abbr.* (**экваториальный воздух**) equatorial air.
эв— *see* **эй—**.
эваку/ационный *a.*, **—ация** *f.* evacuation; **—ированный** *a.* evacuated; **—ировать** *v.* evacuate.
Эвальд Ewald.
эвапор/ация *f.* evaporation, vaporization; **—ограф** *m.* recording evaporimeter, atmograph; **—ометр** *m.* evaporimeter.
эвгедральн/ость *f.*, **—ый** *a.* euhedral.
эвгранитовый *a.* eugranitic.
эвдиалит *m.* eudialyte.
эвдидимит *m.* eudidymite.
эвдиометр *m.* eudiometer; **—ический** *a.* eudiometric; **—ия** *f.* eudiometry.
эвднофит *m.* eudnophite.
Эвдокс, —а *see* **Евдокс, —а.**
эвекц/ионный *a.* evectional; **—ия** *f.* evection.
эвердур *m.* Everdur (silicon bronze).
Эвершеда эффект Evershed effect.
эвкайрит *m.* eucairite.
эвклаз *m.* euclase.
Эвклид Euclid; **эвклидова геометрия** Euclidean geometry.
эвколит *m.* eucolite.
эвкриптит *m.* eucryptite.
эвксенит *m.* euxenite.
эвлит/ин *m.* eulytine. **—ит** *m.* eulytite.
эвольвент/а *f.*, **—ный** *a.* evolvent; involute.
эволюта *f.* evolute.
эволюц/ионировать *v.* evolve; **—ионный** *a.* evolution, evolutionary; **—ия** *f.* evolution.
эвпирхроит *m.* eupyrchroite.
эвралит *m.* euralite.
эвристический *a.* heuristic.
эврит *m.* eurite.
эвсинхит *m.* eusynchite.
эвстатический *a.* eustatic.
эвтаксит *m.* eutaxite; **—овый** *a.* eutaxic.
эвталлит *m.* euthallite.
эвтект/ика *f.*, **—ический** *a.* eutectic; **—оид** *m.*, **—оидный** *a.* eutectoid.
эвхроит *m.* euchroite.
эгейит *m.* egueïite.
эгида *f.* aegis.
эгирин *m.* aegirine, aegirite, acmite; **э.-авгит** *m.* aegirine-augite.
Эгнеля закон Egnell law.
ЭД *abbr.* [**электродинамические** (**приборы**)] electrodynamic (apparatus).
Эдди теорема Eddy theorem.
Эдисона эффект (**явление**) Edison effect.
Эдкока *see* **Адкока.**
эдр *suffix* —hedron; **—ический** *suffix* —hedral.
э.д.с. *abbr.* (**электродвижущая сила**) electromotive force (emf).
Эдьюкейтор Educator (reactor).
э. ед. *abbr.* (**электронная единица**) electronic unit.
эжектор *m.*, **—ный** *a.* ejector, ejector pump.
эзаидрит *m.* esaidrite.
ЭЗО *abbr.* (**этилцеллюлозная защитная оболочка**) ethylcellulose protective coating.
ЭИН *abbr.* [**Энергетический институт** (**Академии наук СССР**)] Institute of Power Engineering (of the Academy of Sciences, USSR).
эй— *prefix* eu—, ei—; *see also* **эв—**.
Эйбл Able (rocket system).
эйзенстассфуртит *m.* eisenstassfurtite.
Эйкена закон Eucken law.
эйкозан *m.* eicosane.
эйконал *m.* eikonal.
эйконоген *m.* eiconogen.
эйксенит *m.* euxenite.
Эйлера отношение Euler relation; **числа Э.** E. numbers; **формула Э.-Маклорена** E.-Maclaurin formula; **Э.-Маскерони постоянная** E.-Mascheroni constant; **эйлеров** *a.* Euler, Eulerian.
Эйнштейна закон Einstein law; **эффект Э.-де Хааза** E.-de Haas effect.
эйнштейн/ий *m.* einsteinium (E); **—овская частота** (**тепловых колебаний**) Einstein frequency; **—овское искривление** Einstein deflection effect.
Эйри *see* **Эри.**
Эйринга формула Eyring formula.
эйфельский ярус Eifelian stage.
эйхбергит *m.* eichbergite.
эйхвальдит *m.* eichwaldite.
Эйхенвальда опыт Eichenwald experiment.

эйч-металл *m.* Aich metal (copper-zinc-iron alloy).

эка— *prefix* eka—.

экв *abbr.* (**эквивалент**) equivalent.

Экватор Equateur (French thermonuclear device).

экватор *m.* equator.

экваториальн/ый *a.* equatorial; **э. выступ** equatorial bulge; **—ая зона затишья** doldrums; **—ое поворотное устройство** equatorial mounting.

экв. ед. *abbr.* (**эквивалентная единица**) equivalent unit.

экви— *prefix* equi—.

эквивалент *m.* equivalent; **э. антенны** artificial (or dummy) antenna; **—ность** *f.* equivalence; **—ный** *a.* equivalent.

экви/волюминальный *a.* equivoluminal; **—градиентный** *a.* equigradient.

эквидистантн/ость *f.* equidistance; **—ый** *a.* equidistant.

эквилибр *m.* equilibrium, balance; **—ировать** *v.* equilibrate, balance.

экви/молекулярный *a.* equimolecular; **—молярный** *a.* equimolar; **—потенциальный** *a.* equipotential; **—скалярный** *a.* equiscalar; **—фазный** *a.* equiphase.

ЭКГ *abbr.* (**электрокардиограмма**) electrocardiogram.

экдемит *m.* ecdemite.

экз. *abbr.* (**экземпляр**) copy; (**экземпляры**) copies.

экз— *prefix* ex—; *see also* **экс—**.

экзальтация рефракции optical exaltation.

экзамен *m.*, **—ационный** *a.* examination; **вступительный э.** entrance examination; **выдержать э.** pass an examination; **выпускной э.** final examination; **держать э.** take an examination; **провалиться на —е** fail an examination; **—овать** *v.* examine.

экзегетерический *a.* exegetic.

экземпляр *m.* copy; specimen.

экзогенный *a.* exogenous, exogenetic, exogenic.

экзоморф/изм *m.* exomorphism; **—ный** *a.* exomorphic.

экзосмо/с *m.* exosmosis; **—тический** *a.* exosmotic.

экзосфера *f.* exosphere.

экзотерический *a.* exoteric.

экзотерм/ический, —ный *a.* exothermic; **—ичность** *f.* exothermicity.

экзотический *a.* exotic.

экзо/энергетический, —эргический *a.* exoergic.

экипаж *m.* crew.

экипиров/анный *a.* equipped, furnished; **—ать** *v.* equip, furnish; **—ка** *f.* equipment; equipping; **—очный** *a.* equipment.

экке́р *m.* (surv.) cross-staff; **зеркальный э.** optical square.

эклеит *m.* eakleite.

эклиметр *m.* clinometer, inclinometer.

эклипти/ка *f.*, **—ческий** *a.* ecliptic; **наклонность —ки** obliquity of the ecliptic.

Экмана спираль Ekman spiral.

экономайзер *m.* economizer.

эконометр *m.* econometer.

эконом/ика *f.* economics; **—ист** *m.* economist; **—ить** *v.* economize, save.

экономич/еский *a.* economical; **—еская игла** economizer needle; **—ность** *f.* economy; **—ный** *a.* economical.

эконом/ия *f.* economy, saving; **—ность** *f.* economy; **—ный** *a.* economical.

экран *m.* screen, shield; baffle, deflector; **э. с темным изображением** dark-trace screen.

экранизация *see* **экранирование.**

экраниров/ание *n.*, **—ка** *f.* screening, shielding; (geo.) masking; **коэффициент —ания** screening number (or constant); **—анный** *a.* screened, shielded; **—анный тетрод** screen-grid tetrode; **—ать** *v.* screen, shield.

экранирующ/ий *a.* screening, shielding; **—ая сетка** screen grid; **—ее облако** obscuring cloud.

экс— *prefix* ex—; *see also* **экз—**.

эксгаустер *m.* exhauster, exhaust fan; aspirator.

эксикатор *m.* exsiccator, desiccator.

экситон *m.*, **—ный** *a.* exciton.

экситрон *m.* excitron.

экскав/атор *m.* excavator; power shovel; **—аторный** *a.* excavator, excavation; **—ация** *f.* excavation.

экскурс *m.* excursion; digression; **—ион-**

ный *a.* excursion; —**ия** *f.* excursion, trip, tour.

Экснера заслоночная теория Exner barrier theory.

экспан/дер *m.* expander; —**дирование** *n.* expanding; —**сиометр** *m.* expansion gauge; —**сионный** *a.*, —**сия** *f.* expansion.

экспедировать *v.* dispatch, expedite.

экспедиц/ионный *a.* expeditionary; dispatch; —**ия** *f.* expedition; dispatch office.

экспеллер *m.* expeller.

экспендер *see* **экспандер.**

эксперим. *abbr.* (**экспериментальный**) experimental.

эксперимент *m.* experiment; **э. внутри реактора** (nucl.) in-pile experiment; —**ально** *adv.* experimentally; —**альный** *a.* experimental; research; —**альный реактор** experimental reactor; research reactor; —**атор** *m.* experimenter; —**ирование** *n.* experimentation; —**ировать** *v.* experiment.

эксперт *m.* expert; examiner, inspector; —**иза** *f.* expert examination (or opinion); committee of experts.

экспликация *f.* explanation.

эксплоат— *see* **эксплуат—.**

эксплуататор *m.* exploiter; —**ский** *a.* exploiting.

эксплуатационн/ый *a.* operation, operational, working; exploitation; **э. режим** operating conditions; —**ое испытание** performance (service, maintenance) test; —**ые качества** performance (characteristics); —**ые расходы** operating costs.

эксплуат/ация *f.* operation, working, running; maintenance; exploitation; **ввести в —ацию** put into operation; **условия —ации** operating conditions; —**ировать** *v.* operate, run, work; exploit; —**ирующийся** *a.* in operation.

экспозиция *f.* exposition, exhibition, display; (phot.) exposure.

экспон/ат *m.* exhibit; —**ент** *m.* exhibitor; (math.) exponent, index; —**ента** *f.* exponential (function); —**ентный,** —**енциальный** *a.* exponential; —**енциально** *adv.* exponentially; —**енциальное время** mean life; —**ировать** *v.* exhibit; expose.

экспонометр *m.* exposure meter; (x-ray) intensitometer.

экспорт *m.*, —**ировать** *v.*, —**ный** *a.* export; —**ирование** *n.* exportation.

экспресс *m.* express; **э.-анализ** rapid (or proximate) analysis; **э.-лаборатория** field laboratory; —**ный** *a.* express, (very) rapid.

экспромтом *adv.* impromptu.

экспропри/ация *f.* expropriation; —**ировать** *v.* expropriate.

экстензометр *m.* extensometer.

экстенсивн/ость *f.* extensiveness; —**ый** *a.* extensive.

экстерн *m.* external student, extern.

экстинкция *f.* extinction.

экстра— *prefix* extra—.

экстрагент *m.* extracting agent, extractant.

экстрагир/ование *n.* extraction; —**ованный** *a.* extracted; —**овать** *v.* extract; —**уемость** *f.* extractibility; —**уемый** *a.* extractable; —**ующий** *a.* extracting; —**ующий слой** extract layer.

экстрак/т *m.* extract; —**тивный** *a.* extractive; —**тор** *m.* extractor; —**ционный** *a.* extraction, extractive; —**ционная перегонка** extractive distillation; —**ция** *f.* extraction.

экстраординарный *a.* extraordinary; **э. профессор** adjunct professor.

экстраполиров/ание *n.* extrapolation; —**анный** *a.* extrapolated; —**ать** *v.* extrapolate.

экстраполяц/ионный *a.*, —**ия** *f.* extrapolation; —**ионная ионизационная камера** extrapolation ionization chamber.

экстраток *m.* extra current.

экстрем/аль *f.*, —**альный** *a.*, —**мум** *m.* extremal, extremum, extreme; —**альный принцип** extremum (or variational) principle; —**изировать** *v.* extremize.

экстренн/ый *a.* special; urgent; —**ая остановка** (reactor) scram.

экструдинг *m.* extrusion; extruding.

эксцентрик *m.*, —**овый** *a.* eccentric; cam; —**овый вал** camshaft; —**овый привод** cam drive.

эксцентри/цитет *m.*, **—чность** *f.* eccentricity; **—ческий, —чный** *a.* eccentric.
эксцесс *m.* (stat.) excess, kurtosis.
эктропит *m.* ectropite.
эл. *abbr.* (**электрический**) electric; (**электронный**) electron.
эластанс *m.* elastance.
эластичн/ость *f.* elasticity; **—ый** *a.* elastic.
эластомер *m.* elastomer.
эл.-графич. *abbr.* (**электронно-графический**) electron diffraction.
элгуйарит *m.* elhuyarite.
элеватор *m.*, **—ный** *a.* elevator.
Электра Electra.
электрет *m.* electret.
электриз/атор *m.* electrizer; **—ация** *f.*, **—ование** *n.* electrification, electrization; **—ация трением** triboelectrification; **—ованный** *a.* electrified; **—овать** *v.* electrify, electrize; **—уемый, —ующийся** *a.* electrifiable.
электрик *m.* electrician.
электрифи/кация *f.* electrification; **—цированный** *a.* electrified; **—цировать** *v.* electrify.
электрическ/и *adv.* electrically; **—ий** *a.* electric, electrical; *see also* **электро—**; **—ая прочность** electric (or dielectric) strength; **—ая станция** electric power plant; **—ое сродство** electroaffinity; **эффект —ого ветра** electric wind effect.
электричество *n.* electricity.
электро— *prefix* electro—, electric.
электроакуст/ика *f.* electroacoustics; **—ический** *a.* electroacoustic.
электро/анализ *m.* electroanalysis; **—баллистика** *f.* electroballistics; **—биология** *f.* electrobiology.
электровалентн/ость *f.* electrovalence; **—ый** *a.* electrovalent.
электровоз *m.* electric locomotive.
электрогальван/изация *f.* electrogalvanizing; **—ический** *a.* electrogalvanic.
электрогенератор *m.* electric generator; **—ный** *a.* generator; electricity-generating.
электрогониометр *m.* electrogoniometer.
электрограф/ический *a.* electrographic; **—ия** *f.* electrography.
электрод *m.* electrode; **э. последующего ускорения** intensifier (or post-acceleration) electrode; **износ —ов** electrode consumption.
электродвигатель *m.*, **—ный** *a.* electric motor; **э. короткозамкнутый** squirrel-cage motor.
электродвижущ/ий *a.* electromotive; **э. ряд** electromotive series; **—ая сила** electromotive force (emf).
электродиализ *m.* electrodialysis.
электродинам/ика *f.* electrodynamics; **—ический** *a.* electrodynamic; **—ометр** *m.* electrodynamometer.
электродный *a.* electrode; **э. потенциал** electrode (or electrolytic) potential.
электродуг/а *f.* electric arc; **—овая сварка** arc welding.
электро/емкость *f.* capacity; **—звуковой** *a.* electroacoustic; **—золь** *m.* electrosol; **—измерительный прибор** electrical measuring instrument (or meter).
электрокалор/иметр *m.* electrocalorimeter; **—ический** *a.* electrocaloric.
электрокапиллярн/ость *f.* electrocapillarity; **—ый** *a.* electrocapillary; **—ые явления** electrocapillarity.
электро/кардиограф *m.* electrocardiograph; **—кимограф** *m.* electrokymograph.
электрокинет/ика *f.* electrokinetics; **—ический** *a.* electrokinetic.
электролиз *m.* electrolysis; **подвергать —у** electrolyze; **—ация** *f.* electrolyzing; **—ер** *m.* electrolyzer, electrolytic cell; **—ный** *a.* electrolysis, electrolytic; **—ованный** *a.* electrolyzed; **—овать** *v.* electrolyze.
электролит *m.* electrolyte; **—ический, —ный** *a.* electrolytic; **—ический элемент** electrolytic cell; **—ическое осаждение** *see* **электроосаждение**; **—ическое покрытие** electrodeposition.
электролюминесцен/тный *a.* electroluminescent; **—ция** *f.* electroluminescence.
электромагн/етизм *m.* electromagnetism; **—ит** *m.* electromagnet; **—итизация** *f.* electromagnetization; **—итный** *a.* electromagnetic; **—итный**

измерительный прибор moving-iron instrument.

электромегафон *m.* electrical megaphone.

электромер *m.* electromer; **—ия** *f.* electromerism; **—ный** *a.* electromeric.

электрометаллургия *f.* electrometallurgy.

электрометр *m.* electrometer; **э. с вибрирующим язычком** vibrating-reed electrometer; **—ический** *a.* electrometer, electrometric; **—ическая лампа** electrometer tube; **—ия** *f.* electrometry.

электромехани/ка *f.* electromechanics; **—ческий** *a.* electromechanical.

электромиограф *m.* electromyograph.

электромонтер *m.* electrician.

электромотор *m.* electric motor; **—ный** *a.* electromotive.

электромощность *f.* electric power.

электрон *m.* electron; (met.) Electron (magnesium-base alloy); **э. проводимости** conduction electron; **—вольт** *m.* electronvolt; **—ика** *f.* electronics; **—ирование** *n.* electronation.

электронно— *prefix* electronic, electron; *see also* **электроно—**; **э.-активное ядро** electron-emitting nucleus; **э.-волновая лампа** electron-wave tube; **э.-дырочная пара** electron-hole pair; **э.-дрырочный переход** *p-n* junction; **э.-лучевая трубка** (*or* **лампа), э.-лучевой прибор** cathode-ray tube; electron-beam tube; **э.-оптический** *a.* electron-optical, opto-electronic; **э.-оптический преобразователь** image converter; **э.-оптическое изображение** electron micrograph; **э.-световой индикатор** (**настройки**) electron-ray indicator tube.

электронн/ый *a.* electron, electronic; (semicond.) *n*-type; **э. микроскоп** electron microscope; **э. осциллоскоп** cathode-ray oscilloscope; **э. парамагнитный резонанс** electron paramagnetic resonance (EPR); **э. полупроводник** *n*-type semiconductor; **э. проектор** electron projector; **э. прожектор, —ая пушка** electron gun; **э. умножитель** electron multiplier; **э. фотоумножитель** photomultiplier tube, multiplier phototube; **—ая зона** conduction band; **—ая лампа** electron tube; vacuum tube; **—ая линза** electron lens; **—ая оболочка** electron shell; **—ая оптика** electron optics; **—ая проводимость** *n*-type conductivity; **—ая связь** electron coupling; beam coupling.

электроно— *prefix* electronic, electron; *see also* **электронно—**; **э.-акцептор** *m.* electron acceptor; **э.-грамма** *f.* electron-diffraction pattern.

электронограф *m.* electron-diffraction camera; **—ический** *a.*, **—ия** *f.* electron diffraction.

электронодонор *m.*, **—ный** *a.* electron donor.

электроно/поточный *a.* electron-stream; **—сродство** *n.* electron affinity.

электрооборудование *n.* electrical equipment.

электроопт/ика *f.* electro-optics; **—ический** *a.* electro-optical.

электро/осадитель *m.* electrical precipitator, electrostatic precipitator; **—осаждение** *n.* electrodeposition, electroplating; **—осмос** *m.* electro-osmosis (electroendosmosis).

электроотрицательн/ость *f.* electronegativity; **—ый** *a.* electronegative.

электро/очистка *f.* electrical precipitation (for gases); **—питание** *n.* electric power supply.

электропередача *f.* electrotransmission.

электропечь *f.* electric furnace; **дуговая э.** electric arc furnace.

электропиролиз *m.* electropyrolysis.

электроплав/ильный *a.*, **—ка** *f.* electro-smelting.

электропокрытие *n.* electrodeposition, electroplating.

электрополиров/анный *a.* electropolished; **—ка** *f.* electropolishing, electrolytic polishing.

электро/положительный *a.* electropositive; **—привод** *m.* electric drive.

электропровод/ка *f.* (electric) wiring; **—ность** *f.* electrical conductivity; **—ящий** *a.* conducting.

электро/разведка *f.* electrical prospecting; **—резка** *f.* (electric) arc cutting.

электросвар/ка *f.*, **—очный** *a.* electric welding.

электро/свечение *n.* electroluminescence; **—сеть** *f.* electric system (or wiring); power lines; **—сила** *see* **электромощность**; **—синтез** *m.* electrosynthesis.

электроскоп *m.* electroscope; **—ический** *a.* electroscopic; **—ия** *f.* electroscopy.

электро/сопротивление *n.* electrical resistance; **—сталь** *f.* electric steel; **—станция** *f.* electric power station (or plant).

электростати/ка *f.* electrostatics; **—ческий** *a.* electrostatic.

электростенолиз *m.* electrostenolysis.

электрострикц/ионный *a.* electrostrictional; **—ия** *f.* electrostriction.

электротеллур/ическое поле telluric field, earth electric field; **—ограф** *m.* electrotellurograph.

электротерапия *f.* electrotherapy.

электротерм/ический *a.* electrothermal; **—ия** *f.* electrothermics.

электротехни/к *m.* electrician; electrical engineer; **—ка** *f.* electrical technology, electrical engineering; **—ческий** *a.* electrotechnical, electrical-engineering; **—ческая сталь** transformer steel, electrical sheet.

электротипия *f.* electrotyping.

Электроточприбор *abbr.* (**Завод точных электрических приборов**) Precision Electrical Instruments Plant.

электро/тяга *f.* electric traction; **—физиология** *f.* electrophysiology; **—фильтр** *m.* electric separator (or precipitator); **—фон** *m.* electrophone; **—фор** *m.* electrophorus.

электрофорез *m.* electrophoresis; **—ный** *a.* electrophoretic.

электрофорная машина electrostatic (static, induction) machine.

электрохим/ический *a.* electrochemical; **э. ряд** electrochemical (or electromotive) series; **—ия** *f.* electrochemistry.

электро/ход *m.* motor ship; **—централь** *f.* electric power plant; **—часы** *pl.* electric clock; **—эндосмос** *m.* electroendosmosis; **—энергия** *f.* electric energy (or power); **—энцефалограф** *m.* electroencephalograph; **—ядерный** *a.* electronuclear.

электрум *m.* electrum (natural gold-silver alloy).

элемент *m.* element; (elec.) cell; **гальванический э.** galvanic (or voltaic) cell; **жидкостный э., мокрый э., наливной э.** wet cell; **э. с воздушной деполяризацией** air cell; **сухой э.** dry cell.

элементарн/ость *f.* elementary character; **—ый** *a.* elementary, unit; elemental; (**полный**) **—ый анализ** ultimate analysis; **—ый объем** volume element; **—ая длина** length (line, distance) element; **—ая площадка** area element; **—ая частица** elementary (or fundamental) particle; **—ая ячейка** unit cell.

элементный *a.* element; (elec.) cell.

элео— *prefix* eleo—, elaeo—.

элерон *m.* aileron.

элиазит *m.* eliasite.

элимин/атор *m.* eliminator; **—ация** *f.* elimination; **—ировать** *v.* eliminate.

элинвар *m.* Elinvar (iron-nickel alloy).

элит *m.* ehlite.

эллахерит *m.* oellacherite.

эллинг *m.* covered shipyard; airship shed.

эллипс *m.* ellipse; **э. рассеивания** (stat.) ellipse of concentration; **—оид** *m.* ellipsoid; **—оидальный** *a.* ellipsoidal.

эллиптич/ески *adv.* elliptically; **—еский** *a.* elliptic, elliptical; **—ность** *f.* ellipticity.

эл.-магн. ед. *abbr.* (**электромагнитная единица**) electromagnetic unit (emu).

элонгация *f.* elongation.

эл.-оптич. *abbr.* (**электронно-оптический**) electron-optical.

элотрон *m.* elotron.

э. л. с. *abbr.* (**эффективная лошадиная сила**) effective horsepower.

эл.-ст. ед. *abbr.* (**электростатическая единица**) electrostatic unit.

ЭЛТ *abbr.* (**электронно-лучевая трубка**) cathode-ray tube.

Эльзассер Elsasser.

Эльма огонь, святого Э. огонь St. Elmo's fire.

эльсвортит *m.* ellsworthite.

Эльстера и Гейтеля эффект Elster and Geitel effect.

элю/ант *m.* eluant; **—ат** *m.* eluate.

элюв/иальный *a.* eluvial; **—ий** *m.* eluvium.

элю/ирование *n.*, **—ция** *f.* elution; **—ировать** *v.* elute; **—ирующий** *a.* eluting; **—триация** *f.* elutriation.

эмаграмма *f.* emagram.

эмалевый *a.* enamel.

эмалиров/анный *a.* enameled; **—ать** *v.* enamel; **—ка** *f.*, **—очный** *a.* enameling.

эмал/итовый *a.*, **—ь** *f.* enamel.

эманационн/ый *a.* emanation, emanating; **—ая способность** emanating power; **—ая съемка** emanation prospecting.

эманация *f.* emanation; emanon; **э. актиния** actinon; **э. радия** radon; **э. тория** thoron.

эманий *m.* emanium (Em).

эманирован/ие *n.* emanation, emanating; **коэффициент —ия** emanating power.

эманометр *m.* emanometer.

эмблема *f.* emblem.

эмбрион *m.* embryo; **—альный** *a.* embryonic.

эмбритит *m.* embrithite.

эмденовская функция Emden function.

ЭМИЗ *abbr.* (**Электромеханический инструментальный завод**) Electromechanical Instruments and Apparatus Plant.

эмиссионн/ый *a.* emission, emissive, emitting; **э. микроскоп** emission microscope; **—ая способность** emissive power, emissivity; **—ая туманность** emission nebula; **—ая характеристика** emission characteristic.

эмиссия *f.* emission.

эмит/ировать *v.* emit; **—тер** *m.* emitter; **—терный переход** emitter junction.

эмпир/изм *m.*, **—ика** *f.* empiricism, experience, experiments; **—ический** *a.* empirical, experimental.

эмплектит *m.* emplectite.

эмульг/атор *m.* emulsifier; **—ация** *f.*, **—ирование** *n.* emulsification; **—ирующий агент** emulsifying agent, emulsifier.

эмульсер *m.* air lift.

эмульсионн/ый *a.* emulsion; **—ая камера** (*or* **пачка**) emulsion (or pellicle) stack.

эмульсиров/ание *n.* emulsification; **—анный** *a.* emulsified; **—ать** *v.* emulsify.

эмульсифик/атор *m.* emulsifier; **—ационный** *a.* emulsification, emulsifying; **—ация** *f.* emulsification.

эмульс/ия *f.* emulsion; **—оид** *m.* emulsoid.

эмфатический *a.* emphatic.

эмфолит *m.* empholite.

эмшер *m.* Emscherian stage.

эналит *m.* enalite.

энантиоморф *m.* enantiomorph; **—изм** *m.* enantiomorphism; **—ный** *a.* enantiomorphous.

энантиотроп/ия *f.* enantiotropy; **—ный** *a.* enantiotropic.

энгессеровая сила Engesser load.

энгидрос *m.* enhydros.

эндекаэдр *m.* hendecahedron; **—ический** *a.* hendecahedral.

Эндимион Endymion (lunar crater).

эндлихит *m.* endlichite.

эндо— *prefix* endo—.

эндовибратор *m.* cavity resonator.

эндоморф *m.* endomorph; **—ный** *a.* endomorphic; **—оз** *m.* endomorphism.

эндосмо/с *m.* endosmosis; **—тический** *a.* endosmotic.

эндотерм/ический, —ный *a.* endothermic; **—ичность** *f.* endothermicity.

эндоэнергетический *a.* endoergic.

эндоэргический *a.* endoergic.

энергети/к *m.* power engineer; **—ка** *f.* power engineering; power; **—ческий** *a.* energy, power; energetic; **—ческий реактор** power reactor; **—ческая отдача** energy efficiency.

энергичн/о *adv.* energetically, vigorously; **—ый** *a.* energetic, vigorous; **—ая реакция** vigorous reaction.

энерг/ия *f.* energy, power; **э. покоя** rest energy; **э. связи** binding energy; **э. сцепления** cohesive (or binding) energy; **возбуждать —ию** energize.

энерго— *prefix* power, energy.

Энергоакадемия *abbr.* (**Энергетическая академия**) Academy of Power Engineering.

энерговыделен/ие *n.* energy release; **плотность —ия** power density.

энерго/реактор *m.* power reactor; **—силовая станция, —станция** *f.* power plant; **—система** *f.* power system; **—съем** *m.* power output.

энзим *m.*, **—ный** *a.* enzyme.

ЭНИА *abbr.* (**Научно-исследовательская электротехническая ассоциация**) Electrotechnical Research Association.

Эниветок (атолл) Eniwetok.

энигматит *m.* aenigmatite.

ЭНИН *abbr.* [**Энергетический институт (им. Г. М. Кржижановского)**] G. M. Krzhizhanovskii Institute of Power Engineering.

Энке Encke (lunar crater).

Энке комета Encke comet.

эннеаэдр *m.* enneahedron; **—ический** *a.* enneahedral.

энн/ый *a.* unspecified; *n*th; **в —ой степени** to the *n*th power (or degree).

энольный *a.* enolic.

эн.-сист. *abbr.* (**энергосистема**) power system.

энтальпия *f.* enthalpy.

энтр. ед. *abbr.* (**энтропийная единица**) entropy unit.

энтропия *f.* entropy.

энц. *abbr.* (**энциклопедический**) encyclopedic.

энциклопед/ический *a.* encyclopedic; **—ия** *f.* encyclopedia.

эолов/о-обломочный *a.* anemoclastic; **—ый** *a.* eolian, windborne.

ЭОП *abbr.* (**электронно-оптический преобразователь**) image-converter tube.

эосфорит *m.* eosphorite.

эоцен *m.* Eocene epoch; **—овый** *a.* Eocene.

эпейроген/ез, —езис *m.* epeirogenesis; **—етический, —ический** *a.* epeirogenic; **—ия** *f.* epeirogeny.

эпи— *prefix* epi—.

эпибуланжерит *m.* epiboulangerite.

Эпиген Epigenes (lunar crater).

эпиген/езис *m.* epigenesis; **—етический** *a.* epigenetic; **—ный** *a.* epigene.

эпидиаскоп *m.* epidiascope.

эпидидимит *m.* epididymite.

эпизодический *a.* incidental; irregular, sporadic.

эпизона *f.* epizone.

Эпик Öpik.

эпикадмиевый *a.* epicadmium.

эпимер, —ид *m.* epimer, epimeride; **—ный** *a.* epimeric.

эпи/параклаз *m.* epiparaclase, overthrust; **—положение** *n.* epi-position; **—породы** *pl.* epirocks; **—проекция** *f.* episcope projection.

эпи/рогенезис *see* **эпейрогенез**; **—скоп** *m.* episcope; **—таксия** *f.* epitaxy.

эпителий *m.* epithelium.

эпи/тепловой, —термальный, —термический *a.* epithermal; **—трохоида** *f.* epitrochoid; **—фокус** *m.* epifocus; **—центр** *m.* epicenter; zero point.

эпицикл *m.* epicycle; **—ический** *a.* epicyclic; **—оида** *f.* epicycloid.

Эплтона слой Appleton layer.

эпоксисоединение *n.* epoxy compound.

эпо/ха *f.* epoch, age, era, period, time; **метод наложения —х** superposed-epoch method.

э.п.р. *abbr.* (**электронный парамагнитный резонанс**) electron paramagnetic resonance (EPR).

эпюр *m.*, **—а** *f.* diagram, curve.

эра *f.* era.

Эратосфена решетка sieve of Eratosthenes.

эрбий *m.* erbium (Er).

эрг *m.* erg.

эргодическ/ий *a.* ergodic; **—ое свойство** ergodicity.

эргометр *m.* ergometer.

эренвертит *m.* ehrenwerthite.

Эренфеста теорема Ehrenfest theorem.

Эри Airy (lunar crater).

Эри интеграл Airy integral; **Э. точки** A. points.

Эридан Eridanus (Eri) (constellation).

Эрике Ehricke.

эринит *m.* erinite.

эриохальцит *m.* eriochalcite.

эритрин *m.* erythrin; erythrite; **—овый** *a.* erythrin.

эритросидерит *m.* erythrosiderite.

эритроцит *m.* erythrocyte, red blood corpuscle.

Эрленмейера колба Erlenmeyer flask.

Эрлиха теория Ehrlich theory.

Эрмита многочлены (полиномы) Hermite polynomials.

эрмитов, —ский *a.* Hermitian; **—ость** *f.* Hermitian character.

эродиров/анный *a.* eroded; **—ать** *v.* erode.

эроз/ивный *a.* erosive; **—ионный** *a.* erosion, erosional; **—ия** *f.* erosion.

Эрос Eros.

Эротосфен Eratosthenes (lunar crater).

эрратический *a.* erratic.

Эрстед Oersted (lunar crater).

эрстед *m.* oersted; **—ит** *m.* oerstedite; **—метр** *m.* oerstedmeter.

эрстит *m.* Oerstit (magnetic alloy).

Эртеля тензор Ertel tensor.

Эру печь Héroult furnace.

эрубесцит *m.* erubescite.

эрудиция *f.* erudition.

эруптивный *a.* eruptive.

э.с. *abbr.* (**эрмитово-сопряженный**) Hermitian conjugate.

эскалатор *m.* escalator.

эскарп *m.* scarp, escarpment.

эскер *m.* esker.

эскиз *m.* sketch, draft, outline; **—ный** *a.* sketch; sketchy; **—ный проект** draft; **—ная карта** sketch map.

эсобразный *a.* sigmoid.

Эспи-Кеппена теория Espy-Koeppen theory.

эссенция *f.* essence.

Эссона коэффициент Esson coefficient.

эстакада *f.* trestle bridge; pier.

эстамп *m.* print, plate.

эстезиометр *m.* esthesiometer.

Эстонская ССР Estonian SSR.

эстрада *f.* platform, stage.

Эст. ССР *abbr. see* **Эстонская ССР.**

эстуар/иевый *a.* estuarine; **—ий** *m.* estuary.

эта *pron. f.* this, that.

этаж *m.* story, floor; **—ный** *a.* story, floor; storied; stepped, graduated; multiple-stage.

эталон *m.* standard; standard instrument (or tool); (opt.) etalon; **—ный** *a.* standard, reference; calibration, calibrating; **—ный элемент** standard cell.

эталониров/ание *n.* standardizing; calibration; **—анный** *a.* standardized; calibrated; **—ать** *v.* standardize; calibrate.

этан *m.*, **—овый** *a.* ethane; **—ол** *m.* ethanol, ethyl alcohol.

этап *m.* stage, step.

Этвеша опыт Eötvös experiment; **Э.-Рамзая-Шильда коэффициент** E.-Ramsay-Shield coefficient.

этерификация *f.* esterification; etherification.

ЭТИ *abbr.* (**Энциклопедия технических измерений**) Encyclopedia of Technical Measurements.

эти *pron. pl.* these, those.

этика *f.* ethics.

этикетка *f.* label.

этил *m.*, **—овый** *a.* ethyl; **хлористый э.** ethyl chloride; **—ен** *m.* ethylene; **—енгликол** *m.* ethylene glycol; **—овый спирт** ethyl alcohol.

этиология *f.* etiology.

этит *m.* aetites, eaglestone.

этич/еский, —ный *a.* ethical.

это *pron. n.* this, that, it; **для —го** for this purpose; **до —го** thus far; **при —м** at the same time; in this connection; being; *see also under* **при; при всем —м** in spite of all this, for all this.

этот *pron. m.* this, that.

Эттингсгаузена эффект Ettingshausen effect.

эфемер/идное время ephemeris time; **—иды** *pl.* (astr.) ephemeris; **—ный** *a.* ephemeral.

эфесит *m.* ephesite.

эфир *m.* ether; ester; (specif.) diethyl ether; **кислотный э., сложный э.** ester; **простой э.** ether; **серный э.** sulfuric ether; diethyl ether; **этиловый э.** ethyl ether; **—ный** *a.* ester; ether, etheric, ethereous, ethereal; **—ное масло** essential oil.

эфлоресценция *f.* efflorescence.

эфф. *abbr.* (**эффективный**) effective, efficient.

эффект *m.* effect; **э. на прибор** instrumental response.

эффективн/ость *f.* efficiency; effectiveness, efficacy; sensitivity; **э. источника** source strength; **предел —ости** effective range; **—ый** *a.* effective; efficient, efficacious; workable; sensitive (to); **—ая мощность** effective power; **—ое сечение** cross section.

эффектный *a.* effective; spectacular.
эффуз/ивный *a.* (petr.) effusive, extrusive; **—ия** *f.* effusion; **—ор** *m.* effusor.
эхо *n.* echo; **—заградитель** *m.* echo suppressor; **—локация** *f.* echo ranging; **—лот** *m.* echo sounder, sonic depth finder; **—скоп** *m.* echoscope.
Эчисона *see* **Ачесона.**
эшафот *m.* scaffold.
эшвегеит *m.* eshwegeite.
эшелетт *m.* echelette grating.
эшелле *n.* echelle grating.
эшеллит *m.* echellite.
эшелон *m.*, **—ный** *a.* echelon.
эшинит *m.* eschynite, aeschynite.
ЭЭГ *abbr.* (**электроэнцефалограмма**) electroencephalogram.

Ю

ю. *abbr.* (**южный**) southern.
Ю [*in steel mark* (**алюминий**)] aluminum (Al).
Ю. *abbr.* (**юг**) south.
юбилей *m.*, **—ный** *a.* anniversary, jubilee.
юб/ка *f.*, **—очный** *a.* skirt; (elec.) petticoat (of insulator); **—очный изолятор** petticoat (or bell) insulator.
ю.-в. *abbr.* (**юго-восточный**) southeastern.
юг *m.* south.
юго/-восток *m.* southeast; **ю.-восточный** *a.* southeast, southeastern; **ю.-запад** *m.* southwest; **ю.-западный** *a.* southwest, southwestern.
Югославия Yugoslavia; *see also* **ФНРЮ.**
югославский *a.* Yugoslav.
южн. *abbr. see* **ю.**
Южная Гидра Hydrus (Hy) (constellation); **Ю. Корона** Corona Australis (CrA) (constellation); **Ю. Рыба** Piscis Austrinus (PsA) (constellation).
южнее *adv.* to the south (of).
южн/ый *a.* south, southern, southerly; **ю. полярный круг** Antarctic Circle; **—ая полярность** south-seeking polarity; **—ое (полярное) сияние** aurora australis.
Южный Крест Crux (Cru) (constellation).
Южный Ледовитый океан Antarctic Ocean.
Южный Треугольник Triangulum Australe (TrA) (constellation).
ю.з. *abbr.* (**юго-западный**) southwestern.
Ю.-З. *abbr.* (**юго-запад**) southwest.
Юз Hughes.
Юинг Ewing.
юинтаит *m.* uintaite.
Юкава потенциал Yukawa potential.
юлианский календарь Julian calendar.
Юлинга эффект Uehling effect.
Юм-Розери правило Hume-Rothery rule.
юмохоит *m.* umohoite.
Юнга модуль Young modulus; **Ю. расположение** Y. apparatus.
ЮНЕСКО *abbr.* (**Организация Объединенных Наций по вопросам образования, науки и культуры**) United Nations Educational, Scientific and Cultural Organization (UNESCO).
Юнона Juno (rocket).
юн/ость *f.* youth; (geo.) immaturity; **—ошеский** *a.* youthful; junior; **—ый** *a.* young, youthful; immature.
Юпитер Jupiter.
юра *see* **юрский период.**
юри/дический *a.* juridical, legal; **—сдикция** *f.* jurisdiction.
юрский период Jurassic period.
юстиров/ание *n.*, **—ка** *f.* adjustment, positioning, aligning; **—ать** *v.* adjust, position, align; **—очный магнит** positioning magnet.
ютагит *m.* utahite.
юталит *m.* utahlite.

Я

я *pron.* I.

ябло/ко *n.* apple; **глазное я.** eyeball; **—чный** *a.* (chem.) malic; apple.

яв/ить *see* **являть**; **—ка** *f.* appearance; presence; **—ление** *n.* phenomenon; effect; occurrence; appearance.

являть *v.* show, display, exhibit, manifest; **—ся** *v.* appear; be.

явно— *prefix* phanero—.

явно *adv.* evidently, clearly, obviously; explicitly; **—зернистый, —кристаллический** *a.* phanerocrystalline.

явн/ость *f.* evidence, obviousness, clearness; explicitness; **—ый** *a.* evident, obvious, manifest, apparent; clear, definite, distinct; explicit; **—ый полюс** (elec.) salient pole; **—ая функция** explicit function.

явств/енность *f.* clearness, distinctness; **—енный** *a.* clear, distinct; **—овать** *v.* be clear (obvious, evident, apparent); appear.

яд *m.* poison.

яд. ед. *abbr.* (**ядерная единица**) nuclear unit.

ядерно— *prefix* nuclear.

ядерн/о-активный *a.* nuclear-active; **—ый** *a.* nuclear; **—ая техника** nuclear engineering; **—ая фотопластинка** nuclear track plate; **—ая фотоэмульсия** nuclear emulsion.

ядовит/ость *f.* toxicity; **—ый** *a.* poisonous, toxic; noxious.

ядр/о *n.* nucleus; core, kernel; main body; (math.) kernel; (chem.) ring; **атомное я.** atomic nucleus; **я. дислокации** dislocation center; **я. диффузии** diffusion kernel; **я. конденсации** condensation nucleus (or center); **я.-мишень** target nucleus; **я. отдачи** recoil nucleus; **я. сечения** (elast.) core of section; **я. смещения** displacement kernel.

ядротехника *f.* nuclear engineering, nucleonics.

язвин/а *f.* pit; **—ы** *pl.* pitting.

язык *m.* tongue; language; **я. колокола** bell clapper; **на —е . . .** in terms of.

языч/ковый *a.* tongue; reed; **вибрационный я. электрометр** vibrating reed electrometer; **—ный** *a.* tongue; lingual; **—ок** *m.* tongue; catch, lug; reed.

яичко *n.* (small) egg.

яйце— *prefix* egg, ovi—.

яйце/видный, —образный *a.* egg-shaped, oviform, ovoid, oölitic, oval.

яйцо *n.* egg.

Якоби многочлены (полиномы) Jacobi polynomials.

якобиан *m.* Jacobian.

якобсит *m.* jacobsite.

якобы *adv.* supposedly, allegedly; as if.

якор/ный *a.*, **—ь** *m.* anchor; (elec.) armature.

Якутская АССР Yakut ASSR.

ялпаит *m.* jalpaite.

ям/а *f.* pit, hole; **воздушная я.** air pocket; **потенциальная я.** potential well; **—ка** *f.* small pit, hole, cavity; **центральная —ка** fovea (of retina).

Яна-Теллера эффект Jahn-Teller effect.

янв. *abbr. see* **январь.**

январь *m.* January.

янит *m.* janite.

янозит *m.* janosite.

Яноши Janossy.

янтарь *m.* amber; **черный я.** jet.

янтинит *m.* janthinite.

Януса-Шура-Лерера метод Janus-Shur-Lehrer method.

яп., япон. *abbr.* (**японский**) Japanese.

Япония Japan.

японский *a.* Japanese.

яр *m.* steep bank.

ярд *m.* yard.

ярк/ий *a.* bright, brilliant; vivid; **я. пример** striking example; **—ое свидетельство** graphic evidence.

ярко/-красный *a.* bright-red; **—мер** *m.* lucimeter; **—стная температура** brightness (or luminance) temperature.

яркост/ь *f.* luminance, luminosity; brightness, brilliance; vividness; **пороговая я.** absolute threshold of luminance; **разность —и** luminance difference threshold.

ярлит *m.* jarlite.

ярлы/к, —чок *m.* label, tag.

ярмо *n.* yoke.

ярозит *m.* jarosite.

ярус *m.* story, floor; (geo.) stage; level; **облачный я.** cloud level; —**ный** *a.* story, floor; stage; multistage.

Ясель Praesepe.

ясн/о *adv.* clearly, distinctly, evidently; it is clear; **я. выраженный** clearly expressed; pronounced; —**ость** *f.* clearness, clarity, lucidity; —**ый** *a.* clear; distinct; lucid; apparent, evident.

яулингит *m.* jaulingite.

ячеист/ый *a.* cellular, porous; —**ая резина** foam rubber; —**ая циркуляция** cellular circulation.

ячейк/а *f.* cell; mesh (of network or screen); (elec.) section, stage, unit, element; **я. фильтра** (elec.) filter section; —**овый** *a.* cellular.

яшм/а *f.* jasper.

Ящерица Lacerta (Lac) (constellation).

ящи/к *m.* box; container; drawer; **я. матрицы** matrix block; **потенциальный я.** square potential well; —**чный** *a.* box; block.

Appendix

The following ruled pages are provided for convenience in recording new Russian words and their English equivalents, additional equivalents for words or phrases in the present vocabulary, and felicitous translations of phrases not obvious from the given equivalents for the words therein.

Abbreviations

a.	adjective
abbr.	abbreviation
acc.	accusative
acous.	acoustics
adv.	adverb
aero.	aerodynamics, aeronautics
astr.	astronomy, astrophysics
bio.	biology, biophysics
chem.	chemistry
comp.	comparative
conj.	conjunction
cont.	continued
cosm.	cosmic rays
cryst.	crystallography
dat.	dative
elast.	elasticity
elec.	electricity, electronics
esp.	especially
Ex.	example
f.	feminine
fluor.	fluorescence
gen.	genitive
geo.	geology, geophysics
geod.	geodesy
geom.	geometry
hyd.	hydrodynamics
imp.	imperative
instr.	instrumental
m.	masculine
mach.	machinery
mag.	magnetism
math.	mathematics
mech.	mechanics
med.	medicine
mes.	meson physics
met.	metals, metallurgy
meteor.	meteorology
micros.	microscopy
mil.	military
min.	mining
mol.	molecular physics
mus.	music
n.	neuter
naut.	nautical
nucl.	nuclear physics, nuclear power
obs.	obsolete
opt.	optics
petr.	petrology
phot.	photography
photom.	photometry
pl.	plural
plast.	plasticity
prep.	preposition, prepositional
pron.	pronoun
quant.	quantum mechanics, quantum electrodynamics
rad.	radio, radar
rel.	relativity
seis.	seismology
semicond.	semiconductors
sing.	singular
sol.	solid state physics
spec.	specifically
spect.	spectroscopy
stat.	statistics
surv.	surveying
tech.	technology
telev.	television
therm.	thermodynamics, heat
v.	verb